THE

STONEHAM CATALOGUE

OF

BRITISH STAMPS

1840 - 2005

Thirteenth Edition

Published by

MACHIN COLLECTORS CLUB
8 JANNYS CLOSE
AYLSHAM, NORFOLK, NR11 6DL
ENGLAND

£15.95

First edition:	February 1978
Second edition:	November 1978
Third edition:	September 1978
Fourth edition:	September 1980
Fifth edition:	September 1981
Sixth edition:	August 1982
Seventh edition:	September 1984
Eight edition:	November 1985
Ninth edition:	October 1989
Tenth edition:	October 1981
Eleventh edition:	August 1985
Twelfth edition:	September 1998
Thirteenth edition:	April 2006

Published by The Machin Collectors Club
8 Jannys Close, Aylsham, Norfolk, NR11 6DL U.K.
Telephone/Fax: 01263 733586
email: machins@supanet.com
web site: www.machins.org
Printed in Great Britain

Index to Advertisers

Contents

Contents

Foreword

Welcome to the thirteenth edition of Stoneham which marks the twenty eighth anniversary of the catalogue. Over the years many changes have taken place to improve the scope and ease of use of this publication, but none as comprehensive as the changes that have been incorporated here.

The stamp market over recent years has seen a great revival. Whether it is for investment purposes or for the more traditional pleasure of the hobby is open to conjecture, but prices are changing regularly, and mostly upwards, so the need was for a catalogue that made it easy to identify and value GB stamps, reflected true market prices and was low cost so that collectors could afford the latest edition. I think we have achieved all these goals with the catalogue you are now reading.

There were some fundamental changes that I thought needed to be incorporated into this edition. The first, and most obvious, is the introduction of full colour throughout. This facility has been utilised as much as possible to aid the identification of any single item within these pages. Secondly, for modern Great Britain collectors, separate sections have been introduced. For example booklets are now divided into their own specific sub-sections - Prestige, Counter, Vending (Machine) and 'Window' books. Prices have also been introduced for 'cylinder' books (where applicable) with the cheapest variety being included. 'Smilers' sheets are now included with prices for stamp/label pairs from the sheets. Self Adhesive issues have their own new Section and another new section (as 'trailed' in the twelfth edition) is 'Used Abroad'.

For those of you who are interested in a more in-depth study of Machins and modern booklets and material you will find more details, including prices, in the Machin Collectors Club specialised catalogue featured on Page G51 and elsewhere.

In limited cases some renumbering has taken place, but this has only been done where absolutely necessary (such as the separating of the Counter and Vending (Machine) books.

One of the great traditions of Stoneham catalogue since its first publication has been the inclusion of *GENUINE* market prices. The tradition is continued in this edition. Every section of the catalogue has been reviewed and up to date prices are included for all sections. This has been achieved with the help and co-operation of the many dealers who specialise in the various fields listed. I must say here that I have been overwhelmed by the help offered in bringing this catalogue back into being. From the many dealers and collectors who have offered stamps and other material for illustration, to dealers, auction houses and specialist collectors who have offered their expertise in pricing the thouands of stamps, books etc. listed within. Acknowledgements are on the opposite page, but I would like to add my personal thanks publicly to all those mentioned - Thank you.

Every care has been taken in the preparation of this catalogue, but inevitably some errors may have occured. If so, I apologise in advance, especially to all the contributors listed opposite, and ask you to contact me with your observations in whichever way suits you best.

We hope you thoroughly enjoy using this new Stoneham catalogue and if you have any ideas or suggestions for improving it still further, or are able to provide new information, we will be very pleased to hear from you.

Melvyn Philpott

Aylsham, April 2006

Acknowledgements

The introduction of colour to this catalogue meant that every illustration had to re-scanned. Many of the contributors below very kindly provided material for this, but I must thank MCC member Ronnie Briggs especially, who spent many hours scanning, cropping, straightening etc. the images contained within.

Further thanks go to all of the following dealers, MCC members and individuals without whose contribution this publication would never have reached the bookshelf - Many thanks to you all.

M W Arnold	Ian Beckett	Tony Bellew
John Bennie	Jim Bond	John Brain
Ian De La Rue Brown	Ross Candlish	Tony Child
Andrew Claridge	Paul Dauwalder	Stanley Gibbons Ltd
Alan Grant	Frank Goldberg	Chris Harman
Tony Hender	Mike and Sue Holt	Mike Jackson
Andrew G.Lajer	Grahame W. Mann	Peter Mollett
Brian Morris	Alan Musry	Jim Nicholson
Tom Pierron	Norman Sharpe	James Skinner
Alec Withell		

For the technically minded this catalogue was compiled using Adobe Creative Suite CS2®:

Adobe Indesign® Adobe Photoshop® Adobe Illustrator®

on a custom built computer supplied by Aylsham Computer Centre, Aylsham, NORFOLK

Explanation and Abbreviations

Prices. All prices quoted are in English Pounds. Prices over £10 are shown with the £ sign. Less than ten pounds, the amount is shown in decimal form, without the £ sign. e.g. 9.50- nine pounds 50 pence. 50 - 50 pence.
The market prices shown are strictly related to the condition of the stamps, and these are specified at the beginning of most sections. Older issues of stamps in exceptional condition will always command a large premium.

Price Column Symbols

U/M - Unmounted mint, never hinged
M/M - Mounted mint, light hinge mark
F/U - Fine used
A/U - Average used
✉ - Stamp on cover

First Day Covers. Commemorative issues are priced as being illustrated covers with circular 'First Day of Issue' handstamps or special illustrated postmarks. Plain covers are worth up to 60% less. The only exceptions are the commemorative issues of King George V where illustrated covers are very rare. From the 1964 Shakespeare issue, plain covers have no greater value than the equivalent value of the used stamps.

Paper and Gums. Whilst certain variations in paper did apply to earlier issues, and these are listed when significant, the Machin decimal issues have provided a whole new area of study for collectors. The various paper and gum combinations are shown separately in this section under the conventional abbreviations.
These are:
GA - Gum Arabic. The original type of gum, with a more or less shiny surface.
PVA - Polyvinyl Alcohol gum, colourless with a matt surface.
PVAD or **Dex.** - Polyvinyl Alcohol gum with dextrin added, matt surface but with a greenish blue tinge.
OCP - Original Coated Paper, slightly creamy to white, but does not fluoresce under ultra violet light.
FCP - Fluorescent Coated Paper, generally whiter than OCP, and fluorescent under ultra violet light.
FBO - Fluorescent Brightening agent Omitted from paper.
ACP - Advanced Coated Paper, appears very bright under ultra violet light
Low OBA - Low Optical Brightening Agent - appears dull like PCP.
OFNP - OBA Free Non Phosphor paper.
OFPP - OBA Free Phosphorised paper.

Phosphor Bands. The position of the bands are abbreviated throughout in the following form:
CB - centre band. LB - side band at left. RB - side band at right. 2B - two bands, one at each side. AOP - 'All over' phosphor, either PPP or PCP.
PPP - Pre-printed phosphor (all over). PCP - Phosphor coated paper (all over). PCPI - Matt surface. PCP2 - Shiny surface.

CBar or 2Bar indicates that band(s) are short at the top *and* bottom

There are different coloured phosphor bands, which react in different manners under an ultra-violet light. These were applied to the Wilding issues, and are now included in this catalogue. Furthermore, the Machin series saw the introduction of Yellow and Blue fluors. These are described in the introductory notes for this series starting on Page G1.

Colours and Shades. The colour and shade descriptions for the older (classic) issues may not be considered very accurate by modem colour/shade standards, but they are traditional and have become recognised and accepted over many years.

Throughout this catalogue, colour/shade descriptions have been abbreviated when necessary, and in the following manner:

bis. - bistre
car. - carmine
grn. - green
och. - ochre
redd. - reddish
ult. - ultramarine
bt. - bright
p1. - pale
bl. - blue
chest. - chestnut
ind. - indigo
ol. - olive
sep. - sepia
ver. - vermilion
dk. - dark
blk. - black
choc. - chocolate
mag. - magenta
or. - orange
scar. - scarlet
vio. - violet
dl. - dull
brn. - brown
cin. - cinnamon
mar. - maroon
pur. - purple
sl. - slate
yel. - yellow
dp. - deep
brz. - bronze
emer. - emerald
myr. - myrtle
pr. - Prussian
tur. - turquoise
multi. - multicoloured
lt. - light

Other Abbreviations

Horiz. - horizontal
photo. - photogravure
inv. - inverted
(TL) - traffic light (gutter pair)
litho. - lithography
typo. - typography
M.C. - Maltese Cross
vert. - vertical
perf. - perforation
wmk. - watermark.

Illustrations Definitive issues are full size and commemorative issues are generally three-quarters size. Booklet panes are half size.

Issue Dates These are expressed in the British style, i.e. day/month/year

Fine Used Stamps and Their Scarcity

Queen Victoria - Line Engraved and Surface Printed

It is important for collectors to realise that from 1840 and certainly in the succeeding 50 years cancellations were designed to completely deface the stamps and in fact were called "obliterators". The Maltese Cross and later the Barrel Oval of 1844 were the first to be used and it is only when one of these has not been centrally applied to the stamp. i.e. Queen Victoria's profile left clear that the term fine used is applied. In reality the even greater use of superlatives is applied to stamps that exist in these conditions, and it is why of course on imperforate issues this condition with four clear margins can command a considerable premium.

On Surface Printed issues the Duplex cancellation, which came into use in 1853. appears most prevalent, but it was still intended to be an obliterator, and was supposed to be applied so that the number in bars defaced the stamp whilst the adjoining CDS (circular date stamp) was left clear on the left hand side to be read by postal clerks. It is therefore an exception to find these stamps with a CDS cancel and is due either to misapplication of the handstamp, or they were used telegraphically or for other Post Office purposes.

Most higher values (2d to £5) were used on overseas mail, parcels, registered packages and international telegraphs, as well as internal Post Office accounting. In the latter case once the stamp has been removed from the "form" it is impossible to be sure how it was used and these are now accepted by collectors. The stamps suffered very heavy and often smudgy cancellations and the incidence of a fine CDS postmark is small, is highly collectable and of course worth a premium.

King Edward VII

The majority of low values, i.e. ½d and 1d are found with CDS, having been used by both rural and larger post offices to cancel the colossal volume of mail in the form of postcards, which was at its peak in the Edwardian period. The Duplex cancellation was still in use and with it a squared circle, and in 1902 a machine cancel with the wavy lines also came into use.

Higher denomination stamps from 1d were mainly used on parcels and overseas mail, but also very often, either on their own or in combination, on Inland Parcel Post slips, which meant they received a cancellation in the form of a CDS. The Channel Island CDS was also used on Edward VII high values 2s 6d - £1 as a receipt for payment of tobacco duty.

Kings George V, Edward VIII and George VI

As machine cancellations were now well established, this, coupled with the introduction of slogan postmarks. had the result that almost all mail passing through Head Post Offices was cancelled with anything but a CDS.

The wide use of the Double Circle and Single Circle CDS at almost all other Post Offices meant that the majority of low value stamps, i.e. ½d to 2d are readily found in fine used condition, but above that value it is much more difficult. As with previous reigns a clear CDS on a high value stamp commands a premium.

It is possible to find George V stamps with Duplex cancellations and squared circles. These postmarks were not supposed to be used but were not withdrawn, and when discovered do add an element of interest to a collection.

Queen Elizabeth II

An enormous number of different postmarks are now in use. CDS, double CDS, machine cancels, slogans, meter marks, registered and parcel cancels to name but a few.

Really fine single circle date stamps are just as difficult to find and equally as elusive on the high values. Stamps with parts of 'First Day of Issue' postmarks are totally acceptable. as postally used.

Furthermore, genuine postally used examples of the modern Machin issues are often sought, and found, in kiloware. But how do you put a value on the many hours spent finding them?

A Guide to Fakes and Repairs - Be on Your Guard!

Regretfully the incidence of stamps that are being repaired continues to grow particularly for scarcer items where demand continues to motivate prices. The following points should help you in sorting out the wheat from the chaff.

Q.V. Line Engraved Issues

Beware of re-backed impcrforate stamps, especially the 1840 Id black and 2d blue, and the 3 embossed issues. Tests to check whether the stamp has been re-backed are as follows:

1. Immerse stamp in Ronosol - This will show any thickening of the paper as a line and, as a re-hacked stamp has in effect an extra thickness, it will show up as a clear line in the liquid.
2. Ultra violet light - If a modern glue has been used this will give a slight fluorescence which of course will end where the new paper meets the old.
3. A good quality magnifying glass - To see where the design has been painted in, especially in the margins and on the corners, as it is quite normal for re-backed copies to start life as slightly cut down 3 margin examples!

A further warning on the line engraved issues

Take extra care when purchasing copies on cover as this is a very neat way of getting rid of a stamp which has a 'thin' or tear. Unused copies should also be treated with great care as frequently they are found to be chemically cleaned and re-gummed. In the late 19th century many people used to thread stamps on cotton to make decorations, and holes were made by the needle piercing the stamp.
Finally, beware of faked coloured postmarks (e.g. Maltese Crosses), and also faked postmarks on cover, especially the rarer ones.

Q.V. Surface Printed Issues

The following are points to watch when purchasing Surface Printed.

1. Cleaned off postmarks - These can easily be spotted with an ultra violet lamp.
2. High values with fiscal cancellations cleaned off - Use an ultra violet lamp.
3. Repairs to used stamps utilising portions of other stamps - Usually found on small piece or part of an envelope.
4. Re-gumming - To check use all the following methods:
   (a) High powered glass to check between perfs for gum on face.
   (b) Place stamp face down in palm of hand and the top and bottom edges should curl up; if they stay flat or curl the other way it is 90% certain that the stamp has been re-gummed.
   (c) Lightly draw fingers across edge of perfs; if the perfs appear sharp and hard to the touch, this is again an indica tion of re-gumming.
5. Re-perfing - Normally found on cut down wing margin copies. but this is also a method of making a slightly spoilt stamp appear acceptable by re-perfing it and making it smaller to cover up any tears. etc.
6. Repaired Perforations - When a stamp has missing perforations an expert repairer can add perfs. to make the stamp appear sound. Immersing the stamp in Ronosol, with special artention to the perfs. should show up any repairs or added perforations.
7. Colours changed by water immersion - Many surface printed stamps are printed in fugitive inks and any moisture will affect the colour. A good example is the 1883 Lilac and Green issue.
8. Fiscal cancellations covered by faked postmarks - again usually found on small piece or part cover.
9. Facsimiles of the High Values cut out and used with faked postmarks.
10. Altered plate numbers. These are manufactured by scratching out and/or bleaching.
11. Blued paper. This can be artificially created by soaking a stamp in a very mild solution of ink.

Kings George V, George VI and Queen Elizabeth II

Some of the foregoing problems also exist with these reigns and the special points to watch are painted in or scratched out varieties, i.e. the "Pencf" flaw, "Q" for "0" and "no cross on crown" on George V issues.
First Day Covers from the 1924 Wembley Exhibition up to the 1966 World Cup Winners issue are known with forged post-marks. Rare shades can be created by chemical means, the 1935 Silver Jubilee Prussian Blue is an example and should be purchased only with a recognised certificate. Toned paper varieties can be chemically created. Cleaned and re-gummed High Values. Missing colour varieties artificially produced by chemical or other means. e.g. Christmas 1966 issues - Queen's head removed with surgical spirit. These can be easily detected under UV light.

Graphite line varieties created with Indian ink or Letraset, and phosphor bands applied with nail varnish. Both of the latter are easily detected by the fact that the genuine graphite lines never get on the face of the stamp or between the perfs., and phosphor bands react under an ultra violet lamp.

The foregoing warnings cover the most obvious areas, and the collector should always take great care to examine valuable stamps before acquisition.

Watermark Detection

As many collectors are aware the second biggest problem after colour (shades) in collecting GB. stamps, is the detection of the watermark. After a quick look through this catalogue you will notice how the watemark can radically affect the scarcity and value of stamps. Various products have come on to the market purporting to be the answer to watermark detection, but only one has had real success. This works on the principle that a watermark is a thinning of the paper, and therefore, can he made to show up by using a specially designed ink sachet and a roller which theoretically "fills in" the thinner portions created by the watermark and shows the outline as a darker colour. It is also effective on stamps on postcards and covers provided that the card or cover itself has no watermark and has no embossed or relief pattern. "Ronosol" lighter fuel works reasonably well when used against a black plastic background and there are various proprietary brands of watermark fluid which do the same basic task. However, fluids are not successful on certain types of paper especially that used on QEII postage dues, and of course, are completely incapable of showing the watermark of a stamp on cover.

There are also watermark detectors of the light emitting variety which use filters to show up the watermark the devices using a combination of light and pressure are probably the most successful types for detecting watermarks.

With experience one can detect watermarks by looking for the differences where the watermarks are limited e.g. the shape of the Crown. Watermarks can also be seen on occasions by holding the stamp in a horizontal position near a good source of light, like a window.

All illustrations of watermarks are as viewed from the ***back*** of the stamp

Controls

Control letters were introduced in 1884 on the 1d lilac Die II. to aid in the financial control of stocks. The control was not part of the plate and was changed or replaced when necessary. In the Victorian period, only the 1d Lilac and ½d 'Jubilee' issues had control letters. For both these issues, the control was located in the bottom margin under the eleventh stamp. The letters were changed irregularly, about twice a year.

The system was continued for the ½d and 1d Edwardian stamps, and the control letter was at first changed annually in October. In 1903, the Inland Revenue suggested adding a number to represent the year. The letter was then changed about April and each year the number appeared with two different letters. For the Edwardian ½d value, the control was located under the second stamp, except for controls 'A' and 'B' which were under the eleventh. All the 1d controls are located under the eleventh stamp.

George V controls were used for all values from ½d to 1s. The control was located under the second stamp, except the 1d value where it is found under the eleventh. Controls printed at Somerset House each had a full stop after the letter. In 1912, 1914 and from 1918 to 1924 inclusive, there appeared three letters with each year number, otherwise there were two controls for each year.

The system continued for the photogravure issues, but the control was then etched into the cylinder. When this had to be changed, the old one was filled in and a new one etched. The use of controls continued through the brief reign of King Edward VIII into that of King George VI, and was discontinued in 1947.

Many different types of perforating machine were used, giving rise to different combinations of marginal perforation. As far as controls are concerned, the perforation types can be simplified to the basic two type; the margin being either imperforate (I) or perforated through (P).

Notes applicable to all Controls listed in this catalogue

Detailed listings of controls of all definitive issues from 1887- 1947 together with Postage Due controls can be found at the back of the catalogue.

The pricing policy is based on the value of single mounted mint stamps with control attached, all in fine condition and with upright watermark, up to and including the King George V Block Cypher definitives. In the ease of all issues from 1934 where cylinder numbers were printed in the margins besides the control, prices are for corner pairs, comer blocks of four or six as appropriate.

All pre QE2 commemorative issues are priced as cylinder control blocks of six with the exception of the 1929 Postal Union Congress which is priced for single stamps.
Later issues had the fractional type of control. and in a number of cases the control is found with a surrounding box of lines or part box, thus -

X 35	or	X 35	or	X 35	or	X 35	or	X 35

Where these exist, the price is followed by a symbol (*). With one or two rare exceptions the price is broadly the same for all degrees of boxing.

Watermark varieties and rare shades with control are not separately priced, but would he approximately 10% more than the price of the equivalent stamp without control.

Stamps with 'Official' overprints exist with control in the same issues as the appropriate plain stamps. These are generally scarce and are shown in the listings.

Where no prices are shown, i.e. blank areas in the tabulations, the controls either do not exist, or if marked with a star are very rare and therefore not priced.

Collecting and Pricing Stamps on Cover

Once again, the prices of stamps on cover are included and the following notes set out the principles which have guided the editors in assessing prices. It will be appreciated that every cover is different in some detail, and that consequently prices are not mandatory and should be taken as a guide only, when an individual cover is being valued. The term 'on cover' refers to the various types of Envelopes. Wrappers, Folders, Entires or Postcards used to carry correspondence. Stamps "on piece" do not qualify, and should generally be priced at the same value as the stamp or stamps alone. "On piece" refers to stamps cut out from the paper but with the postmark intact.

The Envelope was the same as we know it today with a gummed flap at the back, but frequently having a wax seal.
The Wrapper was quite simply a piece of paper wrapped around a folded letter sheet and fastened with a wax seal.
A Folded Entire was a letter sheet, usually a double page folded, interlocked and again fastened with a wax seal.
Postcards can be plain or illustrated.
Printed Postal Stationery to which extra stamps have been applied.

These were all used during the reign of Queen Victoria, but later only the Envelopes, Postcards and Postal Stationery survived.

Prices of Covers

Queen Victoria - Line Engraved and Surface Printed issues

All the prices in this catalogue relate to covers with average Used or stamps Grade Ill. Please refer to the illustrations and descriptions given on the relevant pages. For other grades the price should be adjusted upwards or downwards by the same percentages quoted.

Kings Edward VII, George V, Edward VIII and George VI issues

All the prices relate to covers with Fine Used stamps, having light neat cancellations and leaving the entire stamp design clearly and easily seen. Heavy cancellations and other defects can reduce the values to as little as 30% or less of the quoted catalogue prices. A stamp neatly tied to the cover by a circular date stamp applied to the corner and leaving two thirds or more of the design completely clear may be classified as Superb Used, and would carry a premium of 50 - 100% above the catalogue price.

Mulreadys

Designed by William Mulready, engraved by John Thompson and printed by William Clowes.

'Mulreadys' were introduced at the same time as adhesive labels on 6th May 1840. They were designed by William Mulready and printed in sheets of 12. Each impression on the sheet had its own unique number that could be substituted, if worn or damaged. Mulreadys were used as a convenient mode of advertising and many collectors have found it to be a rewarding study. Generally they were of a commercial nature and used by insurance companies. Banks, Tax Offices and many other organisations.

No.		Colour	Unused	F/U
1840 (6 May)				
Envelope				
MU1	1d	**Black**	£100	£110
MU1a		Red Maltese Cross	-	£125
MU1b		Black Maltese Cross	-	£110
MU1c		1844 cancel	-	£250
MU1d		Advertisement	£180	£200
MU1e		First Day Use	-	£3000

Printed from six forms with 80 unique numbers known.

No.		Colour	Unused	F/U
Envelope				
MU3	2d	**Blue**	£140	£500
MU3a		Red Maltese Cross	-	£500
MU3b		Black Maltese Cross	-	£500
MU3c		1844 cancel	-	£750
MU3d		First Day Use	-	£22000

Printed from one forme with 13 unique numbers known.

No.		Colour	Unused	F/U
Wrapper				
MU2	1d	**Black**	£100	£120
MU2a		Red Maltese Cross	-	£120
MU2b		Black Maltese Cross	-	£120
MU2c		1844 cancel	-	£225
MU2d		Advertisement	-	£250
MU2e		First Day Use	-	£2250

Printed from six formes with 78 unique numbers known.

No.		Colour	Unused	F/U
Wrapper				
MU4	2d	**Blue**	£140	£500
MU4a		Red Maltese Cross	-	£550
MU4b		Black Maltese Cross	-	£500
MU4c		1844 cancel	-	£600
MU4d		Advertisement	-	£900
MU4e		First Day Use	-	£12000

Printed from one forme with 12 unique numbers known.

Beginning with the Penny Black issued on 6 May I840 and Twopence Blue, issued 2 days later; the four values ½d, Id, 1½d and 2d spanned a period of usage of just forty years. They have presented a complex study for collectors of British stamps. In the following pages the main varieties are listed according to shade, watermarks, plate numbers, dies, alphabets and papers. The different plates, except where they are shown on the stamp design, can only be identified by minute detail differences.

Inverted watermark varieties for almost all of these stamps are recorded and we now list them.

The prices stated relate to stamps that comply with the following conditions:

Imperforate Issues

Mounted Mint (M/M) Stamps should have four clear margins, at least 75% original gum and be reasonably lightly hinged. Stamps without gum must be purchased with caution as many line engraved issues have been chemically cleaned to remove postmarks and pen cancels. Stamps with large margins and/or margins with inscriptions are worth a considerable premium.

Used This is probably the most difficult area to describe as so much depends on the eye of the beholder. For example, under Grade I category the cancel on the Grade II illustration would be quite acceptable to the majority of collectors. The descriptions of the margins are also problematical: most text books state that the top quality stamps should have large even margins. However, many stamps have one side or even two that may show some of the adjoining stamp(s) which of course makes it anything but even. The cancellation should be obvious. A clear profile or full crisp cancels is a personal choice. The four categories listed overleaf are suggested as a guide to quality. All the following points should be taken into account.

(a) Margins
(h) The clarity and neatness of cancellation
(c) The back of the stamp
(d) The condition of the surface
(e) Whether it has any creasing
(I) Any tears or pin holes
(g) Any thinning
(h) Has the stamp been chemically cleaned?

Perforated Issues

Mounted Mint (M/M) Stamps should have at least 75% original gum and be reasonably centred.

Average Used (A/U) Please refer to the relevant page for used categories of the Perforated Issues

Used Categories of the Imperforate Issues

Grade	*Price Guide*
 **Grade 1- Superb** Four extra large margins, light sharp and clear obliteration leaving profile reasonably clear. The Back should be clean and perfect with no discolouration. The surface and colour should also be clean and the printing clear.	Fine used price + up to 100%
 **Grade II - Fine Used** Four good margins, clear obliteration, surface and colour clean, with the back showing no discolouration.	As catalogue
 **Grade III - Average Used** Four margins, one or two cut close, but not into the design. Slight discolouration on the back acceptable, the obliteration may he heavier and less distinctive. The surface, however, should have no defects.	As catalogue
 **Grade IV - Sound Used** Margins very close, one or two sides almost cutting into the design. The obliteration may be heavier and the back slightly discoloured but no other defects should be apparent. A stamp that has creases, thins, margins that cut into the design, tears, or rubbing on the face, does not fit any of the categories described. Examples of these would normally cost less than 20% of the Grade Ill price.	Average used price less 50%

Please note that although the above refers primarily to the Maltese Cross cancellation, the same remarks are applicable, in the main, to the 1844 obliterators

Line Engraved Issues 1840 - 1881

Incidence of Inverted Watermarks

by Tony Child

In the eleventh edition we published, for the first time anywhere, a priced list which reflects the relative scarcity of different plates of 1d line engraved stamps. That listing was updated and amended in the twelfth edition and has been further updated and amended for this edition.

The information that follows is based on over 15 years of research and the examination of thousands of 1d line engraved stamps having an inverted watermark. Only stamps which have been examined by the author and the plating checked are taken into account (save where a copy of a certificate from a recognised expertisation committee has been provided). In every case, that plating has been verified by another expert in the plating of 1d line engraved stamps.

While further research will result in revisions to the published information, it can be said with some confidence that the tables below reflect the relative scarcity of different plates. However, perhaps perversely, market prices do not necessarily reflect scarcity. For example:

(a) Plate 1a is the second most common plate of the 1d black issue with inverted watermark but 1d blacks from plate 1a with inverted watermark are often priced higher than stamps from other plates which are less common with that variety.

(b) Plate 107 is generally regarded as the scarcest of the imperforate series of Die I, Alphabet I plates from plates 12-131. Yet plate 107 with inverted watermark is far from being the scarcest plate with inverted watermark. However, plate 107 stamps with that variety continue to attract a substantial premium.

(c) Stamps from the 1d Die II, Alphabet III perforation 14 with watermark Large Crown on white paper with inverted watermark are plentiful. Some of the more common plates with upright watermark are as scarce or, in some cases, scarcer with inverted watermark than plate 64 which is scarce with upright watermark. Yet stamps from plate 64 with inverted watermark continue to fetch high prices. In the recent 'Statham' sale at Grosvenor Auctions, a damaged copy of plate 64 with inverted watermark with a missing corner realised over £1200 (inclusive of buyers premium), a price not consistent with the relative scarcity of that plate.

(d) Stamps from the 1d Die II, Alphabet III, perforation 16, with Watermark Large Crown on white paper with inverted watermark are scarce. But the second most common plate with inverted watermark is plate 45, one of the scarcest plates in that issue with upright watermark. A copy of plate 45 with inverted watermark with a few trimmed perforations realised over £800 (inclusive of buyers premium) in the 'Statham' sale.

(e) The 1864 1d plates issue (letters in all four corners) is very common with inverted watermark although a number of plates are rare in that condition. The key plate (other than 77!) with upright watermark is the scarce plate 225.

This is far from being the scarcest plate with inverted watermark yet continues to command a four figure sum when available.

Notes on Pricing

This is a controversial area. Please read the following notes before considering the price listings. The pricing is for good sound used copies. Fine or very fine copies attract a significant premium. Damaged copies are worth less but copies with relatively minor faults from scarcer plates may retain the 'good used' value.

Multiples with inverted watermarks are scarce and blocks of four (or larger) are rare. Multiples attract a significant premium as do stamps with inverted watermarks on covers or entires. Inverted watermark stamps with distinctive cancellations may be expected to cost more than those with a common or garden numeral cancel.

Imperforate 1d red stamps with inverted watermark are far more common than most of the perforate issues. That is true of both Alphabet I (plates 12 to 131) and Alphabet II (plates 132 to 177) issues. The price listed below is for 4 margin copies. Three margin copies are worth less.

The demand for inverted watermark stamps has increased especially for the 1864 1d plates issue. The demand for earlier issues continues to be constrained by the difficulty for collectors in being sure that a stamp offered as plate 5, for example, is in fact from that plate. There continues to be misplated material on the market. Prices from dealers' lists and auction realisations have been taken into account in the pricing tables, as has the relative scarcity and demand for individual plates. The editor welcomes any information, critical or otherwise, which will add to or improve this listing.

Price Listings

A dash in a column indicates that a particular plate is not known to exist with inverted watermark. A hash (#) indicates that a particular plate is believed not to exist with inverted watermark. Prices may go up as demand increases but may also go down as the incidence of accurately plated copies increases.

1d Blacks

All plates (except plate 10) are known with inverted watermark. Plate 1b is relatively common. Plate 1a is the next most common but is scarce. Plates 2, 4, 5, 8 and 9 are next in order of rarity. Plate 6 is rare. Plate 7 is even rarer. Only one copy has been identified from plates 3 and 11 respectively. The latter was in the Seymour sale but its present whereabouts is unknown. A copy of 'plate 10' was offered on eBay in the last few years but was readily identifiable as being from plate 1b. 85% of all 1d Blacks with inverted watermarks come from plate 1b.

1d Black

Plate		Plate		Plate	
1a	£300	1b	£180	2	£400
3	£1200	4	£400	5	£400
6	£700	7	£1000	8	£400
9	£400	10	-	11	£3000

1d Reds from black plates

Plate		Plate		Plate	
1b	£800	2	-	5	-
8	£1500	9	£1200	10	£1800
11	-				

1d Red, Imperforate, Watermark Small Crown, Plates 12-131, Die I, Alphabet I

Most plates exist with inverted watermark. Imperforate 1d Reds with inverted watermark are relatively common far more so than many of the early perfoarated issues. Plate 24 is by far the most common of the "Maltese Cross" plates, followed by plates 45, 31, 25, 32 and 29. Plate 98 is the Alphabet I plate most commonly found with inverted watermark, closely followed by plate 100. Other relatively common plates are 69, 129, 122, 105, 109, 110, 114, 113, 97, 46, 61, 74, 76, 96, 97, 121 and 124. Prices are for four margin stamps.

Plate		Plate		Plate	
12	£400	13	-	14	£400
15	£200	16	-	17	£100
18	£300	19	£100	20	£200
21	£200	22	£250	23	£400
24	£40	25	£80	26	£200
27	£300	28	£80	29	£80
30	-	31	£60	32	£80
33	£300	34	£100	35	-
36	-	37	£200	38	£200
39	£100	40	£400	41	£80
42	£200	43	£200	44	£200
45	£60	46	£60	47	£250
49	£300	49	-	50	£80
51	£200	52	£200	53	£200
54	£250	55	-	56	£80
57	£200	58	£100	59	£300
60	£80	61	£60	62	£60
63	£100	64	£80	65	£300
66	£80	67	£300	68	£200
69	£40	70	£100	71	£100
72	£80	73	£300	74	£60
75	£300	76	£60	77	-
78	£400	79	£200	80	£100
81	-	82	£200	83	£250
84	£200	85	£200	86	£80
87	£100	88	£100	89	£80
90	£250	91	£80	92	£80
93	£80	94	£100	95	£100
96	£60	97	£60	98	£30
99	£100	100	£30	101	£60
102	£200	103	£100	104	£100
105	£40	106	£100	107	* £250
108	£60	109	£40	110	£40
111	£80	112	£60	113	£60
114	£60	115	£60	116	£80
117	£60	118	£80	119	£100
120	£100	121	£60	122	£40
123	£80	124	£60	125	£100
126	£100	127	£100	128	£80
129	£40	130	£80	131	£100

* A copy of plate 107 with inverted watermark realised over £450 (inclusive of premium) in the "Statham" sale.

1d Red, Imperforate, Watermark Small Crown, Plates 132-177, Die I, Alphabet II

All plates except 176 have been recorded with inverted watermark. Like their Alphabet I counterparts, stamps from this issue with inverted watermark are relatively common. Prices are for four margin stamps.

Plate		Plate		Plate	
132	£100	133	£80	134	£100
135	£80	136	£60	137	£60
138	£100	139	£100	140	£100
141	£60	142	£100	143	£60
144	£400	145	£80	146	£100
147	£100	148	£200	149	£100
150	£100	151	£100	152	£100
153	£60	154	£60	155	£60
156	£60	157	£100	158	£80
159	£100	160	£60	161	£80
162	£100	163	£60	164	£40
165	£80	166	£60	167	£40
168	£40	169	£60	170	£60
171	£80	172	£80	173	£60
174	£200	175	£1500	176	-
177	£1500				

A copy of plate 173 (a common plate with inverted watermark) realised £300 (inclusive of premium) in the "Statham" sale; a copy of plate 177 with inverted watermark (one of three recorded copies) realised over £2500 (inclusive of premium) in the same sale!

1d Die I, Alphabet I, Perf 16 (Archer), Watermark Small Crown, Plates 92 to 101, 107 and 111*

Only plates 99 and 100 have been recorded with inverted watermark. There is only one recorded copy of plate 99 (price £1500) but a number of copies are known from plate 100 (price £500). However, a fine used copy of plate 100 with inverted watermark realised over £1380 (inlusive of prmium) in the "Statham" sale.

* An RPS certificated copy of plate 111 with upright watermark exists.

1d Die I, Alphabet II, Perf 16, Watermark Small Crown, Plates 155, 157, 162 - 204, R1 - R6

All plates have been recorded with inverted watermark except the rare plate 168, the scarce plate 170 and plate R4. Stamps from this issue with inverted watermark are relatively common. Plate 176 is the most common plate with inverted watermark, followed by plates 180, 167, 191, 195, 203, R5, 164, 183, 172 and R5 all of which exist in numbers

Plate		Plate		Plate	
155	£300	157	£250	162	£100
163	£80	164	£40	165	£400
166	£80	167	£40	168	#
169	£100	170	-	171	£150
172	£40	173	£60	174	£100
175	£250	176	£30	178	£100
179	£250	180	£30	181	£150
182	£100	183	£60	184	£100
185	£100	186	£100	187	£150
188	£200	189	£100	190	£40
191	£40	192	£80	193	£100
194	£100	195	£40	196	£200
197	£60	198	£80	199	£100
200	£80	201	£300	202	£80
203	£40	204	£400	R1	£100
R2	£250	R3	£100	R4	-
R5	£40	R6	£80		

1d Die I, Alphabet II, Perf 14, Watermark Small Crown, Plates 194-198, 200-204, R1-R6

All plates are recorded with inverted watermark except the rare plate 195. Stamps from this issue with watermark inverted are scarce although plates 198, 203 and R5 are less scarce than other plates

Plate		Plate		Plate	
194	£400	195	#	196	£200
197	£200	198	£100	200	£300
202	£150	203	£100	204	£400
R1	£250	R2	£200	R3	£150
R4	£250	R5	£100	R6	£150

1d Die II, Alphabet II, Perf 14, Watermark Small Crown, Plates 1-21

All plates are recorded with inverted watermark except plate 13. Stamps from this issue with watermark inverted are generally scarce except plate 5 and, to a lesser extent, plates 1 and 11

Plate		Plate		Plate	
1	£100	2	£150	3	£200
4	£250	5	£80	6	£250
7	£200	8	£150	9	£150
10	£300	11	£100	12	£300
13	-	14	£250	15	£200
16	£400	17	£400	18	£300
19	£200	20	£300	21	£200

1d Die II, Alphabet II, Perf 16, Watermark Small Crown, Plates 1-15

All plates are recorded with inverted watermark except plate 12. Stamps from this issue with inverted watermark are generally scarce except plates 1 and 5 which are relatively common.

Plate		Plate		Plate	
1	£50	2	£100	3	£250
4	£400	5	£60	6	£200
7	£200	8	£200	9	£400
10	£300	11	£300	12	-
13	£350	14	£300	15	£200

1d Die II, Alphabet II, Perf 16, Watermark Large Crown, Plates 1-15, blued paper

Stamps from this issue with inverted watermark are very scarce. Plate 5 is scarce but is the most common (or rather least scarce). To date, only 6 plates have been recorded with watermark inverted. Prices are £200 (plate5), £300 (plate 8), £350 (plates 1 and 2) and £400 (plates 6 and 14).

1d Die II, Alphabet II, Perf 14, Watermark Large Crown, Plates 1-21, blued paper

All plates are recorded with inverted watermark except the rare plate 3 and plate 13. The 'Plate 13' in the "Statham" sale turned out on close examinatuion to be plate 14. This is still a difficult issue to find with watermark inverted but plate 19 is relatively common thus, as are plates 5 and 15.

Plate		Plate		Plate	
1	£150	2	£100	3	#
4	£400	5	£70	6	£250
7	£300	8	£100	9	£250
10	£250	11	£150	12	£150
13	-	14	£100	15	£70
16	£100	17	£400	18	£100
19	£50	20	£150	21	£100

1d Die II, Alphabet III, Perf 14, Watermark Small Crown, Plates 22-27 and 31*

Only plates 24 and 26 have been recorded with inverted watermark. There is only one recorded copy of plate 26 (price £1500) but a number of copies are known from plate 24 (price £400)

* An RPS certificated copy of plate 31 with upright watermark exists.

1d Die II, Alphabet III, Perf 14, Watermark Large Crown, Blued paper, Plates 22-38, 40, 42-49, 53*

Plates 27 and 33 are commonly found with inverted watermark. The next most common plates are 35, 26 and 37. Apart from these, stamps from this issue with watermark inverted are scarce but all plates from 23 to 46 exist thus.

Plate		Plate		Plate	
22	#	23	£400	24	£400
25	£300	26	£60	27	£30
28	£100	29	£300	30	£250
31	£300	32	£100	33	£40
34	£100	35	£60	36	£100
37	£100	38	£100	40	£100
42	£300	43	£200	44	£200
45	£200	46	£200	47	-
48	#	49	#	53	#

* An RPS certificated copy of plate 53 with upright watermark exists.

1d Die II, Alphabet III, Perf 14, Watermark Large Crown, (transitional issues), Plates 27, 31-38, 40, 42-49, 52, 53*, 55

This stamp is not often seen with inverted watermark but plates 27, 33, 34, 36, 37, 38, 44, 46, 47 and 49 have been recorded thus.Plates 44 and 37 are the most common (price £80); other prices are: Plates 27, 33, 34, 36 and 47 - £120; Plates 38, 46 and 49 - £200.

* Most copies of plate 53 are correctly classified as transitional issues although copies do exist in a rose red shade on white paper (but not with watermark inverted!).

1d Die II, Alphabet III, Perf 14, Watermark Large Crown, White paper, Plates 27, 33, 34, 36-39, 41-49, 52, 53, 55-68 and R17

All plates exist with watermark inverted except the rare plate 53. Plates 44, 39 and 42 are very common. Watremark type II is common on plates 39, 68, 66, 57 and R17 but is otherwise quite scarce.

Plate		Plate		Plate	
27	£60	33	£300	34	£40
36	£70	37	£80	38	£100
39	£20	41	£100	42	£25
43	£40	44	£20	45	£300
46	£70	47	£40	48	£50
49	£30	52	£80	53	#
55	£60	56	£80	57	£50
58	£40	59	£200	60	£200
61	£200	62	£100	63	£80
64	* £200	65	£2000	66	£70
67	£250	68	£40	R17	£200

* A copy of plate 64 (with missing corner) realised over £1200 (inclusive of premium) in the "Statham" sale. A copy of plate 65 realised over £2750 (inclusive of premium) in that sale.

1d Die II, Alphabet III, Perf 16, Watermark Large Crown, White paper, Plates 27, 34, 36-38, 42-49, 52, 55-60

This stamp is very scarce with watermark inverted. Only plate 44 is seen with any frequency (price £100). Other plates recorded with watermark inverted are plate 45 (price £300), plate 42 (price £350), and plates 57, 58 and 60 (price £400).

A copy of plate 45 with a few clipped perfs realised over £800 in the "Statham" sale.

1d Die II, Alphabet III, Perf 14, Watermark Large Crown, White paper, Plates 50 and 51.

Both plates exist with watermark inverted and both are found with watermarks type 1 and type 2. Neither plate is scarce with watermark inverted (price £50 each plate)

1d Die II, Alphabet II, Perf 14, Watermark Large Crown, White paper, Plates R15 and R16

Both plates exist with watermark inverted but plate 16 is rare thus. Plate R15 exists with watermarks type 1 and type 2 (price £50). Only two copies have been recorded of plate R16 (watermark type 1) price £300.

1864 1d "plates", Watermark Large Crown, letters in all four corners

This issue with inverted watermark is very much in demand by collectors, partly as a result of the publication os a priced list in previous editions of the Stoneham catalogue and partly because the plate number appears on the face of the stamp. However, buyers should beware that plating is not always straighforward.

All plates exist with inverted watermark except the exceedingly rare plate 77 and possibly plate 93. No authenticated copy of plate 93 with watermark inverted has been seen although many imposters have been, even copies of "plate 93" from important collections. The reason is that poor engraving and/or the effect of a postmark makes plate 83 (the most common plate with inverted watermark) appear as plate 93. Do not accept a plated stamp as being from plate 93 unless it has been compared with an authenticated copy of plate 93 (or the imprimatur sheet) and the position in the corner square of all four letterings match. The editor welcomes receipt of copies of "plate 93" with watermark inverted for verification.

The same is true of plate 191, an exceedingly rare plate with inverted watermark. Copies of plate 101 (a very common plate with inverted watermark) or 181, a scarce plate thus, are often passed off as plate 191. The comments above with regard to plate 93 apply.

As noted, the most common plate with inverted watermark is plate 83, followed by plates 101, 141, 136, 71, 154 and 208. Other plates commonly found with inverted watermark are 74, 84, 86, 133, 158, 167, 176, 201 and 216. Among the scarcest plates with inverted watermark are plates 89, 102, 103, 107, 110, 116, 124, 125, 132, 134, 143, 145, 147, 148, 152, 163, 168, 172, 175,, 181, 182, 183, 184, 191, 193, 194, 206, 211, 212, 213, 215, 217, and plates 219 to 225. There is no correlation between the scarcity of stamps with upright watermark from difficult plates and those difficult plates with inverted watermarks.

Plate	F/U	G/U	Plate	F/U	G/U
71	£25	£15	72	£80	£50
73	£50	£35	74	£40	£25
76	£80	£50	77	#	#
78	£80	£50	79	£50	£35
80	£80	£50	81	£80	£50
82	£100	£75	83	£20	£10
84	£40	£25	85	£50	£35
86	£30	£20	87	£100	£75
88	£40	£25	89	£100	£75
90	£50	£35	91	£50	£35
92	£50	£35	93	-	-
94	£50	£35	95	£80	£50
96	£50	£35	97	£40	£25
98	£40	£25	99	£40	£25
100	£100	£75	101	£20	£10
102	£250	£200	103	£250	£200
104	£80	£50	105	£40	£25
106	£80	£50	107	£100	£75
108	£50	£35	109	£100	£75
110	£150	£110	111	£40	£25
112	£80	£50	113	£50	£35
114	£80	£50	115	£50	£35
116	£150	£110	117	£20	£10
118	£30	£20	119	£50	£35
120	£80	£50	121	£80	£50
122	£80	£50	123	£100	£75

Plate	F/U	G/U	Plate	F/U	G/U
124	£150	£110	125	£120	£90
127	£50	£35	129	£80	£50
130	£80	£50	131	£80	£50
132	£150	£110	133	£40	£25
134	£100	£75	135	£50	£35
136	£25	£15	137	£50	£35
138	£100	£75	139	£80	£50
140	£50	£35	141	£20	£10
142	£80	£50	143	£200	£160
144	£80	£50	145	£300	£250
146	£50	£35	147	£120	£90
148	£100	£75	149	£80	£50
150	£80	£50	151	£80	£50
152	£100	£75	153	£50	£35
154	£25	£15	155	£50	£35
156	£50	£35	157	£30	£20
158	£30	£20	159	£100	£75
160	£40	£25	161	£50	£35
162	£100	£75	163	£100	£75
164	£50	£35	165	£50	£35
166	£80	£50	167	£40	£25
168	£100	£75	169	£40	£25
170	£80	£50	171	£100	£75
172	£100	£75	173	£50	£35
174	£50	£35	175	£200	£160
176	£30	£20	177	£50	£35
178	£100	£75	179	£50	£35
180	£80	£50	181	£200	£160
182	£120	£90	183	£200	£160
184	£120	£90	185	£50	£35
186	£50	£35	187	£80	£50
188	£40	£25	189	£100	£75
190	£40	£25	191	£500	£400
192	£50	£35	193	£120	£90
194	£200	£160	195	£50	£35
196	£100	£75	197	£100	£75
198	£40	£25	199	£80	£50
200	£30	£20	201	£30	£20
202	£50	£35	203	£40	£25
204	£80	£50	205	£100	£75
206	£250	£200	207	£40	£25
208	£25	£15	209	£50	£35
210	£50	£35	211	£120	£90
212	£100	£75	213	£300	£250
214	£80	£50	215	£150	£110
216	£25	£15	217	£300	£250
218	£50	£35	219	£120	£90
220	£150	£110	221	£100	£75
222	£200	£160	223	£300	£250
224	£500	£400	225	£1500	£1000

Engraved by Charles and Frederick Heath
Printer: Perkins, Bacon & Petch

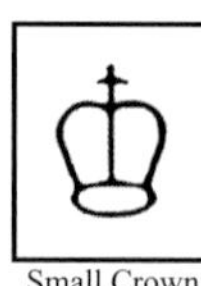

Small Crown Watermark

1840 (6 May) Wmk. Small Crown. White paper. Imperforate

No.			M/M	F/U	G/U	✉
V1	1d	**Greyish black**. Plate 1a	£4000	£200	£120	£275
V1a		Wmk. inverted		£400	£300	
V1b		Grey black (worn plate)	£4200	£200	£120	£275
V1c		Intense black	£4500	£200	£120	£275
V2	1d	**Black.** Plate 1b	£2000	£140	£85	£200
V2a		Wmk. inverted		£250	£180	
V2b		Intense black	£2200	£160	£95	£200
V3	1d	**Black.** Plate 2	£2000	£160	£95	£210
V3a		Wmk. inverted	£4000	£500	£400	
V3b		Intense black	£2000	£160	£95	£210
V3c		Grey black (worn plate)	£2200	£170	£100	£220
V4	1d	**Black.** Plate 3	£2400	£160	£110	£230
V4a		Wmk. inverted		£1800	£1200	
V4b		Grey black	£2400	£180	£110	£220
V5	1d	**Black.** Plate 4	£2000	£160	£100	£210
V5a		Wmk. inverted		£500	£400	
V5b		Intense black	£2200	£160	£100	£210
V6	1d	**Black.** Plate 5	£2000	£150	£100	£210
V6a		Wmk inverted		£500	£400	
V6b		Intense black	£2200	£160	£110	£220
V7	1d	**Black.** Plate 6	£2500	£160	£100	£220
V7a		Wmk. inverted	£4500	£850	£700	
V7b		Intense black	£2500	£160	£100	£220
V8	1d	**Black.** Plate 7	£2500	£160	£100	£220
V8a		Wmk. inverted	£4500	£1200	£1000	
V8b		Greyish black	£2500	£170	£100	£220
V9	1d	**Black.** Plate 8	£3000	£180	£110	£240
V9a		Wmk. inverted	£4800	£500	£400	
V10	1d	**Black.** Plate 9	£3500	£180	£110	£240
V10a		Wmk. inverted		£500	£400	
V11	1d	**Black.** Plate 10	£4500	£275	£175	£400
V11a		Grey black	£4500	£275	£175	£400
V12	1d	**Black.** Plate 11	£5500	£1800	£1200	£3500
V12a		Wmk. inverted			£3000	
V12b		Grey black	£5500	£1800	£1300	£3500
V13	2d	**Blue.** Plate 1 (8.5.40)	£8000	£400	£250	£600
V13a		Wmk. inverted	£4500	£700	£450	
V13b		Deep blue	£8000	£400	£260	£600
V13c		Steel blue	£8000	£420	£270	£650
V13d		Pale blue	£8500	£400	£270	£675
V13e		Milky blue	£9500	£500	£300	£750
V13f		Violet blue	£10500	£800	£475	£1200
V14	2d	**Blue.** Plate 2	£8000	£500	£275	£700
V14a		Wmk. inverted	£14500	£2000	£1500	
V14b		Deep blue	£8000	£500	£275	£720
V14c		Pale blue	£8000	£550	£300	£750

1841 (10 Feb.) Wmk. Small Crown. Blued paper. Imperforate.

Die I. Alphabet I

No.			M/M	F/U	G/U	✉
V15	1d	**Red brown.** Plate 1b	£3000	£150	£90	£225
V15a		Wmk. inverted	£5000	£1200	£800	
V16	1d	**Red brown.** Plate 2	£1200	£120	£75	£175
V17	1d	**Red brown.** Plate 5	£800	£70	£40	£110
V18	1d	**Red brown.** Plate 8	£600	£60	£35	£90
V18a		Wmk. inverted			£1500	
V19	1d	**Red brown.** Plate 9	£600	£60	£35	£95
V19a		Wmk. inverted			£1200	
V20	1d	**Red brown.** Plate 10	£600	£55	£35	£100
V20a		Wmk. inverted			£1800	
V21	1d	**Red brown.** Plate 11	£400	£45	£30	£90

The above stamps were printed from 'black' plates and there are several shades

No.			M/M	F/U	G/U	✉
V22	1d	**Red brown.** Plates 12 - 131	£110	6.00	2.50	£10
V22a		Wmk. inverted	£195	£30	£20	
V22b		Deep red brown	£100	£12	5.00	£14
V22c		Pale red brown	£120	£12	6.00	£17
V22d		Lake red	£1200	£300	£180	£500
V22e		Orange brown	£300	£70	£30	£70
V22f		Red brown on lavender tinted paper. Plates 118 - 131	£400	£85	£40	£80

1841 (3 March) White lines added to design. Wmk Small Crown. Bluish paper. Imperforate.

No.			M/M	F/U	G/U	✉
V23	2d	**Blue.** Plate 3	£1400	£35	£20	£100
V23a		Wmk. inverted	£3000	£300	£190	
V23b		Deep blue	£1500	£40	£22	£110
V23c		Pale blue	£1600	£40	£22	£110
V24	2d	**Blue.** Plate 4	£1200	£40	£20	£100
V24a		Wmk. inverted		£130	£80	
V24b		Deep blue	£1200	£40	£20	£100
V24c		Pale blue	£1200	£40	£20	£100
V24d		Violet blue on thick lavender tinted paper	£2000	£300	£100	£375

1852 (6 Feb.) Change to Alphabet II. Wmk. Small Crown. Bluish paper. Imperforate.

Die I. Alphabet II

No.			M/M	F/U	G/U	✉
V25	1d	**Red brown.** Plates 132 - 175	£125	9.50	4.00	£15
V25a		Wmk. inverted	£600	£40	£30	
V25b		Lake red	£1000	£300	£150	£350
V25c		Orange brown	£300	£50	£18	£55
V25d		Red brown on lavender tinted paper. Plates 132 - 136	£500	£95	£50	£100

1850 Wmk Small Crown. Bluish paper. Archer experimental perf. 16

Die I. Alphabet I

No.			M/M	F/U	G/U	✉
V26	1d	**Red brown.** Plates 92 -101	£800	£250	£150	£750
V26a		Wmk. inverted		£700	£500	

1854 (Feb.) - 55 Wmk. Small Crown. Bluish paper. Perf 16

Die I. Alphabet I

No.			M/M	F/U	G/U	✉
V27	2d	**Deep blue.** Plate 4 (13.5.54)	£1200	£35	£20	£65
V27a		Wmk. inverted		£100	£50	
V27b		Pale blue	£1500	£55	£30	£70

Die I. Alphabet II

No.			M/M	F/U	G/U	✉
V28	1d	**Red brown.** Plates 155, 157, 162 - 204, R1 - R6	£90	6.00	3.00	£10
V28a		Wmk. inverted	£200	£50	£30	
V28b		Yellow brown	£110	£12	6.00	£20
V28c		Brick red	£140	£12	6.00	£20
V28d		Orange brown	£350	£60	£25	£60
V28e		Plum	£600	£120	£50	£120
V29	2d	**Blue.** Plate 5 (28.8.55)	£2000	£150	£70	£200
V29a		Wmk. inverted	£2000	£300	£200	

Die II. Alphabet II

No.			M/M	F/U	G/U	✉
V30	1d	**Red brown.** Plates 1 - 15 (1.3.55)	£120	£12	8.00	£15
V30a		Wmk. inverted	£400	£70	£50	
V30b		Yellow brown	£150	£16	9.00	£18
V30c		Brick red	£160	£17	£10	£20
V30d		Plum	£400	£75	£40	£50

1855 (Jan.) Wmk. Small Crown. Bluish paper. Perf 14

Die I. Alphabet I

No.			M/M	F/U	G/U	✉
V31	2d	**Blue.** Plate 4 (22.2.55)	£1600	£120	£65	£120
V31a		Wmk. inverted		£275	£175	

Die I. Alphabet II

No.			M/M	F/U	G/U	✉
V32	1d	**Red brown.** Plates 194 - 204 R1 - R6	£200	£20	£11	£27
V32a		Wmk. inverted		£150	£100	
V32b		Yellow brown	£210	£20	£12	£25
V32c		Brick red	£220	£40	£25	£40
V32d		Orange brown	£290	£50	£35	£50
V32e		Plum	£450	£100	£50	£85
V33	2d	**Blue.** Plate 5 (5.7.55)	£1700	£120	£60	£120
V33a		Wmk. inverted		£275	£175	

Die II. Alphabet II

No.			M/M	F/U	G/U	✉
V34	1d	**Red brown.** Plates 1 - 21 (28.2.55)	£160	£20	£12	£20
V34a		Wmk. inverted	£375	£120	£80	
V34b		Deep red brown	£200	£20	£10	£20
V34c		Orange brown	£450	£95	£60	£65
V34d		Plum	£650	£150	£70	£100

Die II. Alphabet III

No.			M/M	F/U	G/U	✉
V35	1d	**Red brown.** Plates 22 - 27 (18.8.55)	£950	£200	£130	£500
V35a		Wmk. inverted		£600	£400	

Large Crown Watermark

Large Crown Watermark *(modified and introduced in March 1861)*

1855 (15 May) Wmk. Large Crown. Bluish paper. Perf 16

Die I. Alphabet II

No.			M/M	F/U	G/U	✉
V36	2d	**Blue.** Plate 5 (20.7.55)	£1800	£120	£75	£190
V36a		Wmk. inverted		£350	£250	

Die II. Alphabet II

No.			M/M	F/U	G/U	✉
V37	1d	**Red brown.** Plates 1 - 15 (15.5.55)	£300	£45	£30	£55
V37a		Wmk. inverted		£200	£150	
V37b		Deep red brown	£300	£50	£30	£60

1855 (June) Wmk. Large Crown. Bluish paper. Perf 14

Die I. Alphabet II

No.			M/M	F/U	G/U	✉
V38	2d	**Blue.** Plate 5 (20.7.55)	£750	£16	9.00	£50
V38a		Greenish blue	£850	£18	£10	£60
V38b		Wmk. inverted		£120	£80	

Die I. Alphabet III

No.			M/M	F/U	G/U	✉
V39	2d	**Blue.** Plate 6 (2.7.57)	£900	£16	9.00	£50
V39a		Wmk. inverted		£120	£80	

Die II. Alphabet II

No.			M/M	F/U	G/U	✉
V40	1d	**Red brown.** Plates 1 - 21	£110	7.00	5.00	£10
V40a		Wmk. inverted		£70	£50	
V40b		Yellow brown	£130	£15	8.00	£12
V40c		Plum	£350	£90	£50	£80

Die II. Alphabet III

No.			M/M	F/U	G/U	✉
V41	1d	**Red brown.** Plates 22 - 38, 40, 42 - 49 (8.55)	£75	4.00	2.50	5.00
V41a		Wmk. inverted	£300	£50	£30	
V41b		Brick red	£110	7.00	5.00	6.00
V41c		Brown rose	£110	£12	8.00	9.00
V41d		Orange brown	£175	£20	£12	£10
V41e		Orange red	£175	£20	£12	£20
V41f		Plum	£850	£180	£90	£130
V41g		Deep claret on deep blue paper	£500	£80	£45	£60

1857 Wmk. Large Crown. Cream toned paper. Perf 14

Die II. Alphabet III

No.			M/M	F/U	G/U	✉
V42	1d	**Red orange.** Plates 27 - 55	£130	£30	£17	£22
V42a		Wmk. inverted	£450	£120	£80	
V42b		Orange brown	£140	£30	£15	£20
V42c		Pale red	£170	£30	£15	£20
V42d		Pale rose	£170	£30	£15	£20

1857 (26 Dec.) - 58 New colours on 1d and thin white lines on 2d. Wmk. Large Crown. White paper. Perf. 16

Die I Alphabet III

No.			M/M	F/U	G/U	✉
V43	2d	**Blue.** Plate 6 (1.12.58)	£2700	£140	£95	£195
V43a		Wmk. inverted		£700	£500	

Die II. Alphabet III

No.			M/M	F/U	G/U	✉
V44	1d	**Rose red.** Plates various 27 - 60	£550	£30	£12	£25
V44a		Wmk. inverted		£130	£80	

1856 (Nov) - 63 Wmk. Large Crown. White paper. Perf 14

Die II. Alphabet II

No.			M/M	F/U	G/U	✉
V45	1d	**Rose red.** Plates R15, R16 (1862)	£75	4.00	2.50	7.00
V45a		Wmk. inverted		£75	£50	
V45b		Pale rose red	£75	4.00	2.50	7.00
V45c		Pale red. Plate R15	£125	£50	£20	£35

Die II. Alphabet III

No.			M/M	F/U	G/U	✉
V46	1d	**Rose red.** Plates various 27 - 68, R17 (1856)	£20	3.00	1.50	2.50
V46a		Wmk. inverted	£30	£30	£20	
V46b		Deep rose red (7.56)	£22	3.00	1.50	2.50
V46c		Pale red (4.56)	£50	4.50	2.00	4.50
V46d		Pale rose (3.56)	£50	4.50	2.00	5.00
V46e		Pale rose pink (1863)	£65	5.00	2.00	6.00
V46f		Red brown (1856)	£250	£90	£75	£90
V46g		Bright rose red (3.56)	£175	£35	£15	£25

Die II. Alphabet IV

No.			M/M	F/U	G/U	✉
V47	1d	**Rose red.** Plates 50, 51 (1861)	£85	5.50	3.00	9.00
V47a		Wmk. inverted	£170	£70	£50	
V47b		Pale rose red	£85	5.50	3.00	9.00

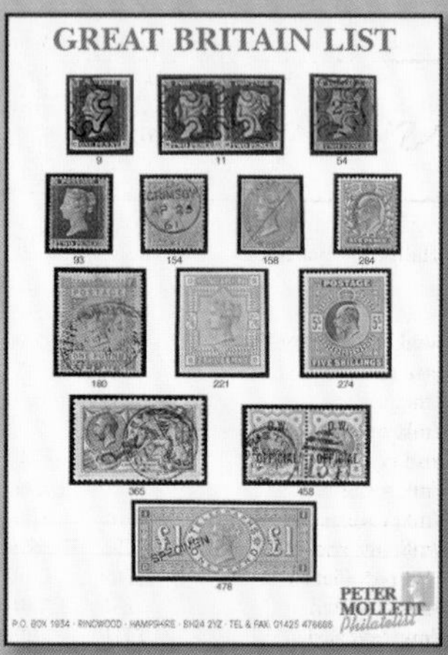

GREAT BRITAIN LIST
PETER MOLLETT Philatelist

POSTAGE
TWO PENCE
TWO PENCE
O.W.
CANCELLED
OFFICIAL
POSTAGE & REVENUE

POSTAGE

Letters in all four corners and plate numbers shown in the design.
Printer: Perkins, Bacon & Co.

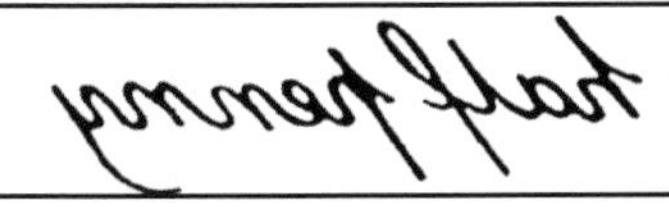

Halfpenny Watermark

Plate Number (20) at right

1870 (1 Oct.) Wmk. Halfpenny. Perf 14

No.			M/M	F/U	G/U	✉
V49	½d	**Rose red.** Plate 1	£80	£40	£20	£75
V49a		Wmk. inverted		£100	£75	
V49b		Wmk. inverted and rev.		£75	£50	
V50	½d	**Rose red.** Plate 3	£60	7.00	3.00	£25
V50a		Wmk. inverted	£120	£75	£50	
V50b		Wmk. reversed	£100	£60	£40	
V50c		Wmk. inv. and rev.	£75	£20	£10	
V51	½d	**Rose red.** Plate 4	£60	7.00	3.00	£20
V51a		Wmk. inverted	£85	£40	£25	
V51b		Wmk. reversed	£110	£80	£50	
V51c		Wmk. inv. and rev.		£50	£40	
V52	½d	**Rose red.** Plate 5	£35	5.00	3.00	£20
V52a		Wmk. inverted		£35	£20	
V52b		Wmk. reversed		£25	£12	
V52c		Wmk. inv. and rev.		£50	£30	
V53	½d	**Rose red.** Plate 6	£50	5.00	3.00	£20
V53a		Wmk. inverted		£40	£30	
V35b		Wmk. reversed		£75	£50	
V53c		Wmk. inv. and rev.		£60	£40	
V54	½d	**Rose red.** Plate 8	£95	£30	£15	£65
V54a		Wmk. inverted		£100	£70	
V54b		Wmk. reversed		£75	£50	
V54c		Wmk. inv. and rev.		£60	£40	
V55	½d	**Rose red.** Plate 9 **	£1500	£250	£170	£850
V55a		Wmk. inv. and rev.		£500	£400	
V56	½d	**Rose red.** Plate 10	£50	5.00	3.00	£20
V56a		Wmk. inverted		£75	£50	
V56b		Wmk. inv. and rev.		£50	£35	
V57	½d	**Rose red.** Plate 11	£50	5.00	3.00	£20
V57a		Wmk. inverted	£120	£60	£40	
V57b		Wmk. reversed		£75	£50	
V57c		Wmk. inv. and rev.		£12	8.00	
V58	½d	**Rose red.** Plate 12	£50	5.00	3.00	£20
V58a		Wmk. reversed		£100	£75	
V58b		Wmk. inv. and rev.	£75	£15	£10	
V59	½d	**Rose red.** Plate 13	£50	5.00	3.00	£20
V59a		Wmk. inverted		£75	£50	
V59b		Wmk. reversed		£30	£20	
V59c		Wmk. inv. and rev.		£60	£40	
V60	½d	**Rose red.** Plate 14	£50	5.00	3.00	£20
V60a		Wmk. reversed		£60	£40	
V60b		Wmk. inv. and rev.		£60	£40	
V61	½d	**Rose red.** Plate 15	£60	9.00	5.00	£20
V61a		Wmk. inverted		£100	£75	
V61b		Wmk. reversed		£70	£50	
V61c		Wmk. inv. and rev.		£70	£50	

No.			M/M	F/U	G/U	✉
V62	½d	**Rose red.** Plate 19	£80	£15	8.00	£40
V62a		Wmk. inverted		£80	£55	
V62b		Wmk. reversed		£70	£50	
V62c		Wmk. inv. and rev.		£80	£55	
V63	½d	**Rose red.** Plate 20	£75	£20	£10	£60
V63a		Wmk. inverted		£80	£55	
V63b		Wmk. reversed		£80	£55	
V63c		Wmk. inv. and rev.	£120	£40	£25	

** Beware of stamps from Plate 19 with the figure '1' obscured or removed

Plate Number (219) at right

1864 (1 April) Wmk. Large Crown. Perf 14

No.			M/M	F/U	G/U	✉
V64	1d	**Rose red.** Plate 71	£24	2.00	1.00	4.00
V64a		Wmk. inverted		£25	£15	
V65	1d	**Rose red.** Plate 72	£24	2.00	1.00	4.00
V65a		Wmk. inverted		£80	£50	
V66	1d	**Rose red.** Plate 73	£24	2.00	1.00	4.00
V66a		Wmk. inverted		£50	£35	
V67	1d	**Rose red.** Plate 74	£20	2.00	1.00	4.00
V67a		Wmk. inverted		£40	£25	
V68	1d	**Rose red.** Plate 76	£20	1.00	60	4.00
V68a		Wmk. inverted		£80	£50	
V69	1d	**Rose red.** Plate 77		£120000	#	#
V70	1d	**Rose red.** Plate 78	£30	1.00	60	4.00
V70a		Wmk. inverted		£80	£50	
V71	1d	**Rose red.** Plate 79	£20	1.50	60	4.00
V71a		Wmk. inverted		£50	£35	
V72	1d	**Rose red.** Plate 80	£20	1.50	1.00	3.00
V72a		Wmk. inverted		£80	£50	
V73	1d	**Rose red.** Plate 81	£27	1.00	60	4.00
V73a		Wmk. inverted		£80	£50	
V74	1d	**Rose red.** Plate 82	£100	3.00	1.10	£10
V74a		Wmk. inverted		£100	£75	
V75	1d	**Rose red.** Plate 83	£120	3.50	2.50	£15
V75a		Wmk. inverted		£20	£10	
V76	1d	**Rose red.** Plate 84	£30	1.50	1.00	5.00
V76a		Wmk. inverted		£40	£25	
V77	1d	**Rose red.** Plate 85	£18	1.50	1.00	3.00
V77a		Wmk. inverted		£50	£35	
V78	1d	**Rose red.** Plate 86	£20	2.00	1.00	3.00
V78a		Wmk. inverted		£30	£20	
V79	1d	**Rose red.** Plate 87	£14	1.50	80	3.00
V79a		Wmk. inverted		£100	£75	
V80	1d	**Rose red.** Plate 88	£130	5.00	2.75	£20
V80a		Wmk. inverted		£40	£25	
V81	1d	**Rose red.** Plate 89	£16	1.50	60	1.00
V81a		Wmk. inverted		£100	£75	
V82	1d	**Rose red.** Plate 90	£15	1.50	60	5.00
V82a		Wmk. inverted		£50	£35	
V83	1d	**Rose red.** Plate 91	£22	3.00	1.50	3.00
V83a		Wmk. inverted		£50	£35	
V84	1d	**Rose red.** Plate 92	£16	1.50	60	3.00
V84a		Wmk. inverted		£50	£35	
V85	1d	**Rose red.** Plate 93	£22	1.50	70	4.00
V85a		Wmk. inverted		-	-	
V86	1d	**Rose red.** Plate 94	£22	2.75	1.25	3.00
V86a		Wmk. inverted		£50	£35	

No.			M/M	F/U	G/U	✉
V87	1d	**Rose red.** Plate 95	£18	1.50	60	3.00
V87a		Wmk. inverted		£80	£50	
V88	1d	**Rose red.** Plate 96	£18	1.50	60	3.00
V88a		Wmk. inverted		£50	£35	
V89	1d	**Rose red.** Plate 97	£18	1.50	70	3.00
V89a		Wmk. inverted		£40	£25	
V90	1d	**Rose red.** Plate 98	£18	3.00	1.75	6.00
V90a		Wmk. inverted		£40	£25	
V91	1d	**Rose red.** Plate 99	£22	2.50	1.10	6.00
V91a		Wmk. inverted		£40	£25	
V92	1d	**Rose red.** Plate 100	£22	1.50	70	£15
V92a		Wmk. inverted		£100	£75	
V93	1d	**Rose red.** Plate 101	£24	4.00	2.25	5.00
V93a		Wmk. inverted		£20	£10	
V94	1d	**Rose red.** Plate 102	£17	1.50	70	3.00
V94a		Wmk. inverted		£250	£200	
V95	1d	**Rose red.** Plate 103	£22	1.50	70	5.00
V95a		Wmk. inverted		£250	£200	
V96	1d	**Rose red.** Plate 104	£27	2.75	1.10	£15
V96a		Wmk. inverted		£80	£50	
V97	1d	**Rose red.** Plate 105	£37	4.00	2.50	£12
V97a		Wmk. inverted		£40	£25	
V98	1d	**Rose red.** Plate 106	£20	1.50	65	4.00
V98a		Wmk. inverted		£80	£50	
V99	1d	**Rose red.** Plate 107	£22	3.00	1.75	6.00
V99a		Wmk. inverted		£100	£75	
V100	1d	**Rose red.** Plate 108	£26	1.50	70	£12
V100a		Wmk. inverted		£50	£35	
V101	1d	**Rose red.** Plate 109	£38	1.50	80	£10
V101a		Wmk. inverted		£100	£75	
V102	1d	**Rose red.** Plate 110	£22	5.00	2.25	8.00
V102a		Wmk. inverted		£150	£110	
V103	1d	**Rose red.** Plate 111	£26	1.50	80	3.00
V103a		Wmk. inverted		£40	£25	
V104	1d	**Rose red.** Plate 112	£29	1.50	80	8.00
V104a		Wmk. inverted		£80	£50	
V105	1d	**Rose red.** Plate 113	£20	6.00	3.00	5.00
V105a		Wmk. inverted		£50	£35	
V106	1d	**Rose red.** Plate 114	£130	7.00	3.25	£10
V106a		Wmk. inverted		£80	£50	
V107	1d	**Rose red.** Plate 115	£45	1.50	80	£10
V107a		Wmk. inverted		£50	£35	
V108	1d	**Rose red.** Plate 116	£36	6.00	3.25	6.00
V108a		Wmk. inverted		£150	£110	
V109	1d	**Rose red.** Plate 117	£20	1.50	60	3.00
V109a		Wmk. inverted		£20	£10	
V110	1d	**Rose red.** Plate 118	£20	1.50	70	3.00
V110a		Wmk. inverted		£30	£20	
V111	1d	**Rose red.** Plate 119	£20	1.50	70	3.00
V111a		Wmk. inverted		£50	£35	
V112	1d	**Rose red.** Plate 120	£12	1.20	60	3.00
V112a		Wmk. inverted		£80	£50	
V113	1d	**Rose red.** Plate 121	£18	5.50	2.50	4.00
V113a		Wmk. inverted		£80	£50	
V114	1d	**Rose red.** Plate 122	£12	1.20	60	3.00
V114a		Wmk. inverted		£80	£50	
V115	1d	**Rose red.** Plate 123	£16	1.50	70	3.00
V115a		Wmk. inverted		£100	£75	
V116	1d	**Rose red.** Plate 124	£12	1.50	50	3.00
V116a		Wmk. inverted		£150	£110	
V117	1d	**Rose red.** Plate 125	£17	1.50	1.00	3.00
V117a		Wmk. inverted		£120	£90	
V118	1d	**Rose red.** Plate 127	£20	2.00	1.00	4.00
V118a		Wmk. inverted		£50	£35	
V119	1d	**Rose red.** Plate 129	£19	2.00	1.00	3.00
V119a		Wmk. inverted		£80	£50	
V120	1d	**Rose red.** Plate 130	£20	1.50	80	3.00
V120a		Wmk. inverted		£80	£50	
V121	1d	**Rose red.** Plate 131	£30	9.00	4.50	6.00
V121a		Wmk. inverted		£80	£50	
V122	1d	**Rose red.** Plate 132	£80	£20	£10	£30
V122a		Wmk. inverted		£150	£110	
V123	1d	**Rose red.** Plate 133	£55	7.50	4.25	£20
V123a		Wmk. inverted		£40	£25	
V124	1d	**Rose red.** Plate 134	£12	1.50	60	3.00
V124a		Wmk. inverted		£100	£75	
V125	1d	**Rose red.** Plate 135	£42	£15	8.00	£15
V125a		Wmk. inverted		£50	£35	
V126	1d	**Rose red.** Plate 136	£78	8.00	5.50	8.00
V126a		Wmk. inverted		£25	£15	
V127	1d	**Rose red.** Plate 137	£13	1.50	70	3.00
V127a		Wmk. inverted		£50	£35	
V128	1d	**Rose red.** Plate 138	£15	1.50	70	3.00
V128a		Wmk. inverted		£100	£75	
V129	1d	**Rose red.** Plate 139	£26	9.00	4.50	£15
V129a		Wmk. inverted		£80	£50	
V130	1d	**Rose red.** Plate 140	£15	1.50	60	3.00
V130a		Wmk. inverted		£50	£35	
V131	1d	**Rose red.** Plate 141	£50	3.00	1.50	£15
V131a		Wmk. inverted		£20	£10	
V132	1d	**Rose red.** Plate 142	£27	9.00	5.00	£12
V132a		Wmk. inverted		£80	£50	
V133	1d	**Rose red.** Plate 143	£20	7.00	3.00	8.00
V133a		Wmk. inverted		£200	£160	
V134	1d	**Rose red.** Plate 144	£50	£10	5.00	£14
V134a		Wmk. inverted		£80	£50	
V135	1d	**Rose red.** Plate 145	£13	1.50	70	3.00
V135a		Wmk. inverted		£300	£250	
V136	1d	**Rose red.** Plate 146	£13	3.00	1.50	3.00
V136a		Wmk. inverted		£50	£35	
V137	1d	**Rose red.** Plate 147	£20	2.00	80	4.50
V137a		Wmk. inverted		£120	£90	
V138	1d	**Rose red.** Plate 148	£20	3.00	1.50	3.00
V138a		Wmk. inverted		£100	£75	
V139	1d	**Rose red.** Plate 149	£20	3.00	1.50	3.00
V139a		Wmk. inverted		£80	£50	
V140	1d	**Rose red.** Plate 150	£12	1.50	60	3.00
V140a		Wmk. inverted		£80	£50	
V141	1d	**Rose red.** Plate 151	£20	6.00	3.50	8.00
V141a		Wmk. inverted		£80	£50	
V142	1d	**Rose red.** Plate 152	£16	3.00	1.25	6.00
V142a		Wmk. inverted		£100	£75	
V143	1d	**Rose red.** Plate 153	£50	6.00	2.50	£25
V143a		Wmk. inverted		£50	£35	
V144	1d	**Rose red.** Plate 154	£14	1.50	60	4.00
V144a		Wmk. inverted		£25	£15	
V145	1d	**Rose red.** Plate 155	£14	1.50	70	4.00
V145a		Wmk. inverted		£50	£35	
V146	1d	**Rose red.** Plate 156	£14	1.50	60	4.00
V146a		Wmk. inverted		£50	£35	
V147	1d	**Rose red.** Plate 157	£14	1.50	60	4.00
V147a		Wmk. inverted		£30	£20	
V148	1d	**Rose red.** Plate 158	£18	1.50	60	3.00
V148a		Wmk. inverted		£30	£20	
V149	1d	**Rose red.** Plate 159	£18	1.50	60	3.00
V149a		Wmk. inverted		£100	£75	
V150	1d	**Rose red.** Plate 160	£18	1.50	60	3.00
V150a		Wmk. inverted		£40	£25	
V151	1d	**Rose red.** Plate 161	£18	5.00	1.50	£12
V151a		Wmk. inverted		£50	£35	
V152	1d	**Rose red.** Plate 162	£16	4.00	1.75	5.00
V152a		Wmk. inverted		£100	£75	
V153	1d	**Rose red.** Plate 163	£16	2.00	70	5.00
V153a		Wmk. inverted		£100	£75	
V154	1d	**Rose red.** Plate 164	£14	2.00	85	6.00
V154a		Wmk. inverted		£80	£50	
V155	1d	**Rose red.** Plate 165	£13	1.50	60	3.00
V155a		Wmk. inverted		£50	£35	
V156	1d	**Rose red.** Plate 166	£13	3.00	1.50	4.00
V156a		Wmk. inverted		£80	£50	
V157	1d	**Rose red.** Plate 167	£13	1.50	60	3.00
V157a		Wmk. inverted		£40	£25	
V158	1d	**Rose red.** Plate 168	£13	5.00	2.00	6.00
V158a		Wmk. inverted		£100	£75	
V159	1d	**Rose red.** Plate 169	£16	5.00	1.10	£10
V159a		Wmk. inverted		£40	£25	
V160	1d	**Rose red.** Plate 170	£12	1.50	60	3.00
V160a		Wmk. inverted		£80	£50	

No.			M/M	F/U	G/U	✉
V161	1d	**Rose red.** Plate 171	£12	1.50	60	3.00
V161a		Wmk. inverted		£100	£75	
V162	1d	**Rose red.** Plate 172	£12	1.50	60	3.00
V162a		Wmk. inverted		£100	£75	
V163	1d	**Rose red.** Plate 173	£20	5.00	3.00	8.00
V163a		Wmk. inverted		£50	£35	
V164	1d	**Rose red.** Plate 174	£12	1.50	60	3.00
V164a		Wmk. inverted		£50	£35	
V165	1d	**Rose red.** Plate 175	£20	3.00	1.20	6.00
V165a		Wmk. inverted		£200	£160	
V166	1d	**Rose red.** Plate 176	£20	3.00	1.20	6.00
V166a		Wmk. inverted		£30	£20	
V167	1d	**Rose red.** Plate 177	£16	1.50	60	3.00
V167a		Wmk. inverted		£50	£35	
V168	1d	**Rose red.** Plate 178	£12	2.00	1.00	£10
V168a		Wmk. inverted		£100	£75	
V169	1d	**Rose red.** Plate 179	£16	2.00	1.00	4.00
V169a		Wmk. inverted		£50	£35	
V170	1d	**Rose red.** Plate 180	£16	3.00	1.00	£15
V170a		Wmk. inverted		£80	£50	
V171	1d	**Rose red.** Plate 181	£13	1.50	60	2.00
V171a		Wmk. inverted		£200	£150	
V172	1d	**Rose red.** Plate 182	£35	2.00	1.25	£14
V172a		Wmk. inverted		£120	£90	
V173	1d	**Rose red.** Plate 183	£16	2.00	1.00	4.00
V173a		Wmk. inverted		£200	£160	
V174	1d	**Rose red.** Plate 184	£12	1.50	60	8.00
V174a		Wmk. inverted		£120	£90	
V175	1d	**Rose red.** Plate 185	£16	2.00	75	£10
V175a		Wmk. inverted		£50	£35	
V176	1d	**Rose red.** Plate 186	£16	2.00	75	8.00
V176a		Wmk. inverted		£50	£35	
V177	1d	**Rose red.** Plate 187	£13	1.50	70	4.00
V177a		Wmk. inverted		£80	£50	
V178	1d	**Rose red.** Plate 188	£19	5.00	2.50	£10
V178a		Wmk. inverted		£40	£25	
V179	1d	**Rose red.** Plate 189	£20	4.00	2.00	£14
V179a		Wmk. inverted		£100	£75	
V180	1d	**Rose red.** Plate 190	£13	3.00	1.75	£14
V180a		Wmk. inverted		£40	£25	
V181	1d	**Rose red.** Plate 191	£12	4.00	2.00	8.00
V181a		Wmk. inverted		£500	£400	
V182	1d	**Rose red.** Plate 192	£14	1.50	60	3.00
V182a		Wmk. inverted		£50	£35	
V183	1d	**Rose red.** Plate 193	£14	1.50	60	6.00
V183a		Wmk. inverted		£120	£90	
V184	1d	**Rose red.** Plate 194	£14	4.00	2.00	8.00
V184a		Wmk. inverted		£200	£160	
V185	1d	**Rose red.** Plate 195	£14	4.00	2.00	4.00
V185a		Wmk. inverted		£50	£35	
V186	1d	**Rose red.** Plate 196	£14	2.00	1.00	6.00
V186a		Wmk. inverted		£100	£75	
V187	1d	**Rose red.** Plate 197	£20	6.00	3.00	£10
V187a		Wmk. inverted		£100	£75	
V188	1d	**Rose red.** Plate 198	£14	3.00	1.50	6.00
V188a		Wmk. inverted		£40	£25	
V189	1d	**Rose red.** Plate 199	£17	3.00	1.50	6.00
V189a		Wmk. inverted		£80	£50	
V190	1d	**Rose red.** Plate 200	£17	1.50	60	8.00
V190a		Wmk. inverted		£30	£20	
V191	1d	**Rose red.** Plate 201	£14	3.00	1.50	4.00
V191a		Wmk. inverted		£30	£20	
V192	1d	**Rose red.** Plate 202	£16	5.00	2.00	£10
V192a		Wmk. inverted		£50	£35	
V193	1d	**Rose red.** Plate 203	£14	7.00	4.00	£10
V193a		Wmk. inverted		£40	£25	
V194	1d	**Rose red.** Plate 204	£15	1.50	60	£10
V194a		Wmk. inverted		£80	£50	
V195	1d	**Rose red.** Plate 205	£15	2.00	70	£14
V195a		Wmk. inverted		£100	£75	
V196	1d	**Rose red.** Plate 206	£15	7.00	4.00	£14
V196a		Wmk. inverted		£250	£200	
V197	1d	**Rose red.** Plate 207	£15	7.00	4.00	£14
V197a		Wmk. inverted		£40	£25	

No.			M/M	F/U	G/U	✉
V198	1d	**Rose red.** Plate 208	£16	8.00	4.50	£16
V198a		Wmk. inverted		£25	£15	
V199	1d	**Rose red.** Plate 209	£15	8.00	4.50	£16
V199a		Wmk. inverted		£50	£35	
V200	1d	**Rose red.** Plate 210	£18	9.00	5.00	£14
V200a		Wmk. inverted		£50	£35	
V201	1d	**Rose red.** Plate 211	£22	£14	8.00	£50
V201a		Wmk. inverted		£120	£90	
V202	1d	**Rose red.** Plate 212	£17	£11	4.00	£30
V202a		Wmk. inverted		£100	£75	
V203	1d	**Rose red.** Plate 213	£17	£10	4.00	£30
V203a		Wmk. inverted		£300	£250	
V204	1d	**Rose red.** Plate 214	£20	£15	6.00	£30
V204a		Wmk. inverted		£80	£50	
V205	1d	**Rose red.** Plate 215	£20	£15	6.00	£30
V205a		Wmk. inverted		£150	£110	
V206	1d	**Rose red.** Plate 216	£20	£15	6.00	£30
V206a		Wmk. inverted		£25	£15	
V207	1d	**Rose red.** Plate 217	£20	4.00	1.75	£30
V207a		Wmk. inverted		£300	£250	
V208	1d	**Rose red.** Plate 218	£18	5.00	2.75	£50
V208a		Wmk. inverted		£50	£35	
V209	1d	**Rose red.** Plate 219	£45	£40	£30	£55
V209a		Wmk. inverted		£120	£90	
V210	1d	**Rose red.** Plate 220	£16	4.00	2.50	£30
V210a		Wmk. inverted		£150	£110	
V211	1d	**Rose red.** Plate 221	£18	£13	7.00	£45
V211a		Wmk. inverted		£100	£75	
V212	1d	**Rose red.** Plate 222	£25	£22	£12	£50
V212a		Wmk. inverted		£200	£160	
V213	1d	**Rose red.** Plate 223	£36	£50	£30	£50
V213a		Wmk. inverted		£300	£250	
V214	1d	**Rose red.** Plate 224	£38	£50	£30	£55
V214a		Wmk. inverted		£500	£400	
V215	1d	**Rose red.** Plate 225	£850	£380	£250	£1000
V215a		Wmk. inverted		£1500	£1000	

Notes - Beware of stamps from Plate 177 with the figure 1 obscured
Prices for 1d red inverted watermarks are for used only, as there is insufficient information at present to provide accurate prices for mint.

No.		M/M	F/U	G/U	✉

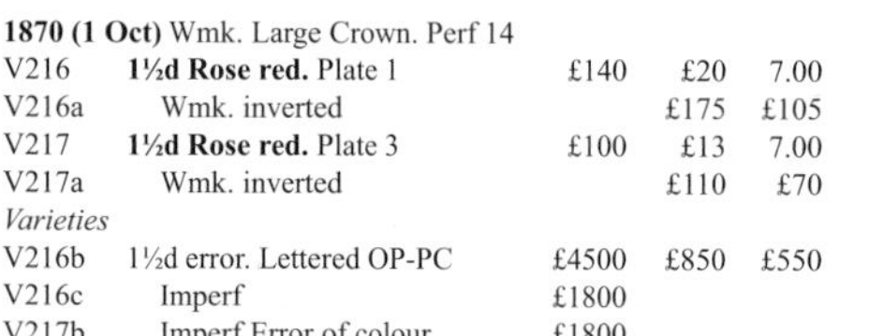

1870 (1 Oct) Wmk. Large Crown. Perf 14

No.		M/M	F/U	G/U	✉
V216	**1½d Rose red.** Plate 1	£140	£20	7.00	£90
V216a	Wmk. inverted		£175	£105	
V217	**1½d Rose red.** Plate 3	£100	£13	7.00	£75
V217a	Wmk. inverted		£110	£70	
Varieties					
V216b	1½d error. Lettered OP-PC	£4500	£850	£550	
V216c	Imperf	£1800			
V217b	Imperf Error of colour	£1800			

Plate 12

1858 (July) Thick white lines. Wmk. Large Crown. Perf. 14

No.		M/M	F/U	G/U	✉
V218	**2d Blue.** Plate 7	£475	£14	7.00	£45
V218a	Wmk. inverted		£400	£300	
V219	**2d Blue.** Plate 8	£370	£12	9.00	£40
V219a	Wmk. inverted		£30	£20	
V220	**2d Blue.** Plate 9	£80	4.00	3.00	£17
V220a	Wmk. inverted	£200	£25	£14	
V221	**2d Blue.** Plate 12	£650	£30	£20	£65
V221a	Wmk. inverted		£100	£80	

1869 (July) Thin white lines. Wmk. Large Crown. Perf. 14

No.		M/M	F/U	G/U	✉
V222	**2d Blue.** Plate 13	£75	5.50	3.50	£20
V222a	Wmk. inverted		£30	£20	
V223	**2d Blue.** Plate 14	£85	7.00	4.00	£20
V223a	Wmk. inverted		£35	£25	
V224	**2d Blue.** Plate 15	£75	7.00	5.00	£25
V224a	Wmk. inverted		£75	£40	

The Embossed issues. introduced in 1847 were unique in British stamp production. Produced at Somerset House on manual presses, each stamp was separately embossed, and consequently the spacing of the impressions was extremely variable from wide margins to overlapping in many instances. It is consequently difficult to find examples with four good margins. The quality of embossing varied from clear sharp impressions to blunted and blurred examples.

The die numbers were inserted in the form of metal plugs in the base of the bust together with the letters "W.W." (the initials of the master engraver William Wyon). The numbers can be read under magnification. but are often illegible due to the embossing having been flattened. These are of slightly less value (approximately 20% less).

Collectors are warned against cut-outs from Postal Stationery using the same design and 'four margin' examples which have been rebacked. The two silk threads go right through the paper, 5mm apart, on the l0d and 1s values and as a consequence it is usually reasonably easy to spot re-backed items. Also, the 6d value is watermarked, whereas the Postal Stationery 6d is without watermark and gum, and does not have a pendant curl. Later examples of the 6d had green tinted gum.

Prices shown in columns one and two are for stamps with margins all round.
Columns 3 & 4 indicate used prices for stamps with 3 clear margins.

Printer: Somerset House

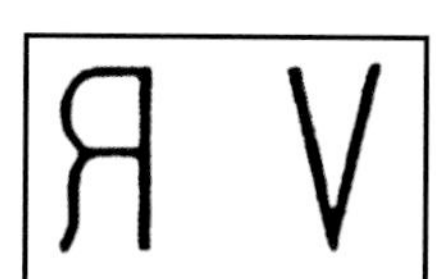

VR Watermark

1847 (1 March) Wmk. VR Imperforate

No.		M/M	F/U	G/U	✉
V225	**6d Mauve**. Die 1WW	£2700	£350	£85	£220
V225a	Wmk. upright	£2000	£360	£90	£230
V225b	Wmk. inverted	£2000	£350	£85	£230
V225c	Wmk. reversed	£2200	£350	£85	£250
V225d	Wmk. inv. and rev.	£2400	£370	£90	£250
V225e	Lilac	£2500	£380	£85	£230
V225f	Purple	£2700	£390	£90	£230
V225g	Violet	£4500	£850	£650	£650

10d on Dickenson silk thread paper (fine used)

1848 (6 Nov.) No Wmk. Dickinson silk thread paper. Imperforate

No.		M/M	F/U	G/U	✉
V226	**10d Brown.** Die W.W.1	£2200	£550	£200	£500
V226a	Deep brown	£2500	£600	£220	
V227	**10d Brown.** Die 2. W.W. (1850)	£2200	£550	£240	£500
V227a	Deep brown	£2500	£650	£220	
V228	**10d Brown.** Die 3. W.W. (1853)	£2200	£500	£220	£500
V228a	Deep brown	£2500	£600	£220	
V229	**10d Brown.** Die 4 W.W. (1854)	£2400	£400	£250	£800
V229a	Deep brown	£1500	£420	£150	
V230	**10d Brown.** Die 5. W.W.*	£27000			

* Only two copies are recorded of V230

1s on Dickinson silk thread paper

1847 (11 Sept.) No Wmk. Dickinson silk thread paper. Imperforate

No.		M/M	F/U	G/U	✉
V231	**1s Green.** Die W.W. 1	£2800	£370	£85	£150
V231a	Deep green	£3000	£400	£105	£200
V231b	Pale green	£2800	£350	£85	£150
V232	**1s Green.** Die W.W. 2	£2800	£380	£80	£150
V232a	Deep green	£3000	£400	£110	£200
V232b	Pale green	£2750	£370	£100	£150

SURFACE PRINTED

The Surface Printed issues form a very interesting part of British stamp production. with a wide variety of shades, watermarks and plate numbers to be collected. All these differences can be readily distinguished contrastmg with the difficulties of the Line Engraved period.

To clarify the listing of stamps for this period they are divided into logical groups as follows:

1. No corner letters
2. Small white corner letters
3. Large white corner letters
4. Large coloured corner letters
5. New design - low values
6. Lilac and Green issue
7. Jubilee issue

All the varieties for each value are listed in sequence within each grouping.

The pricing basis for Surface Printed issues is as follows:

Unmounted mint (U/M) (Jubilee issue only)	Full original gum, well centred, full perforations and good colour.
Mounted Mint (M/M)	At least 75% original gum, full perforations and clean fresh colours.

Fine used and Average Used (F/U, A/U)

Grade I
Superb Used
Well centred with all perforations, true colour and circular date stamp

Grade II
Fine Used
Reasonably centred with all perforations, true colour and light cancel of the period or clear profile.

Grade III
Average Used
Reasonably centred with all perforations and reasonable colour with heavy, but no unsightly cancel.

Grade IV
Sound Used
Could be off centre, possibly one or two short but not missing perforations, reasonable colour and heavy cancel.

WARNING

Re-gumming of stamps is becoming more prevalent, and this abuse can be detected in two possible ways.

1. Place the stamps face down in the palm of the hand and the heat of the hand should cause the edges of the stamp to curl upwards. If it remains flat or curls towards the palm then it is almost certainly re-gummed.

2. Examination with a magnifying glass should reveal any gum that has crept onto the face off the stamp or particularly around the fibres of the perforations.

Stamps that have no gum or have been cleanly regummed are worth approximately 20% of the mounted mint prices, provided they have retained their original colours.

Wing Margins on Surface Printed Issues

All the issues on paper watermarked Emblems, Spray and the three varieties of Garter were printed in sheets consisting of panes. These were broken up on distribution. The panes consisted of normal sized stamps apart from the left and right respectively. They are known as wing margins. It has not always been fashionable to collect wing margins and often the margins have been removed and reperforated. Reperforated examples can be detected easily with a knowledge of the letter combinations that make up wing margin stamps.

EMBLEMS AND SPRAY - D, F. II or I in S.E. corner of stamp.

GARTER - F or G in SE. corner of stamp.

The issues of 1855 - 62 did not have corner letters but did have wing margins.

The 4d and 3d on Large Garter exist correctly with and without wing margins. Official action was taken to remove some of their wing margins with the result that the ‘F’ and ‘G’ stamps here can be found with and without, and in the case of the 8d. with a guillotined edge.

SURFACE PRINTED “ABNORMALS”

The Printers, De La Rue, were obliged to submit samples of each new plate to Somerset House for approval before starting production. Up to six sheets were sent, one of which was retained as the Imprimatur Sheet.

Occasionally it appears some portions of the remaining sheets were perforated and used. probably unofficially. If approval for production was given, then there would be no way of differentiating these stamps apart from a pre-issue dated postmark. However, sometimes due to a change of policy on colour or paper, etc., the issue did not proceed. These stamps, although used, had never crossed the Post Office counter and are classified as Abnormals. These are by their nature very rare, sought after and valuable. The condition is generally poor but as always with such rare items it detracts little from their value.

There are amongst the Imprimaturs eight potential Abnormals of which no copies have yet been found - we list these with a price for the Imprimatur copies outside the Official Archives.

No corner letters

Printer De La Rue & Co.

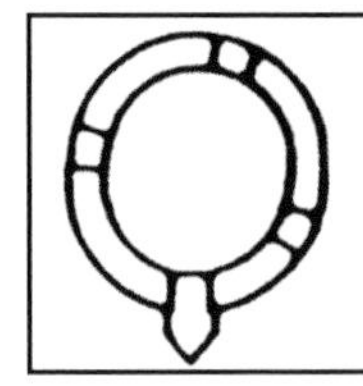

Small Garter Watermark

1855 (31 July) Wmk. Small Garter. Blue glazed paper. Perf 14

No.			M/M	F/U	G/U	✉
V234	**4d**	**Carmine**	£2400	£150	£75	£150
V234a		Wmk. inverted		£370	£220	
V234b		Bright carmine	£2400	£150	£75	£150
V234c		Deep carmine	£2500	£170	£80	£160
V234d		Pale carmine	£2400	£150	£80	£160
V235	**4d**	**Carmine** on white paper	£3500	£350	£220	£600

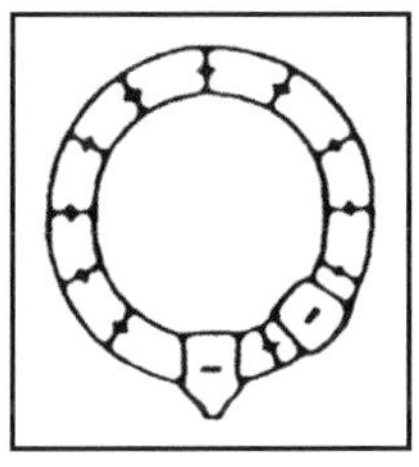

Medium Garter Watermark

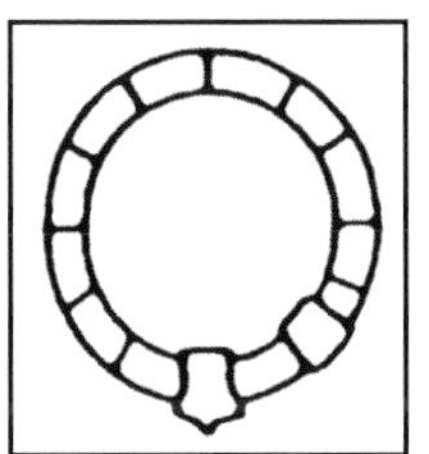

Large Garter Watermark

1856 (25 Feb.) Wmk. Medium Garter. Blue glazed paper. Perf 14

No.			M/M	F/U	G/U	✉
V236	**4d**	**Carmine**	£2800	£180	£85	£160
V236a		Wmk. inverted		£380	£200	
V236b		Pale carmine	£2800	£180	£85	£180
V236c		Deep carmine	£2900	£190	£85	£190

1856 (Sept.) Wmk. Medium Garter. White paper. Perf 14

No.			M/M	F/U	G/U	✉
V237	**4d**	**Pale carmine**	£2200	£190	£90	£280
V237a		Wmk. inverted		£275	£170	

1856 (1 Nov.) New colour. Wmk. Medium Garter. White paper. Perf 14

No.			M/M	F/U	G/U	✉
V238	**4d**	**Rose**	£2200	£180	£100	£220
V238a		Deep rose	£2300	£190	£100	£250

1857 (Jan.) Wmk. Large Garter. White paper. Perf 14

No.			M/M	F/U	G/U	✉
V239	**4d**	**Rose**	£470	£22	£14	£35
V239a		Wmk. inverted		£55	£34	
V239b		Rose carmine	£500	£22	£14	£45
V240	**4d**	**Rose** carmine on thick glazed paper	£1400	£70	£35	£110

1856 (21 Oct.) Wmk. Emblems. Perf 14

No.			M/M	F/U	G/U	✉
V241	**6d**	**Lilac.** Plate (1)	£380	£45	£15	£80
V241a		Wmk. inverted		£85	£20	
V241b		Wmk. inv. and rev		£95	£50	
V241c		Wmk. reversed		£200	£100	
V241d		Pale lilac	£400	£45	£15	£50
V241e		Deep lilac	£475	£50	£20	£60

1856 (1 Nov.) Wmk. Emblems. Perf 14

No.			M/M	F/U	G/U	✉
V242	**1s**	**Green**	£550	£75	£30	£85
V242a		Wmk. inverted		£150	£95	
V242b		Wmk. reversed		£400	£225	
V242c		Pale green	£550	£75	£30	£85
V242d		Deep green	£1200	£175	£75	£180

Small white corner letters

Printer: De La Rus & Co.

Plate numbers shown in brackets do not appear on the design

Without dots
Unshaded spandrels

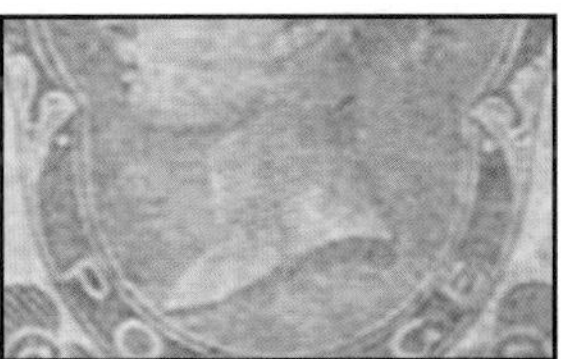

Abnormal
Plate (3) with dots added

1862 (2 May) Wmk. Emblems. Perf 14

No.			M/M	F/U	G/U	✉
V243	**3d**	**Carmine rose.** Plate (2)	£550	£120	£55	£110
V243a		Wmk. inverted		£185	£110	
V243b		Pale carmine rose	£550	£120	£55	£110
V243c		Wmk. inverted		£185	£100	
V243d		Deep carmine rose	£850	£150	£75	£180
Varieties						
VAB1	3d	Plate (2) with shaded spandrels. Abnormal	£4500	£6000		
VAB1a		Imprimatur	£1500			
VAB2	3d	Plate (3) with dots added Line perf 14. Abnormal	£3800	£4500		
VAB2a		Imprimatur	£1200			

1862 (15 Jan.) Wmk. Large Garter. Perf 14

No.			M/M	F/U	G/U	✉
V244	**4d**	**Pale red.** Plate (3)	£380	£35	£15	£55
V244a		Wmk. inverted		£85	£35	
V244b		Bright red	£400	£40	£20	£65

1863 (16 Oct.) Hairlines added to corners. Wmk. Large Garter. Perf 14

No.			M/M	F/U	G/U	✉
V245	**4d**	**Pale red.** Plate (4)	£380	£30	£15	£50
V245a		Wmk. inverted		£75	£30	
V245b		Bright red	£420	£35	£20	£55

1862 (1 Dec.) Wmk. Emblems. Perf 14

No.			M/M	F/U	G/U	✉
V246	**6d**	**Lilac.** Plate (3)	£420	£35	£15	£60
V246a		Wmk. inverted		£95	£65	
V246b		Deep lilac	£850	£40	£20	£75

1864 (20 April) Hairlines added to corners. Wmk. Emblems. Perf 14

No.			M/M	F/U	G/U	✉
V247	**6d**	**Lilac.** Plate (4)	£850	£60	£25	£85
V247a		Wmk. inverted		£115	£70	

1862 (15 Jan) Wmk. Emblems. Perf 14

No.			M/M	F/U	G/U	✉
V248	**9d**	**Bistre.** Plate (2)	£1200	£170	£85	£250
V248a		Wmk. inverted		£250	£140	
V248b		Wmk. reversed		£250	£140	
V248c		Straw	£1200	£170	£85	£250
Varieties						
VAB3	9d	Plate (3) with hairlines				
		Abnormal	£6500	£3500		
VAB3a		Imprimatur	£2200			

1862 (1 Dec.) Wmk. Emblems. Perf 14

No.			M/M	F/U	G/U	✉
V249	**1s**	**Green.** Plate *	£800	£75	£35	£95
V249a		Wmk. inverted		£120	£70	
V249b		Wmk. inv. and rev.		£120	£70	
V249c		Wmk. reversed				
V249d		Deep green	£1000	£110	£50	£125

* Plate 2 was used, although shown as a '1'

No.			M/M	F/U	G/U	✉
Varieties						
VAB4	1s	Plate 2 with hairlines				
		Abnormal	£11000			
VAB4a		Imprimatur	£6000			

Large white corner letters

Printer: De La Rue & Co.

Emblems Watermark

Spray Watermark

1865 (1 March) Wmk. Emblems. Perf 14

No.			M/M	F/U	G/U	✉
V250	**3d**	**Rose.** Plate 4	£450	£50	£25	£65
V250a		Wmk. inverted		£140	£90	
Varieties						
VAB5	3d	Rose Plate 5. Abnormal				
		Imprimatur	£800			

1867 (July) Wmk. Spray. Perf 14

No.			M/M	F/U	G/U	✉
V251	**3d**	**Rose.** Plate 4	£230	£75	£40	£100
V251		Wmk. inverted	£750	£200	£120	
V252	**3d**	**Rose.** Plate 5	£220	£25	£10	£40
V252a		Wmk. inverted	£350	£70	£40	
V252b		Deep rose	£220	£25	£10	£40
V253	**3d**	**Rose.** Plate 6	£220	£25	£10	£40
V253a		Wmk. inverted	£350	£75	£40	
V254	**3d**	**Rose.** Plate 7	£260	£25	£10	£45
V254a		Wmk. inverted	£370	£75	£20	
V255	**3d**	**Rose.** Plate 8	£200	£20	7.00	£40
V255a		Wmk. inverted	£320	£85	£50	
V256	**3d**	**Rose.** Plate 9	£230	£25	7.00	£40
V256a		Wmk. inverted	£350	£95	£60	
V257	**3d**	**Rose.** Plate 10	£300	£45	£10	£70
V257a		Wmk. inverted	£600	£175	£100	

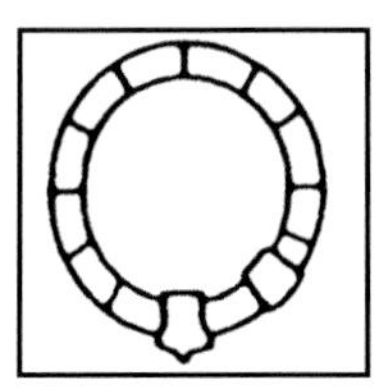

Large Garter Watermark

1865 (4 July) Wmk. Large Garter. Perf 14

No.			M/M	F/U	G/U	✉
V258	**4d**	**Vermillion.** Plate 7	£250	£30	£10	£35
V259	**4d**	**Vermillion.** Plate 8	£220	£30	£10	£35
V259a		Wmk. inverted	£230	£30	£18	
V260	**4d**	**Vermillion.** Plate 9	£200	£20	£10	£35
V260a		Wmk. inverted	£220	£20	£10	
V261	**4d**	**Vermillion.** Plate 10				
V261a		Wmk. inverted	£240	£30	£15	£35
V262	**4d**	**Vermillion.** Plate 11				
V262a		Wmk. inverted	£200	£25	£12	£25
V263	**4d**	**Vermillion.** Plate 12	£200	£22	£10	£35
V263a		Wmk. inverted	£220	£22	£10	
V264	**4d**	**Vermillion.** Plate 13	£200	£25	£12	£35
V265	**4d**	**Vermillion.** Plate 14	£260	£25	£10	£40

With hyphen

Without hyphen

Hexagonal

1865 (1 April) SIX-PENCE hyphenated. Wmk. Emblems. Perf 14

No.			M/M	F/U	G/U	✉
V266	**6d**	**Lilac.** Plate 5	£370	£35	£15	£40
V266a		Wmk. inverted		£75	£50	
V266b		Wmk. reversed		£120	£75	
V266c		Deep lilac	£420	£40	£17	£50

No.			M/M	F/U	G/U	✉
V267	**6d**	**Lilac.** Plate 6	£850	£60	£25	£70
V267a		Wmk. inverted		£100	£50	
V267b		Deep lilac	£950	£70	£30	£95

1867 (21 June) SIX-PENCE hyphenated. Wmk. Spray. Perf 14

No.			M/M	F/U	G/U	✉
V268	**6d**	**Lilac.** Plate 6	£420	£40	£18	£50
V268a		Wmk. inverted		£110	£70	
V268b		Deep lilac	£450	£40	£20	£50
V268c		Violet	£420	£40	£20	£50
V268d		Purple	£420	£45	£20	£60

1869 (8 March) SIX PENCE without hyphen. Wmk. Spray. Perf 14

No.			M/M	F/U	G/U	✉
V269	**6d.**	**Mauve** Plate 8	£260	£25	£10	£30
V269a		Wmk. inverted		£90	£50	
V269b		Violet	£260	£25	£10	£30
V270	**6d.**	**Mauve** Plate 9	£260	£25	£10	`£30
V270a		Wmk. inverted		£95	£60	
Varieties						
VAB6	6d	Mauve. Plate 10 Abnormal				£14000
VAB6a		Imprimatur				£3500

1872 (12 April) New colour and hexagonal design. Wmk. Spray. Perf 14

No.			M/M	F/U	G/U	✉
V271	**6d**	**Chestnut**	£235	£22	£10	£40
V271a		Wmk. inverted		£100	£70	
V271b		Chestnut	£280	£30	£12	£45
V271c		Pale buff	£280	£25	£15	£45
V272	**6d**	**Pale buff.** Plate 12 (30.10.72)	£950	£110	£40	£150
V272a		Wmk. inverted		£200	£130	
Varieties						
VAB7	**6d**	**Chestnut.** Plate 12. Abnormal		£1500		
VAB7a		Imprimatur		£1200		

1865 (1 Dec.) Wmk. Emblems. Per 14

No.			M/M	F/U	G/U	✉
V273	**9d**	**Straw.** Plate 4	£1000	£220	£110	£320
V273a		Wmk. inverted		£375	£250	
Varieties						
VAB8	9d	Straw. Plate 5 . Abnormal	£10000			
VAB8a		Imprimatur	£2200			

1867 (3 Oct.) Wmk. Spray. Perf 14

No.			M/M	F/U	G/U	✉
V274	**9d**	**Straw.** Plate 4	£500	£100	£40	£120
V274a		Wmk. inverted		£225	£140	
V274b		Pale straw	£500	£100	£40	£120
V274c		Deep straw	£575	£110	£45	£130

1867 (1 July) Wmk. Sprat. Perf 14

No.			M/M	F/U	G/U	✉
V275	**10d**	**Red brown.** Plate 1	£1000	£140	£45	£200
V275a		Wmk. inverted		£300	£180	
V275b		Pale red brown	£1000	£140	£45	£200
V275c		Deep red brown	£1200	£180	£90	£210
Varieties						
VAB9	10d	Red brown. Plate 1. Wmk. Emblems. Abnormal		£18000		
VAB10	10d	Red brown. Plate 2. Wmk. Spray. Abnormal	£12500	£4200		
VAB10a		Imprimatur	£2200			

1865 (Feb.) Wmk. Emblems. Perf 14

No.		M/M	F/U	G/U	✉
V276	**1s. Green.** Plate 4	£700	£50	£15	£45
V276a	Wmk. inverted		£150	£85	
V276b	Wmk. inv. and rev.		£100	£70	
Varieties					
VAB11	1s. Green. Plate 5. Abnormal				
VAB11a	Imprimatur	£700			

1867 (13 July) Wmk. Spray. Perf 14

No.		M/M	F/U	G/U	✉
V277	**1s. Pale green.** Plate 4	£220	£25	£10	£35
V277a	Wmk. inverted	£650	£60	£35	
V277b	Deep geen	£280	£25	£10	£35
V278	**1s. Pale green.** Plate 5	£290	£12	7.00	£35
V278a	Wmk. inverted			£70	
V279	**1s. Pale green.** Plate 6	£300	£12	7.00	£30
V279a	Wmk. inverted			£70	
V280	**1s. Pale green.** Plate 7	£300	£35	£15	£65
V280a	Wmk. inverted		£140	£90	

1867 (1 July) Wmk. Spray. Perf 14

No.		M/M	F/U	G/U	✉
V281	**2s Deep blue.** Plate 1	£1200	£90	£45	£250
V281a	Wmk. inverted		£225	£170	
V281b	Dull blue	£1200	£100	£45	£250
V281c	Pale blue	£1400	£100	£45	£250
V281d	Milky blue	£2700	£500	£220	£800
V281e	Cobalt	£6500	£1400	£700	£3500
Varieties					
VAB12	2s Blue. Plate 3. Abnormal		£4000		
VAB12a	Imprimatur	£2400			

1880 (27 Feb) New colour. Wmk. Spray. Perf 14

No.		M/M	F/U	G/U	✉
V282	**2s Pale brown.** Plate 1	£6000	£1400	£850	£10000
V282a	Wmk. inverted		£2200	£1000	
V282b	Brown	£6000	£1500	£850	£10000

Large white corner letters

Printer: De La Rue & Co.

Maltese Cross Watermark

Large Anchor Watermark

1887 (1 July) Wmk. Maltese ross. Perf 15½ x 15

No.			M/M	F/U	G/U	✉
V284	5s	**Rose.** Plate 1	£1850	£200	£85	
V284a		Pale rose	£1850	£200	£85	
V285	5s	**Rose.** Plate 2	£2400	£250	£100	
Varieties						
VAB13		5s Rose. Plate 4. Abnormal				
VAB13a		Imprimatur	£4000			

1882 (25 Nov.) Wmk. Large Anchor. Perf 14#

No.			M/M	F/U	G/U	✉
V286	5s	**Rose.** Plate 4	£5000	£950	£400	
V287	5s	**Rose.** Plate 4 on blued paper	£5000	£1000	£450	

1868 (26 Sept.) Wmk. Maltese Cross. Perf 15½ x 15

No.			M/M	F/U	G/U	✉
V288	10s	**Grey green.** Plate 1	£18000	£1100	£450	

1883 (Feb.) Wmk. Large Anchor. Perf 14

No.			M/M	F/U	G/U	✉
V289	10s	**Grey green.** Plate 1	£24000	£1500	£850	
V290	10s	**Grey green.** Plate 1 on blued paper	£24000	£1600	£900	

1883 (Feb.) Wmk. Maltese Cross. Perf 15½ x 15

No.			M/M	F/U	G/U	✉
V291	£1	**Brown lilac.** Plate 1	£27000	£1900	£1000	

1883 (Feb.) Wmk. Large Anchor. Perf 14

No.			M/M	F/U	G/U	✉
V292	£1	**Brown lilac.** Plate 1	£33000	£3500	£1200	
V293	£1	**Brown lilac.** Plate 1 on blued paper	£35000	£3500	£1200	

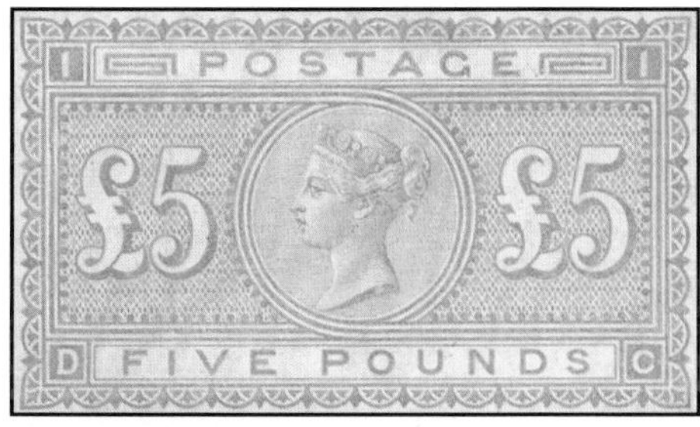

1882 (21 March) Wmk. Large Anchor. Perf 14

No.			M/M	F/U	G/U	✉
V294	£5	**Orange.** Plate 1	£5500	£3000	£1800	
V295	£5	**Orange.** Plate 1 on blued paper	£17500	£4750	£2500	

Large coloured corner letters
Printer: De La Rue & Co.

Small Anchor Watermark

1875 (1 July) Wmk. Small Anchor. Perf 14

A. Blued paper

No.			M/M	F/U	G/U	✉
V296	2½d	**Rose mauve.** Plate 1	£270	£70	£35	£75
V296a		Wmk. inverted	£675	£125	£70	
V297	2½d	**Rose mauve.** Plate 2	£3000	£600	£350	£750
V298	2½d	**Rose mauve.** Plate 3			£1700	£5000

B. White paper.

No.			M/M	F/U	G/U	✉
V299	2½d	**Rose mauve.** Plate 1	£200	£30	£10	£30
V299a		Wmk. inverted	£450	£85	£55	
V300	2½d	**Rose mauve.** Plate 2	£200	£30	£10	£30
V300a		Wmk. inverted	£550	£100	£70	
V301	2½d	**Rose mauve.** Plate 3	£290	£60	£20	£75
V301a		Wmk. inverted	£850	£120	£75	
Varieties						
V300b	2½d	error of lettering LH-FL	£8500	£900	£600	£2500
VAB14	2½d	Rose mauve. Plate 4 Abnormal				
VAB14a		Imprimatur	£850			
VAB15	2½d	Rose mauve. Plate 5. Abnormal				
VAB15a		Imprimatur	£850			

Orb Watermark

Imperial Crown Watermark

1876 (16 May) Wmk. Orb. Perf 14

No.			M/M	F/U	G/U	✉
V302	2½d	**Rose mauve.** Plate 3	£300	£65	£20	£65
V302a		Wmk. inverted	£800	£120	£70	
V303	2½d	**Rose mauve.** Plate 4	£200	£20	£10	£25
V303a		Wmk. inverted	£300	£55	£35	
V304	2½d	**Rose mauve.** Plate 5	£200	£20	£10	£25
V304a		Wmk. inverted	£400	£60	£35	
V305	2½d	**Rose mauve.** Plate 6	£200	£20	£10	£25
V305a		Wmk. inverted	£400	£45	£30	
V306	2½d	**Rose mauve.** Plate 7	£200	£20	£10	£25
V306a		Wmk. inverted	£400	£45	£30	
V307	2½d	**Rose mauve.** Plate 8	£200	£20	£10	£25
V307a		Wmk inverted	£450	£60	£35	
V308	2½d	**Rose mauve.** Plate 9	£200	£20	£10	£25
V308a		Wmk inverted	£500	£70	£45	
V309	2½d	**Rose mauve.** Plate 10	£270	£25	£10	£30
V309a		Wmk. inverted	£450	£75	£475	
V310	2½d	**Rose mauve.** Plate 11	£200	£20	£10	£25
V310a		Wmk inverted	£450	£55	£30	
V311	2½d	**Rose mauve.** Plate 12	£200	£20	£10	£25
V311a		Wmk inverted	£450	£60	£35	

No.			M/M	F/U	G/U	✉
V312	2½d	**Rose mauve.** Plate 13	£200	£20	£10	£25
V312a		Wmk. inverted	£450	£60	£35	
V313	2½d	**Rose mauve.** Plate 14	£200	£20	£10	£25
V313a		Wmk. inverted	£450	£60	£35	
V314	2½d	**Rose mauve.** Plate 15	£200	£20	£10	£25
V314a		Wmk. inverted	£450	£60	£35	
V315	2½d	**Rose mauve.** Plate 16	£200	£20	£10	£25
V315a		Wmk. inverted	£500	£60	£35	
V316	2½d	**Rose mauve.** Plate 17	£700	£150	£80	£250
V316a		Wmk. inverted	£1500	£275	£175	

1880 (5 Feb.) New colour. Wmk. Orb. Perf.14

No.			M/M	F/U	G/U	✉
V317	2½d	**Blue.** Plate 17	£160	£25	£10	£30
V317a		Wmk. inverted	£270	£30	£55	
V318	2½d	**Blue.** Plate 18	£160	£20	£10	£30
V318a		Wmk. inverted	£275	£80	£50	
V319	2½d	**Blue.** Plate 19	£160	£20	£10	£30
V319a		Wmk. inverted	£275	£65	£45	
V320	2½d	**Blue.** Plate 20	£160	£20	£10	£30
V320a		Wmk. inverted	£260	£65	£45	

1881 (23 March) Wmk. Imperial Crown. Perf.14

No.			M/M	F/U	G/U	✉
V321	2½d	**Blue.** Plate 21	£150	£12	5.00	£24
V322	2½d	**Blue.** Plate 22	£90	8.00	4.00	£17
V323	2½d	**Blue.** Plate 23	£90	8.00	4.00	£17
V323a		Wmk. inverted		£200	£120	

Surcharged '3d'

1873 (5 July) Wmk. Spray. Perf.14

No.			M/M	F/U	G/U	✉
V324	3d	**Rose.** Plate 11	£200	£20	7.00	£25
V324a		Wmk. inverted	£375	£120	£75	
V325	3d	**Rose.** Plate 12	£200	£20	7.00	£25
V325a		Wmk. inverted	£400	£120	£75	
V326	3d	**Rose.** Plate 14	£200	£20	7.00	£30
V326a		Wmk. inverted	£400	£80	£50	
V327	3d	**Rose.** Plate 15	£200	£20	7.00	£25
V327a		Wmk. inverted	£450	£80	£50	
V328	3d	**Rose.** Plate 16	£200	£20	7.00	£25
V328a		Wmk. inverted	£450	£80	£50	
V329	3d	**Rose.** Plate 17	£200	£20	7.00	£25
V330	3d	**Rose.** Plate 18	£200	£20	7.00	£25
V330a		Wmk. inverted	£450	£80	£50	
V331	3d	**Rose.** Plate 19	£200	£30	£12	£35
V331a		Wmk. inverted	£450	£100	£70	
V332	3d	**Rose.** Plate 20	£220	£35	£20	£60
V332a		Wmk. inverted	£450	£90	£60	
Varieties						
VAB16	3d	Rose. Plate 21. Abnormal				
VAB16a		Imprimatur	£800			

1881 (Feb.) Wmk. Imperial Crown. Perf. 14

No.			M/M	F/U	G/U	✉
V333	3d	**Rose.** Plate 20	£250	£50	£25	£100
V333a		Wmk. inverted		£200	£110	
V334	3d	**Rose.** Plate 21	£200	£35	£18	£80
V334a		Wmk. Inverted		£200	£100	

1883 (1 Jan.) Surcharged '3d' in carmine. Wmk. Imperial Crown. Perf. 14

No.			M/M	F/U	G/U	✉
V335	3d	**Surcharge on 3d lilac.** Plate 21	£200	£75	£40	£150
V335a		Wmk. inverted	-			

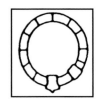

Large Garter Watermark

1876 (1 March) Wmk. Large Garter. Perf. 14

No.			M/M	F/U	G/U	✉
V336	4d	**Vermilion.** Plate 15	£750	£160	£70	£250
V336a		Wmk. inverted	-	£350	£200	
Varieties						
VAB17	4d	Vermilion. Plate 16. Abnormal	-		£13500	
VAB17a		Imprimatur	£3000			

1877 (12 March) New colour. Wmk. Large Garter. Perf. 14

No.			M/M	F/U	G/U	✉
V337	4d	**Sage green.** Plate 15	£300	£100	£40	£175
V337a		Wmk. inverted	-	£220	£130	
V338	4d	**Sage green.** Plate 16	£270	£100	£35	£175
V338a		Wmk. inverted	-	£200	£120	
Varieties						
VAB18	4d	Sage green. Plate 17. Abnormal	-	£9000		
VAB18a		Imprimatur	£3000			

1880 (15 Aug.) New colour. Wmk. Large Garter. Perf. 14

No.			M/M	F/U	G/U	✉
V339	4d	**Grey brown.** Plate 17	£850	£175	£95	£300
V339a		Wmk. inverted	-	£500	£350	

1880 (9 Dec.) Wmk. Imperial Crown. Perf. 14

No.			M/M	F/U	G/U	✉
V340	4d	**Grey brown.** Plate 17	£180	£30	£10	£40
V340a		Wmk. inverted	-	£275	£175	
V340b		Pale grey brown	£180	£30	£10	£40
V341	4d	**Grey brown.** Plate 18	£180	£30	£10	£40
V341a		Wmk. inverted	-	£275	£175	

Surcharged '6d'

1874 (31 March) Wmk. Spray. Perf. 14

No.			M/M	F/U	G/U	✉
V342	6d	**Grey.** Plate 13	£200	£25	£10	£50
V342a		Wmk. inverted	£450	£100	£70	
V343	6d	**Grey.** Plate 14	£200	£25	£10	£50
V343a		Wmk. inverted	£450	£100	£70	
V344	6d	**Grey.** Plate 15	£200	£25	£10	£50
V344a		Wmk. inverted	£450	£100	£70	
V345	6d	**Grey.** Plate 16	£200	£25	£10	£50
V345a		Wmk. inverted	£450	£100	£70	

No.			M/M	F/U	G/U	✉
V346	**6d**	**Grey.** Plate 17	£300	£50	£30	£100
V346a		Wmk. inverted	£750	£175	£125	
Varieties						
VAB19	6d	Buff. Plate 13. Abnormal	-	£9000		
VAB19a		Imprimatur	£2500			
VAB20	6d	Grey. Plate 18. Abnormal	-	-		
VAB20a		Imprimatur	£750			

1881 (1 Jan.) Wmk. Imperial Crown. Perf. 14

No.			M/M	F/U	G/U	✉
V347	**6d**	**Grey.** Plate 17	£180	£35	£15	£60
V347a		Wmk. inverted	-	£300	£200	
V348	**6d**	**Grey.** Plate 18	£180	£35	£15	£60

1883 (1 Jan.) Surcharged '6d' in carmine. Wmk. Imperial Crown. Perf. 14

No.			M/M	F/U	G/U	✉
V349	**6d**	**Surcharge on 6d lilac.** Plate 18	£240	£75	£35	£175
V349a		Wmk. inverted	£850	£400	£250	

V350

V350B

1876 (11 Sept.) Wmk. Large Garter. Perf. 14

No.			M/M	F/U	G/U	✉
V350	**8d**	**Orange.** Plate 1	£375	£120	£45	£200
V350a		Wmk. inverted	-	£350	£200	
V350B	**8d**	**Purple-brown** (unissued)	£5000			
Varieties						
VAB21	8d	Orange. Plate 2. Abnormal	-	-		
VAB21a		Imprimatur	£1800			

1873 (1 Sept.) Wmk. Spray. Perf. 14

No.			M/M	F/U	G/U	✉
V351	**1s**	**Green.** Plate 8	£280	£50	£30	£70
V351a		Wmk. inverted	£650	£90	£60	
V352	**1s**	**Green.** Plate 9	£280	£50	£30	£70
V353	**1s**	**Green.** Plate 10	£280	£60	£30	£70
V354	**1s**	**Green.** Plate 11	£280	£50	£25	£70
V355	**1s**	**Green.** Plate 12	£250	£30	£15	£80
V356	**1s**	**Green.** Plate 13	£250	£30	£15	£80
V356a		Wmk. inverted	£600	£100	£70	
Varieties						
VAB22	1s	Green. Plate 14. Abnormal	-	£14000		
VAB22a		Imprimatur	£2750			

1880 (14 Oct.) New colour. Wmk. Spray. Perf. 14

No.			M/M	F/U	G/U	✉
V357	**1s**	**Orange brown.** Plate 13	£1200	£220	£100	£300
V357a		Wmk. inverted	£2500	£400	£280	

1880 (29 May) Wmk. Imperial Crown. Perf. 14

No.			M/M	F/U	G/U	✉
V358	**1s**	**Orange brown.** Plate 13	£260	£50	£25	£90
V358a		Wmk. inverted	£650	£275	£175	
V359	**1s**	**Orange brown.** Plate 14	£260	£50	£25	£90
V359a		Wmk. inverted	£650	£300	£175	
Varieties						
VAB23	1s	Purple. Plate 13. Abnormal	-	-		
VAB23a		Imprimatur	£900			
VAB24	1s	Purple. Plate 14 and line perf. 14. Abnormal *	£2500	£4000		
VAB24a		Imprimatur	£900			

* This stamp originates from the 'Stamp Committee of 1890' Souvenir Stamp Collection.

New designs. Low values 1880 - 83.
Printer: De La Rue & Co.

Imperial Crown Watermark

1880 (1 Jan.) - 84 Wmk. Imperial Crown. Perf. 14

No.			M/M	F/U	G/U	✉
V360	**½d**	**Deep green** (14.10.80)	£12	3.00	2.00	5.00
V360a		Wmk. inverted	-	£200	£150	
V360ab		No watermark	£4000			
V360b		Pale green	£12	3.00	2.00	5.00
V361	**1d**	**Venetian red**	4.00	2.00	1.00	4.00
V361a		Wmk. inverted	-	£150	£100	
V362	**1½d**	**Venetian red** (14.10.80)	£50	£20	8.00	£40
V363	**2d**	**Rose** (8.12.80)	£70	£25	£10	£60
V363a		Wmk. inverted	£750	£375	£300	
V363b		Deep rose	£75	£25	£15	£60
V363c		Pale rose	£75	£25	£15	£60
V364	**5d**	**Indigo** (15.3.81)	£250	£45	£20	£90
V364a		Wmk. inverted	-	£2750	£2000	
		Set of 5	£375	£95	£40	

Penny lilacs 1881 - 1901.
Printer: De La Rue & Co.

Die I
14 dots in each corner

Die II
16 dots in each corner

1881 (12 July) Wmk. Imperial Crown. Perf. 14. A. Die I.

No.			M/M	F/U	G/U	✉
V365	**1d**	**Lilac**	£60	£10	4.00	7.00
V365a		Pale lilac	£60	£10	4.00	7.00
V365b		Wmk. inverted	-	-	£350	
V365c		Bluish lilac	£250	£40	£20	£50
B. Die II						
V366	**1d**	**Lilac** (12.12.81)	1.00	20	10	1.00
V366a		Wmk. inverted	£35	£25	20	
V366b		No watermark	£400	-	-	
V366c		Deep purple	2.00	40	20	1.00
V366d		Mauve	2.00	40	20	1.00
V366e		Bluish lilac	£250	£70	£35	£75

For controls on this issue, please refer to the section on controls.

No.			M/M	F/U	G/U	✉

Large coloured corner letters

Printer: De La Rue & Co.

Large
Anchor Watermark

1883 (2 July) - 84 Wmk. Anchor. Perf. 14

No.			M/M	F/U	G/U
A. Blued paper					
V367	**2s6d**	**Lilac**	£950	£400	£200
V368	**5s**	**Rose**	£4000	£1200	£500
V369	**10s**	**Ultramarine**	£17000	£3000	£1700
V369a		Cobalt	£22000	£4000	£2000
B. White paper					
V370	**2s6d**	**Lilac** (1884)	£180	£50	£20
V370a		Wmk. inverted		£3500	£2700
V370b		Deep lilac	£180	£50	£20
V371	**5s**	**Rose**	£280	£75	£30
V371a		Wmk. inverted		£3750	
V371b		Crimson	£280	£75	£30
V372	**10s**	**Ultramarine**	£775	£250	£100
V372a		Pale ultramarine	£775	£250	£100
V372b		Cobalt	£11000	£3500	£1000

Large white corner letters

Imperial Crown
Watermark

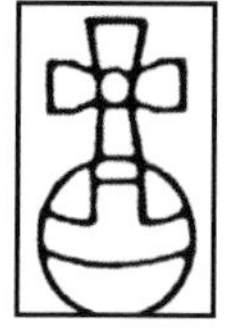

Orb
Watermark

1884 (1 April) Wmk. Three Imperial Crowns. Perf. 14

No.			M/M	F/U	G/U
V373	**£1**	**Brown lilac**	£15000	£1300	£500
V373a		Wmk. inverted	-	£5000	
Varieties					
V373b	£1	Broken frame, lettered JC	£13000	£1750	£800
V373c	£1	Broken frame, lettered TA	£13000	£1750	£800

1888 (1 Feb.) Wmk. Three Orbs. Perf. 14

No.			M/M	F/U	G/U
V374	**£1**	**Brown lilac**	£25000	£2000	£950
Varieties					
V374a	£1	Broken frame, lettered JC	£30000	£2500	£1100
V374b	£1	Broken frame, lettered TA	£30000	£2500	£1100

1891 (27 Jan.) Wmk. Three Imperial Crowns. Perf. 14

No.			M/M	F/U	G/U
V375	**£1**	**Green**	£1600	£425	£250
V375a		Wmk. inverted	£30000	-	£2850
Varieties					
V375b	£1	Broken frame, lettered JC	£4000	£800	£425
V375c	£1	Broken frame, lettered TA	£4000	£800	£425

Lilac and Green issue

Printer: De La Rue & Co.

Coloured letters in all four corners except for the ½d.

Imperial Crown Watermark

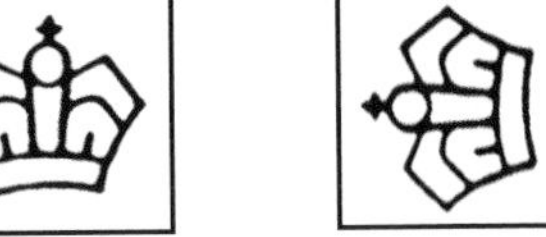

Watermark sideways (from the back)

1883 (1 Aug.) 9d only, **1884 (1 April)** all other values. Wmk. Imperial Crown (sideways to right on 2d, 2½d, 6d and 9d). Perf. 14

No.			M/M	F/U	G/U	✉
V376	½d	**Slate blue**	5.00	1.50	50	4.00
V376a		Wmk. inverted	-	-	£40	
V377	1½d	**Lilac**	£30	£12	5.50	£25
V377a		Wmk. inverted	£100	£75	£30	
V378	2d	**Lilac**	£50	£20	8.00	£30
V378a		Wmk. sideways-inverted	-	-	£150	
V379	2½d	**Lilac**	£25	4.00	2.00	£10
V379a		Wmk. sideways-inverted	-	-	£150	
V380	3d	**Lilac**	£50	£25	9.00	£35
V380a		Wmk. inverted	-	-	£150	
V381	4d	**Dull green**	£95	£45	£22	£125
V382	5d	**Dull green**	£95	£50	£25	£130
V382A		Line under 'd', unissued	£5500			
V383	6d	**Dull green**	£115	£50	£25	£130
V383a		Wmk. sideways-inverted	-	-	£850	
V384	9d	**Dull green**	£240	£175	£65	£350
V384a		Wmk. sideways-inverted	£625	£200	£70	
V385	1s	**Dull green**	£160	£90	£40	£200
V385a		Wmk. inverted	-	-	£500	
		Set of 10	£675	£400	£155	

All prices quoted are for stamps in the correct colour. Washed examples or colour changelings have little value.

Unless stated otherwise, prices from this point forwards are for U/M (never hinged), M/M and F/U. On cover prices remain where appropriate.

The 'Jubilee' issue

Printer: De La Rue

Duty plate Die I

Duty plate Die II

Imperial Crown Watermark

1887 (1 Jan.) - 1900 Wmk. Imperial Crown. Perf. 14 (comb)

No.			U/M	M/M	F/U	✉
V386	½d	**Vermilion**	1.20	60	15	3.00
V386a		Wmk. Inverted	£30	£20	£40	
V386b		Pale vermilion	1.50	50	15	3.00
V386c		Orange vermilion	1.50	50	15	4.00
V386d		Deep vermilion	£12	6.00	2.00	4.00
V387	½d	**Dull blue green** (17.4.1900)	1.25	50	20	3.00
V387a		Wmk. inverted	£30	£20	£45	
V387b		Bright blue green	2.00	1.00	30	3.00
V388	1½d	**Pale purple and pale green**	£13	6.00	1.50	£20
V388a		Wmk. inverted	£500	£375	£250	
V388b		Purple and pale green	£15	8.00	1.50	£20
V388c		Deep purple and pale green	£20	£14	2.00	£20
V389	2d	**Grey green and carmine**	£18	£9	3.50	£15
V389a		Wmk. inverted	£550	£350	£250	
V389b		Yellow green and carmine	£20	£9	3.50	£20
V389c		Deep green and carmine	£40	£16	7.50	£30
V389d		Green and vermilion	£300	£200	£100	£400
V390	2½d	**Purple** on blue paper	£12	7.00	70	7.00
V390a		Wmk. inverted	£850	£550	£375	
V390b		Pale purple on blue paper	£15	5.00	70	7.00
V390c		Deep purple on blue paper	£20	9.00	80	8.00
V391	3d	**Purple** on yellow paper	£25	9.00	1.20	£15
V391a		Wmk. inverted	-	£1500	£500	
V391b		Deep purple on yellow paper	£25	8.00	95	£15
V391c		Purple on orange paper (1890)	£500	£250	£95	£300
V392	4d	**Green and deep brown**	£28	£12	6.00	£30
V392a		Wmk. inverted	£850	£400	£300	
V392b		Green and purple brown	£28	£13	6.00	£30
V392c		Green and deep chocolate brown	£55	£25	8.00	£30
V393	4½d	**Green and carmine** (15.9.92)	5.00	3.50	£14	£70
V393a		Wmk. inverted	-	-	£400	
V393b		Deep green and carmine	8.50	4.50	£15	£70
V393c		Green and dull scarlet	£12	7.00	£18	£100
V393d		Green and deep bright carmine	£800	£350	£200	£750
V394	5d	**Dull purple & blue** (Die I)	£475	£170	£30	£150
V395	5d	**Dull purple & blue** (Die II)	£35	£14	6.00	£35
V395a		Wmk. inverted	-	-	£500	
V395b		Dull purple & bright blue	£35	£15	6.00	£35
V396	6d	**Purple** on rose red paper	£25	£12	6.00	£55
V396a		Wmk. inverted	£1500	£1200	£700	
V396b		Deep purple on rose red	£25	£12	5.00	£55
V396c		Slate purple on rose red	£30	£15	5.00	£55
V397	9d	**Dull purple and blue**	£50	£25	£20	£120
V397a		Wmk. inverted	£1400	£1000	£450	
V397b		Slate purple and blue	£50	£25	£20	£120
V397c		Dull purple and bright blue	£50	£25	£20	£120

No.			U/M	M/M	F/U	✉
V398	10d	**Dull purple and carmine** (24.2.90)	£37	£25	£20	£130
V398a		Wmk. inverted	£1400	£900	£500	
V398b		Dull purple and dull scarlet	£100	£60	£45	£175
V398c		Dull purple and deep bright carmine	£320	£180	£75	£250
V399	1s	**Dull green**	£340	£95	£30	£125
V399a		Wmk. inverted	£900	£550	£550	
V399b		Grey green	£250	£100	£30	£140
V400	1s	**Green and carmine** (11.7.1900)	£48	£32	£55	£600
V400a		Wmk. inverted	£700	£450	£600	
		Set of 14	£460	£165	£125	

No.	M/M	F/U	G/U	✉

Warning

Many of the colours are highly fugitive, especially the 1½d, 2d, 4d, 4½d, 9d and both 1s values. Any contact with water seriously affects these colours.

No. M/M F/U G/U No. M/M F/U G/U

Overprinted by De La Rue & Co.

Collectors are warned that examples of all the 'official' overprints are known to have been forged, and great care should be taken in purchasing the scarcer and higher priced stamps. Some guidance in checking the authenticity of overprints is given below:

(a) Exact comparison with a known genuine overprint.
(b) The impression should be easily read from the back of the stamp as the overprint usually has a heavy impression.
(c) The postmark should obviously be on top of the overprint, and many forged examples can be detected by the overprint being on top of the postmark
(d) If in doubt, obtain an expert opinion and a certificate.

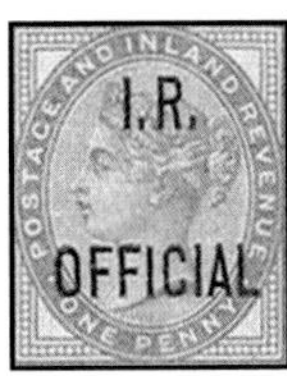

1882 - 1901 Inland Revenue. Surface printed issues overprinted 'I.R. OFFICIAL' in two lines in black. Wmk. Imperial Crown. Perf. 14

No.			M/M	F/U	G/U
1881 Large coloured corner letters					
V401	6d	**Grey** (30.10.82)	£170	£20	£15
1880 - 84 Low values					
V402	½d	**Deep green** (28.10.82)	£27	£10	5.00
V402a		Pale green	£30	£12	6.00
V403	½d	**Slate blue** (8.5.85)	£25	6.00	3.00
1881 1d Lilac					
V404	1d	**Lilac** (Die II) (27.9.82)	2.00	70	35
V404a		Wmk. inverted	-	-	£750
V404b		Blue-black overprint	£200	£40	£25
1883 - 84 'Lilac and Green' issue					
V405	2½d	**Lilac** (12.3.85)	£200	£40	£25
V406	1s	**Dull green** (12.3.85)	£3000	£550	£350
1887 - 1900 'Jubilee' issue					
V407	½d	**Vermilion** (21.8.88)	3.50	1.00	60
V408	½d	**Blue green** (4.01)	4.50	7.00	4.50
V409	2½d	**Purple** on blue paper (20.10.89)	£45	6.00	3.50
V410	6d	**Purple** on rose paper (14.6.01)	£200	£20	£15
V411	1s	**Green** (15.3.89)	£300	£30	£20
V412	1s	**Green and carmine** (12.01)	£1200	£400	£300

1885 - 1902 High values overprinted 'I.R. OFFICIAL' in two lines in black. Wmk. Large Anchor. Perf. 14

No.			M/M	F/U	G/U
1885 (12 March) A. Blued paper					
V413	5s	**Rose**	£4500	£500	£400
V414	10s	**Ultramarine**	£8000	£2500	£1900
1890 (March) B. White paper					
V415	5s	**Rose**	£2200	£700	£400
V415a		Blue-black overprint	£2500	£900	£500
V416	10s	**Ultramarine**	£3500	£900	£600
V416a		Blue-black overprint	£3500	£1200	£750
V416b		Cobalt	£8500	£1800	£800

No.			M/M	F/U	G/U
1885 (12 March) Wmk. Three Imperial Crowns. Perf. 14					
V417	£1	**Brown lilac**	£22000	£11000	
1890 (March) Wmk. Three Orbs. Perf. 14					
V418	£1	**Brown lilac**	£29000	£14000	
1892 (13 April) Wmk. Three Imperial Crowns. Perf. 14					
V419	£1	**Green**	£4000	£800	£550

1883 - 1900 Government Parcels. Surface printed issues overprinted 'GOV^{T}. PARCELS' in two lines in black. Wmk. Imperial Crown. Perf. 14

No.			M/M	F/U	G/U
1881 Large coloured corner letters					
V420	1s	**Orange brown.** Plate 13 (1.7.83)	£650	£70	£35
V421	1s	**Orange brown.** Plate 14 (1.7.83)	£1100	£120	£60
1881 1d Lilac					
V422	1d	**Lilac** (Die II) (6.97)	£50	£10	5.00
V422a		Wmk. inverted	£2500	£1500	£850
1883 - 84 'Lilac and Green' issue					
V423	1½d	**Lilac** (30.4.86)	£180	£30	£12
V424	6d	**Dull green** (30.4.86)	£1100	£250	£100
V425	9d	**Dull green** (1.8.83)	£950	£150	£80
1887 - 1900 'Jubilee' issue					
V426	1½d	**Dull purple & green** (20.10.87)	£25	3.50	2.00
V427	2d	**Green and carmine** (24.10.91)	£45	8.00	4.00
V428	4½d	**Green and carmine** (9.92)	£95	£60	£25
V428a		Wmk. inverted	-	£2000	£1000
V429	6d	**Purple** on rose paper (19.12.87)	£45	£10	7.00
V430	9d	**Dull purple and blue** (21.8.88)	£75	£20	8.00
V431	1s	**Green** (25.3.90)	£140	£60	£30
V432	1s	**Green and carmine** (11.1.1900)	£170	£90	£30

1896 - 1902 Office of Works. Surface printed issues overprinted 'O.W. OFFICIAL' in two lines in black. Wmk. Imperial Crown. Perf. 14

No.			M/M	F/U	G/U
1881 1d Lilac					
V433	1d	**Lilac** (Die II) (24.3.96)	£90	£20	£10
1887 - 1900 'Jubilee' issue					
V434	½d	**Vermilion**	£100	£40	£25
V435	½d	**Blue green**	£120	£45	£30
V436	5d	**Purple and blue** (Die II)	£1100	£170	£100
V437	10d	**Dull purple and carmine**	£1700	£360	£220

½d, 1d

2½d, 6d

1896 - 1901 War Office. Surface printed issues overprinted 'ARMY OFFICIAL' in two lines in black. Wmk. Imperial Crown. Perf. 14

No.			M/M	F/U	G/U
1881 1d Lilac					
V438	**1d**	**Lilac** (Die II) (1.9.96)	2.00	50	25
1887 - 1900 'Jubilee' issue					
V439	**½d**	**Vermilion** (1.9.96)	3.00	50	25
V439a		Wmk. inverted	£400	£250	-
V440	**½d**	**Blue green** (4.1.1900)	3.00	4.00	2.00
V440a		Wmk. inverted	£400	£250	-
V441	**2½d**	**Purple** on blue paper (1.9.96)	£15	12.50	8.50
V442	**6d**	**Purple** on rose paper (7.11.1901)	£40	£20	£12

1902 (19 Feb.) Board of Education. Surface printed issues overprinted 'BOARD OF EDUCATION' in three lines in black. Wmk. Imperial Crown. Perf. 14

No.			M/M	F/U	G/U
1887 - 1900 'Jubilee' issue					
V443	**5d**	**Purple and blue** (Die II)	£1300	£175	£110
V444	**1s**	**Green and carmine**	£3250	£1400	£950

Introductory Notes

It is recommended that identification is best carried out by a series of elimination's and the following chart provides a degree of guidance.

Certain printings can be positively distinguished by perforation size (e.g. Harrison Perf. 15 x 14) or the chalky paper test - lightly rub the surface of the margin of the stamp with a small piece of silver and the chalk surface paper will react with a black mark that looks like a pencil stroke. This can be removed with a light rubber. All chalky papers, with the exception of the 6d, are De La Rue printings.

The exercise then continues with the clues listed. Quality of printing, gum, centring, perforations, date of cancel (when available), plus the differences illustrated below, and finally a comparison of the various shades of colour.

USED STAMPS - beware colour changes being produced by water immersion on the following values - ½d, 1½d, 2d, 3d, 4d green and brown, 5d, 6d, 9d, 10d and 1s, as many of the colours were highly fugitive, especially the greens and purples. Those stamps with affected colours (washed out and pale) are worth very much less.

A

B

X

Y

A	**DE LA RUE**	Shading lines around the crown are light and gradually darken towards the frame sides.
B	**HARRISON** (Somerset House 6d)	Shading lines are virtually the same depth from frame to edge of crown giving a 'halo' effect.
X	**DE LA RUE**	Top 'frame' line to right of value tablet extending upwards (appears to be a single line) is always very thin and/or indistinct.
Y	**SOMERSET HOUSE**	The same 'frame' line is distinct and thick.

PRINTERS	DE LA RUE		HARRISON		SOMERSET HOUSE	
Perf. size	14	14	14	15 x 14	14	14
Paper type	Ordinary, smooth and coated	Chalky	Ordinary, less smooth		Ordinary, less smooth, Plate glazed, appears chalky, but does not react to silver test	
Quality of printing	Fine		Coarser		Coarser	
Gum	Yellowish		Colourless (See Note II)		Colourless	
Centreing	Good		Poor		Less poor	
Perforations	Generally clean		Often ragged		Often ragged	
Date of cancel	From 1902, seldom after 1910		From 1911		From 1911	
½d	See Illustration A		See Illustration B	*		
1d	See Illustration A		See Illustration B some shades also fluoresce gold	*		
1½ d	See Illustration X Dull purple Slate purple	C			See Illustration Y Reddish purple Slate purple	
2d	Green is yellowish or bluish	C			Green is dull to deep greyish	
2½d	Straight blues See Illustration A		Duller blues See Illustration B	*		
3d	Paper appears chalky when not so	C	Purple appears as shades of brown on lemon paper	*		
4d Bi-colour	Only De La Rue	C				
4d Orange	Finer impression, brownish, pale to deep orange		White specks in solid background. Coarser impression. Bright orange shades	*		
5d	Purple and slate purple	C			Reddish tinge to purple	
6d	See Illustration A dull and slate purple (does not fluoresce)	C			See Illustration B Reddish purples, some fluoresce (see Note I)	C
7d	No olive tinge to grey black				Grey is tinged with olive	
9d	Purple is dull or slate	C			Purple is reddish	
10d	Purple is dull or slate	C			Purple is reddish	
1s	Pale bluish green shades	C			Pale to dark green	
2s 6d	Lilac and dull purple (does not fluoresce)	C			Reddish to deep black purple. Dull greyish purple (fluoresces gold)	
5s	Carmine (shows on reverse)				Carmine-reds	
10s	Pale to deep ultramarine				Coarse printing: dull pale to deep ultramarine	
£1	Bluish green				Less bluish but deeper green	

Notes:

(I) 6d Dickinson Paper. Somerset House experimental printing
A coated paper that does not react to the silver test. Shades are dull to deep rose purple with white gum

(II) There is exception to the colourless gum on the printing of the Harrison Penny value, a small printing was made with a double gum - very yellowish, as a result of complaints from the public that the stamps did not appear to be gummed at all. The last of the 6d Somerset House also had yellow gum, but the shades of deep purple were quite different from De La Rue.

6d Somerset House also had yellow gum, but the shades of deep purple were quite different from De La Rue

C Denotes chalky paper variety exists

* Variety exists (Perf. 15 x 14)

Printer: De La Rue in Typography

½d, 1d, 6d

Imperial Crown Watermark

1902 (1 Jan) - 11 Wmk. Imperial Crown. Perf. 14

A. Ordinary paper

No.			U/M	M/M	F/U	✉
E1	½d	**Blue green**	1.50	50	20	25
E1a		Wmk. inverted	£2000	£1500	£700	
E1b		Dull blue green	1.50	50	20	25
E1c		Deep blue green	9.50	5.50	60	70
E2	½d	**Yellow green** (26.11.04)	1.50	50	15	25
E2a		Wmk. inverted	£20	8.50	3.00	5.00
E2b		Pale yellow green	1.50	50	15	25
E2c		Wmk. inverted	£20	8.50	3.00	5.00
E3	1d	**Scarlet**	1.50	50	10	25
E3a		Wmk. inverted	6.00	3.75	95	3.00
E3b		Bright scarlet	1.50	50	10	25
E3c		Wmk. inverted	6.00	3.75	1.50	4.00
E3d		Deep bright scarlet	5.00	2.75	50	75
E3e		Rose carmine	£16	9.00	3.50	6.50
E3f		Deep rose carmine	£35	£28	£10	£15
E3g		Blood-red A	£350	£225	£55	£85
E3h		Deep blood-red A	£750	£495	£95	£125
E4	1½d	**Dull purple and green** (21.3.02)	£50	£20	6.00	£15
E4a		Slate purple & green	£55	£22	8.00	£15
E4b		Wmk. Inverted		£500		
E4c		Deep slate purple & green	£70	£45	8.00	£15
E5	2d	**Yellowish green & carmine** (25.3.02)	£55	£25	8.00	£20
E5a		Grey green & carmine	£55	£25	8.00	£20
E5b		Yellowish green & carmine*	£100	£70	£40	£60
E5c		Yellowish green & vermilion (1903)	£240	£160	£40	£60
E6	2½d	**Ultramarine**	£20	£10	2.00	7.00
E6a		Pale ultramarine	£20	£10	2.00	7.00
E6b		Deep ultramarine	£30	£15	6.00	7.00
E6c		Wmk. inverted	-		£1200	
E7	3d	**Dull purple** on yellow paper (orange yellow back) (20.3.02)	£50	£20	3.00	£15
E7a		Deep purple on yellow paper (orange yellow back)	£55	£25	3.00	£15
E7b		Wmk. inverted	-	£1000	-	
E8	4d	**Green and brown** (27.3.02)	£70	£30	£10	£20
E8a		Green and grey brown	£70	£30	£10	£20
E8b		Wmk. inverted	-	-	£1600	
E8c		Green and chocolate brown	£80	£35	£10	£20
E9	4d	**Pale orange** (1.11.09)	£25	6.00	8.00	£20
E9a		Red orange	£25	6.00	6.00	£20
E9b		Brown orange	£175	£115	£85	£135
E10	5d	**Dull purple and ultramarine** (14.5.02)	£80	£25	7.00	£25
E10a		Slate purple and ultramarine	£80	£25	7.00	£25
E11	6d	**Slate purple**	£50	£22	6.00	£25
E11a		Pale dull purple	£50	£22	6.00	£25
E12	7d	**Grey black** (4.5.10)	8.00	4.00	£10	£100
E12a		Pale grey black	£25	£15	£20	£100
E12b		Deep grey black	£100	£60	£95	£220
E12c		Very deep grey black Ä	£180	£120	£150	£250
E13	9d	**Dull purple & ultramarine** (7.4.02)	£130	£40	£35	£120
E13a		Slate purple and ultramarine	£150	£40	£35	£120
E13b		Slate purple and deep ultramarine	£125	£75	£35	£120
E14	10d	**Dull purple and carmine** (3.7.02)	£140	£45	£30	£145
E14b		Slate purple and carmine	£140	£45	£30	£145
E14c		Slate purple and bright carmine *	£220	£140	£75	£200
E14d		Slate purple & carmine pink	£500	£300	£85	£220
E15	1s	**Dull green and carmine** (24.3.02)	£130	£45	£10	£85
E15a		Dull green & bright carmine	£130	£45	£10	£85
E15b		Dull green and bright carmine *	£200	£130	£75	£175
		Set of 15	£650	£200	£85	

Varieties

No.			U/M	M/M	F/U	✉
E16	2d	Tyrian plum (1910). Unissued	£50000			
E17	2½d	Purple on blue paper. Unissued	£40000	£35000		
E14a	10d	No cross on crown	£395	£275	£150	£300

B. Chalk surfaced paper

No.			U/M	M/M	F/U	✉
E18	1½d	**Pale dull purple and green** (6.9.05)	£50	£25	8.00	£15
E18a		Slate purple & bluish green	£50	£25	8.00	£15
E18b		Deep slate purple and bluish green	£70	£35	9.00	£15
E19	2d	**Grey green & carmine** (6.9.05)	£50	£22	9.00	£25
E19a		Deep grey green and scarlet	£55	£25	9.00	£25
E19b		Grey green and scarlet	£55	£25	9.00	£25
E19c		Pale blue green & carmine	£100	£55	£15	£40
E19d		Wmk. inverted	£1400	£900	-	

No.			U/M	M/M	F/U	✉
E20	3d	**Purple** on lemon paper (lemon back) (31.3.06)	£60	£20	8.00	£20
E20a		Pale purple on lemon paper (lemon back)	£60	£20	8.00	£20
E20b		Dull reddish purple on yellow paper (lemon back)	£275	£100	£27	£40
E20c		Pale reddish purple on orange yellow paper (orange yellow back)	£220	£100	£25	£60
E20d		Dull purple on orange yellow paper (orange yellow back)	£220	£100	£30	£100
E21	4d	**Green and chocolate brown** (19.1.06)	£40	£20	£10	£25
E21a		Deep green and chocolate brown	£40	£20	£10	£25
E21b		Wmk. inverted	-	-	£1200	
E22	5d	**Dull purple and ultramarine** (19.5.06)	£85	£30	£10	£25
E22a		Slate purple and ultramarine	£75	£25	£10	£25
E22b		Wmk. inverted	£1000	£750	£750	
E22c		Deep slate purple and ultramarine	£90	£35	£10	£25
E23	6d	**Dull purple** (1.10.05)	£50	£20	9.00	£30
E23a		Slate purple	£50	£20	9.00	£30
E23b		Pale dull purple	£50	£20	9.00	£30
E23c		Wmk. inverted	-	-	£300	
E24	9d	**Dull purple & ultramarine** (29.6.05)	£125	£50	£30	£120
E24a		Slate purple and ultramarine	£130	£50	£30	£120
E24b		Slate purple and pale ultramarine	£130	£50	£35	£180
E24c		Wmk. inverted	-	-	£1200	
E24d		Slate purple and deep ultramarine	£180	£120	£50	£150
E25	10d	**Dull purple and carmine** (6.9.05)	£130	£45	£35	£150
E25a		Slate purple and carmine	£130	£45	£35	£150
E25c		Dull purple and scarlet (9.10)	£130	£50	£40	£150
E25e		Slate purple and scarlet	£130	£60	£40	£150
E25f		Slate purple & deep carmine	£300	£200	£90	£300
E25g		Slate purple & deep carmine (shiny)	£1500	£1000	£300	£1000
E26	1s	**Dull green and carmine** (6.9.05)	£130	£50	£20	£120
E26a		Dull green & scarlet	£130	£50	£20	£120
E26b		Deep dull green & scarlet	£130	£50	£20	£120
E26c		Dull green & pale carmine	£130	£50	£20	£120
		Set of 9 (cheapest)	£600	£250	£90	

Varieties

No.			U/M	M/M	F/U	✉
E25b	10d	No cross on crown	£350	£200	£125	£300
E25d	10d	No cross on crown	£350	£200	£125	£300

1911 (3 May - Nov.) Wmk. Imperial Crown.
Printer: Harrison and Sons in Typography
A. Perf. 14

No.			U/M	M/M	F/U	✉
E27	½d	**Dull yellow green** (3.5.11)	2.50	1.50	70	2.00
E27a		Wmk. inverted	£27	£14	£15	£35
E27b		Dull green	2.50	1.25	40	1.00
E27c		Deep dull green	9.00	6.00	2.00	6.00
E27d		Pale bluish green	£45	£26	£20	£30
E27e		Wmk. sideways	-	-	£15000	
E27f		Deep dull yellow green (blotchy)	£50	£35	£25	£50
E27g		Olive green	£55	£45	£20	£50
E27h		Bright green (6.11)	£250	£175	£100	£200
E27i		Deep bright green	£250	£175	£100	£200
E28	1d	**Rose red** (3.5.11)	5.00	2.75	5.50	7.50
E28a		No watermark	£40	£27	£85	
E28b		Wmk. inverted	£20	£15	£17	£30
E28c		Deep rose red	8.00	4.50	5.50	7.00
E28d		Pale rose carmine	£50	£35	7.00	£20
E28e		Wmk. inverted	£50	£32	9.00	£20
E28f		Rose carmine	£50	£30	9.00	£20
E28g		Wmk. inverted	£60	£35	£15	£35
E28h		Aniline rose *	£150	£100	£95	£180
E28i		Wmk. inverted	£150	£100	£95	£200
E28j		Intense rose red Ä	£275	£200	£85	£300
E28k		Deep rose carmine	£295	£225	£75	£150
E28m		Aniline pink *	£800	£500	£180	£600
E29	2½d	**Bright blue** (10.7.11)	£90	£30	£15	£30
E29a		Dull blue	£90	£30	£15	£30
E29b		Deep bright blue	£110	£50	£30	£35
E29c		Wmk. inverted	£700	£495		
E29d		Deep dull blue	£130	£90	£45	£60
E30	3d	**Purple** on lemon (12.9.11)	£100	£70	£130	£400
E30a		Grey purple on lemon	£100	£70	£130	£400
E30b		Grey on lemon	£3500	£2800	-	
E31	4d	**Bright orange** (13.7.11)	£105	£45	£80	£100
E31a		Deep bright orange	£110	£55	£80	£100
		Set of 5	£280	£140	£170	

B. Perf. 15 x 14

No.			U/M	M/M	F/U	✉
E32	½d	**Dull green** (30.10.11)	£45	£27	£25	£45
E32a		Pale bluish green	£50	£30	£25	£45
E32b		Deep dull green	£65	£40	£30	£45
E32c		Deep dull green (blotchy)	£800	£550	£250	£450
E33	1d	**Rose carmine** (5.10.11)	£25	£15	7.50	£20
E33a		Pale rose carmine	£25	£15	7.50	£30
E33b		Deep rose carmine	£35	£20	12.50	£20
E33c		Rose red	£45	£25	£16	£30
E33d		Deep rose red	£70	£50	£30	£50
E33e		Intense rose red	£450	£300	£95	£200
E34	2½d	**Bright blue** (14.10.11)	£35	£20	7.00	£20
E34a		Dull blue	£35	£20	7.00	£20
E34b		Wmk. inverted	-	-	£400	
E34c		Deep dull blue	£65	£45	£16	£25
E34d		Deep bright blue	£65	£45	£10	£25
E35	3d	**Purple** on lemon (22.9.11)	£45	£25	5.00	£20
E35a		Grey purple on lemon	£60	£27	5.00	£20
E35b		Grey on lemon	£2700	£2200		
E36	4d	**Bright orange** (22.11.11)	£40	£20	7.00	£40
E36a		Deep bright orange	£45	£25	7.00	£40
E36b		Very deep orange	£85	£65	£20	
		Set of 5	£120	£75	£40	

1911 (13 July) - 13 Wmk. Imperial Crown. Perf. 14
Printer: Somerset House in Typography
A. Ordinary paper

No.			U/M	M/M	F/U	✉
E37	1½d	**Dull purple and green** (13.7.11)	£40	£20	£10	£40
E37a		Dull reddish purple & green	£60	£25	£10	£40
E37b		Dull reddish purple and bright green	£40	£20	£10	£40
E37c		Slate purple and green	£37	£20	£12	£40
E37d		Deep plum and deep green	£200	£130	£55	£75
E37e		Deep plum and pale green	£250	£140	£65	£75
E37f		Reddish purple and bright green	£75	£35	£12	£50
E37g		Reddish purple and yellow green	£75	£35	£12	£50
E38	2d	**Deep dull green and red** (8.8.11)	£35	£15	£10	£30
E38a		Grey green & bright carmine	£35	£15	£10	£30
E38b		Deep dull green and carmine	£40	£17	£10	£30
E38c		Deep dull green and bright carmine	£40	£17	£12	£35

No.			U/M	M/M	F/U	✉
E39	5d	**Deep dull reddish purple and bright blue** (7.8.11)	£35	£17	£10	£40
E39a		Deep reddish purple and bright blue	£35	£17	£10	£40
E39b		Deep plum and cobalt blue	£35	£17	£12	£40
E39c		Pale plum and cobalt blue *	£75	£50	£18	£40
E40	6d	**Dull purple *** (31.10.11)	£30	£20	£10	£50
E40a		Pale dull purple	£50	£27	£12	£50
E40b		Reddish purple *	£35	£20	£12	£60
E40d		Pale reddish purple	£45	£22	£14	£65
E40e		Dark purple	£40	£25	£15	£65
E40f		Royal purple *	£75	£40	£65	£250
E40g		Deep reddish purple *	£75	£40	£20	£65
E40h		Dull lilac *	£200	£150	£75	£140
E41	7d	**Slate grey** (1.8.12)	£15	£10	£12	£130
E41a		Pale grey	£17	£12	£14	£130
E41b		Deep slate grey (5.13)	£125	£80	£40	£150
E42	9d	**Dull reddish purple and blue** (24.7.11)	£95	£40	£40	£140
E42a		Deep dull reddish purple and blue	£140	£65	£45	£140
E42b		Reddish purple and light blue	£140	£65	£50	£150
E42c		Slate purple & cobalt blue *	£150	£70	£50	£160
E42d		Deep dull reddish purple and deep bright blue	£160	£70	£55	£175
E42e		Deep plum and cobalt blue	£150	£70	£55	£175
E43	10d	**Dull reddish purple and carmine** (9.10.11)	£100	£45	£40	£175
E43a		Dull purple and scarlet	£120	£60	£45	£195
E43b		Deep dull purple and carmine	£120	£60	£45	£200
E43d		Deep plum and carmine	£120	£60	£45	£220
E43e		Deep dull purple and scarlet	£150	£70	£50	£230
E43f		Dull reddish purple and scarlet	£165	£110	£70	£250
E43g		Dull reddish purple and aniline scarlet *	£320	£200	£80	£270
E43h		Dull purple and deep scarlet	£275	£190	£100	£300
E43i		Dull reddish purple and aniline pink *	£375	£250	£190	£450
E44	1s	**Green & carmine** (17.7.11)	£100	£40	£15	£100
E44a		Green and scarlet	£135	£45	£18	£120
E44b		No watermark	£1800	£1200	-	
E44c		Wmk. inverted	£130	£90	-	
E44d		Deep green and scarlet	£105	£40	£15	£120
E44e		Green and bright scarlet	£120	£50	£17	£130
E44f		Dark green and scarlet	£150	£70	£30	£150
		Set of 8 (cheapest)	£440	£240	£120	
Varieties						
E40c	6d	No cross on crown	£600	£400	£250	£650
E43c	10d	No cross on crown	£1000	£750	£250	£500

B. Chalk surfaced paper

No.			U/M	M/M	F/U	✉
E45	6d	**Deep plum** (7.13)	£40	£20	£70	£150
E45b		Bright magenta (31.10.11)	£7500	£4500	!	
E45c		Pale plum	£95	£65	£75	£120
Variety						
E45a	6d	No cross on crown	£600	£400	£250	£450

C. "Dickinson" coated paper

No.			U/M	M/M	F/U	✉
E46	6d	**Dull purple** (3.13)	£250	£150	£120	£300
E46a		Dull reddish purple	£260	£160	£130	£300
E46b		Deep dull reddish purple	£280	£170	£150	£400

* Fluorescent reaction when viewed under an ultra violet lamp.

! These stamps are impossible to identify in used condition.

Ä Only purchase with a certificate of authenticity.

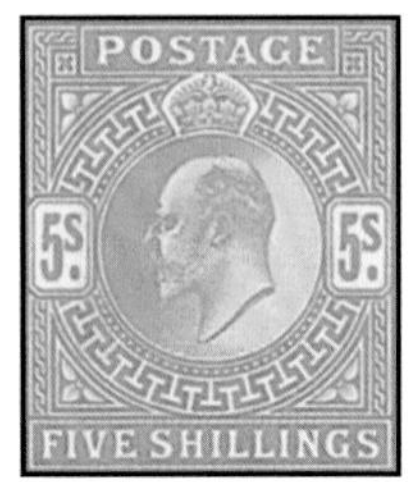

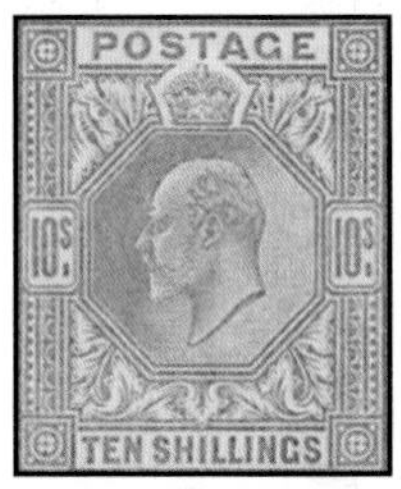

Large Anchor Watermark

Imperial Crown Watermark

1902 (5 April) - 1905 Wmk. Large Anchor. Perf. 14
Printer: De La Rue & Co. in Typography.
A. Ordinary paper.

No.			U/M	M/M	F/U
E47	**2s6d**	**Lilac**	£360	£130	£75
E47a		Wmk. inverted	£2500	£1500	£850
E47b		Slate purple	£370	£140	£75
E48	**5s**	**Bright carmine**	£450	£170	£85
E48a		Deep bright carmine	£450	£170	£85
E48b		Wmk. inverted	-	-	£2000
E49	**10s**	**Ultramarine**	£950	£350	£250
E49a		Deep ultramarine	£1000	£375	£275

B. Chalk surfaced paper

No.			U/M	M/M	F/U
E50	**2s6d**	**Dull purple** (7.10.1905)	£360	£160	£85
E50a		Pale dull purple	£380	£160	£90
E50b		Slate purple	£400	£175	£100
E50c		Wmk. inverted	£3000	£1700	£1200

1902 (16 July) Wmk. Three Imperial Crowns. Perf. 14

No.			U/M	M/M	F/U
E51	**£1**	**Dull blue green**	£1500	£900	£450
E51a		Wmk. inverted		£20000	
		Set of 4	£3100	£1300	£850

1911 (27 Sept.) - 12 Wmk. Large Anchor. Perf. 14
Printer: Somerset House in Typography

No.			U/M	M/M	F/U
E52	**2s6d**	**Dark purple**	£360	£140	£90
E52a		Wmk. inverted			-
E52b		Dull reddish purple	£360	£140	£90
E52c		Pale dull reddish purple	£380	£150	£90
E52d		Dull greyish purple *	£600	£350	£200
E53	**5s**	**Carmine** (29.2.12)	£500	£180	£100
E53a		Carmine red	£500	£180	£100
E54	**10s**	**Blue** (14.1.12)	£950	£350	£270
E54a		Bright blue	£950	£390	£280
E54b		Deep blue	£1000	£400	£300

1911 (3 Sept.) Wmk. Three Imperial Crowns. Perf. 14

No.			U/M	M/M	F/U
E51	**£1**	**Deep green**	£1400	£850	£450
		Set of 4	£3200	£1500	£800

* Fluorescent (gold) reaction under an ultra violet lamp.

Overprinted by De La Rue & Co.

1902 (4 Feb.) - 1904 Inland Revenue. De La Rue printings overprinted "I.R. OFFICIAL" in two lines in black. Wmk. Imperial Crown. Perf. 14

No.			U/M	M/M	F/U
E56	**½d**	**Blue green**	£25	£12	2.00
E57	**1d**	**Scarlet**	£20	£8	1.00
E58	**2½d**	**Ultramarine** (19.2.02)	£950	£550	£80
E59	**6d**	**Dull purple** (14.3.04)	£140000	£100000	£70000
E60	**1s**	**Green and carmine** (29.4.02)	£1300	£800	£250

1902 (29April) Wmk. Large Anchor. Perf. 14

No.			U/M	M/M	F/U
E61	**5s**	**Carmine**	£12000	£7000	£3500
E62	**10s**	**Ultramarine**	£50000	£30000	£17000

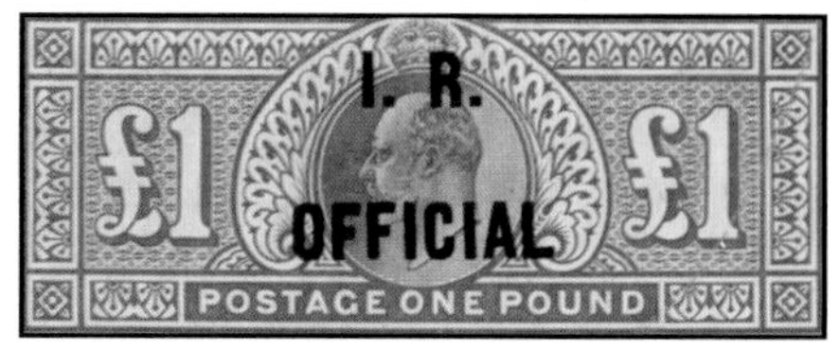

1902 (29April) Wmk. Three Imperial Crowns. Perf. 14

No.			U/M	M/M	F/U
E63	**£1**	**Dull blue green**	£35000	£25000	£12000

Controls	Prices for a M/M single stamp	
½d	Letter A	£90
	Letter B	£90
1d	Letter A	£90
	Letter B	£90

1902 (19 Feb. - Dec.) Government Parcels. De La Rue printings overprinted 'GOV[T]. PARCELS' in two lines in black. Wmk. Imperial Crown. Perf. 14

No.			U/M	M/M	F/U
E64	**1d**	**Scarlet** (30.10.02)	£40	£20	6.00
E65	**2d**	**Green and carmine** (29.4.02)	£110	£80	£20
E66	**6d**	**Dull purple**	£220	£140	£20
E67	**9d**	**Purple & ultramarine** (28.8.02)	£400	£275	£60
E68	**1s**	**Green and carmine** (17.12.02)	£800	£500	£90

Controls	Prices for a M/M single stamp	
1d	Letter A	£150

1902 (11 Feb.) - 1903 Office of Works. De La Rue printings overprinted 'O.W. OFFICIAL' in two lines in black. Wmk. Imperial Crown. Perf. 14

No.			U/M	M/M	F/U
E69	**½d**	**Blue green**	£400	£300	£80
E70	**1d**	**Scarlet**	£400	£300	£80
E71	**2d**	**Green and carmine** (29.3.02)	£1200	£800	£200
E72	**2½d**	**Ultramarine** (20.3.02)	£1400	£1000	£300
E73	**10d**	**Purple and carmine** (28.5.03)	£15000	£11000	£3000

Controls	Prices for a M/M single stamp	
½d	Letter A	£900
	Letter B	£900
1d	Letter A	£900
	Letter B	£900

½d, 1d, 6d

ARMY

OFFICIAL

6d (1903)

1902 (11 Feb.) - 1903 War Office. De La Rue printings overprinted 'ARMY OFFICIAL' in two lines in black. Wmk. Imperial Crown. Perf. 14

No.			U/M	M/M	F/U
E74	**½d**	**Blue green**	4.00	2.50	1.00
E75	**1d**	**Scarlet**	3.00	2.00	1.00
E76	**6d**	**Dull purple** (23.8.02)	£100	£50	£30
E77	**6d**	**Dull purple** (9.03)	£1300	£900	£450

Controls	Prices for a M/M single stamp	
½d	Letter A	£50
	Letter B	£50
1d	Letter A	£50
	Letter B	£50

1902 (19 Feb.) - 1904 Board of Education. De La Rue printings overprinted 'BOARD OF EDUCATION in three lines in black. Wmk. Imperial Crown. Perf. 14

No.			U/M	M/M	F/U
E78	**½d**	**Blue green**	£120	£80	£20
E79	**1d**	**Scarlet**	£120	£80	£20
E80	**2½d**	**Ultramarine**	£2200	£1400	£130
E81	**5d**	**Purple and blue** (6.2.04)	£10000	£2500	£2500
E82	**1s**	**Green and carmine**(23.12.02)	£65000	£40000	£20000

Controls	Prices for a M/M single stamp	
½d	Letter A	£200
1d	Letter A	£225

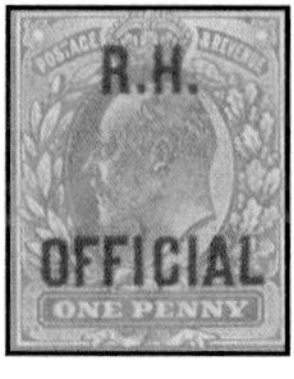

1902 (19 Feb. - April) Royal Household. De La Rue printings overprinted 'R.H. OFFICIAL' in two lines in black. Wmk. Imperial Crown. Perf. 14

No.			U/M	M/M	F/U
E83	**½d**	**Blue green** (29.4.02)	£280	£180	£120
E84	**1d**	**Scarlet**	£280	£140	£95

Controls	Prices for a M/M single stamp	
½d	Letter A	£800
1d	Letter A	£800

No.			U/M	M/M	F/U

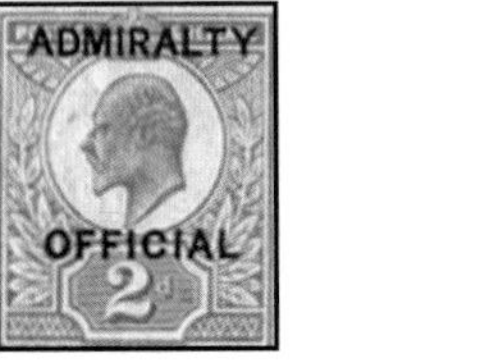

Setting I
(thin)

ADMIRALTY
OFFICIAL

Setting II
(thick and narrow)

1902 (3 March) - 04 The Admiralty. De La Rue printings overprinted 'ADMIRALTY OFFICIAL' in two lines in black. Wmk. Imperial Crown. Perf. 14

A. Setting I

No.			U/M	M/M	F/U
E85	½d	**Blue green**	£25	£14	7.00
E86	1d	**Scarlet**	£15	9.00	3.00
E87	1½d	**Purple and green**	£180	£100	£40
E88	2d	**Green and carmine**	£250	£140	£65
E89	2½d	**Ultramarine**	£300	£190	£65
E90	3d	**Purple on yellow**	£250	£170	£70

B. Setting II

No.			U/M	M/M	F/U
E91	½d	**Blue green**	£35	£20	£10
E92	1d	**Scarlet**	£35	£20	6.00
E93	1½d	**Purple and green**	£500	£350	£110
E94	2d	**Green and carmine**	£850	£650	£350
E95	2½d	**Ultramarine**	£1200	£900	£400
E96	3d	**Purple on yellow**	£750	£550	£120

J. A. C. Harrison' sketch based on
Bertram Mackennal's 'coinage' head.

The early issues of King George V were generally considered unsuccessful due to the inexperience of the recently appointed printers - Harrison & Sons - and the use of Downey's three quarter face portrait. Some adaptations were made to the two values in use (½d and 1d) which lead to Dies 1B and 2. Despite many paper and ink trials it was decided to adopt a profile head for all the low values to 1s. Several types were considered and the final work was based on Bertram Mackennal's coinage head (½d, 1½d, 2d, 3d and 4d values) and medal head (1d, 2½d - large size, the rest 5d to 1s smaller size). Mackennal also designed the frames for the ½d to 4d, G.W. Eve designed the rest.

Some of the 1912-13 printings were done at Somerset House but apart from these and the 6d values, Harrison were the printers until 1924, when Waterlow took over the contract. The 6d value, which also had a wide fiscal use, was printed by Somerset House until 1934. There were also very small printings by Somerset House of the 2½d in 1917 and the 1½d in 1926, to help in emergencies. Harrison regained the contract in 1934, commencing with the final 'block cypher' issues.

Probably the most interesting area from this period are the shades. It started with a period of experimentation, then the First World War interrupted supplies of some dyes used in the inks which led to improvisation. A vast range of shades are available for collectors and some wonderful studies can be produced. In addition, all the shades can be collected with a variety of watermarks - inverted, reversed, inverted and reversed - as well as upright and indeed, none at all. The varieties may be also combined with the controls issued.

The High Values were produced by three printers - Waterlow, De La Rue and Bradbury, Wilkinson - and were again based on the work of Bertram Mackennal. The stamps were recess printed and the master die engraved by J.A.C. Harrison. Harrison was also responsible for the 1924/25 Wembley, 1929 P.U.C. £1 engravings and much other work of this period.

The conditions that led to the wide range of shades in the low values applied even more so to the High Values, because the printing process was more reflective and a wide quality of papers and gums had to be used.

Pricing

The basis for pricing of stamps of this reign is as follows:

Unmounted Mint (U/M)	Full original gum, full perforations and good colour.
Mounted Mint (M/M)	Lightly hinged, full perforations and clear colour without toning.
Fine Used (F/U)	Clear and light postmark on a reasonably well centred stamp, with full perforations.

½d Die 1A

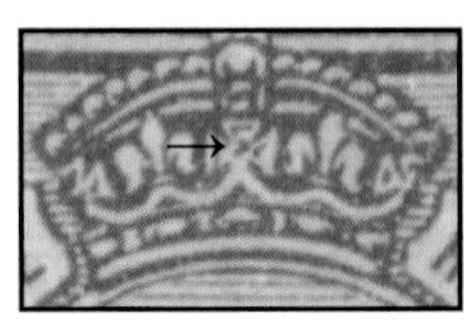

½d Die 1B

1d Die 1A

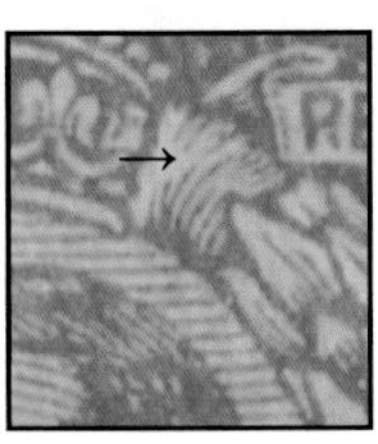

1d Die 1B

Type 1
Die 1A or 1B

Type 2
Die 2

Type 3
Die 1A or 1B

Type 4
Die 2

Downey Head Issues 1911 - 12

½d **DIE 1A** Centre jewel of cross in middle of crown is suggested by a comma (arrowed). Top scale on right hand dolphin ends with a triangle.

DIE 1B Centre jewel in crown is suggested by a crescent (arrowed). Top scale on right hand dolphin has only two sides.

DIE 2 One thick line in ornament above 'FP' of 'Halfpenny' compared with two thinner lines on Dies 1A and 1B (arrowed). The beard has also been lightened and is better defined.

1d **DIE 1A** The second line of shading is complete on the ribbon at the right of the crown (arrowed). On the large leaf that overlaps the right hand side ribbons, there is a line of shading to the left of the central line.

DIE 1B The second line of shading on the ribbon is broken (arrowed); on the leaf the line of shading is much smaller.

DIE 2 The lion is shaded and the beard is more defined (arrowed); the ends of the ribbons above the figures '1' are removed.

Imperial Crown Watermark

Royal Cypher Watermark

1911 (22 June) Wmk. Imperial Crown. Types 1 and 3. Die 1A. Perf. 15 x 14 Printers: Harrison & Sons and Somerset House

No.			U/M	M/M	F/U	✉
G1	½d	**Green**	4.00	2.00	50	1.00
G1a		Pale green	5.25	3.00	50	1.00
G1b		Deep green	£11	6.00	1.00	2.00
G1c		Bluish green	£260	£200	£75	
G2	1d	**Carmine red**	4.00	2.50	40	1.00
G2a		Wmk. inverted	£275	£175	£175	
G2b		No watermark	£400	£200	£450	
G2c		Wmk. sideways	-	-	£12000	
G2d		Carmine red. Chalky paper	£200	£150	-	
G2e		Pale carmine red	5.00	3.00	30	1.00
G2g		Carmine	£13	7.00	2.50	2.00
G2h		Pale carmine	£15	8.00	1.00	2.00
G2i		Deep carmine red	£25	£15	4.00	4.50
G2j		Rose pink	£75	£45	£15	£30
G2k		Deep carmine, varnish ink	£1500	£1200	*	
Varieties						
G1d	½d	Green. Perf. 14	£3500	£3000	£200	£300
G2f	1d	No cross on crown	£300	£185	£100	£300

No. G2l, Perf 14, is probably a colour trial and has been deleted.

1911 - 12 Wmk. Imperial Crown. Types 1 and 3. Die 1B. Perf. 15 x 14

No.			U/M	M/M	F/U	✉
G3	½d	**Bright green**	6.00	3.00	50	1.00
G3a		Wmk. inverted	7.00	4.00	2.50	£10
G3b		Green	£15	8.00	50	1.00
G3c		Wmk. sideways	-	-	£2250	
G3d		Yellow green	9.00	6.00	65	1.00
G3e		Pale bright green	£10	6.00	65	1.00
G3f		Deep green	£20	£10	5.50	7.50
G3g		Bright yellow green	£20	£12	5.00	£10
G3h		Bluish green	£145	£95	£40	£90
G3i		Very deep green	£275	£210	£45	£100
G3j		Deep green, varnish ink	£1500	£1200	*	
G4	1d	**Carmine**	7.50	4.00	30	1.00
G4a		Wmk. inverted	9.00	5.00	2.50	4.00
G4b		Pale carmine	8.00	4.00	30	1.00
G4d		Bright carmine	£13	8.00	1.00	1.25
G4e		Carmine red	£10	6.50	50	1.00
G4f		Pale carmine red	£11	7.50	75	1.25
G4g		Deep carmine	£25	£13	1.00	1.25
G4h		Deep bright carmine	£50	£30	4.00	7.00
G4i		Rose pink	£70	£40	£10	£20
G4j		Carmine, varnish ink	£1500	£1200	*	
G5	1d	**Scarlet** (6.12)	£21	£14	6.50	8.00
G5a		Wmk. inverted	£20	£14	5.00	7.50
G5b		No watermark	£750	£500	£500	
G5c		Bright scarlet	£21	£14	6.00	7.00
G5d		Pale scarlet	£35	£25	6.00	£12
G5e		Aniline scarlet	£135	£85	£60	£90
Varieties						
G4c	1d	No cross on crown	£300	£225	£170	£250

1912 (Aug.) Wmk. Royal Cypher. Types 1 and 3. Die 1B. Perf. 15 x 14

No			U/M	M/M	F/U	✉
G6	½d	**Green**	£35	£20	£11	£16
G6a		Wmk. inverted	£32	£20	£11	£16
G6b		Wmk. inv. and rev.	£350	£250	£250	
G6c		Wmk. reversed	£350	£250	£175	
G6d		No watermark	£750	£500	£500	
G6e		Pale green	£35	£20	£11	£16
G6f		Deep green	£55	£30	£15	£25
G6g		Deep green, varnish ink	£1500	£1200	*	
G7	1d	**Scarlet** (6.12)	£15	8.00	6.00	£10
G7a		Wmk. inverted	£14	8.00	5.00	5.00
G7b		Wmk. inv. and rev.	£350	£250	£100	
G7c		Wmk. reversed	£300	£200	£200	
G7d		Bright scarlet	£15	8.00	6.00	£10
G7e		Pale scarlet	£20	£12	8.00	£12
G7f		Deep bright scarlet	£45	£35	9.00	£14
G7g		Bright scarlet, varnish ink	£1500	£1200		

Cross on crown

No cross on crown

1912 (1 Jan) Wmk. Imperial Crown. Types 2 and 4. Die 2. Perf. 15 x 14

No			U/M	M/M	F/U	✉
G8	½d	**Green**	5.00	2.00	25	1.00
G8b		Wmk. inverted	£300	£200	£140	
G8c		Yellow green	5.50	2.50	25	1.00
G8d		Pale green	9.00	5.00	50	1.00
G8e		Deep green	£11	7.00	1.00	1.50
G8f		Bright yellow-green	£18	£12	1.50	2.00
G8g		Myrtle green	£85	£55	9.00	£15
G8h		Bluish green	£75	£55	£16	£25
G9	1d	**Scarlet**	3.25	1.25	20	1.00
G9b		Wmk. inverted	£175	£125	£90	
G9c		Bright scarlet	3.50	1.25	15	1.00
G9d		Wmk. inverted	£175	£125	£100	
G9e		Deep bright scarlet	4.00	2.00	50	1.00
G9f		Very deep bright scarlet	£65	£50	£20	£30
G9g		Aniline scarlet	£150	£95	£40	£60
Varieties						
G8a	½d	No cross on crown	£60	£45	£25	£35
G9a	1d	No cross on crown	£50	£35	£15	£25
G9da	1d	No cross on crown	£175	£125	£100	
G9h	1d	No cross on crown	£500	£375	£300	£400

1912 (Aug.) Wmk. Royal Cypher. Types 2 and 4. Die 2. Perf. 15 x 14

No			U/M	M/M	F/U	✉
G10	½d	**Green**	5.00	2.50	30	1.00
G10b		Wmk. inverted	£95	£50	£45	
G10c		Wmk. inv. and rev.	8.00	5.00	3.00	
G10d		Wmk. reversed	£75	£50	£40	
G10e		No watermark	£300	£200	£150	
G10f		Pale green	5.50	2.75	35	1.00
G10g		Deep green	6.00	3.50	1.25	1.50
G10h		Yellow green	6.00	3.50	1.25	2.00

No.			U/M	M/M	F/U	✉
G11	**1d**	**Scarlet**	3.50	2.00	30	1.00
G11b		Wmk. inverted	£16	£10	6.00	
G11c		Wmk. inv. and rev.	£16	£10	6.00	
G11d		Wmk. reversed	£20	£15	£12	
G11e		No watermark	£250	£175	£150	
G11f		Bright scarlet	4.00	2.25	35	1.00
G11g		Deep bright scarlet	£25	£18	1.50	1.75
Varieties						
G10a	½d	No cross on crown	£90	£60	£40	£60
G11a	1d	No cross on crown	£60	£40	£30	£45

Multiple Royal
Cypher Watermark

1912 (Oct.) Wmk. Multiple Royal Cypher. Types 2 and 4. Die 2. Perf. 15 x 14

No.			U/M	M/M	F/U	✉
G12	**½d**	**Green**	8.00	4.50	2.00	2.50
G12c		Wmk. inverted	9.00	6.00	3.50	4.50
G12d		Wmk. inv. and rev.	£20	£15	£18	
G12e		Wmk. reversed	£11	7.00	5.00	
G12f		Wmk. sideways	-	-	£1000	
G12g		Yellow green	8.50	5.00	3.50	5.00
G12h		Pale green	£10	5.00	3.50	5.00
G12i		Deep green	£15	9.00	4.50	5.00
G13	**1d**	**Scarlet**	9.00	5.00	2.50	5.00
G13c		Wmk. inverted	£10	6.00	8.00	
G13d		Wmk. inv. and rev.	£400	£300	£200	
G13e		Wmk. reversed	£95	6.00	8.00	
G13f		Wmk. sideways	£90	£60	£75	
G13g		Bright scarlet	£15	8.50	3.25	6.00
G13h		Deep bright scarlet	£55	£40	7.00	8.00
Varieties						
G12a	½d	No cross on crown	£100	£70	£55	£60
G12b		Imperforate	£95	£65	-	
G13a	1d	No cross on crown	£80	£50	£50	£70
G13b		Imperforate	£85	£60	-	

* These stamps should only be purchased with a certificate

Have you read the notes at the beginning of the catalogue?

Royal Cypher
Watermark

1912 (Aug.) - 22 Wmk. Royal Cypher. Perf. 15 x 14. 6d on chalky paper
Printers: Harrison & Sons and Somerset House

No			U/M	M/M	F/U	✉
G14	**½d**	**Green** (1913)	40	20	10	15
G14a		Wmk. inverted	2.00	1.00	1.00	2.00
G14b		Wmk. inv. and rev.	3.00	2.00	1.50	
G14c		Wmk. reversed	£15	9.00	8.00	
G14d		No watermark	£50	£35	£25	
G14e		Bright green	40	20	10	15
G14f		Deep green	4.50	2.00	1.50	2.00
G14g		Pale green	4.50	2.00	1.50	2.00
G14h		Deep bright green	5.00	3.00	1.50	2.00
G14i		Yellow green	5.00	3.00	1.00	1.50
G14j		Cobalt green	£20	£13	2.00	2.50
G14k		Apple green	£13	8.00	3.00	4.00
G14l		Blue green	£25	£17	7.00	7.00
G14m		Pale olive green	£65	£40	£12	£15
G14n		Olive green	£65	£45	£12	£15
G14o		Bright yellow green	£30	£20	*	
G14p		Very pale green	£150	£125	*	
G14q		Deep cobalt green	£235	£195	*	
G14r		Very deep green	£195	£150	*	
G14s		Myrtle green	£200	£150	*	
G14t		Deep myrtle green	£650	£550	*	

No.			U/M	M/M	F/U	✉
G14u		Very yellow (cyprus) green	£3500	£2500	*	
G15	1d	**Scarlet** (10.12)	30	15	10	15
G15a		Wmk. inverted	2.00	1.00	1.00	2.00
G15b		Wmk. inv. and rev.	2.50	1.25	1.50	
G15c		Wmk. reversed	£22	£12	8.00	
G15d		No watermark	£45	£30	£25	
G15e		Bright scarlet	40	15	10	15
G15f		Bright scarlet. 'Q' for 'O'	£155	£100	£100	£125
G15g		Vermilion	3.00	2.00	40	50
G15h		Brick red	3.00	2.00	65	80
G15i		Deep scarlet	8.00	4.50	55	60
G15j		Carmine red	6.50	3.75	1.00	1.25
G15k		Deep bright scarlet	£20	£12	2.00	2.25
G15l		Pale rose red	£11	6.00	1.50	2.00
G15m		Pale red	£11	6.00	1.00	1.25
G15n		Bright carmine red	£20	£12	2.50	3.00
G15o		Deep brick red	£60	£45	3.00	4.00
G15p		Scarlet vermilion	£90	£65	6.00	7.00
G15q		Orange vermilion	£130	£110	£40	£45
G15r		Deep carmine red	£295	£240	5.00	6.00
G15s		Pink	£295	£240	*	
G15t		Deep orange vermilion	£295	£225	£85	£120
G16	1½d	**Red brown** (10.12)	4.00	2.00	10	15
G16a		Wmk. inverted	5.00	2.50	1.00	3.00
G16b		Wmk. inv. and rev.	7.00	5.00	2.50	
G16c		Wmk. reversed	£12	8.00	8.00	
G16d		Red brown. 'PENCF'	£225	£170	£200	£300
G16e		Deep red brown	4.00	2.00	50	60
G16f		Chestnut	2.50	1.50	35	40
G16g		Chestnut. 'PENCF'	£100	£80	£75	£15
G16h		Chocolate brown	8.00	5.00	50	60
G16ha		No watermark	£150	£90	£70	
G16j		Orange brown	5.00	3.00	50	60
G16k		Pale red-brown	£10	5.00	80	90
G16l		Yellow brown	£12	6.00	3.00	4.00
G16m		Bright yellow brown	£14	8.00	3.50	4.00
G16n		Deep chocolate brown	£65	£40	6.00	7.00
G16o		Bright chestnut	£60	£40	7.50	9.00
G16p		Deep yellow brown	£70	£40	£12	£15
G16q		Bright orange brown	£55	£40	£15	£18
G16r		Chocolate	£195	£160	£45	£55
G16s		Very deep red brown	£225	£165	£45	£55
G16t		Brown	£325	£275	*	
G16u		Pale brown	£400	£3510	*	
G17	2d	**Orange** (Die I)	1.75	1.00	25	60
G17a		Wmk. inverted	£11	7.00	4.00	£12
G17b		Wmk. inv. and rev.	6.00	4.00	3.00	
G17c		Wmk. reversed	£11	7.00	8.00	
G17d		No watermark	£85	£60	£30	
G17e		Bright orange	3.00	1.75	40	75
G17f		Reddish orange	3.50	2.00	40	75
G17g		Pale orange	6.50	4.00	60	1.00
G17h		Deep bright orange	£13	8.00	1.25	2.00
G17i		Orange yellow	5.00	3.00	1.00	2.00
G17j		Brown orange	£35	£20	3.00	5.50
G17k		Deep reddish orange	£90	£70	£15	£30
G17l		Intense bright orange	£1400	£1000	*	
G18	2d	**Orange** (Die II) (9.21)	3.75	2.00	75	1.00
G18a		Wmk. inverted	£14	8.00	£12	£20
G18b		Wmk. inv. and rev.	£23	£15	£20	
G18c		Wmk. reversed	-	-	-	
G18d		No watermark	£425	£300	£300	
G18e		Pale orange	4.00	2.20	1.00	1.50
G18f		Bright orange	7.00	5.00	1.25	2.50
G18g		Deep orange	£12	7.00	1.50	3.00
G19	2½d	**Bright blue** (10.12)	9.00	5.00	1.00	2.00
G19a		Wmk. inverted	£40	£20	£30	
G19b		Wmk. inv. and rev.	£15	9.00	£12	
G19c		Wmk. reversed	£15	£10	£12	
G19d		No watermark	£375	£250	£250	
G19e		Blue	9.00	5.00	1.00	2.00
G19f		Cobalt blue	9.00	5.00	1.50	3.00
G19g		Pale blue	£15	9.00	1.25	2.50
G19h		Dull blue	£12	7.00	1.25	2.50
G19i		Ultramarine	£18	£10	1.75	3.50

No			U/M	M/M	F/U	✉
G19j		Deep blue	£15	£10	1.25	2.50
G19k		Powder blue	£25	£15	1.50	3.00
G19l		French blue	£70	£50	1.00	2.00
G19m		Milky blue	£25	£15	6.00	£12
G19n		Violet blue	£20	£12	6.00	£12
G19o		Cobalt violet blue	£20	£15	6.00	£12
G19p		Deep bright blue	£200	£175	*	
G19q		Royal blue	£275	£200	*	
G19r		Dull Prussian blue	£550	£450	*	
G19s		Indigo blue	£1400	£950	*	
G19t		Pale milky blue	£950	£750	*	
G20	3d	**Violet** (10.12)	3.50	2.25	45	1.00
G20a		Wmk. inverted	£70	£35	£35	
G20b		Wmk. inv. and rev.	£15	£10	£15	
G20c		Wmk. reversed	£100	£70	£50	
G20d		No watermark	£135	£100	£100	
G20e		Bluish violet	7.50	4.00	70	1.50
G20f		Pale violet	7.50	4.00	1.00	2.25
G20g		Bright violet	6.00	3.50	1.00	2.25
G20h		Dull violet	5.00	3.00	1.25	2.75
G20i		Lavender violet	£14	8.00	1.25	2.75
G20j		Dull reddish violet	£10	6.00	1.00	2.25
G20k		Reddish violet	£15	9.00	2.00	5.00
G20l		Heliotrope	£30	£20	2.00	5.00
G20m		Brownish violet	£50	£30	3.00	7.00
G20n		Very deep violet	£100	£65	8.00	£20
G20o		Very pale violet	£175	£135	*	
G21	4d	**Grey green** (1.13)	8.00	3.50	60	1.00
G21a		Wmk. inverted	£18	9.00	£25	
G21b		Wmk. inv. and rev.	£30	£18	£11	
G21c		Wmk. reversed	£60	£35	£20	
G21d		No watermark	£175	£135	£80	
G21e		Slate green	8.00	3.50	60	1.00
G21f		Pale grey green	£18	£10	70	1.25
G21g		Pale slate green	£25	£15	70	1.25
G21h		Bluish green grey	£25	£15	3.00	7.00
G21i		Deep grey green	£30	£20	4.00	7.00
G21j		Deep slate green	£170	£120	3.50	8.00
G22	5d	**Brown** (6.13)	8.00	4.00	1.00	2.50
G22a		Wmk. inverted	£375	£275	£275	
G22b		Wmk. inv. and rev.	£150	£100	£100	
G22c		Reddish brown	£18	£10	1.00	2.50
G22d		Yellow brown	£11	5.00	1.00	2.50
G22e		Yellow brown. No wmk	£375	£300	£300	
G22f		Ginger brown	£23	£14	3.00	6.00
G22g		Ochre brown	£100	£75	4.00	9.00
G22h		Bistre brown	£1501	£100	£12	£18
G23	6d	**Reddish purple.** Chalky (8.13)	£13	7.00	60	1.00
G23a		Wmk. inverted	£30	£17	£30	
G23b		Wmk. inv. and rev.	£25	£15	£15	
G23c		Wmk. reversed	£600	£400	£500	
G23d		No watermark	£200	£175	£400	
G23e		Pale reddish purple	£15	8.50	1.25	1.75
G23f		Rosy mauve	£13	6.00	70	1.25
G23g		Purple	£17	8.00	75	1.30
G23h		Plum	£17	9.00	75	1.75
G23i		Deep reddish purple	£25	£13	1.00	1.75
G23j		Dull purple	£22	£12	3.00	3.50
G23k		Slate purple	£120	£80	9.50	£25
G24	6d	**Reddish purple.** Chalky. Perf. 14 (1921)	£85	£50	£45	£90
G25	7d	**Olive** (8.13)	£13	8.00	5.00	6.00
G25a		Wmk. inverted	£35	£17	£40	
G25b		Wmk. inv. and rev.	£1850	£1650	-	
G25c		No watermark	£235	£175	£175	
G25d		Olive grey	£16	£10	2.50	6.00
G25e		Sage green	£70	£35	5.50	£14
G25f		Bronze green	£50	£35	9.00	£20
G26	8d	**Black on yellow**	£30	£15	8.00	£20
G26a		Wmk. inverted	£95	£60	£100	
G26b		Wmk. inv. and rev.	£1250	£1000	£1250	
G26c		Wmk. reversed	£90	£60	£250	
G26d		No watermark	£1250	£1000	£1250	
G26e		Black on yellow buff (granite paper)	£30	£15	8.00	£20

No.			U/M	M/M	F/U	✉
G27	9d	**Agate** (6.13)	£12	7.00	1.75	5.00
G27a		Wmk. inverted	£80	£40	£50	
G27b		Wmk. inv. and rev.	£45	£30	£35	
G27c		No watermark	£300	£250	£250	
G27d		Pale agate	£18	£10	2.50	6.50
G27e		Deep agate	£18	£10	1.75	5.00
G27f		Very deep agate	£450	£350	*	
G28	9d	**Olive green** (9.22)	£110	£50	£16	£50
G28a		Wmk. inverted	£550	£375	£500	
G28b		Wmk. inv. and rev.	£400	£300	£500	
G28c		Pale olive green	£135	£50	£16	£50
G28d		Deep olive green	£170	£60	£18	£60
G29	10d	**Turquoise blue** (8.13)	£20	£10	8.00	£10
G29a		Wmk. inverted	£900	£700	£700	
G29b		Wmk. inv. and rev.	£135	£95	£80	
G29c		Greenish blue	£22	£15	8.00	£10
G29d		Pale turquoise blue	£22	£15	8.00	£10
G29e		Bright turquoise blue	£30	£18	8.00	£10
G29f		Deep turquoise blue	£80	£50	£15	£20
G30	1s	**Bistre brown** (8.13)	£16	9.00	75	2.00
G30a		Wmk. inverted	£135	£65	£50	
G30b		Wmk. inv. and rev.	£35	£25	£30	
G30c		No watermark	£850	£700	£700	
G30d		Deep bistre brown	£25	£15	1.00	3.00
G30e		Olive bistre	£25	£15	1.25	3.50
G30f		Pale buff brown	£25	£15	1.25	3.50
G30g		Buff brown	£25	£15	1.25	3.50
G30h		Pale olive bistre	£25	£15	1.25	3.50
G30i		Olive brown	£60	£40	1.75	3.50
G30j		Fawn brown	£110	£75	2.50	7.00
G30k		Deep bronze brown	£525	£435	*	
		Set of 14	£110	£55	£16	

Multiple Royal Cypher Watermark

1913 (Aug.) Wmk. Multiple Royal Cypher. Perf. 15 x 14

No.			U/M	M/M	F/U	✉
G31	½d	**Green**	£90	£60	£60	£150
G31a		Wmk. inverted	£275	£200	£325	
G31b		Bright green	£90	£60	£60	£150
G31c		Wmk sideways			£15000	
G32	1d	**Scarlet**	£250	£115	£100	£450
G32a		Wmk. inverted	£525	£350	£325	
G32b		Dull scarlet	£250	£115	£125	£450
		Set of 2	£330	£165	£170	

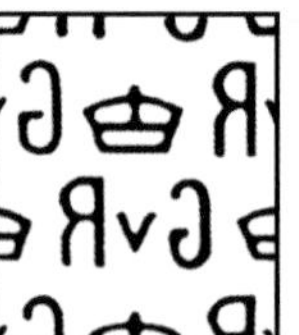

Multiple Block Cypher Watermark

Experimental Watermark

1924 (April) Wmk. Multiple Block Cypher. Perf. 15 x 14 Printers: Harrison & Sons, Waterlow & Sons and Somerset House.

No			U/M	M/M	F/U	✉
G33	½d	**Green**	30	15	5	10
G33a		Wmk. inverted	3.00	1.50	30	2.00
G33b		Wmk. sideways	8.00	5.00	2.50	7.50
G33c		Pale green	60	40	15	10
G33d		Bright green	30	15	5	10
G33e		Deep green	2.50	1.50	20	25
G33f		Deep bright green	5.50	3.50	25	30
G33g		Yellow green	£15	£10	2.00	2.50
G34	1d	**Scarlet**	50	20	5	10
G34a		Wmk. inverted	3.00	1.50	30	2.00
G34b		Wmk. sideways	£20	£10	8.00	£18
G34c		Scarlet. Inverted 'Q' for 'O'	£300	£200	£130	£500
G34d		Pale scarlet	70	30	10	15
G34e		Scarlet vermilion	70	30	15	20
G34f		Deep scarlet vermilion	£22	£15	1.50	1.75
G35	1½d	**Red brown**	40	30	5	10
G35c		Wmk. inverted	1.50	75	25	2.00
G35d		Wmk. sideways	£10	5.00	2.50	7.50
G35e		Yellow brown	50	35	10	15
G35f		Deep red brown	3.00	2.00	15	20
G35g		Orange brown	3.00	2.00	25	30
G35h		Chestnut	2.50	1.50	25	30
G35i		Bright chestnut	3.00	2.00	35	40
G35j		Chocolate brown	5.25	3.75	40	45
G35k		Deep yellow brown	6.00	4.00	40	45
G35l		Bright yellow brown	7.50	4.50	55	60
G35m		Pale red brown	£15	£10	2.50	2.75
G36	2d	**Orange** (Die II)	1.00	60	20	25
G36a		Wmk. inverted	£15	£10	£12	
G36b		Wmk. sideways	£125	£45	£40	£180
G36c		No watermark	£350	£250	£250	
G36d		Yellow orange	2.50	1.60	20	25
G36e		Deep orange	5.00	3.00	40	45
G36f		Pale yellow orange	£10	6.00	55	60
G36g		Deep yellow orange	£20	£12	75	80
G37	2½d	**Blue**	5.00	2.75	35	50
G37a		Wmk. inverted	£25	£18	£30	
G37b		No watermark	£500	£350	£500	
G37c		Pale blue	7.00	4.00	45	60
G37d		Bright blue	5.00	3.00	50	75
G37e		Ultramarine	9.00	5.00	65	90
G38	3d	**Violet**	9.00	3.50	35	50
G38a		Wmk. inverted	£20	£15	£30	
G38b		Deep violet	£11	7.00	65	90
G38c		Pale violet	£19	8.00	40	60
G38d		Bright violet	£13	8.00	50	75
G38e		Pale reddish violet	£20	£10	1.00	1.50
G38f		Deep brownish violet	£30	£20	2.00	3.00
G39	4d	**Grey green**	£12	7.00	60	1.00
G39a		Wmk. inverted	£50	£75	£40	
G39b		Deep grey green	£17	£10	60	1.00
G39c		Very deep grey green	£30	£20	3.50	5.00
G40	5d	**Brown**	£20	£12	1.00	2.00
G40a		Wmk. inverted	£40	£25	£40	
G40b		Deep brown	£30	£23	1.00	2.00
G40c		Reddish brown	£60	£40	1.50	3.00
G40d		Bright ochre brown	£22	£13	1.50	3.00
G40e		Deep ochre brown	£45	£30	2.00	3.50

No.			U/M	M/M	F/U	✉
G41	6d	**Reddish purple.** Chalky. (1936)	£10	7.00	60	90
G41a		Wmk. inverted	£30	£20	£40	
G41b		Wmk. inv. and rev.	£150	£95	£150	
G41c		Rosy-mauve. Chalky	£18	£12	60	90
G41d		Deep reddish purple. Chalky	£18	£11	75	1.00
G41e		Plum. Chalky	£20	£12	75	1.00
G42	6d	**Purple** (1934)	3.00	1.50	20	30
G42a		Wmk. inverted	£30	£20	£35	
G42b		Rosy-mauve (1926)	6.00	3.50	20	30
G42c		Reddish purple	5.00	3.00	20	30
G42d		Pale rosy mauve	8.00	5.00	20	30
G42e		Deep reddish purple	6.00	3.75	40	60
G42f		Deep purple	9.00	5.00	40	60
G43	9d	**Olive green**	£12	7.00	1.00	2.00
G43a		Wmk. inverted	£50	£30	£45	
G43b		Deep olive green	£15	£10	1.00	2.00
G43c		Pale olive green	£15	£10	1.00	2.00
G43d		Olive yellow green	£45	£25	7.50	£15
G44	10d	**Turquoise blue**	£45	£20	£10	£30
G44a		Wmk. inverted	£900	£700	£550	
G44b		Dull greenish blue	£50	£26	£11	£35
G44c		Deep greenish blue	£65	£35	£12	£35
G44d		Deep dull greenish blue	£65	£35	£16	£40
G45	1s	**Bistre brown**	£25	£14	30	60
G45a		Wmk. inverted	£275	£175	£275	
G45b		Buff brown	£33	£20	30	60
G45c		Fawn brown	£40	£26	30	60
G45d		Pale buff brown	£40	£20	45	90
G45e		Deep fawn brown	£100	£45	3.50	7.00
		Set of 12	£110	£65	9.50	

Varieties

G35a	1½d	Red-brown. Tête-bêche pair	£250	£210	£220	G35b
	1½d	Red-brown. Tête-bêche gutter pair	£300	£250	£250	

Photogravure

Over a period of two years, stamps were printed with reduced design sizes to accommodate more accurate perforating of the stamps. The formats and sizes listed refer to the design and not the measurement of the whole stamp.

Multiple Block
Cypher Watermark

1934 (20 Aug.) Wmk. Multiple Block Cypher. Perf. 15 x 14

Large Format (18.6 x 22.5mm)

No			U/M	M/M	F/U	✉
G46	1d	**Scarlet** (24.9)	1.50	80	1.00	1.50
G46a		Bright scarlet	1.50	80	1.00	1.50
G46b		Wmk. inverted	£80	£50	£60	
G47	1½d	**Red brown**	1.25	75	1.00	1.50
G47a		Bright red brown	1.25	75	70	1.50
G47b		Wmk. inverted	£140	£80	£105	
		Set of 2	3.50	1.75	1.70	

1934 Wmk. Multiple Block Cypher. Perf. 15 x 14

Intermediate Format (18.3 x 22.2mm)

No			U/M	M/M	F/U	✉
G48	½d	**Green**	50	25	50	1.00
G48a		Bluish green	1.00	50	50	1.00
G48b		Wmk. inverted	£20	£14	£18	£55
G49	1d	**Scarlet**	8.00	5.00	1.00	1.50
G49a		Bright scarlet	9.00	5.00	1.00	1.50
G49b		Pale scarlet	£15	£10	3.00	1.00
G49c		Wmk. inverted	£20	£14	£18	£55
G50	1½d	**Red brown**	8.00	3.50	75	1.00
G50a		Wmk. inverted	£13	8.00	8.00	£25
G51	2d	**Orange**	3.50	2.25	1.00	1.50
G51a		Bright orange	3.50	2.25	1.00	1.50
		Set of 4	£15	8.50	3.00	

1935 - 36 Wmk. Multiple Block Cypher. Perf. 15 x 14

Small Format (18.0 x 21.7mm)

No.			U/M	M/M	F/U	✉
G52	½d	**Green**	25	10	5	10
G52a		Bluish green	25	10	5	10
G53	1d	**Scarlet**	35	20	5	10
G53a		Bright scarlet	50	30	5	10
G54	1½d	**Red brown**	25	10	5	10
G54a		Bright red brown	25	10	5	10
G55	2d	**Orange**	60	35	10	20
G55a		Bright orange	75	45	10	20
G56	2½d	**Bright blue** (18.3.35)	1.50	1.00	30	90
G56a		Ultramarine	1.75	1.25	30	90
G57	3d	**Violet** (18.3.35)	1.50	1.00	30	90
G57a		Reddish violet	1.50	1.00	30	1.00
G57b		Wmk. inverted			£2500	
G58	4d	**Deep grey green** (2.12.35)	2.00	1.25	30	1.25
G58a		Wmk. inverted			£2500	
G58b		Blackish green	£10	5.00	1.00	4.00
G59	5d	**Yellowish brown** (17.2.35)	6.00	3.50	50	2.00
G59a		Deep yellow brown	8.50	4.50	50	2.00
G60	9d	**Deep olive green** (2.12.35)	£11	7.00	60	2.50
G61	10d	**Turquoise blue** (24.2.36)	£17	8.50	5.50	£25
G62	1s	**Bistre brown** (24.2.36)	£19	9.00	50	2.00
		Set of 11 values	£50	£30	7.50	

1935 Wmk. Multiple Block Cypher inverted (ex booklets)

No			U/M	M/M	F/U	✉
G52a	½d	**Green**	£10	7.50	1.25	6.00
G53a	1d	**Scarlet**	£10	7.50	1.25	6.00
G54a	1½d	**Red brown**	2.00	1.75	50	2.00
		Set of 3 values	£20	£15	2.75	

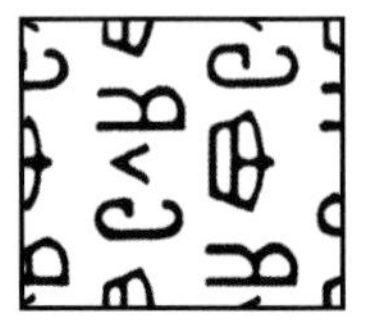

1935 Wmk. Multiple Block Cypher sideways

No			U/M	M/M	F/U	✉
G52b	½d	**Green**	£10	7.00	4.00	£15
G53b	1d	**Scarlet**	£12	8.00	6.50	£25
G54b	1½d	**Red brown**	6.00	4.00	3.50	£15
G55b	2d	**Orange**	£130	£55	£75	£250
		Set of 4	£150	£70	£80	

'SEAHORSES'

Guide Notes To Assist Identification

Four printings were made during this issue and major problems only arise when attempting to differentiate between the first Waterlow printing and the De La Rue issue.

The Bradbury Wilkinson printings were a different size to the others - the stamps being 22.5mm to 23mm in height against the 22mm of the other two printers. On many examples, they also printed a small coloured guide dot centred between the top frame line and the top of the stamp.

The second Waterlow printing was re-engraved, the most obvious difference being the crossed lines behind the King's head.

When sorting 'Seahorses' we suggest the following steps be taken:

Step 1 Check for crossed lines behind the King's head, all stamps with this are Waterlow re-engraved.

Step 2 Measure the height of the remaining stamps and all stamps measuring 22.5mm to 23mm are Bradbury Wilkinson.

All remaining stamps are either Waterlow or De La Rue. The following chart will help collectors to sort the first Waterlow and De La Rue printings.

	Waterlow	**De La Rue**
Gum	White, evenly applied.	Streaky and yellowish.
Perfs	Teeth, evenly spaced.	Upper teeth on both sides are wider than the rest. Holes are always smaller and undulating.
Colours		
2s6d	Sepia to deep sepia. Colours do not show through.	Yellow and brown shades. Colours often show through.
5s	Rose carmine shades. Colours do not show through.	Pale carmine * to deep carmine. Colour invariably shows through
10s	Indigo blue shades.	Pale blue * to deep blue.

* *The pale shades on De La Rue were caused by plate wear and are quite distinct.*

Waterlow
De La Rue
Bradbury Wilkinson

Waterlow
Re-engraved

Royal Cypher Watermark

1913 (July) Wmk. Royal Cypher. Perf. 11 x 12
Printer: Waterlow Bros. & Layton

No.			U/M	M/M	F/U
G63	**2s6d**	**Sepia brown**	£350	£100	£80
G63a		Deep sepia brown	£350	£100	£80
G64	**5s**	**Carmine red**	£600	£230	£130
G64a		Rose carmine	£600	£230	£130
G64b		Pale rose carmine	£600	£230	£130
G65	**10s**	**Indigo blue**	£900	£400	£250
G65a		Indigo	£900	£400	£250
G66	**£1**	**Dull blue green**	£3000	£1800	£800
G66a		Green	£3000	£1800	£800
G66b		Deep green	£3000	£1800	£800
		Set of 4	£4700	£2400	£1250

1915 (Dec.) Wmk. Royal Cypher. Perf. 11 x 12
Printer: De La Rue & Co.

No.			U/M	M/M	F/U
G67	**2s6d**	**Pale brown**	£300	£160	£100
G67a		Pale brown (worn plate)	£300	£160	£100
G67b		Wmk. inverted	£1100	£650	£650
G67c		Wmk. reversed	£1000	£575	£550
G67d		Seal brown	£350	£200	£160
G67e		Wmk. inverted	£1100	£650	£650
G67f		Wmk. reversed	£1100	£575	£650
G67g		Grey brown	£350	£200	£100
G67h		Yellow brown	£320	£180	£100
G67i		Wmk. inverted	£1100	£650	£550
G67j		Wmk. reversed	£1000	£450	£450
G67k		Wmk. inverted and reversed	£2700	£1800	-
G67l		No watermark	£3000	-	-
G67m		Pale yellow brown	£320	£180	£100
G67n		Deep yellow brown	£320	£180	£100
G67o		Wmk. inverted	£1100	£450	£550
G67p		Wmk. reversed	£1000	£500	£550
G67q		Bright yellow brown	£350	£190	£110
G67r		Very deep brown	£1100	£700	£475
G67s		Wmk. inverted	£2000	£1100	£1000
G67t		Wmk. reversed	£1500	£850	£450
G67u		Blackish brown	£1000	£700	£500
G67v		Cinnamon brown	£1200	£875	£500
G68	**5s**	**Bright carmine**	£700	£275	£180
G68a		Pale carmine (worn plate)	£700	£275	£180
G68b		Carmine	£700	£275	£180
G68c		Wmk. inverted	£2500	£1400	£900
G68d		Wmk. reversed	£2500	£1400	£700
G68e		Wmk. inverted and reversed	£3000	£1800	£700
G68f		No watermark	£3000	£1400	£1200
G69	**10s**	**Blue**	£1900	£1000	£450
G69a		Wmk. inverted and reversed	-	£4700	-
G69b		Pale blue	£1900	£1000	£400
G69c		Deep blue	£1900	£1000	£500
G69d		Deep blue (worn plate)	£1900	£1000	£500
G69e		Deep bright blue	£3000	£2500	£1500
G69f		Bright Cambridge blue	£4500	£2500	£2200
		Set of 3	£2800	£1400	£800

1918 (Dec.) Wmk. Royal Cypher. Perf. 11 x 12
Printer: Bradbury Wilkinson & Co.

No			U/M	M/M	F/U
G70	**2s6d**	**Olive brown**	£180	£55	£20
G70a		Chocolate brown	£180	£55	£20
G70b		Pale brown	£180	£55	£30
G70c		Reddish brown	£180	£55	£30
G71	**5s**	**Rose red**	£300	£95	£30
G71a		Rose carmine	£300	£95	£30
G72	**10s**	**Dull blue**	£480	£170	£100
G72a		Dull grey blue	£480	£170	£100
		Set of 3	£850	£320	£140

1918 (Dec.) Re-engraved. Wmk. Royal Cypher. Perf. 11 x 12 Printer: Waterlow & Sons

No			U/M	M/M	F/U
G73	**2s6d**	**Chocolate brown**	£85	£45	£12
G73a		Reddish brown	£85	£55	£15
G74	**5s**	**Bright rose red**	£300	£90	£45
G75	**10s**	**Indigo**	£450	£160	£50
		Set of 3	£780	£290	£100

1924 (3 April) British Empire Exhibition 1924. Wmk. Multiple Block Cypher. Line perf. 14
Printer: Waterlow & Sons in Recess

No.			U/M	M/M	F/U	✉
G76	**1d**	**Scarlet**	5.00	3.00	4.00	6.00
G76a		Comb perf. 14	5.00	3.00	4.00	6.00
G77	**1½d**	**Brown**	£12	7.00	7.00	£12
G77a		Comb perf. 14	£12	7.00	7.00	£12
		Set of 2	£16	9.00	£10	
		First Day Cover				£300

1925 (9 May) British Empire Exhibition 1925. Dated '1925'. Wmk. Multiple Block Cypher. Comb perf. 14
Printer: Waterlow & Sons in Recess

No.			U/M	M/M	F/U	✉
G78	**1d**	**Scarlet**	9.00	6.00	6.00	£18
G79	**1½d**	**Brown**	£38	£20	£27	£65
		Set of 2	£45	£25	£30	
		First Day Cover				£1000

Large Royal Cypher Watermark

1929 (10 May) Postal Union Congress, London 1929. Wmk. Multiple Block Cypher. Perf. 15 x 14
Printer: Waterlow & Sons in Typography

No			U/M	M/M	F/U	✉
G80	**½d**	**Green**	2.25	1.00	25	30
G81	**1d**	**Scarlet**	2.50	1.00	75	1.50
G82	**1½d**	**Purple brown**	1.00	50	25	30
G83	**2½d**	**Blue**	£16	8.00	7.00	£15
G83b		Pale Blue	£20	£14	8.00	£18
		Set of 4	£20	9.50	7.50	
		First Day Cover				£250

Wmk. Large Royal Cypher. Perf. 12
Printer: Bradbury, Wilkinson & Co. in Recess

No			U/M	M/M	F/U	✉
G84	**£1**	**Black**	£700	£400	£400	£1000
		First Day Cover				£2500

1929 Wmk. inverted

No			U/M	M/M	F/U	✉
G80a	½d	Green	£18	9.00	9.00	£30
G81a	1d	Scarlet	£18	9.00	9.00	£30
G82a	1½d	Purple brown	6.00	2.00	3.00	£15
G83a	2½d	Blue	£850	£550	£350	
G83c		Pale Blue	£850	£550	£350	
		Set of 3 (½d to 1½d)	£38	£20	£18	

1929 Wmk. sideways

No			U/M	M/M	F/U	✉
G80b	½d	Green	£60	£35	£25	£100
G81b	1d	Scarlet	£80	£50	£50	£150
G82b	1½d	Purple brown	£50	£35	£25	£90
		Set of 3	£175	£90	£90	

1935 (7 May) Silver Jubilee. Wmk. Multiple Block Cypher. Perf. 15 x 14
Printer: Harrison & Sons in Photogravure

No			U/M	M/M	F/U	✉
G85	**½d**	**Green.** Type I	10	5	5	10
G85b		Green. Type III	£10	5.00	4.25	8.00
G86	**1d**	**Scarlet.** Type I	45	30	25	40
G86b		Scarlet. Type III	£10	5.00	4.25	9.00
G87	**1½d**	**Red brown.** Type I	40	25	10	15
G87b		Red brown. Type III	1.75	1.00	1.00	5.00
G88	**2½d**	**Blue**	4.00	2.75	3.00	£10
G88		Prussian blue	£3500	£3000	£2500	
		Set of 4	5.00	3.00	3.25	
		First Day Cover				£125

TYPE II. Wmk. Inverted

No			U/M	M/M	F/U	✉
G85a	½d	Green	£10	5.00	4.00	£10
G86a	1d	Scarlet	£10	5.00	5.00	£17
G87a	1½d	Red brown	1.75	1.00	1.50	5.00
		Set of 3	£20	£10	9.00	

VISA

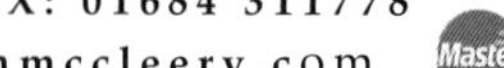
MasterCard

PTS

Silver Jubilee Types

There are three types of the ½d, 1d and 1½d values. The first type is from the sheet printing and the other two from booklets.

Type I	Ex sheets	Upright watermark
Type II	Ex booklet	All with watermark inverted
Type III	Ex booklet	Upright watermark

½d Type I

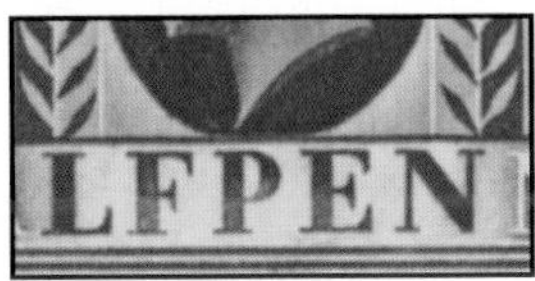

½d Type III

½d Type I - the 'FPE' of 'Halfpenny' is solid throughout whereas in Type III it is shaded at the bottom and solid at the top. The two lines underneath 'Halfpenny' are also noticeably thinner on the booklet printing.

1d Type I

1d Type III

1d Type I & Type III - are the most difficult to differentiate. Although the shading within the crown on the right is deeper in Type III, the easiest method of distinguishing Type III is to check the perforations to see if they have been cut straight on either the top or bottom, proving that they are from booklets.

½d Type I

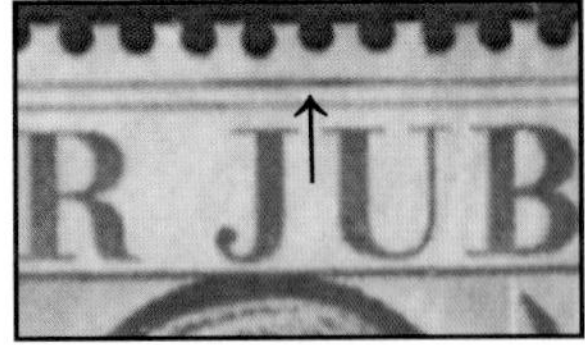

1½d Type I

1½d Type I - the two lines above 'Silver Jubilee' are evenly printed whereas in Type III there is a definite thickening of the frame line above 'JU' of 'JUBILEE'.

King Edward VIII

Printer: Harrison and Sons

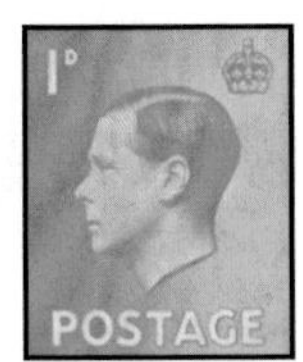

Multiple Crown E8R
Watermark

1936 (1 Sept) Wmk. Multiple Crown E8R. Perf. 15 x 14

No.			U/M	M/M	F/U	✉
ED1	**½d**	**Green**	10	6	15	40
ED2	**1d**	**Scarlet**	14	7	15	40
ED3	**1½d**	**Red brown**	14	9	15	45
ED4	**2½d**	**Bright blue**	18	11	40	3.50
		Set of 4	40	27	50	

1936 Wmk. inverted

No.			U/M	M/M	F/U	✉
ED1a	½d	Green	5.50	2.10	1.80	6.50
ED2a	1d	Scarlet	5.50	2.40	1.80	7.00
ED3a	1½d	Red brown	60	30	40	3.00
		Set of 3	9.50	4.40	4.00	

King George VI

Printer: Harrison & Sons in Photogravure

Multiple Crown GVIR Watermark

No			U/M	M/M	F/U	✉
1937 (10 May) Dark Colours. Wmk. Multiple Crown GVIR. Perf. 15 x 14						
B1	**½d**	**Green**	10	5	15	15
B2	**1d**	**Scarlet**	10	5	15	15
B3	**1½d**	**Red brown** (30.7.37)	10	5	15	15
B4	**2d**	**Orange** (31.1.38)	90	40	15	25
B5	**2½d**	**Ultramarine**	15	5	15	20
B6	**3d**	**Violet** (31.1.38)	2.20	1.10	40	1.65
B7	**4d**	**Grey green** (21.11.38)	20	15	20	80
B8	**5d**	**Brown** (21.11.38)	1.50	80	30	1.50
B9	**6d**	**Purple** (30.1.39)	90	50	15	60
B10	**7d**	**Emerald green** (27.2.39)	2.50	1.40	60	1.25
B11	**8d**	**Carmine** (27.2.39)	3.50	1.50	50	1.50
B12	**9d**	**Olive green** (1.5.39)	3.50	1.70	45	1.50
B13	**10d**	**Turquoise blue** (1.5.39)	3.00	1.70	45	1.50
B14	**11d**	**Plum** (29.12.47)	1.40	1.05	70	2.75
B15	**1s**	**Bistre brown** (1.5.39)	4.00	1.70	15	55
		Set of 15	£24	9.50	3.50	

No			U/M	M/M	F/U	✉
1937 (Aug.) Wmk. inverted						
B1a	**½d**	**Green**	5.00	2.00	30	2.50
B2a	**1d**	**Scarlet**	£22	6.00	1.40	£28
B3a	**1½d**	**Red brown**	8.00	2.20	30	3.50
B4a	**2d**	**Orange** (6.40)	£29	9.75	2.10	£35
B5a	**2½d**	**Ultramarine** (6.40)	£29	10.75	1.90	£28
		Set of 5	£75	£27	5.00	

No			U/M	M/M	F/U	✉
1938 (Jan.) Wmk. sideways						
B1b	**½d**	**Green**	40	15	25	3.00
B2b	**1d**	**Scarlet** (2.38)	12.50	5.50	3.85	£15
B3b	**1½d**	**Red brown** (2.38)	55	25	40	3.00
B4b	**2d**	**Orange** (2.38)	£27	£15	17.50	£55
B5b	**2½d**	**Ultramarine** (6.40)	£40	£15	£15	£65
		Set of 5	£80	£29	£30	

No			U/M	M/M	F/U	✉
1941 (21 July) Pale colours Wmk. Multiple Crown GVIR. Perf. 15 x 14						
B16	**½d**	**Pale green** (1.9.41)	10	5	10	15
B17	**1d**	**Pale scarlet** (11.8.41)	10	5	10	20
B18	**1½d**	**Pale red brown** (28.9.42)	25	30	25	40
B19	**2d**	**Pale orange** (6.10.41)	20	15	20	40
B20	**2½d**	**Light ultramarine** (21.7.41)	10	5	10	30
B21	**3d**	**Pale violet** (3.11.41)	70	45	20	75
		Set of 6	1.00	90	90	

No			U/M	M/M	F/U	✉
1942 (March) Wmk. inverted						
B16a	**½d**	**Pale green**	2.00	1.00	30	3.00
B19a	**2d**	**Pale orange**	1.30	1.00	55	5.00
B20a	**2½d**	**Light ultramarine**	70	40	40	75
		Set of 3	4.00	2.40	1.00	

No			U/M	M/M	F/U	✉
1942 (June) Wmk. sideways						
B17a	**1d**	**Pale scarlet** (10.42)	1.90	1.15	1.40	8.50
B19a	**2d**	**Pale orange** (6.42)	8.50	6.25	6.75	£25
B20b	**2½d**	**Light ultramarine** ('42)	5.00	5.00	3.50	£28
		Set of 3	£14	9.50	9.50	

1950 (2 Oct.) New colours**.** Wmk. Multiple Crown GVIR. Perf. 15 x 14

No.			U/M	M/M	F/U	✉
B22	½d	**Pale orange** (3.5.51)	15	10	10	15
B22a		Orange	20	10	10	15
B23	1d	**Light ultramarine**	15	10	10	15
B24	1½d	**Pale green**	20	10	20	45
B25	2d	**Pale red brown**	30	15	20	45
B25a		Bright red brown	60	25	25	60
B26	2½d	**Scarlet**	10	10	10	25
B27	4d	**Light ultramarine**	70	60	60	75
		Set of 6	1.10	75	1.00	

1951 (May). Wmk inverted

No.			U/M	M/M	F/U	✉
B22a	½d	**Pale orange**	10	5	20	75
B23a	1d	**Light ultramarine** (3.52)	1.75	85	50	4.00
B24a	1½d	**Pale green** (3.52)	1.75	75	1.50	4.50
B25a	2d	**Pale red brown**	2.50	1.25	2.50	5.50
B26a	2½d	**Scarlet**	50	25	30	3.00
		Set of 5	5.75	2.75	5.00	

1951 (3 May) Wmk. sideways

No.			U/M	M/M	F/U	✉
B23b	1d	**Light ultramarine** (5.51)	20	10	20	75
B24b	1½d	**Pale green** (14.9.51)	90	45	1.00	7.00
B25b	2d	**Red brown** (5.51)	30	15	50	5.00
B25d		Bright red brown	75	40	75	2.50
B26b	2½d	**Scarlet**	45	25	40	2.00
		Set of 4	1.60	85	1.90	

Large Crown GVIR Watermark

1939 (21 Aug.) - 48 Wmk. Large Crown GVIR. Perf.14
Printer: Waterlow & Sons in Recess

No			U/M	M/M	F/U	✉
B28	2s6d	**Brown** (4.9.39)	£30	15.50	4.00	£18
B29	2s6d	**Yellow green** (9.3.42)	5.00	2.00	20	1.25
B30	5s	**Red** (21.8.39)	10.50	5.50	75	3.00
B31	10s	**Dark blue** (30.10.39)	£150	£65	£14	£80
B31a		Steel blue	£160	£80	£20	£95
B32	10s	**Ultramarine** (30.11.42)	£18	9.50	3.50	£12
B33	£1	**Brown** (1.10.48)	7.50	6.00	9.50	£100
		Set of 6	£200	£90	£27	

1951 (3 May) 'Festival' issue. Wmk. Large Crown GVIR. Perf.11 x 12
Printer: Waterlow & Sons in Recess

No		U/M	M/M	F/U	✉
B34	**2s6d Yellow green**	5.00	2.50	40	90
B35	**5s Red**	£11	5.50	1.00	4.00
B36	**10s Ultramarine**	12.50	8.00	3.50	£25
B37	**£1 Brown**	£19	11.75	8.50	£75
	Set of 4	45	£24	9.50	

Printer: Harrison &Sons in Photogravure. Perf. 15 x 14 (except where shown)

Multiple Crown GVIR Watermark

1937 (13 May) Coronation

No.			U/M	M/M	F/U	✉
B38	**1½d**	**Maroon**	18	10	10	40
		First Day Cover				£20

Cylinder control block of six - A37 2.50

1940 (6 May) Centenary of First Adhesive Postage Stamps. Perf. 14½ x 14

No.			U/M	M/M	F/U	✉
B39	**½d**	**Green**	10	10	10	30
B40	**1d**	**Scarlet**	30	15	15	55
B41	**1½d**	**Red Brown**	25	15	35	1.00
B42	**2d**	**Orange**	35	25	40	60
B43	**2½d**	**Ultramarine**	1.10	45	35	40
B44	**3d**	**Violet**	1.60	1.00	1.30	£20
		Set of 6	2.60	2.00	2.30	
		First Day Cover				£25

Cylinder control block of six - G40

½d - 1.75	1d - 2.50	1½d - 3.50
2d - 2.00	2½d - 9.00	3d - £35

1946 (11 June) Victory

No.			U/M	M/M	F/U	✉
B45	**2½d**	Ultramarine	6	5	10	15
B46	**3d**	**Violet**	8	5	10	15
		Set of 2	15	10	15	
		First Day Cover				£40

Cylinder control block of six - S46

2½d - 90 3d - 1.00

1948 (26 April) Royal Silver Wedding (£1 Perf. 14 x 15)

No.			U/M	M/M	F/U	✉
B47	**2½d**	**Ultramarine**	10	5	10	10
B48	**£1**	**Blue**	£20	£14	£17	£35
		Set of 2	£20	£14	£17	£35
		First Day Cover				£275

1948 (10 May) Channel Islands Liberation

No.			U/M	M/M	F/U	✉
B49	**1d**	**Scarlet**	5	5	10	20
B50	**2½d**	**Ultramarine**	10	10	15	40
		Set of 2	11	12	25	
		First Day Cover (C. I. pmk)				£10

1948 (29 July) Olympic Games

No.			U/M	M/M	F/U	✉
B51	**2½d**	**Ultramarine**	10	5	10	10
B52	**3d**	**Violet**	10	8	15	40
B53	**6d**	**Bright purple**	50	15	30	60
B54	**1s**	**Brown**	1.50	25	50	1.50
		Set of 4	1.00	45	70	
		First Day Cover				£40

No.			U/M	M/M	F/U	✉	No.
1949 (10 Oct.) Universal Postal Union							
B55	**2½d**	**Ultramarine**	5	5	10	30	
B56	**3d**	**Violet**	15	8	22	40	
B57	**6d**	**Bright purple**	25	15	32	60	
B58	**1s**	**Brown**	50	30	60	1.50	
		Set of 4	70	50	1.00		
		First Day Cover				£12	

No.			U/M	M/M	F/U	✉	No.
1951 (3 May) Festival of Britain							
B59	**2½d**	**Scarlet**	10	5	10	20	
B60	**4d**	**Ultramarine**	15	10	20	30	
		Set of 2	20	13	30		
		First Day Cover				£8	

Introductory Notes

Source

There can be a considerable difference in the scarcity of any single stamp just through its source. The source of each stamp can easily be identified by looking at the condition of the perforation on each side, which can be either cut or torn.

Guillotined perforations

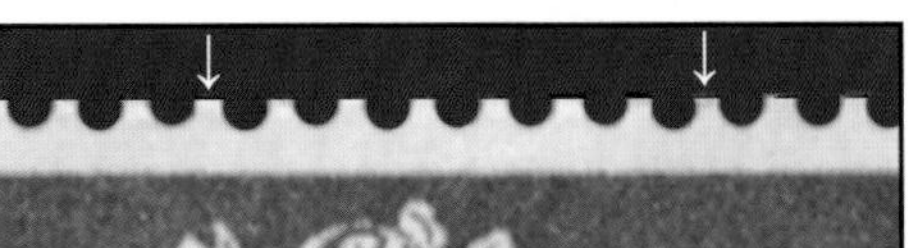

Torn perforations with fibrous ends

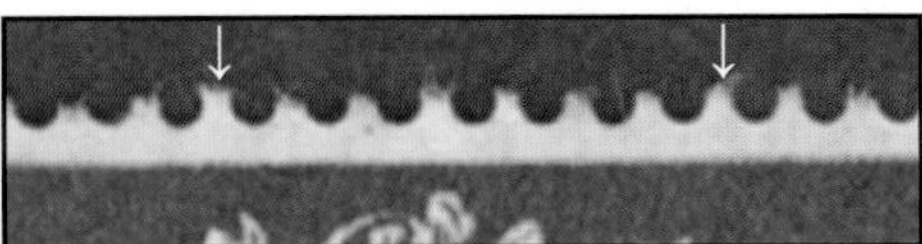

On the illustrations below the arrows indicate guillotined <u>edges</u>

Sheet Stamps: These have torn perforations on all four sides

Horizontal and Sideways Coil Stamps: These have guillotined perforations on the top and bottom

Vertical Coil Stamps: These have guillotined perforations at the left and right

Stamps from coils made up from sheets (that is those coils which also include coil joins) have the sheet margins at the vertical sides of the sheets (in the case of vertical coils) or from the horizontal sides of the sheets (in the case of horizontal coils) removed by tearing. The result of this is that upright watermark coils stamps do exist with perforations on three edges torn and just one side guillotined.

Booklet Stamps from Panes of Two: These have top and bottom perforations guillotined are usually supplied with margin attached to distinguish them from Horizontal coil stamps.

Booklet Panes of Four: These have guillotined perforations on one side (left or right) or on two adjacent sides (bottom/left). Stamps with guillotined perforations on bottom/right adjacent two sides can be from booklet panes of four **or** six.

Booklet Stamps from Panes of Six: These have guillotined perforations on one side (top or bottom) or on two adjacent sides.

Pane of two Pane of four Pane of six

All Wilding issues were printed by Harrison and Sons Ltd in Photogravure.

Watermark Tudor Crown Upright

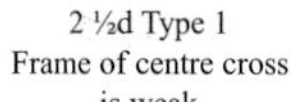

2 ½d Type 1
Frame of centre cross
is weak

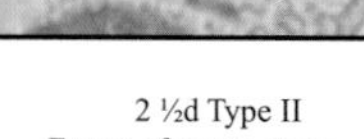

2 ½d Type II
Frame of centre cross
strengthened

No.			U/M	M/M	F/U
1952 (5 Dec.)		**Perf. 15 x 14**			
W1	**½d**	**Orange red** - Sheets (31.8.53)	5	5	10
W1a		Book pane BP75	25	15	20
W1b		Book pane BP76	75	45	
W1c		Book pane BP77	1.50	35	
W1d		Vertical coil	50	25	
W1e		Horizontal coil			
W2	**1d**	**Deep ultramarine** - Sheets (31.8.53)	10	8	15
W2a		Book pane BP78	2.50	1.50	
W2b		Book pane BP79	1.25	70	
W2c		Book pane BP80	1.50	85	
W2d		Book pane BP81	£75		
W2e		Book pane BP82	8.50	4.50	
W2f		Book pane BP83	8.50	4.50	
W2g		Vertical coil	4.00	2.40	
W2h		Horizontal coil	2.50	1.35	
W3	**1½d**	**Green** - sheets	5	5	10
W3a		Book pane BP84	25	15	
W3b		Book pane BP85	1.50	80	
W3c	**1½d**	**Deep green** - sheets	25	12	
W3d		Book pane BP8	25	15	
W3e		Book pane BP85	1.00	60	
W3f		Book pane BP86	1.50	85	
W3g		Vertical coil	75	40	1.00
W4	**2d**	**Red brown** - Sheets (31.8.53)	10	5	10
W4a		Book pane BP87	4.50	2.40	
W4b		Vertical coil			
W5	**2½d**	**Carmine red** - Sheets. Type I	7	4	10
W5a		Vertical coil	12.50	7.00	
W6		Carmine red. Type II			
		Book pane BP88 (5.53)	45	30	50
W7	**3d**	**Deep violet** - Sheets (18.1.54)	1.00	65	25
W7a		Vertical coil			
W7b		Horizontal coil			
W8	**4d**	**Ultramarine** - Sheets (2.11.53)	1.75	95	60
W8a		Horizontal coil	5.50	2.90	
W9	**5d**	**Brown** - Sheets (6.7.53)	50	30	1.00
W10	**6d**	**Red purple** - Sheets (18.1.54)	2.30	1.40	40
W10a		Vertical coil			
W11	**7d**	**Pastel green** - Sheets (8.2.54)	4.40	2.90	2.00
W12	**8d**	**Cerise** - Sheets (6.7.53)	28	14	50
W13	**9d**	**Greyish green** - Sheets (8.2.54)	11.75	6.50	2.00
W14	**10d**	**Deep blue** - Sheets (8.2.54)	9.50	5.00	2.00
W15	**11d**	**Plum** - Sheets (8.2.54)	17.50	9.50	8.50
W16	**1s**	**Bistre brown** - Sheets (6.7.53)	28	15	30
W17	**1s3d**	**Deep green** - Sheets (2.11.53)	2.60	1.50	85
W18	**1s6d**	**Grey blue** - Sheets (2.11.53)	9.00	5.00	1.75

Watermark Tudor Crown Sideways

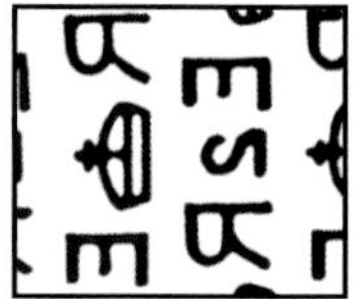

No.			U/M	M/M	F/U
1954 (8 Oct.)		Wmk. Tudor Crown sideways			
W3s	**1½d**	**Green** - Sideways coil (15.10.54)	20	10225	
W4s	**2d**	**Red brown** - Sideways coil	35	20	50
W5s	**2½d**	**Carmine red** - Sideways coil 15.4.54)			
		Type 1	3.10	1.65	4.00

Watermark Tudor Crown Inverted

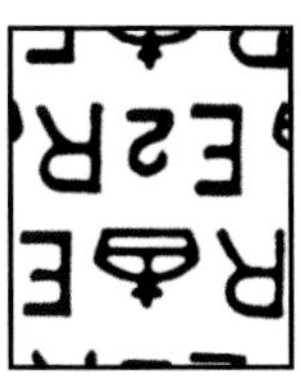

1954 (March). Wmk. Tudor Crown inverted

No.			U/M	M/M	F/U
W1ia	½d	**Orange red** - Book pane BP75a	45	25	35
W1ib		Book pane BP76a	75	40	
W2ia	1d	**Deep ultramarine** - Book pane BP78a	4.00	2.25	1.50
W2ib		Book pane BP79a	5.50	3.00	
W2ic		Book pane BP81a	£75	£50	
W2id		Book pane BP82a	8.50	4.50	
W2ie		Book pane BP83a	8.50	4.50	
W3ia	1½d	**Green** - Book pane BP84a	28	15	30
W3ib		Book pane BP85a	1.25	65	
W4ia	2d	**Red brown** - Book pane BP87a	£17	9.50	£10
W6ia	2½d	**Carmine red** - Book pane BP88a (Type II)	20	10	40

Coil join pairs

No.			U/M	M/M	F/U
W1cj	½d	**Orange red**	90		
W2cj	1d	**Deep ultramarine**	1.00		
W7cj	3d	**Deep violet**	1.50		
W7cja	3d	**Deep violet** (vert.)	2.00		
W8cj	4d	**Ultramarine**	4.00		
W10cj	6d	**Red purple** (vert.)	5.00		

Watermark St. Edwards Crown

1955 (Sept.) Wmk. St. Edward's Crown. Perf. 15 x 14

No.			U/M	M/M	F/U
W19	½d	**Orange red** - Sheets	10	5	10
W19a		Book pane BP89	25	13	
W19b		Book pane BP90	75	40	
W19c		Book pane BP91	1.75	95	
W19d		Vertical coil	35	20	
W19e		Horizontal coil	25	15	
W20	1d	**Deep ultramarine** - Sheets (19.9.55)	18	10	10
W20a		Book pane BP92	45	25	
W20b		Book pane BP93	1.00	55	
W20c		Book pane BP94	1.75	95	
W20d		Book pane BP95	4.50	2.50	
W20e		Vertical coil	3.50	1.80	
W20f		Horizontal coil	3.50	1.80	
W21	1½d	**Green** - Sheets (9.55)	12	7	10
W21a		Book pane BP96	45	25	
W21b	1½d	**Deep green** -Sheets	35	20	10
W21c		Book pane BP96	35	20	
W21d		Book pane BP97	1.25	70	
W21e		Book pane BP98	1.75	90	
W21f		Vertical coil	2.50	1.30	
W22	2d	**Red brown** - Sheets (6.9.55)	12	7	15
W22a		Book pane BP99	5.00	2.60	
W22b		Vertical coil	1.75	1.20	
W23	2d	**Light red brown** - Sheets (17.10.56)	12	10	15
W23a		Book pane BP100	2.50	1.30	
W23b		Vertical coil	3.50	1.80	
W24	2½d	**Carmine red** (Type I) - Sheets (28.9.55)	10	10	15
W24a		Vertical coil	1.50	1.00	
W25		Carmine red (Type II) - Sheets	55	15	85
W25a		Book pane BP101	20	15	
W26	3d	**Deep violet** - Sheets (17.7.56)	15	9	15
W26a		Book pane BP102	65	35	
W26b		Book pane BP103	3.50	1.80	
W26c		Vertical coil			
W26d		Horizontal coil			
W27	4d	**Ultramarine** - Sheets (14.11.55)	80	50	35
W27a		Vertical coil			
W27b		Horizontal coil	4.00	2.25	
W28	5d	**Brown** - Sheets (21.9.55)	3.25	1.75	2.50
W29	6d	**Red purple** - Sheets (20.12.55)	2.60	1.40	75
W29a		Vertical coil			
W30	6d	**Deep claret** - Sheets (8.5.58)	2.20	1.30	65
W30a		Vertical coil			
W31	7d	**Pastel green** - Sheets (23.4.56)	£27	£16	6.00
W32	8d	**Cerise** - Sheets(21.12.55)	3.40	2.00	75
W33	9d	**Greyish green** - Sheets (15.12.55)	10.50	7.00	1.50
W34	10d	**Deep blue** - Sheets (22.9.55)	10.50	6.00	1.50
W35	11d	**Plum** - Sheets (28.10.55)	50	30	40
W36	1s	**Bistre brown** - Sheets (3.11.55)	£12	5.50	40
W37	1s3d	**Deep green** - Sheets (27.3.56)	£16	8.50	90
W38	1s6d	**Grey blue** - Sheets (27.3.56)	£14	8.00	85

Watermark St. Edwards Crown Inverted

1955 (Sept.) Wmk. St. Edward's Crown inverted

No.			U/M	M/M	F/U
W19ia	½d	**Orange red** - Book pane BP89a	10	5	15
W19ib		Book pane BP90a	45	30	
W20ia	1d	**Deep ultramarine** - Book pane BP92a	35	20	30
W20ib		Book pane BP93a	75	40	
		Book pane BP95a	4.50	2.50	
W21ia	1½d	**Green** - Book pane BP96a	30	18	20
		Book pane BP97a	75	40	
W22ia	2d	**Red brown** - Book pane BP99a	6.00	3.50	3.70
W23ia	2d	**Light red brown** - Book pane BP100a (1.57)	4.50	2.50	2.00
W25ia	2½d	**Carmine red** (Type II) - Book pane BP101a	15	10	25
W26ia	3d	**Deep violet** - Book pane BP102a (1.10.57)	1.50	85	90
W26ib		Book pane BP103a	3.50	1.80	

Watermark St. Edwards Crown Sideways

1956 (7 March) Wmk. St. Edward's Crown sideways

No.			U/M	M/M	F/U
W21s	**1½d**	**Green** - Sideways coil	10	5	20
W22s	**2d**	**Red brown** - Sideways coil (31.7.56)	15	5	25
W23s	**2d**	**Light red brown** - Sideways coil (5.3.57)	4.35	2.50	1.75
W25s	**2½d**	**Carmine red** (Type II) - Sideways coil (23.3.56)	1.00	60	40
W26s	**3d**	**Deep violet** - Sideways coil (9.12.57)	7.95	4.50	6.00

Coil join pairs

No.			U/M	M/M	F/U
W19cj	**½d**	**Orange red**	30		
W20cj	**1d**	**Deep ultramarine**	50		
W21cj	**3d**	**Deep violet**	50		
W21cja		Deep violet (vert.)	60		
W22cj	**4d**	**Ultramarine**	2.50		
W22cja		Ultramarine (vert.)	3.00		
W29cj	**6d**	**Red purple** (vert.)	7.50		
W30cj	**6d**	**Claret** (vert.)	5.00		

Graphite Lined Issue

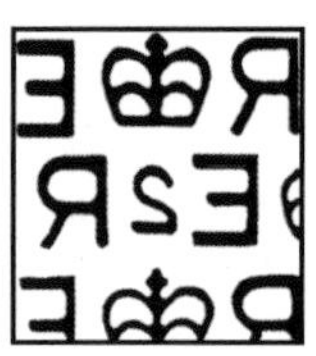

This issue was introduced in the Southampton postal area, for the experimental use of an automatic letter facing machine.

1957 (19 Nov.) Graphite lined. Wmk. St. Edward's Crown. Perf. 15 x 14. Two vertical graphite lines on back under gum, except 2d value with one line only.

No.			U/M	M/M	F/U
W39	**½d**	**Orange red** - Sheets	10	5	10
W39a		Vertical coil	50	30	
W40	**1d**	**Deep ultramarine** - Sheets	25	15	20
W40a		Vertical coil	45	30	
W41	**1½d**	**Green** - Sheets	65	35	2.50
W41a		Horizontal coil	1.75	85	
W42	**2d**	**Light red brown** - Sheets	85	45	75
W42a		Vertical coil	4.75	2.55	
		Horizontal coil	3.75	2.50	
W43	**2½d**	**Carmine red** (Type II) - Sheets	3.75	2.50	2.75
W43a		Horizontal coil	7.50	4.00	
W44	**3d**	**Deep violet** - Sheets	28	20	50
		Horizontal coil	1.75	95	

Coil join pairs

No.			U/M	M/M	F/U
W41cj	**1½d**	**Green**	75		
W42cj	**2d**	**Light red brown**	4.00		
W42cja		Light red brown (vert.)	4.50		
W43cj	**2½d**	**Carmine red**. Type II	£11		
W44cj	**3d**	**Deep violet**	1.25		

Multiple Crowns Watermark Upright Cream Paper

1958 (28 Oct.) Wmk. Multiple Crowns. Cream paper. Perf. 15 x 14

No.			U/M	M/M	F/U
W45	**½d**	**Orange red** - Sheets (25.11.58)	10	5	8
W45a		Book pane BP104	35	20	
W45b		Book pane BP105	1.00	65	
W45c		Vertical coil	35	20	
W45d		Horizontal coil	35	20	
W46	**1d**	**Deep ultramarine** - Sheets (11.58)	25	12	10
W46a		Book pane BP106	35	20	
W46b		Book pane BP107	1.00	65	
W46c		Vertical coil	2.00	1.20	
W46d		Horizontal coil			
W47	**1½d**	**Green** - Sheets (12.58)	20	14	15
W47a		Book pane BP108	75	40	
W47b		Book pane BP109	1.50	85	
W47c	**1½d**	**Deep green** - Sheets	45	30	30
W47d		Book pane BP108	75	45	
W47e		Book pane BP109	1.00	65	
W47f		Vertical coil	1.50	85	
W48	**2d**	**Light red brown** - Sheets (4.12.58)	20	14	10
W48a		Book pane BP110	6.50	3.75	
W48b		Vertical coil	1.75	1.00	
W49	**2½d**	**Carmine red** (Type I) - Sheets (11.9.59)	2.50	1.65	1.00
W49a		Vertical coil			
W50		Carmine red (Type II) - Sheets (4.10.61)	30	20	15
W50a		Book pane BP111	1.75	85	65
W51	**3d**	**Deep violet** - Sheets (8.12.58)	15	10	15
W51a		Book pane BP112	40	25	
W51b		Book pane BP113	2.50	1.40	
W51c		Vertical coil	3.50	1.80	
W52	**4d**	**Ultramarine** - Sheets (29.10.58)	1.50	80	50
W52a		Vertical coil			
W52b		Horizontal coil	3.50	1.85	
W53	**4½d**	**Chestnut red** - Sheets (9.2.59)	50	30	30
W54	**5d**	**Brown** - Sheets (10.11.58)	2.50	1.45	45
W55	**6d**	**Claret** - Sheets (23.12.58)	90	50	20
W55a		Vertical coil	4.50	2.50	
W56	**7d**	**Pastel green** - Sheets (26.11.58)	1.65	85	50
W57	**8d**	**Cerise** - Sheets (24.2.59)	2.50	1.60	60
W58	**9d**	**Greyish green** - Sheets (24.3.59)	2.50	1.60	60
W59	**10d**	**Deep blue** - Sheets (17.6.59)	2.50	1.60	45
W60	**1s**	**Bistre brown** - Sheets (30.10.58)	1.85	1.00	35
W61	**1s3d**	**Deep green** - Sheets (17.6.59)	2.50	1.60	55
W62	**1s6d**	**Grey blue** - Sheets (16.12.58)	10.50	6.00	2.30
		Presentation pack 10s8d. (W35, W45/71) (1960)		£60	
		Presentation pack $1.80 (W35, W45/71) US Edition (1960)		£75	

Multiple Crowns Watermark Inverted Cream Paper

1958 (Nov.) Wmk. Multiple Crowns inverted. Cream paper. Perf. 15 x 14

No.			U/M	M/M	F/U
W45ia	½d	**Orange red** - Book pane BP104a	20	14	15
W45ib		Book pane BP105a	50	35	
W46ia	1d	**Deep ultramarine** - Book pane BP106a	18	10	15
W46ib		Book pane BP107a	60	35	
W47ia	1½d	**Green** - Book pane BP108a	60	40	30
W47ib		Book pane BP109a	1.50	1.00	
W48ia	2d	**Light red brown** - Book pane BP110a (10.4.61)	£72	£40	£30
W50ia	2½d	**Carmine red** (Type II) - Book pane BP112a	3.00	1.70	95
W51ia	3d	**Deep violet** - Book pane BP112a	10	7	10
W51ib		Book pane BP113a	2.50	1.65	

Multiple Crowns Watermark Sideways Left Cream Paper

1958 (24 Oct.) Wmk. Multiple Crowns. Cream paper. Watermark sideways - Crown to left

No.			U/M	M/M	F/U
W45sl	½d	**Orange red** - Book pane BP105b (26.5.61)	1.55	85	30
W46sl	1d	**Deep ultramarine** - Book pane BP107b (26.5.61)	1.55	85	35
W47sl	1½d	**Green** - Book pane BP109b (26.5.61)	4.50	2.50	1.70
W48sl	2d	**Light red brown** - Sideways coil (3.4.59)	1.00	65	50
W49sl	2½d	**Carmine red** (Type I) (10.11.60) Sideways coil	85	45	
W51sl	3d	**Deep violet** - Book pane BP113b	1.55	80	50
W51sla		Sideways coil	2.00	1.10	

Multiple Crowns Watermark Sideways Right Cream Paper

1958 (24 Oct.) Wmk. Multiple Crowns. Cream paper. Watermark sideways - Crown to right

No.			U/M	M/M	F/U
W45sr	½d	**Orange red** - Book pane BP105c (26.5.61)	1.55	85	30
W46sr	1d	**Deep ultramarine** - Book pane BP107c (26.5.61)	1.55	85	35
W47sr	1½d	**Green** - Book pane BP109c (26.5.61)	6.00	3.30	1.90
W51sr	3d	**Deep violet** - Book pane BP113c	1.55	85	50

Coil join pairs

No.			U/M	M/M	F/U
W45cj	½d	**Orange red**	30		
W46cj	1d	**Deep ultramarine**	30		
W47cj	1½d	**Green**	50		
W47cja		Green (vert.)	50		
W52cj	4d	**Ultramarine**	1.00		
W52cja		Ultramarine (vert.)	1.00		
W55cj	6d	**Claret** (vert.)	1.50		

Multiple Crowns Watermark Upright Whiter Paper

Wmk. Multiple Crowns. Whiter paper. Perf. 15 x 14

No.			U/M	M/M	F/U
WW45	½d	**Orange red** - Sheets	5	3	5
WW45a		Book pane BP114	1.50	85	
WW45b		Vertical coil	35	20	
WW45c		Chalky paper - Book pane BP128	1.35	75	
WW46	1d	**Deep ultramarine** - Sheets	6	4	5
WW46a		Book pane BP117	55	30	
WW46b		Vertical coil	40	25	
WW46c		Horizontal coil	65	35	
WW47	1½d	**Green** - Sheets	5	3	10
WW47a		Book pane BP121	2.00	1.10	
WW47b	1½d	**Deep green** - Sheets	30	20	30
WW47c		Book pane BP121	2.75	1.50	
WW47d		Horizontal coil	75	45	
WW48	2d	**Light red brown** - Sheets	5	3	5
WW48a		Vertical coil	1.50	90	
WW49	2½d	**Carmine red** (Type I) - Sheets	5.00	3.50	
WW49a		Vertical coil	10	5	
WW50		Carmine red (Type II) - Sheets	5	5	5
WW50a		Book pane BP123	2.00	1.20	40
WW50b		Chalky paper - Book pane BP129	12	7	
WW51	3d	**Deep violet** - Sheets	5	3	10
WW51a		Book pane BP124	35	20	
WW51b		Vertical coil	1.50	85	
WW52	4d	**Ultramarine** - Sheets	15	10	10
WW52a		Vertical coil			
WW52b		Horizontal coil			
WW52c	4d	**Deep ultramarine** - Sheets	12	7	5
WW52d		Book pane BP126	60	35	
WW52e		Vertical coil	95	55	
WW53	4½d	**Chestnut red** - Sheets	10	5	15
WW54	5d	**Brown** - Sheets	15	9	20
WW55	6d	**Claret** - Sheets	15	9	10
WW55a		Vertical coil	2.75	1.55	
WW56	7d	**Pastel green** - Sheets	22	13	25
WW57	8d	**Cerise** - Sheets	25	15	20
WW58	9d	**Greyish green** - Sheets	25	15	30
WW59	10d	**Deep blue** - Sheets	40	27	20
WW60	1s	**Bistre brown** - Sheets	25	15	15
WW61	1s3d	**Deep green** - Sheets	25	15	15
WW62	1s6d	**Grey blue** - Sheets	2.75	1.50	25

Multiple Crowns Watermark Sideways Left Whiter Paper

No.			U/M	M/M	F/U
WW45sl	½d	**Orange red** - Book pane BP115	1.55	85	
WW45sla	½d	**Orange red** - Book pane BP116	10	5	10
WW46sl	1d	**Deep ultramarine** - Book pane BP118	1.55	85	1.25
WW46sla	1d	**Deep ultramarine** - Book pane BP119-120	45	28	40
WW47sl	1½d	**Green** - Book pane BP122	7.50	4.25	3.00
WW48sl	2d	**Light red brown** - Sideways coil	30	17	25
WW49sl	2½d	**Carmine red** (Type I) - Sideways coil	18	10	20
WW49sla	2½d	**Carmine red** (Type II) - Book pane BP116	35	20	45
WW49slb		Sideways coil	2.90	1.60	
WW51sl	3d	**Deep violet** - Book pane BP125	1.55	85	
WW51sla		Book pane BP119-120	10	5	
WW51sla		Sideways coil	45	25	40
WW52sl	4d	**Ultramarine** - Book pane BP127	35	20	20
WW52sla		Sideways coil	65	35	40

Multiple Crowns Watermark Sideways Right Whiter Paper

No.			U/M	M/M	F/U
WW45sr	½d	**Orange red** - Book pane BP115a	1.55	85	1.25
WW45sra		Book pane BP116a	10	5	
WW46sr	1d	**Deep ultramarine** - Book pane BP118a	1.55	85	1.25
WW46sra		Book pane BP119a	45	25	
WW47sr	1½d	**Green** - Book pane BP122a	7.50	4.00	3.00
WW49sr	2½d	**Carmine red** (Type II) - Book pane BP116a	35	20	45
WW51sr	3d	**Deep violet** - Book pane BP125a	1.55	85	
WW51sra		Book pane BP119a-BP120a	10	5	10
WW52sr	4d	**Ultramarine** - Book pane BP127a	1.20	70	20

Multiple Crowns Watermark Inverted Whiter Paper

No.			U/M	M/M	F/U
WW45i	½d	**Orange red** - Book pane BP114a	55	30	20
WW45ia		Chalky paper - Book pane BP128a	1.35	80	1.50
WW46i	1d	**Deep ultramarine** - Book pane BP117a	45	25	40
WW47i	1½d	**Green** - Book pane BP121a	1.95	1.00	40
WW50i	2½d	**Carmine red** (Type II) - Book pane BP123a	4.50	2.40	1.00
WW50ia		Chalky paper BP129a	30	20	75
WW51i	3d	**Deep violet** - Book pane BP124a	10	8	15
WW52i	4d	**Ultramarine** - Book pane BP126a	1.20	70	35

Multiple Crowns Watermark Graphite Lined

1958 (24 Nov.) Graphite lined. Wmk. Multiple Crowns. Perf. 15 x 14.
Two vertical graphite lines on back under gum, except 2d value with one line only.

No.			U/M	M/M	F/U
W63	½d	**Orange red** - Book pane BP130 (16.6.59)	7.50	4.50	8.00
W63a		Vertical coil	5.00	2.80	
W64	1d	**Deep ultramarine** - Vertical coil (18.12.58)	65	45	85
W64a		Bright ultramarine - Book pane BP131	1.50	85	1.00
W64b		Two lines at left - Vertical coil	75	50	
W64c		Two lines at right - Vertical coil	75	50	
W64d		One line at left - Vertical coil	75	50	
W64e		One line at right - Vertical coil	75	50	
W64f		Three lines - Vertical coil	£15	8.50	
W65	1½d	**Green** - Book pane BP132 (4.8.59)	£50	£30	£35
W66	2d	**Light red brown** - Sheets	4.25	2.50	1.40
W66a		Vertical coil	10.50	6.00	
W67	2½d	**Carmine red** (Type II) - Sheets (9.6.59)	5.00	2.80	5.50
W67a		Book pane BP133	7.50	5.00	
W68	3d	**Deep violet** - Sheets	20	10	15
W68a		Book pane BP134	40	25	
W68b		Vertical coil	7.50	5.00	
W68c		Horizontal coil			
W69	4d	**Ultramarine** - Sheets (29.4.59)	2.00	1.35	2.50
W70	4½d	**Chestnut** - Sheets (3.6.59)	2.60	1.75	1.80

Multiple Crowns Watermark Inverted Graphite Lined

1959 (4 Aug.) Graphite Lined. Wmk. Multiple Crowns inverted

No.			U/M	M/M	F/U
W63i	**½d**	**Orange red** - Book pane BP130a	1.60	95	2.00
W64i	1d	Deep ultramarine - Book pane BP131a	1.00	60	1.30
W65i	**1½d**	**Green** * - Book pane BP132a	£21	£13	£18
W67i	**2½d**	**Carmine red** (Type II) - Book pane BP133a	£35	£20	£29
W68i	**3d**	**Deep violet** - Book pane BP134a	20	12	40

* These stamps are from booklets only and the prices quoted are for stamps with good perforations all round. Trimmed perf. examples can be purchased at a considerable discount.

Coil join pairs

No.			U/M
W66cj	**2d**	**Light red brown** (vert.)	£12
W68cj	**3d**	**Deep violet**	1.50

Phosphor-Graphite St. Edwards Crown Watermark

This further experimental issue was also introduced in the Southampton postal area, the phosphor bands serving the same purpose as the graphite lines to facilitate automatic letter facing.

1959 (18 Nov.) Phosphor and Graphite Lined. Wmk. St. Edward's Crown.
Perf 15 x 14. Two phosphor bands on face and two graphite lines on back, except 2d value with 1 band and 1 graphite line.

No.			U/M	M/M	F/U
W71	**½d**	**Orange red** - Sheets	1.60	95	4.00
W71a		Narrow band left - Sheets	5.25		
W71b		Narrow band right	5.25		
W72	**1d**	**Deep ultramarine** - Sheets	6.50	3.50	6.00
W72a		Narrow band left - Sheets	£10		
W72b		Narrow band right - Sheets	£10		
W73	**1½d**	**Green** - Sheets	1.90	1.10	3.50
W73a		Narrow band left - Sheets	5.00		
W73b		Narrow band right - Sheets	5.00		

Phosphor-Graphite Multiple Crowns Watermark

No.			U/M	M/M	F/U
W74	**2d**	**Light red brown** - Sheets	3.00	1.70	1.50
W75	**2½d**	**Carmine red** (Type II) - Sheets	10.50	6.00	£12
W75a		Narrow band left - Sheets	18.50		
W75b		Narrow band right - Sheets	18.50		
W76	**3d**	**Deep violet** - Sheets	5.75	3.25	4.75
W76a		Narrow band left - Sheets	£13		
W76b		Narrow band right - Sheets	£13		
W77	**4d**	**Ultramarine** - Sheets	9.50	5.00	£12
W77a		Narrow band left - Sheets	17.50		
W77b		Narrow band right - Sheets	17.50		
W78	**4½d**	**Chestnut** - Sheets	£14	£9	5.00
W78a		Narrow band left - Sheets	£40		
W78b		Narrow band right - Sheets	£40		
		Presentation pack 3s8d (W71/78 each x 2) (1960)	£150		
		Presentation pack 50c (W71/78 each x 2) US Edition (1960)	£150		

Variety

No.			U/M	M/M	F/U
W74a	**2d**	**Light red brown**. Error. Wmk. St. Edward's Crown.	87.50	£50	£65
W75a	**2½d**	**Carmine red.** Error. Wmk. St. Edward's Crown.*	£2000	-	-

* This was not officially issued

Multiple Crowns Watermark Green Phosphor

1960 (22 June) Phosphor issue. Wmk. Multiple Crowns. Perf. 15 x 14. Two phosphor bands on face, except where otherwise stated.

No.			U/M	M/M	F/U
W79	**½d**	**Orange red** - Sheets	1.00	60	75
W79a		Book pane BP135	1.25	70	
W79b		Vertical coil	2.50	1.40	
W80	**1d**	**Deep ultramarine** - Sheets	1.00	60	75
W80a		Book pane BP136	1.50	1.00	
W80b		Vertical coil	2.50	1.50	
W81	**1½d**	**Green** - Sheets	1.25	75	80
W81a		Book pane BP137	2.75	1.50	
W82	**2d**	**Light red brown** (left band) - Vertical coil	£20	£12	£18
W82a		(left band) - Sheets	8.25	4.75	
W83	**2½d**	**Carmine red** (Type II) - Sheets	1.50	1.00	1.20
W83a		Book pane BP138	7.50	4.50	
W84	**3d**	**Deep violet** - Sheets	1.00	65	75
W84a		Book pane BP139	1.25	70	
W85	**4d**	**Ultramarine**	5.75	3.00	4.50
W86	**6d**	**Claret** - Sheets	2.75	1.50	2.50
W87	**1s 3d**	**Deep green** - Sheets	6.50	3.50	3.50

Multiple Crowns Watermark Inverted Green Phosphor

No.			U/M	M/M	F/U
W79i	½d	**Orange red** - Book pane BP135a	5.00	2.70	3.75
W80i	1d	**Deep ultramarine** - Book pane BP136a	5.00	2.70	3.75
W81i	1½d	**Green** - Book pane BP137a	£10	6.00	5.00
W83i	2½d	**Carmine red** (Type II) - Book pane BP138a	£115	£65	£60
W84i	3d	**Deep violet** - Book pane BP139a	75	45	50

Multiple Crowns Watermark Blue Phosphor - Cream Paper

No.			U/M	M/M	F/U
W88	½d	**Orange red** - Sheets	20	12	10
W88a		Book pane BP140	65	35	
W88b		Vertical coil	1.50	85	
W89	1d	**Deep ultramarine** - Sheets	75	40	40
W89a		Book pane BP142	1.00	60	
W89b		Vertical coil	1.75	95	
W90	1½d	**Green** - Sheets	50	25	40
W90a		Book pane BP144	1.75	90	
W91	2d	**LB Light red brown** (Photo) - Sheets	£20	£13	£18
W91a		Vertical coil	£30	£16	
W92	2d	**2B Light red brown** (Typo) - Sheets	5.00	2.70	2.50
W92a		Narrow band left - Sheets (Typo)	10.50		
W92b		Narrow band left - Sheets (Typo)	10.50		
W92c		(Photo) - Sheets	1.20	70	
W92d		(Photo) - Vertical coil			
W93	2½d	**2B Carmine red** (Type II) (Photo) - Sheets	3.50	2.00	1.50
W93a		Book pane BP146	7.50	4.00	
W94	2½d	**LB Carmine red** (Type II) (Typo) - Sheets	2.00	1.30	2.00
W94a		(Photo) - Sheets	5.00	2.80	
W94b		Book pane BP147	7.50	4.00	
W95	2½d	**LB Carmine red** (Type I) (Typo) - Sheets	23.50	£15	£21
W96	3d	**Deep violet** - Sheets	1.00	60	80
W96a		Book pane BP148	65	35	
W96b		Vertical coil	3.00	1.60	
W99	4d	**Deep ultramarine** - Sheets	1.85	90	1.30
W100	4½d	**Chestnut** (Typo) - Sheets	2.75	1.50	1.25
W100a		Narrow band left (Typo) - Sheets	8.50		
W100b		Narrow band right (Typo) - Sheets	8.50		
W100c		(Photo) - Sheets	15.00	8.25	7.00
W101	6d	**Claret** (Typo) - Sheets	3.50	2.00	2.00
W101a		Narrow band left (Typo) - Sheets			
W101b		Narrow band right (typo) - Sheets			
W101a		(Photo) - Sheets			
W102	1s 3d	**Deep green** - Sheets	£20	£12	6.50

Multiple Crowns Watermark Sideways Left Blue Phosphor - Cream Paper

No.			U/M	M/M	F/U
W88sl	½d	**Orange red** - Book pane BP141	6.50	4.00	6.00
W89sl	1d	**Deep ultramarine** - Book pane BP143	3.00	1.65	2.00
W90sl	1½d	**Green** - Book pane BP145	6.50	3.50	6.00
W96sl	3d	**Deep violet** - Book pane BP149	3.50	1.80	1.50

Multiple Crowns Watermark Sideways Right Blue Phosphor - Cream Paper

No.			U/M	M/M	F/U
W88sr	½d	**Orange red** - Book pane BP141a	5.25	2.80	4.50
W89sr	1d	**Deep ultramarine** - Book pane BP143a	3.00	1.60	2.00
W90sr	1½d	**Green** - Book pane BP145a	5.25	2.80	4.50
W96sr	3d	**Deep violet** - Book pane BP149a	3.50	1.80	1.50

Multiple Crowns Watermark Inverted Blue Phosphor - Cream Paper

No.			U/M	M/M	F/U
W88i	½d	**Orange red** - Book pane BP140a	55	30	65
W89i	1d	**Deep ultramarine** - Book pane BP142a	75	45	50
W90i	1½d	**Green** - Book pane BP144a	5.75	3.25	3.25
W93i	2½d	**2B Carmine red** (Type II) - Book pane BP146a	£125	£70	£75
W94i	2½d	**LB Carmine red** (Type II) - Book pane BP147a	£20	£12	£10
W96i	3d	**Deep violet** - Book pane BP148a	50	30	50

Multiple Crowns Watermark Blue Phosphor - Whiter Paper

No.			U/M	M/M	F/U
W97	½d	**Orange red** - Sheets	10	5	10
W97a		Book pane BP150	2.00	1.20	
W97b		Vertical coil	75	45	
W98	1d	**Deep ultramarine** - Sheets	85	45	50
W98a		Book pane BP152	1.25	70	
W98b		Vertical coil	1.25	70	
W99	1½d	**Green** - Sheets	12	7	20
WW99a		Book pane BP156	5.50	3.00	
WW100	2d	**2B Light red brown** - Sheets	6.00	3.50	5.00
W100a		Vertical coil	£10	6.50	
W101	2½d	**2B Carmine red** (Type II)			
		Photo - Sheets	30		35
W101a		Typo - Sheets			
W102b		Narrow band left (Typo) - Sheets			
W102c		Narrow band right (Typo) - Sheets			
W103	2½d	**LB Carmine red** (Type II)			
		Typo - Sheets			
W103a		Photo - Sheets	30	17	60
W103b		Photo - Book pane BP158	4.50	2.50	
W104	3d	**2B Deep violet** - Sheets	40	25	35
W104a		Book pane BP159	1.00	60	
W104b		Vertical coil	3.50	2.25	
W105	3d	**LB Deep violet** - Sheets	2.25	1.30	2.00
W105a		Vertical coil	4.50	2.70	
W106	3d	**RB Deep violet** - Sheets	2.25	1.35	2.00
W106a		Vertical coil	5.50	3.00	
W107	4d	**Deep ultramarine** - Sheets	65	35	45
W107a		Book pane BP161	1.50	85	
W108	4½d	**Chestnut** (Typo) - Sheets	1.75	95	65
W108a		Narrow band left (Typo) - Sheets	5.00		
W108b		Narrow band right (Typo) - Sheets	5.00		
W108a		(Photo) - Sheets	10	5	
W109	6d	**Claret** (Typo) - Sheets	£285		
W109a		Narrow band left (Typo) - Sheets			
W109b		Narrow band left (Typo) - Sheets			
W109c		(Photo) - Sheets	50	35	45
W110	1s 3d	**Deep green** - Sheets	90	50	1.10

Multiple Crowns Watermark Sideways Left Blue Phosphor - Whiter Paper

No.			U/M	M/M	F/U
W97sl	½d	**Orange red** - Book pane BP151	8.00	5.00	8.00
W98sl	1d	**Deep ultramarine** - Book pane BP153	3.00	1.60	1.75
WW99sl	1½d	**Green** - Book pane BP157	8.00	5.00	8.00
W104sl	3d	**2B Deep violet** - Book pane BP160	3.50	1.90	1.50
W105sl	3d	**LB Deep violet** - Book pane BP154	£25	£14	£17
W106sl	3d	**RB Deep violet** - Book pane BP155	£25	£14	£17
W107sl	4d	**Deep ultramarine** - Book pane BP162	2.00	1.20	1.50

Multiple Crowns Watermark Sideways Right Blue Phosphor - Whiter Paper

No.			U/M	M/M	F/U
W97sr	½d	**Orange red** - Book pane BP151a	7.50	4.20	7.00
W98sr	1d	**Deep ultramarine** - Book pane BP153a, BP154a	2.75	1.50	1.50
W99sr	1½d	**Green** - Book pane BP157a	7.50	4.00	7.00
W104sr	3d	**2B Deep violet** - Book pane BP160a	3.50	1.90	1.40
W105sr	3d	**LB Deep violet** - Book pane BP154a	£25	£15	£20
W106sr	3d	**RB Deep violet** - Book pane BP155a	£25	£15	£20
W107sr	4d	**Deep ultramarine** - Book pane BP162a	2.00	1.20	1.50

Multiple Crowns Watermark Inverted Blue Phosphor - Whiter Paper

No.			U/M	M/M	F/U
W97i	½d	**Orange red** - Book pane BP150a	1.25	70	75
W98i	1d	**Deep ultramarine** - Book pane BP152a	75	40	50
W99i	1½d	**Green** - Book pane BP156a	£25	£14	£11
W101i	2½d	**LB Carmine red** (Type II) - Book pane BP158a	£25	£14	£13
W104i	3d	**Deep violet** - Book pane BP159a	25	15	30
W107i	4d	**Deep ultramarine** - Book pane BP161a	1.25	70	55

Multiple Crowns Watermark Violet Phosphor - 8mm Bands

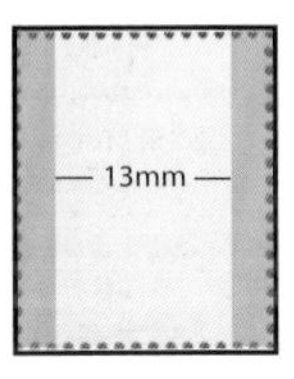

No.			U/M	M/M	F/U
W111	½d	**Orange red** (Typo) - Sheets	35	20	18
W111a		Narrow band left (Typo) - Sheets	3.50		
W111b		Narrow band right (Typo) - Sheets	3.50		
W111c		(Photo) - Vertical coil	45	28	20
W112	1d	**Deep ultramarine** (Typo) - Sheets	17.50	9.00	£7
W112a		Narrow band left (Typo) - Sheets	£70		
W112b		Narrow band right (Typo) - Sheets	£70		
W112c		(Photo) - Sheets	45	25	25
W112b		Book pane BP163	2.00	1.20	
W112c		Vertical coil	1.25	70	
W113	1½d	**Green** - Sheets	90	50	75
W113a		Narrow band left (Typo) - Sheets	4.25		
W113b		Narrow band right (Typo) - Sheets	4.25		
W114	2d	**2B Light red brown** - Sheets	80	50	35
W114a		Vertical coil			
W115	3d	**LB Deep violet** - Sheets	35	20	45
W115a		Book pane BP166	6.50	3.60	
W116a		Vertical coil	2.75	1.50	

No.			U/M	M/M	F/U
W117	3d	**RB Deep violet** - Sheets	35	25	50
W117a		Book pane BP166	1.25	70	
W117b		Vertical coil	2.75	1.60	
W118	4d	**Deep ultramarine** - Sheets	50	30	40
W118a		Book pane BP167	1.00	60	
W119	6d	**Claret** (Typo) - Sheets	7.50	4.00	5.00
W119a		Narrow band left (Typo) - Sheets	£20		
W119b		Narrow band right (Typo) - Sheets	£20		
W120	1s 3d	**Deep green** (Typo) - Sheets	£15	8.00	6.50
W120a		Narrow band left (Typo) - Sheets	£30		
W120b		Narrow band right (Typo) - Sheets	£30		
W120a		(Photo) - Sheets	6.00	3.50	3.50

Multiple Crowns Watermark Sideways Left Violet Phosphor - 8mm Bands

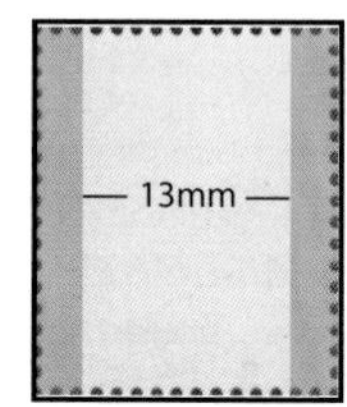

No.			U/M	M/M	F/U
W112sl	1d	**Deep ultramarine** - Book pane BP164-BP165	1.25	70	75
W115sl	3d	**LB Deep violet** - Book pane BP164	2.75	1.85	2.40
W117sl	3d	**RB Deep violet** - Book pane BP165	2.75	1.85	2.40
W118sl	4d	**Deep ultramarine** (Photo) Book pane BP168	60	35	40
W118sla		(Typo) - Book pane BP168b	£10	6.50	£10

Multiple Crowns Watermark Sideways Right Violet Phosphor - 8mm Bands

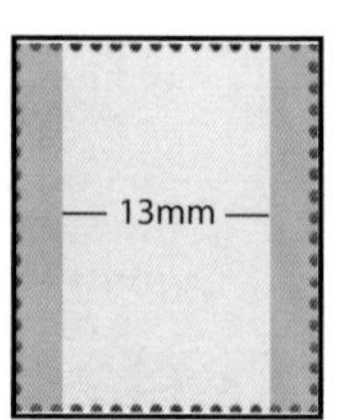

No.			U/M	M/M	F/U
W112sr	1d	**Deep ultramarine** - Book pane BP164a-BP165a	1.25	70	75
W115sr	3d	**LB Deep violet** - Book pane BP164a	2.75	1.85	2.40
W117sr	3d	**RB Deep violet** - Book pane BP165a	2.75	1.85	2.40
W118sr	4d	**Deep ultramarine** (Photo) - Book pane BP168a	60	35	40
W118sra		(Typo) - Book pane BP110c	£10	6.50	£10

Multiple Crowns Watermark Inverted Violet Phosphor - 8mm Bands

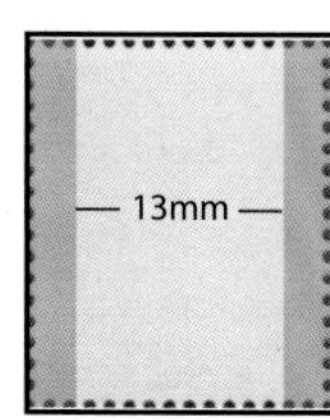

No.			U/M	M/M	F/U
W112i	1d	**Deep ultramarine** - Book pane BP163a	75	40	25
W115i	3d	**LB Deep violet** - Book pane BP166a	£35	£23	£35
W117i	3d	**RB Deep violet** - Book pane BP166a	3.75	1.90	1.75
W118i	4d	**Deep ultramarine** - Book pane BP167a	35	20	25

Multiple Crowns Watermark Violet Phosphor - 9.5mm Bands

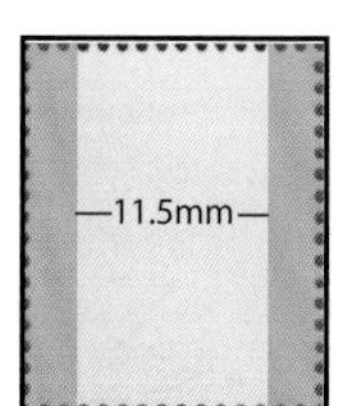

No.			U/M	M/M	F/U
W121	1d	**Deep ultramarine** - Sheets	10	5	5
W121a		Book pane BP169	50	30	
W121b		Vertical coil	1.00	60	
W122	2d	**2B Light red brown** - Sheets	10	5	5
W122a		Vertical coil	75	45	
W123	3d	**CB Deep violet** - Sheets	25	15	20
W123a		Book pane BP172	75	40	
W123b		Vertical coil			
W125	4d	**Deep ultramarine** - Sheets	10	5	8
W125a		Book pane BP173	30	18	
W126	5d	**Brown** - Sheets	12	8	10
W127	6d	**Claret** - Sheets	15	12	10
W127a		Vertical coil	2.50	1.85	
W128	7d	**Pastel green** - Sheets	25	13	10
W129	8d	**Cerise** - Sheets	25	13	15
W130	9d	**Greyish green** - Sheets	30	18	15
W131	10d	**Deep blue** - Sheets	30	18	15
W132	1s	**Bistre brown** - Sheets	25	15	15
W133	1s3d	**Deep green** - Sheets	6.50	3.75	2.00
W134	1s6d	**Grey blue** - Sheets	1.35	85	40

Multiple Crowns Watermark Sideways Left Violet Phosphor - 9.5mm Bands

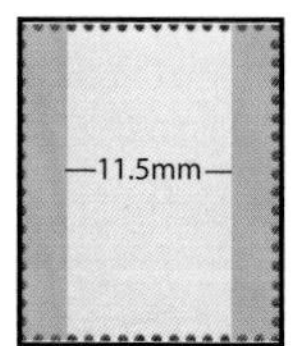

Violet Phosphor - 9.5mm Band Crown to Left

No.			U/M	M/M	F/U
W121sl	1d	**Deep ultramarine** - Book panes BP170-BP171	25	14	20
W122sl	2d	**2B Light red brown** - Sideways coil	18	10	35
W123sl	3d	**CB Deep violet** - Sideways coil	40	25	70
W124sl	3d	**2B Deep violet** - Book panes BP170-BP171	65	40	65
W125sl	4d	**Deep ultramarine** - Sideways coil	35	19	25
W125sla		Book pane BP174	15	8	10

Multiple Crowns Watermark Sideways Right Violet Phosphor - 9.5mm Bands

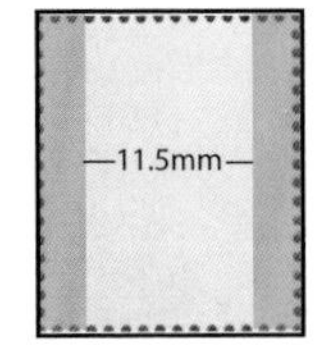

Violet Phosphor - 9.5mm Band Crown to Right

No.			U/M	M/M	F/U
W121sr	1d	**Deep ultramarine** - Book pane BP170a-BP171a	25	13	20
W123sr	3d	**2B Deep violet** - Book pane BP170a-BP171a	65	40	65
W125sr	4d	**Deep ultramarine** - Book pane BP174a	15	8	**10**

Multiple Crowns Watermark Inverted Violet Phosphor - 9.5mm Bands

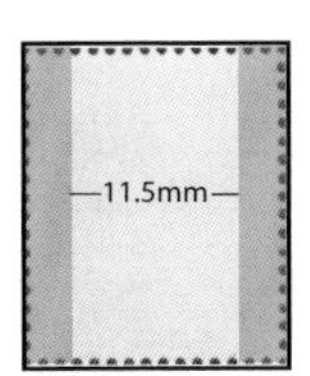

Violet Phosphor - 9.5mm Band Wmk. Inverted

No.			U/M	M/M	F/U
W121i	1d	**Deep ultramarine** - Book pane BP169a	20	12	20
W123i	3d	**CB Deep violet** - Book pane BP172a	1.90	1.25	1.90
W125i	4d	**Deep ultramarine** - Book pane BP173a	15	10	12

Coil Strips

Watermark Tudor Crown Upright

No.				U/M
WCS1	½d	**Orange red**	Vertical	2.50
WCS1a	½d	**Orange red**	Horizontal	
WCS2	1d	**Ultramarine**	Vertical	
WCS2a	1d	**Ultramarine**	Horizontal	
WCS3	1½d	**Green**	Vertical	3.75
WCS4	2d	**Red brown**	Vertical	£12
WCS5	3d	**Deep violet**	Vertical	
WCS5a	3d	**Deep violet**	Horizontal	
WCS6	4d	**Deep Ultramarine**	Horizontal	

Watermark Tudor Crown Sideways

No.				U/M
WCS7	1½d	**Green**	Sideways	90
WCS8	2d	**Red brown**	Sideways	1.80
WCS9	2½d	**Carmine-red** Type II	Sideways	13.75

Watermark St. Edwards Crown Upright

No.				U/M
WCS10	½d	**Orange red**	Vertical	1.25
WCS10a	½d	**Orange red**	Horizontal	1.25
WCS11	1d	**Ultramarine**	Vertical	£10
WCS11a	1d	**Ultramarine**	Horizontal	£10
WCS12	1½d	**Green**	Vertical	£10
WCS13	2d	**Red brown**	Vertical	8.75
WCS13a	2d	**Light Red brown**	Vertical	
WCS14	2½d	**Carmine-red** Type II	Vertical	7.50
WCS15	3d	**Deep violet**	Vertical	
WCS16	4d	**Deep Ultramarine**	Vertical	
WCS16a	4d	**Deep Ultramarine**	Horizontal	£14
WCS17	6d	**Red purple**	Vertical	
WCS17a	6d	**Deep Claret**	Vertical	

Watermark St. Edwards Crown Sideways

No.				U/M
WCS18	1½d	**Green**	Sideways	30
WCS19	2d	**Red brown**	Sideways	35
WCS19a	2d	**Light red-brown**	Sideways	15.50
WCS20	2½d	**Carmine-red** Type I	Sideways	2.40
WCS21	3d	**Deep violet**	Sideways	£32

Watermark St. Edwards Crown Graphite Lined Issue

No.				U/M
WCS22	½d	**Orange red**	Vertical	1.50
WCS23	1d	**Ultramarine**	Vertical	2.70
WCS24	1½d	**Green**	Horizontal	5.00
WCS25	2d	**Light Red brown**	Vertical	£16
WCS25a	2d	**Light Red brown**	Horizontal	22.50
WCS26	2½d	**Carmine-red**	Horizontal	32.50
WCS27	3d	**Deep violet**	Horizontal	6.00

Multiple Crowns Watermark Upright Cream Paper

No.				U/M
WCS28	½d	**Orange red**	Vertical	1.50
WCS28a	½d	**Orange red**	Horizontal	1.25
WCS29	1d	**Ultramarine**	Vertical	4.00
WCS29a	1d	**Ultramarine**	Horizontal	4.50
WCS30	1½d	**Green**	Vertical	6.00
WCS31	2d	**Light Red brown**	Vertical	7.50
WCS32	2½d	**Carmine-red** Type I	Sideways	
WCS33	3d	**Deep violet**	Vertical	£10
WCS34	4d	**Deep Ultramarine**	Vertical	
WCS34a	4d	**Deep Ultramarine**	Horizontal	£15
WCS35	6d	**Red purple**	Vertical	£14

Multiple Crowns Watermark Sideways Left Cream Paper

No.	Value	Description	Orientation	U/M
WCS36	2d	**Light Red brown**	Sideways	3.00
WCS37	2½d	**Carmine-red** Type I	Sideways	2.50
WCS38	3d	**Ultramarine**	Sideways	6.00

Multiple Crowns Watermark Upright Whiter Paper

No.	Value	Description	Orientation	U/M
WCS39	½d	**Orange red**	Vertical	1.25
WCS40	1d	**Ultramarine**	Vertical	1.25
WCS41	1d	**Ultramarine**	Horizontal	1.80
WCS42	1½d	**Green**	Horizontal	4.00
WCS43	2d	**Light Red brown**	Vertical	9.00
WCS44	2½d	**Carmine-red** Type I	Vertical	50
WCS45	3d	**Deep violet**	Vertical	2.00
WCS46	4d	**Deep Ultramarine**	Vertical	2.50
WCS47	6d	**Deep claret**	Vertical	8.75

Multiple Crowns Watermark Sideways Left Whiter Paper

No.	Value	Description	Orientation	U/M
WCS48	2d	**Light Red brown**	Sideways	40
WCS49	2½d	**Carmine-red** Type I	Sideways	50
WCS49a	2½d	**Carmine-red** Type II	Sideways	£10
WCS50	3d	**Deep violet**	Sideways	1.25
WCS51	4d	**Deep ultramarine**	Sideways	3.00

Multiple Crowns Watermark Graphite Lined

Displaced graphite lines as viewed from the back of the stamps.

No.	Value	Description	Orientation	U/M
WCS52	½d	**Orange red**	Vertical	32.50
WCS53	1d	**Ultramarine**	Vertical	3.25
WCS53a	1d	**Ultramarine** - 2 lines at left	Vertical	3.00
WCS53b	1d	**Ultramarine** - 2 lines at right	Vertical	3.00
WCS53c	1d	**Ultramarine** - 1 line at left	Vertical	
WCS53d	1d	**Ultramarine** - 3 lines	Vertical	
WCS54	2d	**Light Red brown**	Vertical	
WCS55	3d	**Deep violet**	Vertical	37.50

Multiple Crowns Watermark Green Phosphor

No.	Value	Description	Orientation	U/M
WCS56	½d	**Orange red**	Vertical	£12
WCS57	1d	**Ultramarine**	Vertical	£12
WCS58	2d	**LB Light Red brown**	Vertical	£80

Multiple Crowns Watermark Blue Phosphor - Cream Paper

No.	Value	Description	Orientation	U/M
WCS59	½d	**Orange red**	Vertical	6.00
WCS60	1d	**Ultramarine**	Vertical	7.50
WCS61	2d	**LB Light Red brown**	Vertical	£100
WCS62	3d	**Deep violet**	Vertical	12.50

Multiple Crowns Watermark Blue Phosphor - Whiter Paper

No.	Value	Description	Orientation	U/M
WCS63	½d	**Orange red**	Vertical	3.00
WCS64	1d	**Ultramarine**	Vertical	5.40
WCS65	2d	**2B Light Red brown**	Vertical	£40
WCS66	3d	**2B Deep violet**	Vertical	£14
WCS66a	3d	**LB Deep violet**	Vertical	22.50
WCS66b	3d	**RB Deep violet**	Vertical	18.00

Multiple Crowns Watermark Violet Phosphor - 8mm Bands

No.	Value	Description	Orientation	U/M
WCS67	½d	**Orange red** (photo)	Vertical	1.50
WCS68	1d	**Ultramarine** (photo)	Vertical	£10
WCS69	2d	**2B Light Red brown**	Vertical	
WCS70	3d	**LB Deep violet**	Vertical	£10
WCS70a	3d	**RB Deep violet**	Vertical	8.00

Multiple Crowns Watermark Violet Phosphor - 9.5mm Bands

No.	Value	Description	Orientation	U/M
WCS71	1d	**Ultramarine**	Vertical	1.60
WCS72	2d	**Light Red brown**	Vertical	3.75
WCS73	3d	**CB Deep violet**	Vertical	
WCS74	6d	**Claret**	Vertical	£15
WCS74a	6d	**Claret, cream paper**	Vertical	12.50

Multiple Crowns Watermark Sideways Left Violet Phosphor - 9.5mm Bands

No.	Value	Description	Orientation	U/M
WCS75	2d	**Light Red brown**	Sideways	40
WCS76	3d	**CB Deep violet**	Sideways	2.00
WCS77	4d	**Ultramarine**	Sideways	1.50

The Castle High Values

To make the distinctions between the three printers as clear as possible we include this chart and comparison guide, which will enable collectors to detect the difference between the printers more easily. Where shades are mentioned we have endeavoured to describe the shades clearly according to the catalogue list. However, where there is a small but distinct difference this has been noted on the chart as a further aid in distinguishing the printers. The basic steps are as follows:

1. Sort by watermark. All those with St. Edward's Crown (1st) are either Waterlow or De La Rue, and those with Multiple Crown Watermarks (2nd) are either the second De La Rue or Bradbury Wilkinson. Those without watermark are Bradbury.
2. Check the Waterlow and De La Rue first watermark against the list below.
3. It is relatively easy to sort the De La Rue from the Bradbury in the Multiple Crown watermark series by the way the paper curls when the face is breathed upon. This is due to the method of printing on the paper web. On De La Rue printings the paper curls vertically, that is top and bottom pull together, whereas on the Bradbury it will curl horizontally, e.g. left and right sides pull together.
4. If used, examples with dated postmarks can be a great help.If difficulties are still experienced the list below should readily solve them. For an inexpensive exercise to help gain experience it is suggested a quantity of good used 2/6d values are obtained for study.

	Wmks.	Waterlow	De La Rue	Bradbury Wilkinson
Paper Type		Cream/lightish cream	Light cream/white	White/chalky
Paper Characteristics		Curls vertically	Curls vertically	Curls horizontally
Watermarks	1st	St. Edwards Crown	St. Edwards Crown	
	2nd		Multiple Crown	Multiple Crown
	Without			None
Perforations	1st	Thick tooth top right	Thin tooth top right	
	2nd		Vert. perf 11.8	Vert. perf 11.9 to 12
Shades				
2s 6d value	1st	Blackish brown	Blackish brown (less blackish tinge)	
	2nd		Blackish brown	Deep black brown
	Without			Deep black brown
5s value	1st	Rose carmine	Rose carmine (noticeably less carmine)	
	2nd		Red	Brownish red
	Without			Brownish red
10s value	1st	Ultramarine	Dull blue	
	2nd		Dull blue	Bright ultramarine
	Without			Bright ultramarine
£1 value	1st	Black	Deep greyish black	
	2nd		Greyish black	Intense black
	Without			Intense black
Print Impression		Very deep, slightly blurred	Soft and sharp	Deep with more detail in diadem

Notes

Some plates of the De La Rue 2nd Watermark had either 1 or 2 coloured plate dots in the bottom margin, row 10, stamp No.1. These marginal pieces are worth 150% premium.

Waterlow and **De La Rue** both used guide marks.

Waterlow - small guide lines 2-3mm at top and bottom, centre and centre left and right of each sheet.

De La Rue - only on the side margins between rows 5 and 6, usually as a 'T' or a cross, which marked a guide 'pinhole'.

Bradbury Wilkinson also used guide holes, row 6, left and right.

Castle High Values

1955 (1 Sept.) Wmk. St. Edward's Crown. Perf. 11 x 12
Printer: Waterlow & Sons in Recess

No.			U/M	M/M	F/U
H1	**2s6d**	**Blackish brown** (23.9.55)	8.50	2.40	70
H2	**5s**	**Rose carmine** (23.9.55)	£21	5.95	1.50
H3	**10s**	**Ultramarine**	£48	£16	6.00
H4	**£1**	**Black**	£68	£28	17.50
		Set of 4	£140	£47	£25

1957 (17 July) - 58 Wmk. St. Edward's Crown. Perf. 11 x 12
Printer: De La Rue (1st) in Recess

No.			U/M	M/M	F/U
H5	**2s6d**	**Blackish brown**	17.95	8.50	1.50
H6	**5s**	**Rose carmine** (30.4.58)	£30	£16	3.20
H7	**10s**	**Dull blue** (25.4.58)	£110	£62	9.50
H8	**£1**	**Black** (28.4.58)	£170	£98	£34
		Set of 4	£299	£180	£48

1959 (15 June) Wmk. Multiple Crowns. Perf. 11 x 12
Printer: De L Rue (2nd) in Recess

No.			U/M	M/M	F/U
H9	**2s6d**	**Blackish brown** (22.7.59)	5.50	2.40	24
H10	**5s**	**Red**	17.50	6.00	45
H11	**10s**	**Blue** (21.7.59)	£22	9.90	1.20
H12	**£1**	**Black** (23.6.59)5	£52	£24	4.60
		Set of 4	£89	£38	5.95
		Presentation Pack	£350		
		Presentation Pack '£1.18s'	£350		
		Presentation Pack '$6.50'	£400		

1963 (1 July) Wmk. Multiple Crowns. Perf. 11 x 12
Printer: Bradbury Wilkinson & Co. in Recess

No.			U/M	M/M	F/U
H13	**2s6d**	**Blackish brown**	12	10	14
H13a		Wmk. inverted	£175	£85	£35
H13b		Chalky paper (30.5.68)	20	10	30
H14	**5s**	**Red** (3.9.63)	85	45	20
H14a		Light brownish red	1.00	60	50
H14b		Wmk. inverted	£125	£60	£30
H15	**10s**	**Ultramarine** (16.10.63)	1.90	1.50	1.25
H16	**£1**	**Black** (14.11.63)	7.00	3.80	3.25
		Set of 4	8.95	5.50	4.50

1967 (4 Dec.) - 68 No watermark. Perf. 11 x 12
Printer: Bradbury Wilkinson & Co. in Recess

No.			U/M	M/M	F/U
H17	**2s6d**	**Blackish brown** (1.7.68)	12	10	20
H18	**5s**	**Brownish red** (10.4.68)	50	30	35
H19	**10s**	**Ultramarine** (10.4.68)	3.70	2.20	1.95
H20	**£1**	**Black**	5.50	2.95	2.50
		Set of 4	6.95	5.50	4.20

Recess Printings

Original '£'

1969 (5 March) No watermark. Perf. 12
Printer: Bradbury Wilkinson & Co. in Recess
PVA Gum

No.			U/M	M/M	F/U
H21	**2s6d**	**Brown**	15	8	15
H22	**5s**	**Red**	75	40	30
H23	**10s**	**Blue**	2.20	1.75	2.40
H24	**£1**	**Black**	1.65	1.30	60
		Set of 4	3.95	3.30	3.20
		First Day Cover			6.50
		Presentation Pack 7	£12		
		German Presentation Pack	£28		

Redrawn '£'

1970 (17 June) - 74. No watermark. Perf. 12
Printer: Bradbury Wilkinson & Co. in Recess

No.			U/M	F/U
A. Post Office paper. PVA Gum				
H25	**10p**	**Cerise** ('all over' phosphor)	50	40
H26	**20p**	**Olive green**	40	10
H27	**50p**	**Blue**	1.00	20
H27a		Uncoated paper	£28	
H27b		Blue ('all over' phosphor) (1.2.73)	1.00	1.00
H28	**£1**	**Black** (6.12.72)	2.50	30
		Set of 4	3.75	90
		First Day Cover (10p-50p)		2.75
		Presentation Pack 18 (10p-50p)	5.00	
		First Day Cover (£1)		3.50
B. Bradbury paper. PVA Gum				
H29	**20p**	**Olive green** (30.11.73)	40	15
H30	**50p**	**Greyish blue** (20.2.74)	1.00	30
H31	**£1**	**Black** (27.9.73)	2.00	40
		Set of 3	3.25	75
		Presentation Pack 38 (20p - £1, any) (25.11.71)	6.00	

Post Office paper is thick and slightly creamy, whereas Bradbury paper is thinner and whiter.

Photogravure Printings

1977 (2 Feb.) - 87 Large format. No watermark. Perf. 14 x 15
Printer: Harrison & Sons in Photogravure
Fluorescent Coated Paper. PVA Dextrin Gum

No.			U/M	F/U
H32	**£1**	**Olive green & pale yellow**	1.50	10
H33	**£1.30**	**Blue green & pale drab** (3.8.83)	4.00	4.00
H34	**£1.33**	**Grey black & pale mauve** (28.8.84)	4.00	4.00
H35	**£1.41**	**Blue green & pale drab** (17.9.85)	4.50	3.00
H36	**£1.50**	**Grey black & pale mauve** (2.9.86)	3.50	1.50
H37	**£1.60**	**Blue green & pale drab** (15.9.87)	3.75	1.50
H38	**£2**	**Purple brown & pale green**	3.00	40
H39	**£5**	**Royal blue & pale pink**	7.50	1.50
		Set of 8	£28	£16
		Gutter pairs (£1, £2, £5)	£25	
		Gutter pair (1.30)	8.00	
		Gutter pair (£1.33)	£10	
		Gutter pair (£1.41)	9.00	
		Gutter pair (£1.50)	7.00	
		Gutter pair (£1.60)	7.50	
		Traffic Light Gutter pairs (£1, £2, £5)	£30	
		Traffic Light Gutter pair (£1.30)	£11	
		Traffic Light Gutter pair (£1.33)	£12	
		Traffic Light Gutter pair (£1.41)	£12	
		Traffic Light Gutter pair (£1.50)	8.50	
		Traffic Light Gutter pair (£1.60)	9.00	
		First Day Cover (1.60)		3.50
		First Day Cover (£1, £2, £5)		£10
		First Day Cover (£1.30)		6.00
		First Day Cover (£1.33)		5.00
		First Day Cover (£1.41)		4.50
		First Day Cover (£1.50)		4.00
		Presentation Pack 91 (£1, £2, £5)	£15	
		Presentation Pack 13 (£1, £2 & £5) (3.3.87)	£18	
		Presentation Pack 14 (£1.60)	4.75	

Castles Series

1988 (18 Oct.) Historic Castles. No watermark. Perf. 15 x 14
Printer: Harrison & Sons in Recess
Fluorescent Coated Paper. PVA Dextrin Gum

No.			U/M	F/U
H40	**£1**	**Green**	2.00	25
H41	**£1.50**	**Burgundy**	2.50	50
H42	**£2**	**Blue**	3.00	75
H43	**£5**	**Brown**	7.50	2.50
		Set of 4	£14	2.50
		Gutter pairs (horizontal)	£35	
		Gutter pairs (vertical)	£35	
		Gutter blocks of four	£75	
		First Day Cover		£25
		Presentation Pack 18	£16	

1992 (24 March)–97. Castles series. Perf 15 x 14 (elliptical). Printed by engraving and recess-printing, with Queen's head in optically variable ink. The four Castles high-value stamps, which all have the silhouetted Queen's head printed in optically variable ink in the top right corner, were first issued, printed by Harrisons (now De La Rue), on 24 March 1992. Re-etched versions of the four, also by Harrisons, appeared at various times during 1994. Examined side by side with the originals, the re-etched Castles give the impression of denser, sharper, more solid images.

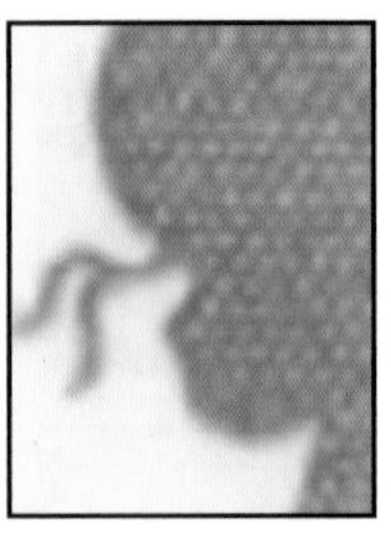
Original

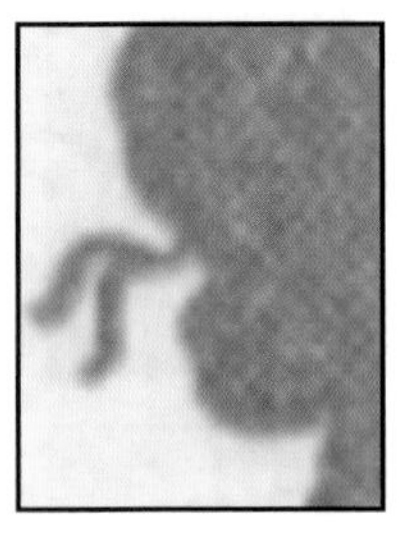
Re-engraved

To identify a single stamp as original or re-engraved when there is nothing to compare it with, study the Queen's head under about 10x magnification. You will find that it is made up of a dense array of fine, crosshatched lines: if the crosshatching forms a mass of diamond patterns, it is the original design; if the patterns are square, it is re-etched. There is also much more detail visible especially around the windows and all the re-engraved issues are slightly deeper in colour as shown below.

Original

Re-engraved

The Carrickfergus Castle design was used for the £1 until 22 August 1995, when it was transferred to the new £3; on the same date a £1 Machin definitive, printed by Enschedé, was issued.

The four designs were engraved afresh in 1997 by Enschedé, whose printings superseded those of Harrisons on 29 July of that year. Comparison of the two printers' work shows the Enschedé versions to be more delicate, refined and finely detailed. Single stamps may be distinguished as Harrison or Enschedé products by close scrutiny of the capital "C" wherever it occurs: the Harrison "C" a upper serif only, the Enschedé "C" has an upper and a lower serif.

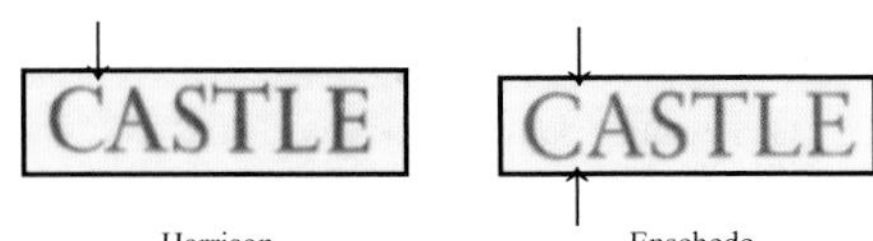

Harrison Enschede

1992 (24 March) Historic Castles.
Printer: Harrison & Sons in Recess
*OBA Free Non Phosphor paper. PVA Dextrin Gum or * PVA Layflat Gum*

No.			U/M	F/U
H44	**£1**	**Green and gold**	2.00	25
H44a	**£1**	Green and gold (re-etched, 2 Dec 94)	4.50	25
H45	**£1.50**	**Burgundy and gold**	.50	50
H45a		Bright magenta and gold (colour error)	£20	
H45b	**£1.50**	Burgundy and gold (re-etched, 26 Oct 94)	2.50	50
H45c	**£1.50**	Burgundy and gold (re-etched, 5 Mar 96) *	3.00	50
H45ca		Creamy opaque paper and brown PVA gum	£18	
H46	**£2**	**Blue and gold**	3.25	75
H46a		Complete offset of blue on gummed side	£45	
H46b		Bright blue and gold (colour error)	£35	
H46c	**£2**	Blue and gold (re-etched, 5 Nov 94)	4.25	75
H46ca		Bright blue and gold (colour error)	£45	
H46d	**£2**	Blue and gold (re-etched, 2 May 96) *	3.50	75
H46da		Ultra-translucent white paper	£10	
H47	**£5**	**Brown and gold**	7.50	2.25
H47a	**£5**	Brown and gold (re-etched, Aug 94)	9.25	2.25
H47aa		Missing Gold (Queen's head)	£275	
H47b	**£5**	Brown and gold (re-etched, 17 Sep 96) *	8.50	2.25
		Set of 4	£22	3.70
		Gutter pairs (horizontal)	£30	
		Gutter pairs (vertical)	£30	
		Gutter blocks of four	£60	
		First Day Cover		£20
		Presentation Pack 25	£15	

1995 (22 August) Historic Castles.
Printer: Harrison & Sons in Recess
OBA Free Non Phosphor paper. PVA Dextrin Gum

No.			U/M	F/U
H48	**£3**	**Violet**	4.50	75
H48a		Complete offset of violet on the gummed side	£25	

1997 (29 July) Historic Castles. No watermark.
Printer: Enschedé in Recess
Optical Free Non Phosphor paper. PVA Dextrin Gum

No.			U/M	F/U
H49	**£1.50**	Burgundy and gold	2.25	25
H50	**£2**	Blue and gold	3.00	50
H51	**£3**	Violet and gold	4.00	75
H51a		Missing Gold (Queen's head)	£650	
H52	**£5**	Brown and gold	7.00	2.25
H52a		Missing Gold (Queen's head)	£3,500	
		Set of 4	£23	5.50
		Gutter pairs (horizontal)	£30	
		Gutter pairs (vertical)	£30	
		Gutter blocks of four	£60	

Britannia Issue

Britannia series. Perf 15 x 14 (two elliptical holes on each horizontal edge). Embossed with braille characters. The £10 stamp has paper with fluorescent coloured fibres and fluorescent ink, which both react under ultra-violet light. On all stamps the fluorescent ink can be seen on the shield, where it appears bright yellow-green. On stamps from part of the printing the wording "TEN POUNDS", which is printed in green ink underneath the value in figures in the lower right corner, has also been printed in fluorescent ink.

1993 (2 March) 'Britannia'. No watermark.
Printer: House of Questa in Litho
OBA-free non-phosphor paper with fluorescent fibres. PVA gum

No.			U/M	F/U
H53	**£10**	**Multicoloured**	£15	7.00
H53a		'TEN POUNDS' in fluorescent ink	£25	
H53aa	**£10**	Missing Silver (Queen's head)	£2500	
		First Day Cover		£18
		Presentation Pack 28	£16	
		PHQ Card	30	£20

Small Format Machin Head

There are many differences between the Enschedé and De La Rue printings. The image is much coarser on De La Rue and the paper is also whiter. Furthermore the gum on the De La Rue printing is whiter, whereas on the Enschedé version the gum has a matt appearance.

Enschedé

De La Rue

1999 (9 Mar.) Small Format Machin Head
Printer: Enschedé in Intaglio
OBA-free non-phosphor paper. PVA gum

No.			U/M	F/U
H54	**£1.50**	**Rust-red**	3.00	1.00
H55	**£2**	**Indigo**	6.50	3.00
H56	**£3**	**Purple**	8.00	4.00
H57	**£5**	**Sepia**	£10	2.50

2000 (11 Apr.) Small Format Machin Head
Printer: De La Rue in Intaglio
OBA-free non-phosphor paper. PVA gum

No.			U/M	F/U
H58	**£1.50**	**Rust-red**	2.80	1.00
H59	**£2**	**Indigo**	4.50	1.50
H60	**£3**	**Purple**	6.50	2.00
H61	**£5**	**Sepia**	9.00	1.50

Introductory Notes

These notes are taken from the Machin Collectors Club Specialised Machin catalogue. They have been abbreviated to cover the listings here and give an excellent introduction to readers who may be interested in taking their interest in Machins further.

The design

The Machin definitives depict a plaster bas-relief of H.M the Queen, sculpted by Arnold Machin, OBE, RA, which was based on photographs taken by Lord Snowdon, supplemented with a number of sittings. This was photographed to produce master negatives used in the production of printing cylinders and plates.

The printers

Between 1967 and December 1979 all the small format Machin definitives were printed in photogravure by Harrison & Sons Ltd. On 12th December 1979 8p stamps printed in photogravure by Joh Enschedé en Zonen of Holland were released and during 1980 stamps printed in offset-lithography by the House of Questa & John Waddington Ltd. appeared. From 1989 onwards offset-lithographed stamps by Walsall Security Printers Ltd. were issued. In 1991 with the 18p value and then between 1993 and 1996 for the 'make-up' values, Joh. Enschedé was the first printer to use computer engraved gravure (its worth noting, however, that these printings did not use the digitally re-mastered head).

A major change occurred during 1997 when a digitally re-mastered head was introduced. In conjunction to this, Royal Mail required all printers to adopt gravure for printing low value definitives. Furthermore, the most famous of the printers of British stamps, since before the first world war, Harrison & Sons Ltd. of High Wycombe, was absorbed into the De La Rue organisation.

In 2003 Questa was absorbed with the De La Rue organisation. The plant at High Wycombe was closed down and the complete operation, including paper stock, presses etc. was transferred to the Questa plant at Byfleet in Surrey. De La Rue have now moved their operation to Dunstable in Bedfordshire.

A further change took place with the demise of the large format high value stamps. At the start of the Machin series the high value series were recess-printed by Bradbury, Wilkinson & Co. Ltd. These were followed by the photogravure Machin head series by Harrison & Sons Ltd. between 1977 and 1988, and then by the Castles first and second issues from Harrison & Sons Ltd which were Recess printed. The re-engraved stamps from Enschedé followed in 1994. In 1999 the Castle high values were then replaced by the normal sized 'Machins' printed by Recess.

All these changes are reflected in the various sections of this catalogue with useful tips on aids to identification.

For clarity the printers are referred to as De La Rue, Harrison, Enschedé, Questa, Waddington and Walsall throughout this catalogue.

Photogravure

This was the main process used for printing Machin definitives until the introduction of computer engraved cylinders (see below) in 1997. Photogravure is an intaglio process, which means the stamp image is etched below the surface of the copper-printing cylinder. The printing area on the copper cylinder consists of minute cells of uniformed size and shape. These cells are all etched to different depths but the background area surrounding the cells is level. On the printing press the surface of the cylinder passes through a duct of liquid ink which fills the cells and also covers the non-printing areas.

As the curved surface of the cylinder emerges from the duct the background is cleaned by a steel (doctor) blade, which scrapes the surplus ink from the surface and allows it to fall back into the ink duct. The surface of the cylinder is then brought into contact with the paper. Although not visible to the naked eye the photogravure-printed stamps have a distinctive screen pattern. When viewed under a magnifying glass, they will reveal line as well as tone made up of minute dots of uniformed size and shape, as a result of the cells depositing a quantity of ink on the paper. Gradations of tone are obtained by etching the cells to different depths, so that more or less ink is carried by the cells and transferred to the paper according to their depth.

So, in photogravure, the screen dots are the same size but the volume of ink deposited on the paper by each cell varies in thickness. In the highlights and middle tones, the thinner films of ink allow more of the white paper to show through. Therefore it appears lighter than the darker areas, which are more deeply etched and deposit a thicker film of ink on the paper. Although photogravure cylinders have a very long life span a back-up cylinder will be made and in some cases such as first and second class issues, several backup cylinders will be produced. Photogravure cylinders are very expensive to produce and to prolong their life even further are often chromium plated. The backup cylinder will come in to use if the original cylinder has to be taken off for repair or to be re-chromed. When repaired the original cylinder will usually go back in to use.

Gravure

In this process the image is directly engraved onto the cylinder by a diamond stylus or laser instead of using a photographic plus acid etching method. The printing process itself is as described above but the resultant image is easily recognised as can be seen from the scans on Page G - 4. Various names have been given to this new system. 'New image' by the Post Office, 'gravure', 'electro mechanical engraving' and 'computer engraved'. As the main difference is in the actual engraving of the cylinder we refer to it as 'gravure'. The term photogravure is no longer used since the 'photo' part is no longer appropriate.

Offset Lithography

This process of printing was, until the introduction of computer engraved cylinders, used by Walsall Security Printers and The House of Questa for the printing of book panes, although Harrison & Sons do use the lithographic process for the printing of their book covers.

Lithography is a planographic printing process where the printing image and the non-printing background are in the same plane, and not raised in relief as in the case of letterpress printing (sometimes referred to as typographic), nor etched into the surface as in photogravure. It can also be referred to as a chemical printing process because it uses the natural repulsion of oil or grease by water as a means of determining which parts of a printing surface shall be inked and which parts remain uninked.

Lithographic plates used for stamp printing are made of a metal, this being either zinc or aluminium. These metal plates are reasonably cheap to produce. Since their life span is fairly short compared to photogravure cylinders, they are easily replaced. This is the main reason why there are so many plate combinations on lithography printed stamps.

The stamp image is put on to the plate photographically, and is done by photographing the original artwork for the stamp. This is then made up into the pane size of either four or ten stamps. The negative is next printed on to the metal plate, which has a thin film of light-sensitive coating on its surface. When exposed to light the coating hardens and on development in water the areas unaffected by light are washed away, leaving the water-insoluble coating as the image printing areas. The negative is correctly positioned and exposed on to the metal plate the required number of times by a 'step and repeat' camera.

The term 'offset lithography' literally means that the image on the plate, (when on the press and inked up), is transferred or offset on to a rubber blanket and then from this blanket the image is transferred to the paper. This is done to give some flexibility between the plate and the paper.

Stamps printed by lithography when only printed in one colour, as with some Regional issues, are very flat with little tonal range, when compared to their photogravure counterparts. For this reason more than one plate is normally used and can be up to four plates, although Walsall used three plates for their first class stamps and Questa used two. Both of these printers used two plates for their second class stamps. Each plate prints a slightly different shade of the colour required and also prints a different part of the stamp. The background is on one plate, the head on a second plate and the background and head combined on a third plate. This third combined plate prints different parts of the head to the second plate.

The blue of the second class stamps only requires two plates to produce the same stamp as that printed by photogravure, these being one plate for the background and the other plate for the head. The direction of printing on lithographic stamps cannot be identified but it would normally be upright or inverted.

Stamps printed by photogravure are very easy to distinguish from the lithographic printed stamps. The simplest way to determine them is under magnification using a x10 glass. The edge of the stamp frame on a photogravure printing has spikes pointing in the direction which it was printed. This will only appear on one edge and will also help to distinguish the direction of print which can be either left, right, upright or inverted. Stamps printed by offset lithography normally have a straight clean edge on all four sides.

The information produced here on the printing of Machin definitives is only very brief but we hope will give an insight into the printing of our stamps and will also help to identify stamps printed by either photogravure or lithography.

It was always intended that Machin's sculpted bust should be reproduced only in photogravure, and many people feel that no completely satisfactory lithographic reproduction has yet been achieved. Offset-lithography is however a much cheaper process, but is also a less secure process i.e. can be forged more easily then gravure.

It is important to remember that for the first twelve years of the design's life, and whilst collectors were developing most of the terminology in use today, Harrisons printed all the small format stamps. When discussing technical aspects of stamp production comparisons are all too often made with the Harrison standard. Lithography is a completely different process and such comparisons are not always valid. In the notes following it may be assumed that references to offset lithography are common to Questa, Waddington & Walsall, those to photogravure are to both Harrisons & Enschedé. Many descriptions are common to both processes but comparisons between actual stamps should be drawn with care. (The computer engraved gravure process is common to all printers).

Recess

This printing process is also referred to as either Intaglio or line engraved. Recess printing falls into the same group of printing methods as gravure in that the design will be cut/etched into the printing plate/cylinder. This is achieved by :-

Recess - engraved lines and dots   Gravure - screened image etching / engraving

Initially, the design will be engraved onto a master die in soft steel. Depending on the complexity of the design this can take many weeks and requires a highly skilled craftsman. This is why the method is generally associated with 'High' values. Once engraved the master die will be hardened. Various methods of taking the master die to the printing plate have been employed for the Machin recess printed stamps :-

£.s.d

From the master die a transfer roller was made and this was used to 'roll' out multiple images onto the printing plate. This consisted of 160 stamp images, arranged into four panes of 40 (5 x 8).

Decimal 'High' values 1970-1977

Again, the master die was used to create a transfer roller which was used to 'roll' out multiple images onto a 'Master' printing plate. This consisted of 100 stamp images, arranged in one pane of 10 x 10. The 'Master' plate is then used to create the working / printing plates. Many printing plates can be created from the 'Master'. This procedure was later revised to produce double pane printing plates.

Decimal small format 'High' values 1999-2003

The small format 'High' values introduced in 1999 used the world renowned master engraver Czeslaw Slania to create the die master for these issues. The value tablet position on the die master was not engraved which enabled the same head to be used for each of the four values - separate engravings were made for each of the value tablets. The same Slania die master was used by both Enschedé and De La Rue. Different techniques were used to manufacture the 'Master' and working plates - a detail account used by De La Rue can be found in the British Philatelic Bulletin June 2001 (Vol 38 No.10). The printing plates were in the main double pane consisting of 100 (10 x 10) in each pane. The Giori press used four of these plates concurrently during printing.

Letterpress

This printing process is also referred to as typography, surface printed or relief printed. The process is effectively the opposite of Recess in that the design is raised above the surface of the printing plate. This method can be described in terms of woodblock printing whereby the parts of the design not to be printed is cut away. This leaves the parts to be printed as raised surfaces which take the ink (the design is in reverse), the woodblock is then pressed against the paper.

It has only been used once to produce the Machin definitive in a booklet pane from the 'Profile on Print' prestige book issued in 1999 (the pane containing 4 x 1st Black NVI and printed by Harrison - the phosphor bands were printed in Litho).

Embossing

The process creates a raised profile of the design in relief by making an impression in the paper, a corollary is the head on a coin or medal. It is not necessary for a coloured ink to be used with this method although one often is.

This process has only been used to produce the Machin definitive in a booklet pane from the 'Profile on Print' prestige book issued in 1999 (the self adhesive pane containing 4 x 1st NVI and printed by Walsall - the value tablet in grey and the phosphor was printed in Litho).

Head Types

Photogravure and Gravure

Four distinct types and several sub-types of varying importance exist. For the stamps with solid backgrounds types A & B have been adopted. Head A shows a flat base to the portrait, head B shows it curved. There are also numerous minor variations between the two types.

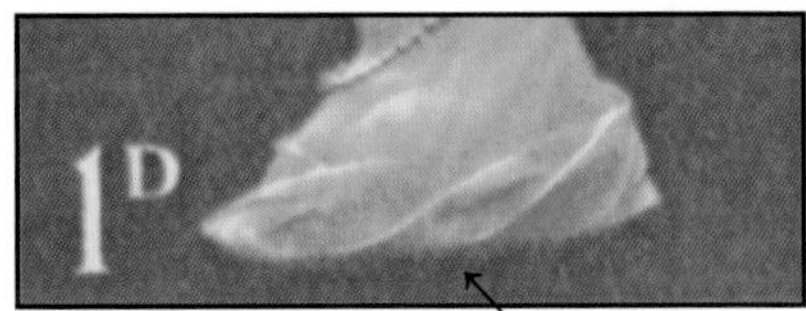

Head A with 'Flat' base

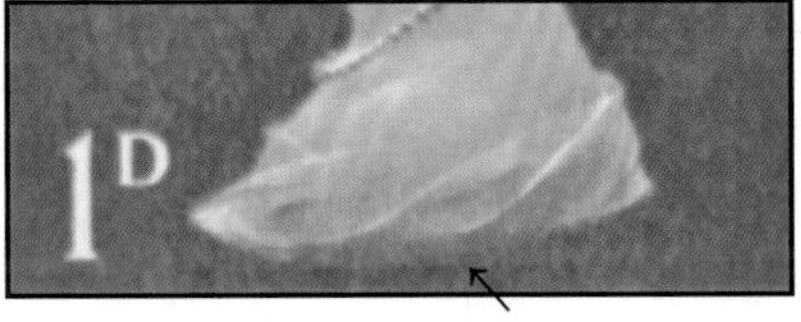

Head B with 'Curved' base

For stamps with a light coloured background which varies in density across the width of the stamp (e.g. the 6p value), head type C is used. For stamps which show evenly toned, light coloured, backgrounds (e.g. the 13p value) head D is used. Head B exists in two major types:- 'B1', the so-called 'small head' used for both the pre-decimal and the decimal issues and 'B2', 'large head'. This was first seen in 1976 and which is very similar except that the portrait is set lower, so that the tip of the bust is much nearer the lower frame line.

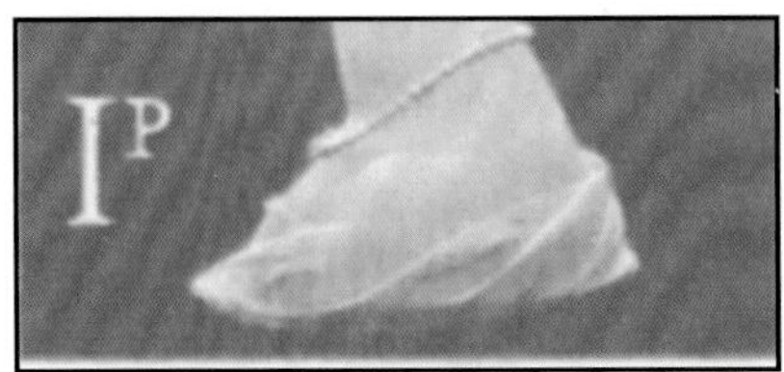

Head B2 with portrait set lower

There is also a missing photogravure-screening dot on the lower frame line near the left corner, common to all 'head B1' printings, which has been 'repaired'. Head C exists in two types - the standard 'head C' was used throughout except for two printings showing the portrait set lower, but as good a variety as 'head B2' above. Head D is consistent throughout except that some show a screen dot missing on the lower frame line, approx. 6.5mm from the left corner. Reduced size versions of all of the above were used for Regional issues, together with a variation of head D which shows a shaded space in the top of the central cross.

The gravure printed normal stamps are the B2 Head but are computer engraved.

Head C with graduated background

Head D with solid line at base

The Millennium head stamps were introduced in the year 2000. Printed by De La Rue, Questa and Walsall, each printer's stamps can be identified without any philatelic aid. Walsall printings show three clear jewels at back of the crown, whilst Questa printings show the top of the crown cut off. Many other differences exist.

De La Rue

Questa

Walsall

Lithography

The situation here is much more confused. The way in which the plastic plates are made has permitted a lot of minor variations and versions of head types A, B, C, D, both full size and reduced for Regional issues. In no case so far, however, has more than one obvious variation been used on any particular value and we list only the basic types, which should be recognisable from the Photogravure illustrations above.

Screened values

A number of printings show 'screened values', the result of the (unintentional) presence of photogravure screening dots in the white value area, or, occasionally, 'screened borders' where the inter-stamp gutters were inadequately masked out during production of the cylinder. Occasionally the whole of a printing is affected. A magnifying glass (x10) is required to detect these popular variations.

Phosphors

Many of the Machin issues have phosphor bands; either one or two set vertically at the centre or side(s) of the stamps. Bands are usually 4mm or from 9.5mm (across pair of stamps), but there have been exceptions, which are shown in the text. Harrison & Enschedé bands were applied by screened photogravure cylinders; Waddington's bands by unscreened typographic plates, and Questa's and Walsall's lithographic stamps by unscreened lithographic plates. All bands are now printed gravure and are unscreened.

From 1967 to 1993 all phosphor had Terephthalic acid as the activator. Harrisons call this Lettalite B3; philatelists generally refer to it as 'violet' or 'B3'. Under UV the phosphorescence is violet. Two errors occurred. A 2½p printing was made using green 'B1' phosphor in error, and the so-called 'jet' printings (see below) are a mixture of violet and green reacting inks, which glow a dirty yellow under the lamp.

From 1986 onwards Harrison's used a new phosphor, similar to 'B3' but using a different, almost transparent, solvent, which makes the bands much less obvious under natural light. This is described as 'A' Phosphor.

All phosphors show some fluorescence as well as phosphorescence. In 1991 a further new phosphor was introduced having strong yellow fluorescence and violet/blue phosphorescence. This is described as 'C'. The level of reaction of the yellow fluorescence varied from a very bright yellow to a pale greyish-yellow.

1995 saw a further change with the phosphor having blue fluorescence and blue/violet phosphorescence. This is described as 'D'. The changes to fluorescence, changes to adhesives from blue to white, and variations in the amount of optical brightening agent in the stamp paper means all collectors need to be vigilant at all times. Regular contact with your suppliers is essential if you wish to maintain the completeness of your collection.

All phosphors, excepting the 'blue' of the Wilding era and errors, have stronger phosphorescence at short wave than long wave. In 1994 a phosphor, which has stronger phosphorescence, such that it can easily be detected with long wave UV lamp was observed. Known, as 'Novaglo', the name of the company understood to manufacture the phosphor. Note that many other stamps show long wave phosphorescence, but are less bright.

For the identification of all different paper and phosphor types short wave and long wave ultraviolet lamps are essential. There are many models available, both battery operated and mains operated. Dual versions (interchangeable short & long wave tubes) are also available. Each lamp type has its own benefits and disadvantages.

Both the short wave and long wave versions are available with and without optical filters. In checking fluorescence of the B3 and 'A' phosphors a short wave with filter version is needed. In checking fluorescence of later phosphors a long wave version (without filter) is preferable.

Phosphor Bands

Normal phosphor banded stamps can have either a single band placed at the centre, left or right or two bands placed at either side. However the width of these can vary depending on several factors. Centre bands can be either 4mm or 4.5mm in width. Two band stamps are usually derived from 9.5mm bands printed across the perforations. Therefore each band (in theory) should be 4.75mm in width. However, as the registraion is not always accurate, the space *between* each band should be measured. As the small format stamps are 21mm wide and, in this case, the bands are 9.5mm wide the resulting space between the bands is 11.5mm.

Phosphor screens

Phosphor screens of 150, 250 and for the 1991 Enschedé stamps only 300 dots per linear inch screens have been used. Both 150 and 250 screens were used for a number of printings and these may be readily identified, with practice, using a x10 or x15 magnifier in good light. The 250 screen is very fine, the 150 much coarser by comparison. In both cases one normally sees a grid (you are seeing the 'streets', not the 'houses'), and it is the density of the grid which is important. Occasionally 150 screens can be seen with the naked eye. Conversely the screen may be 'clogged' in printing. These can be very difficult to distinguish without some experience.

'JET' phosphors

Named after its discoverer, Mr. J.E. Thompson, this is the result of the contamination of violet phosphor with green phosphor ink not intended for stamps. It glows a dirty yellow colour under long wave UV, but is more easily identified by viewing the stamp through a thin film of plastic, such as the front of a Prinz or Hawid mount. This gives a good reaction to long wave UV which is not found on normal 'B3' stamps.

Phosphor under Ink

Much the simplest (and the only reliable non-chemical) method for the identification of these is to hold the stamp up to the light and to look from the gummed side. In the area covered by the phosphor band the stamp is actually lighter than in the non-phosphor area. This is caused by the fact that the first layer of ink (be it colour or phosphor) effectively seals the surface, so that subsequent layers do not soak in well and in consequence more of the ink evaporates off. This effect is best seen on the lighter stamps - 4½p, 6p etc., but is visible on other values.

Short band, Inset and Stepped Bands

Where phosphor bands are short, inset or stepped they are described as such in the text. Please note that all short and inset bands must be clear of the normal perforations (not necessarily the elliptical perforations) to qualify for inclusion in this catalogue.

Perforations

Various perforation gauges have been employed and the main ones are given below:

* Harrison, and De La Rue, stamps are perforated 14¾ x 14;
* The Questa, Walsall and Waddington litho issues were originally perf. 13½ x 14 but this was later changed to perf 14¾ x 14,
* A printing of the Walsall litho 1st class N.V.I. book is known perforated 12¾ x 13 in error,
* The Questa gravure issues are perf. 14 x 14,
* The Walsall gravure sheet printings are perf. 14¾ x 14, whilst the gravure Prestige books are perf. 14 x14, with the Label books being perf 14¾ x 14, but with smaller holes and ellipses,
* The Bradbury Wilkinson High Value issues are perforated 12 x 12,
* The Harrison 'Machin' photogravure high values are 14 x 15.
* The decimal 'Castles' are perforated 15 x 14, as is the £10 'Britannia'.

Unfortunately no two authorities on this subject ever quote quite the same set of figures for the above. We show those most commonly used by collectors.

Perforators

A number of different techniques exist for producing the actual perforation holes. These are broadly as follows:

The 'Comb' perforator

The original type of perforator is still in use after 140 years. These use precisely engineered male and female dies. Perforation is slow but the results are excellent, with perfectly formed 'flat' holes. Minor errors in spacing at the intersection of one strike with another are often noticed.

The 'Kampf' perforator

This perforated the stamps 'in the web' and comprised a precisely engineered 'male' drum, with rows of pins projecting outwards, whilst the female die was a similar drum, but without the pins and blanketed with a thick rubber sheet. The method may be quite crude but it is very effective. The holes, being punched through at speed, are not perfectly circular and the individual discs of paper are frequently not punched out completely and so cling to the edges of the holes.

The Swedish 'Lawnmower' and APS Perforators

These draw the paper over raised 'pimples' to produce the holes in relief and the tops of these are then shaved or ground off with abrasives, from the gummed side. The holes are perfectly circular but 'debris' of paper and gum normally surrounds all or part of the holes and occasionally they are not cut through completely, so that a thin film covers each. This type of perforator has been in use since the late 1960s and Harrison's Ab Produktion Svenska (APS) machine is the latest development.

Straight sided and elliptically perforated stamps

During 1987 the first issues appeared with officially sanctioned straight edges on one or more sides. Since 1993 stamps showing elliptical perforations, as an anti-forgery 'security' measure, have appeared and are now included on almost every issue.

Straight Edge stamps

The vast majority of Machin issues have perforations to which we are all accustomed. Straight edged stamps, which only had a short life span, can therefore be described as imperforate and this is the term that is used throughout this catalogue.

Direction of printing (DOP), Photogravure and Gravure issues only.

This is beyond the scope of this catalogue but can be found in the Machin Collectors Club Specialised catalogue..

Papers

Paper variations have occurred on both the pre-decimal and decimal issues. On the Decimal issue the first type used was OCP (Original Coated Paper), which is off-white to cream in appearance and dull under UV light. FCP (Fluorescent Coated Paper) was introduced during 1971 and is much whiter and more fluorescent under UV light.
Experiments incorporating the phosphor into the paper coating go back to 1968 but large-scale production did not begin until 1979. Five different types are recognised:

* PCP (Phosphor Coated Paper): A largely experimental stock with some minor variations in finish but broadly similar to PCP1 (below) except for the weaker afterglow.
* PCP1 (Phosphor Coated Paper 1): A semi-shiny surface with a strong afterglow.
* PCP2: A highly glossy surface generally producing richly coloured stamps.
* ACP (Advanced Coated Paper): A semi-shiny surface, similar to PCP1, but with a very strong afterglow and appearing bright under UV (as bright as FCP - by comparison PCP/PCP1/PCP2 are as dull as OCP).
* PPP (Phosphor Pre-printed Paper): FCP paper to which an overall phosphor coating (150 screen) was applied under the ink. The surface is very matt and the stamp printing often blotchy.

During 1993 the decision was taken to remove all Optical Brightening Agents from the papers (these are significant pollutants) and three new papers have appeared in consequence.

* OFNP/SA (OBA Free Non-phosphor Paper): This is a paper/gum term and is used in all self-adhesive issues. Reaction to long wave UV light similar to that of OFNP, although the paper texture appears smoother. Note that whilst this is described as coated paper, other papers are also coated.
* OFNP (OBA Free Non-phosphor Paper): Used in conjunction with phosphor bands this replaced FCP.
* OFPP (OBA Free Phosphorised Paper): Replaced PCP/ACP.

Paper varieties

Varnished paper

Varnish was applied to sub standard paper both under and over the phosphor ink (on the 9p violet FCP/PVAD stamp) and was also used on the ½p (Cylinder 8 FCP/PVAD) and the Scottish 12½ p (plate 7A 7B). These two varieties can be easily distinguished by holding the stamp at an angle to the light. Where the phosphor has been applied over the varnish, the bands are quite visible, but where applied under the varnish, they are barely visible.

Translucent paper

Some books have appeared on both 'normal' and translucent papers with some falling in between. To determine the degree of translucency, lay the stamp side face down on a dark surface. Under normal lighting conditions the image will appear clear, if the paper is of the translucent type. It is very difficult to describe in print more accurately than this - comparison is always far more conclusive.

Thin paper

As paper thickness can vary in a normal production run, only those with a marked difference from the normal are listed. As with translucent paper, comparison is recommended for positive identification.

Silicone Coated Paper

This was an experimental coating designed to prevent coil stamps in vending machines sticking together. They can be distinguished (by comparison to a normal stamp) by holding them at an angle to the light looking across the phosphor bands, where they (the phosphor bands) appear much less distinct.

Uncoated Paper

Normal paper has a chalk coating which enhances the printed image. Where this has been omitted the stamp has a flatter appearance, shows no UV reaction and does not respond to the 'silver' test.

Glazed Paper

These stamps show a marked shiny effect most noticeable between the phosphor bands, and are easily recognised when compared to the normal stamp.

Adhesives

The identification of the adhesives used for the Decimal series should prove no problem to you. They are best described as follows: -

GA - Gum Arabic

This is always shiny in appearance and can be verified by looking at the back of the stamp with a x10 glass. You will notice a 'crazy paving' appearance in the adhesive. Gum Arabic also has a tendency to curl very easily and can be confirmed by placing the stamp on your palm - The warmth and moisture from your hand will soon make it curl.

PVA - Polyvinyl Alcohol

PVA is normally matt in appearance although it can sometimes appear with sheen but it lacks the 'crazy paving' effect of Gum Arabic. It does not curl as readily as GA either. The colour of PVA ranges from near white to a light brown but with the differences mentioned above should be easily identified.

In 1994 Harrisons issued some sheets of the 19p on Cylinder 3 using a new formulation of PVA with no dextrin added giving a matt and creamy appearance. It was also noticed that a further printing from Cylinder 3, shortly afterwards, appeared translucent and more white. It was later established that the cause of this was in fact a change of paper thickness and NOT a change to the additive in the adhesive.

PVA (Lay flat) - Non Curl

Introduced gradually since 1996 this adhesive has the property of resisting curling in conditions of high humidity. It is generally very matt in appearance and slightly cream in colour, it is often referred to as 'lay flat'.

PVAD - Polyvinyl Alcohol with Dextrin added

PVAD with the very familiar bluish-green tint has been used in the vast majority of Machin issues; it frequently appears ribbed or mottled. Some printings by the House of Questa have been on paper supplied by Henry Leigh Slater, which has Dextrine adhesive, but with the greenish dye omitted. This reacts chemically as Dextrine (it still contains the starch) but looks very much like PVA. When checking adhesives it is preferable to do so in natural daylight (not direct sunlight), although the modern Halogen hobby lamps may be useful.

Forgeries

Between 1872 and 1993 it seems that no GB stamp was forged, at least not on a commercial basis, or perhaps the forgers were never detected. In the Summer of 1993, copies of the then recently issued 24p rust stamp, which was then the current first class rate, began to appear in the South East of England. The forgers, it seems, had taken advantage of Royal Mail's decision to sell stamps at a discount to retail outlets and gone into business themselves.

We understand that stamps were sold in sheets, or part sheets, and not books, at 20p per stamp. This discount was much greater than that offered by Royal Mail and was obviously attractive to retailers who were not too concerned about buying stamps in this way.

The forged stamps can be easily distinguished by the following characteristics:

* They are perforated gauge 11, instead of the normal 14 or 15,
* The perforated stamps show a peculiar arrangement of holes at the corners of the stamps
* The gum is very shiny,
* The paper quality is very poor,
* The stamps were non-phosphor, which caused letters to be rejected at sorting centres.

About one year later another forgery appeared which was markedly superior to the 24p. This was the so-called 'Questa' 2nd class NVI. This stamp, unlike its predecessor, appeared in books (the covers of which were also forged) and loose panes.

The book and stamps have variously been attributed as rejected Questa printings, or trials, or the result of some nefarious unauthorised activities by an employee or employees at Questa. The House of Questa had always vehemently denied this.

The stamps themselves were produced to a remarkably high standard. The perforations were of the correct gauge, although these extended much further into the wider margin than is usual on normal Questa books. The elliptical security perforations, which must have caused the forgers considerable difficulties, invariably slope to the right.

On some stamps within the pane they are placed slightly higher than on others. The stamps have a central phosphor band, but this produces no afterglow under UV light, although there is some yellow fluorescence under the lamp. On the examples seen, the stamps are a paler blue than the originals and have a blurred appearance. The forgers apparently did not attempt to produce the familiar Questa logo as no plate books have ever been found. The book covers are good enough to fool the general public (with no disrespect!) but again are easily distinguishable as fakes.

The cover is 50mm wide against the normal 48mm and on a thin card. The locking tab is the right shape and in the right place, but slightly larger. The colours used on the outside of the cover are close to the original, although there are minor differences. The facsimile stamp is much darker and again blurred in appearance. This is the most obvious visible sign. Inside, the cover is shiny instead of being matt and those troublesome glue spots, characteristic of all Questa books, are absent.

Although Royal Mail's enquiry's into these forgeries continued for a while, it now seems unlikely, given the time that has passed, that any prosecutions will be made, or indeed whether further information will be made available.

Source Identification

Source

There can be a considerable difference in the value of any single stamp through its source. This guide is NOT comprehensive, but using other attributes such as value, colour, paper/gum combination and phosphor bands, positive source identification should hold no difficulties. Identifying a stamps source is achieved by looking at the perforations on each edge which can be either torn or guillotined.

Guillotined perforations | **Torn perforations with fibrous ends**

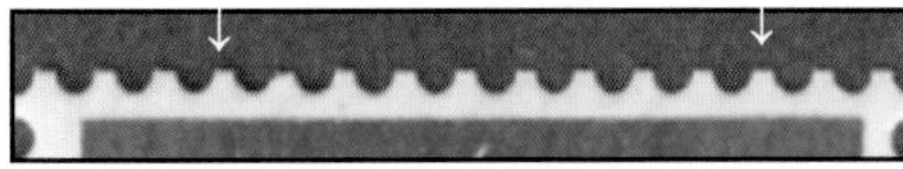

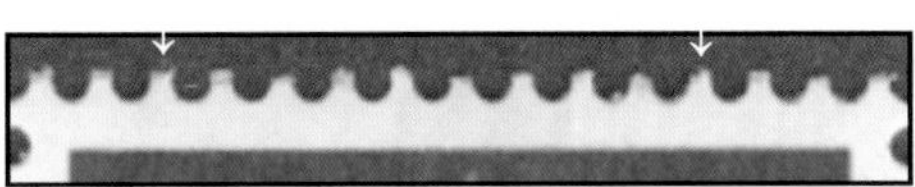

Follow these guidelines and the task is normally straighforward - The arrows on the following illustrations indicate ***guillotined*** edges.

1. On Sheet stamps all four sides are always torn.
3. On Horizontal coils stamps both the top and bottom sides are guillotined.
2. On Vertical coil stamps both the left and right sides are guillotined.

Horizontal coil

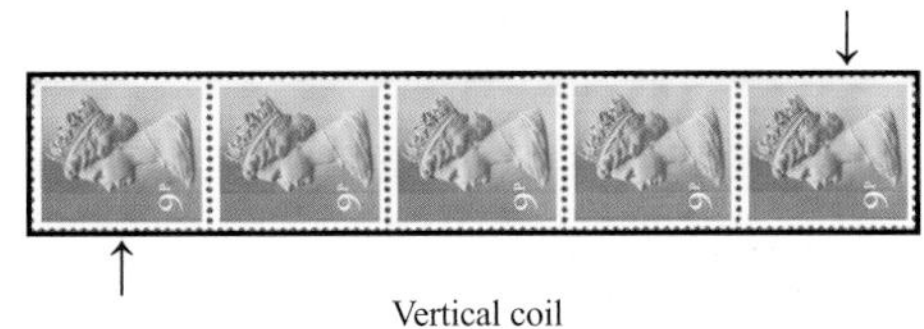

Vertical coil

4. On Machine (Vending) books the left and right sides of the *pane* are guillotined i.e. on any individual stamp either the left or right side is guillotined. The bottom stamps can be either torn or guillotined
5. On Counter books the top, bottom and right edges of the *pane* are guillotined i.e. on any single stamp *either* the top or bottom is guillotined and other sides are torn or, if they are from the end of the pane opposite the selvedge then two adjacent sides are guillotined.

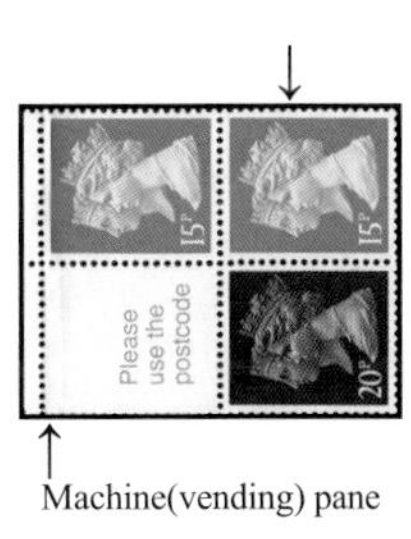

Machine(vending) pane

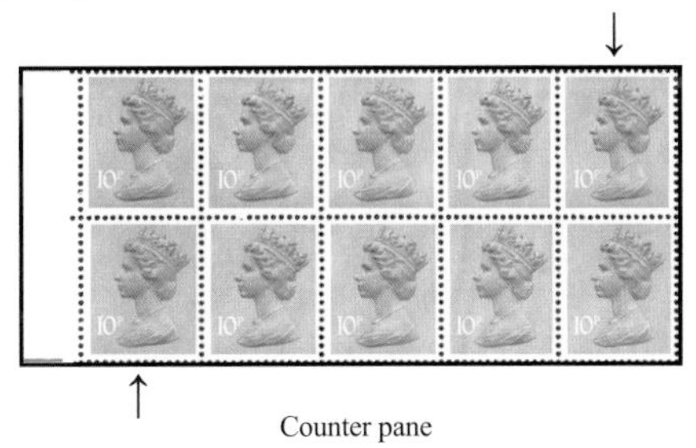

Counter pane

6. On Prestige panes (below right) if the stamps are totally separated from the original pane then all four sides would be torn and this could cause difficulty if there are no other attributes to consider. It is recommended therefore that, whenever possible, stamps from Prestige books be collected with the adjacent selvedge to prove its source.

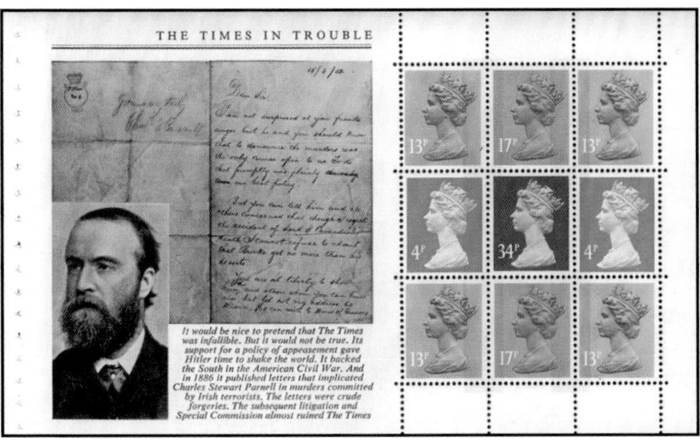

Pre Decimal Machins

2d Type I
Value close to frame edge

2d Type II
Value wide of frame edge

1967 (5 June) - 71. Machin series. No wmk. Perf. 15 x 14. Head types are only shown where relevant. Screen values are not included in these lists, but are to be found in the MCC Specialised catalogue.
Printer: Harrison & Sons in photogravure

Gum Arabic

No.			U/M	F/U
M1	1d	**CB Yellow-olive** - Coil (27.8.69)	40	
M2	2d	**CB Lake brown**, Type II - Sheets (27.8.69)	30	
M3	3d	**CB Deep Violet**, Head A - Sheets (8.8.67)	30	
M3a		Missing phosphor - Sheets	1.25	
M3b		Horizontal coil (2.10.67)	1.50	
M3c		Violet - Sheets	30	
M4	3d	**CB Reddish violet**, Head B - MV coil (27.8.69)	40	
M5	4d	**2B Sepia**, Head A - Sheets (5.6.67)	30	
M5a		Missing phosphor - Sheets, BP175c	4.50	
M5b		Left band omitted - Sheets	£90	
M5c		Right band omitted - Sheets	£80	
M5d		Pane BP175 (21.9.67)	75	
M5e		Vertical coil (15.5.68)		
M5f		Horizontal coil	1.00	
M5g		Broad band left - Horizontal coil	£50	
M5h		Broad band right - Horizontal coil	£35	
M6	4d	**2B Sepia**, Head B1 - Sheets (.8.68)	£1500	
M7	4d	**CB Vermilion**, Head A Pane BP176 (20.2.69)	£20	
M7a		Missing phosphor	£1000	
M8	4d	**CB Vermilion,** Head B - M/V coil	35	
M9	9d	**2B Deep green - Sheets** (8.8.67)	35	
M9a		Missing phosphor	£30	
M10	1s	**2B Pale violet** - Sheets (5.6.67)	40	
M10a		Missing phosphor	£80	
M10b		Left band omitted	£130	
M10c		Right band omitted	£130	
M10d		Bright violet - Sheets (6.68)	1.25	
M11	1s6d	**2B Blue-green & Dark blue** - Sheets (8.8.67)	60	
M11a		Missing phosphor	£15	
M11b		Blue-green omitted	£130	
M11c		Pale & Dark blue - Sheets (12.67)	75	
M11d		Pale & Dark blue, missing phosphor - Sheets (12.67)	£15	
M12	1s9d	**2B Dull orange & Black** - Sheets (5.6.67)	85	
M12a		Missing phosphor	£60	
M12b		Bright orange & black - Sheets (5.6.67)	1.50	
		First Day Cover 4d, 1s, 1s9d (5.6.67)	1.00	
		First Day Cover 3d, 9d, 1s6d (8.8.67)	1.00	

PVA Gum

No.			U/M	F/U
M13	½d	**2B Orange-brown** - Sheets (5.2.68)	15	10
M13a		Missing phosphor	£45	
M14	1d	**2B Olive**, Head A - Sheets (5.2.68)	15	10
M14a		Missing phosphor	£10	
M15	1d	**2B Dull olive**, Head B1 - Sheets (.10.68)	25	
M15a		Left band omitted - Sheets	£80	
M15b		Vertical coil	25	
M15c		Olive - Pane BP177 (25.3.68)	35	
M15d		Missing phosphor - Sheets, coil & pane	2.00	
M16	1d	**2B Yellow-olive** - Panes BP179, BP180 & BP181	35	
M16a		Missing phosphor - Panes BP180b, BP181b	6.00	
M16b		Uncoated paper - Pane SP1b (£1 Cook book)	£90	
M17	1d	**CB Yellow-olive**, Head B2 - Pane BP178 (16.9.68)	40	25
M17a		Missing phosphor	5.00	
M18	2d	**2B Lake brown**, Type I. Head A - Sheets (5.2.68)	25	10
M18a		Missing phosphor	£30	
M19	2d	**2B Lake brown**, Type II. Head B1 - Sheets (2.69)	25	10
M19a		Vertical coil	£10	
M19b		Broad band right - Vertical coil		
M19c		Missing phosphor - Sheets	1.00	
M19d		Horizontal coil	4.00	
M20	3d	**CB Violet**, Head A - Sheets (12.3.68)	20	10
M20a		Missing phosphor - Sheets	3.50	
M20b		Horizontal coil	£25	
M21	3d	**CB Violet,** Head B1 - Pane BP182 (25.3.68)	5.00	
M21a		Missing phosphor - Pane BP182a	£300	
M22	3d	**2B Violet**, Head A - Sheets (20.8.69)	30	20
M22a		Vertical coil	1.50	
M22b		Uncoated paper - Sheets		
M22c		Missing phosphor - Vertical coil	£35	
M23	3d	**2B Violet**, Head B1 - Vertical coil (.3.69)	3.00	
M23a		Missing phosphor - Vertical coil	£275	
M23b		Panes BP180, BP181	50	
M23c		Broad band centre - Panes BP180a, BP181a	4.00	
M23d		Missing phosphor - Panes BP180b, BP181b	£275	
M24	4d	**2B Deep olive-brown**, Head A - Sheets (22.1.68)	25	5
M24a		Missing phosphor - Sheets	£15	
M24b		Pane BP183	30	
M24c		Missing phosphor - Pane BP183b	£15	

No.			U/M	F/U
M25	4d	**2B Deep olive-sepia**, Head B2 - Sheets (.4.68)	25	5
M25a		Missing phosphor - Sheets	2.50	
M25b		Pane BP185	35	
M25c		Broad band left - Pane BP185a	4.50	
M25d		Broad band right - Pane BP185a	4.50	
M25e		Broad band centre - Pane BP185a	4.50	
M25f		Missing phosphor - Pane BP185b	7.00	
M26	4d	**CB Deep olive-brown**, Head A - Sheets (16.9.68)	15	5
M26a		Vertical coil		
M26b		Pane BP184 (16.9.68)	35	
M26c		Missing phosphor - BP184		
M26d		Horizontal coil	2.50	
M27	4d	**CB Deep olive-brown**, Head B1 - Sheets (16.9.68)	15	15
M27a		Missing phosphor - Sheets	£15	
M27b		Panes BP186, BP187		
M27c		Missing phosphor - Pane BP187a		
M28	4d	**CB Vermilion**, Head A - Pane BP188 (6.1.69)	50	10
M28a		Missing phosphor - Pane BP158a	5.00	
M28b		Sheets (.5.69)	20	
M28c		Missing phosphor	1.00	
M28d		Vertical coil	7.50	
M28e		Horizontal coil	17.50	
M29	4d	**CB Vermilion**, Head B2 - Sheets (6.1.69)	15	
M29a		Missing phosphor - Sheets		
M29b		Pane BP189, BP190 (6.1.69)	35	10
M29c		Missing phosphor - Pane BP189a, BP190a		
M29d		Horizontal coil		
M29e		£1 Cook book - Pane SP2/3 (£1 Cook book) (1.12.69)	25	
M29f		Missing phosphor	£10	
M29g		Uncoated paper	12.50	
M30	4d	**LB Vermilion,** Head B2 - Pane BP179 (6.1.69)	75	1.25
M31	4d	**LB Vermillion**, Head B2 - Pane SP1 (£1 Cook book) (1.12.69)	1.00	
M31a		Uncoated paper	£150	
M32	4d	**RB Vermillion**, Head B2 - Pane SP1 (£1 Cook book) (1.12.69)	1.00	
M32a		Uncoated paper	£150	

No.			U/M	F/U
M33	5d	**2B Dark blue** Head A - Sheets (1.7.68)	40	
M33a		Missing phosphor	3.00	
M34	5d	**2B Deep blue**, Head B1 - Sheets (.3.69)	20	
M34a		Missing phosphor - Sheets	3.50	
M34b		Pane BP191 (.3.69)	30	
M34c		Missing phosphor - Pane BP191a	£10	
M34d		Vertical coil	5.00	
M34e		Horizontal coil	3.50	
M34f		£1 Cook book - Panes SP1/4 (1.12.69)	15	
M34g		Uncoated paper - Panes SP1/4 (1.12.69)	£15	
M34h		Missing phosphor - Panes SP1/4 (1.12.69)	£50	
M35	6d	**2B Reddish purple**, Head A - Sheets (5.2.68)	20	15
M35a		Missing phosphor	£15	
M35b		Bright magenta - Sheets	2.00	1.00
M35c		Claret - Sheets (.4.69)	75	20
M35d		Claret, Missing phosphor	£25	
M35e		Magenta, Head B - Vertical coil	£10	4.00
M35f		Claret, Head B - Vertical coil (9.70)	£85	£15
M36	7d	**2B Bright emerald** - Sheets (1.7.68)	30	15
M36a		Missing phosphor	£85	

No.			U/M	F/U
M37	8d	**2B Vermilion**, Head A - Sheets (1.7.68)	20	20
M37a		Missing phosphor	£325	
M38	8d	**2B Light blue**, Head B - Sheets (6.1.69)	50	30
M38a		Missing phosphor	£60	
M39	9d	**2B Deep green** - Sheets (29.11.68)	45	12
M39a		Missing phosphor	£55	
M40	10d	**2B Drab** - Sheets (1.7.68)	40	35
M40a		Missing phosphor	£50	
M40b		Uncoated paper	£20	
M41	1s	**2B Pale violet** - Sheets (26.4.68)	30	10
M41a		Missing phosphor	3.75	
M42	1s6d	**2B Pale blue & Deep blue** - Sheets (29.8.68)	50	10
M42a		Missing phosphor	£12	
M42b		Missing Pale blue	£110	
M42c		Broad band centre	£85	
M42d		Broad band left	£14	
M42e		Broad band right	£14	
M43	1s6d	**Prussian blue & indigo** - Sheets (.5.70)	1.75	15
M43a		Missing phosphor	£25	
M44	1s9d	**2B Bright orange & black - Sheets** (16.11.70)	1.00	20
		Phosphor wash	£75	
		First Day Cover (½d, 1d, 2d, 6d) (5.2.68)		50
		First Day Cover (5d, 7d, 8d, 10d) (1.7.68)		75
		Presentation Pack (No.8) (5.3.69). *Contents:* ½d, 1d, 2d, 3d, 4d red, 5d, 6d, 7d, 8d blue, 9d, 10d, 1s, 1s6d, 1s9d (14v)	6.00	
		German Presentation Pack	£30	

All Over Phosphor (PCP) PVA Gum

No.			U/M	F/U
M45	5d	**Deep Blue** (2B), Head B (1970)	£275	
M46	1s6d	**Prussian blue & indigo** (10.12.69)	45	45

Coil Strip

1969 (27 Aug.) No watermark. Perf. 15 x 14. One phosphor CB.
Gum Arabic

No.			U/M	F/U
MV1	1s	**Coil strip** *Contents:* 2 x 2d, 3d, 1d and 4d vermilion se-tenant.	75	1.00

Decimal Machins

1971 (15 Feb.) - 91. Decimal Machin series.
All are perf. 15 x 14

Printers: Harrison & Sons in Photogravure, except the 8p and 18p both printed by Enschedé in Photogravure

Original Coated Paper - Gum Arabic (OCP/GA)

No.			U/M	F/U
M47	½p	**2B Turquoise**), Head C, MV coil (15.2.71)	30	
M47a		Wide band left	6.00	
M47b		Wide band right	£30	
M47c		Missing phosphor	£65	
M47d		Missing phosphor (screened)	12.50	
M47e		Silicone coated	£40	
M48	1p	**2B Crimson**, Head B1, MV coil (15.2.71)	25	
M48a		Wide band left	6.00	
M48a		Wide band right	£35	
M48b		Missing phosphor	£65	
M48c		Missing phosphor (screened)	12.50	
M48d		Silicone coated	£40	
M49	2p	**2B Dark green**, Head B1, MV coil (15.2.71)	1.00	
M49a		Wide band left	22.50	
M49b		Wide band right	£125	
M49c		Missing phosphor	£175	
M49d		Missing phosphor (screened)	£30	
M49e		Silicone coated	£150	
M50	3p	**2B Ultramarine**, Head B1. Type II Horizontal coil (2.73)	£45	

Original Coated Paper - PVA Gum (OCP/PVA)

No.			U/M	F/U
M51	½p	**2B Turquoise**, Head C - Sheets (15.2.71)	15	10
M51a		Missing phosphor - Sheets	35	
M51b		Pane MP4	1.75	
M51c		Broad band left - Pane MP4a	£40	
M51d		Broad band right - Pane MP4a	£45	
M51e		Broad band centre - Pane MP4a	£80	
M51f		Missing phosphor -Panes MP4a, MP1, MP3a	£35	
M51g		LB omitted - Pane MP3	£50	
M51h		RB omitted - Pane MP3	£50	
M52	½p	**2B Deep Turquoise,** Thick value Pane MP5 (14.4.71)	6.00	1.00
M52a		Broad band left - Pane MP5a	£300	
M52b		Broad band right - Pane MP5a	£375	
M52c		Broad band centre - Pane MP5a	£325	
M52d		Missing phosphor - Pane MP5b	£250	
M53	1p	**2B Dull crimson**, Head B1 - Panes MP6, MP7 (15.2.71)	90	10
M53a		Broad band right - Panes MP6a, MP7a	£45	
M53b		Broad band left - Panes MP6a, MP7a	£55	
M53c		Vertical coil	60	
M53d		Missing phosphor - Vertical coil	£350	
M53e		Thin paper - Vertical coil	£20	
M53f		Very thin value - S/T coil	1.50	
M54	1p	**2B Crimson** - Sheets	15	
M54a		Missing phosphor - Sheets	6.00	
M54b		Left band omitted	£400	
M54c		Right band omitted	£125	
M55	1½p	**2B Black**, Head B1 - Sheets (15.2.71)	20	10
M55a		Missing phosphor - Sheets	£20	
M55b		Uncoated paper - Sheets	£100	
M55c		Panes MP6, MP7	70	
M55d		Broad band left - Panes MP6a, MP7a	£110	
M55e		Broad band right - Panes MP6a, MP7a	£100	
M56	2p	**2B Dark green** - Sheets (15.2.71)	15	15
M56a		Missing phosphor - Sheets	£40	
M56b		Panes MP4, MP5	1.00	
M56c		Broad band left - Panes MP4a, MP5a	£40	
M56d		Broad band right - Panes MP4a, MP5a	£40	
M56e		Broad band centre - Panes MP4a, MP5a	£55	
M56f		Missing phosphor - Panes MP4b, MP5b	£70	
M56g		MV coil	1.00	
M57	2½p	**CB Magenta**, Head C - Sheets (15.2.71)	15	10
M57a		Missing phosphor	£10	
M57b		Thin higher set value - Sheets (Cyl 8)	1.25	
M57c		Missing phosphor - Sheets (Cyl 8)	£70	
M57d		Vertical coil	5.00	
M57e		Horizontal coil	3.50	
M57f		Panes MP8 to MP12	75	
M57g		Missing phosphor - Panes MP8a, MP9a, MP12a	£85	
M58	2½p	**LB Magenta**, Pane MP13	5.25	
M58a		Missing phosphor - Pane MP13a	£80	
M59	3p	**2B Ultramarine**, Head B1, Thin value Sheets (15.2.71)	30	10
M59a		Missing phosphor - Sheets	2.50	
M59b		Panes MP13, MP14, MP16	40	
M59c		Broad band left - Panes MP14, MP16	£200	
M59d		Broad band right - Panes MP14a, MP16a	£200	
M59e		Broad band centre - Panes MP14a, MP16a	£225	
M59f		Left band omitted - Pane MP14	£150	
M59g		Missing phosphor - Pane MP13a, MP16b	£85	
M60	3p	**2B Ultramarine**, Head B1, Thick value Horizontal coil	11.00	
M60a		Vertical coil	4.50	
M61	3½p	**2B Pale olive-grey**, Head C - Sheets	25	30
M61a		Missing phosphor	5.50	
M62	4p	**Ochre-brown** (2B), Head B1 - Sheets (15.2.71)	25	15
M62a		Missing phosphor	£35	
M62b		Missing phosphor (screened)	£10	
M62c		LB omitted	£75	
M62d		RB omitted	£55	

No.			U/M	F/U
M63	5p	**2B Pale violet**, Head C - Sheets (15.2.71)	25	15
M63a		Missing phosphor	£225	
M64	6p	**2B Light green**, Head C - Sheets (15.2.71)	20	15
M64a		Missing phosphor	£50	
M64b		Uncoated paper	£15	
M64c		Very thin value, S/T coil (3.77)	1.50	1.00
M65	7½p	**2B Pale chestnut**, Head C - Sheets (15.2.71)	25	40
M65a		Missing phosphor	£15	
M66	9p	**2B Orange and black**, Head B1 - Sheets (15.2.71)	1.00	45
M66a		Missing phosphor	£80	
M66b		Screened value	1.50	
M66c		Missing phosphor - Screened value	£110	

Original Coated Paper - PVA Dextrin gum. (OCP/PVAD)

No.			U/M	F/U
M67	3½p	**2B Deep olive-green**, Head C. Glazed paper. Paper error. (7.1.74)	£175	£50

Fluorescent Coated Paper - Gum Arabic (FCP/GA)

No.			U/M	F/U
M68	½p	**2B Turquoise**, Head C - Sheets(22.9.72)	15	30
M68a		MV Coil	20	
M68b		Silicone coated - MV coil (22.9.72)	40	
M69	1p	**2B Bright crimson**, Head B1 - MV coil Silicone coated (22.9.72)	30	30
M69a		Silicone omitted	£15	
M69b		Vertical coil	60	
M70	2p	**2B Green**, Head B1 - MV coil Silicone coated (22.9.72)	2.00	75
M70a		Silicone omitted	£40	
M71	2½p	**CB Magenta**, Head C - Sheets, Comb perf (13.9.72)	20	10
M71a		Deep magenta. APS perf.	35	
M71b		Horizontal coil	£22	
M72	3p	**2B Ultramarine**, Head B1 - Sheets (23.8.72)	2.50	85
M72a		Missing phosphor	£20	
M72b		Horizontal coil	£22	
M73	3p	**CB Ultramarine** - Sheets (10.9.73)	1.00	10
M73a		Missing phosphor	£250	
M74	3p	**CB Deep Ultramarine**, Wider set value - Sheets (Cyls 24,31)	25	10

No.			U/M	F/U
M75	4p	**2B Ochre-brown**, Head B1 - Sheets (1.11.72)	30	35
M75a		JET phosphor	£20	
M76	6p	**2B Pale green**, Head C, JET phosphor - Sheets (6.6.73)	1.50	40

Fluorescent Coated Paper - PVA Gum. (FCP/PVA)

No.			U/M	F/U
M77	½p	**2B Bright turquoise**, Head C - Sheets (17.9.71)	30	30
M77a		Missing phosphor - Sheets	£125	
M77b		Pane MP17, MP18	45	
M77c		RB Omitted - Pane MP18	£1000	
M77d		2B + AOP - Pane MP18	£150	
M77e		JET Phosphor - Pane MP18c	£10	
M78	½p	**2B Bright turquoise**, Thick value - Pane MP19	75	45
M78a		Broad band centre - Pane MP19a	£40	
M78b		Missing phosphor - Pane MP19b	£180	
M78c		JET Phosphor - Pane MP19c	5.00	
M79	½p	**2B Pale turquoise**, Thin value - Panes SP7, SP8 (£1 Wedgwood)	65	60
M79a		Broad band left, Panes SP7, SP8	£300	
M79b		Broad band right, Panes SP7, SP8	£300	
M79c		Broad band centre, Panes SP7, SP8	£300	
M79d		Bands front and back, Pane SP8	£200	
M79e		Missing phosphor, Panes SP7, SP8	£325	
M80	½p	**LB Turquoise** Pane SP8 (24.5.72)	£39	£20
M81	1p	**2B Deep crimson**, Head B1 - Sheets (6.10.71)	90	30
M81a		Missing phosphor - Sheets	£65	
M81b		Pane MP20	1.00	
M81c		Missing phosphor - Pane MP20b	£30	
M81d		Broad band left - Pane MP20a	£200	
M81e		Broad band right - Pane MP20a	£200	
M81f		JET Phosphor - Pane MP20c	6.00	
M82	1p	**2B Bright Crimson** - Sheets (Cyl. 1)	1.75	35
M82a		Missing phosphor - Sheets	£35	
M82b		Pane MP20	1.75	
M83	1½p	**2B Black**, Head B1 - Sheets (6.10.71)	75	35
M83a		Missing phosphor - Sheets	£75	
M83b		Pane MP20	1.00	
M83c		Broad band left - Pane MP20a	£195	
M83d		Broad band right - Pane MP20a	£200	
M83e		Missing phosphor - Pane MP20b	£30	
M83f		JET Phosphor - MP20c	6.00	
M84	2p	**2B Green**, Head B1 - Sheets (6.10.71)	1.75	30
M84a		Missing phosphor - Sheets	£300	
M84b		Pane MP19	75	
M84c		Broad band centre - Pane MP19a	£35	
M84d		JET Phosphor - Pane MP19c	6.00	

Thin value   Thick value   Very thin value

No.			U/M	F/U
M85	2½p	**CB Bright Magenta**, Head C, Thin value - Sheets(10.71)	1.50	30
M85a		Missing phosphor - Sheets	£20	
M85b		Pane MP25	2.50	
M85c		Pane SP6 (£1 Wedgwood)	2.50	
M85d		Missing phosphor - Pane SP6	£130	
M86	2½p	**CB Bright Magenta**, Thick value - Panes MP21, MP23, MP24	50	35
M86a		Missing phosphor - Panes MP21a, MP23a MP24a	9.00	
M86b		JET Phosphor - Pane MP23b	£10	
M87	2½p	**CB Pale Bright Magenta**, Thin value - Sheets	60	30
M87a		Missing phosphor - Sheets	£10	
M87b		JET Phosphor	£10	
M87c		Green phosphor - Sheets	5.00	
M88	2½p	**CB Pale Bright Magenta**, Very thin value - Pane SP7 (£1 Wedgwood)	2.50	1.00
M88a		Broad band left - Pane SP7c	£350	
M88b		Broad band right - Pane SP7c	£350	
M88c		Broad band centre - Pane SP7c	£300	
M88d		Missing phosphor - Pane SP7a	£200	
M89	2½p	**LB Magenta** - Thick value - Pane MP13 (24.5.72)	2.50	1.00
M89a		Missing phosphor - Pane MP13a	£35	
M89b		JET Phosphor - Pane MP13b	£45	
M89c		Very thin value - Panes SP7, SP8 (£1 Wedgwood)	2.00	2.00
M89d		Broad band left - Pane SP8a	£395	
M89e		Missing phosphor - Pane SP8b	£400	
M90	2½p	**RB Pale Magenta** - Thin value - Pane SP6 (24.5.72)	2.00	1.00
M90a		Missing phosphor - Pane SP6a	£85	
M90b		Broad band left - Pane SP6b	£350	
M90c		Broad band right - Pane SP6b	£350	
M90d		Broad band centre - Pane SP6b	£300	
M91	2½p	**RB Pale Magenta** - Very thin value - Pane SP7 (24.5.72)	3.50	1.00
M91a		Missing phosphor - Pane SP7a	£200	
M91b		Broad band left - Pane SP7b	£350	
M91c		Broad band right - Pane SP7b	£350	
M91d		Broad band centre - Pane SP7b	£275	
M92	3p	**2B Ultramarine**, Head B1 - Sheets (17.9.71)	60	15
M92a		Missing phosphor - Sheets	£10	
M92b		Panes MP13, MP14, MP16	60	
M92c		Broad band left - Pane MP14a	£150	
M92d		Broad band right - Pane MP14a	£150	
M92e		Missing phosphor - Panes MP13a, MP14b	£10	
M92f		Left band omitted - Pane MP13	£45	
M92g		Right band omitted - Pane MP13	£45	
M92h		JET Phosphor - Sheets	4.50	
M92i		JET Phosphor - Panes MP13b, MP16c	4.50	
M93	3p	**2B Ultramarine**, Thin paper - Sheets	5.00	3.50
M93a		Left band omitted - Sheets	£40	
M93b		Right band omitted - Sheets	£45	
M93c		Missing phosphor - Sheets	£25	
M93d		Pane MP27b	4.00	
M94	3p	**2B Dull Ultramarine** - Panes SP5, SP6 (£1 Wedgwood) (4.7.03)	75	50
M94a		Broad band left - Panes SP5, SP6	£25	
M94s		Broad band right - Panes SP5, SP6	£125	
M94d		Broad band centre - Panes SP5, SP6	£70	
M94d		Missing phosphor - Panes SP5, SP6	£45	
M94e		Wider bands (11mm) - Pane SP6	£10	
M94f		Broad band left - Pane SP6	£250	
M95	3p	**CB Bluish ultramarine** - Sheets (1.74)	60	30
M95a		Pane MP28 (14.11.73)	1.50	
M95b		Thin paper - Pane MP28	2.50	

No.			U/M	F/U
M96	3½p	**2B Bronze green**, Head C - Sheets (7.73)	1.75	
M96a		Pane MP30	1.00	
M96b		Missing phosphor - Pane MP30	£1500	
M97	4p	**2B Ochre-brown**, Head B1 - Sheets (18.7.73)	2.50	
M98	5p	**2B Pale violet** - Sheets 1971)	4.00	
M98a		Missing phosphor - Sheets	£450	
M98b		Right band omitted - Sheets	£1000	
M99	6p	**2B Light green**, Head C - Sheets (18.7.73)	£17	
M100	6½p	**CB Greenish blue**, Head B1 - Sheets (12.75)	£23	
M101	7½p	**2B Pale chestnut**, Head C - Sheets (1971)	2.75	
M101a		Missing phosphor - Sheets	£225	
M102	9p	**2B Orange and sepia**, Head B1 - Sheets (11.71)	2.50	
M102a		Broad band right	£30	
M102b		Missing phosphor	£70	
M103	10p	**2B Orange-brown and deep brown** - Sheets (11.8.71)	50	15
M103a		Missing orange-brown	£175	
M103b		Missing phosphor	£8	
M103b		Left band omitted	£175	
M104	10p	**2B Orange and Butter yellow** - Sheets (11.8.71)	£10	

FCP/PVAD

Several two banded stamps were derived from 8mm bands instead of the normal 9.5mm. To easily distinguish these measure the space *between* the bands as illustrated below.

All are B3 phosphor unless stated otherwise. Colours as before.

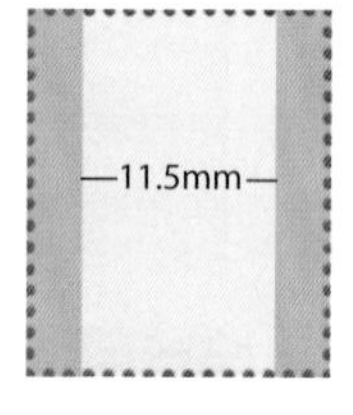

2B stamps from 9.5mm bands

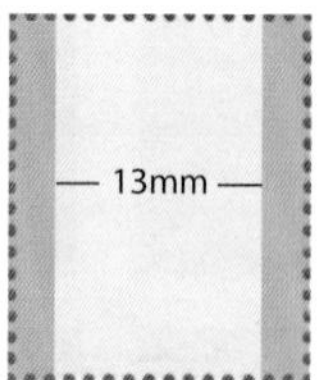

2B stamps from 8mm bands

Thin value

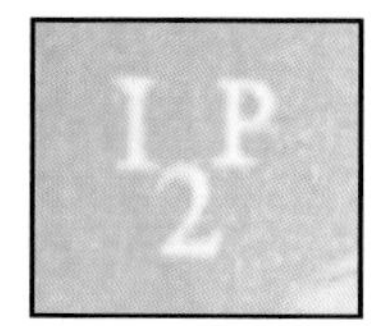

Thick value

No.			U/M	F/U
M105	½p	**2B Turquoise**, Thin value, Head C - Sheets (10.9.73)	10	10
M105a		Missing phosphor - Sheets	1.00	
M105b		Left band omitted - Sheets	£60	
M105c		Right band omitted - Sheets	£60	
M105d		MV Coil	15	
M105e		Broad band centre - MV Coil	75	
M105f		Pane MP31	25	
M105g		Broad band left MP31a	£10	
M105h		Broad band right MP31a	1.50	
M105i		Broad band centre MP31a	1.25	
M106	½p	**2B Bright turquoise** Thick value - Pane MP31 (4.74)	25	30
M106a		Broad band left MP31a	£10	
M106b		Broad band right MP31a	£10	
M106i		Broad band centre MP31a	£150	

No.			U/M	F/U
M107	½p	**2B Deep turquoise**Thin value - MV Coil	25	25
M107a		Broad band centre - MV Coil	£15	
M107b		Missing phosphor - MV Coil	1.50	
M107c		Varnished paper - Sheets	50	
M108	½p	**2B, 8mm Bright Turquoise** Thin value - Pane FP39, FP40	25	15
M108a		Ribbed - Panes FP39, FP40	3.00	
M109	½p	**2B, 8mm Turquoise** Thin value, Panes FP16, FP17	50	30
M109a		Missing phosphor - Pane FP16b, FP17b	5.00	
M110	½p	**2B, 8mm Pale turquoise** Thick value (1.2.82) Panes FP24. FP25	10	15
M111	½p	**CB Bright Turquoise** Thin value - MV Coil (14.12.77)	10	15
M111a		Thick paper - MV Coil		£12
M112	½p	**CB Bright Turquoise** Thick value - Pane FP15 (8.2.78)	10	15
M112a		Missing phosphor - Pane FP15	£10	

Original value

Redrawn value

No.			U/M	F/U
M113	1p	**2B Crimson**, Head B1 Narrow value - Sheets (10.9.73)	10	10
M113a		Glazed paper - Sheets	1.25	
M113b		Pane MP32	20	
M113c		Broad band left - Pane MP32a	£50	
M113d		Broad band right - Pane MP32a	£30	
M113e		Broad band centre - Pane MP32a	£10	
M113e		Missing phosphor - Pane MP32b		
M113g		Imperf. pair - Sheets	£800	
M113h		MV Coil	10	
M113i		Missing phosphor - MV Coil	5.00	
M114	1p	**2B Crimson**, Head B1 Very thin value - MV Coil (3.12.75)	10	10
M114a		Broad band left - MV Coil		
M114b		Broad band centre	1.00	
M115	1p	**2B Crimson**, Head B2 Very thin value - Pane FP13 (10.3.76)	30	10
M115a		Broad band left - Pane FP13	8.00	
M115b		Broad band right - Pane FP13	£10	
M116	1p	**2B, 8mm Crimson**, Head B2 Narrow value Panes FP16, FP17, FP39, FP40 (26.1.77)	60	35
M116a		Missing phosphor - Panes FP16b, FP17b	£7	
M117	1p	**CB Crimson**, Head B1. Very thin value - MV Coil (14.12.77)	10	10
M117a		Thick paper - MV Coil	£10	
M118	1p	**CB Crimson**, Head B1. Thick value - Pane FP1	50	40
M119	1p	**CB Crimson**, Head B2. Very thin value - Pane FP15	65	60
M119a		Missing phosphor - Pane FP15c	5.00	
M120	1p	**CB Crimson**, Head B2. Thick value - Pane FP26	65	60
M120a		Missing phosphor - Pane FP26a	£10	
M121	1p	**CB Crimson**, Head B2. Wide spaced value - Pane FP2	50	45
M122	1p	**RB Crimson A Phosphor** - Pane SP35 (P & O Prestige book)	2.50	1.90

Redrawn Numerals

No.			U/M	F/U
M123	1p	**CB 4mm Crimson** - Pane FP27	40	20
M123a		Missing phosphor - Pane FP27a	£35	
M123b		Imperf. left - Pane FP 19	1.00	
M123c		Imperf. left, Missing phosphor - Pane FP19a	£95	
M124	1p	**CB 4.5mm Crimson** - Panes FP18 FP27	1.75	75
M125	1p	**LB Crimson** - Pane FP3 (20.10.86)	40	20
M125a		Broad band left - Pane FP3	£180	
M125b		Missing phosphor - Pane FP3a	£18	
M126	1p	**RB Crimson - Error** - Pane FP3b	£30	
M127	1½p	**2B Black**, Head B1 - Sheets (12.11.73)	10	10
M127a		Glazed paper - Sheets	1.00	
M127b		Pane MP32	50	
M127c		Broad band left - Pane MP32a	£80	
M127d		Broad band right - Pane MP32a	£50	
M127e		Missing phosphor - Pane MP32b	£275	
M128	2p	**2B Green**, Head B1 - Sheets (10.9.73)	10	10
M128a		Missing phosphor - Sheets	£10	
M128b		Glazed paper - Sheets	1.50	
M128c		MV Coil	15	
M128d		Missing phosphor - MV Coil	£10	
M128e		Broad band left - MV Coil	£10	
M128f		Broad band right - MV Coil	£15	
M128g		Thin paper - MV Coil	£35	
M128h		Pane MP31 (12.11.73)	30	
M128i		Broad band left - MP31a	£10	
M128j		Broad band right - MP31a	£15	
M129	2p	**2B Myrtle green**, Head B2, Value set high - Panes SP11, SP12 (£3 Wedgwood) (16.4.80)	15	15
M129a		6mm Broad band left - Pane SP11a	£80	
M129b		6mm Broad band centre - Pane SP11a	£35	
M129c		9.5mm Broad band left - Pane SP11a	£55	
M129d		9.5mm Broad band centre - Pane SP11a	£35	
M129e		Bands front and back - Panes SP9c, SP12b	£110	
M129f		Missing phosphor - Panes SP11b, SP12a	£20	
M130	2p	**2B Myrtle green**, Head B2, Value set low - Pane SP15 (SG Prestige book) (28.8.79)	1.00	75
M130a		Broad band left - Pane SP15	£70	
M130b		Broad band right - Pane SP15	£75	
M130c		Broad band centre - Pane SP15	£70	
M130d		Bands front and back - Pane SP15	£300	
M130e		Missing phosphor - Pane SP15	£30	
M131	2p	**2B 8mm Myrtle green,** - Panes FP30, FP31 (29.8.79)	30	10
M131a		Short bands at top - Pane FP30	2.50	
M131b		Short band at bottom left - Pane FP30	2.50	
M131c		Short band at bottom right - Pane FP31	2.50	
M131d		Inset left band - Pane FP30	7.50	
M131e		Inset right band - Pane FP31	7.50	
M132	2p	**2B 8mm Myrtle green,** Value set high - Panes FP32, FP33 (4.2.80)	75	25
M132a		Short bands at top - Pane FP32	5.00	
M132b		Short band at bottom left - Pane FP32	5.00	
M132c		Short band at bottom right - Pane FP34	£15	
M132d		Inset left band - Pane FP32	7.50	
M132e		Inset right band - Pane FP34	7.50	
M132f		Broad band left - Pane FP34	£15	
M132g		Broad band right- Pane FP33	£15	
M132h		Missing phosphor - Pane FP33a	7.50	
M133	2½p	**CB Magenta**, Head C - Sheets (8.8.73)	10	10
M134	2½p	**2B Magenta,** Head C - Sheets (21.5.75)	20	30
M135	2½p	**2B 8mm Rose-red -** Panes FP36, FP36a (26.8.81)	25	30
M136	3p	**CB Ultramarine**, Head B1, Thin value - Sheets (10.9.73)	15	20
M136a		Missing phosphor - Sheets	£10	
M137	3p	**CB Ultramarine**, Head B1, Very thin value - Sheets (14.11.73) - Pane MP33	2.50	50

Non-elliptical Decimal - FCP/PVAD Machin Definitives

No.			U/M	F/U
M138	3p	**CB Ultramarine**, Head B1, Thick value - Horizontal coil (11.73)	7.00	1.50
M138a		Band at left (Displaced)	8.00	
M138b		Vertical coil (.4.74)	7.50	
M139	3p	**2B 8mm Bright magenta**, Head B1 - Pane FP24, FP25 (1.2.82)	25	20
M139a		Missing phosphor - Panes FP24a, FP25a	£500	
M139b		All over phosphor - Panes FP24, FP25	£85	
M140	3p	**2B Bright magenta**, Head B2 - Pane SP15 (SG Prestige book) (19.5.82)	1.00	50
M140a		Broad band left - Pane SP15a	£150	
M140b		Broad band right - Pane SP15a	£250	
M140c		Broad band centre - Pane SP15a	£225	
M140d		Missing phosphor - Pane SP15b	£120	
M140e		Bands front and back - Pane SP15c	£650	
M141	3½p	**2B Bronze green**, Head C - Sheets (22.8.73) 40	10	15
M141a		Missing phosphor - Sheets	7.50	
M141b		Right band omitted - Sheets	£130	
M141c		Pane MP34	75	
M141d		Missing phosphor - Pane MP34a	7.50	
M141e		Vertical coil	£11	
M141f		Horizontal coil (.2.74)	2.00	
M142	3½p	**2B Deep Olive-brown**, Head C - Error of colour - Sheets	£700	
M143	3½p	**CB Bronze green**, Head C - Sheets (24.6.74)	30	10
M143a		Side band left (Displaced) - Sheets	5.00	
M143b		Missing phosphor - Sheets	7.50	
M143c		Pane MP35 (23.10.74)	50	
M143d		Missing phosphor - Pane MP35b	£20	
M143e		Horizontal coil (.12.74)	1.00	

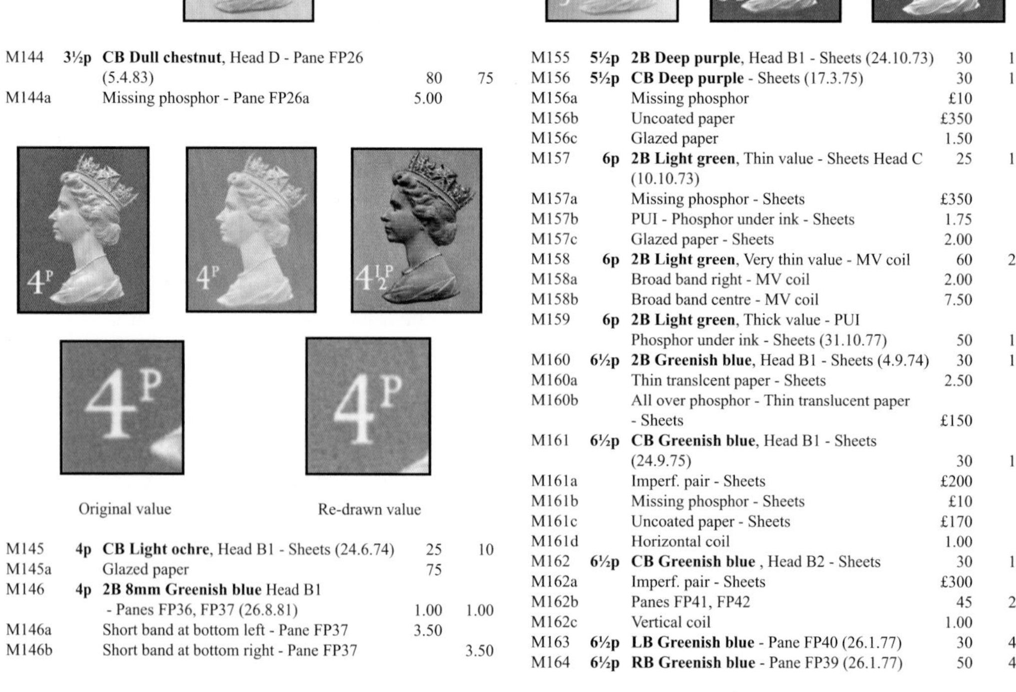

No.			U/M	F/U
M144	3½p	**CB Dull chestnut**, Head D - Pane FP26 (5.4.83)	80	75
M144a		Missing phosphor - Pane FP26a	5.00	

Original value Re-drawn value

No.			U/M	F/U
M145	4p	**CB Light ochre**, Head B1 - Sheets (24.6.74)	25	10
M145a		Glazed paper	75	
M146	4p	**2B 8mm Greenish blue** Head B1 - Panes FP36, FP37 (26.8.81)	1.00	1.00
M146a		Short band at bottom left - Pane FP37	3.50	
M146b		Short band at bottom right - Pane FP37		3.50

4p Re-drawn value

No.			U/M	F/U
M147	4p	**CB Pale greenish blue** - Pane FP27 (3.9.84)	75	75
M147a		Missing phosphor - Pane FP27a	£75	
M148	4p	**LB Greenish blue** - Pane SP27 (The Times Prestige book) (8.1.85)	1.00	75
M148a		Broad band at left - Pane SP25a	£450	
M148b		Missing phosphor - Pane SP25b	£500	
M148c		Bands front and back - Pane SP25c	£375	
M149	4p	**RB Greenish blue** - Pane SP25 (8.1.85)	1.00	1.10
M149a		Bands front and back - Pane SP25c	£375	
M150	4½p	**2B Light grey-blue**, Head D - Sheets (24.10.73)	7.00	15
M151	4½p	**2B Deep steel-blue**, Head D - Sheets (24.10.73)	50	30
M151a		Broad band right - Sheets	8.00	
M151b		Missing phosphor - Sheets	6.00	
M151c		Imperf. pair - Sheets	£300	
M151d		PUI - Phosphor under ink - Sheets	2.00	
M151e		Horizontal coil	75	
M151f		Pane MP36	1.00	
M151g		Missing phosphor - Pane MP36a	£250	
M151h		PUI - Phosphor under ink -Pane MP36b	£35	
M152	5p	**2B Pale violet**, Head C - Sheets (5.6.74)	20	10
M152a		All over phosphor - Sheets	£160	
M152b		Broad band left - Sheets	£10	
M153	5p	**2B Claret**, Head C - Pane FP18 (20.10.86)	1.00	35
M154	5p	**2B Claret**, Head C, 'A' phosphor 4.5mm - Pane FP18a (27.1.87)	1.00	1.00
M154b		Imperf. at left, 4.5mm band - Pane FP19	70	40
M154c		Imperf. at left, 4mm band - Pane FP19b (30.10.87)	1.20	75
M154d		Imperf. at left, missing phosphor - PaneFP19a	£85	

No.			U/M	F/U
M155	5½p	**2B Deep purple**, Head B1 - Sheets (24.10.73)	30	15
M156	5½p	**CB Deep purple** - Sheets (17.3.75)	30	15
M156a		Missing phosphor	£10	
M156b		Uncoated paper	£350	
M156c		Glazed paper	1.50	
M157	6p	**2B Light green**, Thin value - Sheets Head C (10.10.73)	25	15
M157a		Missing phosphor - Sheets	£350	
M157b		PUI - Phosphor under ink - Sheets	1.75	
M157c		Glazed paper - Sheets	2.00	
M158	6p	**2B Light green**, Very thin value - MV coil	60	25
M158a		Broad band right - MV coil	2.00	
M158b		Broad band centre - MV coil	7.50	
M159	6p	**2B Light green**, Thick value - PUI Phosphor under ink - Sheets (31.10.77)	50	15
M160	6½p	**2B Greenish blue**, Head B1 - Sheets (4.9.74)	30	15
M160a		Thin translcent paper - Sheets	2.50	
M160b		All over phosphor - Thin translucent paper - Sheets	£150	
M161	6½p	**CB Greenish blue**, Head B1 - Sheets (24.9.75)	30	10
M161a		Imperf. pair - Sheets	£200	
M161b		Missing phosphor - Sheets	£10	
M161c		Uncoated paper - Sheets	£170	
M161d		Horizontal coil	1.00	
M162	6½p	**CB Greenish blue** , Head B2 - Sheets	30	15
M162a		Imperf. pair - Sheets	£300	
M162b		Panes FP41, FP42	45	20
M162c		Vertical coil	1.00	
M163	6½p	**LB Greenish blue** - Pane FP40 (26.1.77)	30	40
M164	6½p	**RB Greenish blue** - Pane FP39 (26.1.77)	50	40

No.			U/M	F/U
M165	7p	**2B Purple-brown**, Head B1 - Sheets (15.1.75)	30	10
M165a		Missing phosphor - Sheets	5.00	
M165b		Imperf. pair	£300	
M165c		PUI - Phosphor under ink - Sheets	1.00	
M165d		PUI - Missing phosphor	2.50	
M165e		Glazed paper	60	
M166	7p	**CB Purple-brown**, Head B1, Thin value - Sheets (13.6.77)	40	10
M166a		All over phosphor	£750	
M166b		Imperf. pair	£750	
M166c		Horizontal coil (16.11.77),		
M166d		MV coil (14.12.77)	40	
M166e		Thick paper - MV coil (14.12.77)	£20	
M167	7p	**CB Purple-brown** (CB), Head B2, Thin value - Sheets (13.6.77)	20	15
M167a		Imperf. pair	£100	
M167b		Imperf. at top (marginal)	£150	
M167c		Vertical coil (13.6.77)	50	
M167d		Panes FP43, FP44	60	
M168	7p	**CB Chocolate brown** (CB), Head B2, PUI - Phosphor under ink - Sheets	50	20
M169	7p	**CB Purple-brown** (CB), Head B2, Thick value - Pane FP15 (8.2.78)	50	20
		Missing phosphor - Pane FP15c	5.00	

Thin value

Very thin value

No.			U/M	F/U
M170	7p	**LB Red-brown**, Head B2 - Thin value Pane FP29 (13.6.77)	50	25
M170a		Very thin value	1.00	
M170b		Centre *Bar* - Pane FP79 (Christmas book)	50	25
M170c		Centre *Bar* - Plus2 x 1.5mm short bands at top - Pane FP79 (Christmas book)	5.00	
M171	7p	**RB Red-brown**, Head B2 - Thin value Pane FP28 (13.6.77)	50	25
M171a		Very thin value	1.50	
M172	7½p	**2B Pale chestnut**, Head C, Thick value - Sheets (30.4.74)	1.25	50
M172a		Broad band left - Sheets	£300	
M173	7½p	**2B Pale chestnut**, Head C, Thin value - Sheets (30.4.74)	50	40

M180

No.			U/M	F/U
M174	8p	**2B Red**, Head B1 - Sheets (24.10.73)	20	15
M174a		Uncoated paper - Sheets	9.00	
M174b		Glazed paper - Sheets	80	
M174c		PUI - Phosphor under ink - Sheets	3.50	
M175	8p	**CB Red**, Head B1 - Sheets (20.8.79)	25	10
M175a		Imperf. pair - Sheets	£700	
M175b		Uncoated paper - Sheets	£600	
M176	8p	**CB Bright red**, Head B1, Value set right - Pane FP1	25	15
M176a		Short band at top - Pane FP1	2.50	
M176b		MV coil	25	
M176c		All over phosphor wash - MV coil	£375	

No.			U/M	F/U
M177	8p	**CB Bright red**, Head B2 - Pane FP2 (Chambon)	40	25
M177a		Short band at top - Pane FP2	5.00	
M178	8p	**CB Red**, Head B2, value set high Sheets	30	20
M178a		Panes FP45, FP46	60	
M178b		Vertical coil	60	
M179	8p	**CB Red**, Head B1, value set left - Sheets (Halley press)	85	50
M179a		Missing phosphor - Sheets (Halley press)	£500	
M180	8p	**CB Red**, Enschedé printing (sloping 'p') - Sheets (12.12.79)	25	25
M180a		Missing phosphor - Sheets	£180	
M181	8p	**LB 8mm Red**, Head B2 - Pane FP31 (28.8.79)	35	35
M182	8p	**RB 8mm Red**, Head B2 - Pane FP30 (28.8.79)	35	35
M183	8p	**CBar Red**, Head B2 - Pane FP80 (Christmas book) (14.11.79)	60	45
M184	8½p	**2B Light yellow-green**, Head C - Sheets (24.9.75)	40	15
M184a		Left band omitted - Sheets	£200	
M184b		Broad band left - Sheets	£250	
M184c		Imperf. pair - Sheets	£1300	
M184d		Missing phosphor - Sheets	2.50	
		Glazed paper - Sheets	1.25	
M185	8½p	**2B 8mm Yellow green** - Panes FP39, FP40 (26.1.77)	40	20

No.			U/M	F/U
M186	9p	**2B Dull orange and black**, Head B1 - Sheets (22.3.74)	75	15
M186a		Broad band right - Sheets	£40	
M186b		Missing phosphor - Sheets	£100	
M187	9p	**2B Bright orange and black**, Head B1 - Sheets	75	20
M187a		Broad band right - Sheets	2.50	
M187b		Missing phosphor - Sheets	£100	
M187c		Left band omitted - Sheets	£40	
M187d		Right band omitted - Sheets	£40	
M188	9p	**2B Bright violet**, Head C - Sheets (25.2.76)	50	15
M188a		Missing phosphor - Sheets	2.00	
M188b		All over phosphor - Sheets	£85	
M188c		Vertical coil	60	25
M188d		Horizontal coil	60	25
M189	9p	**2B Bright violet**, Head C, Varnish over phosphor - Sheets	2.00	25
M190	9p	**2B Bright violet**, Head C, Varnish under phosphor - Sheets	1.00	20
M190a		Missing phosphor - Sheets		
M191	9p	**2B Dull violet**, Head C - Sheets	50	15
M191a		Imperf. pair - Sheets	£250	
M192	9p	**2B Dull violet**, Head C, PUI - Phosphor under ink - Sheets	50	15
M192a		Imperf. pair - Sheets	£250	
M193	9p	**2B 8mm Violet**, Head C - Panes FP28, FP29	40	15
M194	9p	**2B Bluish violet**, Head C - Sheets	60	15
M194a		All over phosphor wash - Sheets	£10	
M194b		Left band omitted - Sheets	£35	
M194c		Right band omitted - Sheets	£35	
M194d		Missing phosphor - Sheets	6.00	
M194e		Panes FP49, FP50	60	
M195	9p	**2Bar Pale bluish violet**, Head C - Pane FP79 (Christmas book)	50	20
M195a		Additional CB at top - Pane FP79	4.00	

No.			U/M	F/U
M196	9½p	**2B Purple**, Head C - Sheets (25.2.76)	25	15
M196a		Missing phosphor - Sheets	£15	
M196b		Left band omitted - Sheets	£25	
M196c		Right band omitted - Sheets	£25	
M196d		Bright purple magenta. Error of colour	£2500	
M197	10p	**2B Orange and deep brown**, Head B1 - Sheets Cyl 8A (12.11.73)	40	15
M198	10p	**2B Light orange and deep brown**, Head B1 - Sheets, Cyl 5A (12.11.73)	1.00	25
M198a		Imperf. pair - Sheets, Cyl 5A	£2000	

Original value

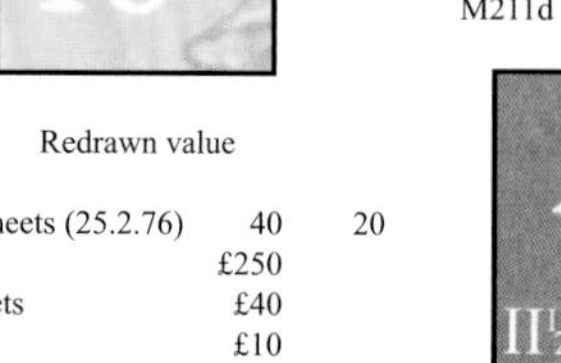

Redrawn value

No.			U/M	F/U
M199	10p	**2B Light orange**, Head D - Sheets (25.2.76)	40	20
M199a		Imperf. pair - Sheets	£250	
M199b		All over phosphor wash - Sheets	£40	
M199c		Broad band at right - Sheets	£10	
M200	10p	**2B Light orange**, Head D - PUI (Phosphor under ink) - Sheets (25.2.76)	50	25
M200a		Imperf. top marginal pair	£500	
M201	10p	**2B 10mm Light orange**, Head D, Chambon printing - Sheets	45	25
M201a		Missing phosphor - Sheets	1.75	
M201b		Gutter pair - Sheets	1.20	
M201c		Gutter pair, Missing phosphor - Sheets	£20	
M201d		Left band omitted - Sheets	£85	
M201e		Right band omitted - Sheets	£85	
M202	10p	**2B 8mm Light orange**, Head D - Panes FP30, FP31	35	15
M202a		Missing phosphor - Panes FP30a, FP31a	4.50	
M203	10p	**CBar Light orange**, Head D - Pane FP80 (Christmas book)	75	
M204	10p	**CB Light orange** - Sheets (4.2.80)	30	15
M204a		Imperf. pair	£225	
M204b		Missing phosphor	5.00	
M204c		All over phosphor wash	£50	
M204d		Solid all over phosphor	£300	
M204e		Imperf. pair	£250	
M204f		Panes FP51, FP52	40	
M204g		Panes SP10, SP12 (£3 Wedgwood)	40	
M204h		Broad band left - Pane SP12	£550	
M204i		Bands front and back - Pane SP12b	£150	
M205	10p	**LB 8mm Light orange** Pane FP33 (4.2.80)	50	35
M205a		Missing phosphor - Pane FP33a	5.00	
M206	10p	**LB Light orange** Pane SP12 (£3 Wedgwood)	1.50	25
M206a		Bands front and back - Pane SP12b	£350	
M207	10p	**RB 8mm Light orange** - Pane FP32 (4.2.80)	50	35
M207a		Broad band left - Pane FP32	7.50	
M207b		Broad band right - Pane FP32	7.50	
M207c		Missing phosphor - Pane FP 33a	5.00	
M208	10p	**CBar Light orange**, Head D - Pane FP81 (Christmas book)	50	20
M208a		Missing phosphor - Pane FP81a	£10	

Redrawn value

No.			U/M	F/U
M209	10p	**2B Light orange** - Pane SP23 (Christian Heritage prestige book)	£10	4.90
M209a		Bands front and back - Pane SP23	£900	
M209b		Missing phosphor - Pane SP23a	£1750	

No.			U/M	F/U
M210	10½p	**2B Yellow**, Head D - Sheets (25.2.76)	40	20
M210a		All over phosphor error	5.50	
M211	10½p	**2B Dull blue** - Sheets (26.4.78)	35	30
M211a	11p	**2B Brown red**, Head D - Sheets (25.2.76)	35	10
M211b		Imperf. pair - Sheets	£1500	
M211c		Missing phosphor - Sheets	4.50	
M211d		PUI (Phosphor under ink) - Sheets	1.00	

No.			U/M	F/U
M212	11½p	**CB Drab**, Head B2 - Sheets (14.1.81)	50	20
M212a		Imperf. pair - Sheets	£300	
M212b		Panes FP54, FP55	60	
M212c		Phosphor wash - Pane FP55	£60	
M212d		Vertical coil	1.00	
M213	11½p	**CBar Drab**, Head B2 - Pane FP82 (Christmas book)	50	20
M214	11½p	**LB 8mm Drab**, Head B1 - Pane FP37 (26.8.81)	40	30
M215	11½p	**LB 8mm Drab**, Head B2 - Pane FP17 (26.1.81)	40	30
M215a		Missing phosphor - Pane FP17b	£10	
M215b		Pane FP56 (6.5.81)	40	30
M216	11½p	**RB 8mm Drab**, Head B1 - Pane FP36 (26.8.81)	40	40
M217	11½p	**RB 8mm Drab**, Head B2 - Pane FP16 (26.1.81)	40	30
M217a		Missing phosphor - Pane FP16b	£10	
M217b		Pane FP56 (6.5.81)	40	30
M218	12p	**2B Yellow green**, Head C - Panes SP9, SP12 (£3 wedgwood) (16.4.80)	40	20
M218a		6mm Broad band left - Panes SP9, SP12	£50	
M218b		6mm Broad band right - Panes SP9, SP12	£100	
M218c		6mm Broad band centre - Panes SP9, SP12	£35	
M218d		9.5mm Broad band left - Panes SP9, SP12	£45	
M218e		9.5mm Broad band right - Panes SP9, SP12	£70	
M218f		9.5mm Broad band centre - Panes SP9, SP12	£25	
M218g		Bands front and back - Panes SP9, SP12	£85	
M218h		Missing phosphor - Panes SP9, SP12	7.50	
M219	12p	**2B 8mm Yellow green**, Head C - Pane FP33 (25.6.80)	40	25
M219a		Broad band left - Pane FP33	7.50	
M219b		Broad band right - Pane FP33	7.50	
M219c		Missing phosphor - Pane FP33a	7.50	
M220	12p	**2B 8mm Yellow green**, Value set high - Panes FP32, FP34	75	30
M221	12p	**2Bar Yellow green**, Head C - Pane FP81 (Christmas book)	65	
M221a		Missing phosphor - Pane FP81a	£10	
M221b		Left band omitted - Pane FP81	£50	
M221c		Right band omitted - Pane FP81	£60	
M222	12p	**CB 4mm Emerald green**, Head B2 - Sheets (29.10.85)	30	15
M222a		Missing phosphor - Sheets	8.00	
M222b		‘A’ phosphor - Sheets (.6.86)	45	
M222c		All over phosphor wash	£10	
M222d		Panes FP58, FP59	50	
M222e		Missing phosphor - Panes FP58a, FP59a	8.00	
M222f		Pane FP20	50	
M222g		Vertical coil	50	
M222h		Horizontal coil	50	

No.			U/M	F/U
M223	12p	**CB 4.5mm Emerald green**, Head B2 - Pane SP30 (B. Rail book) (29.10.85)	50	25
M223a		Missing phosphor - Pane SP30a	£30	
M223b		CB displaced to right - Pane SP30	7.50	
M224	12p	**CB 4.5mm Emerald green**, Head B2, 5 point star underprint - Sheets (29.10.85)	50	25
M224a		Band displaced right - Sheets	9.50	
M225	12p	**LB Emerald green** - Panes FP60, FP61 (14.1.86)	75	50
M225a		Pane SP31 (B. Rail book)	75	
M225b		Broad band left - Pane SP31a	£200	
M225c		Missing phosphor - Pane SP31b	£70	
M225d		Bands front and back - Pane SP31c	£400	
M226	12p	**RB Emerald green** - Panes FP60, FP61 (14.1.86)	75	50
M226a		Pane SP31 (B. Rail book)	75	
M226b		Bands front and back - Pane SP31	£400	

M232/M245

M230

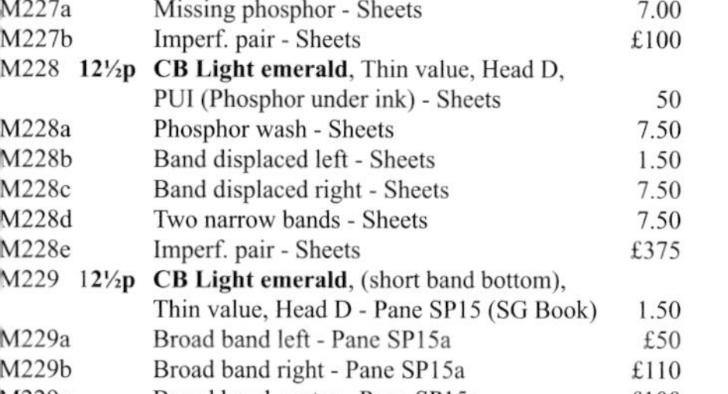

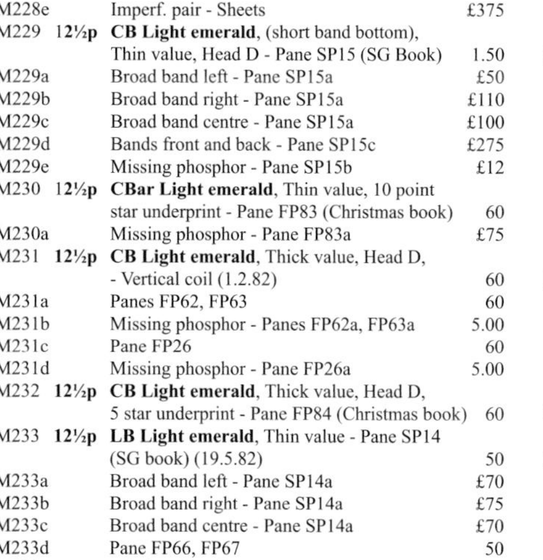

No.			U/M	F/U
M227	12½p	**CB Light emerald**, Thin value, Head D - Sheets (27.1.82)	25	10
M227a		Missing phosphor - Sheets	7.00	
M227b		Imperf. pair - Sheets	£100	
M228	12½p	**CB Light emerald**, Thin value, Head D, PUI (Phosphor under ink) - Sheets	50	25
M228a		Phosphor wash - Sheets	7.50	
M228b		Band displaced left - Sheets	1.50	
M228c		Band displaced right - Sheets	7.50	
M228d		Two narrow bands - Sheets	7.50	
M228e		Imperf. pair - Sheets	£375	
M229	12½p	**CB Light emerald**, (short band bottom), Thin value, Head D - Pane SP15 (SG Book)	1.50	35
M229a		Broad band left - Pane SP15a	£50	
M229b		Broad band right - Pane SP15a	£110	
M229c		Broad band centre - Pane SP15a	£100	
M229d		Bands front and back - Pane SP15c	£275	
M229e		Missing phosphor - Pane SP15b	£12	
M230	12½p	**CBar Light emerald**, Thin value, 10 point star underprint - Pane FP83 (Christmas book)	60	
M230a		Missing phosphor - Pane FP83a	£75	
M231	12½p	**CB Light emerald**, Thick value, Head D, - Vertical coil (1.2.82)	60	25
M231a		Panes FP62, FP63	60	
M231b		Missing phosphor - Panes FP62a, FP63a	5.00	
M231c		Pane FP26	60	
M231d		Missing phosphor - Pane FP26a	5.00	
M232	12½p	**CB Light emerald**, Thick value, Head D, 5 star underprint - Pane FP84 (Christmas book)	60	25
M233	12½p	**LB Light emerald**, Thin value - Pane SP14 (SG book) (19.5.82)	50	30
M233a		Broad band left - Pane SP14a	£70	
M233b		Broad band right - Pane SP14a	£75	
M233c		Broad band centre - Pane SP14a	£70	
M233d		Pane FP66, FP67	50	
M233e		Missing phosphor - Pane FP66a, FP67a	£10	
M233f		Panes SP17, SP18 (Royal Mint book)	60	
M233g		Bands front and back - Panes SP17c, SP18c	£100	
M234	12½p	**LB Light emerald**, Short band at top, Thin value - Pane SP15 (SG book)	1.25	35
M234a		Bands on front and back - Pane SP15c	£300	
M235	12½p	**LB Light emerald**, Thin value set high - Pane SP17 (SG book)	1.50	40
M235a		Missing phosphor - Pane SP17b	£140	
M236	12½p	**RB Light emerald**, Thin value - Pane SP14 (SG book) (19.5.82)	50	30
M236a		Pane FP66, FP67 (5.4.83)	50	
M236b		Missing phosphor - Pane FP66a, FP67a	£10	
M236c		Panes SP17, SP18 (Royal Mint book) (14.9.93)	60	
M236d		Bands front and back - Panes FP17c, FP18c	£100	

No.			U/M	F/U
M237	12½p	**RB Light emerald**, Thin value set high - Pane SP17 (Royal Mint book)	1.50	75
M238	12½p	**LB 8mm Light emerald**, Thin value - Panes FP24, FP25	50	30
M238a		Pane SP14 (SG book)	50	
M238b		8mm Broad band left - Pane SP14a	£35	
M238c		8mm Broad band right - Pane SP14a	£35	
M238d		8mm Broad band centre - Pane SP14a	£150	
M238e		Bands front and back - Pane SP14c	£80	
M238f		Missing phosphor - Pane SP14b	£10	
M239	12½p	**LB 8mm Light emerald**, Thick value - Panes FP64, FP65	50	25
M239a		Missing phosphor - Panes FP64a, FP65a	£300	
M240	12½p	**RB 8mm Light emerald**, Thin value - Panes FP24, FP25	50	25
M240a		Missing phosphor - Pane FP24a, FP25a	£375	
M240b		Pane SP14 (SG book)	50	
M240c		Bands front and back - Pane SP14c	£100	
M241	12½p	**RB 8mm Light emerald**, Thick value - Panes FP64, FP65	50	25
M241a		Missing phosphor - Panes FP64a, FP65a	£300	

> 8mm side banded stamps are best collected se-tenant to distinguish from the normal 9.5mm derived types

No.			U/M	F/U
	12½p	**2B Light emerald** - Error pane		
M242		Left band short at top and bottom - Panes FP64b, FP65b	£25	
M242a		Right band short at top and bottom - Panes FP64b, FP65b	£25	

No.			U/M	F/U
M243	13p	**CB 4mm Chestnut** - Sheets (28.88.84)	30	20
M243a		Imperf. pair - Sheets	£1000	
M243b		Pane FP27	30	
M243c		Missing phosphor - Pane FP27a	6.00	
M243d		Panes FP68, FP70	30	
M243e		Missing phosphor - Panes FP68b, FP70b	6.00	
M243f		Pane FP18	30	
M243g		Horizontal coil	30	
M243h		Band at right - Horizontal coil	7.50	
M243i		Vertical coil	30	
M244	13p	**CB 5mm Chestnut** - Pane SP26 (The Times book)	60	30
M244a		Missing phosphor - Pane SP26a	£75	
M244b		Bands front and back - Pane SP26b	£100	
M245	13p	**CB Chestnut** - 5 point star underprint - Panes FP69, FP71 (Christmas book) (1.12.86)	50	30
		Missing phosphor - Panes FP69a, FP71a	£1400	
M246	13p	**LB Chestnut** - Panes FP73, FP74 (3.9.84)	60	30
M246a		Panes SP22, SP23, SP24 (Heritage book) (4.9.84), SP27 (Times book) (8.1.85)	70	
M246b		Missing phosphor - SP22a, SP23a, SP24b (4.9.84), SP27b (Times book) (8.1.85)	£50	
M246c		Broad band left - Pane SP24a	£100	
M246d		Broad band right - Pane SP24a	£140	
M246e		Broad band centre - Pane SP24a	£100	
M246f		Pane FP21	60	
M246g		Error Pane, Pane FP3b	60	

No.			U/M	F/U
M247	13p	**RB Chestnut** - Panes FP73, FP74 (3.9.84)	60	25
M247a		Panes SP22, SP24 (Heritage book) (4.9.84), SP25 (Times book) (8.1.85)	70	
M247b		Missing phosphor - SP22a, SP23b, SP24b (4.9.84), SP25b (Times book) (8.1.85)	£50	
M247c		Pane FP3	60	
M247d		Missing phosphor - Pane FP3a	£40	
M248	13p	**2B Chestnut** - Error panes FP73a, FP74a Left band short at top and bottom	7.50	
M248a		Right band short at top and bottom	7.50	
M249	13p	**CB 4.5mm Chestnut,** 'A' phosphor, Pane FP18a	50	25
M249a		Imperf. at right - Pane FP19	50	
M249b		Missing phosphor - Pane FP19a	£25	
M250	13p	**CB 4mm Chestnut,** 'A' phosphor, Sheets (27.1.87)	40	25
M250a		Imperf. pair - Sheets	£900	
M250b		Missing phosphor - Sheets	7.50	
M250c		Panes FP68a, FP70a	40	
M250d		Missing phosphor - FP68b, FP70b	7.50	
M250e		Screened value - FP68a , FP70a	1.00	
M250f		Panes SP34, SP35 (P & O book) (3.3.87)	40	
M250g		Pane FP4, FP72 Window books (4.8.87)	40	
M250h		Imperf. at right - Pane FP19b (20.10.87)	1.00	
M251	13p	**LB 4mm Chestnut**, 'A' phosphor - Pane FP21a (27.1.87)	1.00	35
M251a		Pane FP3e	1.00	
M251b		Imperf. at left - Pane FP22	2.50	
M251c		Displaced bands giving 2B stamps - Pane FP22	£15	
M252	13p	**RB 4mm Chestnut**, 'A' phosphor - Pane FP3c (27.1.87)	1.00	35
M252a		Missing phosphor - Pane FC3d	£15	
M252b		Pane SP35	1.00	
M253	14p	**2B 8mm Grey blue** - Panes FP16, FP17 (26.1.81)	50	30
M253a		Missing phosphor - Pane FP16b, FP17b	£40	
M253b		Left band omitted - Pane FP16, FP17	£70	
M253c		Right bad omitted - Pane FP16, FP17	£70	
M253d		Panes FP56, FP57	50	
M253e		Left band short at top and bottom, Panes FP56, FP57	1.00	
M253f		Right band short at top and bottom, Panes FP56, FP57	1.00	
M254	14p	**2Bar Grey blue -** Pane FP82 (Christmas book)	1.00	35
M255	14p	**CB Dark blue**, 'A' phosphor - Sheets (23.8.88)	45	25
M255a		AOP wash - Sheets	£10	
M255a		Pane FP5, FP110	45	
M255b		Panes FP75, FP76	45	
M255c		Missing phosphor - Panes FP75a, FP76a	£35	
M255d		Imperf. at top, Panes FP6, FP78	60	25
M255e		Imperf. at top, Missing phosphor - Pane FP6a, FP78a	£10	
M255f		Imperf. at bottom, Panes FP6, FP78	60	25
M255g		Imperf. at bottom, Missing phosphor - Pane FP6a, FP78a	£10	
M255h		Imperf. at top and right - Pane FP7	7.50	
M255i		Imperf. at top and right, Missing phosphor - Pane FP7a	£10	
M255j		Imperf. at bottom and right - Pane FP7	7.50	
M255k		Imperf. at bottom and right, Missing phosphor - Pane FP7	£10	
M256	14p	**RB Dark blue**, 'A' phosphor Imperf. at left - Pane FP23	75	35
M256a		Imperf. at left, Missing phosphor - Pane FP23a	£300	
M257	14p	**RB Dark blue**, 'A' phosphor, Comb perf - Pane FP8	1.50	85
M257a		APS perf - Pane FP8	1.50	
M257b		Missing phosphor - Pane FP8b	7.50	

No.			U/M	F/U
M258	15p	**CB Light blue** - Sheets (26.9.89)	45	30
M258a		Imperf. pair - Sheets	£450	
M258b		Missing phosphor - Sheets	£12	
M258c		Vertical coil	50	
M258d		Horizontal coil	1.50	
M259	15p	**LB Light blue** - Pane FP9	1.25	45
M259a		Missing phosphor - Pane FP9a	£150	
M259b		Inset band - Pane FP9	2.00	
M259c		Stepped band at top - Pane FP9	2.50	
M260	15p	**RB Light blue** - Pane SP47 (London Life book) (20.3.90)	1.25	1.10
M261	15½p	**2B 8mm Pale violet**, Thick value - Panes FP64, FP65 1.2.82)	45	40
M261a		Left band short at top -Panes FP64, FP65	1.50	
M261b		Left band short at bottom -Panes FP64, FP65	1.50	
M261c		Left band short at top -Panes FP64, FP65	1.50	
M261d		Right band short at top -Panes FP64, FP65	1.50	
M261e		Right band short at bottom -Panes FP64, FP65	1.50	
M261f		Left band short at top and bottom - Panes FP64, FP65	1.00	
M261g		Right band short at top and bottom - Panes FP64, FP65	1.00	
M261h		Missing phosphor - Pane FP64a, FP65a		
M262	15½p	**2B 9.5mm Pale violet**, Thin value - Panes SP13, SP16 (SG Book)	50	45
M262a		6mm Broad band left - Panes SP13a, SP16a	£50	
M262b		6mm Broad band right - Panes SP13a, SP16a	£50	
M262c		6mm Broad band centre - Panes SP13a, SP16a	£50	
M262d		9.5mm Broad band left - Panes SP13a, SP16a	£50	
M262e		9.5mm Broad band right - Panes SP13a, SP16a	£50	
M262f		9.5mm Broad band centre - Panes SP13a, SP16a	£50	
M262g		Bands front and back - Panes SP13c, SP16c	£250	
M262h		Missing phosphor - Panes SP13b, SP16b	£10	
M262i		Solid AOP - Pane SP13	£125	
M263	15½p	**2Bar Pale violet**, Thick value, 10 point star underprint - Pane FP83 (Christmas book)	50	45
M263a		Missing phosphor - Pane FP83a	£100	
M263b		Left band omitted -Pane FP83	£175	
M263c		Right band omitted - Pane FP83	£175	
M264	15½p	**LB 8mm Pale violet**, Error panes FP64b, FP65b	£60	
M265	15½p	**RB 8mm Pale violet**, Error panes FP64b, FP65b	£60	
M266	16p	**2B Drab** - Panes FP66, FP67 (5.4.83)	1.00	50
M266a		Left band short top and bottom - Panes FP66, FP67	1.25	
M266b		Right band short top and bottom - Panes FP66, FP67	1.25	
M266c		Missing phosphor - Panes FP66a, FP67a	£70	
M266d		Left band omitted, Pane FP66	£60	
M266e		Right band omitted, Pane FP66	£60	

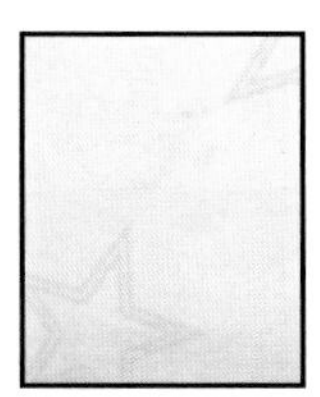

M271

No.			U/M	F/U
M267	17p	**2B Grey blue** - Panes FP60, FP61, FP73, FP74 (3.9.84)	60	30
M267a		Left band short at top and bottom - Panes FP60, FP61, FP73, FP74	1.00	
M267b		Right band short at top and bottom - Panes FP60, FP61, FP73, FP74	1.00	
M267c		Left band short at top - Panes FP60, FP61	2.50	
M267d		Left band short at bottom - Panes FP60, FP61	2.50	
M267e		Left band short at top and bottom - Panes FP73, FP74	1.25	
M267f		Right band short at top and bottom - Panes FP73, FP74	1.25	
M267g		Panes SP23, SP27 (Heritage, Times panes respectively), SP31, SP32 (B. Rail book)	60	
M267h		Missing phosphor - Panes SP23a, SP27b, SP31b	£300	
M267i		Broad band left - Panes SP27a, SP31a	£300	
M267j		Bands front and back - Panes SP23a, SP27c, SP31c	£300	
M267k		Right band short at top - Pane SP23	2.00	
M267l		Right band short at bottom - Pane SP23	2.00	
M268	17p	**2B Grey blue** 250 Screen - Pane FP10	75	30
M268a		Short bands at top - Pane FP10	3.50	
M269	17p	**LB Grey blue**, Error panes FP73a, FP74a	£13	
M270	17p	**RB Grey blue**, Error panes FP73a, FP74a	£13	
M271		**2B Grey blue**, Multiple star underprint - Pane FP11 (4.11.85)	50	
M271a		Short bands at top - Pane FP11	1.50	
M271b		Left band stepped at top - Pane FP11	2.50	
M271c		Left band inset - Pane FP11	2.25	
M271d		Short bands at bottom - Pane FP11	£10	
M271e		Left band omitted - Pane FP11	£50	
M271f		Right band omitted - Pane FP11	£45	
M271g		Missing phosphor - Pane FP11a	£12	
M272	17p	**CB Dark blue** - Sheets (4.9.90)	50	40
M272a		Screened value - Sheets	45	
M272b		Imperf. pair - Sheets	£1000	
M272c		Vertical coil	50	
M273	17p	**LB Dark blue** Pane FP12 (4.9.90)	50	50
M273a		Missing phosphor - Pane FP12a	£10	
M273b		Stepped band at top - Pane FP12	50	
M273c		Short band bottom - Pane FP12	2.50	
M274	17p	**RB Dark blue** - Pane FP12 (4.9.90)	1.00	65
M274a		Short band bottom - Pane FP12	6.00	
M274b		Imperf. at left - Pane FP38	75	
M274c		Imperf. at left - Short band top - Pane FP38	1.00	
M274d		Imperf. at left - Missing phosphor - Pane FP38a	£25	
M275	18p	**2B Dull olive grey** - Pane FP21 (20.10.86)	1.00	35
M275a		Short band at top left - Pane FP3	2.00	
M275b		Short band at top right - FP3, FP21	1.50	
M275c		Left band stepped at top - Pane FP21	1.75	
M275d		Left band inset - Pane FP21	1.75	
M275e		Broad band left - Pane FP3	£275	
M275f		Missing phosphor - Pane FP3a	£25	
M276	18p	**2B Dull olive grey,** Screened value - Pane FP21 (20.10.86)	6.00	4.50
M276a		Left band short at top - Pane FP21	£15	
M276b		Left band stepped at top - Pane FP21	17.50	
M276c		Left band inset - Pane FP21	£20	
M276d		Right band short at top - Panes FP3, FP21	£15	

No.			U/M	F/U
M277	18p	**2B Dull olive grey,** 'A' phosphor - Panes FP21a, SP35 (P&O book)	1.00	60
M277a		Left band short at top - Panes FP3b, FP3c	1.00	
M277b		Left band stepped at top - Pane FP21a	1.50	
M277c		Left band inset - Pane FP21a	1.50	
M277d		Right band short at top - Panes FP3b, FP3c	1.00	
M277e		Broad band left - FP7c	£275	
M277f		Missing phosphor Pane FP3a	£28	
M278	18p	**2B Dull olive grey**, Screened value , 'A' phosphor - Pane FP21a	£10	
M278a		Left band short at top - Pane FP3c	£15	
M278b		Left band stepped at top - Pane FP21a	£15	
M278c		Left band inset - Pane FP21a	£15	
M278d		Right band short at top - Pane FP3c FP21a	£15	
M278e		Imperf. at left - Pane FP22	1.50	
M278f		Imperf. at left, Right band short at top - Pane FP22	1.75	
M278g		Imperf. at right - Pane FP22	1.00	
M278h		Imperf. at right, Right band short at top - Pane FP22	1.25	
M278i		Imperf. at right, Left band inset - Pane FP22	1.25	

No.			U/M	F/U
M279	18p	**CB (Offset left) Bright green** - Sheets	40	25
M279a		Imperf. pair - Sheets (10.9.91)	£325	
M279b		Screened value - Sheets	1.00	
M279c		Vertical coil (16.9.91)	40	
M279d		Missing phosphor - Vertical coil	£15	
M280	18p	**CB (Offset left) Deep bright green** - Sheets	2.00	95
M281	19p	**2B Orange red,** APS perf , Inset bands, - Panes FP8, FP8a (5.9.88)	85	50
M281a		Comb perf, Inset bands - Panes FP8, FP8a	85	50
M281b		Missing phosphor - Pane FP8b	4.50	
M281c		Right band inset, left band stepped at top APS perf - Pane FP8	1.00	
M281d		Right band inset, left band stepped at top Comb perf - Pane FP8	1.00	
M281e		Right band inset - Pane FP8	2.00	
M281f		Bands short at bottom - Pane FP8	2.00	
M281g		Imperf. at right - Pane FP23	1.00	
M281h		Imperf. at right, Right band stepped at top - Pane FP23	3.00	
M281i		Imperf. at right, Right band inset - Pane FP23	1.00	
M281j		Imperf. at right, Missing phosphor - Pane FP23a	£350	
M282	20p	**2B Dull purple** - Sheets (25.2.76)	55	25
M282a		Broad band	£18	

No.			U/M	F/U
M283	20p	**2B Black** - Pane SP47 (London Life book)	1.00	90
		Left band inset - Pane FP9	1.50	
		Left band inset and both bands short at top - Pane FP9	2.00	
		Missing phosphor - Pane FP9a	£475	
M284	22p	**2B (RB 4mm and inset) Orange**		
		Imperf. at right - Pane FP38 (4.9.90)	75	60
		Right band stepped at top - Pane FP38	1.50	
		Missing phosphor - Pane FP38a	£13	

M285	22p	**2B (Both bands 4mm and inset) Orange**		
		Pane FP38 (4.9.90)	1.25	55
		Short bands at top - Pane FP38	1.50	
M286	22p	**2B (RB 5mm and inset) Orange**		
		Pane FP38	75	45
		Left band stepped at top - Pane FP38	1.50	
M285	22p	**2B (Both bands 5mm and inset) Orange**		
		Pane FP38	1.50	60
		Short bands at top - Pane FP38	3.00	
M286	26p	**2B Rosine**, 'A' Phosphor - Pane SP35 (P & O book) (3.3.87)	5.00	3.00
M287	31p	**2B Mauve** - Pane SP31 (B. Rail book) (18.3.86)	6.00	4.00
M287a		Broad band left - Pane SP31a	£1000	
M287b		Bands front and back - Pane SP31c	£850	
M287c		Missing phosphor - Pane SP31b	£900	
M288	34p	**2B Ochre brown**, - Pane SP27 (Times book) (8.1.85)	5.00	4.00
M288a		Broad band left - Pane SP27a	£1000	
M288b		Bands front and back - Pane SP27c	£1000	
M288c		Missing phosphor - Pane SP27b	£900	
M289	50p	**2B Ochre** - Sheets (2.2.77)	1.25	25
M289a		Imperf. pair - Sheets	£550	
M290	50p	**Drab ochre**, (Non phosphor) - Sheets (21.5.80)	1.25	40
M290a		Imperf. pair - Sheets	£450	
M291	50p	**Ochre** - Sheets (Cyl 35) (13.3.90)	1.25	50
M291a		Deep yellow-ochre (Cyl 36) (.10.90)	1.50	
M292	50p	**2B Bistre** - Pane SP47 (London Life book) (20.3.90)	3.00	2.00
M293	75p	**Grey black**, Head B2 - Sheets (26.7.88)	1.25	1.25
M293a		Screened value - Sheets	2.50	

Phosphor Pre-printed Paper-PVA Dextrin Gum (PPP/PVAD)

M294	1p	**Crimson,** Head B1 - Sheets (10.10.79)	20	10
M295	2p	**Myrtle green,** Head B2 - Sheets (10.10.79)	20	10
M295a		Missing phosphor	£200	
M296	10p	**Orange brown,** Head D - Sheets (3.10.79)	50	30
M296a		Missing phosphor in pair with normal	£375	
M296b		Panes FP85, FP86 (3.10.79)	50	
M296c		Pale orange brown - Panes FP85, FP86	2.50	50
M296d		Vertical coil (14.11.79)	50	

Phosphor Coated Paper-PVA Dextrin Gum (PCP/PVAD)

This was an experimental coating and has a very short lived afterglow.

M297	4½p	**2B Grey blue** - Sheets (13.11.74)	50	30
M299	8½p	**Yellow green,** Head C (24.3.76)	40	30

PCP1-PVA Dextrin Gum (PCP1/PVAD)

M300	½p	**Turquoise,** Head C - Sheets (10.12.80)	15	10
M300a		Imperf. pair -Sheets	£250	
M300b		RD coil	15	
M300c		Fluorescent brightener omitted - RD coil	£950	
M301	1p	**Crimson,** Head B1 - Sheets (12.12.79)	15	10
M302	1p	**Crimson**, Head B2 -Sheets	15	10
M302a		Thick value - RD 13p coil	20	
M303	2p	**Pale green,** Head B2 - Sheets	20	10
M303a		Imperf. pair - Sheets	£1300	

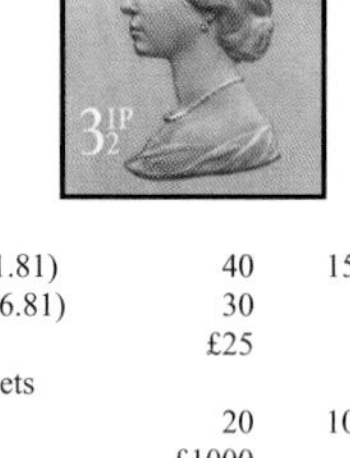

M304	2½p	**Rose red**, Head C. - Sheets (14.1.81)	40	15
M304a		Bright rose red - RD 11½p coil (6.81)	30	
M304b		Fluorescent Brightener omitted	£25	
M305	3p	**Bright magenta**, Head B1 - Sheets (22.10.80)	20	10
M305a		Imperf. pair	£1000	
M305b		Phosphor missing from coating - Sheets	£130	
M306	3p	**Magenta**, Head B2 - Sheets	20	10
M307	3p	**Pink**, Head B1 - RD 11½p coil	25	10
M307a		Fluorescenet brightener omitted - RD coil	5.00	
M308	3½p	**Dull chestnut**, Head D - Sheets (30.3.83)	30	20

M309	4p	**Greenish blue**, Head B1 - RD 12½p coil (30.12.81)	15	10
M309a		Fluorescent Brightener omitted - RD 12½p coil	£350	
M310	4p	**Pale greenish blue,** Head B2 - RD 13p coil (14.4.84)	30	10
M311	5p	**Pale violet**, Head C - Sheets (10.10.79)	30	15
M312	7p	**Brick red**, Head B2 - Sheets (29.10.85)	1.50	1.25

M313	10p	**2B Orange brown** (Chambon printing), Head D - Sheets (20.8.79)	35	25
M313a		Gutter pair	1.50	
		Missing phosphor - Sheets	£100	

No.			U/M	F/U
M313	**10p**	**Orange brown,** Head D - Sheets (10.10.79)	23	20
M314	**10p**	**CB Orange brown** - Sheets (4.2.80)	75	30
M315	**11½p**	**Ochre brown,** Head B2 - Sheets (15.8.79)	50	20
M316	**12p**	**Yellow green**, Head C - Sheets (30.1.80)	40	25
M316a		Panes FP89, FP90	40	
M316b		Vertical coil	40	
M317	**12½p**	**CB Light emerald**, Head D - Sheets	3.50	1.00
M317a		Imperf. pair - Sheets	£2000	

No.			U/M	F/U
M318	**13p**	**Olive grey**, Head C - Sheets (15.8.79)	45	25
M319	**13½p**	**Reddish brown**, Head B2 - Sheets (30.1.80)	45	30
M320	**14p**	**Grey**, Head D - Sheets (14.1.81)	40	20
M320a		Panes FP91, FP92 (26.1.81)	40	
M320b		Fluorescent Brightener omitted - Panes FP91a, FP92a	2.50	

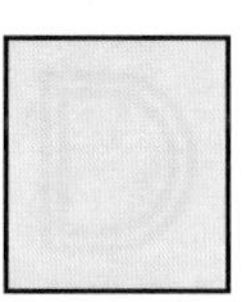

M322b/M329

No.			U/M	F/U
M320	**15p**	**Ultramarine**, Head B2 - Sheets (15.8.79)	40	20
M321	**15½p**	**Pale violet**, Head C - Sheets (14.1.81)	40	20
M321a		Imperf. pair	£300	
M321b		Fluorescent Brightener omitted	£14	
M321c		Vertical coil	50	25
M322	**16p**	**Pale drab,** Head D - Panes FP95, FP97 (5.4.83)	40	25
M322a		Vertical coil	40	
M322b		'D' underprint in blue -Panes FP96, FP98 (10.8.83)	55	

No.			U/M	F/U
M323	**16½p**	**Pale chestnut**, Head D - Sheets (27.1.82)	50	40
M324	**17p**	**Light emerald**, Head D - Sheets (30.1.80)	45	20
M324a		Fluorescent Brightener omitted - Sheets	1.25	
M325	**17p**	**Slate blue**, Head D - Sheets (30.3.83)	50	25
M326		Panes FP99, FP101	50	
M327		Pane FP88	50	
M328		Vertical coil	50	
M329		'D' underprint in blue - Panes FP100, FP102 (5.3.85)	60	
M330	**17p**	**2B Slate blue** (Paper error) - Pane FP87	£65	
M331		Short bands at top - Pane FP87	£130	
M332	**17½p**	**Pale chestnut**, Head D - Sheets (30.1.80)	50	35

No.			U/M	F/U
M333	**18p**	**Violet**, Head C - Sheets (14.1.81)	50	40
M334	**18p**	**Olive grey**, Head C - Panes FP103, FP104 (27.1.82)	60	30
M334a		Vertical coil	60	
M335	**19½p**	**Olive grey**, Head C - Sheets (27.1.82)	1.50	1.00

No.			U/M	F/U
M336	**20p**	**Dull purple**, Head D - Sheets (10.10.79)	60	
M337	**20½p**	**Ultramarine**, Head B2 - Sheets (30.3.83)	1.00	50
M337a		Imperf. pair - Sheets	£1200	
M338	**22p**	**Blue**, Head B2 - Sheets (22.10.82)	55	20
M338a		Imperf. pair - Sheets	£225	
M338b		Missing phosphor - Sheets	£650	
M338c		Experimental (ribbed) coating - Sheets	1.00	

No.			U/M	F/U
M339	**23p**	**Brown red**, Head D - Sheets (30.3.84)	1.00	40
M339a		Imperf. pair -Sheets	£1300	
M340	**25p**	**Dull purple**, Head C - Sheets (12.80)	1.50	
M341	**26p**	**Red**, Head B2 - Sheets (27.1.82)	70	

No.			U/M	F/U
M342	**28p**	**Deep violet,** Head C - Sheets (30.3.83)	75	
M342a		Imperf. pair - Sheets	£1100	
M343	**29p**	**Ochre brown**, Head B2 - Sheets (27.1.82)	2.00	75
M344	**31p**	**Mauve**, Head C - Sheets (30.3.83)	1.00	
M345	**34p**	**Ochre brown**, Head B2 - Sheets (28.8.84)	1.00	

No.			U/M	F/U

PCP2-PVA Dextrin Gum (PCP2/PVAD) Colours are as PCP1

No.			U/M	F/U
M346	½p	**Turquoise,** Head C - Sheets	25	15
M346a		Imperf. pair - Sheets	£175	
M346b		RD coil	25	
M347	1p	**Deep crimson**, Head B1 - Sheets (.12.79)	20	10
M348	1p	**Deep crimson**, Head B2 - Sheets (.83)	£10	10
M349	2p	**Deep green**, Head B2 - Sheets (.12.79)	20	10
M350	2p	**Pale green**, Head B2 - Sheets (.80)	35	15
M350a		Imperf. pair - Sheets	£1250	
M351	2½p	**Rose red**, Head C - Sheets	20	10
M352	3p	**Bright magenta**, Head B1 - Sheets	30	15
M352a		Imperf. pair - Sheets	£1250	
M353	4p	**Greenish blue,** Head B1 - RD coil	£275	
M354	5p	**Pale lilac**, Head C - Sheets (.11.80)	30	15
M355	12p	**Lime green**, Head C - Sheets (.7.80)	1.50	75
M355a		Bright Lime green - Sheets	80	70
M356	14p	**Grey,** Head D - Sheets (14.1.81)	50	30
M356a		Panes FP106, FP107 (26.1.81)	50	
M356b		Phantom CB - Panes FP106, FP107	3.50	
M356c		Vertical coil (11.3.81)	50	
M357	15p	**Ultramarine**, Head B2 - Sheets (1.80)	1.50	75
M357a		Deep ultramarine - Sheets (1980)	55	25
M358	15½p	**Dull violet**, Head C - Sheets (14.1.81)	50	35
M359a		Panes FP108, FP109	2.50	
M360	16½p	**Deep chestnut**, Head D - Sheets (27.1.82)	2.00	75
M361	17p	**Bright emerald,** Head D - Sheets (30.1.80)	2.25	
M362	17½p	**Light brown,** Head D - Sheets (30.1.80)	1.50	
M363	18p	**Deep violet**, Head C - Sheets (14.1.81)	50	35
M364	20p	**Deep dull purple**, Head D - Sheets (10.10.79)	50	20
M365	22p	**Deep blue**, Head B2 - Sheets (22.10.80)	60	25
M366	25p	**Deep purple**, Head B2 - Sheets (14.1.81)	70	50
M367	29p	**Olive-sepia** - Sheets (.82)	4.50	3.50

Advanced Coated Paper-PVA Dextrin Gum (ACP/PVAD)

No.			U/M	F/U
M368	1p	**Claret**, Head B1 - Sheets Experimental coating (short afterglow)	2.50	2.50
M369		Normal afterglow	65	
M370	1p	**Claret,** Head B2, Narrow value set high - Sheets (7.1.86)	25	10
M371	1p	**Claret,** Head B2, Thick value set high Horizontal coil (23.6.87)	35	20
M372	1p	**Claret,** Head B2, Thick value - RD coil (18.3.88)	50	25
M373	1p	**Claret,** Head B2, Very thin value - Sheets (Cyls 15,17) (.9.88)	25	10
M373a		Imperf. pair - Sheets	£1000	

Re-drawn value

No.			U/M	F/U
M374	1p	**Claret** - Vertical coil (26.7.88)	35	
		Pane FP112 (10.9.91)	35	
M375	2p	**Olive green**, Head B2 - Sheets (26.7.88)	15	10
M375a		Imperf. pair		
M375b		Screened value 926.7.88)	65	
M375c		RD 14p coil (5.9.88)	60	
M376	2p	**Deep green**, Head B2. Imperf. at left - Pane FP113 (10.9.91)	45	20
M377	2p	**Deep green**, Head B2. Imperf. at right - Pane FP113 (10.9.91)	45	20
M378	3p	**Magenta**, Head B2 - Sheets	40	25
M378a		Pane SP19 (Royal mint book) (14.9.93)	1.25	
M379	3p	**Bright magenta**, Head B1 - Sheets	25	10

Re-drawn value

No.			U/M	F/U
M380	3p	**Bright magenta**, Sheets (21.1.92)	30	15
M381		RD 15p coil (10.10.89)	85	
M382		Thin paper - RD 15p coil	2.50	

No.			U/M	F/U
M383	3½p	**Dull chestnut**, Head D - Pane SP19 - Royal Mint book (14.9.83)	90	40
M384	4p	**Greenish blue**, Head B2 - RD 13p & 14p coils (18.3.88)	30	15

Re-drawn value

No.			U/M	F/U
M385	4p	**Greenish blue** - RD 18p coil (1.10.93)	35	15
M386	4p	**Greenish blue**, Screened value - Sheets	25	15
M386a		Imperf. pair - Sheets	£1500	
M386b		RD 15p & 17p coils ((10.10.89)	25	
		Thin paper RD 15p coil	1.00	
M387	5p	**Dull red brown**, Head B2 - Sheets (26.7.88)	25	10
M387a		Screened value - Sheets	65	
M387b		Imperf. pair - Sheets	£1500	
M387c		RD 17p & 18p coils (27.11.90)	25	

No.			U/M	F/U
M388	6p	**Lime green** - Sheets (10.9.91)	25	15
M389	10p	**Orange brown**, - Sheets (16.7.85)	30	15

Re-drawn value

No.			U/M	F/U
M390	10p	**Light tan**, Head B2 (4.9.90)	25	25

No.			U/M	F/U
M391	15½p	**Pale violet,** Head C - Sheets (1983)	3.00	1.00
M392	16p	**Drab**, Head D - Sheets (30.3.83)	40	15
M392a		Imperf. pair - Sheets	£125	
		Panes SP19, SP20 (Royal Mint book)	40	
M393	17p	**Grey blue**, Head D - Sheets (19.6.84)	45	20
M393a		Imperf. pair - Sheets	£250	
M393b		Panes SP21, SP28, SP29 (Heritage, Times and B. Rail books respectively)	45	

No.			U/M	F/U
M394	**18p**	**Olive green**, Head B2 - Sheets (28.8.84)	50	30
M394a		Screened value - Sheets	3.00	
M394b		Imperf. pair (Screened value) - Sheets	£80	
M394c		Pane SP33 (P&O book)	50	
M394d		Panes FP122, FP123	50	
M394e		Pane FP114, FP124	50	
M394f		Vertical coil	50	
M395	**19p**	**Dull orange red**, Head B2 - Sheets (23.8.88)	40	25
M395a		Imperf. pair - Sheets	£500	
M395b		Panes FP115, FP127	40	
M395c		Pane FP125	40	
M395d		Vertical coil	40	
M396	**19p**	**Dull orange red**, - Imperf. at top - Panes FP116, FP117, FP128	75	35
M397	**19p**	**Dull orange red**, - Imperf. at bottom - Panes FP116, FP117, FP128	75	35
M398	**19p**	**Dull orange red**, - Imperf. at top and right - Pane FP117 (24.1.89)	6.50	4.50
M399	**19p**	**Dull orange red**, - Imperf. at right and bottom - Pane FP117 (24.1.89)	6.50	
M400	**20p**	**Turquoise green,** Head B2 - Sheets (23.8.88)	35	30
M401	**20p**	**Black**, Head B2 APS perf. - Sheets (2.10.89)	35	35
M401a		Imperf. pair -Sheets	£600	
M410b		Screened value - Sheets	2.75	
M401c		Horizontal coil	35	
M401d		Vertical coil	35	
M402	**20p**	**Black**, Imperf. at left - Pane FP121	1.00	75
M402a		Screened value - Pane FP121	3.00	
M403	**20p**	**Black**, Imperf. at right - Pane FP121	1.00	75
M403a		Screened value - Pane FP121	3.00	

No.			U/M	F/U
M404	**22p**	**Dark blue** - Experimental coating -Sheets	2.50	1.75
M405	**22p**	**Bright green**, Head B2 - Sheets (28.8.84)	40	35
M405a		Screened value - Sheets	1.25	
M405b		Imperf. pair	£1000	
M406	**22p**	**Orange,** - Sheets (4.9.90)	50	30
M406a		Screened value - Sheets	70	
M406b		Imperf. pair, Screened value - Sheets	£400	
M406c		Vertical coil	50	
M406d		Low OBA - Sheets	3.50	
M406e		Low OBA, Screened value - Sheets	2.50	
M407	**23p**	**Light green**, Head B2 - Sheets (23.8.88)	70	25

No.			U/M	F/U
M408	**24p**	**Violet**, Head B2 - Sheets (28.8.84)	1.25	45
		Screened value - Sheets	2.25	
M409	**24p**	**Indian red**, Head B2 - Sheets (26.9.89)	75	65
M409a		Imperf. pair - Sheets	£1800	
M410	**24p**	**Brown,** Head B2 - Sheets (10.9.91)	2.00	90
M410a		Low OBA, screened value - Sheets	1.50	
M410b		Imperf. pair - Sheets	£700	
M410c		Pane FP112 (10.9.91)	45	45
M411	**24p**	**Brown,** Imperf. at left - Pane FP113	60	35
M412	**24p**	**Brown,** Imperf. at right - Pane FP113	60	35

26p Type I 26p Type II

No.			U/M	F/U
M413	**26p**	**Red**, Head B2, Type I - Sheets (1984)	65	25
M413a		Imperf. pair - Sheets (1984)	£550	
M414		Type II - Pane FP118 (4.8.87)	3.50	1.75
M414a		Screened value - FP118	6.50	
M415	**26p**	**Stone**, Head B2 - Sheets (4.9.90)	65	45

No.			U/M	F/U
M416	**27p**	**Rust brown**, Head B2 - Sheets (23.8.88)	1.00	40
M416a		Screened value (part) - Sheets	4.50	
M417	**27p**	**Rust brown**, Imperf. at top (11.10.88) - Pane FP120	4.00	2.50
M418	**27p**	**Rust brown**, Imperf. at bottom - Pane FP120	4.00	
M419	**27p**	**Mauve**, Head B2 - Sheets (4.9.90)	55	50
M420	**28p**	**Dull violet**, Head C - Sheets (21.10.86)	80	60

No.			U/M	F/U
M421	**28p**	**Yellow ochre**, Head B2 - Sheets (23.8.88)	65	50
M422	**28p**	**Slate**, Head B2 - Sheets (10.9.91)	55	50
M423	**29p**	**Purple**, Head B2 - Sheets (26.9.89)	1.25	50

No.			U/M	F/U
M424	**30p**	**Sage green**, Head B2 - Sheets (26.9.89)	2.25	75
M242a		Screened value - Sheets	90	
M425	**31p**	**Mauve**, Head C - Sheets (17.9.85)	90	65
M425a		Imperf. pair -Sheets	£1100	
M426	**31p**	**Blue**, Head B2 - Sheets (4.9.90)	85	75

No.			U/M	F/U
M427	**32p**	**Dark turquoise**, Head B2 - Sheets (23.8.88)	6.50	4.50
M427a		Screened value - Sheets	85	
M427b		Imperf. pair, screened value - Sheets	£1600	

No.			U/M	F/U
M428	33p	**Emerald**, Head B2 - Sheets (4.9.90)	70	55
		Vertical coil	70	
M429	34p	**Ochre brown**, Head B2 - Sheets (24.6.86)	1.00	50

No.			U/M	F/U
M430	34p	**Slate**, Head B2 - Sheets (26.9.89)	90	70
M431	34p	**Purple**, Head B2 - Sheets (10.9.91)	65	60
M432	35p	**Dark brown**, Head B2 - Sheets (23.8.88)	9.00	
M432a		Screened value - Sheets	1.00	65
M432b		Imperf. pair, screened value - Sheets	£1300	

No.			U/M	F/U
M433	35p	**Deep yellow**, Head B2 - Sheets (10.9.91)	80	80
M433a		Deep bright yellow - Sheets	1.00	90
M434	37p	**Red** - Sheets (26.9.89)	1.25	90
M435	39p	**Bright mauve**, Head B2 - Sheets (10.9.91)	90	65
M435a		Screened value - Sheets	1.75	
M435b		Vertical coil (11.2.92)	90	
M436	50p	**Sand**, Head B2 - Sheets (21.1.92)	1.25	50
M436a		Imperf. pair - Sheets	£1500	

1996 (6 February). Perf. 15 x 14. Two phosphor bands
Printer: Harrison & Sons in photogravure

OFPP/PVAD

No.			U/M	F/U
M437	4p	**New blue** - RD 19p coil (30.1.95)	30	30
M438	5p	**Claret** - RD coil (30.1.95)	35	30

OFNP/PVAD

No.			U/M	F/U
M439	25p	**Salmon pink** - RD coil (16.1.96)	4.00	

Photogravure

Litho
Image tends to look 'flat'

Printed by Waddington in Lithography

1980 (30 Jan.) - 86. No watermark.

FCP/PVA - Perf. 13½ x 14

No.			U/M	F/U
LM1	4p	**2B Greenish blue**, - Sheets (30.1.80)	15	20
LM1a		Missing phosphor - Sheets	£1300	
LM1b		Imperforated right marginal - Sheets		
LM2	20p	**2B Deep purple and dull purple** - Sheets (21.5.80)	75	25
LM2a		Dull purple and dull purple. Error of colour (stamp appears in one colour)	£350	

PCP/PVAD - Perf. 13½ x 14

No.			U/M	F/U
LM3	4p	**Greenish blue** - Sheets (11.81)	20	10
LM4	20p	**Deep purple and dull purple** - Sheets (11.81)	85	20
LM4a		Deep purple brown and dull purple - Sheets (10.85)	1.75	50

ACP/PVAD - Perf. 13½ x 14

No.			U/M	F/U
LM5	4p	**Greenish blue** - Sheets (2.86)	6.50	4.50
LM6	20p	**Deep purple and dull purple** - Sheets (.2.86)	4.50	3.50

Printed by Questa in Lithography

FCP/PVAD - Perf. 13½ x 14

No.			U/M	F/U
LM7	75p	**Black** - Sheets (30.1.80)	2.50	1.00
LM7a		Imperf. at right (marginal)	£225	

PCP/PVA - Perf. 13½ x 14

No.			U/M	F/U
LM8	5p	**Pale lilac** - Sheets (10.81)	35	20
LM8a		Imperf. at right (marginal)	£450	

PCP/PVAD - Perf. 13½ x 14

No.			U/M	F/U
LM9	2p	**Green**, Type I - Sheets (21.5.80)	20	10
LM10	5p	**Pale lilac** - Sheets (21.5.80)	20	10
LM11	5p	**Pale lake brown** - Sheets (21.1.82)	35	15

OCP/PVA - Perf. 15 x 14

No.			U/M	F/U
LM12	75p	**Black** - Sheets (28.2.84)	2.25	1.00

FCP/PVA - Perf. 15 x 14

No.			U/M	F/U
LM13	13p	**CB Pale chestnut** - Pane SP38 (FT book) (9.2.88)	50	35
LM14	13p	**LB Pale chestnut** - Pane SP39 (FT book) (9.2.88)	50	35
LM15	13p	**RB Pale chestnut** - Pane SP39 (FT book) (9.2.88)	50	35
LM16	14p	**CBar Dark blue** - Pane LP1 (11.10.88)	1.40	55
LM16a		Short bar at top - Pane LP1	2.50	
LM16b		Short bar at bottom - Pane LP1	2.50	
LM17	17p	**CB Dark blue** - Panes SP49, SP52 (Agatha Christie book) (19.3.91)	55	45
LM17a		Missing phosphor - Panes SP49a, SP52a	£200	

No.			U/M	F/U
LM18	18p	**2B Grey olive** - Pane SP39 (FT book) (9.2.88)	3.50	3.50
LM18a		Double print (various degrees) - SP39	£600	
LM18b		Blackish olive - Pane SP39	£35	
LM19	18p	**CB Bright green** - Pane SP58 (Tolkien book) (27.10.92)	65	35
LM20	18p	**RB Bright green** - Pane SP59 (27.10.92)	85	50
LM20a		Short additional band upper left - Pane SP59	4.00	
LM21	22p	**2B Bright yellow green** - Pane SP39 (9.2.88)	4.50	4.50

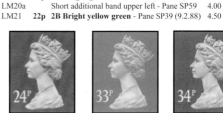

No.			U/M	F/U
LM22	24p	**2B Chestnut** - Pane SP59 (Tolkien book) (27.10.92)	1.00	75
LM22a		Left band short at top - Pane SP59	4.00	
LM23	33p	**2B Emerald** - Pane SP55 (Wales book) (25.9.92)	1.00	75
		Missing phosphor - Pane SP55a	£550	
LM24	34p	**2B Ochre brown** - Pane SP39 (FT book) (9.2.88)	3.50	3.50

75p Type I

75p Type II

No.			U/M	F/U
LM25	39p	**2B Bright mauve** - Pane SP59 (Tolkien book) (27.10.92)	1.00	1.00
LM25a		Short bands at top - Pane SP59	4.50	
LM26	75p	**Black.** Type I - Sheets (7.10.86)	2.50	2.25
LM27	75p	**Black and pale grey brown**. Type II - Sheets (23.2.88)	7.00	4.00

FCP/PVAD - Perf. 15 x 14

No.			U/M	F/U
LM28	75p	**Black**. Type I - Sheets (19.2.85)	3.00	2.00

PCP/PVAD - Perf. 15 x 14

No.			U/M	F/U
LM29	2p	**Deep green** - Sheets (10.7.84)	20	10
LM30	5p	**Pale lake brown** - Sheets (21.2.84)	40	15

ACP/PVA - Perf. 15 x 14

No.			U/M	F/U
LM31	2p	**Deep green and light yellow green** - Sheets (23.2.88)	40	35
LM32	19p	**Orange red**, - Pane LP2 (11.10.88)	1.00	75
LM33	22p	**Orange red** - Pane SP51 (Agatha Christie book) (19.3.91)	60	45
LM34	24p	**Chestnut** - Panes SP57, SP60 (Tolkien book) (27.10.92)	60	45
LM35	33p	**Emerald** - SP51 (Agatha Christie book) (19.3.91)	1.20	1.00

ACP/PVAD - Perf. 15 x 14

No.			U/M	F/U
LM36	2p	**Deep green** - Sheets (25.2.86)	20	10
LM37	4p	**Greenish blue** - Sheets (13.5.86)	40	40
LM37a		Double impression - Sheets	£500	
LM38	5p	**Pale lake brown** - Sheets	40	10
LM39	18p	**Grey olive** - Panes SP37, SP40 (FT book) (9.2.88)	60	40
LM40	20p	**Deep sepia and purple** - Sheets (13.5.86)	85	45

OFNP/PVA - Perf. 15 x 14

No.			U/M	F/U
LM41	33p	**2B Emerald** - Pane SP64 (Beatrix Potter book) (10.10.93)	1.00	1.00
LM42	39p	**2B Bright mauve** - Pane SP64 (Beatrix Potter book) (10.10.93)	1.25	1.25

OFNP/PVA - C (Yellow) fluor phosphor

No.			U/M	F/U
LM43	18p	**LB Bright green** - Pane SP64 (B. Potter book) (10.8.93)	1.50	1.50
LM43a		Short band at top left	4.00	4.00
LM43b		Short band at bottom left	4.00	4.00
LM43c		Two side bands		
LM43d		Side band right		
LM43e		CB offset left		
LM43f		Missing phosphor	£300	£300
LM44	33p	**2B Light emerald** - Pane SP64 (B. Potter book) (10.8.93)	1.25	1.25
LM44a		Short band at top right	4.00	4.50
LM44b		Short band at bottom right	4.00	4.50
LM44c		Broad band left		
LM44d		Broad band right		
LM44e		Missing phosphor	£375	£375
LM45	39p	**2B Bright mauve** - Pane SP64 (B. Potter book) (10.8.93)	1.50	1.50
LM45a		Short band at top right	4.50	4.50
LM45b		Short band at bottom right	4.50	4.50
LM45c		Single 4mm CB		
LM45d		Single 4mm LB		
LM45e		Double impression		
LM45f		Missing phosphor	£475	£475

Printed by Walsall in Lithography

FCP/PVA - Perf 14

No.			U/M	F/U
LM46	14p	**RB Dark blue,** Imperf. at left - Pane LP3 (25.4.89)	1.00	1.00
LM46a		Missing phosphor - Pane LP3a	£225	
LM47	19p	**2B Orange red,** Imperf. at left -Pane LP3 (25.4.89)	1.50	1.50
LM47a		Band short at bottom, LB short at top - Pane LP3	2.00	
LM47b		Missing phosphor - Pane LP3a	£350	
LM48	19p	**2B Orange red,** Imperf. at right -Pane LP3 (25.4.89)	1.00	1.00
LM48a		Bands short at top - Pane LP3	2.00	
LM48b		Bands short at bottom - Pane LP3	2.50	
LM48c		Missing phosphor - Pane LP3a	£175	
LM49	29p	**2B Purple,** Imperf. at top - Pane LP4 (2.10.89)	2.50	1.50
LM50	29p	**2B Purple,** Imperf. at bottom - Pane LP4 (2.10.89)	2.50	1.50
LM51	29p	**2B Purple,** Imperf. at top and right - Pane LP4 (2.10.89)	2.50	1.50
LM52	29p	**2B Purple**, Imperf. at right and bottom - Pane LP4 (2.10.89)	2.50	1.50

ACP/PVA - Perf 14

No.			U/M	F/U
LM53	29p	**Purple,** Imperf. at top - Pane LP6 (17.4.90)	2.50	2.00
LM54	29p	**Purple,** Imperf. at bottom - Pane LP6 (17.4.90)	2.50	2.00
LM55	29p	**Purple,** Imperf. at top and right - Pane LP6 (17.4.90)	2.50	2.00
LM56	29p	**Purple,** Imperf. at right and bottom - Pane LP6 (17.4.90)	2.50	2.00
LM57	31p	**Blue,** Imperf. at top - Pane LP7 (17.9.90)	1.00	65
LM57a		Low OBA - Pane LP7a	1.10	
LM58	31p	**Blue,** Imperf. at bottom - Pane LP7 (17.9.90)	1.00	65
LM58a		Low OBA - Pane LP7a	1.10	
LM59	33p	**Emerald,** Imperf. at top - Pane LP8 (16.9.91)	85	80
LM60	33p	**Emerald,** Imperf. at bottom - Pane LP8 (16.9.91)	85	80
LM61	39p	**Bright mauve,** Imperf. at top - Panes LP9, LP10 (16.9.91)	90	80
LM62	39p	**Bright mauve,** Imperf. at bottom - Panes LP9, LP10 (16.9.91)	90	80

ACP/PVAD - Perf 14

No.			U/M	F/U
LM63	2p	**Deep green,** Imperf. at left - Pane LP5 (9.2.93)	60	40
LM64	2p	**Deep green,** Imperf. at right - Pane LP5 (9.2.93)	60	40
LM65	24p	**Brown,** Imperf. at left - Pane LP5 (9.2.93)	60	50
LM66	24p	**Brown,** Imperf. at right - Pane LP5 (9.2.93)	60	50
LM67	33p	**Emerald,** Imperf. at top - Pane LP11 (8.9.92)	1.50	1.00
LM68	33p	**Emerald,** Imperf. at bottom - Pane LP11 (8.9.92)	1.50	1.00

Printed by Harrison in Photogravure

Perf. 15 x 14 elliptical.

OFPP/PVAD

No.			U/M	F/U
SM1	25p	**Salmon-pink** - Sheets	55	55
SM1a		Imperforate pair - Sheets	£400	
SM1b		Panes EP1, EP2, EP3 ((1.11.94)	60	
SM1c		Vertical coil	75	
SM2	35p	**Deep yellow** - Vertical coil (1.11.93)	3.50	1.00
SM3	41p	**Stone** - Vertical coil (1.11.93)	4.00	1.00

OFNP/PVAD - C (yellow) fluor

No.			U/M	F/U
SM4	19p	**CB Olive-green** - Sheets	60	45
SM4a		Imperforate pair - Sheets	£250	
SM4b		Missing phosphor - Sheets	£100	
SM4c		Two narrow side bands - Sheets	£120	
SM4d		Narrow band at right	£175	
SM4e		Vertical coil	75	
SM4f		Bottom of value filled in - Vertical coil	2.75	
SM4g		Deep olive-green - Sheets (Cyl 4)	1.00	
SM5	19p	**CB Deep Olive-green,** Thick opaque paper - Sheets	3.50	
SM6	25p	**2B Salmon-pink** - Sheets (20.12.94)	65	55
SM6a		Panes EP4, EP5 and EP6	65	
SM6b		Short bands at top - Pane EP5 (6.6.95)	1.25	
SM6c		Translucent paper - Sheets	1.25	
SM6d		Broad band at left - Translucent paper	£25	
SM6e		Vertical coil (16.5.95)	1.25	

OFNP/PVA(Layflat) - C (yellow) fluor phosphor

No.			U/M	F/U
SM7	19p	**CB Olive-green** (19.7.94)	75	55
SM7a		Thinner paper, whiter gum	1.25	

OFNP/PVAD - D (blue) fluor

No.			U/M	F/U
SM8	19p	**CB Olive-green** - Sheets (28.7.95)	50	45
SM8a		Screened value - Sheets	3.00	
SM8b		Vertical coil (.10.95)	55	
SM9	19p	**CB Deep olive-green**, Opaque paper - Sheets	90	
SM9a		Translucent paper - Sheets	65	
SM10	20p	**CB Bright green** - Sheets (25.6.95)	45	45
SM10a		Imperforate pair - Sheets	£325	
SM10b		Value set high (Cyl 14) - Sheets	60	
SM11	25p	**2B Salmon-pink** - Sheets (.8.95)	65	65
SM11a		Panes EP5a, EP6a	65	
SM11b		Short bands at top - Pane EP5a	4.00	
SM11c		Missing phosphor	£22	
SM11d		Vertical coil	5.00	
SM12	26p	**2B Reddish brown** - Sheets (25.6.96)	60	55
SM12a		Screened value - Sheets	4.00	
SM13	26p	**2B Deep reddish brown** - Sheets	1.25	75

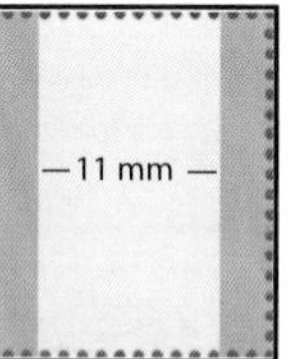

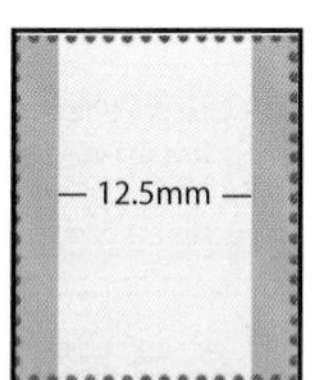

There are two varieties of phosphor bands on the 37p, 43p and 63p Vertical coil stamps. For simplicity these are described as either 11mm or 12.5mm which refers to the space *between* the bands as shown above.

No.			U/M	F/U
SM14	37p	**2B 11mm Amethyst** - Vertical coil (8.7.96)	1.00	1.00
SM14a		**2B 12.5mm** - Vertical coil	2.75	
SM15	43p	**2B 11mm Chocolate-brown** - Vertical coil (8.7.96)	1.00	1.00
SM15a		**2B 12.5 mm** - Vertical coil	2.50	
SM16	63p	**2B 11mm Light emerald** - Vertical coil (12.12.96)	1.25	1.25
SM16a		**2B 12.5mm** - Vertical coil (12.12.96)	3.50	

OFNP/PVA(Layflat) - D (blue) fluor phosphor

No.			U/M	F/U
SM17	20p	**CB Bright green** - Sheets (1.2.97)	1.25	1.00
SM18	25p	**2B Salmon-pink** - Sheets (.8.95)	9.00	5.00
SM19	26p	**2B Pale reddish brown** - Sheets (28.2.97)	1.25	1.25
SM19a		Reddish brown - Sheets (Cyl 6)	2.00	

Printed by Harrison/De La Rue in Gravure

OFNP/PVA (Layflat) - D (blue) fluor

No.			U/M	F/U
SM20	1p	**2B Reddish crimson** - Sheets (1.4.97)	10	10
SM21	2p	**2B Deep grey-green** - Sheets (27.5.97)	15	10
SM22	4p	**2B New blue** - Sheets (27.5.97)	20	15

No.			U/M	F/U
SM23	5p	**2B Claret** - Sheets (27.5.97)	25	20
SM24	6p	**2B Lime green** - Sheets (1.4.97)	30	25
SM25	7p	**2B Light grey** - Sheets (20.4.99)	30	25
		Imperforate pair - Sheets	£1000	

No.			U/M	F/U
SM26	8p	**2B Deep yellow** - Sheets (25.4.00)	30	25
SM27	10p	**2B Deep orange** - Sheets (27.5.97)	30	35
SM27a		Dull Brownish-orange - Sheets	85	
SM28	19p	**CB Yellowish olive** - Sheets (20.4.99)	40	35
SM28a		Additional narrow band at left - Sheets	3.00	
SM28b		Additional narrow band at right - Sheets	3.00	
SM29	19p	**CB Deep olive** - Sheets (.4.99)	90	50
SM30	19p	**CB Olive-green** - Sheets (9.8.99)	90	50

No.			U/M	F/U
SM31	20p	**CB Bright green** - Sheets (29.4.97)	45	40
SM31a		Imperforate pair - Sheets	£350	
		Pale bright green - Sheets	1.00	
SM32	20p	**RB Bright green** - Pane SP78 (BBC book) (23.9.97)	95	80
SM33	20p	**2B Bright green** - Sheets (.2.98)	40	35
SM34	26p	**2B Reddish brown** - Sheets	50	40
SM34a		Imperforate pair - Sheets	£290	
SM34b		Pane SP78 (BBC book) (23.9.97)	55	65
SM35	26p	**Chocolate brown** - Sheets (18.4.98)	1.10	75

No.			U/M	F/U
SM36	26p	**2B Gold** - Sheets (29.4.97)	60	55
SM36a		Imperforate pair - Sheets	£2000	
SM36b		Pane SP77 (BBC book) (23.9.97)	60	
SM36c		Short bands at top - Pane SP77	2.50	
SM36d		Short bands at bottom - Pane SP77	2.50	
SM36e		Left band inset - Pane SP77	1.95	
SM36f		Right band inset - Pane SP77	1.95	

No.			U/M	F/U
SM37	30p	**2B Olive-grey** - Sheets (12.5.97)	60	55
SM38	30p	**2B Deep Olive-grey** - Sheets (24.7.98)	1.50	
SM38a		Imperforate pair - Sheets		
SM39	31p	**2B Royal purple** - Sheets (7.8.97)	60	55
SM40	33p	**2B Slate blue** - Sheets (25.4.00)	55	

No.			U/M	F/U
SM41	37p	**2B Bright mauve** - Sheets (7.8.97)	75	75
SM41a		Vertical coil (26.8.97)	75	
SM42	37p	**2B Grey-black** , Dull fluor - Sheets (4.7.02)	75	60
SM42a		Bright fluor - Pane SP135 (Letters by night book) (16.3.04)	1.25	
SM43	38p	**2B Ultramarine** - Sheets (20.4.99)	65	55

No.			U/M	F/U
SM44	39p	**2B Bright magenta** - Sheets (27.5.97)	75	75
SM44a		Imperforate pair - Sheets	£750	
SM45	40p	**2B Greyish blue** - Sheets (20.4.99)	70	65
SM46	41p	**2B Rosine** - Sheets (20.4.99)	95	80

No.			U/M	F/U
SM47	42p	**2B Grey-green** - Sheets (4.7.02)	85	75
SM48	43p	**2B Sepia brown** - Sheets (1.4.97)	80	80
SM48a		Vertical coil (26.8.97)	1.00	
SM49	44p	**2B Stone** - Sheets (20.4.99)	85	75

No.			U/M	F/U

No.			U/M	F/U
SM50	45p	**2B Bright mauve** - Sheets (20.4.99)	75	55
SM51	47p	**2B Sea green** - Sheets (4.7.02)	95	75
SM52	50p	**2B Ochre** - Sheets (1.4.97)	1.00	95

No.			U/M	F/U
SM53	63p	**2B Light emerald** - Sheets (13.8.97)	1.10	1.00
SM54	64p	**2B Sea-green** - Sheets (20.4.99)	1.10	1.00
SM55	65p	**2B Greenish-blue** - Sheets (25.4.00)	1.10	1.00

No.			U/M	F/U
SM56	68p	**2B Stone** - Sheets (06.02)	1.15	1.00
SM57	£1	**2B Bluish violet** - Sheets (1.4.97)	1.75	1.75
SM57a		Imperforate pair - Sheets	£650	

OFPP/PVA(Layflat)

All from Jeffrey Matthews Miniature Sheet

No.			U/M	F/U
SM58	4p	**New blue** (22.5.00)	50	
SM59	5p	**Claret**	50	
SM60	6p	**Lime green**	60	
SM61	10p	**Deep orange**	70	
SM62	31p	**Royal purple**	1.10	
SM63	39p	**Bright magenta**	1.30	
SM64	64p	**Sea green**	2.50	
SM65	£1	**Bluish-violet**	3.50	

Printed by Enschedé in Photogravure

OFNP/PVAD

No.			U/M	F/U
E18a	18p	**CB Bright green (Yellow phosphor)**	40	45

OFNP/PVA - C (yellow) fluor phosphor

No.			U/M	F/U
EE1	1p	**2B Crimson** (unvarnished) (8.6.93)	30	30
EE1a		4 mm varnish bands (20.4.94)	80	
EE1b		2 mm varnish bands	80	
EE2	2p	**2B Deep green** (2 mm varnish bands) (11.4.95)	30	30
EE4	4p	**2B New blue** (4 mm varnish bands) (14.12.93)	35	35
EE4a		2 mm varnish bands (13.9.94)	1.00	

No.			U/M	F/U
EE5	5p	**2B Claret** (unvarnished) (8.6.93)	35	35
EE5aa		2 mm varnish bands	1.00	
EE6	6p	**2B Lime green** (unvarnished) (27.4.93)	35	35
EE6a		Wide left band and narrow right band	1.50	
EE6b		2 mm varnish bands	1.00	
EE6c		Missing phosphor	-	
EE10	10p	**2B Orange** (unvarnished) (8.6.93)	40	40
EE10a		Deep orange, 4 mm varnish bands	1.00	
EE10b		Deep orange, 2 mm varnish bands (14.2.95)	1.00	

No.			U/M	F/U
EE20	20p	**2B Sea-green** (4 mm varnish bands) (14.12.93)	45	45
EE20a		2 mm varnish bands (28.8.94)	1.10	
EE29	29p	**2B Light grey** (unvarnished) (26.10.93)	60	60
EE29a		4 mm varnish bands (25.4.94)	1.20	
EE29b		2 mm varnish bands (31.3.95)	1.20	

No.			U/M	F/U
EE30	30p	**2B Grey-green** (unvarnished) (27.7.93)	60	60
EE30a		4 mm varnish bands	1.25	
EE30b		2 mm varnish bands (23.11.94)	1.25	

EE35	35p	**2B Deep yellow** (unvarnished) (17.8.93)	65	65
EE35a		4 mm varnish bands (9.6.94)	1.40	
EE35b		2 mm varnish bands (28.6.95)	1.40	
EE35c	35p	**CB Lime green**	85	75
EE36	36p	**2B Ultramarine** (unvarnished) (26.10.93)	70	70
EE36a		4 mm varnish bands	1.40	
EE36b		2 mm varnish bands (12.5.95)	1.40	

EE38	38p	**2B Rosine** (unvarnished) (26.10.93)	75	75
EE38a		2 mm varnish bands (25.1.94)	1.40	
EE38b		Imperf. pair	£175	
EE38c		2 mm varnish bands, Novaglo phosphor	2.75	
EE41	41p	**2B Stone** (unvarnished) (26.10.93)	75	75
EE41a		Drab (2 mm varnish bands) (23.6.94)	1.40	
EE50	50p	**2B Ochre** (4 mm varnish bands) (14.12.93)	1.00	1.00
EE50a		2 mm varnish bands (14.7.94)	1.50	

OFNP/PVA Tinted - D (blue) fluor phosphor

(25p unvarnished, others with 2 mm varnish bands)

EE1c	1p	**2B Crimson** (15.2.96)	30	25
EE2a	2p	**2B Deep green** (16.11.95)	30	55
EE4b	4p	**2B New blue** (2.11.95)	45	40
EE5b	5p	**2B Claret** (14.3.96)	40	40
EE10c	10p	**2B Deep orange** (10.1.96)	50	45
EE25	25p	**2B Bright salmon-pink** (10.10.95)	75	65
EE25a		'Rogue' Layflat paper	7.50	
EE29c	29p	**2B Light grey** (18.1.96)	1.00	85
EE30c	30p	**2B Grey-green** (26.3.96)	1.25	1.00
EE35d	35p	**2B Deep yellow** (18.12.95)	1.00	90
EE38d	38p	**2B Rosine** (8.1.96)	1.00	90
EE41b	41p	**2B Stone** (11.8.95)	1.20	1.00
EE41c		Pale grey-brown (2.5.96)	1.75	
EE43	43p	**2B Rosine** (25.6.96)	1.25	1.00
EE50b	50p	**2B Stone** (21.2.96)	1.50	1.20
EE50c		Imperf. pair	-	
EE100	£1	**2B Bluish violet** and Iriodin ink (22.8.95)	2.50	2.00

OFNP/PVA White - D (blue) fluor phosphor

(25p unvarnished, others with 2 mm varnish bands)

No.			U/M	F/U
EE1d	1p	**2B Crimson** (29.4.96)	50	25
EE2b	2p	**2B Deep green** (25.5.96)	35	55
EE4c	4p	**2B New blue** (1.8.96)	40	40
EE5c	5p	**2B Claret** (4.10.96)	50	40
EE5d		Deep reddish claret, mottled background	75	
EE6d	6p	**2B Lime green** (26.3.96)	40	35
EE10d	10p	**2B Deep orange** (13.9.96)	80	45
EE20	20p	**2B Sea-green** (26.3.96)	1.30	1.10
EE25	25p	**2B Deep salmon-pink** (20.10.95)	90	65
EE30d	30p	**2B Grey-green** (26.3.96)	1.00	1.00
EE31	31p	**2B Deep purple** (25.6.96)	70	65
EE37	37p	**2B Amethyst** (25.6.96)	75	70
EE39	39p	**2B Bright magenta** (25.6.96)	80	75

EE43a	43p	**2B Chocolate-brown** (25.6.96)	1.00	95
EE50d	50p	**2B Ochre** (14.11.96)	1.50	1.20
EE63	63p	**2B Light emerald** (25.6.96)	1.20	1.10
EE100a	£1	**2B Bluish violet** (fluorescent ink) and Iriodin ink (27.6.96)	2.50	2.00
EE100b		Bluish violet (without fluorescence)	3.25	
EE100c		Iriodin ink stops short of base of design	5.50	

Printer: Enschedé in Gravure

EEG42	42p	**2B Sage green** - Pane SP136 (Glory of the Garden book) (25.5.04)	1.50	
EEG47	47p	**2B Sea green** - Pane SP136 (Glory of the Garden book) (25.5.04)	1.65	

Printed by Questa in lithography

On the Questa Litho printings with elliptical perfs there are two types of ellipse - A(r) and B(s) - and also two fluor types. These are beyond the scope of this work, but full details may be found in the MCC Specialised Machin catalogue.

Colours similar to Enschedé Printings

OFNP/PVA - C (yellow) fluor phosphor

No.			U/M	F/U
EQL6	6p	**2B Lime green** - Pane SP66 (N. Ireland book) (26.7.94)	5.00	4.00
EQL10	10p	**2B Deep orange** - Pane SP70 (Nat. Trust book) (25.4.95)	2.50	2.00
EQL10a		Short bands at bottom	4.75	
EQL18	18p	**LB Bright green** - Pane SP64 (B. Potter book) (10.8.93)	2.00	1.50
		Short band at top - Pane SP64	8.00	
		Short band at bottom -Pane SP64	8.00	
		Two side bands - Pane SP64		
		Missing phosphor - Pane SP64a	£350	
EQL19	19p	**LB 4mm Olive-green** - Panes SP66 (N. Ireland book) (26.7.94), SP70 (Nat. Trust book) (25.4.95)	1.00	90
EQL19a		Short additional band at bottom right - Pane SP70	3.25	
EQL19b		4.75 mm left band - Pane SP72 (25.4.95)	75	
EQL19c	19p	**RB 4mm Olive-green** - Pane SP70 (Nat. Trust book) (25.4.95)	1.00	90
EQL19d		Short additional band at bottom left - Pane SP70	3.25	
EQL19e		4.75 mm right band - SP72 (Nat. Trust book) (25.4.95)	75	
EQL25	25p	**2B Salmon-pink** - Panes SP66 (N. Ireland book) (26.7.94), SP70 (Nat. Trust book) (25.4.95)	80	70
EQL25a		Short band at top right - Pane SP66	4.00	
EQL25b		Left band inset - Pane SP70	6.00	
EQL30	30p	**2B Grey-green** - Pane SP70 (Nat. Trust book) (25.4.95)	2.60	2.25
		Left band inset - Pane SP70	£15	
EQL33	33p	**2B Light emerald** - Pane SP64 (B. Potter book) (10.8.93)	1.75	
EQL33a		Right band short at top - Pane SP64	9.00	
EQL33b		Right band short at bottom - Pane SP64	9.00	
EQL33c		Missing phosphor - Pane SP64a	£450	
EQL35	35p	**2B Deep yellow** - Pane SP70 (Nat. Trust book) (25.4.95)	1.50	1.3
EQL35a		Short bands at top	£13	
EQL39	39p	**Bright mauve** - Pane SP64 (B. Potter book) (10.8.93)	1.90	
EQL39a		Right band short at top - Pane SP64	9.00	
EQL39b		Right band short at bottom - Pane SP64	9.00	
EQL39c		Double/triple impression - Pane SP64	£300	
EQL39d		Missing phosphor - Pane SP64a	£500	
EQL41	41p	**2B Drab** - Pane SP70 (Nat. Trust book) (25.4.95)	1.75	1.50

OFNP/PVA - D (blue) fluor phosphor

No.			U/M	F/U
EQL1	1p	**2B Crimson** - Pane EP14 (8.7.96)	50	30
EQL1a		Short bands at top - Pane EP14		
EQL1b		Short bands at bottom - Pane EP14	5.50	
EQL1c		Broad band at right - Pane EP14	£150	
EQL1d		Missing phosphor - Pane EP14a	£500	
EQL20	20p	**CB Bright green** - Panes EP14, EP16 (8.7.96)	1.00	90
EQL20a		Short bands at top - Panes EP14, EP16	£15	
EQL20b		Short bands at bottom - Pane EP14	£12	
EQL20c		Missing phosphor - Pane EP14a, EP16a	£175	
EQL20d		Narrow band at left - Pane EP14	£125	
EQL25	25p	**2B Salmon-pink** - Panes EP13, EP15 (19.12.95)	65	55
EQL25a		Pane SP77 (Euro '96 book)	3.50	
EQL25b		Broad band left - Pane SP77	£500	
EQL26	26p	**2B Red-brown** - Panes EP14, EP16 (8.7.96)	60	55
EQL26a		Short bands at top - Panes EP14, EP16	£15	
EQL26b		Short bands at bottom - Panes EP14	£15	
EQL26c		Inset left band - Panes EP14	£15	
EQL26d		Inset right band - Panes EP14	£15	
EQL26e		Broad band at right- Panes EP14	£150	
EQL26f		Missing phosphor	£45	

Printed by Questa in Gravure

OFNP/PVA - C (yellow) fluor phosphor

No.			U/M	F/U
EQG1	1p	**2B Crimson** - Pane EP21 (1.12.98)	50	35
EQG1a		'Invisible' phosphor - Pane EP21	£10	
EQG1b	1p	**2B Deep Crimson** - Pane EP22 (26.4.99)	50	35
EQG1c		Short bands at top - Pane EP22	3.00	
EQG1d		Short bands at bottom and additional Short CB at bottom	7.50	
EQG1f	1p	**2B (10mm) Crimson** - Pane SP98 (World Changers book) (21.9.99)	1.25	1.00
EQG1g		Short bands at top - Pane SP98	55	
EQG1h		Right band inset and short bands at top - SP98	3.25	
EQG1i		Right band inset - Pane SP98	5.00	
EQG1j	1p	**2B Crimson (Added OBA)** - Pane EP22	1.50	90
EQG1k		Short bands at top - Pane EP22	5.00	
EQG2	2p	**2B Green** - Pane EP22 (26.4.99)	50	35
EQG2a		Short bands at top - Pane EP22	3.25	
EQG2b	2p	**2B Green (Added OBA)** - Pane EP22 (31.7.99)	1.50	90
EQG2c		Short bands at top - Pane EP22	5.00	
EQG19	19p	**CB Olive-green** - Panes EP22, EP24	75	50
EQG19a		Additional narrow band at left -Pane EP22	£12	
EQG19b		Additional narrow band at right - Pane EP22	£12	
EQG19c	19p	**CB 5mm Bistre** - Pane SP98	1.00	75
EQG19d	19p	**CB Olive-green (Added OBA)** - Panes EP22, EP24 (31.7.89)	1.50	1.00
EQG19e		Additional narrow band at left -Pane EP22	£12	
EQG19f		Additional narrow band at right - Pane EP22	£12	
EQG20	20p	**CB Bright green** - Panes EP21, EP23 (1.12.98)	1.25	90
EQG20a		Short band at top - Pane EP23	4.50	
EQG20b		'Invisible' phosphor - Pane EP21	£25	
EQG26	26p	**2B Red-brown** - Pane EP21	65	45
EQG26a		Short bands at bottom - Pane EP21	£15	
EQG26b		Right band inset - Pane EP21	5.00	
EQG26c		'Invisible' phosphor - Pane EP21	7.50	
EQG26A	26p	**2B 10mm Chestnut** - Pane SP98 (World Changers book)	2.00	1.50
EQG26Aa		Right band inset	5.00	
EQG26B	26p	**2B Red-brown (Added OBA)** - Pane EP22 (31.7.99)	1.25	90
EQG26Ba		Left band inset - Pane EP22	5.00	
EQG26Bb		Right band inset - Pane EP22	£15	

Printed by Walsall in Lithography

OFNP/PVA (Cream) - C (yellow) fluor phosphor

No.			U/M	F/U
EWL25	25p	**2B (Inset) Deep salmon-pink** - Pane EP7 (1.11.93)	1.00	90
EWL25a		Short bands at top - Pane EP7	5.00	
EWL25b		Short bands at bottom - Pane EP7	5.00	
EWL25c		Double broad bands at right - Pane EP7	£65	
EWL25d		One narrow band at right - Pane EP7	£175	
EWL25e		One band at left, two bands at right - Pane EP7	£40	
EWL35	35p	**2B (Inset) Deep yellow** - Pane EP8 (1.11.93)	1.10	1.00
EWL35a		Inset left band - Pane EP8	4.00	
EWL35b		Inset right band - Pane EP8	4.50	
EWL35c		**Two** Full bands - Pane EP8	£10	
EWL41	41p	**2B (Inset) Stone** - Pane EP10 (1.11.93)	1.15	1.00
EWL41a		Left band inset - Pane EP10	£18	
EWL41b		Right band inset - Pane EP10	£18	
EWL41c		Missing phosphor		
EWL41d		One band at left, two bands at right	-	
EWL60	60p	**2B Slate-blue** (Inset left band) - Pane EP11 (9.8.94)	2.50	1.75
EWL60a		Inset right band - Pane EP11 (9.8.94)	4.00	
EWL60b		Full bands - pane EP11 (16.9.95)	5.50	

OFNP/PVA (White) - C (yellow) fluor phosphor

No.			U/M	F/U
EWL35d	35p	**2B Deep yellow** - Pane EP8	3.00	1.00
EWL41e	41p	**2B Stone** - Pane EP10	2.00	1.00
EWL41f		4mm CB (OR) - Pane EP10	£500	
EWL41g		Broad band left - Pane EP10	£500	
EWL60c	60p	**2B Slate-blue** - Pane EP11	2.25	1.75

OFNP/PVA (White) - D (blue) fluor phosphor

No.			U/M	F/U
EWL35e	35p	**2B Deep yellow** - Pane EP8a (20.10.95)	1.25	75
EWL35f		Left band inset - Pane EP8a (19.3.96)	1.30	
EWL35g		Right band inset - Pane EP8a (19.3.96)	1.30	
EWL37	37p	**2B Amethyst** - Pane EP9 (8.7.96)	4.50	3.50
EWL37a		Right band inset - Pane EP9 (8.7.96)	1.75	
EWL37b		Left band inset - Pane EP9 (8.7.96)	1.75	
EWL41h	41p	**2B Stone** - Pane EP10a (19.3.96)	4.50	1.50
EWL41i		Left band inset - Pane EP10a (19.3.96)	1.50	
EWL41j		Right band inset - Pane EP10a	1.50	
EWL60d	60p	**2B Slate-blue** - Pane EP11a (19.3.96)	4.50	1.90
EWL60e		Left band inset - Pane EP11a(19.3.96)	2.00	
EWL60f		Right band inset - Pane EP11a	2.00	
EWL63	63p	**2B Light emerald** - Pane EP12 (8.7.96)	1.00	1.00
EWL63a		Left band inset - Pane EP12 (8.7.96)	1.00	
EWL63b		Right band inset - Pane EP12	4.50	
EWL63c		Missing phosphor -Pane EP12a	£500	

Printed by Walsall in Gravure

OFNP/PVA - D (blue) fluor phosphor

No.			U/M	F/U
EWG10	10p	**2B Deep orange** - Pane SP88 (Breaking Barriers book) (13.10.98)	1.25	1.00
EWG10a		Short bands at top - Pane SP88	7.50	
EWG10b		Short bands at bottom - Pane SP88	£22	
EWG19	19p	**RB Bistre** - Pane SP101 (Special by Design book) (15.2.00)	1.00	95
EWG19a		Short band at top - Pane SP101	6.50	
EWG19b		Right band inset - Pane SP101	4.00	
EWG19c		Right band inset and Short band at top - Pane SP101	7.50	
EWG30	30p	**2B Grey-green** - Pane EP17 (5.5.98)	50	50
EWG37	37p	**2B Amethyst** - Pane EP18 (26.8.97)	80	75
EWG37a		Shiny printing - Pane EP18 (5.5.98)	1.10	
EWG38	38p	**2B Ultramarine** - Pane EP19 (26.4.99)	80	70
EWG38a	38p	**2B Ultramarine** (Smaller design) - Pane SP101 (Special by Design book) (15.2.00)	5.00	4.00
EWG38b		Left band short at top - Pane SP101	1.25	
EWG38c		Right band inset - Pane SP101	£25	
EWG38d		Right band inset and Left band short at top - Pane SP101	8.00	
EWG39	39p	**2B Light grey** - Pane SP140 (Bronte sisters book) (24.2.05)	1.75	1.30
EWG40	40p	**2B Greyish-blue** - Pane EP20	80	60
EWG42	42p	**2B Sage green** - Pane SP140 (Bronte sisters book) (24.2.05)	1.80	1.50
EWG43	43p	**2B Chocolate-brown** - Pane SP88 (Breaking Barriers book) (13.10.98)	1.25	1.00
EWG43a		Short bands at top - Pane SP88	8.00	
EWG43b		Short bands at bottom - Pane SP88	£20	
EWG43c		Right band inset - Pane SP88	5.00	
EWG43d		Right band stepped at top - Pane SP88	£25	
EWG43e	43p	**2B Sepia-brown** - Pane SP86 (Breaking Barriers book) (13.10.98)	1.25	1.00
EWG43f		Short bands at bottom -Pane SP86	£20	
EWG43g		Left band inset - Pane SP86	£23	
EWG63	63p	**2B Light emerald** - Pane EP21 (26.8.97)	1.25	1.00
EWG63a		Shiny printing	1.50	
EWG64	64p	**2B Sea green** - Pane EP22	1.25	1.20
EWG65	65p	**2B Greenish-blue** - Pane EP23	1.30	1.25

De La Rue ATN Printings
(formerly known as Byfleet)

Printed by De La Rue on the ATN press in Gravure with Dlw phosphor/fluor.

These were formerly known as 'Byfleet' printings, and are easily differentiated from the earlier gravure printings by the bright blue fluorescence.

In co-operation with other Machin dealers, this catalogue, and the Machin Collectors Club, have now sub divided these further into three gum types. These are:-

ATN(l) Layflat gum
ATN (t) Tinted gum ATN (c) Cream PVA gum

On the printings with tinted gum - ATN(t) - different papers are known which are variously described as Bright Intermediate or Dull, these descriptions meaning the reaction of the paper when viewed under long wave UV. However with single stamps it is virtually impossible to distinguish between the bright or intermediate papers *unless* you have a marginal example. In these listings we show single stamps as either Dull or Bright/Intermediate. For collectors who do collect marginal single stamps or who specialise in Cylinder or Date blocks you will find the complete listings of ALL paper varieties in the Machin Collectors Club specialised catalogue - and also a monthly update in the MCC's Newsletters.

Please note that prices for phosphor band varieties are difficult to determine with any accuracy at this time. However, all known varieties are listed, and with current prices where known.

ATN (l) - Layflat gum

No.			U/M	F/U
ATN(l)20	20p	**2B Bright green**	50	
ATN(l)20a		Left band inset	7.50	
ATN(l)20b		Right band inset		
ATN(l)20c		Short band top	6.00	
ATN(l)20d		Dark shade. from 04/03/03 printing		
ATN(l)20e		Phosphor/fluor wash from 04/03/03 printing		
ATN(l)33	33p	**2B Slate blue**	60	
ATN(l)33a		Left band inset	£12	
ATN(l)33b		Short band top		
ATN(l)35	35p	**2B Sepia-brown**	60	

No.			U/M	F/U
ATN(l)39	39p	**2B Light grey**	60	
ATN(l)39a		Left band inset	8.50	
ATN(l)39b		Right band inset		
ATN(l)39c		Short band bottom		
ATN(l)40	40p	**2B Greenish-blue**	80	
ATN(l)43	43p	**2B Pale emerald**	85	

ATN (t) - Tinted Gum

No.			U/M	F/U
ATN(t)1	1p	**2B Crimson** - Bright/Inter. paper	10	
ATN(t)1a		Left band inset	4.00	
ATN(t)1b		Right band inset	4.00	
ATN(t)1c		Short band at top	£10	
ATN(t)1d		Short band at bottom	5.00	
ATN(t)2	2p	**2B Deep green** - Bright/Inter. paper	15	
ATN(t)2a		Left band inset	3.50	
ATN(t)2b		Right band inset	7.00	
ATN(t)2c		Short band top	8.00	
ATN(t)4	4p	**2B New blue** - Dull paper	20	
ATN(t)4a		Left band inset		
ATN(t)4b		Right band inset		
ATN(t)4Aa	4p	**2B New blue** - Bright/Inter. paper	20	
ATN(t)4Ab		Left band inset	3.50	
ATN(t)4Ac		Right band inset		

No.			U/M	F/U
ATN(t)5	5p	**2B Claret** - Dull paper	25	
ATN(t)5a		Left band inset	9.00	
ATN(t)5b		Short band top	5.50	
ATN(t)5Aa	5p	**2B Claret** - Bright/Inter. paper	25	
ATN(t)5Ab		Left band inset	8.00	
ATN(t)5Ac		Short band top		
ATN(t)7	7p	**2B Bright magenta** - Bright/Inter. paper	30	
ATN(t)7a		Right band inset		
ATN(t)8	8p	**2B Deep yellow** - Bright/Inter. paper	30	
ATN(t)8a		Left band inset		
ATN(t)8b		Short band top		

No.			U/M	F/U
ATN(t)9	9p	**2B Orange** - Bright/Inter. paper	35	
ATN(t)9a		Left band inset	£11	
ATN(t)10	10p	**2B Deep orange** - Bright/Inter. paper	35	
ATN(t)10a		Left band inset		
ATN(t)10b		Right band inset	6.50	
ATN(t)10c		Short band bottom	4.50	
ATN(t)10a		Phosphor/fluor wash		
ATN(t)10b		Dark shade		
ATN(t)10c		Dark shade - Phosphor/fluor wash		

No.			U/M	F/U
ATN(t)20	20p	**2B Bright green** - Bright/Inter. paper	40	
ATN(t)20a		Left band inset	4.00	
ATN(t)20b		Right band inset		
ATN(t)20c		Short band top		
ATN(t)20d		Short band bottom		
ATN(t)20a		Dark shade		
ATN(t)20b		Pale shade		
ATN(t)20Aa	20p	**2B Bright green** - Dull paper	65	
ATN(t)20A		Left band inset		
ATN(t)33	33p	**2B Slate blue** - Bright paper	50	
ATN(t)33a		Left band inset	6.00	
ATN(t)34	34p	**2B Lime green** - Bright/Inter. paper	50	
ATN(t)34a		Left band inset	4.50	
ATN(t)34b		Right band inset		
ATN(t)34c		Short band top		
ATN(t)34Aa	34p	**2B Lime green** - Dull paper	75	
ATN(t)34Ab		Left band inset		
ATN(t)34Ac		Right band inset		
ATN(t)35	35p	**2B Sepia-brown** - Bright/Inter. paper	50	
ATN(t)35a		Left band inset	12.50	
ATN(t)35b		Short band top		
ATN(t)35Aa	35p	**CB Lime green** - Bright/Inter. paper	50	

No.			U/M	F/U
ATN(t)37	37p	**2B Grey-black** - Inter. paper	55	
ATN(t)37a		Short band top	6.00	
ATN(t)39	39p	**2B Light grey** - Inter. paper	60	
ATN(t)40	40p	**2B Greenish-blue** - Bright/Inter. paper	60	
ATN(t)40a		Left band inset	6.00	
ATN(t)41	41p	**2B Red** - Bright paper		
ATN(t)41a		Left band inset	5.00	
ATN(t)42	42p	**2B Grey-green** - Bright/Inter. paper	75	
ATN(t)42a		Left band inset		
ATN(t)43	43p	**2B Pale emerald** - Inter. paper	80	
ATN(t)43a		Right band inset		

No.			U/M	F/U
ATN(t)46	46p	**2B Old Gold** - Bright/Intermediate paper		
ATN(t)47	47p	**2B Sea green** - Dull paper		
ATN(t)47Aa	47p	**2B Sea green** - Bright/Intermediate paper		
		Left band inset	12.50	
ATN(t)50	50p	**2B Ochre** - Bright/Inter. paper	95	
ATN(t)50a		Left band inset		
ATN(t)50b		Right band inset		
ATN(t)50c		Short band top		
ATN(t)50d		Short band bottom	6.50	

No.			U/M	F/U
ATN(t)68	68p	**2B Stone** - Inter. paper		
ATN(t)68a		Left band inset	6.00	
ATN(t)68b		Short band top	6.00	
ATN(t)100	£1	**2B Bluish-violet** - Dull paper		
ATN(t)100Aa	£1	**2B Bluish-violet** - Bright/Inter. paper	1.80	
ATN(t)100Ab		Left band inset	8.00	
ATN(t)100Ac		Right band inset		
ATN(t)100Ad		Short band top		
ATN(t)150	£1.50	**2B Rust-red** - Inter. paper	2.50	
ATN(t)150a		Short band bottom	5.00	

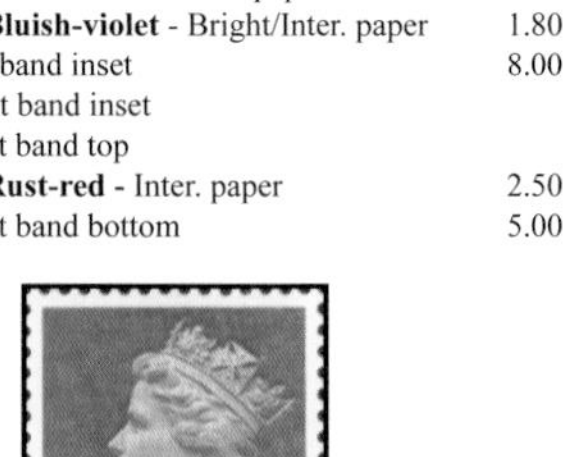

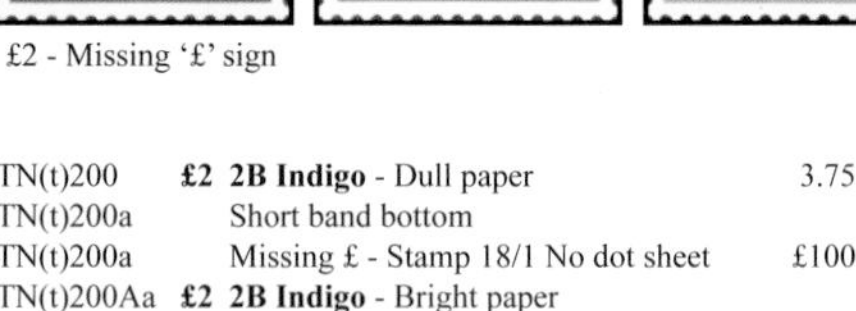

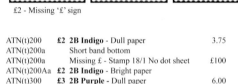

£2 - Missing '£' sign

No.			U/M	F/U
ATN(t)200	£2	**2B Indigo** - Dull paper	3.75	
ATN(t)200a		Short band bottom		
ATN(t)200a		Missing £ - Stamp 18/1 No dot sheet	£100	
ATN(t)200Aa	£2	**2B Indigo** - Bright paper		
ATN(t)300	£3	**2B Purple** - Dull paper	6.00	
ATN(t)500	£5	**2B Slate-blue** - Inter. paper	8.50	

ATN (c) - Cream PVA Gum

No.			U/M	F/U
ATN(c)1	**1p**	**2B Crimson**	15	
		Left band inset	7.50	
		Right band inset	7.50	
		Short band top		
		Short band bottom		
ATN(c)2	**2p**	**2B Deep green**	15	
		Left band inset	4.00	
		Short band top	7.50	
ATN(c)5	**5p**	**2B Claret**		

No.			U/M	F/U
ATN(c)35	**35p**	**2B Lime green CB**	65	
ATN(c)47	**47p**	**2B Sea green**	85	
ATN(c)50	**50p**	**2B Ochre**	95	

No.			U/M	F/U
ATN(c)100	**£1**	**2B Bluish-violet**	1.50	
ATN(c)1st	**1st**	**2B Gold**	65	
		Left band inset		
		Short band top	6.00	
		Short band bottom	6.50	

Multi-Value Coil Strips

All coil stamps were printed by Harrisons

OCP/GA

No.			U/M	F/U
MC1	2 x ½p	**2B Turquoise, 2 x 1p 2B Crimson** and **2p 2B Green** (15.2.71)	95	
MC1a		Broad band at left	£25	
MC1b		Broad band at right	£125	
MC1c		Missing phosphor (screened)	£30	
MC1d		Silicone coated	£200	

OCP/PVA

No.			U/M	F/U
MC2	2 x ½p	**2B Turquoise, 1p 2B Crimson, 2p 2B Green** and **6p 2B Light green** (3.77)	2.75	

FCP/GA

No.			U/M	F/U
MC3	2 x ½p	**2B Turquoise, 2 x 1p 2B Crimson** and **2p 2B Myrtle-green** with silicone coating (9.72) As MC1	2.50	
MC3a		Silicone omitted	£15	

FCP/PVAD

No.			U/M	F/U
MC4	2 x ½p	**2B Turquoise, 2 x 1p 2B Crimson** and **2p 2B Green** (4.74) As MC1	50	
MC4a		Broad band	£40	
MC4b		Missing phosphor	7.50	
MC4c		Thin paper	£40	
MC5	2 x ½p	**2B Turquoise, 1p 2B Crimson, 2p 2B Dark green** and **6p 2B Light green** (3.12.75) As MC2	65	
MC5a		Broad band	2.00	
MC5b		Broad band at right	7.00	

No.			U/M	F/U
MC6	2 x ½p	**CB Turquoise, 2 x 1p CB Crimson** and **7p CB Purple-brown** (14.12.77)	55	
MC6a		Screened value on 7p	9.50	
MC6b		Thick paper	3.00	

No.			U/M	F/U
MC7	2 x 1p	**CB Crimson, 8p CB Rosine** *plus* 2 x "be properly addressed" and "use the postcode" labels (16.1.80)	45	
MC7a		'All over' phosphor error	£250	

PCP1/PVAD

No.			U/M	F/U
MC8	½p	**Turquoise** and **3 x 4p Greenish blue** (30.12.81)	65	
MC8a		Fluorescent Brightener Omitted (mounted)	£175	
MC8b		FBO (unmounted mint)	£1500	
MC8a		PCP2. Fluorescent Brightener Omitted (mounted)	£125	

No.			U/M	F/U
MC9	1p	**Crimson** and **3 x 4p Greenish blue** (14.8.84)	65	

No.			U/M	F/U
MC10	2½p	**Rose-red** and **3 x 3p Dull red magenta** (6.81)	65	
MC10a		Fluorescent Brightener Omitted	£35	

ACP/PVAD

No.			U/M	F/U
MC11	1p	**Crimson** and **3 x 4p Greenish blue** (18.3.88)	45	

No.			U/M	F/U
MC12	2p	**Green** and **3 x 4p Pale blue** (5.9.88)	1.95	

No.			U/M	F/U
MC13	3p	**Bright magenta** and **3 x 4p New blue** (10.10.89)	1.00	

No.		U/M	F/U

MC14	5p **Dull red-brown** and **3 x 4p New blue** (27.11.90)	85	
MC15	**2 x 5p Dull red-brown** and **2 x 4p New blue** (1.10.91)	75	

OFPP/PVAD

MC16	**3 x 5p Dull red-brown** and **4p New blue** (31.1.95	75	

Single Value Coil Strip

No.		U/M	F/U
SC1	**5 x 25p Salmon pink** - Redaers digest coil strip (6.2.96)	£20	

Stamps inscribed 1st or 2nd class were issued on 22nd August 1989 for a trial period. Partly, their purpose was to avoid stock returns from retail outlets when postal rate changes came into operation.

1989 (22 Aug.) - 90

Printed by Harrison in Photogravure

Perf. 15 x 14

FCP/PVAD

No.			U/M	F/U
HN1	2nd	**CB Bright blue,** Imperf. at top - Panes CP1, CP2	65	50
HN2	2nd	**CB Bright blue,** Imperf. at top and right, Pane CP1	3.00	2.00
HN3	2nd	**CB Bright blue,** Imperf. at bottom - Panes CP1, CP2	65	50
HN4	2nd	**CB Bright blue.** Imperf. at bottom and right - Panes CP1	3.00	2.00
HN5	2nd	**RB Bright blue** - Pane SP47 (London Life book) (20.3.90)	2.50	1.40
HN6	2nd	**CB Dark blue** Imperf. at top - Pane CP3 (7.8.90)	50	45
HN7	2nd	**CB Dark blue** ,Imperf. at bottom - Pane CP3	50	45
HN8	1st	**2B Black** Pane SP47 (London Life book) (20.3.90)	2.50	1.40

ACP/PVAD

No.			U/M	F/U
HN9	1st	**Black,** Imperf. at top - Panes CP4, CP5	70	60
HN10	1st	**Black,** Imperf. at top and right - Pane CP4	4.00	5.00
HN11	1st	**Black,** Imperf. at bottom - Pane CP4, CP5	70	60
HN12	1st	**Black,** Imperf. at bottom and right - Pane CP4	4.00	5.00
HN13	1st	**Orange-red,** Imperf. at top - Pane CP6 (7.8.90)	50	50
HN14	1st	**Orange-red,** Imperf. at bottom - Pane CP6	50	50
		First Day Cover (22.8.89)		1.50

Printed by Questa in Lithography

Perf. 15 x 14

FCP/PVA

No.			U/M	F/U
QN1	2nd	**CBar Bright blue** - Pane CP7, CP7a (19.8.89)	60	45
QN1a		Short band at top - Pane CP7	2.00	
QN1b		Short band at bottom - Pane CP7	2.00	
QN2	2nd	**CBar Dark blue** - Pane CP8 (7.8.90)	75	85
QN2a		Short band at top - pane CP8	2.00	
QN2b		Short band at bottom - Pane CP8	2.00	
QN3	2nd	**RB 4.5mm Bright blue** - Pane SP55 (Wales book) (25.2.92)	95	85
QN3a		Missing phosphor - Pane SP55a	£700	
QN4	2nd	**RB 3.5mm Bright blue** - Pane SP59 (Tolkien book) (27.10.92)	1.00	85
QN4a		Short additional band at top left - Pane SP59	4.00	
QN5	1st	**2B Orange-red** - Pane SP59 (Tolkien book) (27.10.92)	1.25	1.00
QN5a		Left band short at top - Pane SP59	4.50	
QN6	1st	**2B Orange-red** - Pane SP55 (Wales book) (25.2.92)	1.00	75
QN6a		Missing phosphor - Pane SP55	£750	

ACP/PVA

No.			U/M	F/U
QN7	1st	**Black** - Panes CP9, CP9b (19.9.89)	1.00	1.10
QN7a		Low OBA -Panes CP9a, CP9c	1.40	
QN8	1st	**Orange-red** - Pane CP10 (6.8.91)	60	50

ACP/PVAD

No.			U/M	F/U
QN9	1st	**Orange-red** - Pane CP11 (7.8.90)	40	

OFNP/PVA - C (Yellow) fluor

No.			U/M	F/U
QN10	1st	**2B Orange-red** - Pane SP63 (B. Potter book) (10.8.93)	1.50	1.25
QN10a		Left band inset - Pane SP63	9.00	
QN11	2nd	**LB Bright blue** - Pane SP64 (B. Potter book) (10.8.93)	1.00	95
QN11a		Short additional band at top right - Pane SP64	2.50	
QN11b		Short additional band at bottom right - Pane SP64	2.50	
QN11c		Missing phosphor - Pane SP64a	£325	

Printed by Walsall in Lithography

Perf. 14

FCP/PVA

No.			U/M	F/U
WN1	2nd	**CB Bright blue,** Imperf. at top - Pane CP12 (22.8.89)	40	50
WN1a		Short band at top - Pane CP12	5.00	
WN2	2nd	**CB Bright blue,** Imperf. at top and right - Pane CP12	1.25	70
WN3	2nd	**CB Bright blue,** Imperf. at bottom - Pane CP12	40	50
WN4	2nd	**CB Bright blue,** Imperf. at bottom and right - Pane CP12	1.25	70
WN5	2nd	**CB Dark blue,** Imperf. at top - Panes CP13, CP16 (7.8.90)	45	40
WN5a		Short band at top - pane CP13	£15	
WN6	2nd	**CB Dark blue,** Imperf. at bottom - Panes CP13, CP16	45	40
WN6a		Short band at bottom - Pane CP16	5.00	
WN7	1st	**2B Black,** Imperf. at top - Pane CP15 (22.8.89)	1.00	1.00
WN7a		Missing phosphor - Pane CP15a	£150	
WN8	1st	**2B Black,** Imperf. at top and right - pane CP15	1.25	1.00
WN8a		Missing phosphor - Pane CP15a	£150	
WN9	1st	**2B Black,** Imperf. at bottom - Pane CP15	1.00	1.00
WN9a		Missing phosphor - Pane CP15a	£150	
WN10	1st	**2B Black,** Imperf. at bottom and right - Pane CP51	1.25	1.00
WN10a		Missing phosphor - Pane CP15a	£150	

FCP/PVAD

No.			U/M	F/U
WN11	2nd	**CB Bright blue,** Imperf. at top (16.3.93)	40	50
WN12	2nd	**CB Bright blue,** Imperf. at bottom	40	50

ACP/PVA

No.			U/M	F/U
WN13	1st	**Orange-red** Imperf. at top - Panes CP19, CP20 (7.8.90)	50	50
WN13a		Low OBA - Panes CP19a, CP20a	50	
WN14	1st	**Orange-red,** Imperf. at bottom - Panes CP19, CP20	50	50
WN14a		Low OBA - Panes CP19a, CP20a	50	

Perf 13

No.			U/M	F/U
WN15	1st	**Orange-red,** Imperf. at top - Pane CP21 (10.90)	1.50	85
WN15a		Low OBA - Pane CP21a	1.75	
WN16	1st	**Orange-red,** Imperf. at bottom - Pane CP21	1.50	85
WN16a		Low OBA - Pane CP21a	1.75	
		First Day Cover (7.8.90)		1.50

ACP/PVAD

No.			U/M	F/U
WN17	1st	**Orange-red** Imperf. at top - Panes CP22, CP23 (9.2.93)	50	30
WN18	1st	**Orange-red**, Imperf. at bottom - Panes CP22, CP23	50	30

1993 (6 April). Perf 15 x 14 (elliptical).

Printed by Harrison in Photogravure

OFPP/PVAD

No.			U/M	F/U
HNE1A	1st	**Orange-red** - Panes CP27, CP28 (6.4.93)	55	30
HNE1Aa		Translucent paper	4.50	

OFNP/PVAD - C (Yellow) fluor

No.			U/M	F/U
HNE2A	2nd	**CB Bright blue** - Panes CP24 (7.9.93)	1.60	
HNE2Aa		Translucent paper - Pane CP24	50	25
HNE1B	1st	**2B Orange-red** - Pane CP26 (4.4.95)	65	30
HNE1Ba		Translucent paper - Pane CP26	2.00	

OFNP/PVAD - D (Blue) fluor

No.			U/M	F/U
HNE2B	2nd	**CB 4mm Bright blue** - Pane CP24a (28.7.95)	1.10	75
HNE2C	2nd	**CB 4.5mm Bright blue** - Pane CP24a	90	70
HNE2Ca		Vertical coil (8.7.96)	90	
HNE2Cb		Translucent paper - Pane CP24a	2.50	
HNE2D	2nd	**CB 4.5mm Deep bright blue** - Pane CP25	1.10	85
HNE2Da		Translucent paper - Pane CP25 (6.8.96)	2.00	

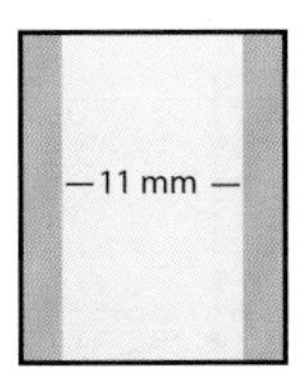

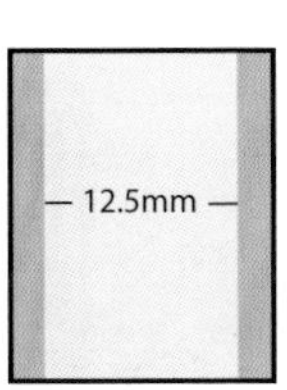

There are two varieties of phosphor bands on the 1st Vertical coil stamps. For simplicity these are described as either 11mm or 12.5mm which refers to the space *between* the bands as shown above.

No.			U/M	F/U
HNE1C	1st	**2B Orange-red** - Pane CP26a (28.7.95)	1.00	85
HNE1Ca		Translucent paper - CP26a	3.25	
HNE1Cb		Vertical coil, 11mm (8.7.96)	1.00	
HNE1Cc		Vertical coil, Screened value, 11mm (8.7.96)	7.00	
HNE1Cd		Vertical coil, 12.5mm	2.50	
HNE1Ce		Vertical coil, Screened value, 12.5mm	11.00	

OFNP/PVA (Layflat) - D (Blue) fluor

No.			U/M	F/U
HNE2E	2nd	**CB Bright blue** - Pane CP29 (.4.97)	3.00	70
HNE1D	1st	**2B Orange-red** - Pane CP30 (.4.97)	3.25	85

Printed by Walsall in Lithography

OFNP/PVA - C (Yellow) fluor

No.			U/M	F/U
WNE2A	2nd	**CB Bright blue**, Cream gum, - Panes CP35, CP36 (6.4.93)	60	45
WNE2Aa		Short band at bottom	£18	
WNE2B	2nd	**CB Bright blue**, White gum - Pane CP35	1.75	
WNE1A	1st	**2B (Both inset) Orange-red**, Cream gum - Panes CP37, CP39 (6.4.93)	65	50
WNE1Aa		Bands short at bottom, Both bands inset - Pane CP39	4.75	
WNE1Ab		Right band inset - Pane CP39	£15	
WNE1Ac		Double broad band left - Panes CP37, CP39	£175	
WNE1Ad		Double broad band right - Panes CP37, CP39	£125	
WNE1Ae		One 4mm Centre band - Panes CP37, CP39	£200	
WNE1Af		Missing phosphor - Pane CP39a	£200	
WNE1Ag		One band at left, two bands at right - Pane CP39	£45	
WNE1B	1st	**2B (Left inset) Orange-red**, Cream gum - Panes CP37, CP39 (6.4.93)	1.95	1.50
WNE1C	1st	**2B (Right inset) Orange-red**, Cream gum - Panes CP37, (6.4.93)	1.95	1.50
WNE1D	1st	**2B Orange-red**, White gum - Panes CP37, CP39 (6.4.93)	1.00	
WNE1Da		Short bands at top - CP37, CP39	£10	
WNE1Db		Left band inset - Panes CP37, CP39	7.50	
WNE1Dc		Right band inset - Panes CP37, CP39	7.50	
WNE1Dd		Missing phosphor - Panes CP37, CP39	£175	

OFNP/PVA - D (Blue) fluor

No.			U/M	F/U
WNE2C	2nd	**CB Bright blue**, White gum - Pane CP35a	85	55
WNE1E	1st	**2B Orange-red**, Dull fluor - Panes CP38, CP40	85	65
WNE1Ea		Left band inset - Panes CP38, CP40	4.50	
WNE1Eb		Right band inset - Panes CP38, CP40	4.50	
WNE1F	1st	**2B Orange-red**, Bright fluor - Panes CP38, CP40	1.00	80
WNE1Fa		Short bands at bottom - Pane CP40	6.50	
WNE1Fb		Short bands at bottom, Right band inset - Pane CP40	£10	
WNE1Fc		Left band inset - Pane CP40	£10	
WNE1Fd		Right band inset - Pane CP40		

Printed by Questa in Lithography

Thick value

Thin value

Questa used two types of perforator which resulted in two distinct ellipse shapes as illustrated below. The first has a rounded or 'rugby ball' shape and is known as A(r), whereas the second is straighter or 'sausage' shaped and is known as B(s). A further difference on the Questa printings is the gum colour which is either cream or white. Either or both of these can make a considerable difference to the value of a stamp.

Ellipse Type A(r)

Ellipse Type B(s)

OFNP/PVA - C (Yellow) fluor

No.			U/M	F/U
QNE2A	**2nd**	**CBar Bright blue**, Cream gum, A(r) ellipse Sheets (6.4.93)	60	45
QNE2Aa		Pane CP31 - (6.4.93)	60	
QNE2Ab		Short band at top - Pane CP31	3.00	
QNE2Ac		Short band at bottom -Pane CP31	3.00	
QNE2Ad		Missing phosphor - CP31a	£175	
QNE2Ae		Very weak phosphor - CP31	4.50	
QNE2B	**2nd**	**CBar Bright blue**, Cream gum, B(s) ellipse Sheets (.10.94)	£15	
QNE2Ba		Short band at bottom only - Sheets	£20	
QNE2C	**2nd**	**CB Bright blue**, Cream gum, A(r) ellipse Pane CP32	60	45
QNE2D	**2nd**	**CBar Bright blue**, White gum, B(s) ellipse Sheets (7.10.94)	1.50	
QNE2Da		Short band at top only - Sheets	3.75	
QNE2Db		Short band at bottom only - Sheets	7.50	
QNE2Dc		Reduced fluor - Pane CP32 (22.2.95)	£30	
QNE2E	**2nd**	**CB Bright blue**, White gum, A(r) ellipse Pane CP32	1.75	1.50
QNE2Ea		Missing phosphor - Pane CP32	£175	
QNE2Eb		Reduced fluor - Pane CP32	2.00	
QNE1A	**1st**	**2B Orange-red**, Thin value, Cream gum, A(r) ellipse - Sheets & Boots M/S	60	45
QNE1Aa		Bands short at bottom - Sheets & Boots M/S	7.50	
QNE1Ab		Left band inset - Boots M/S	£15	
QNE1Ac		Right band inset - Boots M/S	£15	
QNE1Ad		Missing phosphor - Boots M/S	£850	
QNE1B	**1st**	**2B Orange-red**, Thick value, Cream gum, A(r) ellipse - Panes CP33, CP34	1.00	75
QNE1Ba		Short bands at top - Pane CP33	5.00	
QNE1Bb		Short bands at bottom - Pane CP33	7.50	
QNE1Bc		Left band inset - Pane CP33	£15	
QNE1Bd		Right band inset - Pane CP33	12.50	
QNE1Be		Missing phosphor - Pane CP34a		
QNE1C	**1st**	**2B Orange-red**, Thin value, Cream gum, B(s) ellipse - Boots M/S	£30	

No.			U/M	F/U
QNE1D	**1st**	**2B Orange-red**, Thin value, White gum, A(r) ellipse - Pane CP33	1.00	
QNE1Da		Reduced fluor - Pane CP33	4.00	
QNE1E	**1st**	**2B Orange-red**, Thin value, White gum, B(s) ellipse - Pane CP33, Boots M/S	2.00	
QNE1Ea		Short bands at top - Boots M/S	£22	
QNE1Eb		Short bands at bottom - Pane CP33		
QNE1Ec		Left band inset - Boots M/S	£10	
QNE1Ed		Right band inset - Boots M/S	£15	

OFNP/PVA - D (Blue) fluor

No.			U/M	F/U
QNE2F	**2nd**	**CB 4mm Bright blue**, B(s) ellipse - Pane CP32a (28.7.95)	1.00	75
QNE2G	**2nd**	**CB 4mm Bright blue**, A(r) ellipse - Pane CP32a	£30	
QNE2H	**2nd**	**CBar 4mm Deep bright blue**, B(s) ellipse - Sheets (14.11.95)	1.00	85
QNE2Ha		Short band at bottom only - Sheets	£15	
QNE2I	**2nd**	**CB 4mm Bright blue**, B(s) ellipse - Pane CP32a (20.4.96)	1.50	1.25
QNE2Ia		3.5mm Narrow weak phosphor band - Pane CP32a	5.00	
QNE2J	**2nd**	**CB 4.5mm Bright blue**, B(s) ellipse - Sheets (5.10.96)	1.50	1.00
QNE2Ja		Short band at bottom - Sheets	£25	
QNE1F	**1st**	**2B Orange-red**, B(s) ellipse - Pane CP33a (28.7.95)	1.00	85
QNE1Fa		Sheets (14.11.95), Boots M/S (11.9.95)	1.00	
QNE1Fb		Left band inset - Boots M/S	£15	
QNE1Fc		Missing phosphor - Boos M/S	£600	
QNE1G	**1st**	**2B 8mm Orange-red**, B(s) ellipse - Pane CP33a (7.9.98)	1.00	85
QNE1Ga		Pane SP93 (Profile on Print book)	1.00	
QNE1Gb		Short bands at top - Pane SP93	£22	
QNE1H	**1st**	**2B 7mm Orange-red**, A(r) ellipse - Sheets	£10	
QNE1I	**1st**	**2B 8mm Orange-red**, A(r) ellipse - Pane SP93 (Profile on Print book)	1.50	1.25

Printer: Enschedé in Litho

OFNP/PVA - D (Blue) fluor

No.			U/M	F/U
ENE1A	**1st**	**2B Orange-red**, Dull violet fluor - Unbranded M/S	75	50
ENE1B	**1st**	**2B Orange-red**, Bright violet fluor - Unbranded M/S	7.50	5.75
ENE1Ba		Short bands at top- Unbranded M/S	£20	
ENE1Bb		Short bands at bottom- Unbranded M/S	£20	
ENE1C	**1st**	**2B Orange-red**, Bright turquoise fluor - Unbranded M/S	£30	

Printed by Harrison/De La Rue in Gravure

OFNP/PVAD - D (Blue) fluor

No.			U/M	F/U
HNEG2A	2nd	**CB Bright blue** - Vertical coil (Trial issue) (8.7.96)	2.50	2.00

OFNP/PVA Layflat - D (Blue) fluor

No.			U/M	F/U
HNEG2B	2nd	**CB Bright blue** - Pane CP40	95	50
HNEG2Ba		Vertical coil (24.9.97)	95	
HNEG1A	1st	**2B Gold**, Dull fluor - Pane CP44 (21.4.97)	1.10	55
HNEG1Aa		Pane SP80 (BBC book) (23.9.97)	1.10	
HNEG1Ab		Left band stepped at top - Pane SP80	17.50	
HNEG1Ac		Left band stepped at bottom - Pane SP80	10.00	
HNEG1Ad		Right band stepped at top - Pane SP80	17.50	
HNEG1Ae		Right band stepped at bottom - Pane SP80	10.00	
HNEG1B	1st	**2B Gold**, Bright fluor - Pane SP135 (Letters by night book) (16.3.04)	1.00	55
HNEG1C	1st	**2B Orange-red** - Vertical coil (29.4.97)	1.00	
HNEG1Ca		Pane CP41(18.11.97)	1.00	
HNEG1D	1st	**2B Deep orange-red** - Pane SP89 (Profile on Print book) (16.2.99)	1.00	55
HNEG1Da		Short bands at top - Pane SP89	6.00	
HNEG1Db		Short bands at bottom - Pane SP89	4.00	
HNEG1Dc		Left band inset - Pane SP89	3.00	
HNEG1Dd		Right band inset - Pane SP89	3.25	
HNEG1De		Left band stepped at top - Pane SP89	15.00	
HNEG1Df		Left band stepped at bottom - Pane SP89	17.50	
HNEG1Dg		Right band stepped at top - Pane SP89	15.00	
HNEG1Dh		Right band stepped at bottom - Pane SP89	25.00	
HNEG1Di		Broad band left - Pane SP89	£13	
HNEG1Dj		4.5mm CB OL - Pane SP89	£13	
HNEG1E	1st	**2B Millennium** - Sheets (6.1.00)	75	50

OFPP/PVAD - D (Blue) fluor

No.			U/M	F/U
HNEG1F	1st	**2B Millennium** - Her Majesty's stamps miniature sheet (23.5.00)	1.50	1.00

Printed by Walsall in Gravure

On the Walsall Gravure printings there are two types of both the fluor level and the finish. The fluor level can be either Dull or Bright, and you will need a long wave UV lamp to detect this. The finish can either appear matt or glossy. Both these terms are used in the following Walsall listing. All are rotary perfs unless otherwise stated.

On some stamps there are also two types of Ellipse similar to the Questa types illustrated earlier.

OFNP/PVA - D (Blue) fluor

No.			U/M	F/U
WNEG2A	2nd	**CB Bright blue**, Dull fluor, Matt finish - Sheets (29.4.97)	75	50
WNEG2B	2nd	**CB Deep bright blue**, Dull fluor, Matt finish - Pane CP45 (26.8.97)	1.00	
WNEG2C	2nd	**CB Bright blue**, Dull fluor, Matt finish, Comb perfs - Pane CP45 (.10.97)	1.50	
WNEG2D	2nd	**CB Deep bright blue**, Bright fluor, Glossy finish - Pane CP45 (.11.97)	75	
WNEG2E	2nd	**CB Deep bright blue**, Bright fluor, Glossy finish, Comb perfs - Sheets	1.50	
WNEG2Ea		Pane CP45 (.11.97)	1.50	
WNEG2F	2nd	**CB Bright blue**, Bright fluor, Matt finish - Panes SP116 (Gracious Accession book), SP128 (Perfect Coronation book) (2.6.03), SP140 (Bronte sisters book) (24.2.05)	95	
WNEG2G	2nd	**LB Bright blue**, Bright fluor, Glossy finish, - Pane SP87 (Breaking barriers book) (13.10.98)	1.00	75
WNEG2Ga		Short band at top - Pane SP87	8.50	
WNEG2Fb		Short band at bottom - Pane SP87	£20	
WNEG2H	2nd	**RB Bright blue**, Bright fluor, Glossy finish, - Pane SP87 (Breaking barriers book) (13.10.98)	1.20	75
WNEG2Ha		Short band at top - Pane SP87	£20	
WNEG2Hb		Short band at bottom - Pane SP87	£20	
WNEG2I	2nd	**2B Deep bright blue**, Bright fluor, Glossy finish (Very pale Queen's head), A(r) ellipse - Sheets (13.4.99)	1.10	60
WNEG2J	2nd	**2B Deep bright blue**, Bright fluor, Glossy finish (Very pale Queen's head), B(s) ellipse - Sheets (13.4.99)	1.10	
WNEG1A	1st	**2B Pale gold**, Head 1, Dull fluor, Shiny finish - Sheets (21.4.97)	1.00	50
WNEG1B	1st	**2B Pale gold**, Head 2, Dull fluor, Shiny finish - Pane CP48 (30.5.97)	2.00	95
WNEG1C	1st	**2B Pale gold**, Head 2, Bright fluor, Shiny finish, Comb perfs - Pane CP48 (.10.97)	£20	
WNEG1D	1st	**2B Pale gold**, Head 2, Bright fluor, Shiny finish - Pane CP48 (30.5.97)	2.50	1.20

No.			U/M	F/U
WNEG1E	1st	**2B Deep gold**, Head 2, Dull fluor, Matt finish - Pane CP48 (21.4.97)	1.50	75
WNEG1F	1st	**2B Deep gold**, Head 2, Bright fluor, Matt finish - Sheets (21.4.97)	1.25	65
WNEG1Fa		Pane CP48 (21.4.97)	1.25	
WNEG1G	1st	**2B Gold** - Panes SP122 (Across the Universe book) (24.9.02), SP128 (Perfect Coronation book) (2.6.03)	1.25	75
WNEG1H	1st	**2B Pale orange-red**, Dull fluor, Matt finish - Pane CP46 (26.8.97)	75	60
WNEG1Ha		Missing phosphor - Pane CP46a	£200	
WNEG1I	1st	**2B Pale orange-red**, Dull fluor, Matt finish, Comb perfs - Pane CP46 (.10.97)	3.00	1.50
WNEG1J	1st	**2B Bright orange-red**, Dull fluor, Matt finish, Comb perfs - Pane CP49 (18.11.97)	1.25	75
WNEG1K	1st	**2B Bright orange-red**, Bright fluor, Matt finish - Sheets (18.11.97)	1.00	
WNEG1Ka		Pane CP46 (.11.97)	1.00	
WNEG1L	1st	**2B Bright orange-red**, Bright fluor, Matt finish, Comb perfs - Pane CP46 (10.97)	1.50	80
WNEG1La		Left band ommited - Pane CP46	£300	
WNEG1Lb		Missing phosphor - Pane CP46a	£600	
WNEG1M	1st	**2B Bright orange-red**, Bright fluor, Glossy finish, Comb perfs - Panes CP46, CP50 (3.98)	90	65
WNEG1N	1st	**2B Pale orange-red**, Bright fluor, Glossy finish, Comb perfs - Pane CP46 (.3.98)	1.50	
WNEG1Na		Left band inset - Pane CP46	£25	
WNEG1O	1st	**2B Pale orange-red**, Bright fluor, Glossy finish, A(r) ellipse, Very pale Queen's head - Panes CP41E, CP41F (.3.98)	1.25	75
WNEG1Oa		Short bands at bottom - Pane CP41F	£15	
WNEG1Ob		Left band inset - Pane CP41E	4.50	
WNEG1P	1st	**2B Pale orange-red**, Bright fluor, Glossy finish, B(s) ellipse, Very pale Queen's head - Sheets (25.5.99)	1.25	75
WNEG1Q	1st	**2B Millennium**, Perf 15 - Pane CP50	1.00	
WNEG1R	1st	**2B Millennium**, Dull fluor, Perf 14 - Pane SP99 (Special by Design book) (15.2.00)	1.00	75
WNEG1Ra		Bright fluor - Pane SP110 (Treasury of Trees book)	1.10	95
WNEG'E'A	E	**2B Deep blue**, Bright fluor, Glossy finish - Pane CP47 (19.1.99)	75	60
WNEG'E'B	E	**2B Dark blue**, Bright fluor, Matt finish - Panes SP116 (Gracious Accession book), SP122 (Across the Universe book)	1.25	95

Printed by Questa in Gravure

No.			U/M	F/U
QNEG2A	2nd	**CB Bright blue**, Perf 14, patchy uneven background - Pane CP51 (1.12.98)	95	75
QNEG2B	2nd	**CB Deep bright blue**, Perf 14, smooth even background - Pane CP51	1.50	95
QNEG2C	2nd	**CB Dull mid-blue**, Perf 14, smooth even background - Pane CP51	1.00	80
QNEG2D	2nd	**CB Bright blue**, Perf 15 - Panes CP54, CP55 CP56 (27.4.00)	70	50
QNEG2Da		Short band at top - Panes CP54, CP55	4.50	
QNEG2Db		Additional narrow band at left - Pane CP54	£10	
QNEG2Dc		Additional narrow band at right - Pane CP54	£10	
QNEG2Dd		Narrow band at right - Pane CP55	8.00	
QNEG1A	1st	**2B Orange-red**, Perf 14 - Pane CP52 (1.12.98)	90	75
QNEG1B	1st	**2B Orange-red**, Perf 15 - Panes CP54, CP55, CP56 (27.4.00)	90	70
QNEG1Ba		Short bands at top - Pane CP54	4.50	
QNEG1Bb		Short bands at top, Left band inset - Pane CP54	5.50	
QNEG1Bc		Short bands at top, Right band inset - Pane CP54	6.50	
QNEG1Bd		Left band stepped at top -Pane CP54	£15	
QNEG1Be		Right band stepped at top - pane CP54	£15	
QNEG1Bf		Broad band left - Pane CP55a	£18	
QNEG1C	1st	**2B Millennium**, Perf 14 - Pane CP53	95	75
QNEG1Ca		Perf 15 - Pane SP104 (Life of the Century book) (4.8.00)	1.00	
QNEG1Cb		Left band inset - Pane SP104	£20	

Printed by Enschedé in Gravure

No.			U/M	F/U
ENEG1A	1st	**2B Gold** - Panes SP125 (Microcosmos book) (25.2.03), SP136 (Glory of the Garden book) (25.5.04)	1.00	75
ENEG1A	E	**2B Dark blue** - Pane SP125 (Microcosmos book) (25.2.03)	1.30	1.20

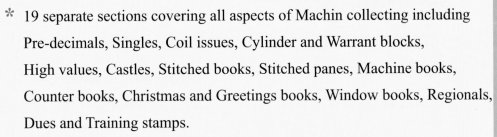

Greetings Card Miniature Sheets ('Boots Labels')

The greetings card miniature sheet, also known as the "Boots" label, consists of a single 1st class NVI at the centre of a rectangular pane that also bears informative and publicity text. It is rouletted from each bottom corner to the centre of the top edge to enable it to be folded round one corner of a greetings card. It was originally printed by Questa for Boots, with the Boots logo above the stamp, and presented in a sealed transparent pack with a Boots greetings card. Later versions were printed without the logo, first by Questa and then by Enschedé.

The Questa unbranded printings have either shorter spacing between the rouletting holes or longer spacing. The Questa version with Boots logo and blue fluor (SLMS3) only exists folded as it was always found with a greetings card, but all the others are known unfolded from philatelic outlets.

1994 (17 Aug.) Perf 15 x 14 (elliptical). Two phosphor bands.

Printed by Questa in Lithography
(Boots logo)

OFNP/PVA - C (Yellow) fluor

No.			U/M	F/U
SLMS1	1st	**2B Bright orange-red** (sheet 85 x 43 mm), A(r) Ellipse, Cream gum (17.8.94)	2.00	1.50
SLMS1a		Short bands at bottom	£20	
SLMS1b		Left band inset	£15	
SLMS1c		Right band inset	£15	
SLMS1d		Missing phosphor	£800	
SLMS2	1st	**2B Bright orange-red** (sheet 85 x 42 mm), B(s) Ellipse, White gum (.10.94)	2.00	1.50
SLMS2a		Short bands at top	£20	
SLMS2b		Left band inset	£12	
SLMS2c		Right band inset	£17	
SLMS3	1st	**2B Bright orange-red** (sheet 85 x 42 mm), B(s) Ellipse, Cream gum (.10.94)	£30	

Printed by Questa in Lithography
(Boots logo)

OFNP/PVA - D (Blue) fluor

No.			U/M	F/U
SLMS4	1st	**2B Bright orange-red**, B(s) Ellipse, White gum(25.9.95)	5.00	5.00
SLMS4a		Right band inset	£15	
SLMS4b		Missing phosphor	£550	

1995 (11 Sep.) Perf 15 x 14 (elliptical). Two phosphor bands

Printed by Questa in Lithography
(Unbranded)

OFNP/PVA - D (Blue) fluor

No.			U/M	F/U
SLMS5	1st	**2B Bright orange-red**, Short spacing (11.9.95)	1.00	75
SLMS6	1st	**2B Bright orange-red**, Long spacing (10.98)	£10	75
SLMS6a		Mixed ellipses (B(s) to the left, A(r) to the right	£80	

Printed by Enschedé in Lithography
(Unbranded)

OFNP/PVA - D (Blue) fluor

No.			U/M	F/U
SLMS7	1st	**2B Bright orange-red** , Dull fluor, violet tint to fluor (29.4.97)	90	90
SLMS8	1st	**2B Bright orange-red** , Bright fluor, violet tint to fluor (29.4.97)	9.00	
SLMS8a		Short bands at top	£20	
SLMS8b		Short bands at bottom	£20	
SLMS9	1st	**2B Bright orange-red** , Bright fluor, turquoise tint to fluor (29.4.97)	£30	

The Penny Black (1840) Anniversary Stamps

To mark the 150th Anniversary of the 1840 1d Black, special 'double head' design stamps were issued on 10 January 1990. The first five stamps were issued as commemoratives and for the next nine months also served as definitives, alongside the subsequent booklet stamps.

1990 (10 Jan.) Perf. 15 x 14

Printed by Harrison in Photogravure

FCP/PVAD

No.			U/M	F/U
PB1	15p	**CB Light blue** - Sheets (10.1.90)	65	30
PB1a		Screened value - Sheets	1.75	
PB1b		Imperforate pair - Sheets	£1250	
PB2		Imperf. top - Pane AP2 (30.1.90)	60	35
PB3		Imperf. bottom - Pane AP2 (30.1.90)	60	35
PB4	15p	**LB Light blue** - Pane AP1 (30.1.90)	1.50	1.50
PB4a		Left band clear of perfs -Pane AP1	2.00	1.75
		Left band stepped at top - Pane AP1	2.00	
PB5	15p	**RB Light blue** - Pane SP47 (London Life book) (20.3.90)	2.50	2.00
PB6	20p	**2B Black and buff**, - Pane AP1	1.50	1.00
PB6a		Left band inset - Pane AP1 (30.1.90)	2.00	1.80
PB6b		Short bands at top and Left band inset - Pane AP1	2.25	
PB7	29p	**2B Purple** - Pane SP47 (London Life book)	6.00	6.50

ACP/PVAD

No.			U/M	F/U
PB8	20p	**Black and pale buff** - Sheets	55	50
PB8a		Imperforate pair - Sheets	£1300	
PB8b		Low OBA - Sheets	1.00	
PB8c		Shift 2½mm to top of buff - Sheets	5.00	
PB8d		Shift 3mm to bottom of buff - Sheets	£10	
PB8e		Shift 5mm to bottom of buff - Sheets	£14	
PB9	20p	**Imperf**. at top - Panes AP3, AP5 (30.1.90)	80	60
PB10		Imperf. at top and right - Pane AP3 (17.4.90)	1.50	1.10
PB11		Imperf. at bottom - Panes AP3, AP5 (30.1.90)	50	60
PB12		Imperf. bottom and right - Pane AP3 (17.4.90)	1.50	1.10
PB13		Imperf. at left - Pane AP4 (30.1.90)	1.00	75
PB14		Imperf. at right - Pane AP4 (30.1.90)	85	65
PB15		Very dull paper - Pane SP48 (London Life book) (20.3.90)	£50	
PB16	29p	**Mauve** - Sheets (10.1.90)	1.10	80
PB17	34p	**Slate** - Sheets (10.1.90)	90	85
PB17a		Low OBA - Sheets	1.50	
PB18	37p	**Red** - Sheets	1.20	90
		Presentation Pack 204	3.75	

1990 (3 May) 'Stamp World 90', London Miniature Sheet
Printed in Photogravure and recess

No.			U/M	F/U
MS6	£1	**Miniature sheet** containing 20p stamp	3.00	2.75
MS6a		Missing Black (Recess printing)	£7500	
MS6b		Missing Cream (Recess printing)	£4000	
MS6c		Imperforate	£3500	
MS6d		Imperforate. First Day Cover	£3500	
MS6e		Recess printing inverted (background)	£4500	
		Souvenir Book	£20	

Printed by Questa in Lithography

Perf. 15 x 14

FCP/PVA

No.			U/M	F/U
PB19	15p	**CBar Light blue** - Pane AP6 (17.4.90)	1.25	1.10
PB19a		Short band at top - Pane AP6	3.00	
PB19b		Short band at bottom - Pane AP6	3.00	

ACP/PVAD

No.			U/M	F/U
PB20	20p	**Black.** Low OBA - Pane AP7 (17.4.90)	1.25	1.25
PB20a		Normal OBA - Pane AP7	£45	

Printer: Walsall Security Printers in Lithography. Perf. 14

FCP/PVA

No.			U/M	F/U
PB21	15p	**CB Light blue.** Imperf. at top - Pane AP8 (30.1.90)	1.00	80
PB22		Imperf. at top and right - Pane AP8	1.00	1.30
PB23		Imperf. at bottom - Pane AP8	1.00	80
PB24		Imperf. at bottom and right - Pane AP8	1.00	1.30

ACP/PVA

No.			U/M	F/U
PB25	20p	**Black and buff**, Low OBA, Imperf. at left - Pane AP10 (30.1.90)	1.25	90
PB26		Low OBA, Imperf. at right - Pane AP10	1.00	75
PB27		Imperf. at top, Low OBA - Pane AP12 (30.1.90)	1.50	90
PB28		Imperf. at top and right, Low OBA - Pane AP12	1.50	1.20
PB29		Imperf. at bottom, Low OBA, - Pane AP12	1.50	75
PB30		Imperf. at bottom and right, Low OBA - Pane AP12	1.50	1.20

ACP/PVAD

No.			U/M	F/U
PB31	20p	**Black and buff.** Imperf. at top - Pane AP12 (30.1.90)	1.00	90
PB32		Imperf. at top and right- Pane AP12	1.75	1.20
PB33		Imperf. at bottom - Pane AP12	1.00	75
PB34		Imperf. at bottom and right - Pane AP12	1.75	1.20

Printer: Walsall Security Printers in Gravure

OFNP/PVA

No.			U/M	F/U
PB30	1st	**2B Black and buff** - Pane SP102 (Special by Design book) (15.2.00)	1.00	

No. U/M F/U No. U/M F/U

'Wilding' Design Decimal Definitives and £1 Dulac Design

2002 (5 Dec.) Widlings Definitive Collection I

Wildings Definitive Collection I

2003 (20 May.) Widlings Definitive Collection II

Wildings Definitive Collection II

2003 (2 June) Pane from 'A Perfect Coronation' Prestige Book

SP131 - pane from 'A Perfect Coronation' Prestige book

2000 (23 May) Her Majesty's Stamps miniature sheet

Her Majesty's Stamps Miniature Sheet
(Printed on Phosphorised paper)

2002 (5 Dec.) Wildings Definitive collection

No.			U/M	F/U
WD1	**1p**	**2B Orange** - 1st Wildings Min. sheet	30	40
WD2	**2p**	**2B Ultramarine** - 1st Wildings Min. sheet	30	40
WD4	**4p**	**2B Deep lilac** - 2nd Wildings Min. sheet	30	40
WD5	**5p**	**2B Brown** - 1st Wildings Min. sheet	30	40
WD8	**8p**	**2B Ultramarine** - 2nd Wildings Min. sheet	30	40
WD10	**10p**	**2B Purple** - 2nd Wildings Min. sheet	35	45
WD20	**20p**	**CB Bright green** - 2nd Wildings Min. sheet	50	55
WD28	**28p**	**2B Bronze-green** - 2nd Wildings Min. sheet	75	90
WD33	**33p**	**2B Brown** - 1st Wildings Min. sheet	80	95
WD34	**34p**	**2B Brown-purple** - 2nd Wildings Min. sheet	95	1.10
WD37	**37p**	**2B Magenta** - 1st Wildings Min. sheet	1.10	1.30
WD42	**42p**	**2B Prussian blue** - 2nd Wildings Min. sheet	1.30	1.50
WD47	**47p**	**2B Bistre-brown** - 1st Wildings Min. sheet	1.50	1.70
WD47a		Pane SP131* (Perfect coronation book)	3.50	4.00
WD50	**50p**	**2B Green** - 1st Wildings Min. sheet	1.60	1.70
WD68	**68p**	**2B Grey-blue** - 2nd Wildings Min. sheet	2.00	2.25
WD68a		Pane SP131* (Perfect coronation book)	3.50	4.00
WD1st	**1st**	**2B Green** - 1st Wildings Min. sheet	1.00	1.25
WD2nd	**2nd**	**CB Carmine-red** - 1st Wildings Min. sheet	75	90
WD'E'	**E**	**2B Chestnut** - 2nd Wildings Min. sheet	1.10	1.30
WDM	**1st**	**Millennium** - Her Majesty's stamps miniature sheet	1.10	1.30
WD100	**£1**	**2B Dulac design** - Pane SP131* Watermarked paper (Perfect coronation book)	£25	£28
WD100a	**£1**	**Dulac design,** Unwatermarked, Phosphorised paper - Her Majesty's stamps miniature sheet	£6	£7

Pane SP131 is on Watermarked paper

QE2 Commemorative (Special) Issues

Please note that prices for Cylinder Blocks, which include all the plate numbers, can be for blocks of four, six eight Etc. depending on the stamp format.

1953 (3 June) Coronation. Wmk. Tudor Crown.

No.			U/M	M/M	F/U
C1	**2½d**	Carmine red	15	10	10
C2	**4d**	Ultramarine	60	45	50
C3	**1s3d**	Olive green	3.50	2.50	1.70
C4	**1s6d**	Slate blue	4.50	3.50	3.10
		Set of 4	7.70	6.00	5.00
		Set of 4 Cylinder Blocks	£60		
		First Day Cover			£29

1957 (1 Aug.) World Scout Jubilee Jamboree

No.			U/M	M/M	F/U
C5	**2½d**	Rolling Hitch	10	5	10
C6	**4d**	'Coming to Britain'	20	15	30
C7	**1s3d**	Globe and Compass	1.90	1.60	1.95
		Set of 3	1.95	1.60	2.10
		Set of 3 Cylinder Blocks	£15		
		First Day Cover			£11

1957 (12 Sept.) 46th Parliamentary Conference

No.			U/M	M/M	F/U
C8	**4d**	Light Blue	35	25	42
		First Day Cover			£80
		Cylinder Block	2.80		

1958 (18 July) 6th British Empire and Commonwealth Games

No.			U/M	M/M	F/U
C9	**3d**	Welsh Dragon	8	5	10
C10	**6d**	Flag and Emblem	25	18	25
C11	**1s3d**	Welsh Dragon	1.00	70	1.00
		Set of 3	1.10	80	1.00
		Set of 3 Cylinder Blocks	8.50		
		First Day Cover			£50
Varieties					
C9a	3d	'Specimen'		£20	
C10a	6d	'Specimen'		£20	
C11a	1s3d	'Specimen'		£20	

Multiple Crowns Watermark

This watermark was used for all commemoratives up to and including the 1967 Wild Flowers. From the 1967 British Paintings issue all commemoratives to date have been issued with no watermark, unless otherwise stated.

1960 (7 July) Tercentenary of General Letter Office. Perf. 14 x 15 (1s3d)

No.			U/M	M/M	F/U
C12	**3d**	Postboy of 1660	10	5	10
C12a		Chalky paper	60	30	50
C13	**1s3d**	Posthorn of 1660 (wmk sideways)	1.50	1.00	1.50
		Set of 2	1.50	1.25	2.00
		Set of 2 Cylinder Blocks	£11		
		First Day Cover			£24

1960 (19 Sept.) 1st Anniversary European Postal and Telecommunications Conference

No.			U/M	M/M	F/U
C14	**6d**	Green & reddish purple	40	30	45
C15	**1s6d**	Brown & deep blue	5.20	2.60	3.30
		Set of 2	5.35	2.70	3.00
		Set of 2 Cylinder Blocks	£40		
		First Day Cover			23.50
Variety					
C15a	1s6d	Shift 3mm to bottom of brown	£35		

1961 (28 Aug.) Post Office Savings Bank Centenary Timson Press.
Perf. 14 x 15 (2½d)

No.			U/M	M/M	F/U
C16	**2½d**	Thrift Plant (wmk. sideways)	22	12	16
C17	**3d**	Growth of Savings	18	10	10
C17a		Perforated through side margin	£13		
C18	**1s6d**	Thrift Plant	1.00	70	85
		Set of 3	1.00	75	75
		Set of 3 Cylinder Blocks	7.00		
		First Day Cover			£31

Thrissell Press

No.			U/M	M/M	F/U
C19	**2½d**	Thrift Plant (wmk. sideways)	1.10	75	1.10
C20	**3d**	Growth of Savings	20	15	30

Varieties

No.			U/M	M/M	F/U
C16a	2½d	Missing Black (Queen's portrait)	£17000		
C16b		Black shift 1mm right	£500		
C17b	3d	Missing Orange-brown (squirrel, leaves etc.)	£195		£175
C19a	2½d	Missing Red	£4500		
C20a	3d	Missing Orange-brown (squirrel, leaves etc.)	£750		£450

The 2½d Timson portrait is a dull olive-tinged black and is much more shaded. The portrait on the Thrissell is lighter and grey-black.

On the 3d Timson printing the portrait is distinct with highlights and deep shadows. On the 3d Thrissell printing the portrait shows a definite dullness and lacks any contrast.

1961 (18 Sept.) C.E.P.T. Conference, Torquay

No.			U/M	M/M	F/U
C21	**2d**	C.E.P.T.	10	10	10
C22	**4d**	Doves and Emblem	10	10	10
C23	**10d**	Doves and Emblem	13	20	13
		Set of 3	20	25	20
		Set of 3 Cylinder Blocks	2.00		
		First Day Cover			4.50

Varieties

No.			U/M	M/M	F/U
C21a	2d	Missing Orange	£8000		
C23a	10d	Missing Yellow-green (doves)	£9750		
C23b		Missing Turquoise	£2500		
C23c		Pale green shift	£75		
C23d		Turquoise shift	£25		

1961 (25 Sept.) Commonwealth Parliamentary Conference
Perf. 14 x 15 (1s3d)

No.			U/M	M/M	F/U
C24	**6d**	Hammer Beam Roof	17	10	20
C25	**1s3d**	Westminster(wmk. sideways)	90	75	1.05
		Set of 2	90	80	1.10
		Set of 2 Cylinder Blocks	7.00		
		First Day Cover			£18

Varieties

No.			U/M	M/M	F/U
C24a	6d	Missing Gold (Beam Roof)	£750		
C25a	1s3d	Missing Blue (Queen's portrait)	£12750		
C25b	1s3d	Missing Green (dry print)	£12500		

PHOSPHOR BANDS

All the following issues were also printed on an experimental basis with 3 vertical phosphor bands or 1 phosphor band where indicated. These experimental issues were initially distributed only from Post Offices in the Southampton area.

1962 (14 Nov.) National Productivity Year. On both the 2½d and 3d values, the watermark is normally inverted.

Ordinary

No.			U/M	M/M	F/U
C26	**2½d**	Units of Productivity	10	5	10
C26a		Deep green & bright carmine-red	20	10	15
C26b		Olive green & carmine red	20	10	15
C27	**3d**	National Productivity	10	5	10
C28	**1s3d**	Unified Productivity	1.00	60	1.00
		Set of 3	1.00	70	1.00
		Set of 3 Cylinder Blocks	7.50		
		First Day Cover			£22

Phosphor

No.			U/M	M/M	F/U
C29	**2½d**	Units of Productivity (1 band)	25	15	30
C30	**3d**	National Productivity	95	75	75
C31	**1s3d**	Unified Productivity	12.40	£10	£11
		Set of 3	£13	£10	11.25
		Set of 3 Cylinder Blocks			
		First Day Cover			£85

Varieties

No.			U/M	M/M	F/U
C27a	3d	Missing Blue (Queen's portrait, etc.)	£1200		
C28a	1s3d	Missing Blue (Queen's portrait, etc.)	£6500		
C30a	3d	Missing left phosphor band	£40		

1963 (21 March) Freedom from Hunger

Ordinary

No.			U/M	M/M	F/U
C32	**2½d**	Campaign Emblem	10	5	10
C33	**1s3d**	Children of Three Races	1.00	60	1.00
		Set of 2	1.10	60	1.10
		Set of 2 Cylinder Blocks	£8		
		First Day Cover			£17

No.			U/M	M/M	F/U
Phosphor					
C34	**2½d**	Campaign Emblem	1.00	50	1.00
C35	**1s3d**	Children of Three Races	12.50	8.25	£11
		Set of 2	£2.70	£10	£11
		Set of 2 Cylinder Blocks	£21		
		First Day Cover			£19.50

1963 (7 May) Paris Postal Conference Centenary The normal watermark on this issue is inverted.

No.			U/M	M/M	F/U
Ordinary					
C36	**6d**	Green & lilac	20	10	20
		First Day Cover			8.50
		Cylinder Block	1.50		
Phosphor					
C37	**6d**	Green & lilac	3.10	2.30	3.10
		First Day Cover			16.50
Cylinder Block			£24		
Variety					
C37a	6d	Missing Green (leaves)		£2250	£1000

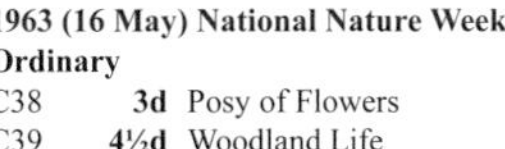

1963 (16 May) National Nature Week

No.			U/M	M/M	F/U
Ordinary					
C38	**3d**	Posy of Flowers	10	5	10
C39	**4½d**	Woodland Life	10	10	15
		Set of 2	15	12	20
		Set of 2 Cylinder Blocks			
		First Day Cover			9.25
Phosphor					
C40	**3d**	Posy of Flowers	30	20	20
C41	**4½d**	Woodland Life	1.40	60	1.50
		Set of 2	1.40	70	1.50
		Set of 2 Cylinder Blocks	£11		
		First Day Cover			17.50

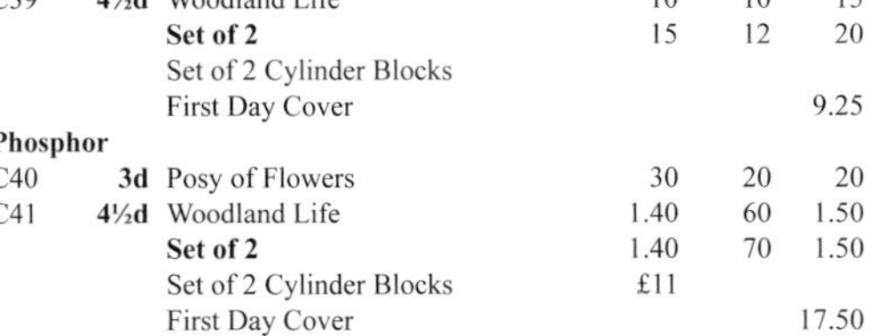

1963 (31 May) 9th International Lifeboat Conference

No.			U/M	M/M	F/U
Ordinary					
C42	**2½d**	Rescue at Sea	10	5	10
C43	**4d**	19th Century Lifeboat	30	20	40
C44	**1s6d**	Lifeboatmen	1.20	90	1.00
		Set of 3	1.30	1.00	1.20
		Set of 3 Cylinder Blocks	£10		
		First Day Cover			£18

No.			U/M	M/M	F/U
Phosphor					
C45	**2½d**	Rescue at Sea	70	35	70
C46	**4d**	19th Century Lifeboat	60	40	60
C47	**1s6d**	Lifeboatmen	£21	£15	£12
		Set of 3	22.25	£15	12.20
		Set of 3 Cylinder Blocks	£180		
		First Day Cover			£26

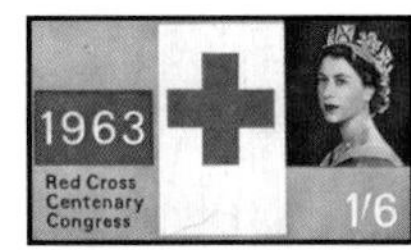

1963 (15 Aug.) Red Cross Centenary Congress

No.			U/M	M/M	F/U
Ordinary					
C48	**3d**	Red & violet	10	5	10
C49	**1s3d**	Red, blue & grey	1.40	90	1.25
C50	**1s6d**	Red, blue & bistre	1.40	90	1.60
		Set of 3	2.40	1.70	2.75
		Set of 3 Cylinder Blocks	£19		
		First Day Cover			£18
Phosphor					
C51	**3d**	Red & violet	85	60	60
C52	**1s3d**	Red, blue & grey	£21	£11	£14
C53	**1s6d**	Red, blue & bistre	£15	£7	£12
		Set of 3	33.85	£25	£24
		Set of 3 Cylinder Blocks	£270		
		First Day Cover			£38
Varieties					
C48a	3d	Missing Red (Cross)	£5000		
C48b	3d	Shift 2mm to bottom of Red	8.00		
C51a	3d	Missing Red (Cross)	£8000		

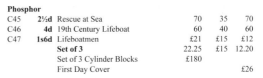

1963 (3 Dec.) Opening of C.O.M.P.A.C. Cable

No.			U/M	M/M	F/U
Ordinary					
C54	**1s6d**	Commonwealth Cable	1.00	85	90
		Cylinder Block	7.50		
		First Day Cover			£12
Phosphor					
C55	**1s6d**	Commonwealth Cable	7.20	4.50	7.70
		Cylinder Block	£57		
		First Day Cover			17.50
Varieties					
C54a	1s6d	Missing Black (cable)	£3500		
C54b	1s6d	'Cancelled'			

1964 (23 April) Shakespeare Festival

2s6d value recess printed by Bradbury, Wilkinson & Co. (Perf. 11 x 12)

No.			U/M	M/M	F/U
Ordinary					
C56	**3d**	Midsummer Nights Dream	10	5	10
C57	**6d**	Twelfth Night	16	10	15
C58	**1s3d**	Romeo & Juliet	50	25	50
C58a		Wmk. inverted	£550		
C59	**1s6d**	Henry V	80	55	45
C59a		Wmk. inverted			£1250
C60	**2s6d**	Hamlet	80	55	1.10
C60a		Wmk inverted	£335		
C60b		Black	£500		£200
		Set of 5	1.80	1.20	2.20
		Set of 5 Cylinder Blocks	£14		
		First Day Cover			£6
		Presentation Pack	£12		
Phosphor					
C61	**3d**	Midsummer Nights Dream	15	15	15
C62	**6d**	Twelfth Night	75	50	75
C63	**1s3d**	Romeo & Juliet	2.80	2.00	3.00
C63a		Wmk. inverted	£110	£30	£50
C64	**1s6d**	Henry V	3.00	2.00	3.20
		Set of 4	6.00	4.00	6.95
		Set of 4 Cylinder Blocks	£45		
		First Day Cover			£8
Variety					
C59a	1s6d	White Knight. Shift 5mm to right of Violet	£125		

1964 (1 July) 20th International Geographical Congress

No.			U/M	M/M	F/U
Ordinary					
C65	**2½d**	Urban	10	5	10
C66	**4d**	Industrial	30	20	30
C66a		Wmk. inverted	£425		
C67	**8d**	Forestry	50	30	70
C67a		Wmk. inverted	£450		
C68	**1s6d**	Nuclear	1.60	90	1.25
C68a		Wmk. inverted	£20		
		Set of 4	1.70	1.10	1.80
		Set of 4 Cylinder Blocks	£13		
		First Day Cover			£10
		Presentation Pack	£95		
Phosphor					
C69	**2½d**	Urban (1 band)	25	15	30
C70	**4d**	Industrial	1.00	70	1.10
C71	**8d**	Forestry	2.20	1.60	2.00
C72	**1s6d**	Nuclear	£10	8.00	£9
		Set of 4	11.50	8.00	9.50
		Set of 4 Cylinder Blocks	£90		
		First Day Cover			£27
Varieties					
C66a	4d	Missing Violet (4d etc.)	£195		£110
C66b	4d	Missing Red-brown	£5500		
C66c	4d	Missing Violet and Red-brown	£290		
C66d	4d	Shift 1mm to left of violet (4d, etc.)	£15		
C67b	8d	Missing Green (grass)	£9750		£4000

1964 (5 Aug.) International Botanical Congress

No.			U/M	M/M	F/U
Ordinary					
C73	**3d**	Spring Gentian	10	5	10
C74	**6d**	Dog Rose	20	15	20
C75	**9d**	Honeysuckle	70	50	1.00
C75a		Wmk. inverted	£40		
C76	**1s3d**	Waterlily	1.00	75	1.00
C76a		Wmk. inverted	£500		
		Set of 4	1.80	1.25	2.00
		Set of 4 Cylinder Blocks	£14		
		First Day Cover			£12
		Presentation Pack	£95		
Phosphor					
C77	**3d**	Spring Gentian	30	15	11
C78	**6d**	Dog Rose	1.70	1.20	1.50
C79	**9d**	Honeysuckle	2.00	1.50	3.00
C80	**1s3d**	Waterlily	£10	6.50	7.50
		Set of 4	12.50	8.50	10.50
		Set of 4 Cylinder Blocks			
		First Day Cover			£22
Varieties					
C73a	3d	Missing Blue	£5000		
C73b	3d	Perf. shift 2.5mm to right	£30		
C73c	3d	Missing Sage-green	£7250		
C75b	9d	Missing Green (Leaves)	£6250	£4000	£2000
C76b	1s3d	Missing Yellow (flowers)	£30000		

1964 (4 Sept.) Opening of the Forth Road Bridge

No.			U/M	M/M	F/U
Ordinary					
C81	**3d**	Black, ultramarine & purple	10	5	10
C82	**6d**	Black, blue & maroon	20	10	15
C82a		Wmk. inverted	1.00	80	1.00
		Set of 2	20	10	20
		Set of 2 Cylinder Blocks	1.50		
		First Day Cover			£3
		Presentation Pack	£375		

No.			U/M	M/M	F/U
Phosphor					
C84	**3d**	Black, ultramarine & purple	40	30	35
C85	**6d**	Black, blue & maroon	2.20	1.40	2.35
C86		Wmk. inverted	£500	£350	
		Set of 2	2.20	1.50	2.20
		Set of 2 Cylinder Blocks	£17		
		First Day Cover			6.50
Varieties					
C81a	3d	Imperforate top margin	£700		
C82b	6d	Missing Blue	£2750		£1000

1965 (8 July) Sir Winston Churchill Memorial Issue

No.			U/M	M/M	F/U
Ordinary					
C87	**4d**	Black & deep brown (R)	10	5	10
C87a		Wmk. inverted	1.00	60	75
C87b		Black & deep brown (T)	10	5	10
C88	**1s3d**	Black & slate grey	16	10	25
C88a		Wmk. inverted	£70		
		Set of 2	20	12	25
		Set of 2 Cylinder Blocks	1.50		
		First Day Cover			2.20
		Presentation Pack	£45		
Phosphor					
C89	**4d**	Black & deep-brown	20	15	20
C90	**1s3d**	Black & slate grey	1.10	75	1.20
		Set of 2	1.15	70	1.30
		Set of 2 Cylinder Blocks	£9		
		First Day Cover			3.50
Varieties					
C87c	4d	Missing Queen's head (due to paper fold)	£2500		
C87d	4d	Missing Black	£2750		

(R) = Rembrandt Press (T) = Timson Press

The Churchill 4d was printed by the Rembrandt and Thrissell machines. The Rembrandt shows a lack of detail on the face and the Queen's portrait appears dull and out of focus. On the Thrissell printing there is much more detail on the face and the left eyebrow is complete, while the Queen's portrait is much more clearly defined and lighter in shade.

1965 (19 July) 700th Anniversary of Parliament

No.			U/M	M/M	F/U
Ordinary					
C91	**6d**	Simon de Montfort's Seal	15	10	15
C92	**2s6d**	Parliament Buildings	44	30	50
C92a		Wmk inverted	£15		
		Set of 2	45	30	55
		Set of 2 Cylinder Blocks	3.50		
		First Day Cover			7.25
		Presentation Pack	£40		
Phosphor					
C93	**6d**	Simon de Montfort's Seal	40	25	45
C93a		Missing phosphor	£100		
		First Day Cover			10.50
		Cylinder Block	£3		
Varieties					
C91a	6d	Imperf at top (marginal)	£700	£450	£400
C92b	2s6d	Shift 1mm to bottom of Ivory (Queen's portrait)	£45		

1965 (9 Aug.) Centenary of the Salvation Army

No.			U/M	M/M	F/U
Ordinary					
C94	**3d**	Bandsmen and Banner	10	5	10
C95	**1s6d**	Three Salvationists	40	30	55
		Set of 2	45	30	55
		Set of 2 Cylinder Blocks	3.50		
		First Day Cover			£11
Phosphor					
C96	**3d**	Bandsmen and Banner (1 band)	27	15	30
C97	**1s6d**	Three Salvationists	1.10	80	1.20
		Set of 2	1.15	80	1.30
		Set of 2 Cylinder Blocks	£9		
		First Day Cover			£14

1965 (1 Sept.) Commonwealth Arts Festival

No.			U/M	M/M	F/U
Ordinary					
C98	**6d**	Trinidad Carnival Dancers	14	5	15
C99	**1s6d**	Canadian Folk Dancers	45	35	65
		Set of 2	60	30	70
		Set of 2 Cylinder Blocks	£3		
		First Day Cover			£8
Phosphor					
C100	**6d**	Trinidad Carnival Dancers	20	10	25
C101	**1s6d**	Canadian Folk Dancers	1.30	70	1.45
		Set of 2	1.35	70	1.45
		Set of 2 Cylinder Blocks	£10		
		First Day Cover			9.50

1965 (1 Sept.) Joseph Lister Centenary

No.			U/M	M/M	F/U
Ordinary					
C102	**4d**	Carbolic Spray	10	5	10
C103	**1s**	Chemical Symbols	40	25	60
C104		Wmk. inverted	£325		
		Set of 2	40	25	60
		Set of 2 Cylinder Blocks	£3		
		First Day Cover			£7
Phosphor					
C105	**4d**	Carbolic Spray	20	10	20
C106	**1s**	Chemical Symbols	1.30	70	1.40
C106a		Wmk. inverted	£300		
		Set of 2	1.30	65	1.40
		Set of 2 Cylinder Blocks			
		First Day Cover			£9

No.			U/M	M/M	F/U

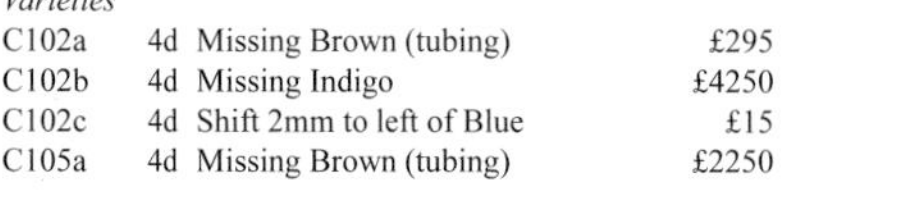

Varieties

No.			U/M	M/M	F/U
C102a	4d	Missing Brown (tubing)	£295		£250
C102b	4d	Missing Indigo	£4250		
C102c	4d	Shift 2mm to left of Blue	£15		
C105a	4d	Missing Brown (tubing)	£2250		

A

B

C

D

E

F

1965 (13 Sept.) 25th Anniversary of the Battle of Britain

Ordinary

No.			U/M	M/M	F/U
C107	4d	Olive green & black (A)	50	30	50
C108	4d	Olive green, grey & black (B)	50	30	50
C109	4d	Olive green, red, blue & grey (C)	50	30	50
C110	4d	Olive green, grey & black (D)	50	30	50
C111	4d	Olive green, grey & black (E)	50	30	50
C112	4d	Olive green, grey, blue & black (F)	50	30	50
C107/112	**4d**	**Block of 6 se-tenant**	3.40	1.90	3.80
C113	**9d**	Black, orange & purple	70	40	80
C113a		Wmk. inverted	£50		
C114	**1s3d**	Multicoloured	60	35	90
C114a		Wmk. inverted	£20		
		Set of 8	3.80	2.10	3.90
		Set of 3 Cylinder Blocks	£30		
		First Day Cover			£11
		Presentation Pack	£39.50		

Phosphor

No.			U/M	M/M	F/U
C115	4d	Olive green & black (A)	85	15	95
C116	4d	Olive green, grey & black (B)	85	15	95
C117	4d	Olive green, red, blue & grey (C)	85	15	95
C118	4d	Olive green, grey & black (D)	85	15	95
C119	4d	Olive green, grey & black (E)	85	15	95
C120	4d	Olive green, grey, blue & black (F)	85	15	95
C115/20	**4d**	**Block of 6 se-tenant**	5.00	2.75	5.70
C121	**9d**	Black, orange & purple	60	40	80
C122	**1s3d**	Multicoloured	70	40	90
C122a		Wmk. inverted	5.00		
		Set of 8	5.70	3.50	5.90
		Set of 3 Cylinder Blocks	£45		
		First Day Cover			£13

Varieties

No.			U/M	M/M	F/U
C112a	4d	Missing Blue			£4000
C114b	1s3d	Shift 2mm to left of Blue (Sky)	£50		
C114c	1s3d	Shift 2mm to right of pale grey (St. Paul's, etc.)	£50		
C114d	1s3d	Shift 12mm to bottom of Black (Queen's portrait & 1s3d)	£150		
C114e	1s3d	Shift 2mm to bottom left of Dark Grey	£30		

1965 (8 Oct.) Opening of Post Office Tower, London

Ordinary

No.			U/M	M/M	F/U
C123	**3d**	Geogian Buildings	10	5	10
C124	**1s3d**	Regents Park	25	15	30
C124a		Wmk inverted	£45		
		Set of 2	25	15	30
		Set of 2 Cylinder Blocks	1.50		
		First Day Cover			£4
		Presentation Pack	3.50		

Phosphor

No.			U/M	M/M	F/U
C125	**3d**	Geogian Buildings (1 side band)	15	10	15
C126	**1s3d**	Regents Park	25	15	30
C126a		Wmk inverted	£25	£15	£1
		Set of 2	25	20	35
		Set of 2 Cylinder Blocks	1.50		
		First Day Cover			4.75
		Presentation Pack	3.50		

Varieties

No.			U/M	M/M	F/U
C123a	3d	Missing Yellow bistre (Tower)	£2250		$750
C124b	1s3d	Shift 1mm to left of Green (Queen's portrait, etc.)	£25		

1965 (25 Oct.) 20th Anniversary of United Nations and International Co-operation Year

Ordinary

No.			U/M	M/M	F/U
C127	**3d**	UN Emblem	10	5	10
C128	**1s6d**	ICY Emblem	45	20	47
C128a		Wmk. inverted			£1750
		Set of 2	45	20	50
		Set of 2 Cylinder Blocks	3.50		
		First Day Cover			£7

Phosphor

No.			U/M	M/M	F/U
C129	**3d**	UN Emblem (1 band)	15	10	15
C130	**1s6d**	ICY Emblem	1.60	90	1.70
		Set of 2	1.70	80	1.65
		Set of 2 Cylinder Blocks	£13		
		First Day Cover			£8

Varieties

No.			U/M	M/M	F/U
C128b	1s6d	Shift 2.5mm to left of Black	£25		
C128c		Imperf. between stamp & top margin	£1500		

1965 (15 Nov.) Centenary of International Telecommunications Union

Ordinary

No.			U/M	M/M	F/U
C131	**9d**	Telecommunications	20	15	20
C131a		Wmk. inverted	£15		
C132	**1s6d**	Radio Waves	40	25	50
C132a		Wmk. inverted	£50		
		Set of 2	55	35	60
		Set of 2 Cylinder Blocks	£4		
		First Day Cover			£8

No.			U/M	M/M	F/U
Phosphor					
C134	**9d**	Telecommunications	40	25	40
C134a		Wmk. inverted	£60		
C135	**1s6d**	Radio Waves	2.50	1.50	2.70
		Set of 2	2.60	1.50	2.70
		Set of 2 Cylinder Blocks	18.50		
		First Day Cover			£10
Varieties					
C131b	9d	Shift 4mm to left of deep Violet	£55		
C131c	9d	Shift 2mm to left of Blue	£45		
C131d	9d	Shift 1mm to top of Red	£35		
C134b	9d	Shift 1mm to left of Black (inscription & Queen's portrait)	£20		
C132b	1s6d	Missing Pink (panel behind Queen's portrait)	£1500		£1350
C132c	1s6d	Shift 8mm to bottom of Pink (panel)	£40		

1966 (25 Jan.) Robert Burns

No.			U/M	M/M	F/U
Ordinary					
C136	**4d**	Black, violet & light blue	10	5	10
C137	**1s3d**	Black, slate blue & orange	25	15	30
		Set of 2	22	15	30
		Set of 2 Cylinder Blocks	1.70		
		First Day Cover			2.50
		Presentation Pack	39.50		
Phosphor					
C138	**4d**	Black, violet & light blue	10	5	15
C139	**1s3d**	Black, slate blue & orange	1.10	60	1.15
		Set of 2	1.10	60	1.15
		Set of 2 Cylinder Blocks	8.50		
		First Day Cover			2.75
Varieties					
C137a	1s3d	Shift 2mm to left of Slate-blue (Background to Queen's portrait)	£65		

1966 (28 Feb.) 900th Anniversary of Westminster Abbey

2s6d value recess printed by Bradbury, Wilkinson & Co. (Perf 11 x 12)

No.			U/M	M/M	F/U
Ordinary					
C140	**3d**	Westminster Abbey	10	5	10
C141	**2s6d**	Fan Vaulting	25	20	40
		Set of 2	30	20	40
		Set of 2 Cylinder Blocks	1.70		
		First Day Cover			3.20
		Presentation Pack	£35		
Phosphor					
C142	**3d**	Westminster Abbey (1 band)	10	5	10
		First Day Cover			6.50
		Cylinder Block	80		
Varieties					
C140a	3d	Shift 1mm to left of Chestnut	£20		

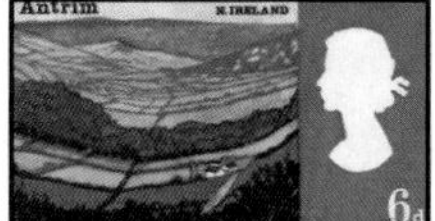

1966 (2 May) Landscapes of the British Isles

No.			U/M	M/M	F/U
Ordinary					
C143	**4d**	Hassocks	10	5	10
C144	**6d**	Antrim	10	8	10
C144a		Wmk. inverted	5.00		
C145	**1s3d**	Harlech	17	10	22
C146	**1s6d**	Cairngorm	17	13	25
C146a		Wmk. inverted	£10		
		Set of 4	35	30	60
		Set of 4 Cylinder Blocks	2.70		
		First Day Cover			£3
Phosphor					
C147	**4d**	Hassocks	10	5	12
C148	**6d**	Antrim	10	5	10
C148a		Wmk. inverted	£30		
C149	**1s3d**	Harlech	17	10	22
C150	**1s6d**	Cairngorm	17	12	25
		Set of 4	45	25	60
		Set of 4 Cylinder Blocks	3.50		
		First Day Cover			3.20
Varieties					
C144b	6d	Missing 'D' in 'AND (SONS)'	£10		
C144c	6d	Shift 1mm to bottom of Emerald green (Mountain tops)	£15		
C146b	1s6d	Shift 2mm to left of Black (trees)	£35		
C146c	1s6d	Shift 2mm to left of Deep Blue (panel behind Queen's head)	£35		
C148b	6d	Missing 'D' in 'AND (SONS)'	5.00		

1966 (1 June) World Cup Football Competition

No.			U/M	M/M	F/U
Ordinary					
C151	**4d**	Players with Ball	10	5	10
C152	**6d**	Goalmouth Melee	10	5	10
C152a		Wmk. inverted	1.00	60	75
C153	**1s3d**	Goalkeeper Saving	15	10	20
C153a		Wmk. inverted	£100		
		Set of 3	30	15	35
		Set of 3 Cylinder Blocks	1.70		
		First Day Cover			£5
		Presentation Pack	9.50		

Phosphor

No.			U/M	M/M	F/U
C154	**4d**	Players with Ball	10	5	10
C155	**6d**	Goalmouth Melee	10	5	10
C156	**1s3d**	Goalkeeper Saving	15	10	20
C156a		Wmk. inverted	1.00	60	75
		Set of 3	25	15	30
		Set of 3 Cylinder Blocks	1.40		
		First Day Cover			7.50
Varieties					
C152b	6d	Missing Black (Goalkeeper, etc.)	£125		£45
C152c	6d	Missing Green (shorts & pitch)	£3250		£1500
C152d	6d	Missing Red (left & right players)	£3750		
C152e	6d	Shift 4mm to left of Black	£45		
C152f	6d	Shift 4mm to left of Red	£125		
C153b	1s3d	Missing Blue (stripes)	£160		
C153c	1s3d	Shift 5mm to bottom of Blue (Arrow by ball)	£45		
C153d	1s3d	Shift 3mm to left of Yellow (Two balls, etc.)	£20		
C155a	6d	Missing Black (Goalkeeper, etc.)	£550		

A 

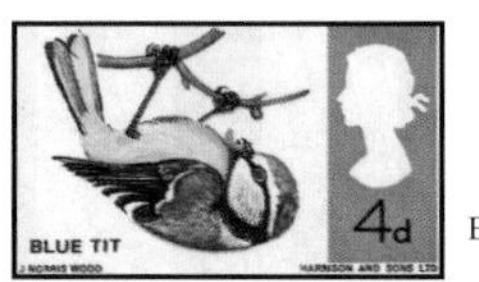 B

C 

D

1966 (8 Aug.) British Birds

Ordinary

No.			U/M	M/M	F/U
C157	4d	Black Headed Gull (A)	12	8	15
C158	4d	Blue Tit (B)	12	8	15
C159	4d	Robin (C)	12	8	15
C160	4d	Blackbird (D)	12	8	15
C157/60	**4d**	**Block of 4 se-tenant**	40	25	50
		Cylinder Block	1.90		
C157/60a		Block of 4. Wmk. inverted	7.50	3.50	4.00
		Cylinder Block			
		First Day Cover			3.50
		Presentation Pack	4.50		
Phosphor					
C161	4d	Black Headed Gull (A)	13	8	15
C162	4d	Blue Tit (B)	13	8	15
C163	4d	Robin (C)	13	8	15
C164	4d	Blackbird (D)	13	8	15
C161/4	**4d**	**Block of 4 se-tenant**	40	25	50
		Cylinder Block			
C161/4a		Block of 4. Wmk. inverted	£35	£15	£25
		Cylinder Block			
		First Day Cover			3.50

Varieties

Prices are for blocks of four unless stated. Brackets indicate stamps affected.

No.			U/M	M/M	F/U
C157/60b	4d	Missing Black, blue, bistre & brown	£6500		
C157a	4d	Missing Black (A) Single	£7500		£3500
C157/60d	4d	Missing Greenish-yellow	£2250		
C157/60e	4d	Missing Red (A & C)	£1500		
C157/60f	4d	Missing Green (A, B & C)	£325		£225
C157/60g	4d	Missing Blue (A & B)	£750		
C157/60h	4d	Missing Bistre (A, B & C)	£375		
C157/60i	4d	Missing Brown (C & D)	£150		
C157/60j	4d	Shift 3mm to top of Red & green (A, B & C)	£225		
C157/60k	4d	Shift 2mm to left of red (A & C)	£135		
C161/64b	4d	Missing Green (A, B & C)	£325		
C161/64c	4d	Missing Blue (A & B)	£7000		
C161/64d	4d	Missing Bistre (A, B & C)	£8750		
C161/64e	4d	Missing Brown (C & D)	£225		
C161/64f	4d	Missing Greenish-yellow	£5500		

1966 (18 Aug.) World Cup Football. England winners

Ordinary

No.			U/M	M/M	F/U
C165	**4d**	England Winners	15	10	15
		Cylinder Block	80		
		First Day Cover			3.50
Variety					
C165a	4d	Shift 2mm to right of blue, red & flesh	£75		

1966 (19 Sept.) British Technology

Ordinary

No.			U/M	M/M	F/U
C166	**4d**	Jodrell Bank	10	5	10
C167	**6d**	British Motor Cars	10	5	10
C168	**1s3d**	SRN6 Hovercraft	10	5	20
C169	**1s6d**	Windscale Reactor	10	5	20
		Set of 4	27	15	50
		Set of 4 Cylinder Blocks	2.00		
		First Day Cover			1.50
		Presentation Pack	7.50		
Phosphor					
C170	**4d**	Jodrell Bank	10	5	10
C171	**6d**	British Motor Cars	10	5	15
C172	**1s3d**	SRN6 Hovercraft	10	5	20
C173	**1s6d**	Windscale Reactor	10	5	20
		Set of 4	35	25	60
		Set of 4 Cylinder Blocks	2.50		
		First Day Cover			1.50
Varieties					
C167a	6d	Missing red (Minis)	£6000		
C167b	6d	Double print of red (Minis)	£250		
C167c	6d	Missing deep blue (Jaguar)	£4750		

A 

 B

C 

 D

E 

 F

1966 (14 Oct.) 900th Anniversary of Battle of Hastings

No.			U/M	M/M	F/U
Ordinary					
C175	4d	Battle Scene (A)	10	5	15
C176	4d	Battle Scene (B)	10	5	15
C177	4d	Battle Scene (C)	10	5	15
C178	4d	Battle Scene (D)	10	5	15
C179	4d	Battle Scene (E)	10	5	15
C180	4d	Battle Scene (F)	10	5	15
C175/80	**4d**	**Strip of 6 se-tenant**	60	30	1.20
C175/80a		Strip of 6. Wmk. inverted	£70		
C181	**6d**	Norman Ship	10	5	15
C181a		Wmk. inverted	£40		
C182	**1s3d**	Horsemen (wmk. sideways)	20	15	20
C182a		Wmk. sideways inverted	£35		
		Set of 8	80	45	1.20
		Set of 3 Cylinder Blocks	£6		
		First Day Cover			2.20
		Presentation Pack	3.75		
Phosphor					
C183	4d	Battle Scene (A)	15	10	20
C184	4d	Battle Scene (B)	15	10	20
C185	4d	Battle Scene (C)	15	10	20
C186	4d	Battle Scene (D)	15	10	20
C187	4d	Battle Scene (E)	15	10	20
C188	4d	Battle Scene (F)	15	10	20
C183/88	**4d**	**Strip of 6 se-tenant**	60	45	1.20
C183/88a		Strip of 6. Wmk. inverted	£35		
C189	**6d**	Norman Ship	10	5	15
C189a		Wmk. inverted	£50		
C190	**1s3d**	Horsemen (wmk. sideways)	20	15	20
C190a		Wmk. sideways inverted	£35		
		Set of 8	80	60	1.20
		Set of 3 Cylinder Blocks	£6		
		First Day Cover			3.50

Varieties

Prices for 4d are for strips of six, however the missing orange only affects Types A, B, C, E & F

No.			U/M	M/M	F/U
C175/80b	4d	Missing Olive-green	£375		
C175/80c	4d	Missing Bistre	£375		
C175/80d	4d	Missing Deep blue	£410		
C175/80e	4d	Missing Orange (A, B, C, E & F)	£375		
C175/80f	4d	Missing Magenta	£375		
C175/80g	4d	Missing Green	£375		
C175/80h	4d	Missing Blue	£375		
C175/80i	4d	Missing Grey	£240		
C179j	4d	Missing Light blue and Grey (single stamp on cover)			£5000
C182a	1s3d	Missing Gold (Queen's head)	£125		
C182b	1s3d	Missing Lilac	£400		
C183/88b	4d	Missing Olive-green	£375		
C183/88c	4d	Missing Bistre	£375		
C183/88d	4d	Missing Deep blue	£410		

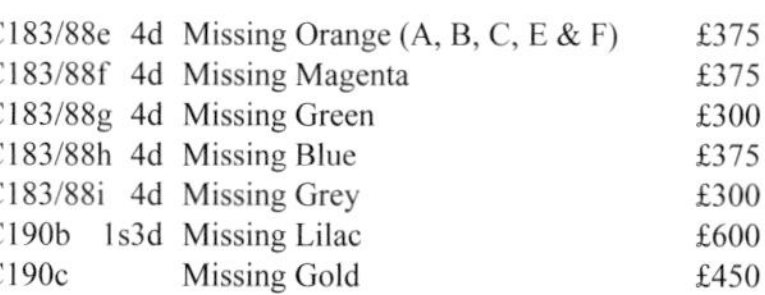

No.			U/M	M/M	F/U
C183/88e	4d	Missing Orange (A, B, C, E & F)	£375		
C183/88f	4d	Missing Magenta	£375		
C183/88g	4d	Missing Green	£300		
C183/88h	4d	Missing Blue	£375		
C183/88i	4d	Missing Grey	£300		
C190b	1s3d	Missing Lilac	£600		
C190c		Missing Gold	£450		

1966 (1 Dec.) Christmas 1966

No.			U/M	M/M	F/U
Ordinary					
C191	**3d**	King	10	5	10
C192	**1s6d**	Snowman	14	10	20
C192a		Wmk. inverted	£15		
		Set of 2	13	10	20
		Set of 2 Cylinder Blocks	1.00		
		First Day Cover			1.25
		Presentation Pack	5.00		
Phosphor					
C193	**3d**	King (1 side band)	10	5	10
C194	**1s6d**	Snowman (2 bands)	14	10	20
C194a		Wmk. inverted	£40		
		Set of 2	13	10	25
		Set of 2 Cylinder Blocks	1.00		
		First Day Cover			1.25
Varieties					
C191a	3d	Missing 'T' in 'SHEMZA'	£2		
C191b	3d	Missing Gold (Queen's head) *	£125		
C192b	1s6d	Missing Pink (Hat)	£1500		
C192c	1s6d	Missing Gold (Queen's head) *	£550		
C193a	3d	Missing 'T' in 'SHEMZA'	£2		
C193b		Missing Gold (Queen's head) *	£525		
C194b	1s6d	Missing Gold	£625		

* Only purchase with a certificate.

1967 (20 Feb.) European Free Trade Association

No.			U/M	M/M	F/U
Ordinary					
C195	**9d**	Multicoloured	10	5	11
C195a		Wmk. inverted	£15	8.00	£10
C196	**1s6d**	Multicoloured	10	10	14
		Set of 2	15	10	20
		Set of 2 Cylinder Blocks	80		
		First Day Cover			1.25
		Presentation Pack	1.60		
Phosphor					
C197	**9d**	Multicoloured	10	5	11
C197a		Wmk. inverted	6.00	2.50	3.25
C198	**1s6d**	Multicoloured	10	10	14
C198a		Wmk. inverted	£15	8.00	£10
		Set of 2	15	10	20
		Set of 2 Cylinder Blocks	80		
		First Day Cover			1.25

Varieties

No.			U/M	M/M	F/U
C195b	9d	Missing Black, Brown, Light Blue & Yellow	£850		
C195c	9d	Missing Lilac	£65		
C195d	9d	Missing Green	£65		
C195e	9d	Missing Brown	£50		
C195f	9d	Missing Light Blue	£65		
C195g	9d	Missing Yellow	£65		
C195h	9d	Shift 3mm of Brown and 1mm of Light Blue to bottom	£35		
C196a	1s6d	Missing Deep Blue	£350		
C196c	1s6d	Missing Brown	£65		
C196d	1s6d	Missing Light Blue	£65		
C196e	1s6d	Missing Yellow	£65		
C196f	1s6d	Missing Blue-grey	£65		
C197b	9d	Missing Lilac	£150		
C197c	9d	Missing Green	£65		
C197d	9d	Missing Brown	£50		
C197e	9d	Missing Light Blue	£65		
C197f	9d	Missing Yellow	£65		
C198b	1s6d	Missing Red	£6500		
C198c	1s6d	Missing Deep Blue	£350		
C198d	1s6d	Missing Brown	£50		
C198e	1s6d	Missing Light Blue	£65		
C198f	1s6d	Missing Blue-grey	£65		

A

B

C

D

1967 (24 April) British Wild Flowers

Ordinary

No.			U/M	M/M	F/U
C199	4d	Hawthorn and Bramble (A)	10	10	10
C200	4d	Bindweed (B)	10	10	10
C201	4d	Ox-eye Daisy (C)	10	10	10
C202	4d	Bluebell (D)	10	10	10
C199/202	**4d**	**Block of 4 se-tenant**	40	30	60
C199/202a		Block of 4 Wmk. inverted	£25		
C203	**9d**	Dog Violet	10	5	15
C203a		Wmk. inverted	5.00		
C204	**1s9d**	Primroses	13	10	17
		Set of 6	55	40	75
		Set of 3 Cylinder Blocks	4.20		
		First Day Cover			£2
		Presentation Pack	2.95		

Phosphor

No.			U/M	M/M	F/U
C205	4d	Hawthorn and Bramble (A)	10	5	15
C206	4d	Bindweed (B)	10	5	15
C207	4d	Ox-eye Daisy (C)	10	5	15
C208	4d	Bluebell (D)	10	5	15
C205/8	**4d**	**Block of 4 se-tenant**	40	20	60
C205/8a		Block of 4 Wmk. inverted	£25		
C209	**9d**	Dog Violet	10	5	15
C210	**1s9d**	Primroses	13	10	17
		Set of 6	35	25	70
		Set of 3 Cylinder Blocks	2.60		
		First Day Cover			£2
		Presentation Pack	3.50		

Varieties

Prices are for blocks of four and the stamps affected are shown in brackets.

No.			U/M	M/M	F/U
C199/202b	4d	Missing reddish-purple (D)	£950		
C199/202c	4d	Missing red (A)	£2500		
C199/202d	4d	Missing slate-purple (A)	£4250		
C205/8b	4d	Missing agate (A, B, C & D)	£7500		
C205/8c	4d	Missing violet (B & D)	£10000		
C205/8d	4d	Missing slate-purple (A)	£300		£500

1967 (10 July) British Paintings

No.			U/M	M/M	F/U
C211	**4d**	Multicoloured	10	5	10
C211a		Missing phosphor	£10		
C212	**9d**	Multicoloured	10	5	15
C212a		Missing phosphor	£450		
C212b		One broad band	£15		
C213	**1s6d**	Multicoloured	10	5	12
C213a		Missing phosphor	£300		
C213b		One broad band	5.00		
		Set of 3	15	10	27
		Set of 3 Cylinder Blocks	1.10		
		First Day Cover			1.20
		Presentation Pack	3.30		

Varieties

No.			U/M	M/M	F/U
C211b	4d	Missing Gold (4d & Queen's head)	£225		
C211c	4d	Missing Light Blue	£6000		
C211d	4d	Shift 3.5mm to right of Gold	£45		
C212c	9d	Missing Black (9d & Queen's head)	£550		£175
C212d	9d	Missing Black (Queen's head), 9d at right	£750		
C212e	9d	Shift 24mm to right of Black (Queen's head & 9d transposed)	£175		
C213c	1s6d	Missing Light Blue	£200		
C213d	1s6d	Missing Grey	£55		
C213e	1s6d	Missing Gold (Queen's head)	£6000		£3000

IMPORTANT NOTE

From this issue all stamps have only 2 vertical phosphor bands except where stated. The price column for Mounted Mint (M/M) is omitted from this date, as collectors prefer Unmounted Mint (U/M) in modern issues.

1967 (24 July) Sir Francis Chichester

No.			U/M	F/U
C214	**1s9d**	Gypsy Moth IV (3 bands)	10	15
		Cylinder Block	75	
		First Day Cover		60

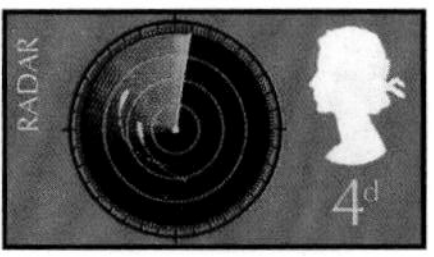

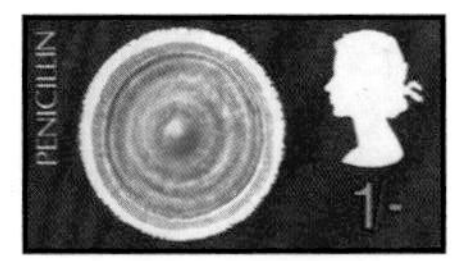

1967 (19 Sept.) British Scientific Discoveries. Wmk. Multiple Crowns

No.			U/M	F/U
C215	**4d**	Radar Screen (3 bands)	10	10
C215a		Missing phosphor	5.00	
C216	**1s**	Penicillium	10	10
C216a		Missing phosphor	£15	
C216b		Wmk. inverted	£10	7.50
C217	**1s6d**	VC10 Jet Engines	10	12
C217a		Missing phosphor	£500	
C217b		Wmk. inverted	£30	£15
C218	**1s9d**	Television (wmk. sideways)	10	15
C218a		Missing phosphor	£500	
		Set of 4	19	25
		Set of 4 Cylinder Blocks	1.50	
		First Day Cover		1.25
		Presentation Pack	2.00	
Variety				
C218b	1s9d	Missing Grey		£4500

1967 (18 Oct.) Christmas 1967

No.			U/M	F/U
C219	**3d**	Adoration of the Shepherds (1 band) (27 Nov.)	10	10
C219a		Missing phosphor	1.00	
C219b		Printed on the gummed side	£400	
C220	**4d**	Madonna and Child	10	10
C220a		Missing phosphor	£100	
C221	**1s6d**	Adoration of the Shepherds (27 Nov.)	10	15
C221a		Missing phosphor	£10	
C221b		One broad band	£30	
		Set of 3	20	25
		Set of 3 Cylinder Blocks	1.50	
		First Day Covers (2)		1.25
Varieties				
C219c	3d	Missing Gold (3d & Queen's head)	£80	
C219d	3d	Missing Rose	£2500	
C219e	3d	Left margin imperforate	£500	
C219e	3d	Missing Yellow	£4000	
C220b	4d	Missing Gold (3d & Queen's head)	£60	£25
C220c	4d	Missing Yellow	£6000	
C221c	1s6d	Missing Gold (Queen's head & value)	£2000	
C221d	1s6d	Missing Ultramarine	£500	
C221e	1s6d	Missing Lemon	£7500	

1967 (27 Nov.) Special Gift Pack

No.			U/M	F/U
YP1		Presentation Pack	1.00	

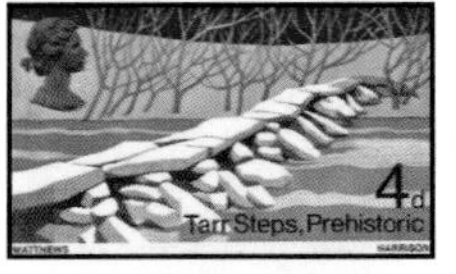

1968 (29 April) British Bridges

No.			U/M	F/U
C222	**4d**	Tarr Steps, Exmoor	10	10
C222a		Missing phosphor	5.00	
C222b		Printed on the gummed side	£20	
C223	**9d**	Aberfeldy	10	11
C223a		Missing phosphor	£15	
C223b		Broad Band	£15	
C224	**1s6d**	Menai	10	15
C224a		Missing phosphor	£16	
C225	**1s9d**	M4 Viaduct	10	17
C225a		Missing phosphor	£10	
C225b		Broad Band	£10	
		Set of 4	19	30
		Set of 4 Cylinder Blocks	1.50	
		First Day Cover		1.20
		Presentation Pack	2.00	
Varieties				
C223c	9d	Missing Ultramarine		£4000
C223d	9d	Missing Gold (Queen's head)	£175	
C224b	1s6d	Missing Reddish orange	£185	
C224c	1s6d	Missing Gold (Queen's head)	£185	
C224d	1s6d	Shift 3mm to bottom of Turquoise-green	£55	
C224e	1s6d	Shift 2mm to bottom of Gold (Queen's head)	£20	
C225c	1s9d	Missing Gold (Queen's head)	£185	
C225d	1s9d	Missing Gold & phosphor	£3500	£1600

1968 (29 May) British Anniversaries

No.			U/M	F/U
C226	**4d**	TUC	10	10
C226a		Missing phosphor	£10	
C227	**9d**	Emmeline Pankhurst	10	12
C227a		Missing phosphor	£10	
C228	**1s**	Sopwith Camel	10	15
C228a		Missing phosphor	£10	
C229	**1s9d**	Captain Cook	10	15
C229a		Missing phosphor	£150	
		Set of 4	19	30
		Set of 4 Cylinder Blocks	1.50	
		First Day Cover		`2.20
		Presentation Pack 1	1.75	

1968 (12 Aug.) British Paintings 1968

No.			U/M	F/U
C230	**4d**	Queen Elizabeth I	10	10
C230a		Missing phosphor	1.00	
C231	**1s**	'Pinkie'	10	11
C231a		Missing phosphor	£10	
C232	**1s6d**	'Ruins of St. Mary'	10	12
C232a		Missing phosphor	£10	
C233	**1s9d**	'The Hay Wain'	10	15
C233a		Missing phosphor	£20	
		Set of 4	20	25
		Set of 4 Cylinder Blocks	1.50	
		First Day Cover		1.25
		Presentation Pack 1	1.75	
		German Presentation Pack	8.50	

Varieties

No.			U/M	F/U
C230b	4d	Missing Gold (Queen's head & 4d)	£200	
C230c		Missing Gold & phosphor	£200	
C230d		Missing Vermilion (face & hands)	£250	
C230e		Missing embossing	£80	
C231b	1s	Missing Gold (Queen's head & 1s)	£4650	
C231c		Missing Gold & phosphor	£250	
C232b	1s6d	Missing Gold (Queen's head & 1/6)	£125	
C232c		Shift 7mm to top of Gold (Queen's head & 1/6)	£35	
C233b	1s9d	Missing Gold, & phosphor	£550	
C233c		Missing Red *	£7500	£1500
C233d		Perf. shift 4mm to top	£45	

* This stamp is of uncertain origin.

1968 (16 Sept.) Collectors Pack 1968

No.		U/M	F/U
YP2	Presentation Pack	3.00	

The Post Office began numbering all Presentation Packs commencing with the 1968 British Paintings issue.

1968 (16 Sept.) Gift Pack 1968

No.		U/M	F/U
YP3	Presentation Pack 3	3.00	
YP3a	German Gift Pack	22.50	

1968 (25 Nov.) Christmas 1968

No.			U/M	F/U
C234	**4d**	Rocking Horse (1 band)	10	10
C234a		Missing phosphor	5.00	
C235	**9d**	Dolls House	10	12
C235a		Missing phosphor	£10	
C236	**1s6d**	Train Set	10	12
C236a		Missing phosphor	£15	
		Set of 3	15	20
		Set of 3 Cylinder Blocks	80	
		First Day Cover		70
		Presentation Pack 4	1.75	
		German Presentation Pack	6.00	

The 4d value was printed on the Rembrandt and Thrissell machines. Either version is worth the same.

Rembrandt: If you imagine a line from the top of the boy's head to the top of the Queen's portrait it should be perfectly horizontal.
Thrissell: The Queen's head is normally lower and also the grey of the boy's pullover is mottled compared with the Rembrandt printing.

Varieties

No.			U/M	F/U
C234b	4d	Missing Vermilion	£225	
C234c	4d	Missing Ultramarine & phosphor	£225	£200
C234d	4d	Missing Gold (Queen's head)	£3500	
C234e	4d	Missing Bistre brown	£3000	
C234f	4d	Shift 2mm to top of Gold (Queen's head) & embossing	£45	
C234g	4d	Shift 11.5mm to bottom of embossing	£35	
C234h	4d	Shift 5mm to left of Ultramarine	£50	
C234i	4d	Missing embossing	5.00	
C235b	9d	Missing Yellow	£70	
C235c	9d	Shift 2mm to bottom of embossing		
C235d	9d	Missing embossing & phosphor	£10	
C235e	9d	Missing embossing	5.00	
C236b	1s6d	Shift 5mm to bottom of embossing	£10	

A

B

C

D

E

1969 (15 Jan.) British Ships

No.			U/M	F/U
C237	**5d**	Queen Elizabeth 2 (1 horizontal band)	10	10
C237a		Missing phosphor	5.00	
C238	**9d**	Elizabethan Galleon (A)	24	27
C238a		Missing phosphor	£10	
C239	**9d**	East Indiaman (B)	24	27
C239a		Missing phosphor	£10	
C240	**9d**	Cutty Sark (C)	24	27
C240a		Missing phosphor	£10	
C238/40	**9d**	**Strip of 3 se-tenant**	60	80
C238/40a		Missing phosphor	£35	
C241	**1s**	SS Great Britain (D)	13	13
C241a		Missing phosphor	£35	
C242	**1s**	RMS Mauretania (E)	13	13
C242a		Missing phosphor	£35	
C241/2	**1s**	**Pair se-tenant**	25	40
C241/2a		Missing phosphor	£75	
		Set of 6	70	1.00
		Set of 3 Cylinder Blocks	5.00	
		First Day Cover		1.75
		Presentation Pack 5	2.50	
		German Presentation Pack	18.50	
		Cunard Presentation Pack	5.00	
Varieties				
C237b	5d	Missing Black (5d, Queen's head & hull)	£950	
C237c	5d	Missing Grey (decks)	£70	
C237d	5d	Missing Red (Cunard, etc.)	£85	
C237e	5d	Missing Red & phosphor	£65	
C237f	5d	Perf. shift 4mm to right ('5' at right)	£40	
C237g	5d	Perf. shift 4mm to top (missing inscription)	£60	
C237h	5d	Perf. shift 4mm to top (inscription above '5')	£35	
C237i	5d	Perf. shift 2mm to top	£25	
C237j	5d	Shift 1mm to top of Grey (superstructure in the sky)	£40	
C238/40b	9d	Missing Red and Blue	£1400	
C238/40c	9d	Missing Blue	£1250	
C238/40d	9d	Shift 5mm to top of Red (Bulwarks in the sky)	£150	
C241/2b	1s	Missing Greenish-yellow	£2500	
C241/2c	1s	Missing Green	£17500	
C241/2d	1s	Missing Carmine (hull)	£15500	
C241/2e	1s	Missing Red	£12500	
C241/2f	1s	Missing Carmine & Red	£13500	

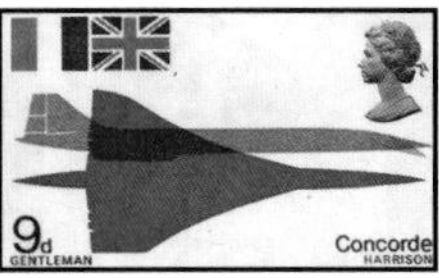

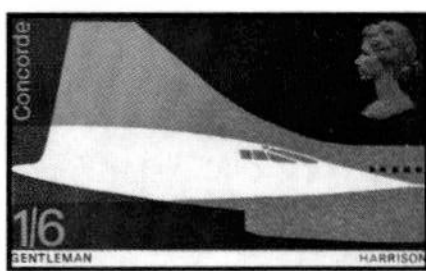

1969 (3 March) First Flight of Concorde

No.			U/M	F/U
C243	**4d**	Concord in Flight	15	10
C243a		Missing phosphor	1.00	
C244	**9d**	Plan and Elevation Views	20	20
C244a		Missing phosphor	£100	
C245	**1s6d**	Concorde's Nose and Tail	20	20
C245a		Missing phosphor	£10	
		Set of 3	50	50
		Set of 3 Cylinder Blocks	3.70	
		First Day Cover		7.50
		Presentation Pack 6	6.50	
		German Presentation Pack	24.50	
Varieties				
C243b	4d	Missing Violet (4d, etc.)	£275	
C243c		Missing Orange (line of fuselage)	£300	£180
C243d		Missing Orange & phosphor	£300	£180
C243e		Shift 2mm to left of Green	£15	
C243f		Missing Violet	£300	£180
C245b	1s6d	Missing Silver (Queen's head)	£300	£180

1969 (2 April) British Anniversaries

No.			U/M	F/U
C246	**5d**	Daily Mail/Vickers FB27	10	10
C247	**9d**	Europa and CEPT Emblems	10	10
C247a		Missing phosphor	£20	
C247b		Uncoated paper	£1500	
C248	**1s**	I.L.O. Emblem	10	10
C248a		Missing phosphor	£10	
C249	**1s6d**	Flags of N.A.T.O	15	17
C249a		Missing phosphor	£10	
C250	**1s9d**	Vickers FB-27	15	20
C250a		Missing phosphor	5.00	
C250b		Uncoated paper	£200	
		Set of 5	28	50
		Set of 5 Cylinder Blocks	2.10	
		First Day Cover		1.50
		Presentation Pack 9	2.75	
		German Presentation Pack	£45	

No.			U/M	F/U
Varieties				
C249b	1s6d	Missing Black	£75	
C249c		Missing Green	£55	
C249d		Missing Green & phosphor	£55	
C249e		Missing Lemon (FDC)		£3500
C250c	1s9d	Shift 3mm to left of Green (globe)	£40	

A

B

C

D

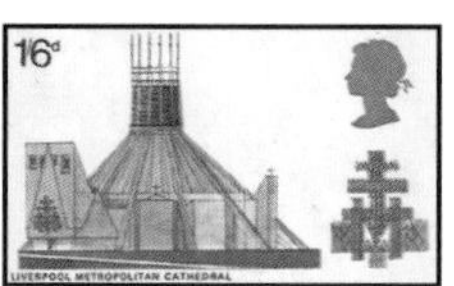

1969 (28 May) British Architecture. Cathedrals

No.			U/M	F/U
C251	**5d**	Durham (A)	10	10
C252	**5d**	York Minster (B)	10	10
C253	**5d**	St. Giles, Edinburgh (C)	10	10
C254	**5d**	Canterbury (D)	10	10
C251/4	**5d**	**Block of 4 se-tenant**	25	50
C255	**9d**	St. Pauls	17	15
C255a		Missing phosphor	£45	
C256	**1s6d**	Liverpool	20	20
C256a		Missing phosphor	£20	
		Set of 6	50	75
		Set of 3 Cylinder Blocks	5.00	
		First Day Cover		1.50
		Presentation Pack 10	1.75	
		German Presentation Pack	£16	

Varieties

Prices are for blocks of four, unless indicated otherwise, and the stamps affected are shown in brackets.

No.			U/M	F/U
C252a	5d	Missing Violet (B)	£3000	
C251/4a	5d	Missing Pale Bluish-violet	£7000	
C251/4b	5d	Missing 'd' after value	£300	
C251/4c	5d	Missing Green	£80	
C251/4d	5d	Imperforate block of 4	£1250	
C255b	9d	Missing Black (9d)	£75	
C255c	9d	Shift 12mm to bottom of Black (9d)	£45	
C255d	9d	Missing Black & Phosphor	£125	
C256b	1s6d	Missing Black (1/6d)	£2500	
C256c	1s6d	Shift 10mm to bottom of Black (1/6d)	£125	
C256d	1s6d	Offset on reverse of Yellow-olive	£50	

A

B

C

1969 (1 July) Investiture of HRH The Prince of Wales

No.			U/M	F/U
C257	**5d**	The Kings Gate (A)	10	15
C257a		Missing phosphor	6.00	
C258	**5d**	The Eagle Tower (B)	10	15
C258a		Missing phosphor	6.00	
C259	**5d**	Queen Eleonor's Gate (C)	10	15
C259a		Missing phosphor	6.00	
C257/9	**5d**	**Strip of 3 se-tenant**	20	50
C257/9a		Missing phosphor	£18	
C260	**9d**	Celtic Cross	15	14
C260a		Missing phosphor	£20	
C261	**1s**	Prince Charles	15	14
C261a		Missing phosphor	£15	
C261b		One broad band	£30	
		Set of 5	35	65
		Set of 3 Cylinder Blocks	3.50	
		First Day Cover		1.50
		Presentation Pack 11	1.75	
		German Presentation Pack	£16	
		Welsh Presentation Pack	£24	

Varieties

Prices for the 5d are for strips of three.

No.			U/M	F/U
C257/9b	5d	Missing Black (5d and inscription)	£650	
C257/9c	5d	Missing Red (Flags)	£1500	
C257/9d	5d	Missing Deep grey (Windows, etc.)	£650	
C257/9e	5d	Missing Green (Flags)	£1500	
C257/9f	5d	Shift 4mm to bottom of Deep olive-grey (Queen's head)	£95	
C257/9g	5d	Missing Pale grey	£12500	
C258g	5d	Missing Pale grey (B)		£3750
C260b	9d	Shift 9mm to bottom of Black (9d, Queen's head & inscription)	£80	

1969 (13 Aug.) Ghandi Centenary Year

No.			U/M	F/U
C262	**1s6d**	Mahatma Ghandi	10	14
C262a		Missing phosphor	5.00	
C262b		Printed on the gummed side	£400	
		Cylinder Block	75	
		First Day Cover		50

1969 (15 Sept.) Collectors Pack

No.			U/M	F/U
CP4		Collectors Year Pack 12	8.50	

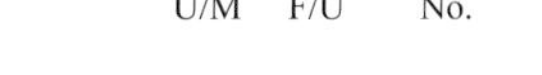

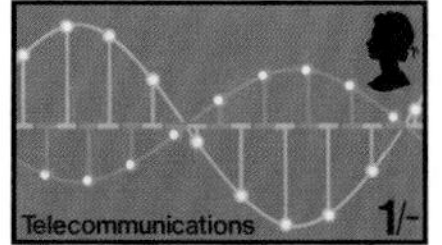

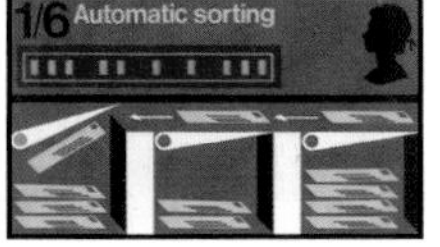

1969 (1 Oct.) Post Office Technology

Printer: De La Rue in Lithography. Perf. 13½ x 14

No.			U/M	F/U
C263	**5d**	National Giro	10	10
C263a		Missing phosphor	5.00	
C263b		One broad band	£15	
C264	**9d**	International Subscriber Dialling	10	15
C264a		One broad band	£15	
C265	**1s**	Pulse Code Modulation	10	15
C265a		Missing phosphor	£300	
C265b		One broad band	£15	
C266	**1s6d**	Automatic Sorting	10	15
C266a		One broad band	£15	
		Set of 4	20	40
		Set of 4 Cylinder Blocks	1.50	
		First Day Cover		1.25
		Presentation Pack 13	1.75	
Variety				
C264b	9d	Perf. shift 4mm to right	£38	

1969 (26 Nov.) Christmas 1969

No.			U/M	F/U
C267	**4d**	Herald Angel (one 8mm centre band)	10	10
C267a		One 4mm centre band	5	5
C268	**5d**	The Three Shepherds	10	10
C268a		Missing phosphor	5.00	
C268b		Perforated right margin	£25	
C269	**1s6d**	The Three Kings	10	15
C269a		Missing phosphor	5.00	
		Set of 3	13	20
		Set of 3 Cylinder Blocks	1.00	
		First Day Cover		60
		Presentation Pack 14	1.75	
Varieties				
C267b	4d	Missing Gold (Queen's head)	£4250	
C268c	5d	Missing Olive brown		£3500
C268d	5d	Missing Gold, Red and Olive brown	£7500	
C268e	5d	Missing Green (centre Shepherd)	£175	
C268f	5d	Missing Light Blue (sheep, etc.)	£65	
C268g	5d	Missing Red (hat & leggings, etc.)	£650	
C268h	5d	Missing Gold (Queen's head)	£425	
C268i	5d	Missing embossing	£20	
C269b	1s6d	Missing Deep slate	£275	
C269c	1s6d	Missing Gold (Queen's head)	£85	
C269d	1s6d	Missing Light Blue	£70	
C269e	1s6d	Missing Yellow	£230	
C269f	1s6d	Missing Violet		
C269g	1s6d	Missing embossing	£10	
C269h	1s6d	Missing embossing & phosphor	£10	

1970 (11 Feb.) British Rural Architecture

No.			U/M	F/U
C270	**5d**	Fife Harding	10	10
C270a		Missing phosphor	5.00	
C271	**9d**	Cotswold Limestone	10	15
C271a		Missing phosphor	£10	
C272	**1s**	Welsh Stucco	10	15
C272a		Missing phosphor	£15	
C273	**1s6d**	Ulster Thatch	10	15
C273a		Missing phosphor	5.00	
		Set of 4	20	45
		Set of 4 Cylinder Blocks	1.50	
		First Day Cover		1.25
		Presentation Pack 15	2.95	
Varieties				
C270b	5d	Missing Dark Grey	£7500	
C270c		Missing Grey (Queen's head)	£5000	
C270d		Missing Lemon	£75	
C270e		Missing Greenish-blue	£3500	
C270f		Shift 1mm to left of Greenish blue (door)	£25	
C271b	9d	Shift 3mm to left of Grey (Queen's head)	£50	
C272b	1s	Missing Light blue	£100	
C273b	1s6d	Missing Turquoise-blue (lawn)	£5000	
C273c		Shift 1mm to right of Lilac	£15	

1970 (1 April) Anniversaries

No.			U/M	F/U
C274	**5d**	Declaration of Arbroath	10	10
C274a		Missing phosphor	£300	
C275	**9d**	Florence Nightingale	10	15
C275a		Missing phosphor	5.00	
C276	**1s**	International Co-operative Alliance	10	15
C276a		Missing phosphor	5.00	
C277	**1s6d**	Mayflower	15	15
C277a		Missing phosphor	5.00	

No.			U/M	F/U
C278	**1s9d**	Royal Astronomical Society	20	20
C278a		Missing phosphor	5.00	
		Set of 5	25	48
		Set of 5 Cylinder Blocks	1.80	
		First Day Cover		1.50
		Presentation Pack 16	1.75	

Varieties

C274b	5d	Missing Emerald (tunics)	£175	
C274c	5d	Missing Gold (Queen's head)	£650	
C274d	5d	Shift 6mm to bottom of Gold (Queen's head)	£35	
C274e	5d	Partial missing Gold (small Queen's head)		
C274f	5d	Dry print of Emerald *	£20	
C275b	9d	Missing Ochre (bedding)	£175	
C275c	9d	Missing embossing	£15	
C275d	9d	Shift 2mm to left of Green (Grey dress)	£20	
C276b	1s	Missing Brown	£135	
C276c	1s	Missing Gold (Queen's head)	£55	
C276d	1s	Missing Green (tablecloth)	£75	
C276e	1s	Missing Green & embossing	£85	£45
C276f	1s	Missing embossing	£15	
C276g	1s	Missing embossing & phosphor	£20	
C277b	1s6d	Missing Emerald (under skirt at left)	£70	
C277d	1s6d	Missing embossing	5.00	
C278b	1s9d	Missing embossing	£75	

* Often mistaken for and sold as Missing Emerald

A

B

C

D

E

1970 (3 June) Literary Anniversaries

C279	5d	Multicoloured (A)	10	12
C280	5d	Multicoloured (B)	10	12
C281	5d	Multicoloured (C)	10	12
C282	5d	Multicoloured (D)	10	12
C279/82	**5d**	**Block of 4 se-tenant**	40	60
C283	**1s6d**	Multicoloured	15	25
C283a		Missing phosphor	5.00	
		Set of 5	40	80
		Set of 3 Cylinder Blocks	3.00	
		First Day Cover		1.20
		Presentation Pack 17	2.50	

Varieties

Prices are for blocks of four

C279/82a	5d	Imperforate block of 4	£800	
C279/82b	5b	Missing Silver	£11000	
C279/82c	5d	Missing Yellow-bistre	£6000	
C279/82d	5d	Missing Light Greenish-blue	£400	
C279/82e	5d	Missing Light Greenish-blue & Silver	£12500	
C283b	1s6d	Missing Blue (1/6)	£7500	
C283c	1s6d	Missing Gold (Queen's head)	£2500	£750
C283d	1s6d	Missing Silver ('Grasmere')	£100	
C283e	1s6d	Missing embossing	5.00	
C283f	1s6d	Missing embossing & phosphor	£20	

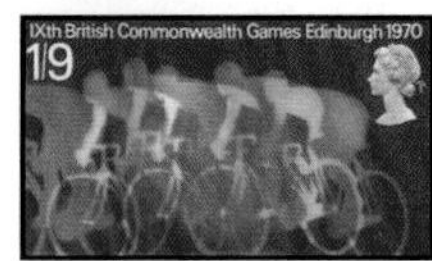

1970 (15 July) 9th Commonwealth Games

Printer: De la Rue in lithography. Perf. 13½ x 14

No.			U/M	F/U
C284	**5d**	Runners	6	10
C284a		Missing phosphor	£200	
C285	**1s6d**	Swimmers	20	20
C285a		Missing phosphor	£60	
C286	**1s9d**	Cyclists	20	27
		Set of 3	36	35
		Set of 3 Cylinder Blocks	2.70	
		First Day Cover		1.25
		Presentation Pack 19	1.75	

Varieties

C284b	5d	Missing Greenish-yellow	£7250	£2750

1970 (14 Sept.) Collectors Year Pack 1970

CP5		Collectors Year Pack Pack 20	7.50	

1970 (18 Sept.) 'Philympia 1970'. International Philatelic Exhibition

C287	**5d**	1d Black	10	10
C287a		Missing phosphor	5.00	
C288	**9d**	1s Green	10	15
C288a		Missing phosphor	£10	
C289	**1s6d**	4d Carmine	20	25
C289a		Missing phosphor	5.00	
		Set of 3	24	30
		Set of 3 Cylinder Blocks	1.80	
		First Day Cover		1.25
		Presentation Pack 21	1.75	

Varieties

C287b	5d	Missing Grey (Queen's head)	£9500	

1970 (25 Nov.) Christmas 1970

No.			U/M	F/U
C290	**4d**	Multicoloured (1 band)	10	10
C290a		Missing phosphor	£60	
C291	**5d**	Multicoloured	10	10
C291a		Missing phosphor	5.00	
C292	**1s6d**	Multicoloured	18	20
C292a		Missing phosphor	5.00	
		Set of 3	19	25
		Set of 3 Cylinder Blocks	1.40	
		First Day Cover		70
		Presentation Pack 22	1.75	

Varieties

No.			U/M	F/U
C290b	4d	Imperforate left margin	£650	
C290c	4d	Missing embossing	£50	
C290d	4d	Shift 15mm to left of embossing - also 2 phosphor bands instead of 1 band		
C291b	5d	Imperforate pair	£250	
C291c	5d	Missing Emerald	£55	
C291d	5d	Missing Gold (Queen's head)		£3500
C291e	5d	Missing embossing	£15	
C291f	5d	Perf. shift 4mm to right		
C292b	1s6d	Missing Salmon	£85	
C292c	1s6d	Missing Ochre	£55	
C292d	1s6d	Missing embossing	£35	

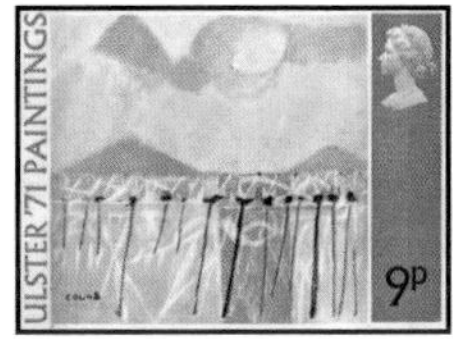

1971 (16 June) 'Ulster 71' Paintings

No.			U/M	F/U
C293	**3p**	A Mountain Road	10	10
C293a		Missing phosphor	5.00	
C294	**7½p**	Deer's Meadow	27	30
C294a		Missing phosphor	£20	
C294b		One broad band	5.00	
C295	**9p**	Slieve na Brock	27	30
C295a		Missing phosphor	£20	
C295b		One broad band	£20	
		Set of 3	40	50
		Set of 3 Cylinder Blocks	3.00	
		First Day Cover		1.35
		Presentation Pack 26A	2.75	

Varieties

No.			U/M	F/U
C293b	3½p	Missing Venetian Red	£4000	
C294c	7½p	Missing Pale olive-grey	£85	
C294d	7½p	Offset on reverse of Grey-blue (panel, Queen's head and inscription)	£55	
C295c	9p	Missing Orange	£1250	
C295d	9p	Shift 4mm to bottom of Grey (sky)	£65	

1971 (28 July) Literary Anniversaries

No.			U/M	F/U
C296	**3p**	John Keats	10	10
C296a		Missing phosphor	5.00	
C297	**5p**	Thomas Gray	15	17
C297a		Missing phosphor	£30	
C298	**7½p**	Sir Walter Scott	20	25
C298a		Missing phosphor	£20	
		Set of 3	40	50
		Set of 3 Cylinder Blocks	3.00	
		First Day Cover		1.40
		Presentation Pack 32	2.75	

Varieties

No.			U/M	F/U
C296b	3p	Missing Gold (Queen's head)	£85	
C296c	3p	Shift 4mm to right of embossing	5.00	
C297b	5p	Missing Gold (Queen's head)	£325	
C298b	7½p	Missing embossing	£35	

1971 (25 Aug.) General Anniversaries

No.			U/M	F/U
C299	**3p**	British Legion	10	10
C299a		Missing phosphor	5.00	
C299b		One broad band	6.00	
C300	**7½p**	City of York	30	35
C300a		Missing phosphor	£10	
C300b		One broad band	£15	
C301	**9p**	Rugby Football	30	35
C301a		Missing phosphor	£400	
C301b		One broad band	£10	
		Set of 3	50	60
		Set of 3 Cylinder Blocks	3.70	
		First Day Cover		1.40
		Presentation Pack 32A	2.75	

Varieties

No.			U/M	F/U
C299c	3p	Missing Black	£11000	£4000
C299d		Missing Olive-brown (faces)	£250	
C299e		Missing Reddish-orange (Nurse's cape)	£275	
C299f		Missing Deep blue (sailor)	£550	
C299g		Shift 1mm to right of Deep Blue	£15	
C299h		Shift 1mm to bottom of Deep Blue	£20	

No.			U/M	F/U
C300c	7½p	Missing Grey	£185	
C300d		Shift 8mm to right of Mauve	£75	
C300e		Shift 1.5mm to right of Black (shield)	£28	
C301c	9p	Missing Olive-brown	£110	
C301d		Missing Light blue	£4000	
C301e		Missing Myrtle green	£7500	£2000
C301f		Missing Lemon	£4000	
C301f		Shift 2mm to right of Yellow (shirts)	£35	
C301g		Shift 3mm to right of Brown (heads, ball and boots)	£75	

1971 (22 Sept.) British Architecture. Modern University Buildings

No.			U/M	F/U
C302	**3p**	Aberystwyth	10	10
C302a		Missing phosphor	5.00	
C303	**5p**	Southampton	17	20
C303a		Missing phosphor	£60	
C304	**7½p**	Leicester	35	40
C304a		Missing phosphor	£10	
C305	**9p**	Essex	50	55
C305a		Missing phosphor	£15	
		Set of 4	80	95
		Set of 4 Cylinder Blocks	6.00	
		First Day Cover		1.35
		Presentation Pack 33	3.50	

Varieties

No.			U/M	F/U
C302b	3p	(Partial) Missing Black (windows)	£8500	
C302c	3p	Shift of Lemon (appears missing)		£4000
C303b	5p	Larger value tablet, due to the use of Cylinder 1A, instead of 2A	£5000	
C305b	9p	Pale Lilac Missing	£2500	

1971 (29 Sept.) Collectors Pack

No.		U/M
CP6	Presentation Pack 34	£20

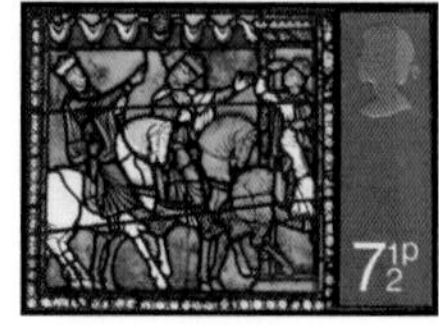

1971 (13 Oct.) Christmas 1971

No.			U/M	F/U
C306	**2½p**	Dream of the Wild (1 band)	10	10
C307	**3p**	Adoration of the Magi	10	10
C307a		Missing phosphor	5.00	
C308	**7½p**	Ride of the Magi	32	45
C308a		Missing phosphor	£10	
C308b		One broad band	£10	
		Set of 3	35	50
		Set of 3 Cylinder Blocks	2.60	
		First Day Cover		1.25
		Presentation Pack 35	2.00	

Varieties

No.			U/M	F/U
C306a	2½p	Imperf. pair	£400	
C307b	3p	Missing Light blue (sky)	£5500	
C307c	3p	Missing Lemon	£135	
C307d	3p	Missing Carmine-rose	£2750	£750
C307e	3p	Missing Gold (Queen's head)	£575	
C307f	3p	Missing Reddish violet	£3000	£750
C307g	3p	Missing embossing	£10	
C307h	3p	Missing embossing & phosphor	£65	
C307i	3p	Shift 1mm to bottom of Blue (panel)	£15	
C307j	3p	Missing Lemon and Carmine-rose		£5500
C308c	7½p	Missing Lemon yellow		£4000
C308d	7½p	Missing Lilac	£575	
C308e	7½p	Missing Emerald	£295	
C308f	7½p	Missing Gold (Queen's head)	£135	
C308g	7½p	Missing embossing	£35	
C308h	7½p	Missing embossing & phosphor	£25	
C308i	7½p	Shift 3mm to bottom of Gold	£15	
C308j	7½p	Shift 2mm to right of Light blue	£18	
C308k	7½p	One broad band on back	£30	
C308l	7½p	One broad diagonal band	£30	

1972 (16 Feb.) British Polar Explorers

No.			U/M	F/U
C309	**3p**	Sir James Clark Ross	10	10
C309a		Missing phosphor	5.00	
C310	**5p**	Sir Martin Frobisher	17	20
C310a		Missing phosphor	£10	
C311	**7½p**	Henry Hudson	35	40
C311a		Missing phosphor	£20	
C312	**9p**	Capt. Robert F. Scott	35	40
C312a		Missing phosphor	£275	
		Set of 4	80	90
		Set of 4 Cylinder Blocks	6.00	
		First Day Cover		1.40
		Presentation Pack 39	2.25	

Varieties

No.			U/M	F/U
C309b	3p	Missing Lemon	£6000	
C309c	3p	Missing Slate black (hair)	£3000	
C309d	3p	Missing Gold (Queen's head)	£90	
C309e	3p	Missing Gold & embossing	£110	
C309f	3p	Missing embossing	£30	
C309g	3p	Missing embossing & phosphor	£25	
C309h	3p	Shift 1mm to bottom of Blue (eyes)	£35	
C309i	3p	Uncoated paper	£2000	
C310b	5p	Missing Gold (Queen's head)	£90	
C310c	5p	Missing Gold & phosphor	£110	
C310d	5p	Missing embossing	£20	
C311b	7½p	Missing Gold (Queen's head)	£295	
C312b	9p	Perf. shift 2mm to left	£20	

1972 (26 April) General Anniversaries

No.			U/M	F/U
C313	**3p**	Tutankhamun	10	10
C314	**7½p**	Coastguard	25	27
C314a		Missing phosphor	£225	
C315	**9p**	Ralph Vaughan Williams	25	27
C315a		Missing phosphor	£30	
		Set of 3	42	55
		Set of 3 Cylinder Blocks	3.15	
		First Day Cover		1.40
		Presentation Pack 40	2.25	

Varieties

No.			U/M	F/U
C313a	3p	Dry print of Black (inscription only)	£1500	
C313b		Imperforate between stamp and bottom margin	£650	
C314b	7½p	Shift 2mm to bottom of Light blue (arms)	£35	
C315b	9p	Missing Brown (face, etc.)	£850	£450
C315c		Missing Gold (Queen's head)	£2500	£1500
C315d		Missing Deep slate	£6000	

1972 (21 June) British Architecture. Old Village Churches

No.			U/M	F/U
C316	**3p**	St. Andrew's, Greenstead	10	10
C316a		Missing phosphor	5.00	
C317	**4p**	All Saints, Earls Barton	25	30
C317a		Missing phosphor	£15	
C318	**5p**	St. Andrews Letheringset	25	30
C318a		Missing phosphor	£20	
C319	**7½p**	St. Andrews, Helpringham	40	50
C319a		Missing phosphor	£10	
C320	**9p**	St. Mary the Virgin, Huish	40	50
C320a		Missing phosphor	£20	
		Set of 5	1.05	1.35
		Set of 5 Cylinder Blocks	7.90	
		First Day Cover		2.50
		Presentation Pack 41	4.00	

Varieties

No.			U/M	F/U
C316b	3p	Missing Gold (Queen's head)	£90	
C316c		Missing Gold & phosphor	£110	
C316d		Missing embossing	£25	
C316e		Missing embossing & phosphor	£15	
C316f		Missing Orange-vermillion		£3500
C316g		Perf. shift 5mm to right (3p at right)	£95	
C316h		Shift 2mm to bottom of Black (detail etc.)	£50	
C316i		Shift 2mm to left of Red (figure)	£35	
C316j		Shift 1mm to bottom of Olive-green (grass)	£30	
C317b	4p	Missing Gold & phosphor (Queen's head)	£4250	£2250
C317c		Missing Violet-blue	£110	
C317d		Missing embossing	£10	
C318b	5p	Missing Gold (Queen's head) & phosphor	£150	
C318c		Missing embossing	£35	
C320b	9p	Missing embossing	£15	
C320c		Shift 1mm to bottom of Red (flowers)	£10	

1972 (24 June) 'Belgica 72'

No.			U/M	F/U
CP7		Souvenir Pack 42	6.00	

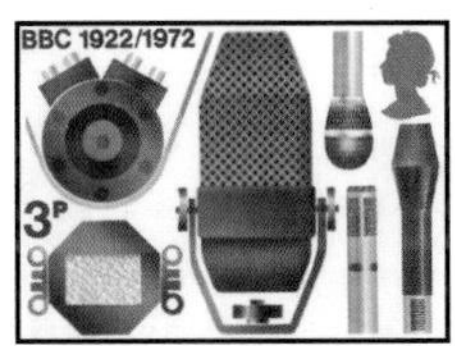

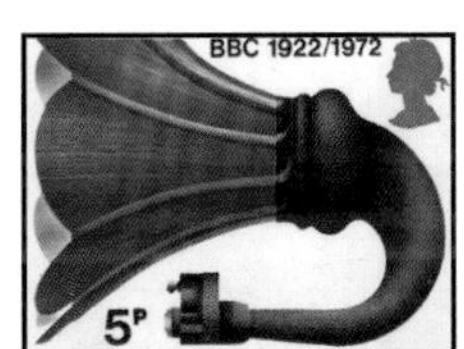

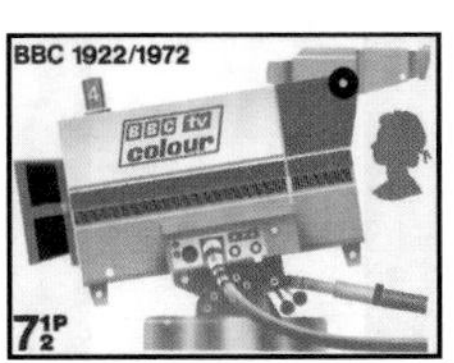

1972 (13 Sept.) British Broadcasting

No.			U/M	F/U
C321	**3p**	Microphone	10	10
C322	**5p**	Loudspeaker	20	20
C322a		Missing phosphor	5.00	
C323	**7½p**	TV Camera	30	35
C323a		Missing phosphor	£10	
C323b		One broad band	£10	

No.			U/M	F/U
C324	**9p**	Oscillator	30	40
C324a		Missing phosphor	£15	
C324b		One broad band	£25	
		Set of 4	70	90
		Set of 4 Cylinder Blocks	5.20	
		First Day Cover		1.45
		Presentation Pack 43	2.25	
		BBC Staff Pack	£20	
Varieties				
C321a	3p	Missing Yellow (terminals)	£4250	
C321b	3p	Shift 2mm to bottom of Yellow (terminals) & Slate (Queen's head) *1	£20	
C323c	7½p	Missing Slate (Queen's head) *2		£2750
C324c	9p	Missing Slate (Queen's head)	£2500	
C324d		Phosphor printed on gum side	£75	

*1 This is often mistaken for the missing yellow.
*2 This stamp is known used on First Day Cover with Edinburgh FDI cancel.

1972 (18 Oct.) Christmas 1972

No.			U/M	F/U
C325	**2½p**	With Trumpet	10	10
C325a		Missing phosphor	£10	
C326	**3p**	Playing Lute	7	10
C326a		Missing phosphor	£5	
C327	**7½p**	Playing Harp	27	27
C327a		Missing phosphor	£10	
		Set of 3	27	30
		Set of 3 Cylinder Blocks	1.90	
		First Day Cover		1.25
		Presentation Pack 44	2.25	
Varieties				
C325b	2½p	Missing Gold	£300	
C325c		Missing Deep grey	£1500	
C325d		Missing embossing	£10	
C325e		Imperf. left margin	£650	
C325f		All colours missing	£50	
C326b	3p	Missing Bright green	£120	
C326c		Missing Red brown	£600	
C326d		Missing Blush violet	£120	
C326e		Missing Lavender	£8500	
C326f		Missing Gold	£550	
C326g		Missing embossing	5.00	
C326h		Missing embossing & phosphor	£10	
C326i		Shift 6mm to bottom left of Bright green	£15	
C326j		Imperforate between stamp and left margin	£650	
C327b	7½p	Missing Ochre	£90	
C327c		Missing embossing	£10	
C327d		Missing embossing & phosphor	£20	
C327e		Missing Blackish-violet	£6500	

1972 (20 Nov.) Royal Silver Wedding
All over phosphor (3p) and without phosphor (20p)
Rembrandt Printing

No.			U/M	F/U
C328	**3p**	Silver, brown and steel blue	10	10
C328a		Missing phosphor	£30	
C329	**20p**	Silver, brown & purple	35	36
		Set of 2	38	37
		First Day Cover		1.25
		Presentation Pack 45	2.60	
		Japanese Pack	4.50	
		Souvenir Pack 46	2.25	

Jumelle Printing

No.			U/M	F/U
C328b	3p	Silver, brown and steel blue	13	13
		Gutter pair	20	20
		Gutter pair (Traffic Light)	£8	£8
Varieties				
C328c	3p	Missing Silver ('Silver Wedding' & 3p)	£350	£200
C328d	3p	Shift 4mm to right of Silver ('Silver Wedding' & 3p)	£30	

Printings The easiest way to identify the two printings is to examine the Duke's head. On the Jumelle printing it is distinct and a lighter shade of brownish-black, on the Rembrandt machine it appears slightly out of focus and is a deeper colour.

Gutter Pairs The Jumelle printing provided a plain gutter through the centre of the sheet - thus providing a new variety for collectors in the form of a gutter pair. This sheet form became standard for all Commemorative stamps from the Horse Chestnut Tree 10p issue of 27th February 1974, but both values of the Royal Wedding issued on 14th November 1973 were also printed with a gutter.

1972 (20 Nov.) Collectors Pack 1972

No.		U/M	F/U
CP8	Presentation Pack 42	13.50	

1973 (3 Jan.) Entry into The European Communities

No.			U/M	F/U
C330	**3p**	Multicoloured	10	10
C331	**5p**	Multicoloured	35	40
C332	**5p**	Multicoloured	35	40
C331/2	**5p**	**Pair se-tenant**	70	85
		Set of 3	65	80
		Set of 2 Cylinder Blocks	2.50	
		First Day Cover		1.25
		Presentation Pack 48	1.45	

1973 (28 Feb.) Tree Planting Year

No.			U/M	F/U
C333	**9p**	Oak Tree (2 band)	17	22
C333a		Missing phosphor	£85	
C333b		One broad band	£20	
		Cylinder Block	1.25	
		First Day Cover		1.25
		Presentation Pack 49	1.10	

Varieties

No.			U/M	F/U
C333b	9p	Missing Black (9p and inscription)	£350	
C333c	9p	Missing Grey (Queen's head)	£300	

From this issue, stamps were printed with 'all over' phosphor unless otherwise stated.

1973 (18 April) British Explorers

No.			U/M	F/U
C334	**3p**	David Livingstone	15	15
C334a		Missing phosphor	£20	
C335	**3p**	H. M. Stanley	15	15
C335a		Missing phosphor	£20	
C334/5	**3p**	**Pair se-tenant**	35	35
C334/5a		Pair missing phosphor	£40	
C336	**5p**	Sir Francis Drake	30	26
C336a		Missing phosphor	£10	
C337	**7½p**	Sir Walter Raleigh	45	30
C337a		Missing phosphor	£200	
C338	**9p**	Charles Sturt	45	30
C338a		Missing phosphor	£30	
		Set of 5	80	90
		Set of 4 Cylinder Blocks	9.50	
		First Day Cover		1.40
		Presentation Pack 50	1.50	

Varieties

Prices for the 3p value are for se-tenant pairs. Singles are worth slightly below half that of the prices quoted.

No.			U/M	F/U
C334/5c	3p	Missing Turquoise (oceans & inscription)	£750	
C334/5d		Missing Light Orange-brown	£700	
C334/5e		Missing Gold (Queen's head)	£110	
C334/5f		Missing Gold and phosphor	£110	
C334/5g		Missing embossing	£50	
C334/5h		Missing embossing and phosphor	£50	
C336b	5p	Missing Grey-black	£625	
C336c		Missing Grey-black and phosphor	£625	
C336d		Missing Sepia (light hair)	£575	
C336e		Missing Gold (Queen's head)	£110	
C336f		Missing embossing	£10	
C336g		Missing embossing and phosphor	£30	
C337b	7½p	Missing Ultramarine (eyes)	£2750	
C337c		Missing Gold (Queen's head)	£2750	
C337d		Shift 2mm to left of Grey-black	£85	
C338b	9p	Missing Greyish black	£1250	
C338c		Double print of Brown-grey (hair and facial features	£800	£600
C338d		Missing Gold (Queen's head)	£110	£45
C338e		Brown-red missing	£500	
C338f		Flesh tones missing	£1000	
C338g		Missing embossing	£30	

1973 (16 May) County Cricket Centenary

No.			U/M	F/U
C339	**3p**	Ochre, black and gold	10	10
C340	**7½p**	Green, black and gold	30	40
C340a		Missing phosphor	£80	
C341	**9p**	Blue, black and gold	40	45
		Set of 3	75	80
		Set of 3 Cylinder Blocks	5.60	
		First Day Cover		1.40
		Presentation Pack 51	2.50	
		Souvenir Booklet	3.50	
		PHQ Card (3p) *	£55	£110

* Used price is for July 1973; the 16 May postmarks were cancelled by favour.

Varieties

No.			U/M	F/U
C339a	3p	Missing Gold (Queen's head)	£2250	
C339b	3p	Missing embossing	310	
C340b	7½p	Missing embossing	£20	
C341a	9p	Missing embossing	£60	

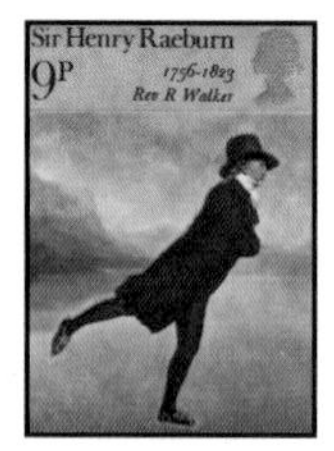

1973 (4 July) British Paintings

No.			U/M	F/U
C342	**3p**	Sir Joshua Reynolds	10	10
C343	**5p**	Sir Henry Raeburn	15	20
C343a		Missing phosphor	£15	
C344	**7½p**	Sir Joshua Reynolds	30	40
C344a		Missing phosphor	5.00	
C345	**9p**	Sir Henry Raeburn	30	40
C345a		Missing phosphor	£75	
		Set of 4	65	70
		Set of 4 Cylinder Blocks	5.00	
		First Day Cover		1.25
		Presentation Pack 52	1.60	

Varieties

C342a	3p	Missing Gold (Queen's head)	£55	
C342b		Missing Gold and embossing	£60	
C342c		Perf. shift 6mm to right (3p at right)	£45	
C343b	5p	Missing Gold (Queen's head)	£65	
C343c		Missing Yellow (Reddish faces)	£475	
C343d		Missing embossing	£20	
C344b	7½p	Missing Gold (Queen's head)	£110	
C344c		Missing Cinnamon	£5250	
C344d		Missing embossing	£15	
C345b	9p	Missing Brownish Rose (paler face) *	£55	
C345c		Missing embossing and phosphor	£100	

* Difficult to identify without some of the selvedge showing the colours.

A 

 B

C 

 D

1973 (15 Aug.) 400th Anniversary of Birth of Inigo Jones

No.			U/M	F/U
C346	**3p**	Court Masque Costumes (A)	15	10
C347	**3p**	St. Pauls Church, Covent Garden (B)	15	10
C346/7	**3p**	**Pair se-tenant**	38	50
C346/7a		Pair missing phosphor	£500	
C348	**5p**	Prince's Lodging, Newmarket (C)	30	40
C349	**5p**	Court Masque Stage Scene (D)	30	40
C348/9	**5p**	**Pair se-tenant**	70	1.05
C348/9a		Pair missing phosphor	£500	
		Set of 4	70	1.20
		Set of 2 Cylinder Blocks	4.50	
		First Day Cover		1.30
		Presentation Pack 53	1.60	
		PHQ Card (3p Type B)	£75	£75

Varieties

The following prices are for se-tenant pairs

No.			U/M	F/U
C346/7b	3p	Deep mauve printed double	£5000	
C346/7c		Shift 5mm to bottom of Gold (Queen's head)	£55	
C346/7d		24mm Black shift - missing value	£500	
C346/7e		24mm Black shift - shifted value	£125	
C346/7f		Extra 9mm band at left	£15	
C348/9b		Extra 9mm band at left	£30	

1973 (12 Sept.) 19th Commonwealth Parliamentary Conference

No.			U/M	F/U
C350	**8p**	View from Whitehall	25	25
C351	**10p**	View from Millbank	25	25
		Set of 2	35	45
		Set of 2 Cylinder Blocks	2.70	
		First Day Cover		1.25
		Presentation Pack 54	1.60	
		Souvenir Booklet 55	3.50	
		PHQ Card (8p)	£20	£25

1973 (14 Nov.) Royal Wedding

No.			U/M	F/U
C352	**3½p**	Violet and silver	10	10
C352a		Missing phosphor	£80	
C353	**20p**	Light brown and silver	40	50
		Set of 2	42	50
		Set of 2 Cylinder Blocks	3.10	
		Gutter Pairs	1.45	1.45
		Gutter Pairs (Traffic light)	£45	£45
		First Day Cover		1.25
		Presentation Pack 56	1.25	
		PHQ Card (3½p)	4.80	7.00

Varieties

C352b	3½p	Imperforate pair	£1850	
C352c	3½p	Miscut gutter pair	£20	
C353a	20p	Missing Silver (Queen's head)	£1750	

Caution: Many stamps show trace of silver colour

A 

 B

C 

 D

E

F

1973 (28 Nov.) Christmas 1973 (Good Ming Wenceslas)

No.			U/M	F/U
PVAD gum				
C354	**3p**	Multicoloured (centre band) (A)	25	10
C355	**3p**	Multicoloured (centre band) (B)	25	10
C356	**3p**	Multicoloured (centre band) (C)	25	10
C357	**3p**	Multicoloured (centre band) (D)	25	10
C358	**3p**	Multicoloured (centre band) (E)	25	10
C354/8	**3p**	**Strip of 5 se-tenant**	1.30	1.60
C359	**3½p**	Multicoloured	10	10
C359a		Missing phosphor	6.00	
		Set of 6	1.30	1.60
		Set of 2 Cylinder Blocks	3.30	
		First Day Cover		1.40
		Presentation Pack 57 (may contain stamps with any of the different gums)	1.60	
Gum Arabic				
C354g	**3p**	Multicoloured (centre band) (A)	20	
C355g	**3p**	Multicoloured (centre band) (B)	20	
C356g	**3p**	Multicoloured (centre band) (C)	20	
C357g	**3p**	Multicoloured (centre band) (D)	20	
C358g	**3p**	Multicoloured (centre band) (E)	20	
C354/8g	**3p**	**Strip of 5 se-tenant**	2.00	
C354/8ga	**3p**	Strip of 5 perf. through side margin	2.50	
PVA gum				
C359p	3½p	Multicoloured	20	
C359pa		Missing phosphor	5.50	

Varieties

The prices quoted for the 3p are for se-tenant strips of five and the stamps affected are shown in brackets.

No.			U/M	F/U
PVAD Gum				
C354/8a	3p	Missing Rosy-mauve (Page boy) (B, C, D & E)	£3500	
C354/8b		Missing Grey-black	£2500	
C354/8c		Imperforate	£1000	
C354/8d		Missing Salmon pink	£10	
C359b	3½p	Missing Rosy mauve (Page boy's robes)	£50	
C359c		Imperforate pair	£350	
C359d		Missing Black (inscription and 3½p)	£60	
C359e		Missing Salmon (faces, etc.)	£50	
C359f		Missing Blue (Page boy's leg and robes)	£150	
C359g		Missing Blue & Rosy mauve (Page boy)	£350	
C359h		Missing Bright Red (King's robe)	£50	
C359i		Missing Red-brown (basket and logs)		£4500
C359j		Missing Gold		£750
C359k		Missing Turquoise-green	£2250	£1000
C359l		Missing phosphor	£10	
Gum Arabic				
C354/8gb	3p	Missing Salmon (floor tiles only) (C)	£10	
PVA Gum				
C359pb	3½p	Imperforate pair	£350	
C359pc		Missing Black (inscription and 3½p)	£60	
C359pd		Missing Blue & Rosy mauve (Page boy)	£350	
C359pe		Missing Rosy mauve (Page boy's robes)	£50	
C359pf		Missing Bright Red (King's robe)	£50	
C359pg		Missing phosphor	£10	

1973 (28 Nov.) Collectors Year Pack 1973

No.		U/M	F/U
CP10	Collectors Year Pack 58	13.50	

PVADextrin gum was used on all the following issues unless otherwise stated.

1974 (27 Feb.) British Trees. Horse Chestnut

No.			U/M	F/U
C360	**10p**	Horse Chestnut	18	20
		Cylinder Block	1.30	
		Gutter pair	75	75
		Gutter pair (Traffic Light)	£25	£25
		First Day Cover		1.25
		Presentation Pack 58	1.10	
		PHQ Card	£54	£55

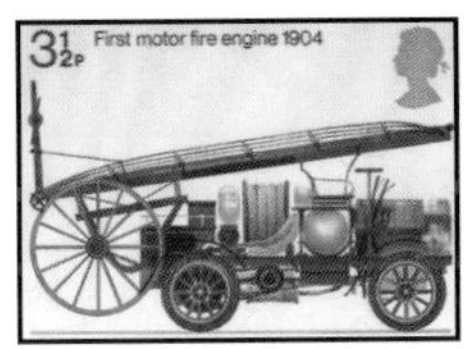

1974 (24 April) 200th Anniversary of The Fire Service

No.			U/M	F/U
C361	**3½p**	Fire Engine 1904	10	10
C361a		PVA Gum	5.00	
C362	**5½p**	Fire Engine 1863	20	20
C362a		Missing phosphor	5.00	
C363	**8p**	Fire Engine 1860	20	35
C364	**10p**	Fire Engine 1766	27	27
		Set of 4	65	70
		Set of 4 Cylinder Blocks	5.00	
		Gutter Pairs	2.30	2.30
		Gutter Pairs (Traffic Light)	£24	£24
		First Day Cover		£2
		Merryweather First Day Cover		5.00
		Presentation Pack 60	1.60	
		PHQ Card (3½p)	£58	£60
Variety				
C361b	3½p	Imperforate pair	£500	

No.			U/M	F/U
1974 (12 June) UPU Centenary				
C365	**3½p**	P & O Packet	10	10
C366	**5½p**	Farman BiPlane	20	20
C367	**8p**	Airmail-blue Van	25	27
C368	**10p**	Imperial Airways	25	30
		Set of 4	50	55
		Set of 4 Cylinder Blocks	3.75	
		Gutter Pairs	1.50	1.50
		Gutter Pairs (Traffic Light)	£20	£20
		First Day Cover		1.25
		Presentation Pack 65	1.60	
Variety				
C365a	3½p	Perf. shift 4mm to top	£45	

No.			U/M	F/U
1974 (10 July) Great Britons				
C369	**4½p**	Robert the Bruce	10	10
C370	**5½p**	Owain Glyndwr	20	30
C371	**8p**	Henry V	35	45
C372	**10p**	The Black Prince	35	30
		Set of 4	65	80
		Set of 4 Cylinder Blocks	4.90	
		Gutter Pairs	2.35	2.35
		Gutter Pairs (Traffic Light)	£28	£28
		First Day Cover		1.75
		Presentation Pack 65	1.60	
		PHQ Cards	£14	£20
Variety				
C372a	10p	Imperf. pair	£625	

No.			U/M	F/U
1974 (9 Oct.) Centenary of Birth of Sir Winston Churchill				
C373	**4½p**	Royal Yacht Squadron	10	10
C374	**5½p**	Prime Minister 1940	30	30
C374a		Missing phosphor	5.00	
C375	**8p**	Secretary for War	40	30
C375a		PVA Gum	75	
C376	**10p**	War Correspondent	40	25
		Set of 4	1.00	80
		Set of 4 Cylinder Blocks	3.80	
		Gutter Pairs	1.70	1.70
		Gutter Pairs (Traffic Light)	£15	£15
		First Day Cover		1.20
		Presentation Pack 66	1.75	
		Souvenir Booklet	1.75	
		PHQ Card (5½p)	2.50	7.00
		PHQ Card missing Silver (Queen's head)	£350	

No.			U/M	F/U
1974 (27 Nov.) Christmas 1974				
C377	**3½p**	Adoration of the Magi (1 right band)	10	10
C377a		Missing phosphor	£10	
C377b		Multicoloured (1 centre band)	11	11
C378	**4½p**	The Nativity	9	10
C379	**8p**	Virgin and Child	20	25
C380	**10p**	Virgin and Child	20	25
		Set of 4	45	52
		Set of 4 Cylinder Blocks	3.40	
		Gutter Pairs	1.60	1.60
		Gutter Pairs (Traffic Light)	£15	£15
		First Day Cover		1.25
		Presentation Pack 67	1.60	
C377c	3½p	(CB) Gutter pair	50	50
C377c	3½p	(CB) Gutter pair (Traffic Light)	6.00	6.00
Variety				
C377c	3½p	Missing Light Stone (background)	£7500	
C377d		Missing Light brown		£3500
1974 (27 Nov.) Collectors Year Pack 1974				
CP11		Collectors Year Pack 68	6.00	

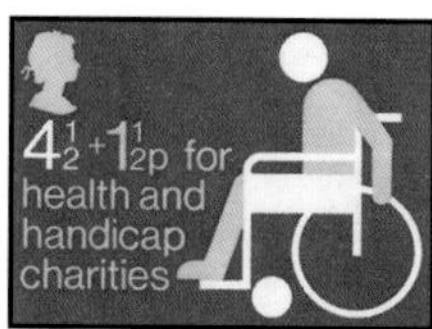

No.			U/M	F/U
1975 (22 Jan.) Charity Issue				
C381	**4½p** + 1½p	Invalid in Wheelchair	10	8
		Cylinder Block	70	
		Gutter Pairs	20	25
		Gutter Pairs (Traffic Light)	50	50
		First Day Cover		50

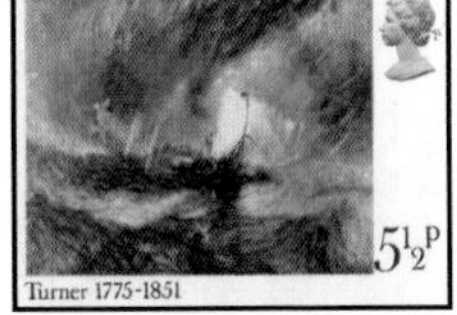

1975 (19 Feb.) 200th Birth Anniversary of J.W. Turner

No.			U/M	F/U
C382	**4½p**	'Peace - Burial at Sea'	10	10
C383	**5½p**	'Snowstorm'	12	12
C384	**8p**	'The Arsenal, Venice'	20	30
C385	**10p**	'St. Laurent'	25	25
		Set of 4	42	47
		Set of 4 Cylinder Blocks	3.10	
		Gutter Pairs	1.05	1.05
		Gutter Pairs (Traffic Light)	2.80	2.80
		First Day Cover		1.25
		Presentation Pack 69	1.60	
		PHQ Card (5½p)	£18	£20

1975 (23 April) European Architectural Heritage Year

No.			U/M	F/U
C386	**7p**	Charlotte Square, Edinburgh	16	10
C387	**7p**	The Rows, Chester	16	10
C386/7	**7p**	**Pair se-tenant**	50	60
C388	**8p**	Greenwich	22	25
C389	**10p**	Windsor	23	25
C390	**12p**	National Theatre	30	25
		Set of 5	65	85
		Set of 4 Cylinder Blocks		
		Gutter Pairs	2.95	2.95
		Gutter Pairs (Traffic Light)	10.50	10.50
		First Day Cover		1.50
		Presentation Pack 70	1.60	
		PHQ Cards (7p's and 8p) (3)	5.00	5.00

1975 (11 June) Sailing. Black - Recess printed

No.			U/M	F/U
C391	**7p**	Dinghies	10	12
C392	**8p**	Racing Keel Boats	18	20
C393	**10p**	Cruising Yachts	22	22
C394	**12p**	Multihulls	30	35
		Set of 4	55	70
		Set of 4 Cylinder Blocks	4.10	
		Gutter Pairs	1.25	1.25
		Gutter Pairs (Traffic Light)	7.50	7.50
		First Day Cover		1.20
		Presentation Pack 71	1.30	
		PHQ Card (8p)	3.00	3.00
Varieties				
C391a	7p	Miscut gutter pair	£28	
C391b	7p	Shift 2mm to bottom of Gold (Queen's head)	£15	
C392a	8p	Missing Black (rigging)	£50	£125
C392b	8p	Missing Gold (Queen's head, 'dry print')	£250	
C394a	12p	Dry print of Rose (white sails)	£10	

1975 (13 Aug.) 150th Anniversary of First Public Steam Railway

No.			U/M	F/U
C395	**7p**	Stephenson's Locomotion	15	10
C396	**8p**	Waverley Class	30	25
C397	**10p**	Caerphilly Castle	30	25
C398	**12p**	High-Speed Train	35	36
		Set of 4	70	70
		Set of 4 Cylinder Blocks	3.25	
		Gutter Pairs	1.65	1.65
		Gutter Pairs (Traffic Light)	4.50	4.50
		First Day Cover		1.80
		Presentation Pack 72	2.50	
		Souvenir Booklet	2.50	
		PHQ Cards	£29	£40

1975 (3 Sept.) 62nd Inter-Parliamentary Conference

No.			U/M	F/U
C399	**12p**	Palace of Westminster	20	20
		Cylinder Block	1.50	
		Gutter pair	35	35
		Gutter pair (Traffic Light)	1.20	1.20
		First Day Cover		1.25
		Presentation Pack 74	90	

1975 (22 Oct.) Bicentenary of the Birth of Jane Austen

No.			U/M	F/U
C400	**8½p**	Emma and Mr Woodhouse	15	10
C401	**10p**	Catherine Moorland	25	20
C402	**11p**	Mr Darcy	30	32
C403	**13p**	Mary and Henry Crawford	30	32
		Set of 4	70	65
		Set of 4 Cylinder Blocks	3.90	
		Gutter Pairs	1.25	1.25
		Gutter Pairs (Traffic Light)	2.95	2.95
		First Day Cover		1.25
		Presentation Pack 75	1.60	
		PHQ Cards	£10	£10

1975 (26 Nov.) Christmas 1975 (Angels)

No.			U/M	F/U
C404	**6½p**	With Harp and Lute (1 band)	11	10
C404a		PVA Gum	1.50	
C405	**8½p**	With Mandolind (phosphor ink)	13	8
C406	**11p**	With Horn	40	35
C407	**13p**	With Trumpet	40	35
		Set of 4	60	65
		Set of 4 Cylinder Blocks	4.50	
		Gutter Pairs	1.20	1.20
		Gutter Pairs (Traffic Light)	2.95	2.95
		First Day Cover		1.25
		Presentation Pack 76	1.60	
	6½p	Gutter pair (PVA)	1.00	
	6½p	Gutter pair (Traffic Light) (PVA Gum)	2.50	

1975 (26 Nov.) Collectors Year Pack 1975

No.			U/M	F/U
CP12		Collectors Year Pack 77	4.00	

1976 (10 March) Centenary of Alexander Graham Bell's First Telephone Transmission

No.			U/M	F/U
C408	**8½p**	Housewife	15	10
C409	**10p**	Policeman	27	20
C410	**11p**	Nurse	35	36
C411	**13p**	Industrialist	40	35
		Set of 4	65	70
		Set of 4 Cylinder Blocks	4.90	
		Gutter Pairs	1.30	1.30
		Gutter Pairs (Traffic Light)	2.95	2.95
		First Day Cover		1.25
		Presentation Pack 78	2.00	
		PHQ Cards	3.00	3.00

Varieties

No.			U/M	F/U
C408a	8½p	Missing Magenta (flowers, vase & picture)	£2000	
C408b		Shift 3mm to bottom of Magenta	£25	
C408c		Imperforate between stamps & bottom margin	£500	
C410a	11p	Imperforate between stamps & bottom margin	£500	

1976 (28 April) Social Reformers

No.			U/M	F/U
C412	**8½p**	Thomas Hepburn	15	10
C413	**10p**	Robert Owen	27	20
C414	**11p**	Lord Shaftesbury	35	36
C415	**13p**	Multicoloured	40	27
		Set of 4	65	70
		Set of 4 Cylinder Blocks	4.90	
		Gutter Pairs	1.30	1.30
		Gutter Pairs (Traffic Light)	2.95	2.95
		First Day Cover		1.25
		Presentation Pack 79	1.75	
		PHQ Card (8½p)	3.00	3.75
Varieties				
C412a	8½p	Shift 2mm to bottom of Deep Grey (moving hands)	£35	
C412b	8½p	Perf. shift 6mm to top (8½p at top)	£40	
C412c	8½p	Perf. shift 3mm to top (8½p bisected)	£25	
C413a	10p	Perf. shift 12mm to bottom (10p above Queen's head)	£50	

1976 (2 June) Bicentenary of American Independence

No.			U/M	F/U
C416	**11p**	Franklin	18	17
		Cylinder Block	1.30	
		Gutter pair	30	30
		Gutter pair (Traffic Light)	80	80
		First Day Cover		1.25
		Presentation Pack 80	75	
		PHQ Card	2.75	2.75

1976 (30 June) Centenary of Royal National Rose Society

No.			U/M	F/U
C417	**8½p**	'Elizabeth of Glamis'	15	12
C418	**10p**	'Grandpa Dickson'	27	20
C419	**11p**	'Rosa Mundi'	30	35
C420	**13p**	'Sweet Briar'	40	30
		Set of 4	65	70
		Set of 4 Cylinder Blocks	4.90	
		Gutter Pairs	1.35	1.35
		Gutter Pairs (Traffic Light)	4.00	4.00
		First Day Cover		1.25
		Presentation Pack 81	1.80	
		PHQ Cards	£14	£20
Variety				
C420a	13p	Missing Black (value only)	£25000	£20000

1976 (4 Aug.) British Cultural Traditions

No.			U/M	F/U
C421	**8½p**	Archdruid	15	10
C422	**10p**	Morris Dancing	21	20
C422a		Missing phosphor	£250	
C423	**11p**	Scots Piper	40	45
C424	**13p**	Welsh Harpist	40	27
		Set of 4	70	70
		Set of 4 Cylinder Blocks	5.20	
		Gutter Pairs	1.35	1.35
		Gutter Pairs (Traffic Light)	3.50	3.50
		First Day Cover		1.25
		Presentation Pack 82	2.00	
		PHQ Cards	7.00	£11

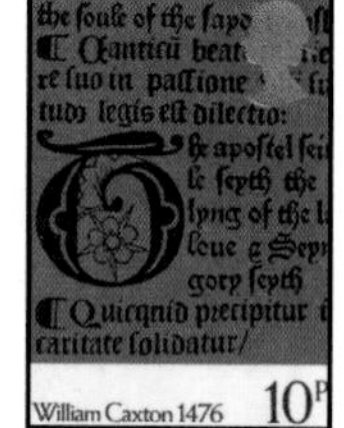

1976 (29 Sept.) 500th Anniversary of the First Printing in Britain

No.			U/M	F/U
C425	**8½p**	Canterbury Tales	15	22
C426	**10p**	Trelyse of Love	21	21
C427	**11p**	Chesse	40	40
C428	**13p**	Early Printing Press	40	30
		Set of 4	90	85
		Set of 4 Cylinder Blocks	6.70	
		Gutter Pairs	1.35	1.35
		Gutter Pairs (Traffic Light)	2.95	2.95
		First Day Cover		1.25
		Presentation Pack 83	1.80	
		PHQ Cards	6.00	7.00

Varieties

			U/M	F/U
C427a	11p	Imperf. at left (marginal)	£1500	
C427b	11p	Shift 4mm to right of Gold (Queen's head)	£35	

1976 (24 Nov.) Christmas 1976

No.			U/M	F/U
C429	**6½p**	Virgin and Child (1 band)	11	10
C430	**8½p**	Angel with Crown	15	10
C431	**11p**	Angel and Sheppherds	30	37
C431a		Uncoated paper	£70	£45
C432	**13p**	The Three Kings	40	30
		Set of 4	57	65
		Set of 4 Cylinder Blocks	4.30	
		Gutter Pairs	1.15	1.15
		Gutter Pairs (Traffic Light)	2.60	2.60
		First Day Cover		1.25
		Presentation Pack 87	2.00	
		PHQ Cards	2.00	2.00

Variety

			U/M	F/U
C429a	6½p	Imperforate pair	£350	
C430a	8½p	Imperforate pair	£400	

1976 (24 Nov.) Collectors Year Pack

No.		U/M	F/U
CP13	Collectors Year Pack 88	6.00	

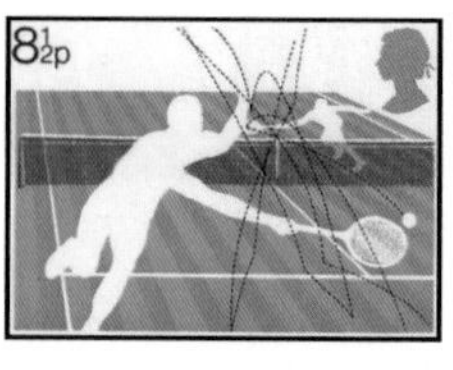

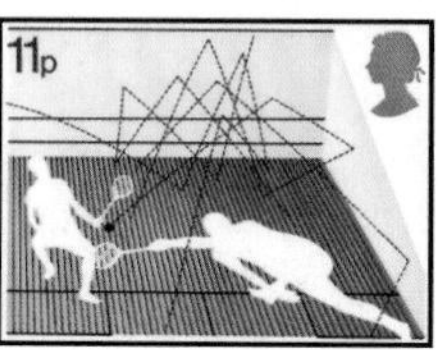

1977 (12 Jan.) Racket Sports

No.			U/M	F/U
C433	**8½p**	Lawn Tennis	15	12
C434	**10p**	Table Tennis	21	21
C435	**11p**	Squash	30	32
C436	**13p**	Badminton	30	27
		Set of 4	65	65
		Set of 4 Cylinder Blocks	4.90	
		Gutter Pairs	1.25	1.25
		Gutter Pairs (Traffic Light)	2.95	2.95
		First Day Cover		1.25
		Presentation Pack 89	1.85	
		PHQ Cards	5.25	5.25

Variety

			U/M	F/U
C433a	8½p	Imperforate pair	£750	
C435a	11p	Imperforate pair	£2000	

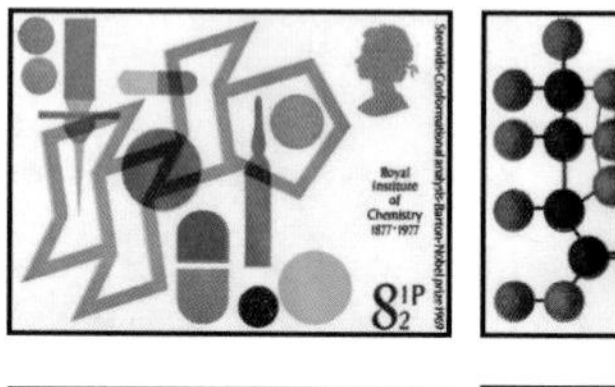

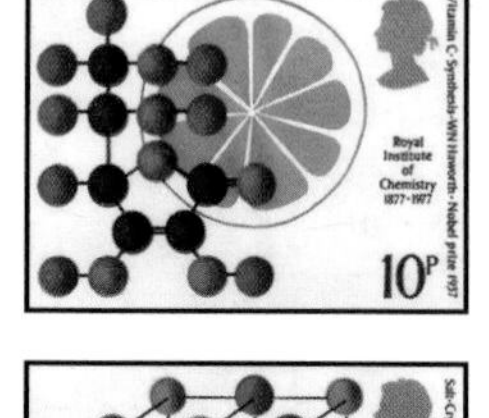

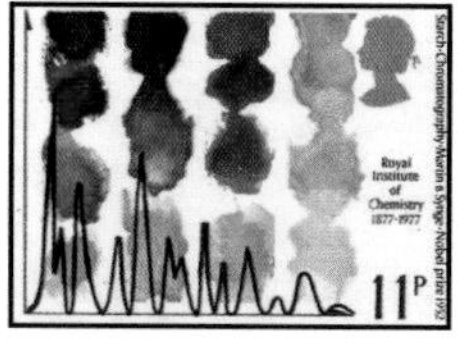

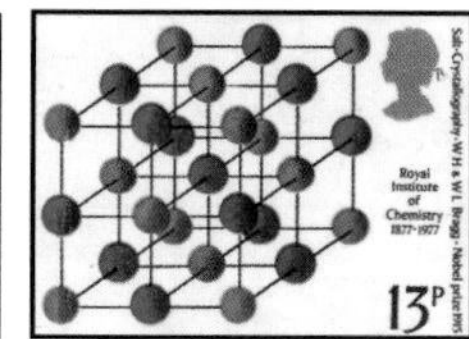

1977 (2 March) Chemistry

No.			U/M	F/U
C437	**8½p**	Steroids	15	10
C438	**10p**	Vitamin C	21	21
C439	**11p**	Starch	30	33
C440	**13p**	Salt	30	27
		Set of 4	65	65
		Set of 4 Cylinder Blocks	4.90	
		Gutter Pairs	1.35	1.35
		Gutter Pairs (Traffic Light)	2.50	2.50
		First Day Cover		1.25
		Presentation Pack 92	1.85	
		PHQ Cards	4.00	4.00

Variety

			U/M	F/U
C437a	8½p	Imperforate pair	£1200	

1977 (11 May) Silver Jubilee

No.			U/M	F/U
C441	**8½p**	Multicoloured	15	10
C442	**9p**	Multicoloured	15	10
C443	**10p**	Multicoloured	20	20
C444	**11p**	Multicoloured	27	25
C445	**13p**	Multicoloured	27	27
		Set of 5	72	55
		Set of 5 Cylinder Blocks	5.50	
		Gutter Pairs	1.85	1.85
		Gutter Pairs (Traffic Light)	2.15	2.15
		First Day Cover		1.35
		First Day Cover (9p only)		40
		Presentation Pack 94 (excludes 9p)	95	
		Souvenir Booklet (excludes 9p)	2.50	
		PHQ Cards	6.00	6.75
Varieties				
C441a	8½p	Imperforate pair	£750	
C443a	10p	Imperforate pair	£1250	
C444a	11p	Imperforate pair	£1250	
C445a	13p	Imperforate pair	£950	

1977 (8 June) Commonwealth Heads of Government

No.			U/M	F/U
C446	**13p**	Gathering of Nations	20	20
		Cylinder Block	1.40	
		Gutter pair	35	35
		Gutter pair (Traffic Light)	50	50
		First Day Cover		50
		Presentation Pack 95	50	
		PHQ Card	2.00	2.00

A

B

C

D

E

1977 (5 Oct.) British Wildlife

No.			U/M	F/U
C447	**9p**	Hedgehog (A)	20	20
C448	**9p**	Hare (B)	20	20
C449	**9p**	Red Squirrel (C)	20	20
C450	**9p**	Otter (D)	20	20
C451	**9p**	Badger (E)	20	20
C447/51	**9p**	**Strip of 5 se-tenant**	85	1.10
		Cylinder Block	2.10	
		Gutter strip of 10	2.00	2.00
		Gutter strip of 10 (Traffic Light)	3.00	3.00
		First Day Cover		1.40
		Presentation Pack 96	85	
		PHQ Cards	1.50	3.75
Variety				
C447/51	9p	Imperforate vertical pair (any)	£600	
C447/51	9p	Imperforate horizontal pair (any)	£1500	

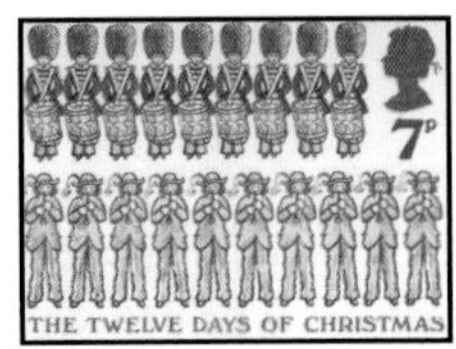

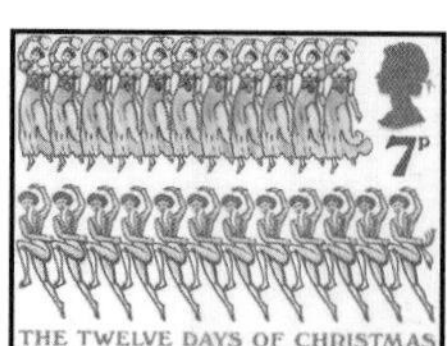

1977 (23 Nov.) Christmas 1977 (Twelve Days of Christmas)

No.			U/M	F/U
C452	**7p**	Three French Hens... (centre band) (A)	15	15
C453	**7p**	Six Geese a Laying... (centre band) (B)	15	15
C454	**7p**	Eight Maids a milking... (centre band) (C)	15	15
C455	**7p**	Ten Pipers Piping,,, (centre band) (D)	15	15
C456	**7p**	Twelve Lords a Leaping... (centre band) (E)	15	15
C452/6	**7p**	**Strip of 5 se-tenant**	60	80
C457	**9p**	A Partridge in a Pear Tree	15	10
		Set of 6	65	80
		Set of 2 Cylinder Blocks	2.60	
		Gutter Pairs	1.35	1.35
		Gutter Pairs (Traffic Light)	2.50	2.50
		First Day Cover		1.25
		Presentation Pack 97	1.25	
		PHQ Cards	1.00	2.10
Variety				
C452/56a	7p	Imperforate strip of 5	£1500	
C457a	9p	Imperforate pair	£1000	

1977 (23 Nov.) Collectors Year Pack 1977

No.		U/M	F/U
CP14	Collectors Year Pack 98	4.00	

1978 (25 Jan.) Energy Resources

No.			U/M	F/U
C458	**9p**	Oil	15	10
C459	**10½p**	Coal	18	18
C460	**11p**	Natural Gas	19	25
C461	**13p**	Electricity	20	20
		Set of 4	60	65
		Set of 4 Cylinder Blocks	4.50	
		Gutter Pairs	1.25	1.25
		Gutter Pairs (Traffic Light)	1.80	1.80
		First Day Cover		1.25
		Presentation Pack 99	1.50	
		PHQ Cards	1.50	2.50

1978 (1 March) British Architecture. Historic Buildings

No.			U/M	F/U
C462	**9p**	Tower of London	15	10
C463	**10½p**	Holyroodhouse	18	18
C464	**11p**	Caernarvon Castle	20	24
C465	**13p**	Hampton Court Palace	20	20
		Set of 4	62	70
		Set of 4 Cylinder Blocks	4.60	
		Gutter Pairs	1.25	1.25
		Gutter Pairs (Traffic Light)	1.80	1.80
		First Day Cover		1.25
		Presentation Pack 100	1.50	
		PHQ Cards	1.25	2.25
MS1	**53½p**	**Miniature Sheet** (in original PO folder)	90	1.10
MS1a		Missing phosphor	£100	
		First Day Cover		1.10
Varieties				
C462a	9p	Imperf. bottom margin	£200	
MS1b	MS	Missing Red (flag on 9p)	£3500	
MS1c	MS	Missing Pale Orange (10p and 13p)	£3500	
MS1d	MS	Missing Yellow-olive (Queen's head)	£4500	
MS1e	MS	Missing Blue	£11000	
MS1f	MS	Imperforate	£4500	

1978 (31 May) 25th Anniversary of the Coronation

No.			U/M	F/U
C466	**9p**	State Coach	15	10
C467	**10½p**	St. Edwards Crown	18	18
C468	**11p**	The Sovereign's Orb	20	25
C469	**13p**	Imperial State Crown	20	20

No.			U/M	F/U
		Set of 4	62	65
		Set of 4 Cylinder Blocks	4.70	
		Gutter Pairs	1.15	1.15
		Gutter Pairs (Traffic Light)	1.80	1.80
		First Day Cover		1.25
		Presentation Pack 101	1.00	
		Souvenir Booklet	2.50	
		PHQ Cards	1.25	2.25

Variety

C469a		Imperforate pair	£75

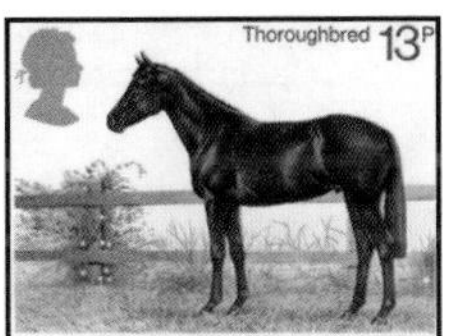

1978 (5 July) Horses. Centenary of the Shire Horse Society.

No.			U/M	F/U
C470	**9p**	Shire Horse	15	10
C471	**10½p**	Shetland Pony	18	18
C472	**11p**	Welsh Pony	20	25
C473	**13p**	Thoroughbred	20	20
		Set of 4	62	65
		Set of 4 Cylinder Blocks	4.70	
		Gutter Pairs	1.20	1.20
		Gutter Pairs (Traffic Light)	1.80	1.80
		First Day Cover		1.25
		Presentation Pack 102	1.05	
		PHQ Cards	1.25	2.25

Variety

C471a	10½p	Imperforate between stamp & bottom margin	£400

1978 (2 Aug.) Cycling. Centenary of the Cyclists' Touring Club.

No.			U/M	F/U
C474	**9p**	Penny-Farthing	15	10
C475	**10½p**	Touring Bicycles	18	18
C476	**11p**	Modern Bicycles	20	25
C477	**13p**	Road-racers	20	20
		Set of 4	62	70
		Set of 4 Cylinder Blocks	4.70	
		Gutter Pairs	1.15	1.15
		Gutter Pairs (Traffic Light)	1.80	1.80
		First Day Cover		1.25
		Presentation Pack 103	90	
		PHQ Cards	1.00	1.50

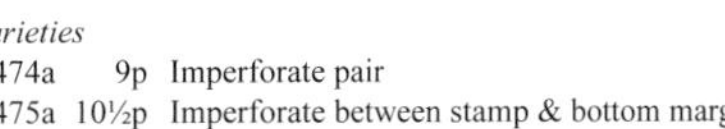

Varieties

No.			U/M
C474a	9p	Imperforate pair	£350
C475a	10½p	Imperforate between stamp & bottom margin	£700
C477a	13p	Imperforate pair	£1000

1978 (22 Nov.) Christmas 1978

No.			U/M	F/U
C478	**7p**	Singing Carols	13	10
C479	**9p**	The Waits	15	10
C480	**11p**	18th Century Singers	20	23
C481	**13p**	'The Boars Head Carol'	22	23
		Set of 4	55	65
		Set of 4 Cylinder Blocks	4.20	
		Gutter Pairs	1.10	1.10
		Gutter Pairs (Traffic Light)	1.80	1.80
		First Day Cover		1.25
		Presentation Pack 104	90	
		PHQ Cards	1.00	1.50

Variety

C478a	7p	Imperforate between stamp & bottom margin	£850
C478b		Imperforate pair	£500
C479a	9p	Imperforate pair	£850
C480a	11p	Imperforate pair	£950

1978 (21 Nov.) Collectors Year Pack 1976

CP15	Collectors Year Pack 105	4.00

1979 (7 Feb.) British Dogs

No.			U/M	F/U
C482	**9p**	Old English Sheepdog	15	10
C483	**10½p**	Welsh Springer	20	22
C484	**11p**	West Highland	20	22
C485	**13p**	Irish Setter	22	22
		Set of 4	60	65
		Set of 4 Cylinder Blocks	4.50	
		Gutter Pairs	1.15	1.15
		Gutter Pairs (Traffic Light)	1.80	1.80
		First Day Cover		1.25
		Presentation Pack 106	1.10	
		PHQ Cards	2.00	2.50

Varieties

No.			U/M	F/U
C483a	10½p	Shift 1½mm to top of Deep Grey (Queen's head) and Black (10½p)	£30	
C484a	11p	Imperforate pair	£1350	
C484a	11p	Imperforate between stamp & bottom margin	£750	

1979 (21 March) British Wild Flowers

No.			U/M	F/U
C486	**9p**	Primrose	15	10
C487	**10½p**	Daffodil	20	20
C488	**11p**	Bluebell	20	22
C489	**13p**	Snowdrop	22	21
		Set of 4	60	65
		Set of 4 Cylinder Blocks	4.50	
		Gutter Pairs	1.15	1.15
		Gutter Pairs (Traffic Light)	1.70	1.70
		First Day Cover		1.25
		Presentation Pack 107	90	
		PHQ Cards	1.00	1.50

Varieties

No.			U/M	F/U
C486a	9p	Imperforate pair	£400	
C487a	10½p	Imperforate vertical pair	£1500	
C487b		Imperforate between stamp & left margin	£1000	
C488a	11p	Imperforate pair	£1300	
C488b	11p	Shift 2mm to left of Silver (Queen's head)	£35	
C489a	13p	Imperforate pair	£850	

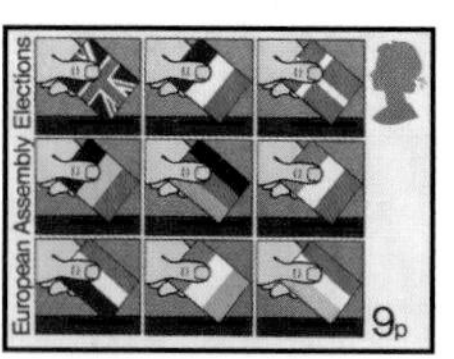

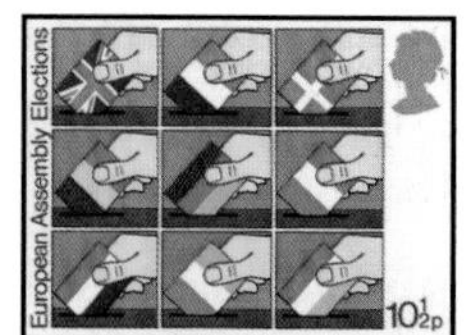

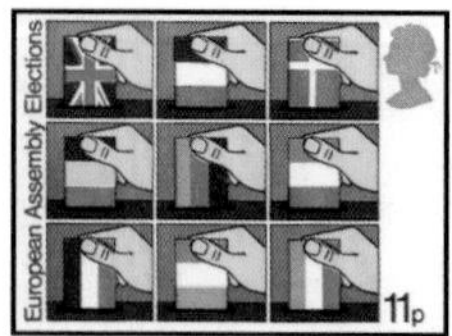

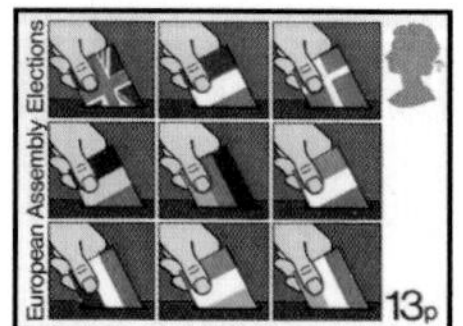

1979 (9 May) Direct Elections to the European Assembly

No.			U/M	F/U
C490	**9p**	Multicoloured	15	10
C491	**10½p**	Multicoloured	20	20
C492	**11p**	Multicoloured	20	22
C493	**13p**	Multicoloured	22	21
		Set of 4	60	65
		Set of 4 Cylinder Blocks	4.50	
		Gutter Pairs	1.15	1.15
		Gutter Pairs (Traffic Light)	1.70	1.70
		First Day Cover		1.25
		Presentation Pack 108	90	
		PHQ Cards	90	1.40

1979 (6 June) Horse Racing

No.			U/M	F/U
C494	**9p**	'Mahmoud'	15	10
C495	**10½p**	'Liverpool National'	20	20
C496	**11p**	'Spring Meeting'	20	22
C497	**13p**	'Dorsett Ferry'	22	20
		Set of 4	60	65
		Set of 4 Cylinder Blocks	4.50	
		Gutter Pairs	1.15	1.15
		Gutter Pairs (Traffic Light)	1.70	1.70
		First Day Cover		1.25
		Presentation Pack 109 (Pack includes a Cartoon insert)	90	
		PHQ Cards	90	1.40

Varieties

No.			U/M	F/U
C494a	9p	Imperforate between stamp & left margin	£850	
C497a	13p	Imperforate between stamp & bottom margin	£100	

1979 (11 July) United Nations 'Year of the Child'

No.			U/M	F/U
C498	**9p**	Peter Rabbit	15	10
C499	**10½p**	Wind in the Willows	25	18
C500	**11p**	Winnie-the-Pooh	30	18
C501	**13p**	Alice in Wonderland	40	25
		Set of 4	90	70
		Set of 4 Cylinder Blocks	6.75	
		Gutter Pairs	1.50	1.50
		Gutter Pairs (Traffic Light)	2.00	2.00
		First Day Cover		1.25
		Presentation Pack 110	2.00	
		PHQ Cards	1.25	1.75

1979 (22 Aug.) Sir Rowland Hill Centenary

No.			U/M	F/U
C502	**10p**	Sir Rowland Hill	15	10
C503	**11½p**	General Post	19	20
C504	**13p**	London Post	20	20
C505	**15p**	Uniform Postage	22	20
		Set of 4	62	65
		Set of 4 Cylinder Blocks	4.70	
		Gutter Pairs	1.28	1.28
		Gutter Pairs (Traffic Light)	1.70	1.70
		First Day Cover		1.25
		Presentation Pack 111	90	
		PHQ Cards	90	1.40
MS2	**59½p**	**Miniature sheet** (24.10.79)	70	70
MS2a		Missing phosphor	£25	
		First Day Cover		75
Varieties				
C502a	10p	Imperforate pair	£2250	
MS2b	MS	Imperforate	£2000	
MS2c	MS	Missing Black and Yellow	£12500	
MS2d	MS	Missing Yellow (10p windows, etc.)	£250	£225
MS2e	MS	Missing Yellow and phosphor	£250	
MS2f	MS	Missing Brown-ochre (15p sky, etc.)	£1750	
MS2g	MS	Missing Brown-ochre, Green and Gold	£5000	
MS2h	MS	Missing Rosine (11½p jacket, etc.)	£1000	
MS2i	MS	Missing Rosine and phosphor	£750	
MS2j	MS	Missing Blue (13p, jacket, sky, etc.)	£5500	
MS2k	MS	Missing Green (10p sky & coat, 15p etc.)	£2500	
MS2l	MS	Missing Brown (15p dress, 11½p, 13p etc.)	£750	
MS2m	MS	Missing Gold (Queen's head)	£250	£225
MS2n	MS	Missing Gold and phosphor	£250	
MS2o	MS	Shift 6mm to top of Green	£175	
MS2p	MS	Shift 2mm to right of Gold	£5	
MS2q	MS	Offset on reverse of Gold (Queen's head)	£350	

There are numerous perforation shifts and colour shifts known of all the colours. This listing therefore is only representative.

1979 (26 Sept.) 150th Anniversary of Metropolitan Police

No.			U/M	F/U
C506	**10p**	Multicoloured	15	10
C507	**11½p**	Multicoloured	17	18
C508	**13p**	Multicoloured	20	20
C509	**15p**	Multicoloured	23	23
		Set of 4	65	67
		Set of 4 Cylinder Blocks	4.50	
		Gutter Pairs	1.35	1.35
		Gutter Pairs (Traffic Light)	1.70	1.70
		First Day Cover		1.25
		Presentation Pack 112	90	
		PHQ Cards	90	1.40

1979 (21 Nov.) Christmas 1979

No.			U/M	F/U
C510	**8p**	The Three Kings	13	10
C511	**10p**	Angel and Shepherds	15	10
C512	**11½p**	The Nativity	17	18
C513	**13p**	Mary and Joseph	20	20
C514	**15p**	The Annunciation	25	20
		Set of 5	80	75
		Set of 5 Cylinder Blocks	5.20	
		Gutter Pairs	1.55	1.55
		Gutter Pairs (Traffic Light)	1.80	1.80
		First Day Cover		1.25
		Presentation Pack 113	95	
		PHQ Cards	90	1.40

No.			U/M	F/U
Varieties				
C510a	8p	Imperforate pair	£400	
C510b		Perf. shift 6mm to top	£50	
C510c		Shift 6mm to bottom of Ochre (horse)	£20	
C510d		Shift 2.5mm to bottom of Ochre, 1mm to bottom of Blue and Violet.	£25	
C511a	10p	Imperforate pair	£850	
C511b		Imperforate between, vertical pair	£450	
C511c		Imperforate between stamp & bottom margin	£800	
C513a	13p	Perf. shift 3mm to top	£14	

1979 (21 Nov.) Collectors Year Pack 1979

No.		U/M	F/U
CP16	Collectors Year Pack 114	5.00	

1980 (16 Jan.) British Birds. Perf 14 x 15

No.			U/M	F/U
C515	**10p**	Kingfisher	15	10
C516	**11½p**	Dipper	16	17
C517	**13p**	Moorhen	20	20
C518	**15p**	Wagtail	25	25
		Set of 4	72	70
		Set of 4 Cylinder Blocks	5.50	
		Set of 4 Gutter Pairs	1.80	2.00
		First Day Cover		1.25
		Presentation Pack 115	90	
		PHQ Cards	85	1.35

A

B

C

D

E

1980 (12 March) 150th Anniversary of the Liverpool & Manchester Railway

No.			U/M	F/U
C519	**12p**	Stephenson's Rocket (A)	20	15
C520	**12p**	First and Second Class Carriages (B)	20	15
C521	**12p**	Third class Carriage (C)	20	15
C522	**12p**	Horsebox and Carriage (D)	20	15
C523	**12p**	Goods Truck and Mailcoach (E)	20	15
	12p	**Strip of 5 se-tenant**	85	90
		Cylinder Block	2.80	
		Strip of 5 Gutter Pairs	2.20	2.20
		First Day Cover		1.25
		Presentation Pack 116	95	
		PHQ Cards	85	1.35
Varieties				
C519/523a		Imperforate strip of 5	£1500	
C519/523b		Missing Lemon yellow	£15000	

Type I
Shading lines above and below Queen's head. are broken

Type II
Shading lines above and below Queen's head are <u>unbroken</u>.

1980 (9 April) London 1980 International Stamp Exhibition. Perf.14½ x 14

No.			U/M	F/U
C524	**50p**	London 1980 (Type I)	75	60
		First Day Cover		1.00
C524a	50p	London 1980 (Type II)	75	60
		First Day Cover		1.25
		Presentation Pack 117	95	
		PHQ Card	35	85

<u>Note</u>: Greenish shades of this stamp are due to problems met with the printing and drying time, and can easily be faked.

1980 (7 May) London 1980 International Stamp Exhibition

No.			U/M	F/U
MS3	75p	**Miniature sheet**	80	1.00
		First Day Cover		50
Variety				
MS3a	MS	Imperforate sheet	£1250	£750

1980 (7 May) London Landmarks. Perf. 14 x 15

No.			U/M	F/U
C525	**10½p**	Buckingham Palace	20	20
C526	**12p**	Albert Memorial	18	10
C527	**13½p**	Royal Opers House	20	20
C528	**15p**	Hampton Court	22	22
C529	**17½p**	Kensington Palace	27	35
		Set of 5	95	95
		Set of 5 Cylinder Blocks	7.30	
		Set of 5 Gutter Pairs	2.40	2.40
		First Day Cover		1.25
		Presentation Pack 118	1.05	
		PHQ Cards	85	1.35
Varieties				
C526a	12p	Imperforate vertical pair	£950	
C527a	13½p	Imperforate pair	£950	
C528a	15p	Perf. shift 3mm to right	£75	
C529a	17½p	Missing Silver (Queen's head)	£450	

1980 (9 July) Europa. Authoresses

No.			U/M	F/U
C530	**12p**	Charlotte Bronte	18	10
C531	**13½p**	George Eliot	20	30
C532	**15p**	Emily Bronte	22	24
C533	**17½p**	Mrs Gaskell	27	25
		Set of 4	82	80
		Set of 4 Cylinder Blocks	6.25	
		Set of 4 Gutter Pairs	2.00	2.00
		First Day Cover		1.25
		Presentation Pack 119	1.55	
		PHQ Cards	85	1.35
Varieties				
C530a	12p	Missing 'P' in value (row 4, stamp 6)	£25	£10
C531a	13½p	Missing Pale Blue	£3000	
C533a	17½p	Imperforate pair and missing Blue	£750	

1980 (4 Aug.) 80th Birthday of the Queen Mother

No.			U/M	F/U
C534	**12p**	The Queen Mother	30	20
		Cylinder Block	1.65	
		Gutter pair	75	80
		First Day Cover		1.25
		PHQ Card	35	65
Varieties				
C534a	12p	Imperforate pair	£1250	
C534b	12p	Perf. shift 3mm to the right	£65	

1980 (10 Sept.) Music. British Conductors. Perf. 14 x 15

No.			U/M	F/U
C535	**12p**	Sir Henry Wood (PCP1)	18	10
C535a		Sir Henry Wood (PCP2)	35	
C536	**13½p**	Sir Thomas Beecham (PCP1)	20	22
C536a		Sir Thomas Beecham (PCP2)	30	
C537	**15p**	Sir Malcolm Sargent (PCP1)	20	22
C537a		Sir Malcolm Sargent (PCP2)	50	
C538	**17½½p**	Sir John Barbirolli (PCP1)	27	25
C538a		Sir John Barbirolli (PCP2)	70	
C538b		Fluorescent Brightener Omitted	1.50	
		Set of 4	85	80
		Set of 4 Cylinder Blocks	6.50	
		Set of 4 Gutter Pairs	2.20	2.20
		First Day Cover		1.25
		FDC wuth 17½p FBO		8.50
		Presentation Pack 120	90	
		PHQ Cards	1.00	1.00

1980 (10 Oct.) Centenary of Sports Organisations. Perf. 14 x 14½
Printers: House of Questa in Lithography

No.			U/M	F/U
C539	**12p**	Running	18	10
C540	**13½p**	Rugby	25	30
C541	**15p**	Boxing	25	30
C542	**17½p**	Cricket	40	30
		Set of 4	80	90
		Set of 4 Cylinder Blocks	6.00	
		Set of 4 Gutter Pairs	2.00	2.00
		First Day Cover		1.255
		Presentation Pack 121	90	
		PHQ Cards	85	1.35
Varieties				
C539a	12p	Missing Gold (Queen's head)	£11500	
C541a	15p	Missing Gold (Queen's head)	£8000	
C541b	15p	Imperforate between stamp & bottom margin	£150	
C541c	15p	Shift 2½mm to right of Gold (Queen's head)	£40	

1980 (19 Nov.) Christmas 1980

No.			U/M	F/U
C543	**10p**	Tree	16	10
C544	**12p**	Candles	18	10
C545	**13½p**	Apples	20	22
C546	**15p**	Crown, Belal	22	22
C547	**17½p**	Holly	27	27
		Set of 5	95	90
		Set of 5 Cylinder Blocks	7.30	
		Set of 5 Gutter Pairs	2.40	2.60
		First Day Cover		1.25
		Presentation Pack 122	90	
		PHQ Cards	1.00	85
Varieties				
C543a	10p	Imperforate between stamp & top margin	£650	
C544a	12p	Imperforate between stamp & bottom margin	£450	

1980 (19 Nov.) Collectors Year Pack 1980

No.		U/M	F/U
CP17	Collectors Year Pack 123	7.00	

1981 (6 Feb.) Europa. Folklore

No.			U/M	F/U
C548	**14p**	St. Valentine's Day	22	12
C549	**18p**	Morris Dancers	27	28
C550	**22p**	Lamastide	35	32
C551	**25p**	Medieval Mummers	35	35
		Set of 4	1.15	1.15
		Set of 4 Cylinder Blocks	8.75	
		Set of 4 Gutter Pairs	2.90	2.90
		First Day Cover		1.25
		Presentation Pack 124	1.95	
		PHQ Cards	1.00	1.50
Varieties				
C548a	14p	Missing Gold (Queen's head)	£7500	
C550a	22p	Perf. shift 5mm to top and major shifts of several colours	£125	

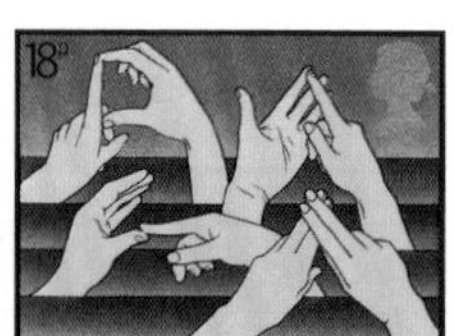

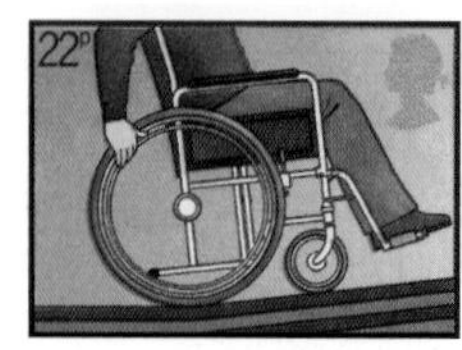

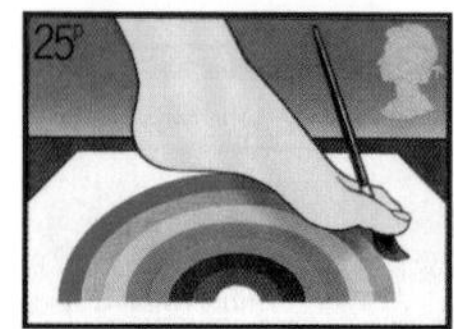

1981 (25 March) International Year of Disabled Persons

No.			U/M	F/U
C552	**14p**	Blind	22	12
C553	**18p**	Deaf	27	28
C554	**22p**	Wheelchair	35	32
C555	**25p**	Painting	35	35
		Set of 4	1.15	1.15
		Set of 4 Cylinder Blocks	9.50	
		Set of 4 Gutter Pairs	2.90	2.90
		First Day Cover		1.25
		Presentation Pack 125	1.05	
		PHQ Cards	1.00	1.50
Variety				
C552a	14p	Imperforate pair ('printers waste')	£500	

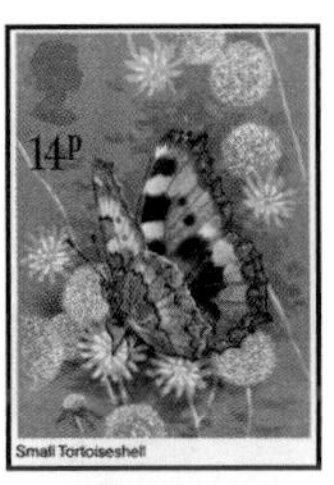

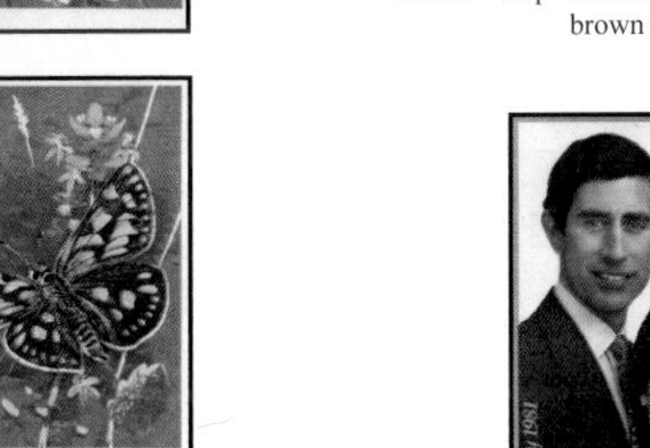

1981 (13 May) Butterflies

No.			U/M	F/U
C556	**14p**	Tortoiseshell	22	12
C557	**18p**	Large Blue	27	35
C558	**22p**	Peacock	35	35
C559	**25p**	Cheq Skipper	35	40
		Set of 4	1.10	1.10
		Set of 4 Cylinder Blocks	8.40	
		Set of 4 Gutter Pairs	2.80	2.80
		First Day Cover		1.25
		Presentation Pack 126	1.05	
		PHQ Cards	1.25	1.75
Varieties				
C556a	14p	Imperforate pair	£2000	
C557a	18p	Shift 4mm to right of Gold (Queen's head)	£20	

1981 (24 June) National Trust

No.			U/M	F/U
C560	**14p**	Glenfinnon	22	12
C561	**18p**	Derwentwater	27	35
C562	**20p**	Stackpole	30	30
C563	**22p**	Giant's Causeway	35	33
C564	**25p**	St. Kilda	35	32
		Set of 5	1.40	1.30
		Set of 5 Cylinder Blocks	10.50	
		Set of 5 Gutter Pairs	3.50	3.50
		First Day Cover		1.20
		Presentation Pack 127	1.20	
		PHQ Cards	1.30	1.80
Varieties				
C562a	20p	Perf. shift 8mm to bottom and shift 13mm to bottom of Gold (Queen's head)	£200	
C563a	22p	Shift 1mm to bottom of Yellow brown (clouds at top left)	£10	

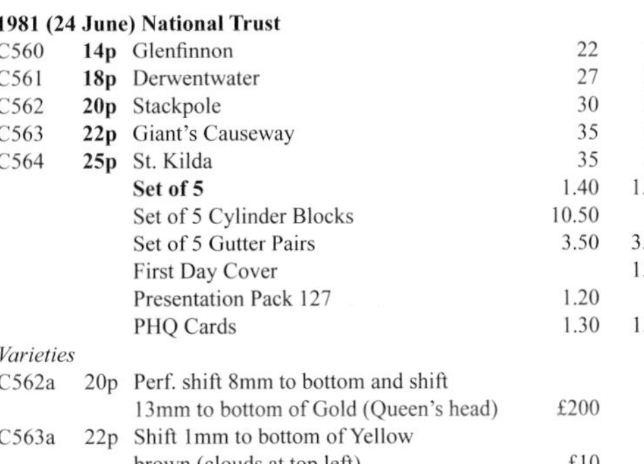

1981 (22 July) Royal Wedding

No.			U/M	F/U
C565	**14p**	Multicoloured	45	20
C566	**25p**	Multicoloured	1.00	75
		Set of 2	1.40	95
		Set of 2 Cylinder Blocks	10.50	
		Set of 2 Gutter Pairs	3.50	3.50
		First Day Cover		2.00
		Presentation Pack 127a	1.40	
		Souvenir Booklet	5.00	
		Japanese Pack	3.50	
		Japanese Pack Reprint	3.00	
		PHQ Cards	65	1.15
Variety				
C565a	14p	Shift 1¼mm to right of Silver (frame,date)		

1981 (12 Aug.) The Duke of Edinburgh Award Scheme. Perf. 14
Printers: John Waddington Ltd. in Lithography

No.			U/M	F/U
C567	**14p**	Expeditions	22	15
C568	**18p**	Skills	30	30
C569	**22p**	Service	35	35
C570	**25p**	Recreation	40	40
		Set of 4	1.15	1.20
		Set of 4 Cylinder Blocks	8.75	
		Set of 4 Gutter Pairs	2.90	2.90
		First Day Cover		1.20
		Presentation Pack 128	1.10	
		PHQ Cards	1.05	1.55

1981 (23 Sept.) Deep Sea Fishing

No.			U/M	F/U
C571	**14p**	Cockle Dredging	21	15
C572	**18p**	Trawl Net	30	30
C573	**22p**	Lobster Potting	35	35
C574	**25p**	Seine Net	45	40
		Set of 4	1.15	1.10
		Set of 4 Cylinder Blocks	8.75	
		Set of 4 Gutter Pairs	2.90	2.90
		First Day Cover		1.20
		Presentation Pack 129	1.10	
		PHQ Cards	1.15	1.65

Samantha Brown, age 5

Tracy Jenkins, age 14

Lucinda Blackmore, age 6

Stephen Moore, age 16

Sophie Sharp, age 8

1981 (18 Nov.) Christmas 1981

No.			U/M	F/U
C575	**11½p**	Father Christmas	18	10
C576	**14p**	Jesus Christ	21	10
C577	**18p**	Flyign Angel	30	35
C578	**22p**	Joseph and Maryl	33	35
C579	**25p**	The Kings	36	35
		Set of 5	1.30	1.25
		Set of 5 Cylinder Blocks	9.75	
		Set of 5 Gutter Pairs	3.25	3.25
		First Day Cover		1.35
		Presentation Pack 130	1.20	
		PHQ Cards	1.35	1.85
Variety				
C575a	11½p	Imperforate between stamp & bottom margin	£450	
C576a	14p	Imperforate pair	£160	

1981 (18 Nov.) Collectors Year Pack

No.		U/M
CP18	Collectors Year Pack 131	8.00

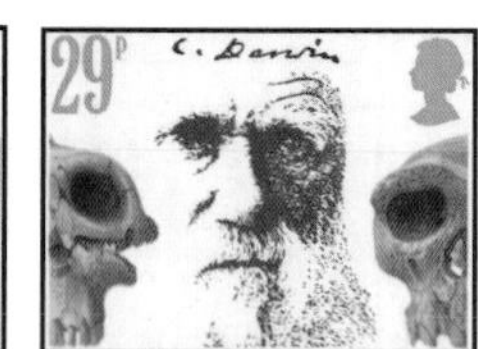

1982 (10 Feb.) Charles Darwin

No.			U/M	F/U
C580	**15½p**	Giant Tortoises	22	18
C581	**19½p**	Iguanas	29	32
C582	**26p**	Finches	38	38
C583	**29p**	Skulls	45	45
		Set of 4	1.30	1.25
		Set of 4 Cylinder Blocks	9.75	
		Set of 4 Gutter Pairs	3.25	3.25
		First Day Cover		1.35
		Presentation Pack 132	1.20	
		PHQ Cards	1.50	2.00

1982 (24 March) Boy Scout and Youth Organisations

No.			U/M	F/U
C584	**15½p**	Boys Brigade	22	18
C585	**19½p**	Girls Brigade	30	35
C586	**26p**	Boy Scouts	40	40
C587	**29p**	Girl Guides	45	50
		Set of 4	1.30	1.35
		Set of 4 Cylinder Blocks	9.75	
		Set of 4 Gutter Pairs	3.25	3.50
		First Day Cover		1.50
		Presentation Pack 133	1.55	
		PHQ Cards	1.65	2.15
Variety				
C585a	19½p	Perf. shift 7mm to left	£150	

1982 (28 April) Europa. British Theatre

No.			U/M	F/U
C588	**15½p**	Ballerina	22	19
C589	**19½p**	Harlequin	40	40
C590	**26p**	Hamlet	50	45
C591	**29p**	Opera Singer	50	50
		Set of 4	1.60	1.50
		Set of 4 Cylinder Blocks	11.90	
		Set of 4 Gutter Pairs	4.00	4.00
		First Day Cover		1.50
		Presentation Pack 134	2.75	
		PHQ Cards	2.00	2.50

1982 (16 June) Maritime Heritage

No.			U/M	F/U
C592	**15½p**	Mary Rose	25	20
C593	**19½p**	Triumph	30	35
C594	**24p**	HMS Victory	40	40
C595	**26p**	HMS Dreadnought	40	45
C596	**29p**	HMS Warspite	50	50
		Set of 5	1.70	1.70
		Set of 5 Cylinder Blocks	12.80	
		Set of 5 Gutter Pairs	4.25	4.25
		First Day Cover		1.60
		Presentation Pack 136	1.95	
		PHQ Cards	2.50	3.00
Varieties				
C592a	15½p	Imperforate pair	£1000	
C592b	15½p	Missing black recess (Mary Rose) *	£2500	£750
C594a	24p	Imperforate between stamp & bottom margin	£400	
C596a	19p	Imperforate pair	£1850	

* A very small number of used examples have been discovered. Buy only with a competent certificate.

1982 (23 July) British Textiles

No.			U/M	F/U
C597	**15½p**	'Strawberry Thief'	22	18
C598	**19½p**	(Steiner & Co.)	30	40
C599	**26p**	'Cherry Orchard'	40	45
C600	**29p**	'Chevron'	50	50
		Set of 4	1.25	1.45
		Set of 4 Cylinder Blocks	9.50	
		Set of 4 Gutter Pairs	3.20	3.20
		First Day Cover		1.50
		Presentation Pack 137	1.20	
		PHQ Cards	2.00	2.50
Varieties				
C597a	15½p	Imperforate pair	£1000	
C598a	19½p	Imperforate vertical pair	£1500	
C598b	19½p	Perf. shift 9mm to right ('19' at right)	£160	
C600a	29p	Perf. shift 2½mm to right	£35	

1982 (8 Sept.) Information Technology

No.			U/M	F/U
C601	**15½p**	Communications	20	20
C601a		PCP2	2.50	
C602	**26p**	Technological Aids	50	65
		Set of 2	60	80
		Set of 2 Cylinder Blocks	4.50	
		Set of 2 Gutter Pairs	1.50	1.50
		First Day Cover		1.25
		Presentation Pack 138	80	
		PHQ Cards	1.00	1.50

Varieties

C601a	15½p	Imperforate pair	£300	
C602a	26p	Imperforate pair	£1250	

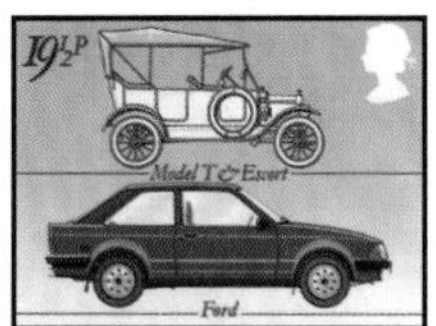

1982 (13 Oct.) British Motor Cars. Perf. 14½ x 14
Printers: House of Questa in Litho.

No.			U/M	F/U
C603	**15½p**	Austin	25	17
C604	**19½p**	Ford	40	50
C605	**26p**	Jaguar	40	40
C606	**29p**	Rolls-Royce	55	70
		Set of 4	1.40	1.50
		Set of 4 Cylinder Blocks	10.50	
		Set of 4 Gutter Pairs	3.50	4.00
		First Day Cover		1.80
		Presentation Pack 139	1.30	
		PHQ Cards	1.75	2.25

Varieties

C604a	19½p	Rose-red, grey & black printed double	£600	
C604b		Imperforate between stamp & right margin	£250	
C606a	29p	Black printed quadruple	£400	
C606b		Black, Bright orange & Carmine-red printed double	£750	
C606c		Shift 2mm to top of Slate	£55	

1982 (17 Nov.) Christmas 1982 (Carols)

No.			U/M	F/U
C607	**12½p**	While Shepperds...	20	10
C608	**15½p**	The Holly and the Ivy	22	12
C608a		Fluorescent Brightener Omitted	1.00	
C609	**19½p**	I Saw Three Ships	30	40
C610	**26p**	We Three Kings	40	40
C611	**29p**	Good King Wenceslas	60	40
		Set of 5	1.40	1.40
		Set of 5 Cylinder Blocks	10.50	
		Set of 5 Gutter Pairs	3.50	3.50
		First Day Cover		1.80
		FDC with 15½p FBO		8.50
		Presentation Pack 140	1.30	
		PHQ Cards	1.85	2.35

Varieties

C608b	15½p	Imperforate pair	£1250	
C608c		Imperforate between stamp & bottom margin	£400	
C609a	19½p	Imperforate pair	£1600	

1982 (17 Nov.) Collectors Year Pack

CP19		Collectors Year Pack 141	£11	

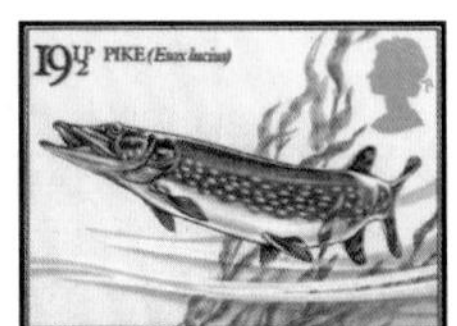

1983 (26 Jan.) British River Fishes

No.			U/M	F/U
C612	**15½p**	Salmon	22	12
C613	**19½p**	Pike	30	45
C614	**26p**	Trout	40	45
C615	**29p**	Perch	60	65
		Set of 4	1.25	1.30
		Set of 4 Cylinder Blocks	9.50	
		Set of 4 Gutter Pairs	3.25	3.25
		First Day Cover		1.80
		Presentation Pack 142	1.25	
		PHQ Cards	1.65	2.15

Varieties

C612a	15½p	Imperforate pair	£1450	
C614a	26p	Imperforate pair	£900	

1983 (9 March) Commonwealth Day

No.			U/M	F/U
C616	**15½p**	Tropical Island	22	18
C617	**19½p**	Desert	40	40
C618	**26p**	Temperate Farmland	40	40
C619	**29p**	Mountain Range	60	60
		Set of 4	1.25	1.30
		Set of 4 Cylinder Blocks	9.50	
		Set of 4 Gutter Pairs	3.25	3.25
		First Day Cover		1.50
		Presentation Pack 143	1.25	
		PHQ Cards	1.65	2.65

1983 (25 May) Europa. British Engineering Achievements

No.			U/M	F/U
C620	**16p**	Humber Bridge	23	20
C621	**20½p**	Thames Flood Barrier	40	50
C622	**28p**	Iolair	60	70
		Set of 3	1.10	1.10
		Set of 3 Cylinder Blocks	8.20	
		Set of 3 Gutter Pairs	2.75	2.75
		First Day Cover		1.30
		Presentation Pack 144	1.85	
		PHQ Cards	1.65	2.65

1983 (6 July) The British Army

No.			U/M	F/U
C623	**16p**	The Royal Scots	23	18
C624	**20½p**	Welsh Fuseliers	35	40
C625	**26p**	Green Jackets	50	50
C626	**28p**	The Irish Guards	50	50
C627	**31p**	Parachute Regiment	50	50
		Set of 5	1.80	1.85
		Set of 5 Cylinder Blocks	13.50	
		Set of 5 Gutter Pairs	4.50	4.80
		First Day Cover		2.40
		Presentation Pack 145	1.60	
		PHQ Cards	1.65	3.65
Varieties				
C625a	26p	Imperforate pair	£1500	
C625b	26p	Perf. shift 6mm to right	£75	
C626a	28p	Imperforate pair		£1750

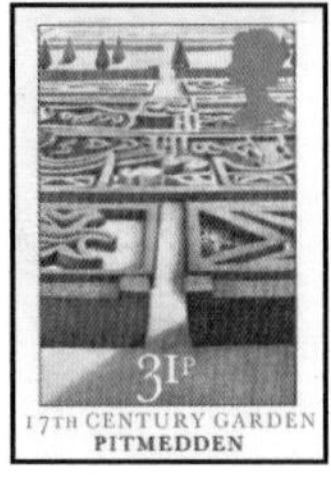

1983 (24 Aug.) British Gardens. Perf. 14
Printers: John Waddington Ltd. in Lithography

No.			U/M	F/U
C628	**16p**	Sissinghurst	35	30
C629	**20½p**	Biddulph Grange	30	40
C630	**28p**	Blenheim	55	40
C631	**31p**	Pitmedden	60	40
		Set of 4	1.30	1.35
		Set of 4 Cylinder Blocks	9.50	
		Set of 4 Gutter Pairs	3.25	3.50
		First Day Cover		1.90
		Presentation Pack 146	1.30	
		PHQ Cards	1.00	3.00

1983 (5 Oct.) British Fairs

No.			U/M	F/U
C632	**16p**	Merry-go-Round	23	20
C633	**20½p**	Big Wheel	35	32
C634	**28p**	Side Shows	40	50
C635	**31p**	Early Produce	50	50
		Set of 4	1.25	1.30
		Set of 4 Cylinder Blocks	9.50	
		Set of 4 Gutter Pairs	3.25	3.50
		First Day Cover		1.90
		Presentation Pack 147	1.30	
		PHQ Cards	1.00	3.00

1983 (16 Nov.) Christmas 1983

No.			U/M	F/U
C636	**12½p**	Christmas Post	20	10
C637	**16p**	The Three Kings	23	12
C638	**20½p**	World of Peace	35	35
C639	**28p**	Light of Christmas	48	50
C640	**31p**	Christmas Dove	45	45
		Set of 5	1.40	1.50
		Set of 5 Cylinder Blocks	10.50	
		Set of 5 Gutter Pairs	3.50	3.50
		First Day Cover		1.85
		Presentation Pack 148	1.35	
		PHQ Cards	1.00	3.00

Varieties

C636a	12½p	Imperforate pair	£950	
C636b	12½p	Shift 2mm to bottom of Red and of Blue, and 3mm to bottom of Yellow	£55	
C637a	16p	Imperforate pair	£950	
C637b	16p	Imperforate between stamp & bottom margin	£450	

1983 (16 Nov.) Collectors Year Pack

CP20		Collectors Year Pack 149	13.50	

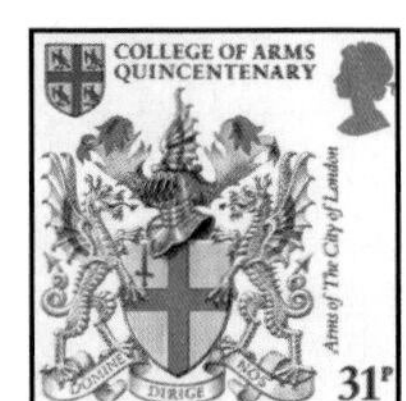

1984 (17 Jan.) Heraldry. Perf. 14½

No.			U/M	F/U
C641	**15p**	College of Arms	23	18
C642	**20½p**	King Richard III	35	35
C643	**28p**	Earl Marshall	45	50
C644	**31p**	City of London	60	60
		Set of 4	1.40	1.45
		Set of 4 Cylinder Blocks	10.50	
		Set of 4 Gutter Pairs	3.50	3.50
		First Day Cover		1.75
		Presentation Pack 150	1.35	
		PHQ Cards	1.25	2.85

Variety

C644a	31p	Imperforate pair	£1750	

1984 (6 March) British Cattle

No.			U/M	F/U
C645	**16p**	Highland Cow	23	18
C646	**20½p**	Chillingham Wild	35	35
C647	**26p**	Hereford Bull	45	45
C648	**28p**	Welsh Black Bull	45	50
C649	**31p**	Irish Moiled Cow	55	50
		Set of 5	1.60	1.70
		Set of 5 Cylinder Blocks	11.90	
		Set of 5 Gutter Pairs	4.00	4.00
		16p Miscur gutter pair	£15	
		First Day Cover		2.20
		Presentation Pack 151	1.60	
		PHQ Cards	1.20	3.00

Variety

C645a	16p	Imperforate vertical pair	£3000	

1984 (10 April) Urban Renewal

No.			U/M	F/U
C650	**16p**	Festival Hall	23	18
C651	**20½p**	Milburngate	35	35
C652	**28p**	Bush House	50	50
C653	**31p**	Commercial Street	60	60
		Set of 4	1.45	1.40
		Set of 4 Cylinder Blocks	10.80	
		Set of 4 Gutter Pairs	3.70	3.70
		26p Miscur gutter pair		£15
		First Day Cover		1.75
		Presentation Pack 152	1.30	
		PHQ Cards	1.30	2.65

Varieties

No.			U/M	F/U
C650a	16p	Perf. shift 3mm to top	£30	
C651a	20½p	Imperforate pair	£1750	
C653a	31p	Imperforate pair	£1750	

1984 (15 May) Europa

No.			U/M	F/U
C654	**16p**	Multicoloured (A)	25	30
C655	**16p**	Multicoloured (B)	25	30
C654/5	**16p**	**Pair se-tenant**	90	1.10
C656	**20½p**	Multicoloured (A)	38	70
C657	**20½p**	Multicoloured (B)	38	70
C656/7	**20½p**	**Pair se-tenant**	1.50	1.55
		Set of 4	2.20	2.30
		Set of 2 Cylinder Blocks	4.50	
		Set of 2 Gutter Blocks	5.50	5.50
		First Day Cover		2.10
		Presentation Pack 153	2.25	
		PHQ Cards	1.40	2.65

Variety

C654/5a	16p	Imperforate pair	£1750	
C656/7a	20½p	Imperforate pair	£1750	

1984 (5 June) London Economic Summit

No.			U/M	F/U
C658	**31p**	Lancaster House	60	55
		Cylinder Block	4.30	
		Gutter pair	1.50	1.50
		First Day Cover		85
		PHQ Cards	45	1.45

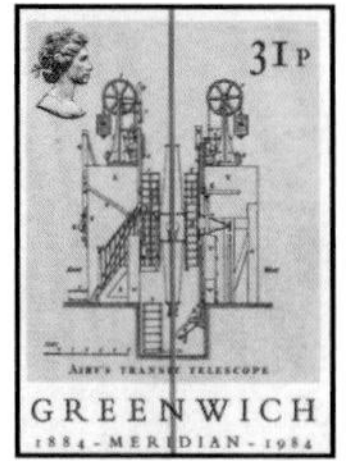

1984 (26 June) Greenwich Meridian. Perf. 14 x 14½
Printers: House of Questa in Lithography

No.			U/M	F/U
C659	**16p**	From Apollo 11	23	20
C660	**20½p**	Chart of Channel	35	35
C661	**28p**	Observatory	45	50
C662	**31p**	Transit Telescope	60	60
		Set of 4	1.40	1.40
		Set of 4 Cylinder Blocks	10.50	
		Set of 4 Gutter Pairs	3.50	3.50
		First Day Cover		1.60
		Presentation Pack 154	1.35	
		PHQ Cards	1.85	2.85
Variety				
C659a	16p	Black printed double		£1750

A

B

C

D

E

1984 (31 July) Royal Mail Coach Run Bicentenary

No.			U/M	F/U
C663	**16p**	Bath Mail Coach (A)	30	35
C664	**16p**	Attack on Exeter Mail (B)	30	35
C665	**16p**	Norwich Mail (C)	30	35
C666	**16p**	Holyhead and Liverpool Mail (D)	30	35
C667	**16p**	Edinburgh Mail (E)	30	35
C663/7	**16p**	**Strip of 5 se-tenant**	1.55	1.60
		Cylinder Block	4.20	
		Gutter Block of 10	3.90	4.00
		First Day Cover		1.75
		Presentation Pack 155	1.40	
		Souvenir Booklet	6.00	
		PHQ Cards	2.00	3.00
Variety				
C666/7	16p	Imperforate pair	£2250	
C663/7		Perf shift 2mm down - Strip of 5 se-tenant	£100	

1984 (25 Sept.) 50th Anniversary of the British Council

No.			U/M	F/U
C668	**17p**	Nigerian Clinic	24	24
C669	**22p**	Violinist, Athens	35	35
C670	**31p**	Building Project	50	50
C671	**34p**	Council Library	60	70
		Set of 4	1.60	1.50
		Set of 4 Cylinder Blocks	12.00	
		Set of 4 Gutter Pairs	4.00	4.00
		Gutter Pairs with 'Ausipex' logo	8.50	8.50
		First Day Cover		1.70
		Presentation Pack 156	1.40	
		PHQ Cards	2.00	3.00
Variety				
C669a	22p	Perf. shift 2mm to left	£10	

1984 (20 Nov.) Christmas 1984

No.			U/M	F/U
C672	**13p**	The Holy Family (1 band)	20	20
C672a		Multiple Star underprint *	25	15
C673	**17p**	Arrival	25	15
C674	**22p**	Shepherd and Lamb	35	35
C675	**31p**	Virgin and Child	60	60
C676	**34p**	Frankinsence	80	80

No.			U/M	F/U
		Set of 5	1.70	1.80
		Set of 5 Cylinder Blocks	13.00	
		Set of 5 Gutter Pairs	4.25	4.25
		First Day Cover		2.40
		First Day Cover 13p (C672a)		3.00
		Presentation Pack 157	1.50	
		PHQ Cards	2.00	3.00

* No. C672a originates from the 1984 Christmas Booklet

Variety

C672a	13p	Imperforate between stamp & bottom margin	£450	
C673a	17p	Imperforate pair	£1750	
C674a	22p	Shift 6mm to bottom of Grey (Queen's head and 22p)	£30	

1984 (20 Nov.) Collectors Year Pack

CP21	Collectors Year Pack 158	17.50	

1984 (20 Nov.) Royal Mail Year Book - 1

YB1	Royal Mail Year Book Book (C641/76)	£32	

1985 (22 Jan.) Famous Trains

C677	**17p**	Flying Scotsman	50	50
C678	**22p**	Golden Arrow	70	65
C679	**29p**	Cheltenham Flyer	50	50
C680	**31p**	Royal Scot	65	60
C681	**34p**	Cornish Riviera	65	60
		Set of 5	2.40	2.45
		Set of 5 Cylinder Blocks	18.00	
		Set of 5 Gutter Pairs	6.00	6.00
		First Day Cover		3.75
		Presentation Pack 159	2.75	
		PHQ Cards	2.50	3.50

Varieties

C677a	17p	Imperforate pair	£1750	
C677b	17p	Perf. shift 3mm to bottom	£75	

1985 (12 March) Insects

C682	**17p**	Bumble Bee	25	20
C683	**22p**	Ladybird	40	40
C684	**29p**	Cricket	50	50
C685	**31p**	Stag Beetle	60	55
C686	**34p**	Dragonfly	60	55
		Set of 5	2.05	2.00
		Set of 5 Cylinder Blocks	7.50	
		Gutter Pairs	4.50	4.50
		First Day Cover		2.70
		Presentation Pack 160	1.80	
		PHQ Cards	2.00	3.00

Varieties

C686a	34p	Imperforate vertical pair	£3500	
C688a	22p	Imperforate between stamp & left margin	£750	

1985 (14 May) Europa. Composers. Perf. 14 x 14½

C687	**17p**	Handel	30	20
C688	**22p**	Holst	70	600
C689	**31p**	Delius	75	70
C690	**34p**	Elgar	75	70
		Set of 4	2.25	2.40
		Set of 4 Cylinder Blocks	17.00	
		Set of 4 Gutter Pairs	5.75	5.75
		First Day Cover		2.70
		Presentation Pack 161	2.75	
		PHQ Cards	1.80	2.80

Varieties

C687a	17p	Imperforate pair	£1500	
C688a	22p	Imperforate pair	£1500	

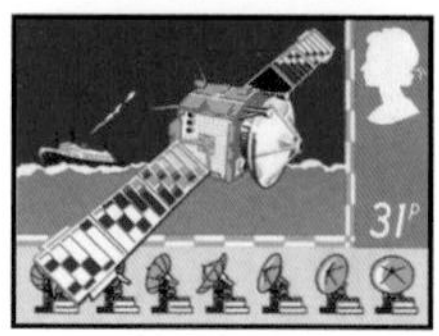

1985 (18 June) Safety at Sea. Phosphor Coated Paper. Perf. 14
Printer: John Waddington Ltd. in Lithography

No.			U/M	F/U
C691	**17p**	Lifeboat	25	25
C692	**22p**	Lighthouse	40	40
C693	**31p**	Satellite	55	65
C694	**34p**	Buoys	60	60
		Set of 4	2.00	1.80
		Set of 4 Cylinder Blocks	15.00	
		Set of 4 Gutter Pairs	5.00	5.00
		First Day Cover		2.70
		Presentation Pack 162	1.50	
		PHQ Cards	1.80	2.80

Variety

C691a	17p	Imperforate between stamp & bottom margin	£500	

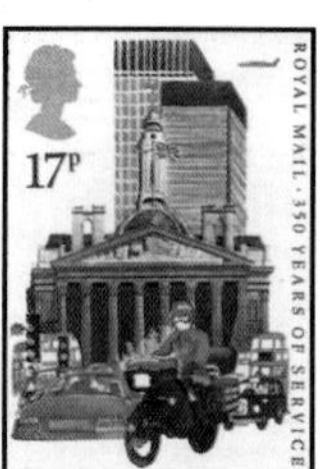

1985 (30 July) 350th Anniversary of Post Office

No.			U/M	F/U
C695	**17p**	Datapost	25	25
C695b		Multiple 'D' underprint *	35	45
C696	**22p**	Rural Postbus	35	35
C697	**31p**	Parcel Delivery	60	70
C698	**34p**	Letter Delivery	60	70
		Set of 4	1.70	1.80
		Set of 4 Cylinder Blocks	12.70	
		Set of 4 Gutter Pairs	4.25	4.25
		First Day Cover		2.25
		Presentation Pack 163	1.50	
		PHQ Cards	2.00	3.00

* No. C695b originates from the £1.53 Discount Booklet

Varieties

C695a	17p	Imperforate pair	£1500	
C697a	31p	Imperforate pair	£1500	
C698a	34p	Imperf. between (vertical pair)	£500	

1985 (3 Sept.) Arthurian Legend

No.			U/M	F/U
C699	**17p**	Arthur and Merlin	25	25
C700	**22p**	Lady of the Lake	35	35
C701	**31p**	Queen Guinevere	60	70
C702	**34p**	Sir Galahad	60	70
		Set of 4	1.70	1.80
		Set of 4 Cylinder Blocks	12.50	
		Set of 4 Gutter Pairs	4.25	4.25
		First Day Cover		2.70
		Presentation Pack 164	1.50	
		PHQ Cards	2.00	3.00

Variety

C699a	17p	Imperforate pair	£2250	

1985 (10 Oct.) British Film Stars. Perf. 14½

No.			U/M	F/U
C703	**17p**	Peter Sellers	25	25
C704	**22p**	David Niven	35	45
C705	**29p**	Charlie Chaplin	60	70
C706	**31p**	Vivien Leigh	60	60
C707	**34p**	Alfred Hitchcock	60	60
		Set of 5	2.60	2.50
		Set of 5 Cylinder Blocks	19.50	
		Set of 5 Gutter Pairs	6.50	6.50
		First Day Cover		2.95
		Presentation Pack 165	2.10	
		Souvenir Booklet	7.50	
		PHQ Cards	1.85	2.85

No.			U/M	F/U

Variety

C707a 34p Shift 15mm to bottom of Silver (Queen's head) £75

1985 (19 Nov.) Christmas 1985

No.			U/M	F/U
C708	**12p**	Principal Boy	20	20
C708c		Multiple star underprint	25	25
C709	**17p**	Genie	25	25
C710	**22p**	Dame	35	45
C712	**31p**	Good Fairy	70	70
C713	**34p**	Panto Cat	70	70
		Set of 5	1.90	1.95
		Set of 5 Cylinder Blocks	14.50	
		Set of 5 Gutter Pairs	4.75	4.75
		First Day Cover		2.80
		Presentation Pack 166	1.60	
		PHQ Cards	2.00	3.00
		Discount Folder (C708c x 50)	£15	

Varieties

No.			U/M	F/U
C708a	12p	Imperforate pair	£1250	
C708b	12p	Perf. shift 5mm to top	£45	
C709a	17p	Imperforate pair	£1750	

1985 (19 Nov.) Collectors Year Pack

No.		U/M
CP22	Collectors Year Pack 167	17.50

1985 (19 Nov.) Royal Mail Year Book - 2

No.		U/M
YB2	Royal Mail Year Book C677/713	£36

1986 (14 Jan.) Industry Year 1986. Phosphor Coated Paper. Perf. 14½ x 14
Printer: House of Questa in Lithography

No.			U/M	F/U
C714	**17p**	Light Bulb	25	20
C715	**22p**	Thermometer	50	50
C716	**31p**	Garden Hoe	70	70
C717	**34p**	Loaf of Bread	70	70
		Set of 4	1.90	2.10
		Set of 4 Cylinder Blocks	14.50	
		Set of 4 Gutter Pairs	4.75	4.75
		First Day Cover		2.85
		Presentation Pack 168	1.60	
		PHQ Cards	1.60	2.60

Varieties

No.			U/M	F/U
C715a	22p	Perf. shift 2.5mm to top	£50	
C715b	22p	Perf. shift 3mm to right	£20	

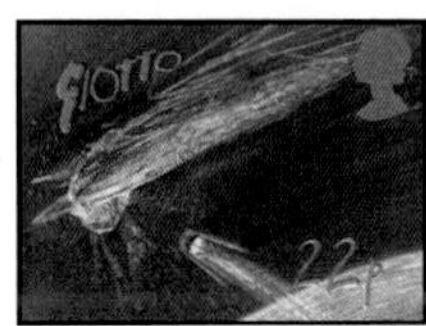

1986 (18 Feb.) Halley's Comet

No.			U/M	F/U
C718	**17p**	Dr. Edmund Haley	25	20
C719	**22p**	Giotto Spacecraft	50	50
C720	**31p**	Twice in a Lifetime	70	70
C721	**34p**	Orbiting	70	70
		Set of 4	1.85	2.10
		Set of 4 Cylinder Blocks	14.00	
		Set of 4 Gutter Pairs	4.70	4.70
		First Day Cover		2.85
		Presentation Pack 169	1.60	
		PHQ Cards	1.75	2.75

Variety

No.			U/M	F/U
C718a	17p	Imperforate between stamp & bottom margin	£1250	

A

B

C

D

1986 (21 April) Sixtieth Birthday of Her Majesty The Queen

No.			U/M	F/U
C722	**17p**	Multicoloured (A)	25	20
C723	**17p**	Multicoloured (B)	25	20
C722/3	**17p**	**Pair se-tenant**	70	70
C724	**34p**	Multicoloured (A)	70	70
C725	**34p**	Multicoloured (B)	70	70
C724/5	**34p**	**Pair se-tenant**	1.60	1.60

No.			U/M	F/U
		Set of 4	2.00	2.20
		Set of 2 Cylinder Blocks	7.90	
		Set of 2 Gutter Blocks	5.00	5.00
		First Day Cover		2.85
		Presentation Pack 170	2.30	
		Souvenir Booklet	7.50	
		PHQ Cards	1.90	2.90
Variety				
C722/3a	17p	Perf. shift 3mm to top	£60	

1986 (20 May) Europa. Nature Conservation. Perf. 14½ x 14

No.			U/M	F/U
C726	**17p**	Barn Owl	25	25
C727	**22p**	Pine Marten	45	45
C728	**31p**	Wild Cat	70	70
C729	**34p**	Toad	70	70
		Set of 4	1.75	1.80
		Set of 4 Cylinder Blocks	13.00	
		Set of 4 Gutter Pairs	4.40	4.50
		First Day Cover		3.25
		Presentation Pack 171	2.75	
		PHQ Cards	1.50	2.50

1986 (17 June) Domesday Book 1086

No.			U/M	F/U
C730	**17p**	Peasants	25	25
C731	**22p**	Freemen	45	50
C732	**31p**	Knight and Retainers	55	75
C733	**34p**	Lord at Banquet	55	70
		Set of 4	1.90	1.95
		Set of 4 Cylinder Blocks	14.50	
		Set of 4 Gutter Pairs	4.75	5.00
		First Day Cover		2.75
		Presentation Pack 172	1.60	
		PHQ Cards	1.50	2.50

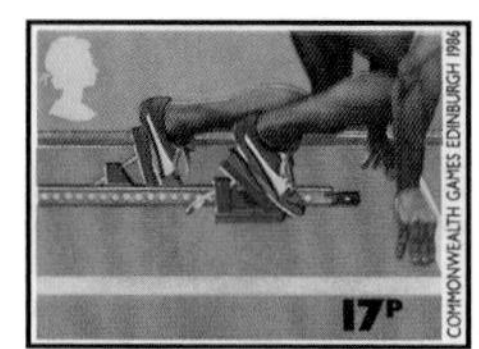

1986 (15 July) Commonwealth Games, Edinburgh and World Hockey Cup, London

No.			U/M	F/U
C734	**17p**	Athletics	25	25
C735	**22p**	Rowing	35	35
C736	**29p**	Weightlifting	60	70
C737	**31p**	Shooting	60	60
C738	**34p**	Hockey	60	60
		Set of 5	2.30	2.35
		Set of 5 Cylinder Blocks	17.50	
		Set of 5 Gutter Pairs	5.75	5.75
		First Day Cover		3.40
		Presentation Pack 173	2.10	
		PHQ Cards	1.70	2.70
Variety				
C735a	22p	Imperforate pair		£750
C738a	34p	Imperforate pair	£1750	

1986 (22 July) Royal Wedding

No.			U/M	F/U
C739	**12p**	Multicoloured (1 band)	35	25
C740	**17p**	Multicoloured	50	35
		Set of 2	80	55
		Set of 2 Cylinder Blocks	5.80	
		Set of 2 Gutter Pairs	2.00	2.00
		First Day Cover		1.25
		Presentation Pack 174	90	
		PHQ Cards	70	1.70
Variety				
C740a	17p	Imperforate pair	£500	

1986 (19 Aug.) Commonwealth Parliamentary Association Conference.
Perf. 14 x 14½

No.			U/M	F/U
C741	**34p**	Multicoloured	62	60
		Cylinder Block	4.50	
		Gutter pair	1.55	1.55
		First Day Cover		1.25
		PHQ Card	40	1.40
Variety				
C741a	34p	Imperforate between (vertical pair)	£300	

1986 (16 Sept) Royal Air Force. Perf. 14½

No.			U/M	F/U
C742	**17p**	Hurricane	25	25
C743	**22p**	Typhoon	42	40
C744	**29p**	DH 9A	60	65
C745	**31p**	Lancaster	70	65
C746	**34p**	Mosquito	70	65
		Set of 5	2.45	2.50
		Set of 5 Cylinder Blocks	18.50	
		Set of 5 Gutter Pairs	6.25	5.25
		First Day Cover		2.95
		Presentation Pack 175	2.10	
		PHQ Cards	1.80	2.80
Varieties				
C742a	17p	Imperforate pair	£1000	
C743a	22p	Missing Pale Green (22p only)*	£450	
C743b	22p	Missing Pale Green (Queen's head only)*	£450	

* Normally sold in se-tenant pairs.Caution is needed with C743a, as many examples show feint traces of pale green.

1986 (18 Nov. - 2 Dec.) Christmas 1986

No.			U/M	F/U
C747	**12p**	Glastonburt Thorn (centre band) (2 Dec.)	40	40
C748	**13p**	Glastonburt Thorn (centre band)	20	20
C748b		Multiple star underprint (2 Dec.)	25	20
C749	**18p**	Tanad Valley Plygain	25	20
C750	**22p**	Hebrides Tribute	50	50
C751	**31p**	Dewsbury Church	80	60
C752	**34p**	Hereford Boy Bishop	70	60
		Set of 6	2.00	2.00
		Set of 6 Cylinder Blocks	15.00	
		Set of 6 Gutter Pairs	5.00	5.00
		Gutter pair 13p (C748b)	75	75
		First Day Cover (5 stamps)		2.80
		First Day Cover (12p)		75
		Presentation Pack 176 (5 stamps)	1.85	
		PHQ Cards (5)	1.80	2.80
		Discount Folder (748b x 36)	8.50	
Variety				
C747a	12p	Imperforate pair	£1200	

The 12p was issued on 2nd December and available until 24th December at Post Offices, however it was still available at the Philatelic Bureau long after that date. The 13p with underprint originated from the Discount Folder that included Gutter Pairs, but these are always folded.

1986 (18 Nov.) Collectors Year Pack

No.		U/M	F/U
CP23	Collectors Year Pack 177	17.50	

1986 (18 Nov.) Royal Mail Year Book - 3

No.		U/M	F/U
YB3	Royal Mail Year Book C714/752	£34	

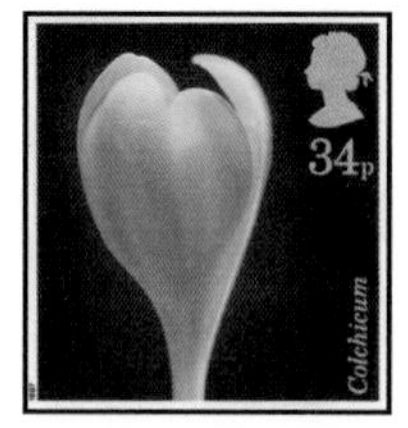

1987 (20 Jan.) Flowers. Perf. 14½ x 14

No.			U/M	F/U
C753	**18p**	Blanket Flower	25	25
C754	**22p**	Glode Thistle	50	50
C755	**31p**	Echeveria	50	70
C756	**34p**	Autumn Crocus	80	75
		Set of 4	1.90	2.00
		Set of 4 Cylinder Blocks	14.50	
		Set of 4 Gutter Pairs	4.75	4.75
		First Day Cover		2.80
		Presentation Pack 178	1.50	
		PHQ Cards	1.50	2.50
Variety				
C755a	31p	Imperforate pair	£1750	
C755b		Imperforate between stamp & left margin	£350	

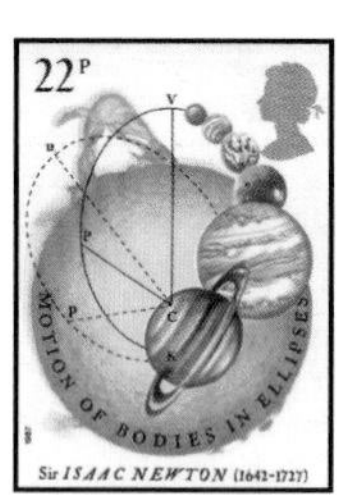

1987 (24 March) Sir Isaac Newton

No.			U/M	F/U
C757	**18p**	Principia Mathmatica	25	25
C758	**22p**	Motion of Bodies	50	60
C759	**31p**	Optick Treatise	70	65
C760	**34p**	System of the World	70	70
		Set of 4	1.90	2.00
		Set of 4 Cylinder Blocks	14.50	
		Set of 4 Gutter Pairs	4.75	4.75
		First Day Cover		2.80
		Presentation Pack 179	1.80	
		PHQ Cards	1.50	2.50
Variety				
C757a	18p	Imperforate pair	£1500	

1987 (12 May) Europa. British Architects in Europe

No.			U/M	F/U
C761	**18p**	Ipswich	25	25
C762	**22p**	Paris	50	60
C763	**31p**	Stuttgart	70	60
C764	**34p**	Luxembourg	70	60
		Set of 4	1.90	1.90
		Set of 4 Cylinder Blocks	14.50	
		Set of 4 Gutter Pairs	4.75	4.75
		First Day Cover		2.80
		Presentation Pack 180	2.75	
		PHQ Cards	1.50	2.50
Variety				
C763a	31p	Imperforate pair	£1500	

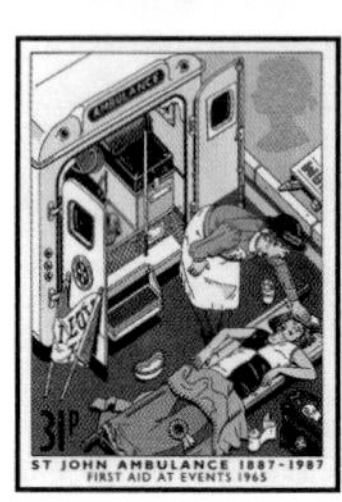

1987 (16 June) St John Ambulance Centenary. Perf. 14 x 14½
Printer: House of Questa in Lithography

No.			U/M	F/U
C765	**18p**	Ashford Litter	25	25
C766	**22p**	Blitz Victim	50	60
C767	**31p**	Volunteer	70	60
C768	**34p**	Air Wing	70	65
		Set of 4	1.90	1.95
		Set of 4 Cylinder Blocks	14.50	
		Set of 4 Gutter Pairs	4.75	4.75
		First Day Cover		2.80
		Presentation Pack 181	1.80	
		PHQ Cards	1.50	2.50
Varieties				
C765a	18p	Black printed double		£850
C765b	18p	Black printed treble		£1500

No.			U/M	F/U

1987 (21 July) Tercentenary of the Revival of the Order of the Thistle.
Perf. 14½

No.			U/M	F/U
C769	**18p**	Lord of Lyon	25	20
C770	**22p**	Heraldic Banner	50	60
C771	**31p**	Scottish Academy	70	65
C772	**34p**	Society of Edinburgh	70	65
		Set of 4	1.90	1.90
		Set of 4 Cylinder Blocks	14.50	
		Set of 4 Gutter Pairs	4.75	4.75
		First Day Cover		2.80
		Presentation Pack 182	1.80	
		PHQ Cards	1.50	2.50
Varieties				
C769a	18p	Imperforate between stamp & bottom margin	£450	
C769b	18p	Imperforate between stamp & bottom and right margin	£750	

1987 (8 Sept.) 150th Anniversary of Queen Victoria's Accession
Printer: Harrison & Sons in photogravure & recess

No.			U/M	F/U
C773	**18p**	Crystal Palace	25	25
C774	**22p**	Great Eastern	50	50
C775	**31p**	Albert Memorial	70	65
C776	**34p**	Diamond Jubilee	70	65
		Set of 4	1.90	1.90
		Set of 4 Cylinder Blocks	14.50	
		Set of 4 Gutter Pairs	4.75	4.75
		First Day Cover		2.80
		Presentation Pack 183	1.80	
		PHQ Cards	1.50	2.50

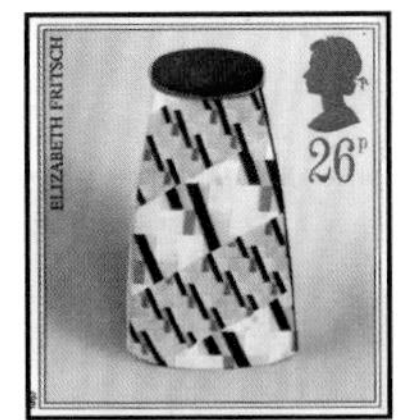

1987 (13 Oct.) Studio Pottery. Perf. 14½ x 14

No.			U/M	F/U
C777	**18p**	Bernard Leach	25	25
C778	**26p**	Elizabeth Fritsch	50	50
C779	**31p**	Lucie Rie	70	65
C780	**34p**	Hans Coper	70	65
		Set of 4	1.90	1.90
		Set of 4 Cylinder Blocks	14.50	
		Set of 4 Gutter Pairs	4.75	4.75
		First Day Cover		2.80
		Presentation Pack 184	1.80	
		PHQ Cards	1.50	2.50
Variety				
C780a	34p	Imperforate vertical strip of three	£2500	

1987 (17 Nov.) Christmas 1987

No.			U/M	F/U
C781	**13p**	Decorating the Tree	25	20
C781a		Multiple star underprint *	30	35
C782	**18p**	Waiting	25	20
C783	**26p**	Sleeping Child	70	70
C784	**31p**	Child Reading	70	70
C784a		Fluorescent Brightener omitted		
C785	**34p**	Child and Snowman	70	70

No.			U/M	F/U
		Set of 5	1.85	2.00
		Set of 5 Cylinder Blocks	13.90	
		Set of 5 Gutter Pairs	4.70	4.70
		Gutter pair 13p (C781a) *	60	1.20
		First Day Cover		2.80
		Presentation Pack 185	1.80	
		PHQ Cards	1.50	2.50
		Discount Folder (C781a x 36)	8.50	

* C781a originates from the Discount Folder, the gutter pair only exists folded.

Variety

C781a	13p	Imperforate between stamp & left margin	£650

1987 (17 Nov.) Collectors Year Pack

CP24	Collectors Year Pack 186	£20

1987 (17 Nov.) Royal Mail Year Book - 4

YB4	Royal Mail Year Book C753/785	£15

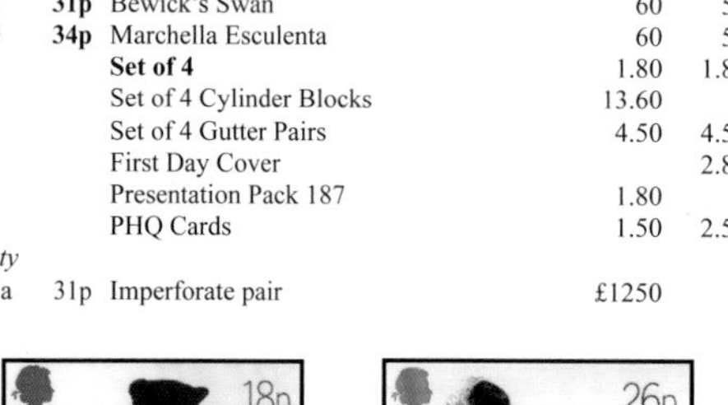

1988 (19 Jan.) The Linnean Society Bicentenary

C786	**18p**	Short Spined Seascorpion	25	25
C787	**26p**	Yellow Waterlily	60	50
C788	**31p**	Bewick's Swan	60	55
C789	**34p**	Marchella Esculenta	60	55
		Set of 4	1.80	1.80
		Set of 4 Cylinder Blocks	13.60	
		Set of 4 Gutter Pairs	4.50	4.50
		First Day Cover		2.80
		Presentation Pack 187	1.80	
		PHQ Cards	1.50	2.50

Variety

C788a	31p	Imperforate pair	£1250

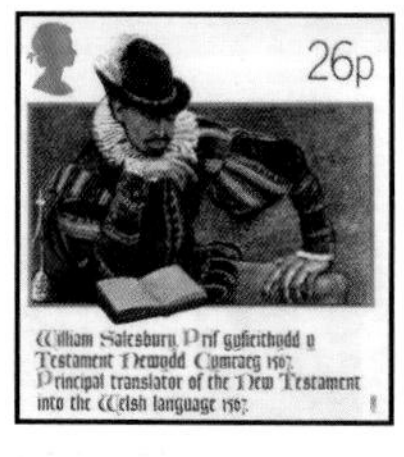

No.			U/M	F/U

1988 (1 March) The Welsh Bible. Perf. 14½ x 14

C790	**18p**	Revd. W. Morgan	25	25
C791	**26p**	William Salesbury	60	65
C792	**31p**	Bishop R. Davies	60	65
C793	**34p**	Bishop R. Parry	60	65
		Set of 4	1.80	1.90
		Set of 4 Cylinder Blocks	13.50	
		Set of 4 Gutter Pairs	4.50	4.50
		First Day Cover		2.70
		Presentation Pack 188	1.80	
		PHQ Cards	1.50	2.50

Varieties

C790a	18p	Imperforate pair	£1250
C791a	26p	Perf. shift 3.5mm to right	£25

1988 (22 March) Sports. Perf. 14½

C794	**18p**	Gymnastics	25	25
C795	**26p**	Downhill Skiing	60	70
C796	**31p**	Tennis	60	70
C797	**34p**	Football	70	70
		Set of 4	1.90	1.90
		Set of 4 Cylinder Blocks	14.50	
		Set of 4 Gutter Pairs	4.75	4.75
		First Day Cover		2.80
		Presentation Pack 189	1.80	
		PHQ Cards	1.50	2.50

1988 (10 May) Europa. Transport

No.			U/M	F/U
C798	**18p**	Mallard	25	25
C799	**26p**	QEII	65	70
C800	**31p**	Glasgow Tram	65	70
C801	**34p**	'HP24'	65	70
		Set of 4	1.80	1.90
		Set of 4 Cylinder Blocks	13.50	
		Set of 4 Gutter Pairs	4.50	4.50
		First Day Cover		2.80
		Presentation Pack 190	2.75	
		PHQ Cards	1.50	2.50

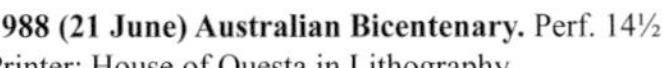

1988 (21 June) Australian Bicentenary. Perf. 14½
Printer: House of Questa in Lithography

No.			U/M	F/U
C802	18p	Early Settler	30	25
C803	18p	Queen Elizabeth II	30	25
C802/3	**18p**	**Se-tenant pair**	70	70
C804	34p	W. G. Grace	70	60
C805	34p	Shakespeare	70	60
C804/5	**34p**	**Se-tenant pair**	1.50	1.70
		Set of 4	2.00	2.10
		Set of 2 Cylinder Blocks	7.50	
		Set of 2 Gutter Blocks	5.00	5.20
		First Day Cover		2.90
		Presentation Pack 191*	1.80	
		Souvenir Booklet	5.00	
		PHQ Cards	1.50	2.50

* Presentation Pack issued by both countries

A

B

C

D

E

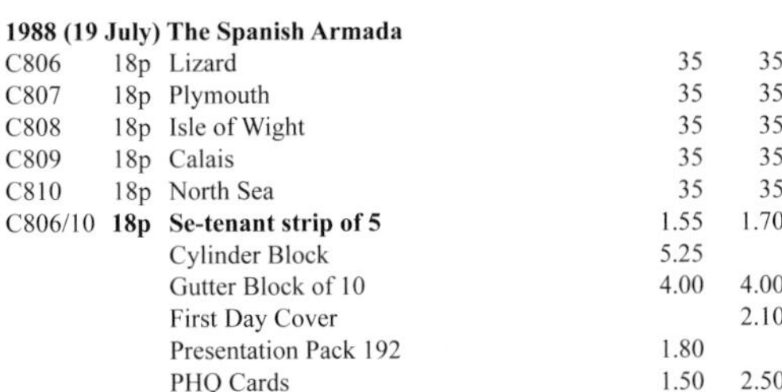

1988 (19 July) The Spanish Armada

No.			U/M	F/U
C806	18p	Lizard	35	35
C807	18p	Plymouth	35	35
C808	18p	Isle of Wight	35	35
C809	18p	Calais	35	35
C810	18p	North Sea	35	35
C806/10	**18p**	**Se-tenant strip of 5**	1.55	1.70
		Cylinder Block	5.25	
		Gutter Block of 10	4.00	4.00
		First Day Cover		2.10
		Presentation Pack 192	1.80	
		PHQ Cards	1.50	2.50

1988 (6 Sept.) Edward Lear

No.			U/M	F/U
C811	**19p**	'Owl and the Pusseycat'	27	22
C812	**27p**	'Lear as a Bird'	50	50
C813	**32p**	'Cat'	70	75
C814	**35p**	'There was a Young..'	70	75
		Set of 4	2.10	2.10
		Set of 4 Cylinder Blocks	15.50	
		Set of 4 Gutter Pairs	5.25	5.25
		First Day Cover		2.80
		Presentation Pack 193	1.80	
		PHQ Cards	1.50	2.50

1988 (27 Sept.) Edward Lear

No.			U/M	F/U
MS4	**£1.35**	**Miniature Sheet**	4.20	4.50
		First Day Cover		5.00

1988 (15 Nov.) Christmas Cards. Perf. 15 x 14

No.			U/M	F/U
C815	**14p**	Journey to Bethlehem (centre band to right)	25	20
C816	**19p**	Shepherd and Star	27	20
C817	**27p**	Three Wise Men	45	45
C818	**32p**	Nativity	75	75
C819	**35p**	The Annunciation	75	75
		Set of 5	2.10	2.10
		Set of 5 Cylinder Blocks	15.90	
		Set of 5 Gutter Pairs	5.25	5.25
		First Day Cover		1.50
		Presentation Pack 194	1.80	
		PHQ Cards	1.50	2.50
Varieties				
C815a	13p	Multicoloured. Error of value	£5000	
		First Day Cover		£1750
		Used		£1000
C816a		Imperforate pair	£750	
C816b		Imperforate bewteen stamp & bottom margin	£100	
C815b	14p	Imperforate pair	£450	
C816a	19p	Imperforate pair	£475	

1988 (15 Nov.) Collectors Year Pack

CP24	Collectors Year Pack 195	£20

1988 (15 Nov.) Royal Mail Year Book - 5

YB5	Royal Mail Year Book C786/819	£18

1989 (17 Jan.) Birds. RSPB Centenary. Perf. 14 x 15

No.			U/M	F/U
C820	**19p**	Puffin	27	27
C821	**27p**	Avocet	45	50
C822	**32p**	Oystercatcher	70	75
C823	**35p**	Gannet	70	75
		Set of 4	2.00	2.10
		Set of 5 Cylinder Blocks	15.25	
		Set of 5 Gutter Pairs	5.00	5.00
		First Day Cover		1.50
		Presentation Pack 196	1.80	
		PHQ Cards	1.60	2.60

A

B

C

D

E

1989 (31 Jan.) Advanced Coated Paper. Perf. 15 x 14

No.			U/M	F/U
C824	**19p**	Rose (A)	3.00	1.50
C825	**19p**	Cupid (B)	3.00	1.50
C826	**19p**	Yachts (C)	3.00	1.50
C827	**19p**	Fruit Bowl (D)	3.00	1.50
C828	**19p**	Teddy Bear (E)	3.00	1.50
	19p	**Strip of 5 se-tenant**	13.50	13.50
		Booklet pane of 10	£30	
		First Day Cover (5v)		12.50

The above are from the first Greetings Book listed on Page

1989 (7 March) Food and Farming Year. Perf. 14 x 14½

No.			U/M	F/U
C829	**19p**	Fruit and Veg	28	25
C830	**27p**	Meat	60	50
C831	**32p**	Dairy	70	70
C832	**35p**	Cereal	70	70
		Set of 4	2.00	2.00
		Set of 4 Cylinder Blocks	14.25	
		Set of 4 Gutter Pairs	5.00	5.00
		First Day Cover		1.40
		Presentation Pack 197	1.80	
		PHQ Cards	1.70	2.70

A

B

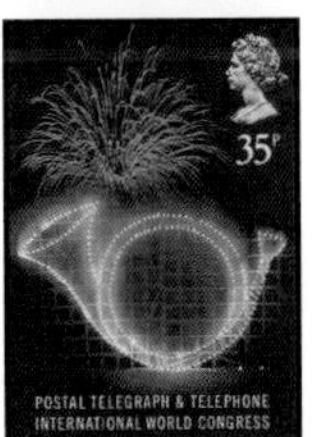

C

D

1989 (11 April) Anniversaries. Perf. 14 x 14½
Printer: House of Questa in Lithography

No.			U/M	F/U
C833	**19p**	Mortar Board (A)	35	25
C834	**19p**	Cross on Ballot Paper (B)	35	25
C833/34	**19p**	**Se-tenant pair**	1.00	1.00
C835	**35p**	Posthorn (C)	50	50
C836	**35p**	Globe (D)	50	50
C835/36	**35p**	**Se-tenant pair**	2.25	2.30
		Set of 4	3.20	3.20
		Set of 2 Cylinder Blocks	7.50	
		Set of 2 Gutter Strips	8.00	8.00
		First Day Cover		1.70
		Presentation Pack 198	2.20	
		PHQ Cards	1.70	2.70

Variety
C836a 35p Error. Inscribed 'One Hundreth Conference....'£4500

1989 (16 May) Europa. Games and Toys. Perf. 14 x 15

No.			U/M	F/U
C837	**19p**	Train and Plane	30	25
C838	**27p**	Bricks	50	45
C839	**32p**	Dice and Ladder	75	80
C840	**35p**	Robot/Boat	75	80
		Set of 4	1.85	1.90
		Set of 4 Cylinder Blocks	13.90	
		Set of 4 Gutter Pairs	7.40	7.40
		First Day Cover		1.70
		Presentation Pack 199	2.75	
		PHQ Cards	1.70	2.70

1989 (4 July) Industrial Archaeology. Perf. 14 x 15

No.			U/M	F/U
C841	**19p**	Ironbridge	28	25
C842	**27p**	Tin Mine	60	50
C843	**32p**	Cotton Mills	70	70
C844	**35p**	Aqueduct	70	70
		Set of 4	1.90	1.90
		Set of 4 Cylinder Blocks	14.50	
		Set of 4 Gutter Pairs	4.75	4.75
		First Day Cover		1.70
		Presentation Pack 200	1.90	
		PHQ Cards	1.70	2.70

1989 (25 July) Industrial Archaeology. Perf. 15 x14

No.			U/M	F/U
MS5	**£1.40**	**Miniature Sheet**	2.90	3.20
		First Day Cover		3.50

The stamp designs in the miniature sheet are in horizontal format.

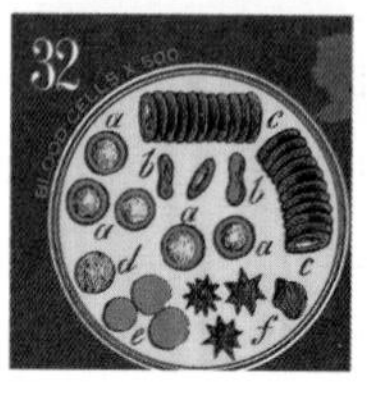

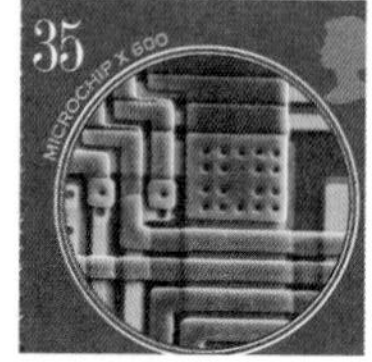

1989 (5 Sept.) Microscopes. Perf 14½ x 14

No.			U/M	F/U
C845	**19p**	Multicoloured	28	25
C846	**27p**	Multicoloured	60	50
C847	**32p**	Multicoloured	70	75
C848	**35p**	Multicoloured	70	70
		Set of 4	1.90	1.90
		Set of 4 Cylinder Blocks	14.50	
		Set of 4 Gutter Pairs	4.75	4.75
		First Day Cover		1.50
		Presentation Pack 201	1.90	
		PHQ Cards	1.70	2.70

A

B

C

D

E

1989 (17 Oct.) Lord Mayor's Show. Perf. 14 x 15

No.			U/M	F/U
C849	20p	Royal Mail Coach (A)	35	30
C850	20p	Escort (B)	35	30
C851	20p	Lord Mayor's Coach (C)	35	30
C852	20p	Passing St. Pauls (D)	35	30
C853	20p	Blues and Royals (E)	35	30
C849/853	**20p**	**Strip of 5 se-tenant**	1.80	1.80
		Cylinder Block	4.20	
		Gutter Strip of 10	4.50	4.80
		First Day Cover		1.50
		Presentation Pack 202	1.85	
		PHQ Cards	1.70	2.70

Variety

C844/8a	Imperforate strip of 5 but with C853 having several blind peforations on the right	£7500	

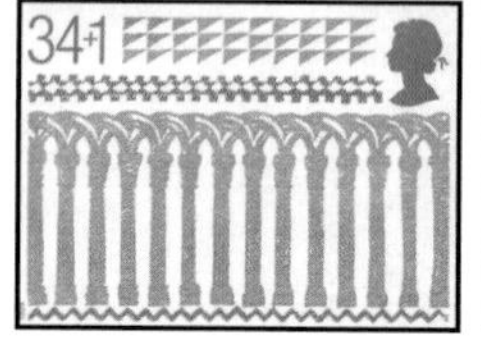

1989 (14 Nov.) Christmas. Charity Issue.

No.			U/M	F/U
C854	**15p**	14th Century Peasants (centre band)	25	25
C855	**15p+1p**	Arches and Roundels (centre band)	30	25
C856	**20p+1p**	Octagen Towers	35	35
C857	**34p+1p**	Arcade	70	80
C858	**37p+1p**	Triple Arch	70	80
		Set of 5	2.10	2.25
		Set of 5 Cylinder Blocks	15.90	
		Set of 5 Gutter Pairs	5.25	5.25
		First Day Cover		1.50
		Presentation Pack 203	1.70	
		PHQ Cards	1.70	2.70

Varieties

C855a	15p+1p	Imperforate pair	£1250	
C856a	20p+1p	Imperforate pair	£1250	

1989 (14 Nov.) Collectors Year Pack

CP26	Collectors Year Pack 204	£21	

1989 (14 Nov.) Royal Mail Year Book - 6

YB6	Royal Mail Year Book C820/858	£18	

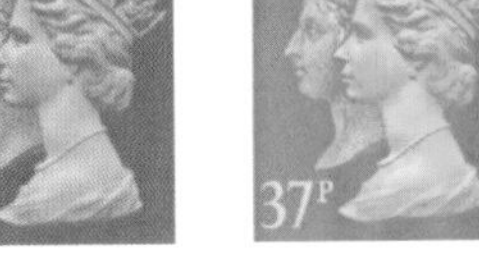
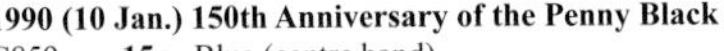

1990 (10 Jan.) 150th Anniversary of the Penny Black

No.			U/M	F/U
C859	**15p**	Blue (centre band)	35	30
C860	**20p**	Black and pale buff	35	35
C861	**29p**	Mauve	70	70
C862	**34p**	Slate	90	90
C863	**37p**	Red	90	90
		Set of 5 *	3.00	3.00
		Set of 5 Cylinder Blocks		
		First Day Cover		3.50
		Presentation Pack 204	3.60	
Variety				
C859a	15p	Imperforate pair	£1250	

* The set of five stamps were issued as commemoratives. This issue is detailed more fully in the definitives section.

1990 (23 Jan.) RSPCA 150th Anniversary. Perf. 14 x 14½
Printer: House of Questa in Lithography

No.			U/M	F/U
C864	**20p**	Kitten	30	30
C865	**29p**	Rabbit	55	60
C866	**34p**	Duckling	70	75
C867	**37p**	Puppy	70	75
		Set of 4	1.90	2.00
		Set of 4 Cylinder Blocks	14.50	
		Set of 4 Gutter Pairs	4.75	4.75
		First Day Cover		1.50
		Presentation Pack 205	2.10	
		PHQ Cards	1.70	2.70
Varieties				
C864a	20p	Missing Silver (Queen's head & 20p)	£200	£45
C865a	29p	Imperforate pair	£1800	
C866a	34p	Missing Silver (Queen's head & 34p)	£450	

A

B

C

D

E

F

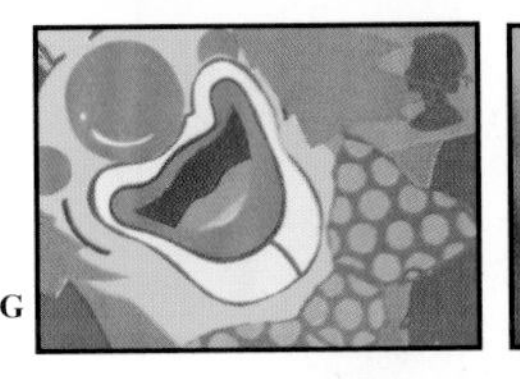
G

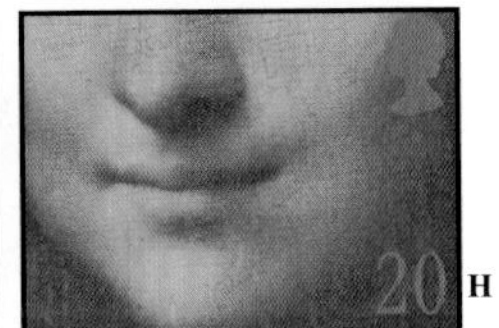
H

I

J

1990 (6 Feb.) 'Smiles'. Fluorescent Coated Paper. Perf. 15 x 14

No.			U/M	F/U
C868	**20p**	Teddy Bear (2 bands) (A)	1.60	1.70
C869	**20p**	Dennis the Menace (2 bands) (B)	1.60	1.70
C870	**20p**	Punch (2 bands) (C)	1.60	1.70
C871	**20p**	Cheshire Cat (2 bands) (D)	1.60	1.70
C872	**20p**	Man in the Moon (2 bands) (E)	1.60	1.70
C873	**20p**	Laughing Policeman (2 bands) (F)	1.60	1.70
C874	**20p**	Clown (2 bands) (G)	1.60	1.70
C875	**20p**	Mona Lisa (2 bands) (H)	1.60	1.70
C876	**20p**	Queen of Hearts (2 bands) (I)	1.60	1.70
C877	**20p**	Stan Laurel (2 bands) (J)	1.60	1.70
	20p	**Booklet pane of 10**	13.50	£14
		First Day Cover		£14

The above are from the second Greetings Book listed on Page

1990 (6 March) Europa 1990

No.			U/M	F/U
C878	**20p**	London 90 (A) *	30	30
C879	**20p**	Glasgow School of Art (B)	45	40
C880	**29p**	Philatelic Bureau	70	50
C881	**37p**	Templeton Carpet	70	60
		Set of 4	2.00	2.00
		Set of 4 Cylinder Blocks	15.00	
		Set of 4 Gutter Pairs	5.00	5.00
		First Day Cover		1.50
		Presentation Pack 206	2.75	
		PHQ Cards	1.70	2.70

* C863 also occurs as a booklet pane of 4 in the £5 London Life booklet.

1990 (10 April) Queen's Awards. Perf. 14 x 14½
Printer: House of Questa in Lithography

No.			U/M	F/U
C882	**20p**	Export	35	35
C883	**20p**	Technology	35	35
C882/883	**20p**	**Se-tenant pair**	70	70
C884	**37p**	Export	85	85
C885	**37p**	Technology	85	85
C884/885	**37p**	**Se-tenant pair**	1.70	1.70
		Set of 4	2.25	2.15
		Set of 2 Cylinder Blocks	5.90	
		Set of 2 Gutter Strips	5.60	5.60
		First Day Cover		1.50
		Presentation Pack 207	2.05	
		PHQ Cards	1.70	2.70

1990 (3 May) 'Stamp World 90', London
Printed in Photogravure and recess

No.			U/M	F/U
MS6	**£1**	**Miniature sheet** containing 20p stamp	2.70	2.75
		First Day Cover		3.00
		Souvenir Book. *Contents:* C854/8 and MS6	£15	
Varieties				
MS6a	£1	Missing Black (Recess printing)	£7500	
MS6b	£1	Missing Cream (Recess printing)	£4000	
MS6c	£1	Imperforate	£3500	
MS6d	£1	Imperforate. First Day Cover		£3500
MS6e	£1	Recess printing inverted (background)	£7500	

1990 (5 June) Kew Gardens, 150th Anniversary

No.			U/M	F/U
C886	**20p**	Cycad	30	30
C887	**29p**	Stone Pine	60	60
C888	**34p**	Willow Tree	85	80
C889	**37p**	Cedar Tree	85	80
		Set of 4	2.40	2.25
		Set of 4 Cylinder Blocks		
		Set of 4 Gutter Pairs	6.00	6.00
		First Day Cover		1.50
		Presentation Pack 208	1.95	
		PHQ Cards	1.70	2.70

1990 (10 July) Thomas Hardy, 150th Birth Anniversary

No.			U/M	F/U
C890	**20p**	Thomas Hardy	40	35
		Cylinder Block	2.90	
		Gutter pair	1.00	1.00
		First Day Cover		1.00
		Presentation Pack 209	80	
		PHQ Card	50	1.50
Variety				
C890a	20p	Imperforate pair	£1350	

1990 (2 Aug.) Queen Mother's 90th Birthday

No.			U/M	F/U
C891	**20p**	Queen Mother	30	30
C892	**29p**	Queen	55	60
C893	**34p**	Duchess of York	70	70
C894	**37p**	Lady Bowes-Lyon	70	70
		Set of 4	2.20	1.80
		Set of 4 Cylinder Blocks	16.50	
		Set of 4 Gutter Pairs	5.50	5.50
		First Day Cover		2.30
		Presentation Pack 210	3.10	
		PHQ Cards	1.80	2.80

1990 (11 Sept.) Awards for Gallantry. Multicoloured designs.

No.			U/M	F/U
C895	**20p**	Victoria Cross	45	50
C896	**20p**	George Cross	45	50
C897	**20p**	Service	45	50
C898	**20p**	Military	45	50
C899	**20p**	Flying	45	50
		Set of 5	1.90	1.90
		Set of 5 Cylinder Blocks	14.50	
		Set of 4 Gutter Pairs	4.80	4.80
		First Day Cover		2.00
		Presentation Pack 211	2.20	
		PHQ Cards	1.95	2.80
Variety				
C895a	20p	Imperforate pair	£1250	

1990 (16 Oct.) Astronomy. Perf. 14 x 14½

No.			U/M	F/U
C900	**22p**	Armagh	30	30
C901	**26p**	Newton	60	45
C902	**31p**	Greenwich	65	70
C903	**37p**	Stonehenge	70	70
		Set of 4	2.00	2.00
		Set of 4 Cylinder Blocks	14.90	
		Set of 4 Gutter Pairs	5.00	5.00
		First Day Cover		2.00
		Presentation Pack 212	2.05	
		PHQ Cards	1.80	2.80
Variety				
C900a	22p	Missing Gold (Queen's head)	£350	

1990 (13 Nov.) Christmas. Snow scenes

No.			U/M	F/U
C904	**17p**	Building a Snowman	25	25
C905	**22p**	Fetching the Tree	30	30
C906	**26p**	Carol Singing	45	45
C907	**31p**	Tobogganing	65	70
C908	**37p**	Ice-Skating	65	70
		Set of 5	2.20	2.20
		Set of 5 Cylinder Blocks	16.50	
		Set of 5 Gutter Pairs	5.50	5.50
		First Day Cover		2.00
		Presentation Pack 213	2.00	
		PHQ Cards	2.20	2.80
		Booklet (10 x 17p)	3.50	
Varieties				
C904a	17p	Imperforate pair	£1350	
C904b	17p	Imperforate top or bottom edge ex Christmas book (pair)	3.00	
C905a	22p	Imperforate pair	£450	

1990 (13 Nov.) Collectors Year Pack

No.		U/M	F/U
CP27	Collectors Year Pack 214	22.50	

1990 (13 Nov.) Royal Mail Year Book - 7

No.		U/M	F/U
YB7	Royal Mail Year Book	£20	

1991 (8 Jan.) Dogs. George Stubbs. Perf. 14 x 14½

No.			U/M	F/U
C909	**22p**	'King Charles Spaniel'	30	30
C910	**26p**	'A Pointer'	45	30
C911	**31p**	'Two Hounds'	60	70
C912	**33p**	'A Rough Dog'	65	70
C913	**37p**	'Fino and Tiny'	65	70
		Set of 5	2.50	2.20
		Set of 5 Cylinder Blocks	18.50	
		Set of 5 Gutter Pairs	6.25	6.25
		First Day Cover		2.20
		Presentation Pack 215	2.15	
		PHQ Cards	1.80	2.50
Varieties				
C894a	22p	Imperforate pair	£800	
C894b		Imperforate between stamp bottom margin	£400	
C896a	31p	Imperforate pair	£800	

A  B

C  D

E  F

G  H

I  J

No.			U/M	F/U

1991 (5 Feb.) 'Good Luck'. Fluorescent Coated Paper. Perf. 15 x 14.

No.			U/M	F/U
C914	**1st**	Bird's Nest (2 bands) (A)	85	65
C915	**1st**	Rainbow (2 bands) (B)	85	65
C916	**1st**	Magpie (2 bands) (C)	85	65
C917	**1st**	Black Cat (2 bands) (D)	85	65
C918	**1st**	Kingfisher (2 bands) (E)	85	65
C919	**1st**	Mallard (2 bands) (F)	85	65
C920	**1st**	Boot (2 bands) (G)	85	65
C921	**1st**	Pot of Gold (2 bands) (H)	85	65
C922	**1st**	Butterflies (2 bands) (I)	85	65
C923	**1st**	Wishing Well (2 bands) (J)	85	65
	1st	**Booklet pane of 10**	8.50	5.90
		First Day Cover		5.70

The above are from the third Greetings Book listed on Page

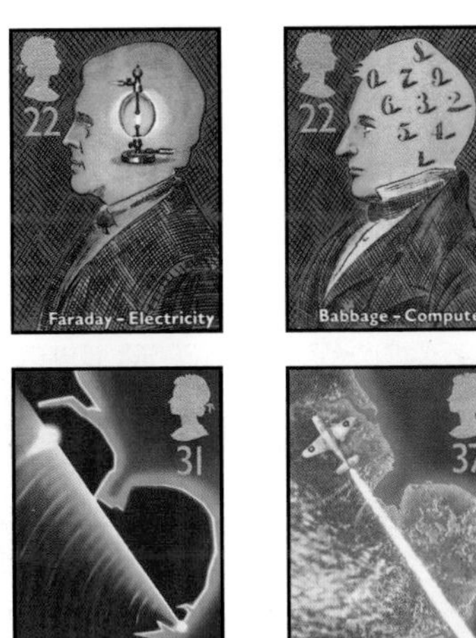

1991 (5 March) Scientific Achievements. Perf. 14 x 15

No.			U/M	F/U
C924	**22p**	Faraday	32	32
C925	**22p**	Babbage	50	60
C926	**31p**	Radar	60	65
C927	**37p**	Gloster Whittle E28/39	60	65
		Set of 4	1.90	1.95
		Set of 4 Cylinder Blocks	14.50	
		Set of 4 Gutter Pairs	4.75	4.75
		First Day Cover		2.00
		Presentation Pack 216	2.05	
		PHQ Cards	1.85	2.90

Variety

C924a	22p	Faraday. Imperforate pair.	£400	

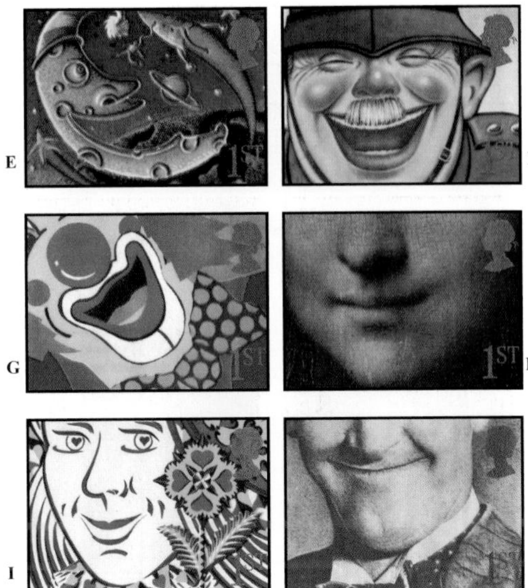

1991 (26 March.) 'Smiles'. Fluorescent Coated Paper. Perf. 15 x 14.
As numbers GS6/15 but inscribed 1st

No.			U/M	F/U
C928	**1st**	Multicoloured (2 bands) (A)	85	60
C929	**1st**	Multicoloured (2 bands) (B)	85	60
C930	**1st**	Multicoloured (2 bands) (C)	85	60
C931	**1st**	Multicoloured (2 bands) (D)	85	60
C932	**1st**	Multicoloured (2 bands) (E)	85	60
C933	**1st**	Multicoloured (2 bands) (F)	85	60
C934	**1st**	Multicoloured (2 bands) (G)	85	60
C935	**1st**	Multicoloured (2 bands) (H)	85	60
C936	**1st**	Multicoloured (2 bands) (I)	85	60
C937	**1st**	Multicoloured (2 bands) (J)	85	60
	1st	**Booklet pane of 10**	8.50	5.95
		First Day Cover		£7

2000 (22 May) The Stamp Show 2000 Smilers sheet

SSP1	C928 to C937 1st (any) with The Stamp Show 2000 label - Set of 10	£20

2001 (3 July) 'Smiles' Smilers sheet

SSP5	C928 to C937 1st (any) with Smiles greeing label Set of 10	£85

2002 (1 Oct.) 1st Smiles from Smilers sheet

No.			U/M	F/U
SSP9		Horizontal strip of two stamps (Teddy and Dennis) and label	4.00	

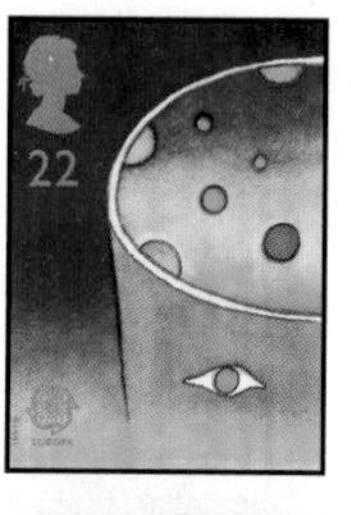

1991 (8 April) Europa. Space

No.			U/M	F/U
C938	22p	Multicoloured	35	35
C939	22p	Multicoloured	35	35
C938/939	**22p**	**Se-tenant pair**	70	70
C940	37p	Multicoloured	85	90
C941	37p	Multicoloured	85	90
C940/941	**37p**	**Se-tenant pair**	1.30	1.40
		Set of 4	1.90	2.00
		Set of 2 Cylinder Blocks	4.90	
		Set of 2 Gutter Strips	4.75	4.75
		First Day Cover		2.00
		Presentation Pack 217	2.75	
		PHQ Cards	1.90	2.80

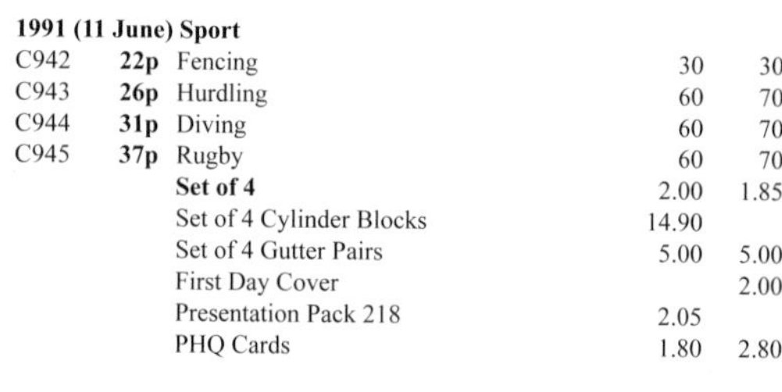

1991 (11 June) Sport

No.			U/M	F/U
C942	**22p**	Fencing	30	30
C943	**26p**	Hurdling	60	70
C944	**31p**	Diving	60	70
C945	**37p**	Rugby	60	70
		Set of 4	2.00	1.85
		Set of 4 Cylinder Blocks	14.90	
		Set of 4 Gutter Pairs	5.00	5.00
		First Day Cover		2.00
		Presentation Pack 218	2.05	
		PHQ Cards	1.80	2.80

1991 (16 July) Roses

No.			U/M	F/U
C946	**22p**	'Silver Jubilee'	30	30
C947	**26p**	'Mme A. Carriere	45	45
C948	**31p**	Rosa Mayesii	52	52
C949	**33p**	'Harvest Fayre'	55	60
C950	**37p**	'Mutabilis'	60	65
		Set of 5	2.30	2.00
		Set of 5 Cylinder Blocks	17.50	
		Set of 4 Gutter Pairs	5.75	5.75
		First Day Cover		2.00
		Presentation Pack 219	2.05	
		PHQ Cards	1.80	2.80
Varieties				
C912a	22p	Missing Silver (Queen's head)	£1000	
C912b	22p	Black printed double		£2500

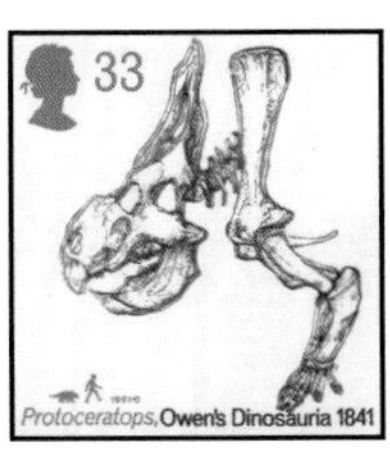

1991 (20 Aug.) Dinosaurs. Perf. 14½ x 14

No.			U/M	F/U
C951	**22p**	Iguanadon	35	30
C952	**26p**	Stegossaurus	50	50
C953	**31p**	Tyrannosaurus	60	60
C954	**33p**	Protocerstops	60	65
C955	**37p**	Triceratops	65	70
		Set of 5	2.60	2.30
		Set of 5 Cylinder Blocks	19.50	
		Set of 5 Gutter Pairs	6.50	6.50
		First Day Cover		2.00
		Presentation Pack 220	2.55	
		PHQ Cards	1.80	2.80

Variety

C917a	22p	Imperforate pair	£1350	
C917b		Imperforate between stamp & bottom margin	£650	

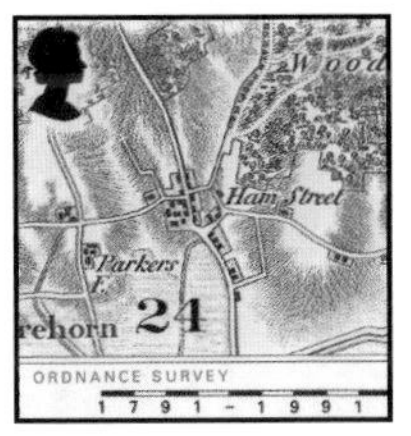

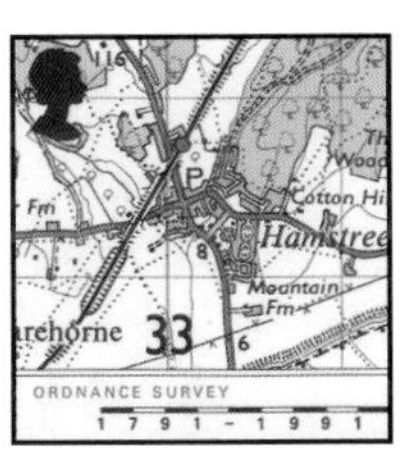

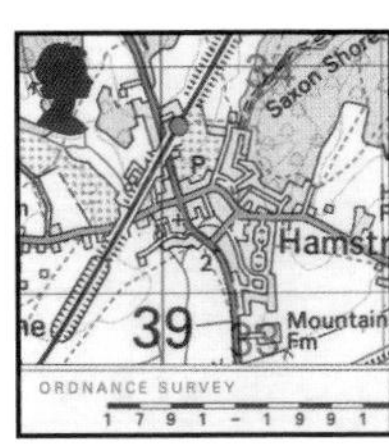

1991 (17 Sept.) Ordnance Survey. Perf. 14½ x 14 Printers: Harrison & Sons (24p, 28p) in Lithography and Recess (24p) and House of Questa in Lithography (33p, 39p)

No.			U/M	F/U
C956	**24p**	Map of 1816	33	33
C957	**28p**	Map of 1906	50	60
C958	**33p**	Map of 1959	65	65
C959	**39p**	Map of 1991	65	65
		Set of 4	2.00	1.90
		Set of 4 Cylinder Blocks	14.90	
		Set of 4 Gutter Pairs	5.00	5.00
		First Day Cover		2.00
		Presentation Pack 221	2.05	
		PHQ Cards	1.80	2.80

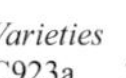

Varieties

No.			U/M	F/U
C923a	26p	Multicoloured. Error of value	£3500	
C923b		Black printed double	£1750	

1991 (12 Nov.) Christmas

No.			U/M	F/U
C960	**18p**	Adoration of the Magi (1 band)	27	27
C961	**24p**	Mary and Jesus	33	33
C962	**28p**	The Holy Family	48	60
C963	**33p**	The Annunciation	55	60
C964	**39p**	The Flight to Egypt	58	60
		Set of 5	2.30	2.15
		Set of 5 Cylinder Blocks	17.50	
		Set of 5 Gutter Pairs	5.75	5.75
		First Day Cover		2.00
		Presentation Pack 222	2.05	
		PHQ Cards	1.80	2.80
		Booklet pane (20 x 18p)	6.50	

Varieties

C960a	18p	Imperforate pair	£1750	
C961a	24p	Black (litho) treble & carmine double	£900	
C961b	24p	Black (litho) and carmine double	£1250	
C961c	24p	Black (litho) double	£1250	

1991 (12 Nov.) Collectors Pack

CP28	Collectors Year Pack 223	22.50	

1991 (12 Nov.) Royal Mail Year Book - 8

YB8	Royal Mail Year Book	£16	

1992 (14 Jan.) The Four Seasons. Winter

No.			U/M	F/U
C965	**18p**	Stag (1 band)	27	27
C966	**24p**	Hare	33	33
C967	**28p**	Fox	48	48
C968	**33p**	Thrush	65	65
C969	**39p**	Sheep	65	65
		Set of 5	2.25	2.20
		Set of 5 Cylinder Blocks	16.90	
		Set of 5 Gutter Pairs	5.65	5.65
		First Day Cover		2.00
		Presentation Pack 224	2.05	
		PHQ Cards	1.80	2.80
		Booklet pane (4 x 39p)	3.00	
Variety				
C932a	24p	Imperforate pair	£400	

A

B

C

D

E

F

G

H

I

J

1992 (28 Jan.) 'Memories'. Fluorescent Coated Paper. Perf. 15 x 14.

No.			U/M	F/U
C970	**1st**	Multicoloured (2 bands) (A)	60	60
C971	**1st**	Multicoloured (2 bands) (B)	60	60
C972	**1st**	Multicoloured (2 bands) (C)	60	60
C973	**1st**	Multicoloured (2 bands) (D)	60	60
C974	**1st**	Multicoloured (2 bands) (E)	60	60
C975	**1st**	Multicoloured (2 bands) (F)	60	60
C976	**1st**	Multicoloured (2 bands) (G)	60	60
C977	**1st**	Multicoloured (2 bands) (H)	60	60
C978	**1st**	Multicoloured (2 bands) (I)	60	60
C979	**1st**	Multicoloured (2 bands) (J)	60	60
	1st	**Booklet pane of 10**	6.00	7.00
		First Day Cover		7.50
		Presentation Pack	7.00	

A

B

C

D

E

1992 (6 Feb.) 40th Anniversary of Accession. Perf. 14½ x 14

No.			U/M	F/U
C980	24p	Multicoloured (2 bands) (A)	75	50
C981	24p	Multicoloured (2 bands) (B)	75	50
C982	24p	Multicoloured (2 bands) (C)	75	50
C983	24p	Multicoloured (2 bands) (D)	75	50
C984	24p	Multicoloured (2 bands) (E)	75	50
	24p	**Strip of 5 se-tenant**	3.00	3.50
		Strip of 5 Missing phosphor	£200	
		Any single stamp Missing phosphor	£32	
		Cylinder Block	6.90	
		Gutter Block of 10	7.50	7.50
		First Day Cover		2.20
		Presentation Pack 225	2.95	
		PHQ Cards	1.80	2.80

1992 (10 March) Lord Tennyson. Perf. 14½ x 14

No.			U/M	F/U
C985	**24p**	Marlin and Vivien	36	38
C986	**28p**	The Millers Daughter	48	50
C987	**33p**	Lady of Shalott	55	58
C988	**39p**	Mariana	60	65
		Set of 4	1.95	2.05
		Set of 4 Cylinder Blocks	14.60	
		Set of 4 Gutter Pairs	4.90	4.90
		First Day Cover		£2
		Presentation Pack 226	2.15	
		PHQ Cards	1.80	2.80

A

B

C

D

E

1992 (7 April) Europa. International Events
Printers: Harrison & Sons in Lithography and Recess (C and D) and House of Questa in Lithography (A, B and E)

No.			U/M	F/U
C989	**24p**	Olympics '92 (A)	40	35
C990	**24p**	Olympics '92 (B)	40	35
C989/990	**24p**	**Se-tenant Pair**	85	90
C991	**24p**	Columbus (C)	36	40
C992	**39p**	Operation Raleigh (D)	60	65
C993	**39p**	Expo '92 Seville (E)	60	65
		Set of 5	2.00	2.30
		Set of 4 Cylinder Blocks	14.50	
		Set of 3 Gutter Pairs & Gutter Strip of 4	7.50	7.50
		First Day Cover		2.00
		Presentation Pack 227	2.75	
		PHQ Cards	2.50	3.50
Variety				
C991a	24p	Missing Cream		£4750

1992 (16 June) The Civil War 1642 - 51

No.			U/M	F/U
C994	**24p**	Pikeman	36	36
C995	**28p**	Drummer	48	50
C996	**33p**	Musketeer	60	65
C997	**39p**	Standard Bearer	60	65
		Set of 4	2.10	2.15
		Set of 4 Cylinder Blocks	15.50	
		Set of 4 Gutter Pairs	5.25	5.25
		First Day Cover		£2
		Presentation Pack 228	2.05	
		PHQ Cards	2.50	3.50
Variety				
C950a	24p	Imperforate pair *	£250	

** Caution, as some are damage (waste)*

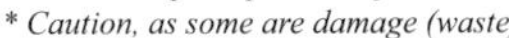

1992 (21 July) Gilbert and Sullivan

No.			U/M	F/U
C998	**18p**	Yeoman of the Guard (1 band)	28	28
C999	**24p**	Gondoliers	36	40
C1000	**28p**	Mikado	48	50
C1001	**33p**	Pirates of Penzance	55	60
C1002	**39p**	Iolanthe	65	65
		Set of 5	2.10	2.20
		Set of 5 Cylinder Blocks	15.75	
		Set of 5 Gutter Pairs	5.25	5.25
		First Day Cover		£2
		Presentation Pack 229	2.15	
		PHQ Cards	2.50	3.50
Variety				
C999a	24p	Imperforate pair	£250	

1992 (15 Sept.) The Environment. Perf. 14 x 14½

No.			U/M	F/U
C1003	**24p**	Acid Rain	36	36
C1004	**28p**	Ozone Layer	48	50
C1005	**33p**	Greenhouse Effect	55	60
C1006	**39p**	Bird of Hope	65	65
		Set of 4	2.00	2.10
		Set of 4 Cylinder Blocks	15.20	
		Set of 4 Gutter Pairs	5.00	5.00
		First Day Cover		£2
		Presentation Pack 230	2.05	
		PHQ Cards	2.50	3.00

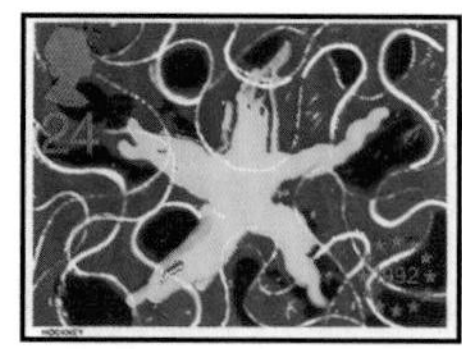
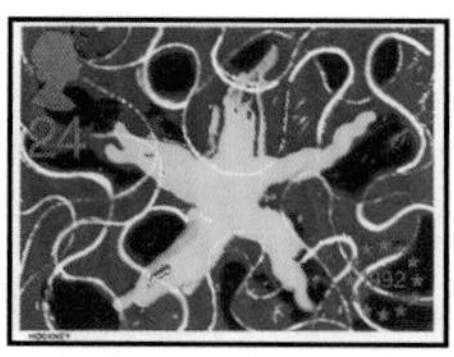

1992 (13 Oct.) Single European Market.

No.			U/M	F/U
C1007	**24p**	Multicoloured	40	35
		Cylinder Block	2.90	
		Gutter pair	1.00	1.00
		First Day Cover		1.00
		Presentation Pack 231	90	
		PHQ Card	40	75

1992 (10 Nov.) Christmas. Stained Glass Windows

No.			U/M	F/U
C1008	**18p**	Angel Gabriel (centre band)	28	28
C1009	**24p**	Mary and Jesus	36	38
C1010	**28p**	King in Crown	40	45
C1011	**33p**	Three Shepherds	50	55
C1012	**39p**	Two Kings with Gifts	70	75
		Set of 5	2.20	2.15
		Set of 5 Cylinder Blocks	16.50	
		Set of 5 Gutter Pairs	5.50	5.50
		First Day Cover		2.00
		Presentation Pack 232	1.95	
		PHQ Cards	2.50	3.50
		Booklet pane (20 x 18p)		

1992 (10 Nov.) Collectors Pack

No.		U/M	F/U
CP29	Collectors Year Pack 233	22.50	

1992 (11 Nov.) Royal Mail Year Book - 9

No.		U/M	F/U
YB9	Royal Mail Year Book	£19	

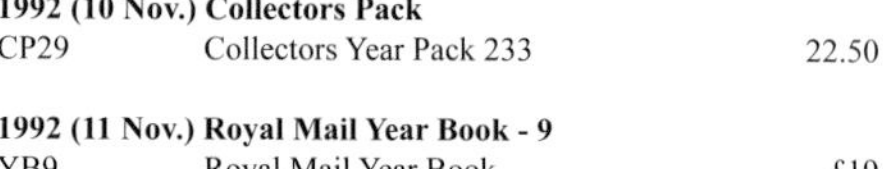

1993 (19 Jan.) Swans

No.			U/M	F/U
C1013	**18p**	Swans Head (1 band)	35	28
C1014	**24p**	Cygnet	70	70
C1015	**28p**	Nesting Pair	80	80
C1016	**33p**	Eggs	1.00	1.00
C1017	**39p**	Mute Swan	1.00	1.00
		Set of 5	3.40	2.50
		Set of 5 Cylinder Blocks	24.90	
		Set of 5 Gutter Pairs	8.50	8.50
		First Day Cover		2.70
		Presentation Pack 234	3.45	
		PHQ Cards	3.50	4.50

A

B

C

D

E

F

G

H

I

J

1993 (2 Feb.) 'Gifts'. Perf. 15 x 14 elliptical

No.			U/M	F/U
C1018	**1st**	Multicoloured (2 bands) (A)	60	60
C1019	**1st**	Multicoloured (2 bands) (B)	60	60
C1020	**1st**	Multicoloured (2 bands) (C)	60	60
C1021	**1st**	Multicoloured (2 bands) (D)	60	60
C1022	**1st**	Multicoloured (2 bands) (E)	60	60
C1023	**1st**	Multicoloured (2 bands) (F)	60	60
C1024	**1st**	Multicoloured (2 bands) (G)	60	60
C1025	**1st**	Multicoloured (2 bands) (H)	60	60
C1026	**1st**	Multicoloured (2 bands) (I)	60	60
C1027	**1st**	Multicoloured (2 bands) (J)	60	60
	1st	**Booklet pane of 10**	5.50	6.00
		First Day Cover		7.50
		Presentation Pack	8.50	
		PHQ Cards	4.00	5.50

No. C also occurs as a pane of 4 in the £6 Beatrix Potter booklet.

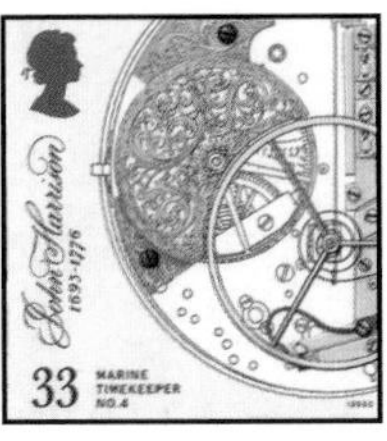

1993 (16 Feb.) Marine Chronometers. Perf. 14½ x 14

No.			U/M	F/U
C1028	**24p**	Front View	36	36
C1029	**28p**	Escapement	50	50
C1030	**33p**	Balance and Spring	60	65
C1031	**39p**	Engraved Back	65	65
		Set of 4	2.00	2.10
		Set of 4 Cylinder Blocks	14.90	
		Set of 4 Gutter Pairs	5.00	5.00
		First Day Cover		2.00
		Presentation Pack 235	2.55	
		PHQ Cards	2.50	3.50

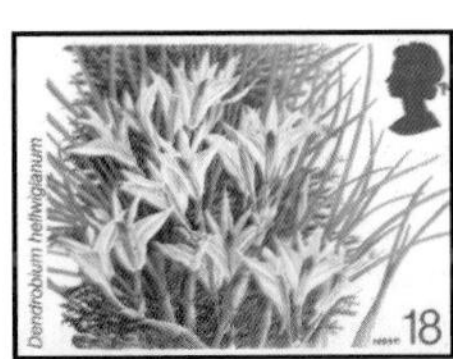

1993 (16 March) Orchids

No.			U/M	F/U
C1032	**18p**	Dendrobium (1 band)	28	28
C1033	**24p**	Paphiopedilum	36	38
C1034	**28p**	Cymbidium	50	50
C1035	**33p**	Vanda Rothschildiana	65	65
C1035a		Year omitted	7.50	7.50
C1036	**39p**	Dendrobium Vexillarius	65	65
		Set of 5	2.40	2.40
		Set of 5 Cylinder Blocks	17.90	
		Set of 5 Gutter Pairs	6.00	6.00
		First Day Cover		2.00
		Presentation Pack 236	2.15	
		PHQ Cards	3.00	4.00

No.			U/M	F/U
Variety				
C1032a	18p	Imperforate pair	£1750	
C1032b		Imperforate between stamp & bottom margin	£450	
C1035a	33p	Coypyright & logo missing	£15	£10

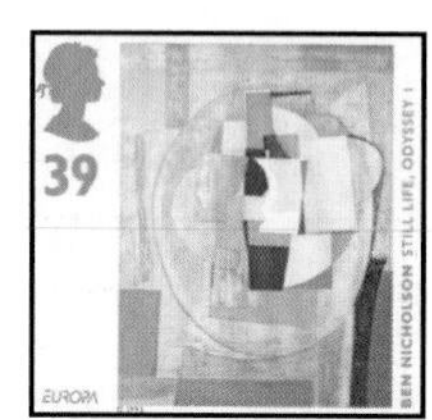

1993 (11 May) Europa. Contemporary Art

No.			U/M	F/U
C1037	**24p**	Henry Moore	35	38
C1038	**28p**	Edward Bawden	50	50
C1039	**33p**	Stanley Spencer	60	65
C1040	**39p**	Ben Nicolson	65	65
		Set of 4	2.00	2.10
		Set of 4 Cylinder Blocks	14.90	
		Set of 4 Gutter Pairs	5.00	5.00
		First Day Cover		2.00
		Presentation Pack 237	2.75	
		PHQ Cards	3.00	4.00

1993 (15 June) Roman Britain

No.			U/M	F/U
C1041	**24p**	Claudius (2 bands)	36	38
C1042	**28p**	Hadrian (2 bands)	50	55
C1043	**33p**	Roman (2 bands)	60	65
C1044	**39p**	'Christ' (2 bands)	65	65
		Set of 4	2.00	2.10
		Set of 4 Cylinder Blocks	14.90	
		Set of 4 Gutter Pairs	5.00	5.00
		First Day Cover		2.00
		Presentation Pack238	2.05	
		PHQ Cards	3.00	4.00

1993 (20 July) Inland Waterways. Perf. 14½ x 14

No.			U/M	F/U
C1045	**24p**	Grand Junction (2 bands)	36	38
C1046	**28p**	Stainforth and Keadby (2 bands)	50	50
C1047	**33p**	Brecknock and Abergavenny (2 bands)	60	65
C1048	**39p**	Crinan (2 bands)	65	65
		Set of 4	2.00	2.10
		Set of 4 Cylinder Blocks	14.90	
		Set of 4 Gutter Pairs	5.00	5.00
		First Day Cover		2.00
		Presentation Pack 239	2.05	
		PHQ Cards	3.00	4.00

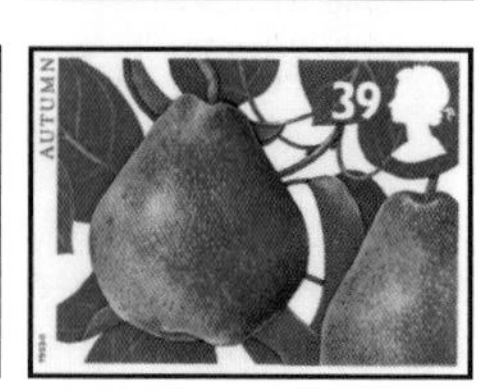

1993 (11 Sept.) The Four Seasons. Autumn

No.			U/M	F/U
C1049	**18p**	Horse Chestnut (1 band)	30	32
C1050	**24p**	Blackberry	36	38
C1051	**28p**	Hazel	40	45
C1052	**33p**	Rowan	50	55
C1053	**39p**	Pear	65	65
		Set of 5	2.30	2.40
		Set of 5 Cylinder Blocks	17.30	
		Set of 5 Gutter Pairs	5.75	5.75
		First Day Cover		2.00
		Presentation Pack 240	2.05	
		PHQ Cards	3.00	4.00

1993 (11 Oct.) Sherlock Holmes. Perf. 14 x 14½

No.			U/M	F/U
C1054	**24p**	Dr. Watson (A)	50	50
C1055	**24p**	Sir Henry (B)	50	50
C1056	**24p**	Lestrade (C)	50	50
C1057	**24p**	Mycroft (D)	50	50
C1058	**24p**	Moriarty (E)	50	50
		Strip of 5 se-tenant	2.50	2.50
		Cylinder Block	5.90	
		Gutter Strip of 10	6.25	6.25
		First Day Cover		2.50
		Presentation Pack 241	2.15	
		PHQ Cards	3.00	4.00

1993 (9 Nov.) Christmas. Dickens' Christmas Carol

No.			U/M	F/U
C1059	**19p**	Bob Cratchit (1 band)	29	34
C1060	**25p**	Mr and Mrs Fezziwig	38	42
C1061	**30p**	Scrooge	50	55
C1062	**35p**	The Prize Turkey	60	65
C1063	**41p**	Scrooge's Nephew	65	70
		Set of 5	2.15	2.25
		Set of 5 Cylinder Blocks	16.00	
		Set of 5 Gutter Pairs	5.40	5.40
		First Day Cover		2.00
		Presentation Pack 242	2.35	
		PHQ Cards	3.00	4.00
Variety				
C1059a	19p	Imperforate pair	£1500	
C1059b	19p	Imperforate at lower margin	£350	

1993 (9 Nov.) Collectors Year Pack

No.		U/M
CP30	Collectors Year Pack 243	£30

1993 (9 Nov.) Royal Mail Year Book - 10

No.		U/M
YB10	Royal Mail Year Book	£24

1994 (18 Jan.) Age of Steam. Railway photographs. Perf. 14½

No.			U/M	F/U
C1064	**19p**	West Highland Line (1 band)	29	34
C1065	**25p**	Kings Cross (2 bands)	38	45
C1066	**30p**	Blyth North (2 bands)	50	55
C1067	**35p**	Wigan Central (2 bands)	60	65
C1068	**41p**	Worc. and Birmingham Canal (2 bands)	65	70
		Set of 5	2.15	2.25
		Set of 5 Cylinder Blocks	16.25	
		Set of 5 Gutter Pairs	5.40	5.40
		First Day Cover		2.50
		Presentation Pack 244	2.80	
		PHQ Cards	3.00	4.00

A

B

C

D

E

F

G

H

I

J

1994 (1 Feb.) 'Messages'. Perf. 15 x 14 elliptical

No.			U/M	F/U
C1069	**1st**	Multicoloured (2 bands) (A)	55	60
C1070	**1st**	Multicoloured (2 bands) (B)	55	60
C1071	**1st**	Multicoloured (2 bands) (C)	55	60
C1072	**1st**	Multicoloured (2 bands) (D)	55	60
C1073	**1st**	Multicoloured (2 bands) (E)	55	60
C1074	**1st**	Multicoloured (2 bands) (F)	55	60
C1075	**1st**	Multicoloured (2 bands) (G)	55	60
C1076	**1st**	Multicoloured (2 bands) (H)	55	60
C1077	**1st**	Multicoloured (2 bands) (I)	55	60
C1078	**1st**	Multicoloured (2 bands) (J)	55	60
	1st	**Booklet pane of 10**	8.50	8.50
		First Day Cover		5.50
		Presentation Pack G4	8.50	
		PHQ Cards	4.00	7.50

1994 (1 March) 25th Anniversary of Investiture of Prince of Wales

No.			U/M	F/U
C1079	**19p**	Castell Y Wan (1 band)	29	34
C1080	**25p**	Ben Arkle	38	43
C1081	**30p**	Mourne Mountains	45	50
C1082	**35p**	Dersingham	53	58
C1083	**41p**	Dolwyddelan	62	67
		Set of 5	2.15	2.25
		Set of 5 Cylinder Blocks	16.25	
		Set of 5 Gutter Pairs	5.40	5.40
		First Day Cover		2.40
		Presentation Pack 245	2.20	
		PHQ Cards	3.00	4.00
		Booklet pane (30p x 4)	2.00	

1994 (12 April) Centenary of the Picture Postcard. Perf. 14 x 14½

No.			U/M	F/U
C1084	**19p**	Blackpool Tower (1 band)	29	34
C1085	**25p**	'Where's my Litle Lad' (2 bands)	38	43
C1086	**30p**	'Wish you were Here' (2 bands)	45	50
C1087	**35p**	Punch and Judy (2 bands)	53	58
C1088	**41p**	Tower Bridge (2 bands)	62	67
		Set of 5	2.15	2.25
		Set of 5 Cylinder Blocks	16.25	
		Set of 5 Gutter Pairs	5.40	5.40
		First Day Cover		2.40
		Presentation Pack 246	2.20	
		PHQ Cards	3.00	4.00

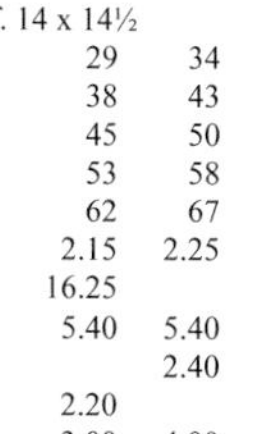

A

B

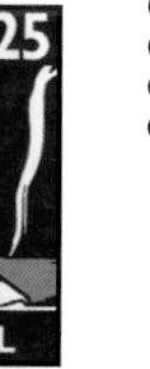

C

D

1994 (3 May) Channel Tunnel. Perf. 14 x 14½

No.			U/M	F/U
C1089	25p	Lion and Cockerel (A)	38	43
C1090	25p	Hands Across the Channel (B)	38	43
C1089/90	**25p**	**Se-tenant pair**	80	80
C1091	41p	Lion and Cockerel (C)	70	75
C1092	41p	Hands Across the Channel (D)	70	75
C1091/92	**41p**	**Se-tenant pair**	1.50	1.50
		Set of 4	2.20	2.20
		Set of 2 Cylinder Blocks	5.50	
		First Day Cover		2.00
		Presentation Pack 247	2.20	
		PHQ Cards	3.00	4.00
Variety				
C1091/2a	41p	Multiple colour shifts to left	£95	
C1091/2b		Imperforate pair	£1250	

A

B

C

D

E

1994 (6 June) D - Day. War photographs. Perf. 14½ x 14

No.			U/M	F/U
C1093	**25p**	RAF Bostons (2 bands) (A)	60	65
C1094	**25p**	HMS Warspite (2 bands) (B)	60	65
C1095	**25p**	Gold Beach (2 bands) (C	60	65
C1096	**25p**	Sword Beach (2 bands) (D)	60	65
C1097	**25p**	Ouistreham (2 bands) (E)	60	65
	25p	**Strip of 5 se-tenant**	2.50	1.95
		Cylinder Block	5.90	
		Gutter Block of 10	6.25	6.25
		First Day Cover		2.40
		Presentation Pack 248	3.20	
		PHQ Cards	3.00	4.00

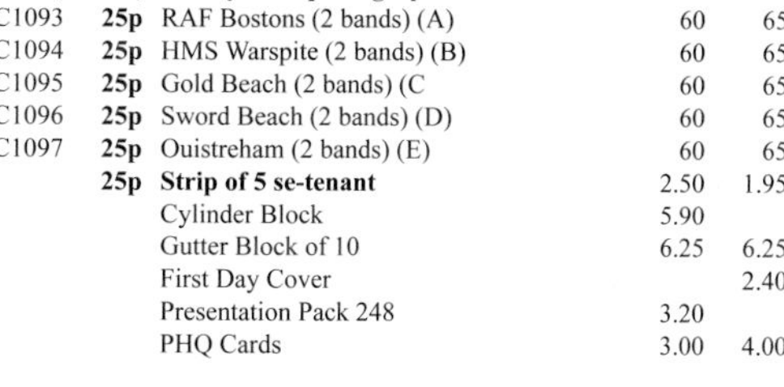

1994 (5 July) Golf

No.			U/M	F/U
C1098	**19p**	St. Andrews (1 band)	29	34
C1099	**25p**	Muirfield (2 bands)	38	43
C1100	**30p**	Carnoustie (2 bands)	45	50
C1101	**35p**	Royal Troon (2 bands)	53	58
C1102	**41p**	Turnberry (2 bands)	70	85
		Set of 5	2.40	2.40
		Set of 5 Cylinder Blocks	18.25	
		Set of 5 Gutter Pairs	6.00	6.00
		First Day Cover		2.00
		Presentation Pack 249	2.30	
		PHQ Cards	3.00	4.00

1994 (2 Aug.) The Four Seasons. Summertime

No.			U/M	F/U
C1103	**19p**	Lanelwedd (1 band)	29	34
C1104	**25p**	Wimbledon	38	43
C1105	**30p**	Cowes	50	55
C1106	**35p**	Lords	53	58
C1107	**41p**	Braemar	60	75
		Set of 5	2.10	2.40
		Set of 5 Cylinder Blocks	15.50	
		Set of 5 Gutter Pairs	5.25	5.25
		First Day Cover		2.00
		Presentation Pack 250	2.20	
		PHQ Cards	3.00	4.00

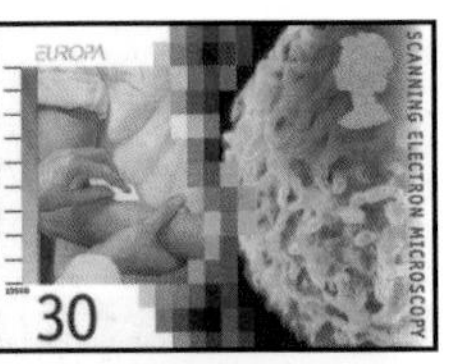

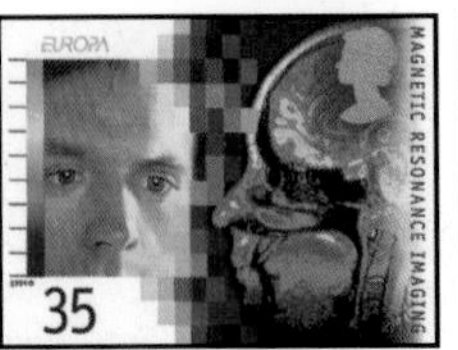

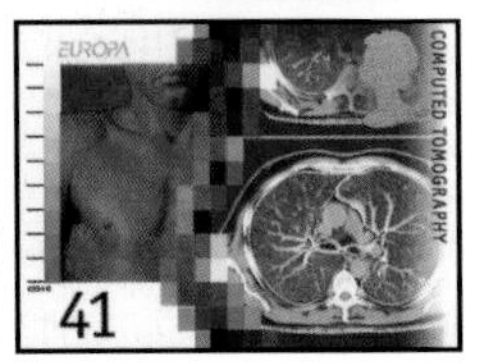

1994 (27 Sept.) Europa. Medical Discoveries. Perf. 14 x 14½

No.			U/M	F/U
C1108	**25p**	Ultrasonic	38	43
C1109	**30p**	Scanning	50	55
C1110	**35p**	Resonance	60	65
C1111	**41p**	Tanography	70	75
		Set of 4	1.90	1.90
		Set of 4 Cylinder Blocks	14.50	
		Set of 4 Gutter Pairs	4.75	4.75
		First Day Cover		2.00
		Presentation Pack 251	2.50	
		PHQ Cards	3.00	4.00
Variety				
C1108a	25p	Imperforate pair	£1750	

1994 (1 Nov.) Christmas. Children

No.			U/M	F/U
C1112	**19p**	Virgin Mary (1 band)	29	34
C1113	**25p**	Three Wise Men	38	43
C1114	**30p**	Virgin and Child	50	55
C1115	**35p**	Shepherds	60	65
C1116	**41p**	Angels	70	75
		Set of 5	2.20	2.35
		Set of 5 Cylinder Blocks	16.25	
		Set of 5 Gutter Pairs	5.50	5.50
		First Day Cover		2.00
		Presentation Pack 252	2.20	
		PHQ Cards	3.00	4.00
Variety				
C1112a	19p	Imperforate pair	£150	
C1112b		Multiple colour shift	£175	
C1114a	30p	Imperforate pair	£2000	

1994 (14 Nov.) Collectors Year Pack

No.		U/M
CP31	Collectors Year Pack 253	22.50

1994 (14 Nov.) Royal Mail Year Book - 11

No.		U/M
YB11	Royal Mail Year Book	£20

No.			U/M	F/U

1995 (17 Jan.) Cats. Perf. 14½ x 14

No.			U/M	F/U
C1117	**19p**	Black Sophie (1 band)	29	34
C1118	**25p**	Siamese and Tabby (2 bands)	38	43
C1119	**30p**	Ginger Chloe (2 bands)	50	55
C1120	**35p**	Tortoiseshell (2 bands)	60	65
C1121	**41p**	Fred (2 bands)	70	75
		Set of 5	2.50	2.45
		Set of 5 Cylinder Blocks	18.50	
		Set of 5 Gutter Pairs	6.25	6.25
		First Day Cover		2.20
		Presentation Pack 254	2.95	
		PHQ Cards	4.50	6.50

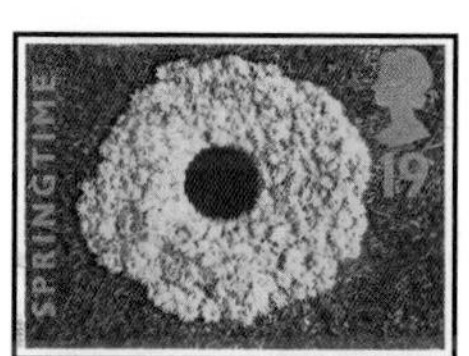

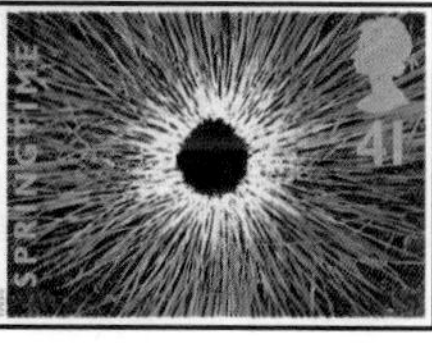

1995 (14 March) The Four Seasons. Springtime

No.			U/M	F/U
C1122	**19p**	Dandelion (1 band)	29	34
C1123	**25p**	Sweet Chestnut Leaves (2 bands)	38	43
C1124	**30p**	Garlic Leaves (2 bands)	50	55
C1125	**35p**	Hazel Leaves (2 bands)	60	65
C1126	**41p**	Spring Grass (2 bands)	70	75
		Set of 5	2.20	2.35
		Set of 5 Cylinder Blocks	16.50	
		Set of 5 Gutter Pairs	5.50	5.50
		First Day Cover		2.20
		Presentation Pack 255	2.20	
		PHQ Cards	4.50	6.50

A

B

C
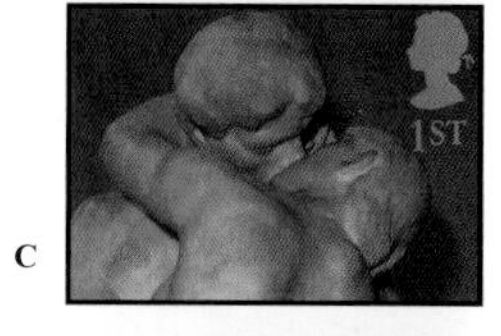

D

E

F

G

H

I

J

1995 (21 March) "Works of Art". Perf. 15 x 14 elliptical

No.			U/M	F/U
C1127	**1st**	Multicoloured (2 bands) (A)	60	60
C1128	**1st**	Multicoloured (2 bands) (B)	60	60
C1129	**1st**	Multicoloured (2 bands) (C)	60	60
C1130	**1st**	Multicoloured (2 bands) (D)	60	60
C1131	**1st**	Multicoloured (2 bands) (E)	60	60
C1132	**1st**	Multicoloured (2 bands) (F)	60	60
C1133	**1st**	Multicoloured (2 bands) (G)	60	60
C1134	**1st**	Multicoloured (2 bands) (H)	60	60
C1135	**1st**	Multicoloured (2 bands) (I)	60	60
C1136	**1st**	Multicoloured (2 bands) (J)	60	60
	1st	**Booklet pane of 10**	5.00	5.00
		First Day Cover		4.75
		Presentation Pack G4	8.50	
		PHQ Cards	3.75	7.50
Varieties:				
	1st	Missing phosphor (Complete booklet)	£8000	
		Missing phosphor (FDC)		£3500
		Missing phosphor (Used single)		£400
		Missing phosphor (unfolded pres. pack)	£5500	

1995 (11 April) National Trust

No.			U/M	F/U
C1137	**19p**	Fireplace (1 band)	29	34
C1138	**25p**	Oak Seedling (2 bands)	38	43
C1139	**30p**	Carved Table Leg (2 bands)	50	55
C1140	**35p**	St. Davids (2 bands)	60	70
C1141	**41p**	Elizabethan Window (2 bands)	70	75
		Set of 5	2.20	2.15
		Set of 5 Cylinder Blocks	16.50	
		Set of 5 Gutter Pairs	5.50	5.50
		First Day Cover		2.20
		Presentation Pack 256	2.20	
		PHQ Cards	4.50	6.50

A

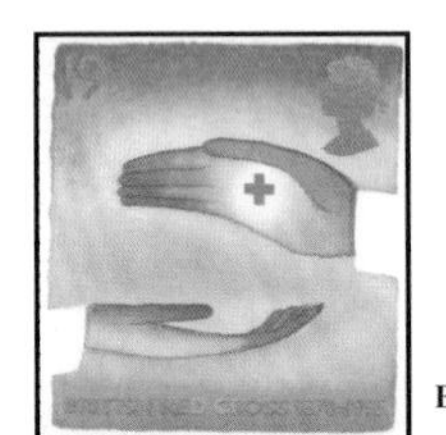
B

C

D

1995 (2 May) Peace

No.			U/M	F/U
C1142	**19p**	Troops (1 band) (A)	35	38
C1143	**19p**	Hand and Red Cross (1 band) (B)	35	38
C1144	**25p**	St. Paul's Cathedral (2 bands) (C)	45	48
C1145	**25p**	Hand and Dove (2 bands) (D)	45	48
C1146	**30p**	UN Hands (2 bands)	60	70
		Set of 5	2.20	2.50
		Set of 5 Cylinder Blocks	16.50	
		Set of 5 Gutter Pairs	5.50	5.50
		First Day Cover		2.20
		Presentation Pack 257	2.60	
		PHQ Cards	4.50	6.50
Variety				
C1145	25p	Imperforate vertical pair	£2750	

2005 (5 July) End of the War 1945 - 2005

No.			U/M	F/U
C1144a	1st	St. Paul's Cathedral	1.75	1.85
MS32		Miniature Sheet	3.50	
		First Day Cover		3.50

1995 (6 June) Science Fiction

No.			U/M	F/U
C1147	**25p**	The Time Machine (2 bands)	38	43
C1148	**30p**	First Men on the Moon (2 bands)	45	50
C1149	**35p**	War of the Worlds (2 bands)	53	58
C1150	**41p**	Shape of Things (2 bands)	70	75
		Set of 4	2.10	2.25
		Set of 4 Cylinder Blocks	15.60	
		Set of 4 Gutter Pairs	5.25	5.25
		First Day Cover		2.20
		Presentation Pack 258	2.35	
		PHQ Cards	4.50	6.50
Variety				
C1147a	25p	Imperforate between stamp & top margin	£150	

A

No.			U/M	F/U

B

C

D

E

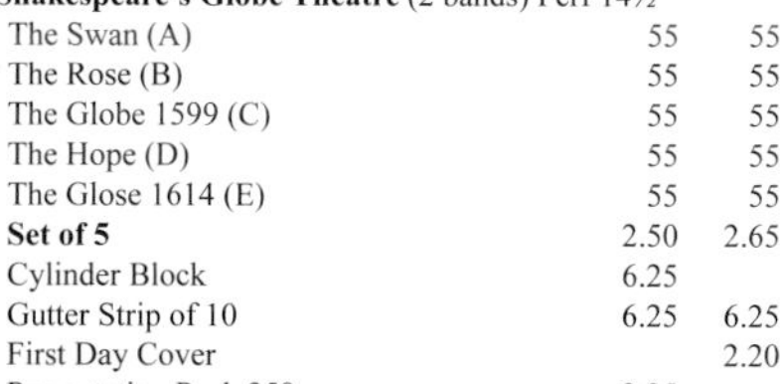

1995 (8 Aug.) Shakespeare's Globe Theatre (2 bands) Perf 14½

No.			U/M	F/U
C1151	**25p**	The Swan (A)	55	55
C1152	**25p**	The Rose (B)	55	55
C1153	**25p**	The Globe 1599 (C)	55	55
C1154	**25p**	The Hope (D)	55	55
C1155	**25p**	The Glose 1614 (E)	55	55
		Set of 5	2.50	2.65
		Cylinder Block	6.25	
		Gutter Strip of 10	6.25	6.25
		First Day Cover		2.20
		Presentation Pack 259	2.35	
		PHQ Cards	4.50	6.50

1995 (5 Sept.) Pioneers of Communications Perf 14½ x 14

No.			U/M	F/U
C1156	**19p**	Rowland Hill - Penny Post (1 band)	35	38
C1157	**25p**	Rowland Hill - Penny Black	45	48
C1158	**41p**	Marconi - Wireless	65	70
C1159	**60p**	Marconi - SOS	1.00	1.10
		Set of 4	2.20	2.25
		Set of 4 Cylinder Blocks	16.50	
		Set of 4 Gutter Pairs	5.50	5.50
		First Day Cover		2.20
		Presentation Pack 260	2.35	
		PHQ Cards	4.50	6.50

Variety

No.			U/M	F/U
C1157	25p	Silver missing	£350	

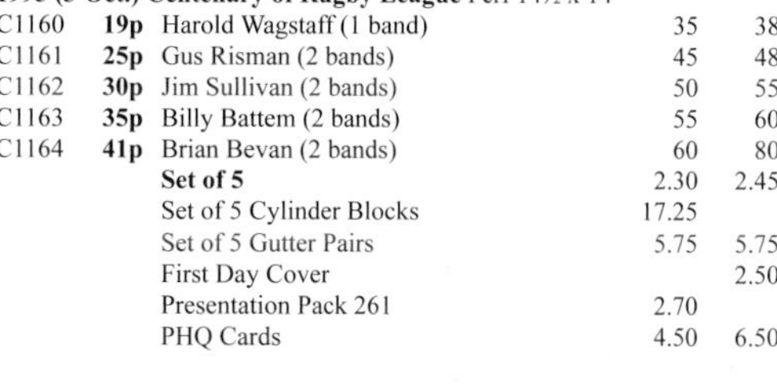

1995 (3 Oct.) Centenary of Rugby League Perf 14½ x 14

No.			U/M	F/U
C1160	**19p**	Harold Wagstaff (1 band)	35	38
C1161	**25p**	Gus Risman (2 bands)	45	48
C1162	**30p**	Jim Sullivan (2 bands)	50	55
C1163	**35p**	Billy Battem (2 bands)	55	60
C1164	**41p**	Brian Bevan (2 bands)	60	80
		Set of 5	2.30	2.45
		Set of 5 Cylinder Blocks	17.25	
		Set of 5 Gutter Pairs	5.75	5.75
		First Day Cover		2.50
		Presentation Pack 261	2.70	
		PHQ Cards	4.50	6.50

No.			U/M	F/U
1995 (30 Oct.) Christmas. Robins Perf 15 x 14				
C1165	**19p**	Letter Box (1 band)	35	38
C1166	**25p**	Holly (2 bands)	45	48
C1167	**30p**	Milk Bottles (2 bands)	50	55
C1168	**41p**	Road Sign (2 bands)	70	67
C1169	**60p**	Door Handle (2 bands)	1.00	95
		Set of 5	2.40	2.35
		Set of 5 Cylinder Blocks	17.90	
		Set of 5 Gutter Pairs	6.00	6.00
		First Day Cover		2.50
		Presentation Pack 262	2.70	
		PHQ Cards	4.50	6.50

2000 (3 Oct.) 19p Christmas Robin from Smilers sheet

SSP2	Strip of two stamps *plus* label	£10

1995 (30 Oct.) Collectors Year Pack

CP32	Presentation Pack 263	22.50

1995 (30 Oct.) Royal Mail Year Book -12

YB12	Royal Mail Year Book	£25

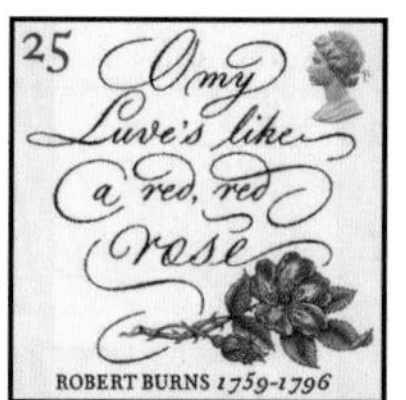

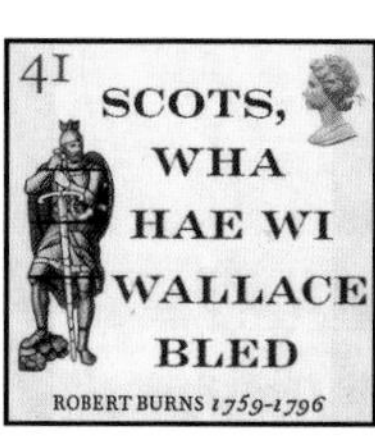

1996 (25 Jan.) Bi-centenary of death of Robert Burns Perf 14½				
C1170	**19p**	'To a Mouse' (1 band)	35	38
C1171	**25p**	'My Luves Like' (2 bands)	50	48
C1172	**41p**	'Scots who Hae' (2 bands)	70	67
C1173	**60p**	'Auld Lang Syne' (2 bands)	1.00	95
		Set of 4	2.50	2.25
		Set of 4 Cylinder Blocks	18.50	
		Set of 4 Gutter Pairs	6.25	6.25
		First Day Cover		2.50
		Presentation Pack 264	2.20	
		PHQ Cards	4.50	6.50

A

B

C

D

E

F

G

H

I

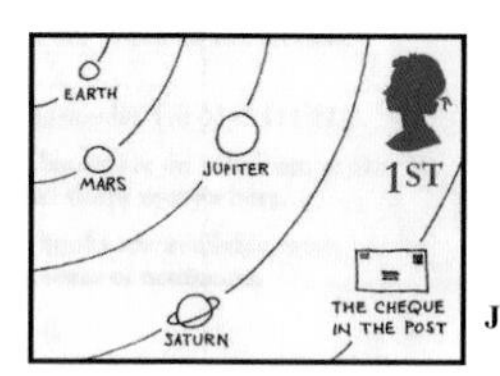

J

No.			U/M	F/U
1996 (26 Feb.) "Cartoons". All over phosphor. Perf. 14½ x 14 elliptical				
C1174	**1st**	Multicoloured (A)	55	60
C1175	**1st**	Multicoloured (B)	55	60
C1176	**1st**	Multicoloured (C)	55	60
C1177	**1st**	Multicoloured (D)	55	60
C1178	**1st**	Multicoloured (E)	55	60
C1179	**1st**	Multicoloured (F)	55	60
C1180	**1st**	Multicoloured (G)	55	60
C1181	**1st**	Multicoloured (H)	55	60
C1182	**1st**	Multicoloured (I)	55	60
C1183	**1st**	Multicoloured (J)	55	60
	1st	**Booklet pane of 10**	8.00	8.00
		First Day Cover		6.00
		Presentation Pack G5	8.50	
		PHQ Cards	4.00	

1996 (11 Nov.) "Cartoons". Two blue phosphor bands. Perf. 14½ x 14 elliptical.

Designs as No's:C1174 - C1183

C1184	**1st**	Multicoloured (2 bands) (A)	55	1.25
C1185	**1st**	Multicoloured (2 bands) (B)	55	1.25
C1186	**1st**	Multicoloured (2 bands) (C)	55	1.25
C1187	**1st**	Multicoloured (2 bands) (D)	55	1.25
C1188	**1st**	Multicoloured (2 bands) (E)	55	1.25
C1189	**1st**	Multicoloured (2 bands) (F)	55	1.25
C1190	**1st**	Multicoloured (2 bands) (G)	55	1.25
C1191	**1st**	Multicoloured (2 bands) (H)	55	1.25
C1192	**1st**	Multicoloured (2 bands) (I)	55	1.25
C1193	**1st**	Multicoloured (2 bands) (J)	55	1.25
	1st	**Booklet pane of 10**	8.00	12.50
		First Day Cover		6.00
		PHQ Cards	4.00	

2001 (18 Dec.) 1st Cartoons from Smilers sheet

No.		U/M	F/U
SSP6	Stamp *plus* label (any)	4.00	

2003 (29 July) Crossword Cartoons from Smilers sheet

No.		U/M	F/U
SSP13	1st Cartoons *plus* label (any)	1.00	
SSP13a	Missing phosphor, set of 10	£500	

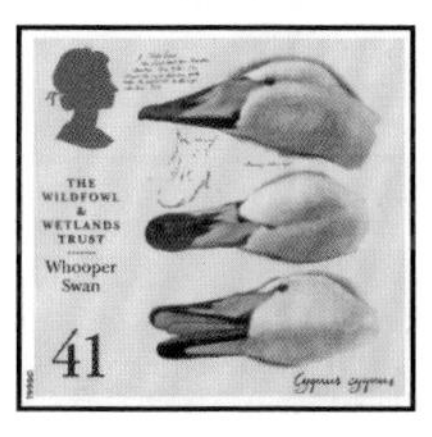

1996 (12 March) 50th Anniversary of Wildfowl and Wetlands Perf 14 x 14½

No.			U/M	F/U
C1194	**19p**	Muscovy Duck (1 band)	35	38
C1195	**25p**	Lapwing	45	48
C1196	**30p**	White-fronted Goose	50	55
C1197	**35p**	Bittern	62	67
C1198	**41p**	Whooper Swan	60	70
		Set of 5	2.20	2.35
		Set of 5 Cylinder Blocks	16.50	
		Set of 5 Gutter Pairs	5.50	5.50
		First Day Cover		2.50
		Presentation Pack 265	2.20	
		PHQ Cards	4.50	

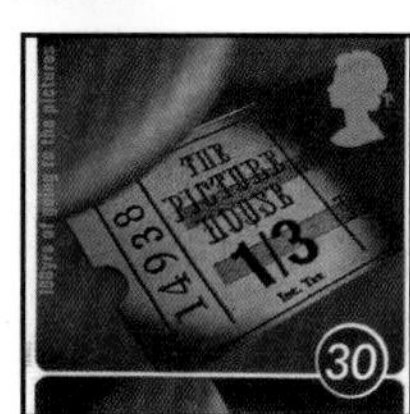

1996 (16 April) Centenary of Cinema Perf 14 x 14½

No.			U/M	F/U
C1199	**19p**	Cinema (1 band)	38	38
C1200	**25p**	Screen Kiss (2 bands)	45	48
C1201	**30p**	Ticket (2 bands)	50	55
C1202	**35p**	Pathe News (2 bands)	65	70
C1203	**41p**	Big Screen Showing (2 bands)	70	80
		Set of 5	2.30	2.50
		Set of 5 Cylinder Blocks	17.50	
		Set of 5 Gutter Pairs	5.75	5.75
		First Day Cover		2.50
		Presentation Pack 266	2.20	
		PHQ Cards	4.50	6.50

1996 (14 May) European Football Championship Perf 14½ x 14

No.			U/M	F/U
C1204	**19p**	Dixie Dean (1 band)	38	38
C1205	**25p**	Bobby Moore (2 bands)	45	48
C1206	**35p**	Duncan Edwards (2 bands)	50	55
C1207	**41p**	Billy Wright (2 bands)	65	75
C1208	**60p**	Danny Blanchflower (2 bands)	70	75
		Set of 5	2.30	2.50
		Set of 5 Cylinder Blocks	17.25	
		Set of 5 Gutter Pairs	5.75	5.75
		First Day Cover		2.50
		Presentation Pack 267	3.00	
		PHQ Cards	4.50	6.50

A

B

C

D

E

1996 (9 July) Olympics and Paralympics - Atlanta Perf. 14½ x 14

No.			U/M	F/U
C1209	**26p**	Sprint Start (2 bands) (A)	40	45
C1210	**26p**	Javelin (2 bands) (B)	40	45
C1211	**26p**	Basketball (2 bands) (C)	40	45
C1212	**26p**	Swimming (2 bands) (D)	40	45
C1213	**26p**	Victory (2 bands) (E)	40	45
		Strip of 5 se-tenant	2.00	2.25
		Cylinder Block		
		Gutter Block of 10	5.00	5.00
		First Day Cover		2.50
		Presentation Pack 268	2.00	
		PHQ Cards	4.50	6.50

Variety

	26p	Imperforate between stamp and left margin only (strip of five)	£750

A B C D E A

2005 (5 Aug.) London 2012 Host City

No.			U/M	F/U
C1209a	**1st**	Sprint Start (2 bands) (D)	40	45
C1210b	**1st**	Javelin (2 bands) (B)	40	45
C1211c	**1st**	Basketball (2 bands) (E)	40	45
C1212d	**1st**	Swimming (2 bands) (C)	40	45
C1213e	**1st**	Victory (2 bands) (A)	40	45
MS33		Complete Miniature Sheet	2.70	2.75
		First Day Cover		3.95
		Presentation Pack		
		PHQ Cards		

1996 (6 Aug.) Europa - Famous Women Perf 14

No.			U/M	F/U
C1214	**20p**	Dorothy Hodgkin (1 band)	30	30
C1215	**26p**	Margot Fonteyn (2 bands)	40	4
C1216	**31p**	Elisabeth Frink (2 bands)	45	50
C1217	**37p**	Daphne Du Maurier (2 bands)	60	70
C1218	**43p**	Marea Hartman (2 bands)	70	80
		Set of 5	2.45	2.55
		Set of 5 Cylinder Blocks	18.25	
		Set of 5 Gutter Pairs	6.20	6.20
		First Day Cover		2.50
		Presentation Pack 269	2.30	
		PHQ Cards	4.50	6.50

No.			U/M	F/U
Variety				
C1215a	26p	Imperforate pair	£300	

1996 (3 Sept.) 50th Anniversary of Children's Television Perf 14½ x 14

No.			U/M	F/U
C1219	**20p**	Muffin the Mule (1 band)	30	30
C1219a		Perf 15 x 14 ex Prestige book	2.50	
C1220	**26p**	Sooty (2 bands)	75	80
C1221	**31p**	Stingray (2 bands)	40	40
C1222	**37p**	Clangers (2 bands)	45	50
C1223	**43p**	Dangermouse (2 bands)	70	70
		Set of 5	2.65	2.65
		Set of 5 Cylinder Blocks	19.75	
		Set of 5 Gutter Pairs	6.75	6.75
		First Day Cover		2.50
		Presentation Pack 270	2.45	
		PHQ Cards	4.50	6.50

1996 (1 Oct.) Classic Sports Cars Perf 14½

No.			U/M	F/U
C1224	**20p**	Triumph (1 band)	30	30
C1225	**26p**	M. G. (2 bands)	40	40
C1226	**37p**	Austin Healey (2 bands)	45	50
C1227	**43p**	Jaguar (2 bands)	70	70
C1228	**63p**	Morgan (2 bands)	90	95
		Set of 5	2.55	2.65
		Set of 5 Cylinder Blocks	19.90	
		Set of 5 Gutter Pairs	6.40	6.40
		First Day Cover		2.50
		Presentation Pack 271	3.15	
		PHQ Cards	4.50	6.50
Varieties				
C1225a	26p	Imperforate pair	£600	
C1226a	37p	Imperforate pair	£750	
C1227a	43p	Imperforate pair	£1100	

1996 (28 Oct.) Christmas Perf 15 x 14

No.			U/M	F/U
C1229	**2nd**	Lo, The Star (1 band)	30	30
C1230	**1st**	Blessed are Thou.. (2 bands)	40	40
C1231	**31p**	Every one to his own City (2 bands)	45	50
C1232	**43p**	and shall be called the Son ...(2 bands)	70	70
C1233	**63p**	I bring you tidings of great joy (2 bands)	1.00	1.05
		Set of 5	2.55	2.65
		Set of 5 Cylinder Blocks	19.25	
		Set of 5 Gutter Pairs	6.40	6.40
		First Day Cover		2.50
		Presentation Pack 272	2.60	
		PHQ Cards	4.50	6.50

1996 (28 Oct.) Collectors Year Pack

No.		U/M	F/U
CP33	Collectors Year Pack 273	22.50	

1996 (28 Oct.) Royal Mail Year Book - 13

No.		U/M	F/U
YB13	Royal Mail Year Book	£23	

A

B

C

D

E

F

G

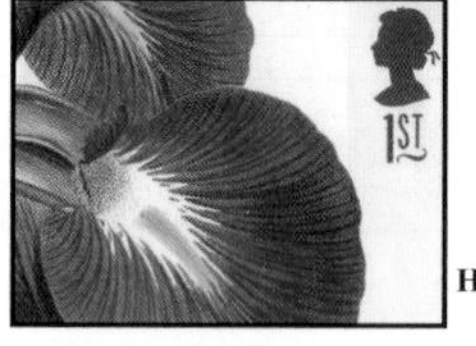

H

I

J

1997 (6 Jan.) "19th Century Flower Paintings". Perf. 14½ x 14 elliptical

No.			U/M	F/U
C1234	**1st**	Multicoloured (2 bands) (A)	55	60
C1235	**1st**	Multicoloured (2 bands) (B)	55	60
C1236	**1st**	Multicoloured (2 bands) (C)	55	60
C1237	**1st**	Multicoloured (2 bands) (D)	55	60
C1238	**1st**	Multicoloured (2 bands) (E)	55	60
C1239	**1st**	Multicoloured (2 bands) (F)	55	60
C1240	**1st**	Multicoloured (2 bands) (G)	55	60
C1241	**1st**	Multicoloured (2 bands) (H)	55	60
C1242	**1st**	Multicoloured (2 bands) (I)	55	60
C1243	**1st**	Multicoloured (2 bands) (J)	55	60
	1st	**Booklet pane of 10**	5.00	5.20
		Set of 10 singles		2.20
		First Day Cover		7.00
		Presentation Pack G6	9.50	
		PHQ Cards	4.50	6.50
Varieties				
		Gold & Phosphor missing (complete book)	£15000	
		Gold & Phosphor missing (pane only)	£8000	

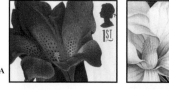

2003 (21 Jan.) 1st Flowers from Smilers sheet

No.		U/M	F/U
SSP11	1st Flowers *plus* label (any)	2.50	
SSP11a	Broad centre band	£50	

A

B

C

D

E

F

G

1997 (21 Jan.) 450th Death Anniversary of Henry VIII Perf. 15 (No. C1244) Perf 14 x 15 (Others)

No.			U/M	F/U
C1244	**26p**	King Henry VIII (A)	70	70
C1245	**26p**	Catherinr of Aragon (B)	50	55
C1246	**26p**	Anne Boleyn (C)	50	55
C1247	**26p**	Jane Seymour (D)	50	55
C1248	**26p**	Anne of Cleaves (E)	50	55
C1249	**26p**	Catherine Howard (F)	50	55
C1250	**26p**	Catherine Parr (G)	50	55
		Set of 7	3.20	3.20
		Se-tenant Strip of 6 C1245-C1250)	3.75	
		Set of 2 Cylinder Blocks	12.50	
		Gutter Pair & Gutter Strip of 12	8.00	8.00

No.			U/M	F/U
		First Day Cover		3.00
		Presentation Pack 274	4.50	
		PHQ Cards	6.00	8.00
Variety				
C1224	26p	King Henry VIII (A) Imperforate pair	£750	

1997 (11 March) Religious Anniversaries Perf 14½

No.			U/M	F/U
C1251	**26p**	St. Columbia in Boat	45	48
C1252	**37p**	St. Columbia on Iona	50	55
C1253	**43p**	St. Augustine with King Ethelbert	70	75
C1254	**63p**	St. Augustines with Model of Cathedral	1.00	1.05
		Set of 4	2.30	2.45
		Set of 4 Cylinder Blocks	17.25	
		Set of 4 Gutter Pairs	5.75	5.75
		First Day Cover		2.00
		Presentation Pack 275	2.35	
		PHQ Cards	3.50	5.50

Dracula

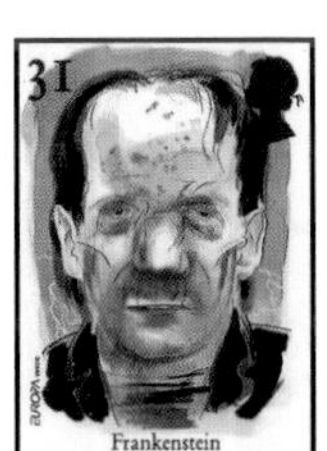
Frankenstein

Dr Jekyll and Mr Hyde

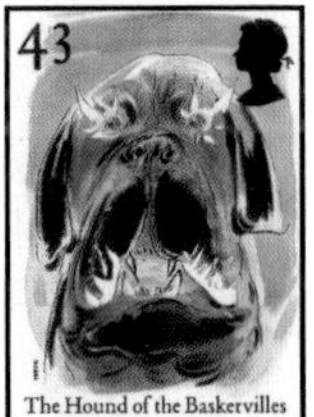
The Hound of the Baskervilles

1997 (13 May) Tales and Legends Perf 14 x 15 - 16mm bands

No.			U/M	F/U
C1255	**26p**	Dracula	1.50	48
C1255a		9mm bands	2.50	
C1256	**31p**	Frankenstein	60	65
C1257	**37p**	Dr Jekyll and Mr Hyde	60	75
C1258	**43p**	Hound of the Baskevilles	2.00	95
C1258a		9mm bands	2.50	
		Set of 4	2.40	2.40
		Set of 4 Cylinder Blocks	17.95	
		Set of 4 Gutter Pairs	6.00	6.00
		First Day Cover		2.50
		Presentation Pack 276	2.20	
		PHQ Cards	3.50	5.50

1997 (10 June) British Aircraft Designers Perf 15 x 14

No.			U/M	F/U
C1259	**20p**	Mitchell - Supermarine (1 band)	35	40
C1260	**26p**	Chadwick - Avro (2 bands)	45	48
C1261	**37p**	Bishop - De Havilland (2 bands)	50	55
C1262	**43p**	Carter - Gloster (2 bands)	80	85
C1263	**63p**	Camm - Hawker (2 bands)	1.10	1.15
		Set of 5	2.90	2.95
		Set of 5 Cylinder Blocks	21.50	
		Set of 5 Gutter Pairs	7.25	7.25
		First Day Cover		2.60
		Presentation Pack 277	3.70	
		PHQ Cards	3.50	5.50

1997 (8 July) 50th Anniversary of the British Horse Society Perf 14½

No.			U/M	F/U
C1264	**20p**	St. Patrick (1 band)	35	40
C1265	**26p**	River Star (2 bands)	45	48
C1266	**43p**	Thompson (2 bands)	70	75
C1267	**63p**	Janus (2 bands)	1.00	1.05
		Set of 4	2.20	2.35
		Set of 4 Cylinder Blocks	16.50	
		Set of 4 Gutter Pairs	5.50	5.50
		First Day Cover		2.60
		Presentation Pack 278	2.60	
		PHQ Cards	3.50	5.50

1997 (12 Aug.) Sub-Post Offices Perf 14½

No.			U/M	F/U
C1268	**20p**	Haroldswick (1 band)	35	40
C1269	**26p**	Painswick (2 bands)	45	48
C1270	**43p**	Beddgelert (2 bands)	70	75
C1271	**63p**	Ballyroney (2 bands)	1.00	1.15
		Set of 4	2.20	2.35
		Set of 4 Cylinder Blocks	16.50	
		Set of 4 Gutter Pairs	5.50	5.50
		First Day Cover		2.60
		Presentation Pack 279	2.60	
		PHQ Cards	3.50	5.50

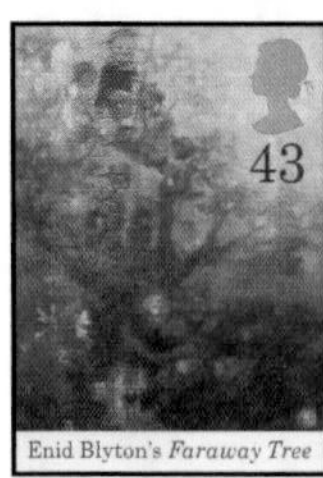

1997 (9 Sept.) Birth Centenary of Enid Blyton Perf 14 x 14½

No.			U/M	F/U
C1272	**20p**	Noddy (1 band)	35	40
C1273	**26p**	Famous Five (2 bands)	45	48
C1274	**37p**	Secret Seven (2 bands)	50	55
C1275	**43p**	Faraway Tree (2 bands)	80	85
C1276	**63p**	Malory Towers (2 bands)	1.00	1.25
		Set of 5	2.60	2.60
		Set of 5 Cylinder Blocks	19.50	
		Set of 5 Gutter Pairs	6.50	6.50
		First Day Cover		2.80
		Presentation Pack 280	2.60	
		PHQ Cards	4.25	6.25

1997 (27 Oct.) Christmas, 150th Anniversary of the Cracker Perf 15 x 14

No.			U/M	F/U
C1277	**2nd**	Santa 'in the Moon' (1 band)	35	40
C1278	**1st**	Santa 'Bursting out' (2 bands)	45	48
C1279	**31p**	Santa 'Riding a Cracker' (2 bands)	48	50
C1280	**43p**	Santa 'Riding a Snowball (2 bands)	70	75
C1281	**63p**	Santa ' Down the Chimney (2 bands)	1.10	1.05
		Set of 5	2.60	2.90
		Set of 5 Cylinder Blocks	19.50	
		Set of 5 Gutter Pairs	6.50	6.50
		First Day Cover		2.80
		Presentation Pack 281	2.60	
		PHQ Cards	2.40	4.40
Variety				
C1277a	2nd	Imperforate pair	£1250	
C1279a	31p	Imperforate pair	£1250	

2000 (3 Oct.) 1st Father Christmas from Smilers sheet

SSP3	Stamp *plus* label	£10

2002 (1 Oct.) 1st Father Christmas from Smilers sheet

No.			U/M	F/U
SSP10		Se-tenant pair *plus* label (any)	2.50	

1997 (13 Nov.) Royal Golden Wedding Perf 15

No.			U/M	F/U
C1282	**20p**	"Driver" - Sepia (1 band)	35	40
C1283	**26p**	"Snowdon" - Blue (2 bands)	45	48
C1284	**43p**	"Driver" - Grey (2 bands)	70	75
C1285	**63p**	"Snowdon" - Grey (2 bands)	1.00	1.15
		Set of 4	2.30	2.30
		Set of 4 Cylinder Blocks	17.25	
		Set of 4 Gutter Pairs	5.75	5.75
		First Day Cover		2.75
		Presentation Pack 282	3.15	
		PHQ Cards	2.00	4.00
Variety				
C1282a	20p	Imperforate pair	£2000	
C1283a	26p	Imperforate pair	£2500	

1997 (13 Nov.) Collectors Pack

		U/M
CP34	Collectors Year Pack 283	£30

1997 (13 Nov.) Royal Mail Year Book - 14

		U/M
CB14	Royal Mail Year Book	£25

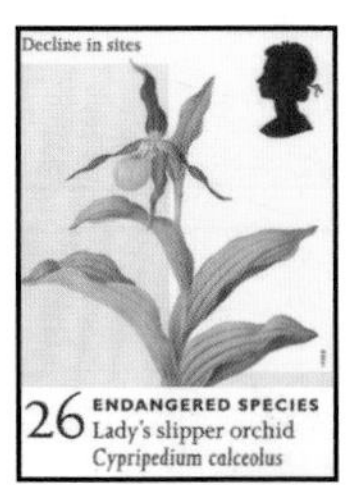

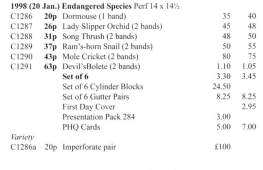

1998 (20 Jan.) Endangered Species Perf 14 x 14½

No.			U/M	F/U
C1286	**20p**	Dormouse (1 band)	35	40
C1287	**26p**	Lady Slipper Orchid (2 bands)	45	48
C1288	**31p**	Song Thrush (2 bands)	48	50
C1289	**37p**	Ram's-horn Snail (2 bands)	50	55
C1290	**43p**	Mole Cricket (2 bands)	80	75
C1291	**63p**	Devil'sBolete (2 bands)	1.10	1.05
		Set of 6	3.30	3.45
		Set of 6 Cylinder Blocks	24.50	
		Set of 6 Gutter Pairs	8.25	8.25
		First Day Cover		2.95
		Presentation Pack 284	3.00	
		PHQ Cards	5.00	7.00
Variety				
C1286a	20p	Imperforate pair	£100	

A

B

C

D

E

1998 (3 Feb.) Diana, Princess of Wales Perf 14 x 15

No.			U/M	F/U
C1292	**26p**	photo by Snowden (1 band)	55	48
C1293	**26p**	photo by John Stilwell (2 bands)	55	48
C1294	**26p**	photo by Snowden (2 bands)	55	48
C1295	**26p**	photo by Tim Graham (2 bands)	55	48
C1296	**26p**	photo by T. Donovan (2 bands)	55	48
		Strip of 5	2.20	2.10
		Cylinder Block	5.50	
		Gutter strip of 10	5.50	5.50
		First Day Cover		2.50
		Presentation Pack	4.00	
		Presentation Pack (Welsh version)	£57	
Variety				
	26p	Imperforate strip of five	£15000	

A

B

C

D

E

1998 (24 Feb.) The Queen's Beasts (2 bands) Perf 15 x 14

No.			U/M	F/U
C1297	**26p**	Lion of England (A)	40	48
C1298	**26p**	Falcon of Plantagenet (B)	40	48
C1299	**26p**	Lion of Mortimer (C)	40	48
C1300	**26p**	Greyhound of Richmond (D)	40	48
C1301	**26p**	Unicorn of Scotland (E)	40	48
		Strip of 5	2.30	2.40
		Cylinder Block	7.70	
		Gutter strip of 10	5.75	5.75
		First Day Cover		2.45
		Presentation Pack 285	2.20	
		PHQ Cards	4.00	6.00
Varieties				
C1297/01	26p	Green missing (strip of five)	£8500	
		Phosphor missing (strip of five)	£25	

1998 (24 Mar.) Lighthouses Perf 15 x 14

No.			U/M	F/U
C1302	**20p**	St. John's Point (1 band)	35	40
C1303	**26p**	The Smalls (2 bands)	45	48
C1304	**37p**	Needles Rock (2 bands)	50	55
C1305	**43p**	Bell Rock (2 bands)	70	75
C1306	**63p**	Eddystone (2 bands)	1.00	1.20
		Set of 5	2.55	2.55
		Set of 5 Cylinder Blocks	19.25	
		Set of 5 Gutter Pairs	6.40	6.80
		First Day Cover		2.70
		Presentation Pack 286	2.75	
		PHQ Cards	4.00	6.00

1998 (23 Apr.) Comedians Perf 15 x 14

No.			U/M	F/U
C1307	**20p**	Tommy Cooper (1 band)	35	40
C1308	**26p**	Eric Morcombe (2 bands)	45	48
C1309	**37p**	Joyce Grenfell (2 bands)	50	55
C1310	**43p**	Les Dawson (2 bands)	80	75
C1311	**63p**	Peter Cook (2 bands)	1.00	1.05
		Set of 5	2.65	2.70
		Set of 5 Cylinder Blocks	19.80	
		Set of 5 Gutter Pairs	6.70	6.70
		First Day Cover		2.70
		Presentation Pack 287	2.75	
		PHQ Cards	4.00	6.00
Varieties				
C1307a	20p	Vermillion printed double	£1500	
C1308a	26p	Vermillion printed double	£250	
C1309a	30p	Value error (mint & FDC)	£1450	£1800

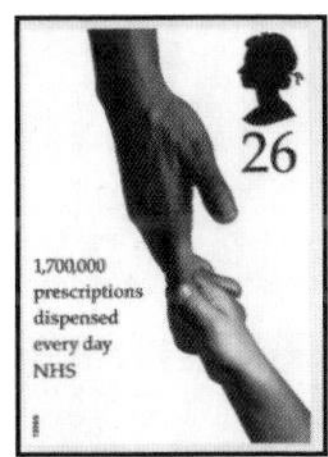

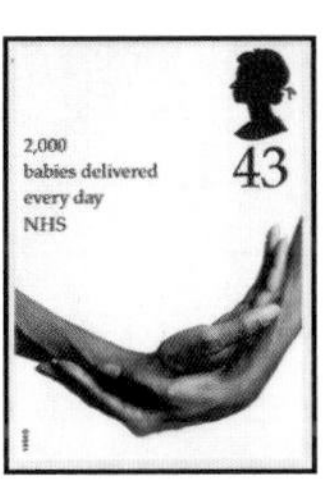

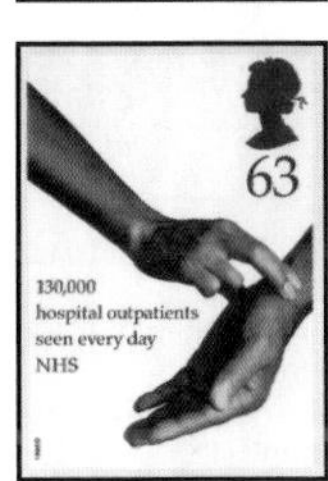

1998 (23 June) 50 Years of NHS Perf 15 x 14

No.			U/M	F/U
C1312	**20p**	10,000 Donors (1 band)	35	40
C1313	**26p**	1,700,000 Prescriptions (2 bands)	45	48
C1314	**43p**	2,000 Babies (2 bands)	70	75
C1315	**63p**	130,000 Outpatients (2 bands)	1.20	1.35
		Set of 4	2.40	2.40
		Set of 4 Cylinder Blocks	17.80	
		Set of 4 Gutter Pairs	6.00	6.00
		First Day Cover		3.00
		Presentation Pack 288	2.40	
		PHQ Cards	4.00	6.00

1998 (21 July) Magical Worlds Perf 15 x 14

No.			U/M	F/U
C1316	**20p**	The Hobbit (1 band)	35	40
C1317	**26p**	Lion, Witch and Wardrobe (2 bands)	45	48
C1318	**37p**	The Phoenix and the Carpet (2 bands)	50	55
C1319	**43p**	The Borrowers (2 bands)	70	85
C1320	**63p**	Through the Looking Glass (2 bands)	1.20	1.35
		Set of 5	2.80	2.60
		Set of 5 Cylinder Blocks	21.50	
		Set of 5 Gutter Pairs	7.00	7.00
		First Day Cover		3.40
		Presentation Pack 289	2.70	
		PHQ Cards	4.00	6.00
Variety				
C1317a	26p	Imperforate pair	£750	

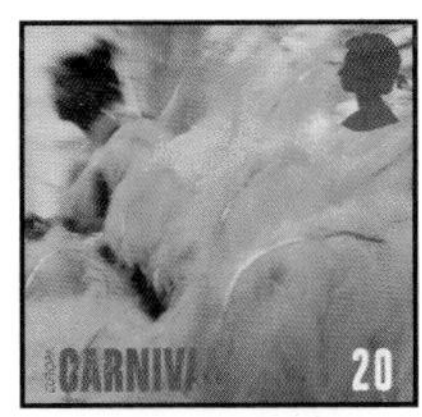

1998 (25 Aug.) Europa Carnival Perf 15 x 14

No.			U/M	F/U
C1321	**20p**	Woman in Yellow (1 band)	35	40
C1322	**26p**	Woman in Blue (2 bands)	45	48
C1323	**43p**	Children (2 bands)	70	75
C1324	**63p**	Child in Green (2 bands)	1.00	1.25
		Set of 4	2.30	2.25
		Set of 4 Cylinder Blocks	16.95	
		Set of 4 Gutter Pairs	5.75	5.75
		First Day Cover		3.00
		Presentation Pack 290	2.40	
		PHQ Cards	4.00	6.00
Variety				
C1321a	20p	Imperforate pair		

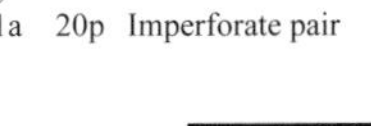

1998 (29 Sep.) Speed Perf 15 x 14

No.			U/M	F/U
C1324	**20p**	Sir Malcolm Campbell (1 centre band)	35	40
C1324a	**20p**	Left band	1.25	1.25
C1324b	**20p**	Right band	1.25	1.25
C1325	**26p**	Sir Henry Seagrave (2 bands)	45	48
C1326	**30p**	John G. Parry Thomas (2 bands)	50	55
C1327	**43p**	John R. Cobb (2 bands)	80	75
C1328	**63p**	Donald Campbell (2 bands)	1.10	1.05
		Set of 5	2.75	2.90
		Set of 5 Cylinder Blocks	21.25	
		Set of 5 Gutter Pairs	6.90	6.90
		First Day Cover		3.00
		Presentation Pack 291	2.95	
		PHQ Cards	4.00	6.00
Variety				
C1325a	26p	Missing Rosine	£2250	

C1324a and C1324b are Perf 14 x 13 and are from 'Breaking Barriers' Prestige Book issued 13th Oct. 1998)

1998 (2 Nov.) Christmas Perf 15 x 14

No.			U/M	F/U
C1329	**20p**	Adoring Angel (1 band)	35	40
C1330	**26p**	Praying Angel (2 bands)	45	48
C1331	**30p**	Angel Playing Pipe (2 bands)	50	55
C1332	**43p**	Angel Playing Lute (2 bands)	80	75
C1333	**63p**	Angel in Prayer (2 bands)	1.00	1.05
		Set of 5	2.75	2.90
		Set of 5 Cylinder Blocks	20.50	
		Set of 5 Gutter Pairs	6.90	6.90
		First Day Cover		3.00
		Presentation Pack 292	2.80	
		PHQ Cards	4.50	6.50
Variety				
C1329a	20p	Imperforate pair	£400	
C1330a	26p	Imperforate pair	£1300	
C1332a	43p	Imperforate pair	£1300	

1998 (2 Nov.) Collectors Year Pack

No.		U/M	F/U
CP35	Collectors Year Pack 293	32.50	

1998 (2 Nov.) Royal Mail Year Book - 15

No.		U/M	F/U
CB15	Royal Mail Year Book	32.50	

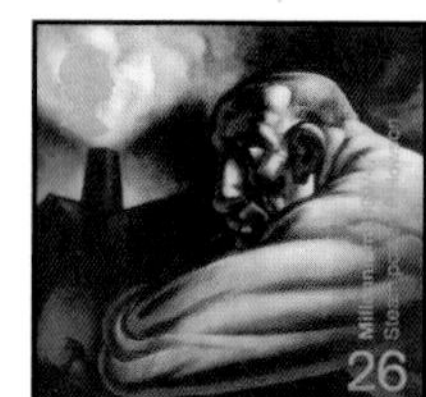

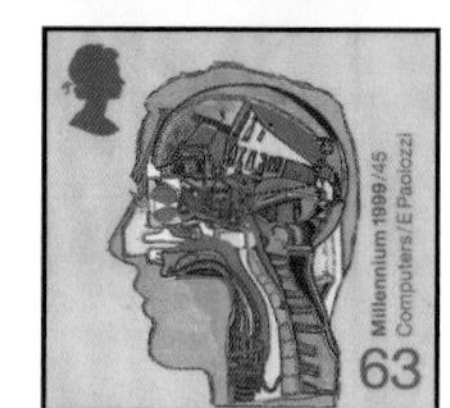

1999 (12 Jan.) Inventors Tale Perf 15 x 14

No.			U/M	F/U
C1334	**20p**	Timekeeping (1 band)	35	40
C1335	**26p**	Steam Power (2 bands)	45	48
C1336	**43p**	Photography (2 bands)	80	80
C1337	**63p**	Computers (2 bands)	1.30	1.30
		Set of 4	2.70	2.70
		Set of 4 Cylinder Blocks	20.00	
		Set of 4 Gutter Pairs	6.75	6.75
		First Day Cover		3.50
		Presentation Pack 294	3.45	
		PHQ Cards	4.50	6.50
Variety				
C1334a	20p	Imperforate pair	£1350	

Perf 13 x 14 - From The World Changers Prestige Book - 21 Sep 1999

No.			U/M	F/U
C1337a	**63p**	Perf 13 x 14	2.00	2.10

1999 (2 Feb.) Travellers Tale Perf 14 x 15

No.			U/M	F/U
C1338	**20p**	Jet Travel (1 band)	35	40
C1339	**26p**	Liberation by Bike (2 bands)	45	48
C1340	**43p**	Linking the Nation (2 bands)	80	80
C1341	**63p**	Cook's Endeavour (2 bands)	1.30	1.50
		Set of 4	2.70	2.70
		Set of 4 Cylinder Blocks	20.00	
		Set of 4 Gutter Pairs	6.75	6.75
		First Day Cover		3.50
		Presentation Pack 295	3.45	
		PHQ Cards	4.50	6.50

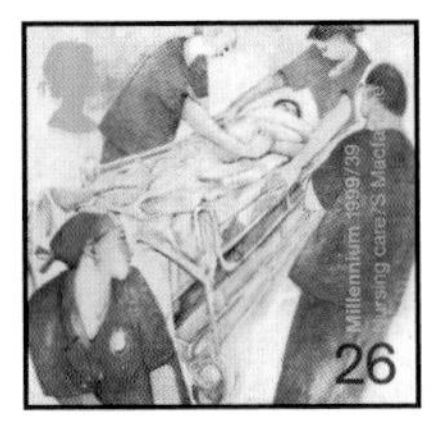

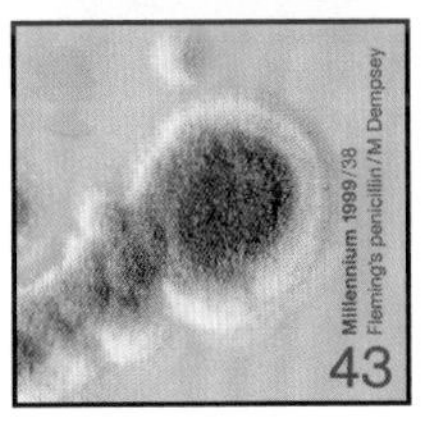

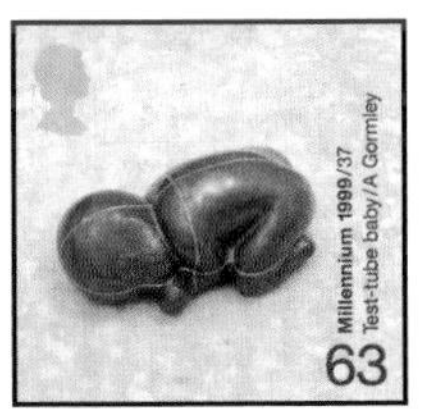

1999 (2 Mar.) Patients Tale Perf 13 x 14

No.			U/M	F/U
C1342	**20p**	Jenner's Vacination (1 band)	35	40
C1343	**26p**	Nursing Care (2 bands)	45	48
C1344	**43p**	Fleming's Penicillin (2 bands)	80	75
C1345	**63p**	Test Tube Baby (2 bands)	1.30	1.30
		Set of 4	2.70	2.70
		Set of 4 Cylinder Blocks	20.00	
		Set of 4 Gutter Pairs	6.75	6.75
		First Day Cover		3.50
		Presentation Pack 296	3.45	
		PHQ Cards	4.50	6.50
Variety				
C1343a	26p	Imperforate pair	£1450	

1999 (6 April) Settler's Tale Perf 14 x 15

No.			U/M	F/U
C1346	**20p**	Migration to Scotland (1 band)	35	40
C1347	**26p**	Pilgrim Fathers (2 bands)	45	48
C1348	**43p**	Destination Australia (2 bands)	80	80
C1349	**63p**	Migration to U.K. (2 bands)	1.30	1.30
		Set of 4	2.70	2.60
		Set of 4 Cylinder Blocks	20.00	
		Set of 4 Gutter Pairs	6.75	6.75
		First Day Cover		3.50
		Presentation Pack 297	3.45	
		PHQ Cards	4.50	6.50
Variety				
C1347a	26p	Imperforate pair	£750	

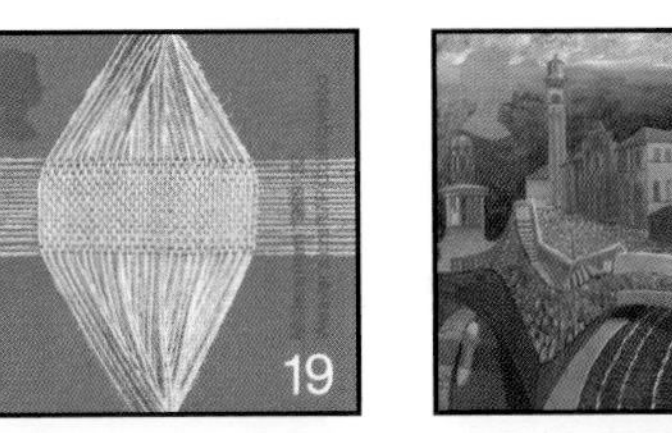

1999 (4 May) Worker's Tale Perf 14 x 15

No.			U/M	F/U
C1350	**19p**	Weaverscraft (1 band)	35	40
C1351	**26p**	Mill Towns (2 bands)	45	48
C1352	**44p**	Ship Building (2 bands)	80	80
C1353	**64p**	City Finance (2 bands)	1.30	1.30
		Set of 4	2.70	2.70
		Set of 4 Cylinder Blocks	20.00	
		Set of 4 Gutter Pairs	6.75	6.75
		First Day Cover		3.50
		Presentation Pack 298	3.45	
		PHQ Cards	4.50	6.50
Varieties				
C1350a	19p	Missing Bronze	£300	
C1350b	19p	Missing Bronze & Phosphor	£300	

1999 (1 June) Entertainers's Tale Perf 14 x 15

No.			U/M	F/U
C1354	**19p**	Mercury's Magic (1 band)	35	40
C1355	**26p**	World Cup (2 bands)	45	48
C1356	**44p**	Dr. Who (2 bands)	80	80
C1357	**64p**	Chaplin's Genius (2 bands)	1.30	1.30
		Set of 4	2.70	2.60
		Set of 4 Cylinder Blocks	20.00	
		Set of 4 Gutter Pairs	6.75	6.75
		First Day Cover		3.50
		Presentation Pack 299	3.45	
		PHQ Cards	4.50	6.50

1999 (15 June) Royal Wedding Perf 14 x 15

No.			U/M	F/U
C1358	**26p**	Portrait (2 bands)	50	55
C1359	**64p**	Profile (2 bands)	1.30	1.30
		Set of 2	1.60	1.70
		Set of 2 Cylinder Blocks	11.25	
		Set of 2 Gutter Pairs	4.00	4.00
		First Day Cover		2.50
		Presentation Pack MO1	1.70	
		PHQ Cards	5.50	6.50
Variety				
C1358a	26p	Imperforate pair	£750	

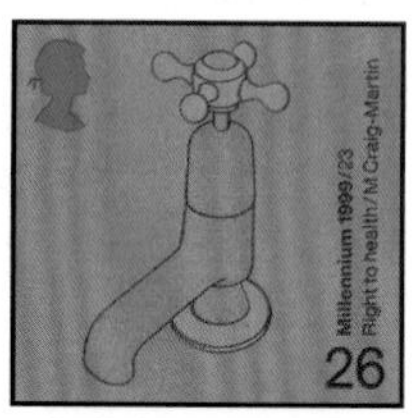

1999 (6 July) Citizens's Tale Perf 14 x 15

No.			U/M	F/U
C1360	**19p**	Equal Rights (1 band)	35	40
C1361	**26p**	Right to Health (2 bands)	45	48
C1362	**44p**	Right to Learn (2 bands)	80	80
C1363	**64p**	First Rights (2 bands)	1.30	1.40
		Set of 4	2.70	2.60
		Set of 4 Cylinder Blocks	20.00	
		Set of 4 Gutter Pairs	6.75	6.75
		First Day Cover		3.50
		Presentation Pack 300	3.45	
		PHQ Cards	5.00	7.00

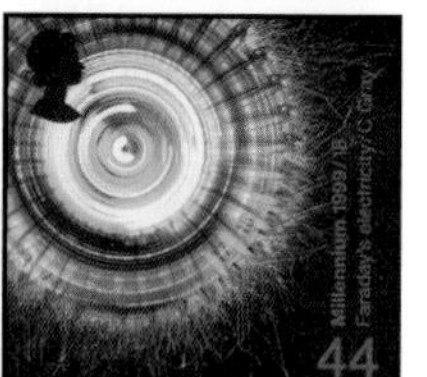

1999 (3 Aug.) Scientist's Tale Perf 13 x 14

No.			U/M	F/U
C1364	**19p**	Decoding DNA (1 band)	35	40
C1365	**26p**	Darwin's Theory (2 bands)	45	48
C1366	**44p**	Faraday's Electricity (2 bands)	80	80
C1367	**64p**	Newton/Hubble (2 bands)	1.30	1.30
		Set of 4	2.70	2.60
		Set of 4 Cylinder Blocks	20.00	
		Set of 4 Gutter Pairs	6.75	6.75
		First Day Cover		3.50
		Presentation Pack 301	3.45	
		PHQ Cards	5.00	7.00
Variety				
C1365a	26p	Imperforate pair	£750	

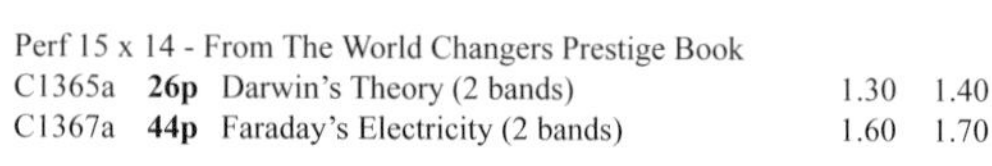

Perf 15 x 14 - From The World Changers Prestige Book

No.			U/M	F/U
C1365a	**26p**	Darwin's Theory (2 bands)	1.30	1.40
C1367a	**44p**	Faraday's Electricity (2 bands)	1.60	1.70

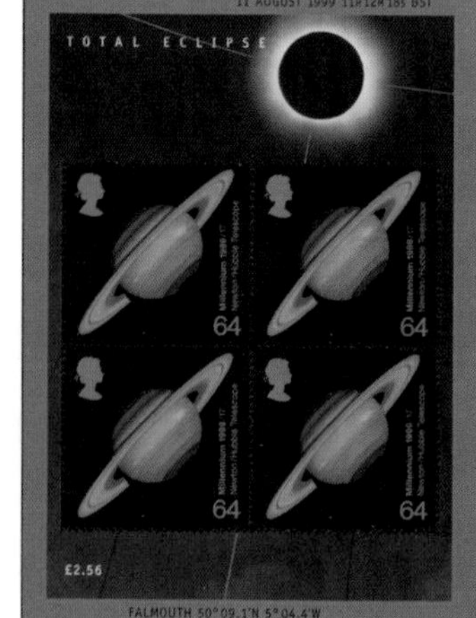

1999 (11 Aug.) Solar Eclipse Miniature sheet Perf 14 x 15

No.			U/M	F/U
MS7	**4 x 64p**	Multicoloured (2 bands)	12.50	12.50
		First Day Cover		12.50
Variety				
MS7A		Impeforate sheet (Mint & FDC)	£3250	£1750

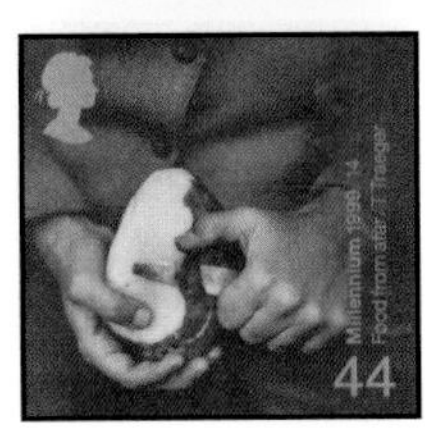

1999 (7 Sep.) Farmers's Tale Perf 14 x 15

No.			U/M	F/U
C1368	**19p**	Upland Landscapes (1 band)	35	40
C1369	**26p**	Horse Plough (2 bands)	45	48
C1370	**44p**	Man Peeling Potato (2 bands)	80	80
C1371	**64p**	Harvester (2 bands)	1.30	1.30
		Set of 4	2.60	2.20
		Set of 4 Cylinder Blocks	19.50	
		Set of 4 Gutter Pairs	6.50	6.50
		First Day Cover		3.50
		Presentation Pack 302	3.45	
		PHQ Cards	5.00	7.00

1999 (5 Oct.) Soldiers's Tale Perf 14 x 15

No.			U/M	F/U
C1372	**19p**	Robert the Bruce (1 band)	35	40
C1373	**26p**	Cavalier and Horse (2 bands)	45	48
C1374	**44p**	War Graves (2 bands)	80	80
C1375	**64p**	Peacekeeping (2 bands)	1.30	1.30
		Set of 4	2.60	2.70
		Set of 4 Cylinder Blocks	19.50	
		Set of 4 Gutter Pairs	6.50	6.50
		First Day Cover		3.50
		Presentation Pack 303	3.45	
		PHQ Cards	5.00	7.00

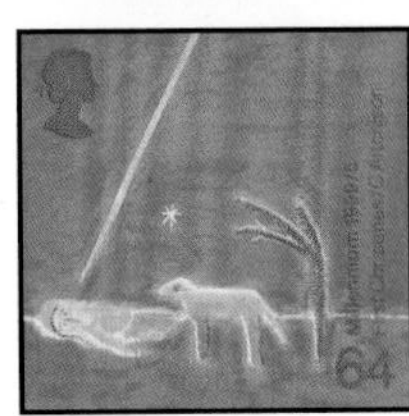

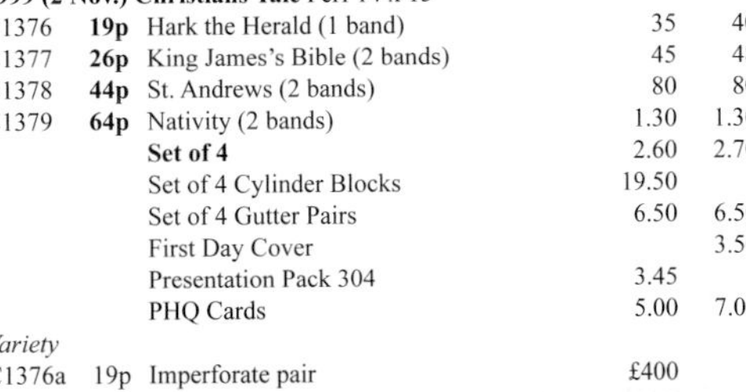

1999 (2 Nov.) Christians Tale Perf 14 x 15

No.			U/M	F/U
C1376	**19p**	Hark the Herald (1 band)	35	40
C1377	**26p**	King James's Bible (2 bands)	45	48
C1378	**44p**	St. Andrews (2 bands)	80	80
C1379	**64p**	Nativity (2 bands)	1.30	1.30
		Set of 4	2.60	2.70
		Set of 4 Cylinder Blocks	19.50	
		Set of 4 Gutter Pairs	6.50	6.50
		First Day Cover		3.50
		Presentation Pack 304	3.45	
		PHQ Cards	5.00	7.00
Variety				
C1376a	19p	Imperforate pair	£400	

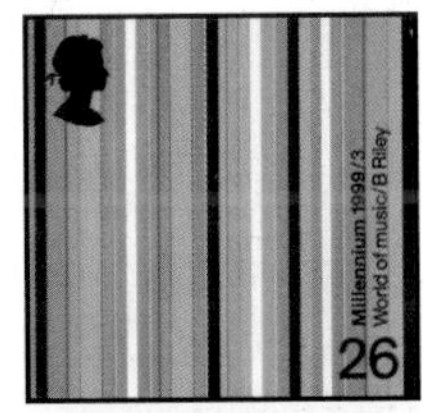

1999 (7 Dec.) Artists Tale Perf 14 x 15

No.			U/M	F/U
C1380	**19p**	World of Stage (1 band)	35	40
C1381	**26p**	World of Music (2 bands)	45	48
C1382	**44p**	World of Literature (2 bands)	80	80
C1383	**64p**	New Worlds (2 bands)	1.30	1.30
		Set of 4	2.60	2.70
		Set of 4 Cylinder Blocks	19.50	
		Set of 4 Gutter Pairs	6.50	6.50
		First Day Cover		3.50
		Presentation Pack 305	3.45	
		PHQ Cards	4.50	6.50

1999 (7 Dec.) Collectors Year Pack

No.		U/M	F/U
CP36	Collectors Year Pack 306	42.50	

1999 (7 Dec.) Royal Mail Year Book - 16

No.		U/M	F/U
YB16	Royal Mail Year Book	49.50	

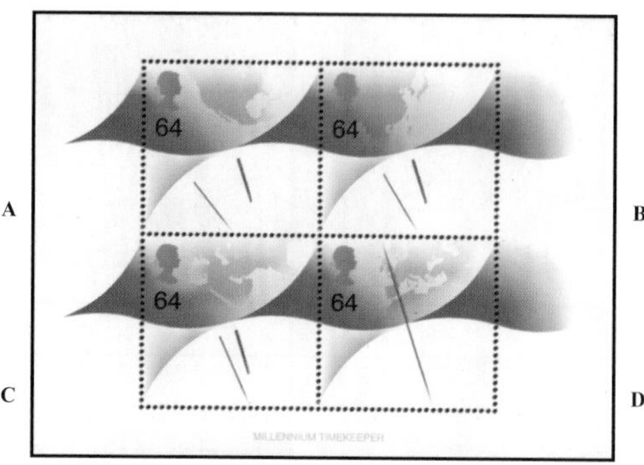

1999 (14 Dec.) Millennium Timekeeper Perf 14 x 15

No.			U/M	F/U
C1384	**64p**	Clockface (2 bands) A	1.30	1.30
C1385	**64p**	Clockface (2 bands) B	1.30	1.30
C1386	**64p**	Clockface (2 bands) C	1.30	1.30
C1387	**64p**	Clockface (2 bands) D	1.30	1.30
		First Day Cover		11.50
		Presentation Pack MO2	£24	
		PHQ Cards	9.00	
MS8	**4 x 64p**	Miniature sheeet	11.50	
MS9	**4 x 64p**	Stamp Show 2000 overprint (22.5.00)	12.50	

2000 (18 Jan.) Millennium 2000 - Above and Beyond Perf 14 x 15

No.			U/M	F/U
C1388	**19p**	Barn Owl (1 band)	35	40
C1389	**26p**	Night Sky (2 bands)	45	48
C1390	**1st**	Night Sky (2 bands) From 'Across the Universe' Prestige Book	2.50	2.50
C1391	**44p**	River Gayte and Mills (2 bands)	80	80
C1392	**64p**	Cape Gannets (2 bands)	1.30	1.30
		Set of 4	2.60	2.50
		Set of 4 Cylinder Blocks	19.50	
		Set of 4 Gutter Pairs	6.50	6.50
		First Day Cover		3.50
		Presentation Pack 307	3.45	
		PHQ Cards	4.50	6.50

C1390 and C1402

		U/M	F/U
	Se-Tenant pair with margins but from 10 x 1st Millennium book	3.50	

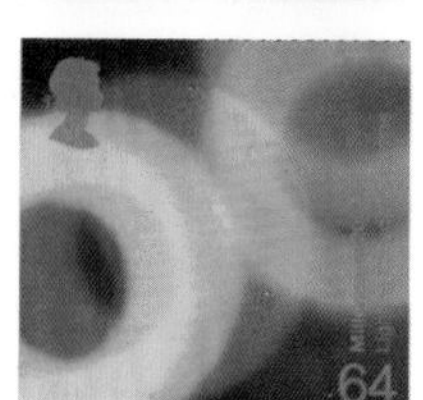

2000 (1 Feb.) Millennium 2000 - Fire and Light Perf 14 x 15

No.			U/M	F/U
C1393	**19p**	Beacons (1 band)	35	40
C1394	**26p**	Phelyffordd Eryri (2 bands)	45	48
C1395	**44p**	Dynamic Earth (2 bands)	80	80
C1396	**64p**	Lighting Croydons Skyline (2 bands)	1.30	1.10
		Set of 4	2.50	2.50
		Set of 4 Cylinder Blocks	18.75	
		Set of 4 Gutter Pairs	6.25	6.25
		First Day Cover		3.50
		Presentation Pack 308	3.45	
		PHQ Cards	4.50	6.50

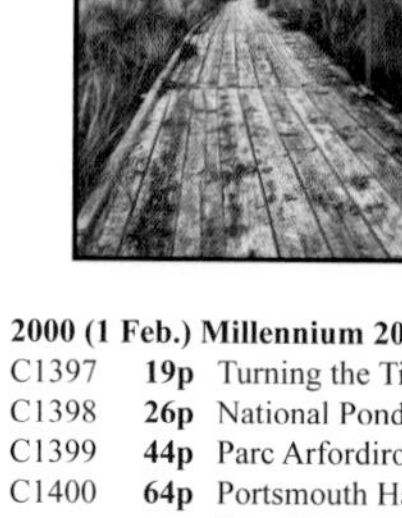

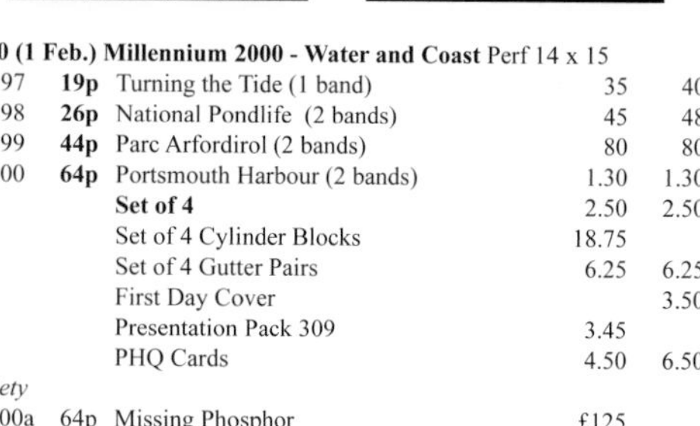

2000 (1 Feb.) Millennium 2000 - Water and Coast Perf 14 x 15

No.			U/M	F/U
C1397	**19p**	Turning the Tide (1 band)	35	40
C1398	**26p**	National Pondlife (2 bands)	45	48
C1399	**44p**	Parc Arfordirol (2 bands)	80	80
C1400	**64p**	Portsmouth Harbour (2 bands)	1.30	1.30
		Set of 4	2.50	2.50
		Set of 4 Cylinder Blocks	18.75	
		Set of 4 Gutter Pairs	6.25	6.25
		First Day Cover		3.50
		Presentation Pack 309	3.45	
		PHQ Cards	4.50	6.50

Variety

C1400a	64p	Missing Phosphor	£125	

No.			U/M	F/U

2000 (4 Apr.) Millennium 2000 - Life and Earth Perf 14 x 15

No.			U/M	F/U
C1401	**2nd**	ECOS (1 band)	35	40
C1402	**1st**	Web of Life (2 bands)	45	48
C1403	**44p**	Earth Centre (2 bands)	80	80
C1404	**64p**	Project SUZY (2 bands)	1.30	1.30
		Set of 4	2.50	2.60
		Set of 4 Cylinder Blocks	18.75	
		Set of 4 Gutter Pairs	6.25	6.25
		First Day Cover		3.50
		Presentation Pack 310	3.45	
		PHQ Cards	4.50	6.50

C1390 and C1402				
		Se-Tenant pair with margins but from 10 x 1st Millennium book	3.50	

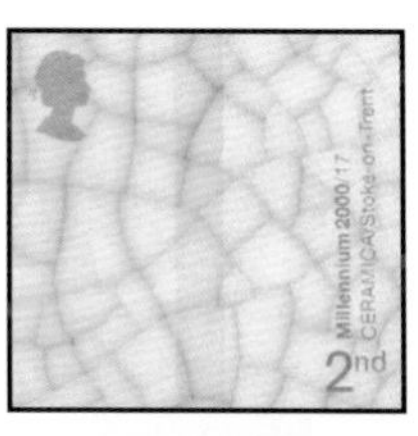

2000 (2 May) Millennium 2000 - Arts and Craft Perf 14 x 15

No.			U/M	F/U
C1405	**2nd**	Cermaica (1 band)	35	40
C1406	**1st**	Tate Modern (2 bands)	45	48
C1407	**45p**	Cycle Network (2 bands)	80	80
C1408	**65p**	The Lowry (2 bands)	1.10	1.10
		Set of 4	2.60	2.70
		Set of 4 Cylinder Blocks	19.50	
		Set of 4 Gutter Pairs	6.50	6.50
		First Day Cover		3.50
		Presentation Pack 311	3.45	
		PHQ Cards	4.50	6.50

2000 (22 May) Stamp Show 2000 Jeffrey Matthews Colour Pallette
Perf 15 x 14

No.		U/M	F/U
MS10	Complete miniature sheet	11.50	11.50
MS10a	Souvenir Wallet	18.00	

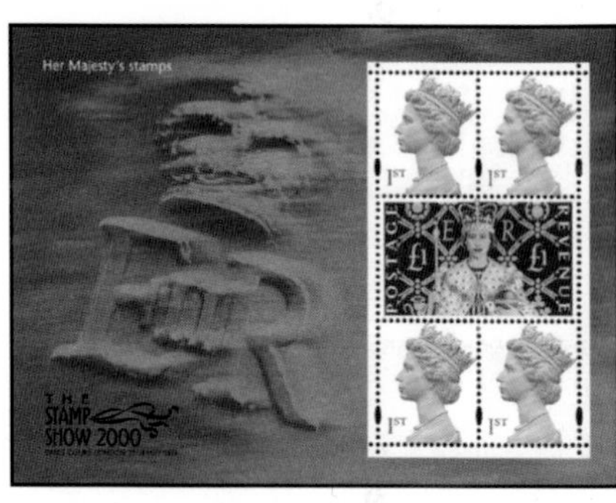

2000 (23 May) Stamp Show 2000 Her Majesty's Stamps
Perf 15 x 14

No.		U/M	F/U
MS11	Complete miniature sheet	11.50	12.50
	Presentation Pack MO3	47.50	

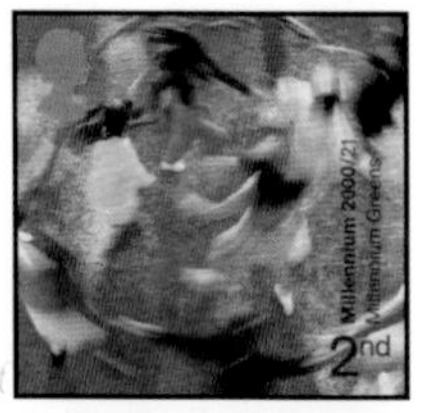

2000 (6 June) Millennium 2000 - People and Places Perf 14 x 15

No.			U/M	F/U
C1409	**2nd**	Millennium Greens (1 band)	35	40
C1410	**1st**	Millennium Bridge, Gateshead (2 bands)	48	53
C1411	**45p**	Mile End Park, London (2 bands)	80	80
C1412	**65p**	On the Meridian Line (2 bands)	1.10	1.10
		Set of 4	2.60	2.70
		Set of 4 Cylinder Blocks	19.50	
		Set of 4 Gutter Pairs	6.50	6.50
		First Day Cover		3.60
		Presentation Pack 312	3.45	
		PHQ Cards	4.50	6.50

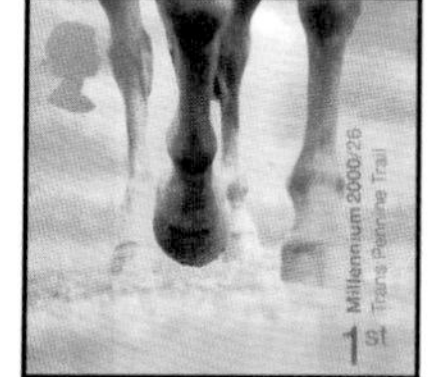

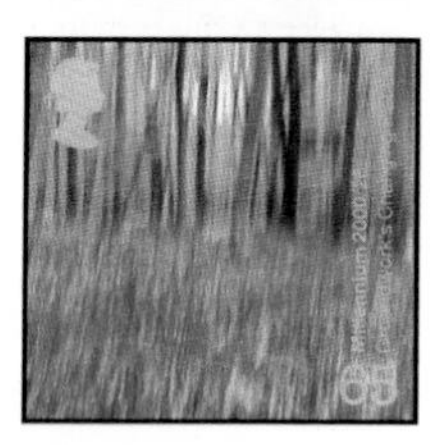

2000 (4 July) Millennium 2000 - Stone and Soil Perf 14 x 15

No.			U/M	F/U
C1413	**2nd**	Strangford Stone (1 band)	35	40
C1414	**1st**	Trans Penine Trail (2 bands)	48	53
C1415	**45p**	Cyclist (2 bands)	80	80
C1416	**65p**	Bluebell Wood (2 bands)	1.20	1.10
		Set of 4	2.50	2.60
		Set of 4 Cylinder Blocks	18.75	
		Set of 4 Gutter Pairs	6.25	6.25
		First Day Cover		3.60
		Presentation Pack 313	3.45	
		PHQ Cards	4.50	6.50

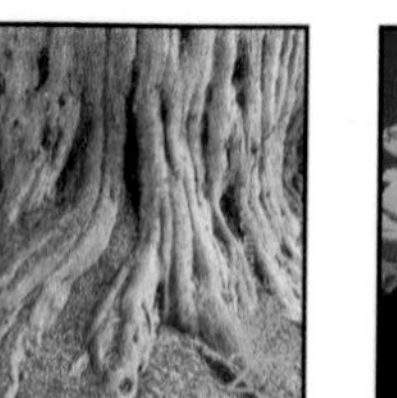

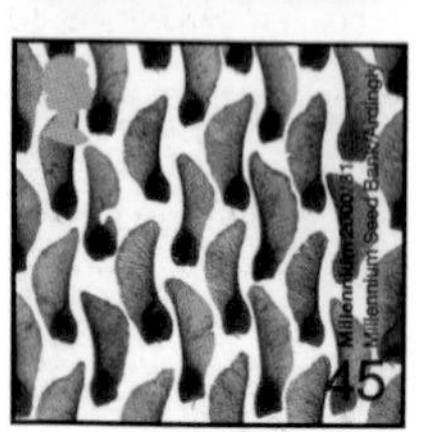

2000 (1 Aug.) Millennium 2000 - Tree and Leaf Perf 14 x 15

No.			U/M	F/U
C1417	**2nd**	Yews (1 band)	35	40
C1418	**1st**	Eden Project (2 bands)	48	53
C1419	**45p**	Seed Bank (2 bands)	80	80
C1420	**65p**	Forest for Scotland (2 bands)	1.10	1.10
		Set of 4	2.60	2.70
		Set of 4 Cylinder Blocks	19.50	
		Set of 4 Gutter Pairs	6.50	6.50
		First Day Cover		3.60
		Presentation Pack 314	3.45	
		PHQ Cards	4.50	6.50

2000 (4 Aug.) Queen Mother's Birthday Perf 15

No.			U/M	F/U
C1421	27p	Queen Mother	3.50	3.50
C1422	27p	Queen Elizabeth II	1.20	1.30
C1423	27p	Prince Charles	1.20	1.30
C1424	27p	Prince William	1.20	1.30
MS12		Complete Miniature sheet	6.50	7.00
		Pane from Prestige Book (4 x C1421)	4.60	5.00
		Pane from Prestige Book (C1421-C1424)	5.00	6.00
		First Day Cover		8.50
		Presentation Pack MO4	11.95	
		PHQ Cards	8.50	
Variety				
MS12a		Imperforate miniature sheet	£3750	

All of the above are from 'The Life of the Century' Prestige book and miniature sheet only.

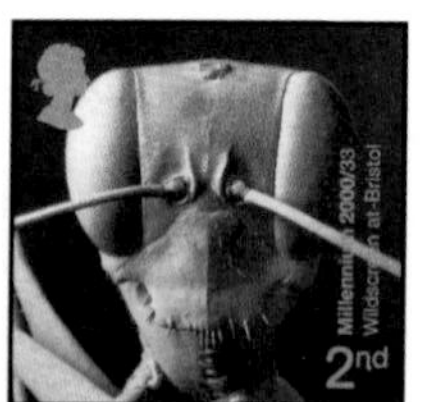

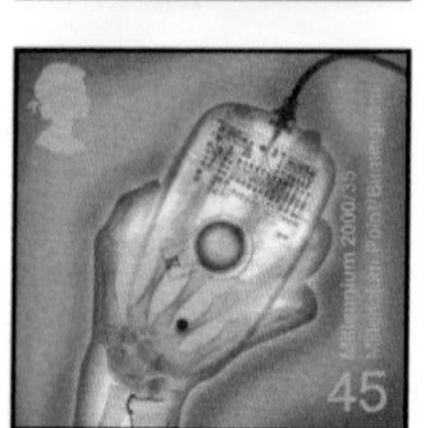

2000 (1 Aug.) Millennium 2000 - Mind and Matter Perf 14 x 15

No.			U/M	F/U
C1425	**2nd**	Wildscreen of Bristol (1 band)	35	40
C1426	**1st**	Norfolk & Norwich Project (2 bands)	48	53
C1427	**45p**	Millennium Point (2 bands)	80	80
C1428	**65p**	SCRAN (2 bands)	1.10	1.10
		Set of 4	2.60	2.70
		Set of 4 Cylinder Blocks	19.50	
		Set of 4 Gutter Pairs	6.50	6.50
		First Day Cover		3.60
		Presentation Pack 315	3.45	
		PHQ Cards	4.00	6.00

No.			U/M	F/U

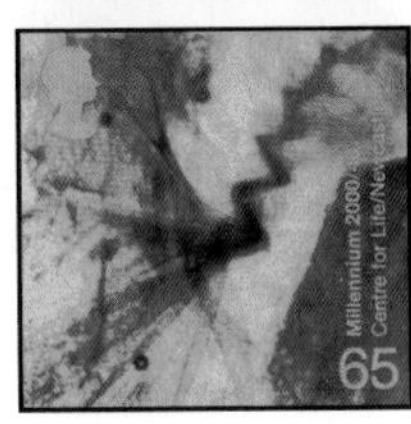

2000 (3 Oct.) Millennium 2000 - Body and Bone
Perf 14 x 15 (C1305) or 13 x 14

No.			U/M	F/U
C1429	**2nd**	Body/The Dome (1 band)	35	40
C1430	**1st**	Hampden Park/Glasgow (2 bands)	48	53
C1431	**45p**	Bath Spa (2 bands)	80	80
C1432	**65p**	Centre for Life (2 bands)	1.10	1.10
		Set of 4	2.60	2.70
		Set of 4 Cylinder Blocks	19.50	
		Set of 4 Gutter Pairs	6.50	6.50
		First Day Cover		3.60
		Presentation Pack 316	3.45	
		PHQ Cards	4.00	6.00

2000 (7 Nov.) Millennium 2000 - Spirit and Faith Perf 14 x 15

No.			U/M	F/U
C1433	**2nd**	St. Edmundsbury (1 band)	35	40
C1434	**1st**	Church Floodlighting (2 bands)	48	53
C1435	**45p**	St. Pattrick Centre (2 bands)	80	80
C1436	**65p**	Mystery Plays/York (2 bands)	1.10	1.10
		Set of 4	2.60	2.70
		Set of 4 Cylinder Blocks	19.50	
		Set of 4 Gutter Pairs	6.50	6.50
		First Day Cover		3.60
		Presentation Pack 317	3.45	
		PHQ Cards	4.00	6.00

Variety

C1433a	2nd	Imperforate pair	£525	
C1434a	1st	Imperforate pair	£500	

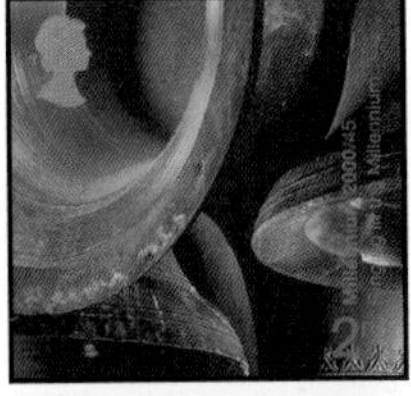
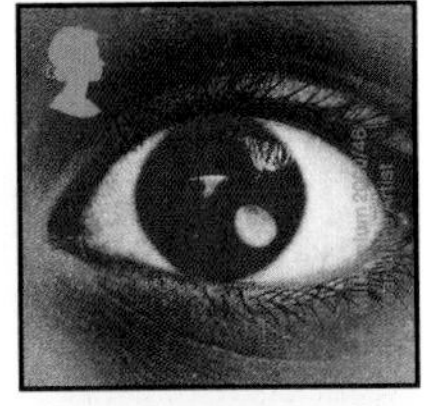

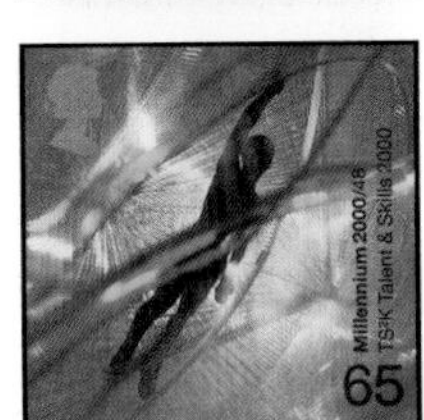

2000 (5 Dec.) Millennium 2000 - Sound and Vision Perf 14 x 15

No.			U/M	F/U
C1437	**2nd**	Ringing in Millennium (1 band)	35	40
C1438	**1st**	Year of the Artist (2 bands)	48	53
C1439	**45p**	Canolff Mileniwn/Cardiff (2 bands)	80	80
C1440	**65p**	TS2K Talent and Skill (2 bands)	1.10	1.10
		Set of 4	2.60	2.70
		Set of 4 Cylinder Blocks	19.50	
		Set of 4 Gutter Pairs	6.50	6.50
		First Day Cover		3.60
		Presentation Pack 318	3.45	
		PHQ Cards	4.00	6.00

2000 (5 Dec.) Collectors Year Pack

CP37	Collectors Year Pack 319	42.50	

2000 (5 Dec.) Royal Mail Year Book - 17

YB17	Royal Mail Year Book	49.50	

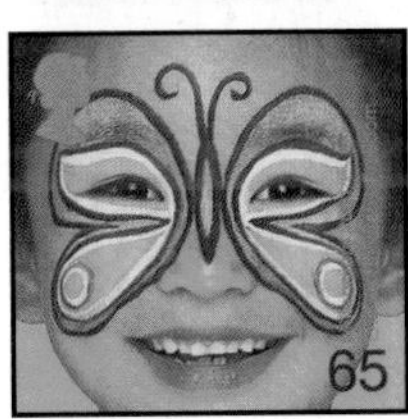

2001 (16 Jan.) New Millennium 2001 - Rights of the Child
Perf 14 x 15

No.			U/M	F/U
C1441	**2nd**	Nurture Children (1 band)	35	40
C1442	**1st**	Listen to Children (2 bands)	48	53
C1443	**45p**	Teach Children (2 bands)	80	80
C1444	**65p**	Ensure Children's Freedom (2 bands)	1.10	1.10
		Set of 4	2.50	2.60
		Set of 4 Cylinder Blocks	18.75	
		Set of 4 Gutter Pairs	6.25	6.25
		First Day Cover		3.25
		Presentation Pack 319	3.45	
		PHQ Cards	4.00	6.00

No.			U/M	F/U

A

B

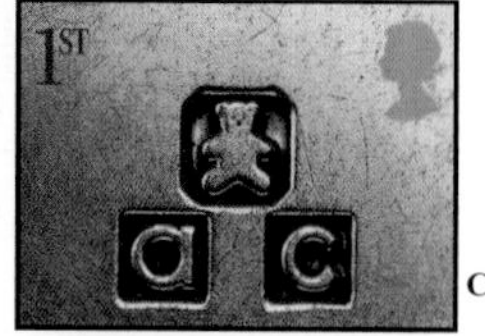
C

D

E

2001 (5 Feb.) Occasions Stamps Printed in gravure Perf 15 x 14

No.			U/M	F/U
C1445	**1st**	Love (A)	65	60
C1446	**1st**	Thanks (B)	65	60
C1447	**1st**	ABC (C)	65	60
C1448	**1st**	Welcome (D)	65	60
C1449	**1st**	Cheers (E)	65	60
		Set of 5	2.70	2.90
		Set of 5 Cylinder Blocks	20.00	
		Set of 5 Gutter Pairs	6.75	6.75
		First Day Cover		3.50
		Presentation Pack MO5	4.50	
		PHQ Cards	4.50	6.50

2001 (5 June) 1st Occasions Printed in Litho from Smilers sheet

No.		
SSP4	Vertical strip of five stamps & five labels	£25
	First Day Cover (Customised sheets) (1.5.01)	£25

2001 (13 Feb.) Cats and Dogs - Self Adhesive Die cut Perf 15 x 14

No.			U/M	F/U
C1450	**1st**	Dog & Man on Bench	80	80
C1451	**1st**	Dog in Bath	80	80
C1452	**1st**	Dog in Pen	80	80
C1453	**1st**	Cat in Bag	80	80
C1454	**1st**	Cat on Gate	80	80
C1455	**1st**	Dog in Car	80	80
C1456	**1st**	Cat at Window	80	80
C1457	**1st**	Dog Behind Fence	80	80
C1458	**1st**	Cat Watching Bird	80	80
C1459	**1st**	Cat in Sink	80	80
		Set of 10	7.50	7.50
		First Day Cover		7.00
		Presentation Pack 320	9.75	
		PHQ Cards	5.00	9.00
Variety				
		Imperforate pane of 10	£3500	

2001 (13 Mar.) The Weather Perf 15

No.			U/M	F/U
C1461	**19p**	Rain (1 band)	35	40
C1462	**27p**	Fair (2 bands)	45	53
C1463	**45p**	Much Rain/Stormy (2 bands)	80	80
C1464	**65p**	Very Dry/Set Fair (2 bands)	1.10	1.10
		Set of 4	2.55	2.60
		Set of 4 Cylinder Blocks	18.90	
		Set of 4 Gutter Pairs	6.40	6.40
		First Day Cover		3.25
		Presentation Pack 321	5.95	
		PHQ Cards	2.00	

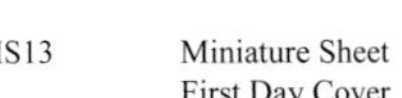

No.			U/M	F/U
MS13		Miniature Sheet	7.00	7.25
		First Day Cover		7.50

2001 (10 Apr.) Centenary of Royal Navy Submarine Service Perf 15 x 14

No.			U/M	F/U
C1465	**2nd**	Vanguard Class	35	40
C1466	**1st**	Swiftsure Class	45	53
C1467	**45p**	Unity Class	80	80
C1468	**65p**	Holland Class	1.10	1.10
		Set of 4	2.35	2.40
		Set of 4 Cylinder Blocks	17.50	
		Set of 4 Gutter Pairs	5.90	5.90
		First Day Cover		3.25
		Presentation Pack 322	4.95	
		PHQ Cards	4.00	6.00

2001 (22 Oct.) Perf 15½ x 15 From 'Unseen & Unheard' Prestige Book

No.			U/M	F/U
C1465a	**2nd**	Vanguard Class	2.00	2.00
C1466b	**1st**	Swiftsure Class	2.00	2.00
C1467c	**45p**	Unity Class	2.50	2.50
C1468d	**65p**	Holland Class	2.50	2.50

2001 (22 Oct.) Miniature Sheet Perf 15½ x 15

No.			U/M	F/U
C1469	**1st**	White Ensign	1.70	1.80
C1470	**1st**	Union Flag	1.70	1.80
C1471	**1st**	Jolly Roger	1.70	1.80
C1472	**1st**	Chief of Defence Flag	1.70	1.80
MS14		Miniature Sheet	3.50	3.00
		First Day Cover		4.00
		Presentatiom Pack MO6	9.75	

Self Adhesive Perf 15½ x 14 Die Cut

No.			U/M	F/U
C1466c	**1st**	Swiftsure Class	32.00	27.00
C1469a	**1st**	White Ensign	8.00	8.00
C1471a	**1st**	Jolly Roger	8.00	8.00

2004 (27 July) 1st Union flag from 'Rule Britannia' Smilers sheet

No.		U/M
SSP20	1st Union flag *plus* label (any)	2.00

2005 (21 June) 1st White Ensign from 'White Ensign' Smilers sheet

No.		U/M
SSP24	Stamp *plus* label (any)	75
SSP24a	Solid all over phosphor	£9

A

B C

D E

2001 (15 May.) 150th Anniversary of First Double Decker Bus
Perf 15 x 14

No.			U/M	F/U
C1473	**1st**	Leyland (A)	48	53
C1474	**1st**	AEC/Daimler (B)	48	53
C1475	**1st**	AEC/Bristol (C)	48	53
C1476	**1st**	Bristol/Leyland (D)	48	53
C1477	**1st**	Daimler/MCW (E)	48	53
		Set of 5	2.30	2.40
		Cylinder Block	7.90	
		Se-tenant Strip of 5	2.30	2.40
		Gutter Strip of 10	5.75	5.75
		First Day Cover		3.00
		Presentation Pack 323	4.95	
		PHQ Cards	4.00	6.00
Variety				
		Imperforate strip of 5	£2000	
		Missing grey	£5000	
MS15		Miniature Sheet		
		First Day Cover		4.50

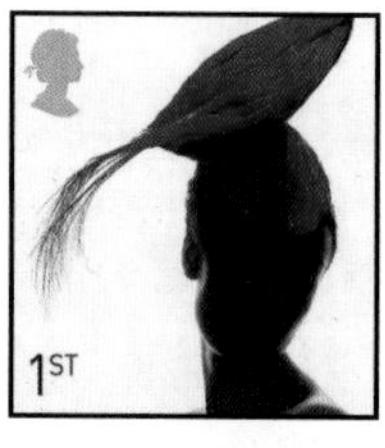

2001 (19 Jun.) Hats Perf 15

No.			U/M	F/U
C1478	**1st**	Multicoloured (Toque Hat)	45	80
C1479	**E**	Multicoloured (Butterfly Hat)	55	60
C1480	**45p**	Multicoloured (Top Hat)	80	75
C1481	**65p**	Multicoloured (Spiral Hat)	1.20	1.30
		Set of 4	2.75	2.80
		Set of 4 Cylinder Blocks	20.50	
		Set of 4 Gutter Pairs	6.90	6.90
		First Day Cover		3.75
		Presentation Pack 324	3.75	
		PHQ Cards	4.00	6.00

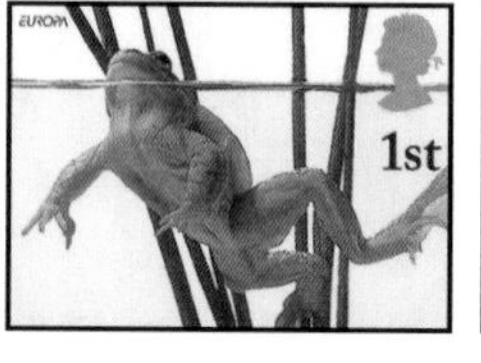

2001 (10 Jul.) Europa - Pond Life Perf 15

No.			U/M	F/U
C1482	**1st**	Common Frog	40	45
C1483	**E**	Great Diving Beetle	60	65
C1484	**45p**	Stickleback	75	80
C1485	**65p**	Hawker Dragonfly	1.10	1.15
		Set of 4	2.80	2.80
		Set of 4 Cylinder Blocks	20.50	
		Set of 4 Gutter Pairs	7.00	7.00
		First Day Cover		3.75
		Presentation Pack 325	3.75	
		PHQ Cards	4.00	6.00

2001 (4 Sep.) Punch and Judy Show Puppets Perf 14 x 15

No.			U/M	F/U
C1486	**1st**	Policeman	50	55
C1487	**1st**	Clown	50	55
C1488	**1st**	Mr Punch	50	55
C1489	**1st**	Judy	50	55
C1490	**1st**	Beadle	50	55
C1491	**1st**	Crocodile	50	55
		Set of 6	2.80	2.90
		Cylinder Block	7.00	
		Gutter Block of 12	7.00	7.00
		First Day Cover		3.50
		Presentation Pack 326	2.95	
		PHQ Cards	6.00	8.00

Self Adhesive Perf 14 x 15½ Die Cut

No.			U/M	F/U
C1488a	**1st**	Multicoloured (Mr Punch)	8.50	8.50
C1489a	**1st**	Multicoloured (Judy)	8.50	8.50

2001 (2 Oct.) Nobel Prizes Perf 15

No.			U/M	F/U
C1492	**2nd**	Multicoloured (Carbon 60 Molecule)	40	45
C1493	**1st**	Multicoloured (Globe Economic Sciences)	45	50
C1494	**E**	Multicoloured (Peace)	60	60
C1495	**40p**	Multicoloured (Physiology and Medicine)	70	75
C1496	**45p**	Multicoloured (Literature)	1.00	1.00
C1497	**65p**	Multicoloured (Physics)	1.00	1.10
		Set of 6	4.00	4.00
		Set of 6 Cylinder Blocks	29.50	

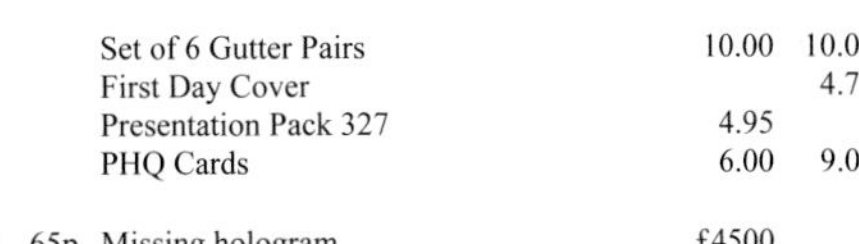

No.			U/M	F/U
		Set of 6 Gutter Pairs	10.00	10.00
		First Day Cover		4.75
		Presentation Pack 327	4.95	
		PHQ Cards	6.00	9.00

Variety

C1495a	65p	Missing hologram	£4500

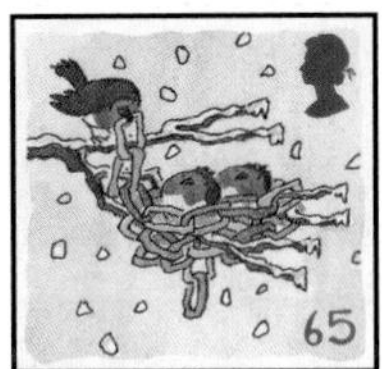

2001 (6 Nov.) Christmas Self Adhesive Perf 15 Die Cut

No.			U/M	F/U
C1498	**2nd**	Robins with Snowman	40	35
C1499	**1st**	Robins on Bird Table	45	50
C1500	**E**	Robins Skating	50	55
C1501	**45p**	Robins with Pudding	65	70
C1502	**65p**	Robins in Paper Chain	1.00	1.10
		Set of 5	3.00	3.20
		Set of 5 Gutter Pairs	7.50	7.50
		First Day Cover		3.75
		Presentation Pack 328	3.40	
		PHQ Cards	5.00	7.50

Variety

C1498a	2nd	Imperforate pair	£500
C1502a	65p	Imperforate pair (stamps & roulleting)	£750
C1502b	65p	Imperforate pair (stamps only)	£275

2003 (30 Sep.) Christmas from Smilers sheet

SSP14	1st Christmas plus label (any)	2.00

2001 (6 Nov.) Collectors Year Pack

CP38	Collectors Year Pack 329	42.50

2001 (6 Nov.) Royal Mail Year Book - 18

YB18	Royal Mail Year Book	47.50

A

B

C D

E

F

G

H

I

J

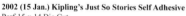

2002 (15 Jan.) Kipling's Just So Stories Self Adhesive
Perf 15 x 14 Die Cut

No.			U/M	F/U
C1503	**1st**	Whale (A)	65	65
C1504	**1st**	Camel (B)	65	65
C1505	**1st**	Rhino (C)	65	65
C1506	**1st**	Leopard (D)	65	65
C1507	**1st**	Elephant (E)	65	65
C1508	**1st**	Kangaroo (F)	65	65
C1509	**1st**	Armadillos (G)	65	65
C1510	**1st**	Crab (H)	65	65
C1511	**1st**	Cat (I)	65	65
C1512	**1st**	Butterfly (J)	65	65
		Set of 10	6.50	6.50
		First Day Cover		5.15
		Presentation Pack 330	9.95	
		PHQ Cards	5.00	7.50

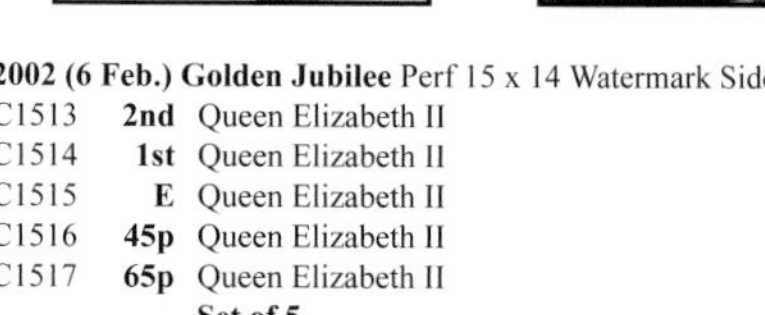

2002 (6 Feb.) Golden Jubilee Perf 15 x 14 Watermark Sideways

No.			U/M	F/U
C1513	**2nd**	Queen Elizabeth II	40	45
C1514	**1st**	Queen Elizabeth II	45	50
C1515	**E**	Queen Elizabeth II	50	55
C1516	**45p**	Queen Elizabeth II	70	75
C1517	**65p**	Queen Elizabeth II	1.15	1.20
		Set of 5	3.00	3.10
		Set of 5 Cylinder Blocks	22.50	
		Set of 5 Gutter Pairs	7.50	7.50
		First Day Cover		3.70
		Presentation Pack 331	3.50	
		PHQ Cards	3.00	5.00

Perf 15 x 14 Watermark Upright From 'A Gracious Accession' Prestige Book

No.			U/M	F/U
C1513a	**2nd**	Queen Elizabeth II	4.50	4.50
C1514a	**1st**	Queen Elizabeth II	2.50	2.50
C1515a	**E**	Queen Elizabeth II	2.50	2.50
C1516a	**45p**	Queen Elizabeth II	3.00	3.00
C1517a	**65p**	Queen Elizabeth II	5.00	5.00

2002 (5 Mar.) Occasions 18mm phosphor bands Perf 15 x 14
Litho Printed by Questa

No.			U/M	F/U
C1518	**1st**	A New Baby	55	60
C1519	**1st**	Love	55	60
C1520	**1st**	Hello	55	60
C1521	**1st**	Moving Home	55	60
C1522	**1st**	Best Wishes	55	60
		Set of 5	2.25	2.35
		Set of 5 Cylinder Blocks	16.90	
		Set of 5 Gutter Pairs	5.65	5.65
		First Day Cover		3.15
		Presentation Pack MO7	2.25	
		PHQ Cards	3.00	5.00

Varieties
18mm phosphor bands Perf 15 x 14

No.			U/M	F/U
C1518a	**1st**	A New Baby	5.00	5.00
C1519a	**1st**	Love	5.00	5.00
C1520a	**1st**	Hello	5.00	5.00
C1521a	**1st**	Moving Home	5.00	5.00
C1522a	**1st**	Best Wishes	5.00	5.00

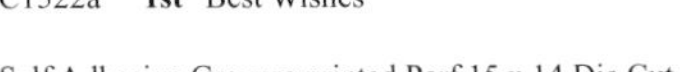

Self Adhesive Gravure printed Perf 15 x 14 Die Cut

No.			U/M	F/U
C1520b	**1st**	Multicoloured (Hello)	3.00	3.00

2001 (23 Apr.) 1st Occasions from Smilers sheet Litho printed

No.		U/M
SSP7	Vertical strip of five stamps & five labels	£10

2004 (30 Jan.) 1st Hello from Hong Kong Smilers sheet

No.		U/M
SSP17	1st *plus* label (any)	2.00

A

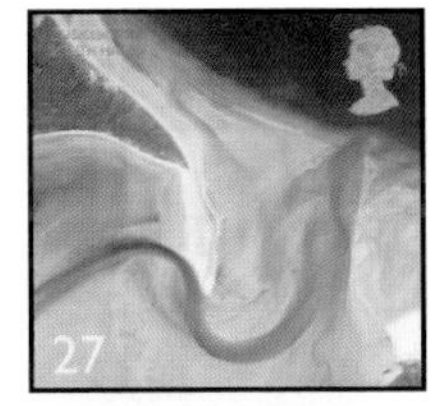
B

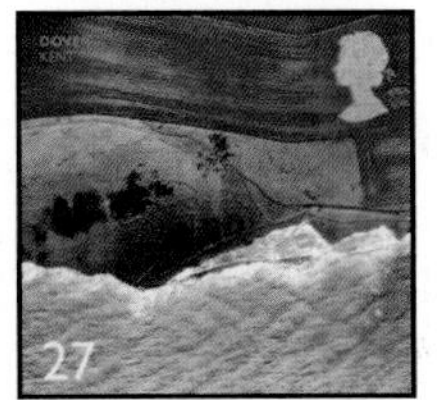
C

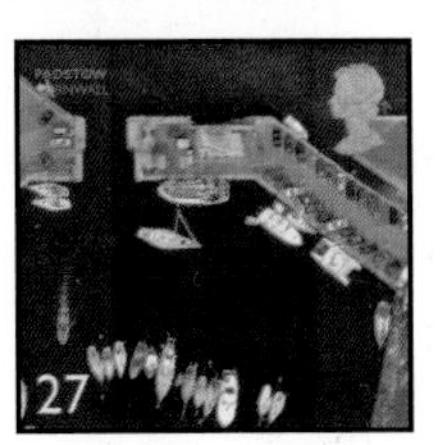
D

E

F

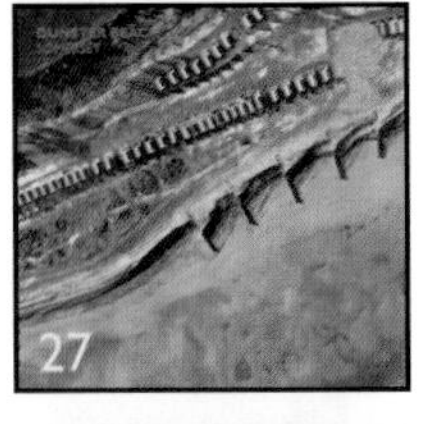
G

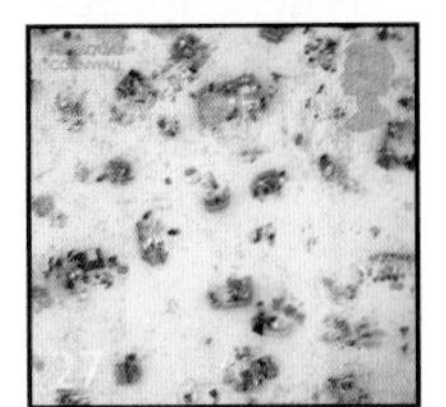
H

I

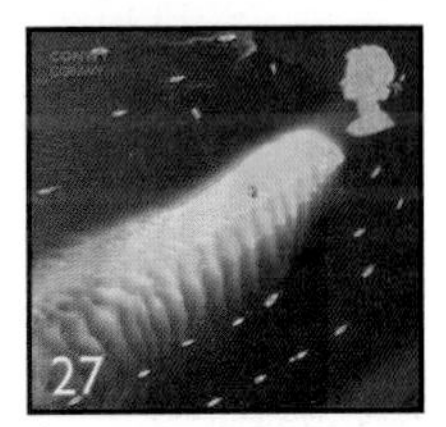
J

2002 (19 Mar.) British Coastlines Perf 15

No.			U/M	F/U
C1523	**1st**	Studland (A)	60	60
C1524	**1st**	Luskentyre (B)	60	60
C1525	**1st**	Dover (C)	60	60
C1526	**1st**	Padstow (D)	60	60
C1527	**1st**	Broadstairs (E)	60	60
C1528	**1st**	St. Abb's Head (F)	60	60
C1529	**1st**	Dunster Beach (G)	66	60
C1530	**1st**	Newquay (H)	60	60
C1531	**1st**	Portrush (I)	60	60
C1532	**1st**	Conwy (J)	60	60
		Set of 10	5.50	5.50
		Cylinder Block	9.75	
		Gutter Block of 20	10.50	10.50
		First Day Cover		5.15
		Presentation Pack 332	4.20	
		PHQ Cards	5.50	8.00

Variety

No.		U/M
C1523/32	Missing silver (block of ten)	£4000

2002 (10 Apr.) Europa Circus Perf 15

No.			U/M	F/U
C1533	**2nd**	Slack Wire	40	45
C1534	**1st**	Lion Tamer	45	50
C1535	**E**	Trick Cycle	55	60
C1536	**45p**	Krazy Kar	65	70
C1537	**65p**	Equestrienne	1.00	1.05
		Set of 5	3.00	3.20
		Set of 5 Cylinder Blocks	22.50	
		Set of 5 Gutter Pairs	7.50	7.50
		First Day Cover		4.20
		Presentation Pack 333	3.20	
		PHQ Cards	3.00	5.00
Variety				
C1535	E	Imperforate pair	£850	

2002 (25 Apr.) The Queen Mother Perf 14 x 15

No.			U/M	F/U
C1538	**1st**	The Queen Mother	45	50
C1539	**E**	The Queen Mother	55	60
C1540	**45p**	The Queen Mother	65	70
C1541	**65p**	The Queen Mother	1.00	1.05
		Set of 4	2.80	3.00
		Set of 4 Cylinder Blocks	20.50	
		Set of 4 Gutter Pairs	7.00	7.00
		First Day Cover		4.00
		Presentation Pack MO8	2.80	
		PHQ Cards	3.00	5.00

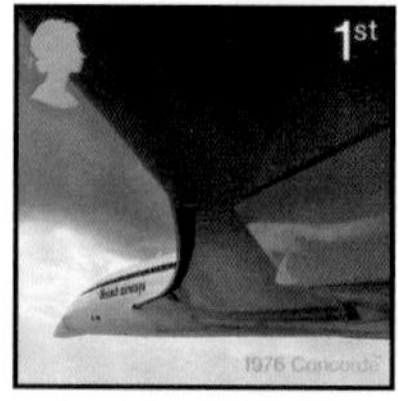

2002 (2 May) Airliners Perf 15

No.			U/M	F/U
C1542	**2nd**	Airbus	40	45
C1543	**1st**	Concorde	45	50
C1544	**E**	Trident	55	60
C1545	**45p**	VC10	65	70
C1546	**65p**	Comet	1.00	1.05
		Set of 5	3.00	3.20
		Set of 5 Cylinder Blocks	22.50	
		Set of 5 Gutter Pairs	7.50	7.50
		First Day Cover		4.20
		Presentation Pack 334	3.20	
		PHQ Cards	4.00	6.00
MS16		Miniature Sheet	4.50	4.60
		First Day Cover		5.00

Self Adhesive Perf 15 x 14 Die Cut

C1543a	**1st**	Concorde	2.50	2.50

A

B

C

D

2002 (21 May) World Cup Printed in Gravure Perf 15

No.			U/M	F/U
C1547	**1st**	Lion and St. George Shield	1.50	1.75
C1548	**1st**	English Flag & Football (A)	75	80
C1549	**1st**	English Flag & Football (B)	75	80
C1550	**1st**	English Flag & Football (C)	75	80
C1551	**1st**	English Flag & Football (D)	75	80
		First Day Cover		3.20
		Presentation Pack 335	2.95	
		PHQ Cards	2.50	3.50

2002 (21 May) 1st Football World Cup, Printed in Litho from Smilers sheet

		U/M	F/U
SSP8	1st *plus* label (any)	2.50	

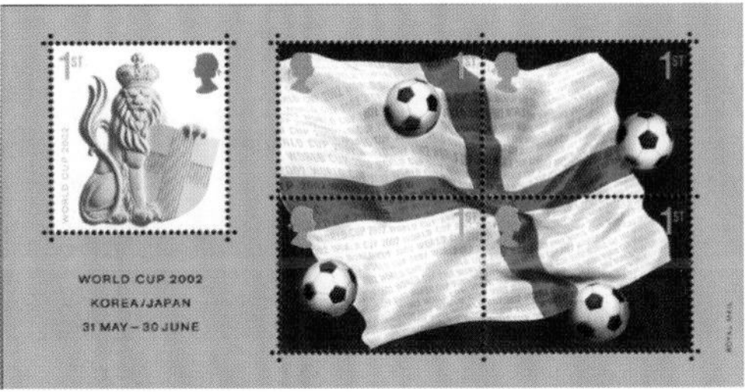

		U/M	F/U
MS17	Miniature Sheet	2.70	2.80

Self Adhesive Perf 15 x 14 Die Cut

			U/M	F/U
C1548a	**1st**	English Flag & Football (A)	3.50	3.50
C1549a	**1st**	English Flag & Football (B)	3.50	3.50

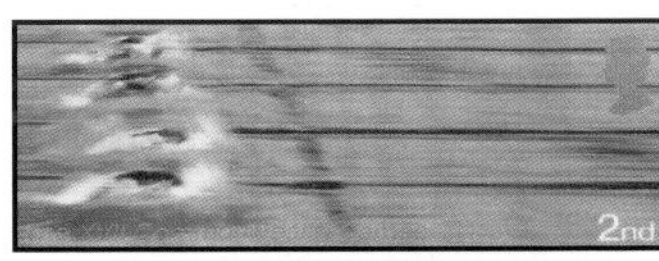

2002 (16 July) The Friendly Games Perf 15

No.			U/M	F/U
C1552	**2nd**	Swimming	40	45
C1553	**1st**	Track	45	50
C1554	**E**	Cycling	55	60
C1555	**47p**	Long Jump	70	75
C1556	**68p**	Disabled	1.30	1.40
		Set of 5	3.40	3.50
		Set of 5 Cylinder Blocks	24.50	
		Set of 5 Gutter Pairs	8.50	8.50
		First Day Cover		4.30
		Presentation Pack 336	3.20	
		PHQ Cards	3.00	5.00

2002 (20 Aug.) Peter Pan Perf 15 x 14

No.			U/M	F/U
C1557	**2nd**	Tinkerbell	40	45
C1558	**1st**	Group	45	50
C1559	**E**	Crocodile	65	70
C1560	**47p**	Hook	90	1.00
C1561	**68p**	Peter	1.30	1.40
		Set of 5	3.50	3.60
		Set of 5 Cylinder Blocks	25.50	
		Set of 5 Gutter Pairs	8.75	8.75
		First Day Cover		4.30
		Presentation Pack 337	3.20	
		PHQ Cards	4.00	6.00

002 (10 Sep.) London Bridges Perf 15 x 14

No.			U/M	F/U
C1562	**2nd**	Millennium	40	45
C1563	**1st**	Tower	45	50
C1564	**E**	Westminster	65	70
C1565	**47p**	Blackfriar's	80	85
C1566	**68p**	London	1.30	1.35
		Set of 5	3.50	3.60
		Set of 5 Cylinder Blocks	25.50	
		Set of 5 Gutter Pairs	8.75	8.75
		First Day Cover		4.30
		Presentation Pack 338	3.20	
		PHQ Cards	3.50	5.50

Self Adhesive Perf 14½ x 14 Die Cut

No.			U/M	F/U
C1563a	**1st**	Tower	1.75	2.00

A

B

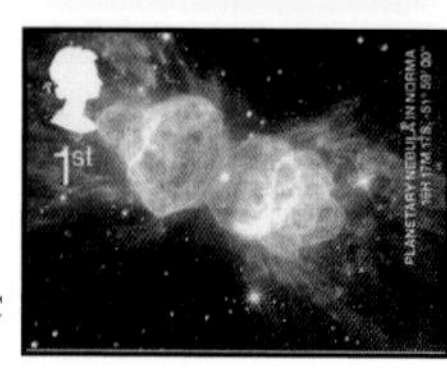
C

D

2002 (24 Sep.) Astronomy Perf 14½ x 14

No.			U/M	F/U
C1567	**1st**	Aquilla (A)	60	65
C1568	**1st**	Pegasus (B)	60	65
C1569	**1st**	Norma (C)	60	65
C1570	**1st**	Circinus (D)	60	65
		Presentation Pack 339	2.75	
		PHQ Cards	3.75	5.50

All the above were from a miniature sheet and Prestige Book pane.

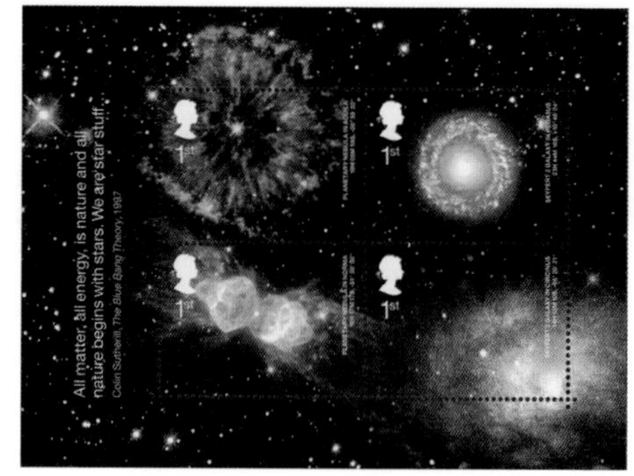

No.		U/M	F/U
MS18	Miniature Sheet	2.60	3.00
	Sheet First Day Cover		3.50
	Prestige Book pane	2.25	2.50

2002 (8 Oct.) Pillar to Post Perf 15 x 14

No.			U/M	F/U
C1571	**2nd**	1857 Box	40	45
C1572	**1st**	1874 Box	45	50
C1573	**E**	1934 Box	60	65
C1574	**47p**	1939 Box	80	85
C1575	**68p**	1980 Box	1.20	1.30
		Set of 5	3.40	3.50
		Set of 5 Cylinder Blocks	25.50	
		Set of 5 Gutter Pairs	8.50	8.50
		First Day Cover		4.50
		Presentation Pack 340	3.20	
		PHQ Cards	3.00	

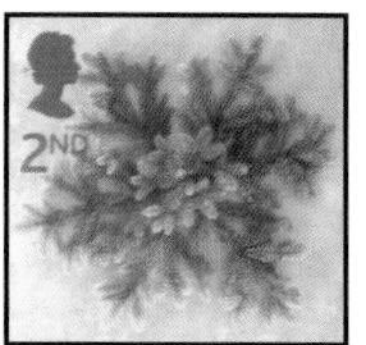

2002 (5 Nov.) Christmas Self Adhesive Perf 15 x 14 Die Cut

No.			U/M	F/U
C1576	**2nd**	Spruce	40	45
C1577	**1st**	Holly	45	50
C1578	**E**	Ivy	60	65
C1579	**47p**	Mistletoe	80	85
C1580	**68p**	Cone	1.20	1.30
		Set of 5	2.70	2.90
		Set of 5 Gutter Pairs	6.75	6.75
		First Day Cover		4.50
		Presentation Pack 341	3.20	
		PHQ Cards	3.00	5.00
Variety				
C1576a	2nd	Imperforate pair	£25	
C1577a	1st	Imperforate pair	£100	

2002 (5 Dec.) Anniversary of Wilding Definitives (1st) Perf 15 x 14

No.		U/M	F/U
MS19	Complete Miniature Sheet	5.50	3.80
	First Day Cover		3.80
	Presentation Pack	3.80	

Individual stamps from this miniature sheet will be found in the definitives section.

2002 (5 Nov.) Collectors Year Pack

CP39	Collectors Year Pack 342	42.50	

2002 (5 Nov.) Royal Mail Year Book - 19

YB19	Royal Mail Year Book	47.50	

A  B 

C  D 

E  F 

G  H 

I  J 

2003 (14 Jan.) Birds of Prey Perf 14½

No.			U/M	F/U
C1581	**1st**	Barn Owl in Flight (A)	55	65
C1582	**1st**	Barn Owl in Flight (B)	55	65
C1583	**1st**	Barn Owl in Flight (C)	55	65
C1584	**1st**	Barn Owl in Flight (D)	55	65
C1585	**1st**	Barn Owl in Flight (E)	55	65
C1586	**1st**	Kestrel in Flight (F)	55	65
C1587	**1st**	Kestrel in Flight (G)	55	65
C1588	**1st**	Kestrel in Flight (H)	55	65
C1589	**1st**	Kestrel in Flight (I)	55	65
C1590	**1st**	Kestrel in Flight (J)	55	65
		Set of 10	4.90	5.00
		Cylinder Block	11.25	
		Gutter Block of 20	12.25	12.25
		First Day Cover		5.50
		Presentation Pack 343	4.25	
		PHQ Cards	4.00	6.00
Varieties				
C1581/90		Missing Brownish grey & Phosphor (Blocks of ten - mint & FDC)	£1750	£1100
C1581/90		Upward shift of all colours except brownish-grey	£1250	

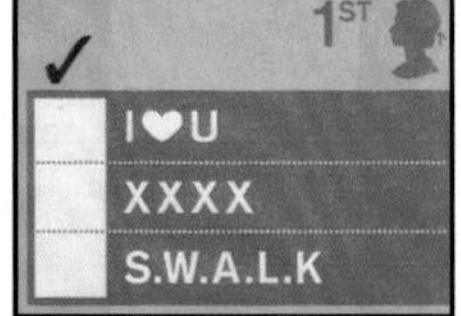

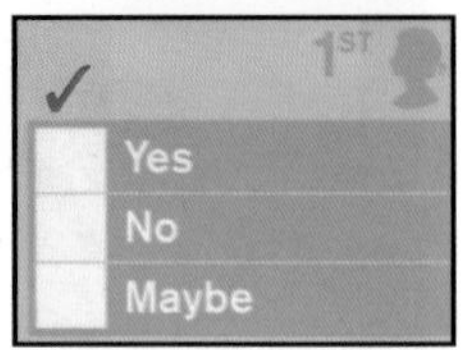

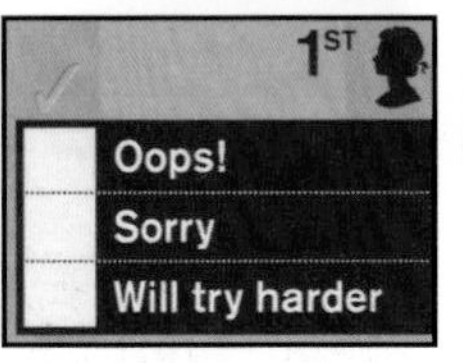

2003 (4 Feb.) Occasions Perf 14½ x 14

No.			U/M	F/U
C1591	**1st**	Gold Star... (A)	55	60
C1592	**1st**	I Love You... (B)	55	60
C1593	**1st**	Angel... (C)	55	60
C1594	**1st**	Yes... (D)	55	60
C1595	**1st**	Oops!... (E)	55	60
C1596	**1st**	I Did it!... (F)	55	60
		Set of 6	2.60	2.70
		Gutter Block of 12	6.50	6.50
		First Day Cover		3.55
		Presentation Pack MO9	2.80	
		PHQ Cards	3.00	5.00

Variety

C1591/6 Imperforate block of six £1550

2003 (4 Feb.) Occasions from Smilers sheet

		U/M
SSP12	1st Occasions *plus* label (any)	2.00

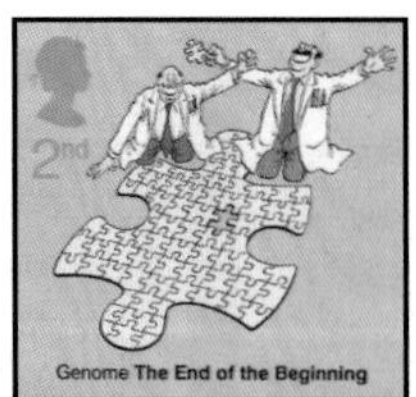

Genome The End of the Beginning

Genome Comparative Genetics

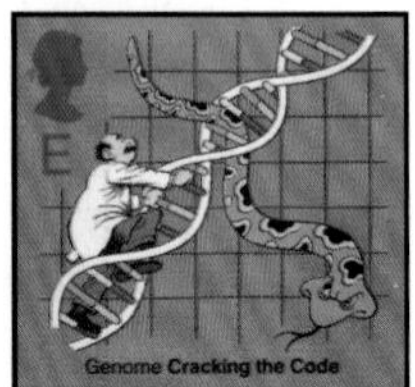

Genome Cracking the Code

Genome Genetic Engineering

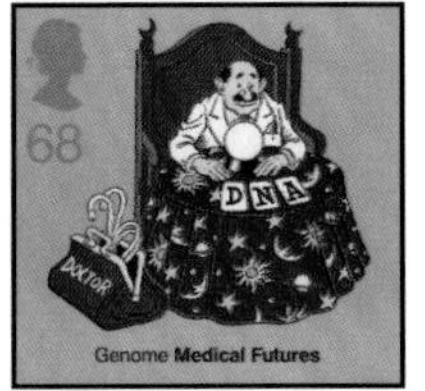

Genome Medical Futures

2003 (25 Feb.) Discovery of DNA Perf 14½

No.			U/M	F/U
C1597	**2nd**	Genome Jigsaw	40	45
C1598	**1st**	Ape and Scientist	45	50
C1598a		Missing phosphor		
C1599	**E**	Snakes and Ladders	60	60
C1600	**47p**	Animal Scientist	80	75
C1601	**68p**	Crystal Ball	1.20	1.30
		Set of 5	3.20	3.40
		Set of 5 Cylinder Blocks	24.50	
		Set of 5 Gutter Pairs	8.00	8.00
		First Day Cover		5.00
		Presentation Pack 344	3.20	
		PHQ Cards	3.00	5.00

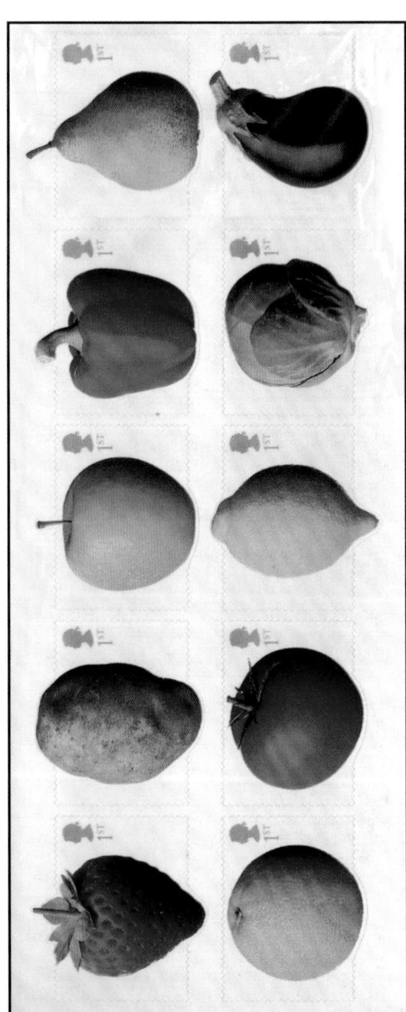

2003 (25 Mar.) Fruit and VegetablesSelf Adhesive Perf 14 Die Cut

No.			U/M	F/U
C1602	**1st**	Strawberry	65	70
C1603	**1st**	Potato	65	70
C1604	**1st**	Apple	65	70
C1605	**1st**	Red Pepper	65	70
C1606	**1st**	Pear	65	70
C1607	**1st**	Orange	65	70
C1608	**1st**	Tomato	65	70
C1609	**1st**	Lemon	65	70
C1610	**1st**	Cabbage	65	70
C1611	**1st**	Aubergine	65	70
		Set of 10	5.40	5.60
		First Day Cover		7.00
		Presentation Pack 345	£32	
		PHQ Cards	6.00	9.50
Variety				
C1602/11		Imperforate sheetlet	£1750	

2003 (29 Apr.) Extreme Endeavours Perf 15 x 14

No.			U/M	F/U
C1612	**2nd**	Amy Johnson	40	45
C1613	**1st**	Everest Team	45	50
C1614	**E**	Freya Stark	55	60
C1615	**42p**	Ernest Shackleton	75	80
C1616	**47p**	Francis Chichester	80	85
C1617	**68p**	Robert F Scott	1.20	1.25
		Set of 6	3.80	4.00
		Set of 6 Cylinder Blocks	27.50	
		Set of 6 Gutter Pairs	9.50	9.50
		First Day Cover		4.80
		Presentation Pack 346	3.80	
		PHQ Cards	3.00	5.00

Self Adhesive Perf 14½ Die Cut

No.			U/M	F/U
C1613a	**1st**	Everest Team	2.75	2.75

2003 (20 May) Anniversary of Wilding Definitives (2nd) Perf 15 x 14

No.		U/M	F/U
MS20	Mixed Values	5.50	5.50
	First Day Cover		3.80
	Presentation Pack	3.80	

Individual stamps from this miniature sheet will be found in the definitives section.

2003 (2 June) Anniversary of the Coronation Perf 14½ x 14

No.			U/M	F/U
C1618	**1st**	Coronation Procession	50	55
C1619	**1st**	Street Party Poster	50	55
C1620	**1st**	The Coronation	50	55
C1621	**1st**	Royal Wall Mosaic	50	55
C1622	**1st**	Cecil Beaton Portrait	50	55
C1623	**1st**	Children's Race	50	55
C1624	**1st**	Marble Arch Procession	50	55
C1625	**1st**	Children at Street Party	50	55
C1626	**1st**	Royal Carriage	50	55
C1627	**1st**	Children and Cakes	50	55
		Set of 10	4.40	4.60
		Cylinder Block	11.00	
		Gutter Block of 20	11.00	11.00
		First Day Cover		5.30
		Presentation Pack 347	12.50	
		PHQ Cards	3.80	6.00
Variety				
C1627a	1st	Image printed double	£1250	

2003 (2 June) Anniversary of the Coronation from Prestige Book
Perf 15 x 14

No.			U/M	F/U
C1628	**£1**	Coronation	25.00	25.00

The 47p and 68p individual stamps from this miniature sheet will be found in the definitives section.

2003 (17 June) Birthday of Prince William Perf 14½

No.			U/M	F/U
C1629	**28p**	Prince William	45	50
C1630	**E**	Prince William	60	70
C1631	**47p**	Prince William	80	85
C1632	**68p**	Prince William	1.20	1.25
		Set of 4	3.00	3.10
		Set of 4 Cylinder Blocks	22.50	
		Set of 4 Gutter Pairs	7.50	7.50
		First Day Cover		4.00
		Presentation Pack 348	16.00	
		PHQ Cards	3.00	5.50

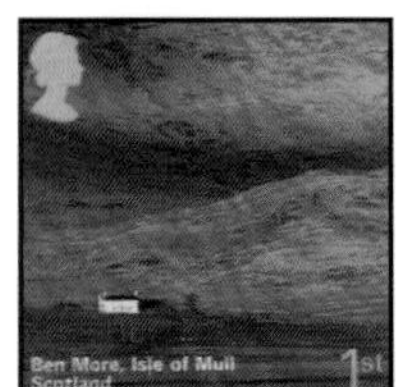

2003 (15 July) A British Journey - Scotland Perf 14½

No.			U/M	F/U
C1633	**2nd**	Loch Assynt	40	45
C1634	**1st**	Ben More	45	50
C1635	**E**	Rothiemurchus	55	60
C1636	**42p**	Dalveen Pass	65	70
C1637	**47p**	Glenfinnan Viaduct	70	75
C1638	**68p**	Papa Little	1.10	1.15
		Set of 6	3.65	3.80
		Set of 6 Cylinder Blocks	27.50	
		Set of 6 Gutter Pairs	9.00	9.50
		First Day Cover		4.75
		Presentation Pack 349	3.80	
		PHQ Cards	3.00	5.00

Self Adhesive Perf 14½ Die Cut

No.			U/M	F/U
C1634a	**1st**	Ben More	2.50	2.50

2003 (12 Aug.) British Pub Signs Perf 14 x 14½

No.			U/M	F/U
C1639	**1st**	The Station	45	50
C1640	**E**	Black Swan	55	60
C1641	**42p**	The Cross Keys	70	75
C1642	**47p**	The Mayflower	85	90
C1643	**68p**	The Barleysheaf	1.30	1.15
		Set of 5	3.60	3.70
		Set of 5 Cylinder Blocks	26.50	
		Set of 5 Gutter Pairs	9.00	9.25
		First Day Cover		4.65
		Presentation Pack 350	3.50	
		PHQ Cards	3.00	5.00

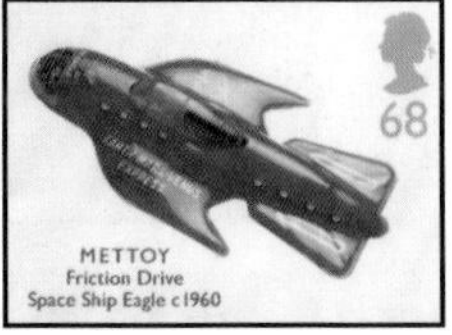

2003 (18 Sep.) Transports of Delight Perf 14 x 14½

No.			U/M	F/U
C1644	**1st**	Biplane	45	50
C1645	**E**	Omnibus	55	60
C1646	**42p**	Locomotive	75	80
C1647	**47p**	Ford Zephyr	80	90
C1648	**68p**	Space Ship	1.30	1.40

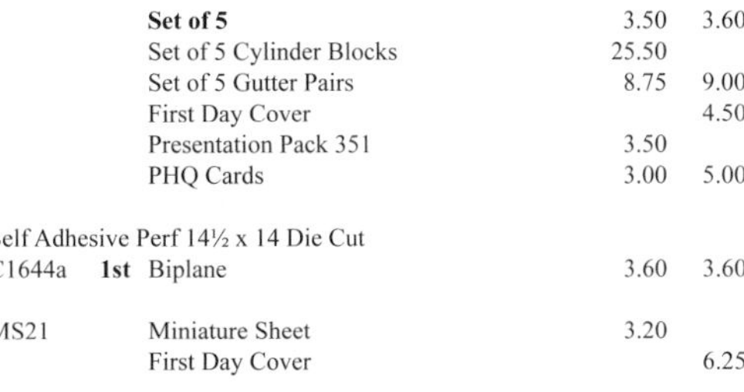

No.			U/M	F/U
		Set of 5	3.50	3.60
		Set of 5 Cylinder Blocks	25.50	
		Set of 5 Gutter Pairs	8.75	9.00
		First Day Cover		4.50
		Presentation Pack 351	3.50	
		PHQ Cards	3.00	5.00
Self Adhesive Perf 14½ x 14 Die Cut				
C1644a	**1st**	Biplane	3.60	3.60
MS21		Miniature Sheet	3.20	
		First Day Cover		6.25

2003 (7 Oct.) The British Museum Perf 14 x 14½

No.			U/M	F/U
C1649	**2nd**	Denytenamun	40	45
C1650	**1st**	Alexander the Great	45	50
C1651	**E**	Sutton Hoo Helmet	65	70
C1652	**42p**	Pavati	75	80
C1653	**47p**	Mask of Xiuhtecuhtli	85	90
C1654	**68p**	Hoa Hakananai	1.30	1.40
		Set of 6	4.00	4.20
		Set of 6 Cylinder Blocks	28.50	
		Set of 6 Gutter Pairs	10.00	10.50
		First Day Cover		4.75
		Presentation Pack 352	3.80	
		PHQ Cards	3.00	5.00

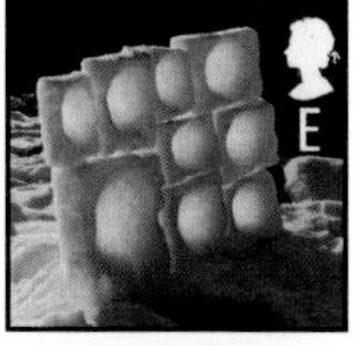

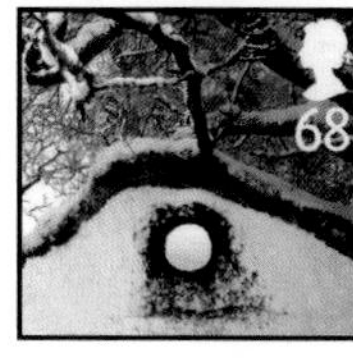

2003 (4 Nov.) Christmas Self Adhesive Perf 14½ x 14 Die cut

No.			U/M	F/U
C1655	**2nd**	Ice Spiral	40	45
C1656	**1st**	Icicle Star	45	50
C1656a	**1st**	Icicle Star (Matrix intact - Post Office Staff Issue)	2.50	
C1657	**E**	Wall of Frozen Snow	65	70
C1658	**53p**	Ice Ball	95	1.00
C1659	**68p**	Ice Hole	1.20	1.30
C1660	**£1.12**	Snow Pyramids	2.00	2.10
		Set of 6	5.20	5.90
		Set of 6 Gutter Pairs	13.00	13.50
		First Day Cover		6.00
		Presentation Pack 353	4.95	
		PHQ Cards	3.00	5.00

2003 (4 Nov) Christmas Ice Sculptures from Smilers sheet

No.		U/M	F/U
SSP15	2nd Ice spiral *plus* label (any)	1.75	
SSP16	1st Icicle star *plus* label (any)	1.75	

2003 (4 Nov.) Collectors Year Pack

No.		U/M	F/U
CP40	Collectors Year Pack 353	£45	

2003 (4 Nov.) Royal Mail Year Book - 20

No.		U/M	F/U
YB20	Royal Mail Year Book	£48	

2003 (19 Dec.) Rugby World Cup Winners Perf 14 x 14½

No.			U/M	F/U
C1661	**1st**	St. George's Flag	65	75
C1662	**1st**	Australia Team	65	75
C1663	**68p**	Rugby World Cup	1.75	1.95
C1664	**68p**	England Team	1.75	1.95
		First Day Cover		
		Presentation Pack M9B	£20	
		PHQ Cards		
MS22		Miniature Sheet	2.80	2.90

2004 (13 Jan.) Classic Locomotives Perf 14 x 14½

No.			U/M	F/U
C1665	**20p**	Gwynedd	30	35
C1666	**28p**	West Lothian	45	50
C1667	**E**	Leicestershire	65	70
C1668	**42p**	Worcestershire	70	75
C1669	**47p**	East Sussex	85	90
C1670	**68p**	Yorkshire	1.30	1.40
		Set of 6	4.00	4.20
		Set of 6 Cylinder Blocks	28.50	
		Set of 6 Gutter Pairs	10.00	10.75
		First Day Cover		6.00
		Presentation Pack 355	27.50	
		PHQ Cards	4.00	6.00
Variety				
C1669a	47p	Imperforate pair	£1000	
C1669b	47p	Missing yellow		
MS23		Miniature Sheet	11.95	11.95
		First Day Cover		20.00

2004 (3 Feb.) Occassions Perf 14 x 14½

No.			U/M	F/U
C1671	**1st**	Postman	60	65
C1672	**1st**	Face	60	65
C1673	**1st**	Duck	60	65
C1674	**1st**	Baby	60	65
C1675	**1st**	Aircraft	60	65
		Set of 5	2.50	2.60
		Set of 5 Cylinder Blocks	18.50	
		Set of 5 Gutter Pairs	6.25	6.50
		First Day Cover		4.00
		Presentation Pack M10	2.80	
		PHQ Cards	3.20	5.00

2004 (3 Feb) Occasions from Smilers sheet

No.		U/M
SSP18	Vertical strip of five stamps & five labels	7.50

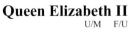

A

B

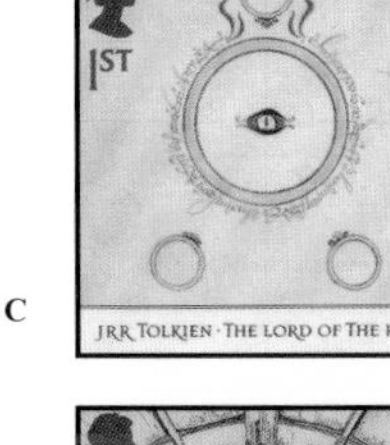

C

D

E

F

G

H

I

J

2004 (26 Feb.) J R Tolkien 50th Anniversary Perf 14 x 14½

No.			U/M	F/U
C1676	**1st**	Middle Earth	55	55
C1677	**1st**	Lothlorien Forest	55	55
C1678	**1st**	Dust Jacket	55	55
C1679	**1st**	1st Rivendell	55	55
C1680	**1st**	Hall at Bag End	55	55
C1681	**1st**	Orthanc	55	55
C1682	**1st**	Doors of Durin	55	55
C1683	**1st**	Barad-dur	55	55
C1684	**1st**	Minas Tirith	55	55
C1685	**1st**	Fangom Forest	55	55
		Set of 10	5.20	5.20
		Cylinder Block	12.50	
		Gutter Block of 20	13.00	13.00
		First Day Cover		6.00
		Presentation Pack 356	8.25	
		PHQ Cards	3.20	5.00

2004 (16 Mar.) Northern Ireland Perf 14 x 14½

No.			U/M	F/U
C1686	**2nd**	Ely Island	30	35
C1687	**1st**	Giant's Causeway	45	50
C1688	**E**	Antrim Mountains	60	65
C1689	**42p**	Mourne Mountains	65	70
C1690	**47p**	Glenelly Valley	75	80
C1691	**68p**	Strangford Lough	1.10	1.20
		Set of 6	3.65	3.85
		Set of 6 Cylinder Blocks	26.50	
		Set of 6 Gutter Pairs	9.25	9.50
		First Day Cover		6.00
		Presentation Pack 357	3.95	
		PHQ Cards	3.00	5.00

Self Adhesive Perf 14½ x 14 Die Cut

C1687a	**1st**	Giant's Causeway	2.00	2.00

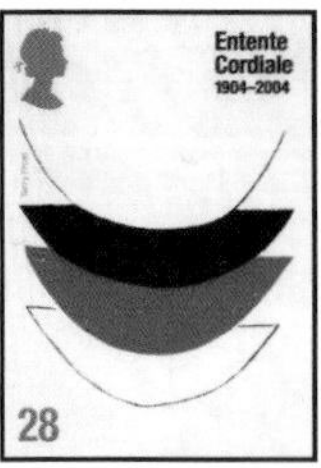

2004 (6 Apr.) Entente Cordiale Perf 14 x 14½

C1692	**28p**	Lace 1 1968	60	60
C1693	**57p**	Coccinelle	1.10	1.10
		Set of 2	1.60	1.65
		Set of 2 Cylinder Blocks	11.50	
		Set of 2 Gutter Pairs	4.00	4.25
		First Day Cover		3.20
		Presentation Pack 358	12.95	
		Presentation Pack (Anglo French)	12.50	
		PHQ Cards	2.00	3.00

2004 (13 Apr.) Ocean Liners Perf 14 x 14½

No.			U/M	F/U
C1694	**1st**	RMS Queen Mary 2	45	50
C1695	**E**	SS Canberra	60	65
C1696	**42p**	RMS Queen Mary	65	70
C1697	**47p**	RMS Mauretania	75	80
C1698	**57p**	SS City of New York	1.00	1.10
C1699	**68p**	PS Great Western	1.20	1.30
		Set of 6	4.40	4.60
		Set of 6 Cylinder Blocks	33.50	
		Set of 6 Gutter Pairs	11.00	11.60
		First Day Cover		5.00
		Presentation Pack 359	4.50	
		PHQ Cards	3.20	5.00
MS24		Miniature Sheet	6.00	6.00
		First Day Cover		10.00
Variety				
C1700		Error of value - 57p printed 53p		

This is from the Ocean Liners Miniature sheet printed before a price rise was granted. These sheets were recalled but a few were found in a dealers stock in the USA.Unlikely to be available as a single!

Self Adhesive Perf 14½ x 14 Die Cut

C1692a	**1st**	RMS Queen Mary 2	2.00	2.10

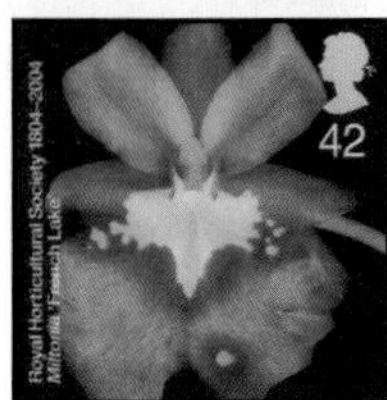

2004 (25 May) Bicentenary of the RHS Perf 14 x 14½

No.			U/M	F/U
C1701	**2nd**	Dianthus	35	40
C1702	**1st**	Dahlia	45	50
C1703	**E**	Clematis	60	65
C1704	**42p**	Miltonia	70	80
C1705	**47p**	Lilium	80	90
C1706	**68p**	Delphinium	1.20	1.30
		Set of 6	3.80	3.90
		Set of 6 Cylinder Blocks	27.50	
		Set of 6 Gutter Pairs	9.50	10.00
		First Day Cover		5.50
		Presentation Pack 360	4.20	
		PHQ Cards	3.20	5.00
MS25		Miniature Sheet	5.50	5.50

Perf 15 x 14 From 'The Glory of the Garden' Prestige Book. These were originally issued in the Flowers Greetings books but perf 14 x 14½ - See page H80

No.			U/M	F/U
C1707	**1st**	Camellia Japonica	3.00	3.00
C1708	**1st**	Tulipa	3.00	3.00
C1709	**1st**	Iris Latifolia	3.00	3.00

2004 (25 May) RHS Smilers sheet

No.			U/M	F/U
SSP19		Stamp with label (any)	2.00	

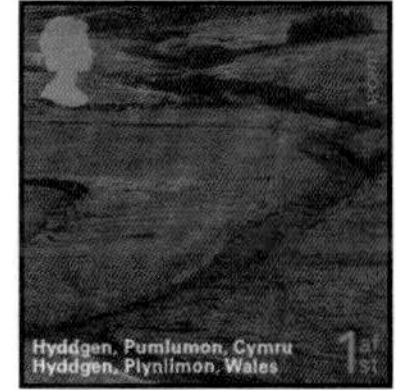

2004 (15 June) Wales Perf 14 x 14½

No.			U/M	F/U
C1710	**2nd**	Barmouth Bridge	35	40
C1711	**1st**	Hydden	45	50
C1712	**40p**	Brecon Beacons	60	65
C1713	**43p**	Rhondda Valley	65	70
C1714	**47p**	Dee Valley	75	80
C1715	**68p**	Marloes Sands	1.10	4.25
		Set of 6	3.70	3.85
		Set of 6 Cylinder Blocks	26.50	
		Set of 6 Gutter Pairs	9.25	9.75
		First Day Cover		5.50
		Presentation Pack 361	4.20	
		PHQ Cards	3.20	5.00

Self Adhesive Perf 14½ x 14 Die Cut

No.			U/M	F/U
C1711a	**1st**	Hydden	4.50	4.50

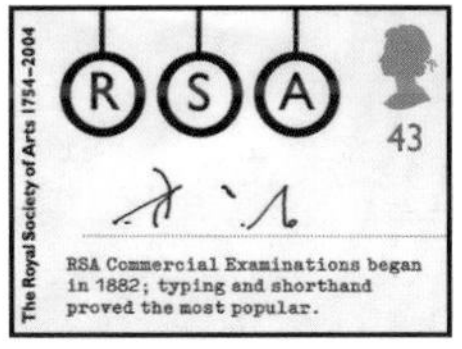

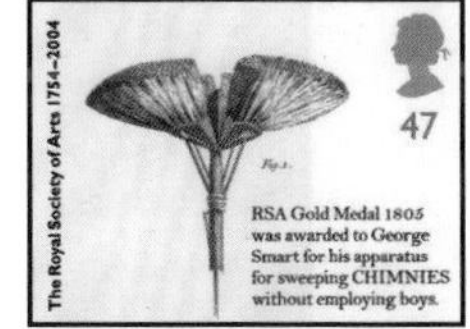

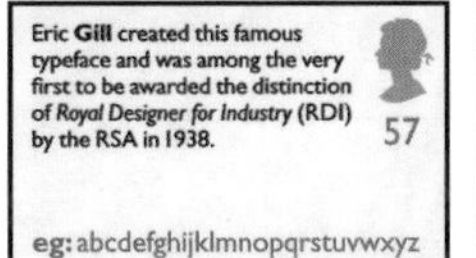

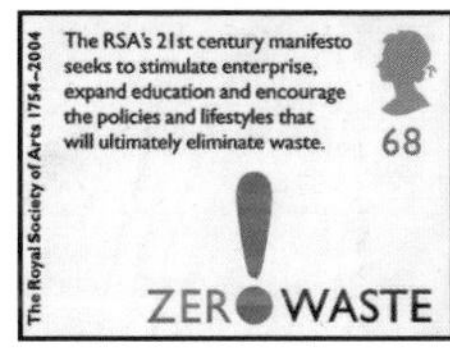

2004 (10 Aug.) 50th Anniversary of the RSA Perf 14 x 14½

No.			U/M	F/U
C1716	**1st**	Sir Rowland Hill	45	50
C1717	**40p**	William Shipley	60	65
C1718	**43p**	Typewriter/Shorthand	70	75
C1719	**47p**	Chimney Sweep	85	90
C1720	**57p**	Gill Typeface	1.00	1.05
C1721	**68p**	Zero Waste	1.30	1.35
		Set of 6	4.40	4.40
		Set of 6 Cylinder Blocks	31.50	
		Set of 6 Gutter Pairs	11.00	11.00
		First Day Cover		6.00
		Presentation Pack 362	4.50	
		PHQ Cards	3.20	5.00

No. U/M F/U

A

B

C

D

E

F

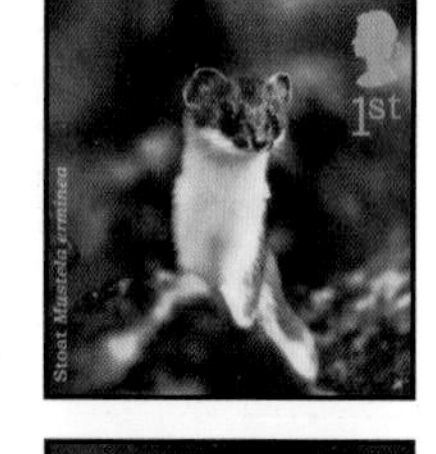

G

H

I

J

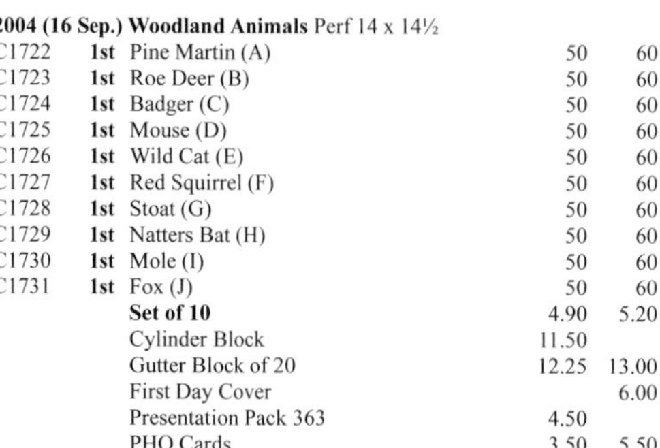

2004 (16 Sep.) Woodland Animals Perf 14 x 14½

No.			U/M	F/U
C1722	**1st**	Pine Martin (A)	50	60
C1723	**1st**	Roe Deer (B)	50	60
C1724	**1st**	Badger (C)	50	60
C1725	**1st**	Mouse (D)	50	60
C1726	**1st**	Wild Cat (E)	50	60
C1727	**1st**	Red Squirrel (F)	50	60
C1728	**1st**	Stoat (G)	50	60
C1729	**1st**	Natters Bat (H)	50	60
C1730	**1st**	Mole (I)	50	60
C1731	**1st**	Fox (J)	50	60
		Set of 10	4.90	5.20
		Cylinder Block	11.50	
		Gutter Block of 20	12.25	13.00
		First Day Cover		6.00
		Presentation Pack 363	4.50	
		PHQ Cards	3.50	5.50

No. U/M F/U

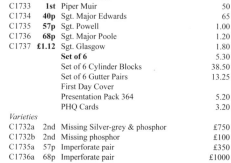

2004 (12 Oct.) 150th Anniversary of the Crimean War Perf 14 x 14½

No.			U/M	F/U
C1732	**2nd**	Pt. McNamara	35	40
C1733	**1st**	Piper Muir	50	60
C1734	**40p**	Sgt. Major Edwards	65	70
C1735	**57p**	Sgt. Powell	1.00	1.10
C1736	**68p**	Sgt. Major Poole	1.20	1.30
C1737	**£1.12**	Sgt. Glasgow	1.80	1.90
		Set of 6	5.30	5.40
		Set of 6 Cylinder Blocks	38.50	
		Set of 6 Gutter Pairs	13.25	13.75
		First Day Cover		7.50
		Presentation Pack 364	5.20	
		PHQ Cards	3.20	

Varieties

No.			U/M	F/U
C1732a	2nd	Missing Silver-grey & phosphor	£750	
C1732b	2nd	Missing phosphor	£100	
C1735a	57p	Imperforate pair	£350	
C1736a	68p	Imperforate pair	£1000	

2004 (2 Nov.) Christmas Perf 14 x 14½

No.			U/M	F/U
C1738	**2nd**	On Snowy Roof	35	40
C1739	**1st**	Sunrise	50	60
C1739a	**1st**	Sunrise (Matrix intact - Post Office Staff Issue)	2.50	
C1740	**40p**	On Roof in Gale	65	70
C1741	**57p**	Umbrella in Rain	1.00	1.10
C1742	**68p**	In Fog on Roof	1.20	1.30
C1743	**£1.12**	Sheltering from Hailstorm	1.70	1.80
		Set of 6	5.25	5.40
		Set of 6 Gutter Pairs	13.25	13.75
		First Day Cover		7.50
		Presentation Pack 365	5.20	
		PHQ Cards	3.20	5.00
MS27		Miniature sheet	4.90	5.10
		First Day Cover		8.00

2004 (2 Nov.) from 'Christmas' Smilers sheet

No.		U/M
SSP21	2nd and label	1.50
SSP21a	1st and label	1.50

2004 (2 Nov.) Collectors Year Pack

No.		U/M
CP41	Collectors Year Pack 366	£48

2004 (2 Nov.) Royal Mail Year Book - 21

No.		U/M
YB21	Royal Mail Year Book	£50

2005 (11 Jan.) Farm Animals Printed in gravure Perf 14½ x 14½

No.			U/M	F/U
C1744	**1st**	Saddle Back Pig	50	60
C1745	**1st**	Khaki Campbell Duck	50	60
C1746	**1st**	Clydesdale Horse	50	60
C1747	**1st**	Shorthorn Cow	50	60
C1748	**1st**	Border Collie Puppy	50	60
C1749	**1st**	Chicks	50	60
C1750	**1st**	Suffolk Sheep	50	60
C1751	**1st**	Bagot Goat	50	60
C1752	**1st**	Norfolk Black Turkey	50	60
C1753	**1st**	Embden Geese	50	60
		Set of 10	4.70	4.90
		Cylinder Block		
		Gutter Block of 20	11.75	12.00
		First Day Cover		6.00
		Presentation Pack 367	4.50	
		PHQ Cards	4.20	6.00

2005 (11 Jan.) from 'Farm Animals' Printed in Litho from Smilers sheet

No.		U/M
SSP23	1st plus *label* (any)	1.50
SSP23a	Set of 10 stamps and labels	£12

2005 (8 Feb.) South West England

No.			U/M	F/U
C1754	**2nd**	Old Harry Rocks	35	40
C1755	**1st**	Wheal Coates, St. Agnes	45	50
C1756	**40p**	Start Point, Start Bay	65	70
C1757	**43p**	Horton Down, Wiltshire	70	75
C1758	**57p**	Chiselcombe, Exmoor	1.10	1.15
C1759	**68p**	St James's Stone, Lundy	1.20	1.25
		Set of 6	3.80	3.90
		Set of 6 Cylinder Blocks	28.50	
		Set of 6 Gutter Pairs	9.50	9.50
		First Day Cover		5.50
		Presentation Pack 368	4.20	
		PHQ Cards	4.20	6.00

2005 (24 Feb.) Jane Eyre Perf 14 x 14½

No.			U/M	F/U
C1760	**2nd**	Mr Rochester	35	40
C1761	**1st**	Jane as Thornfield Hall Burns	45	50
C1762	**40p**	Jane Eyre	65	70
C1763	**57p**	Jane with Adele	1.05	1.10
C1764	**68p**	Jane as a child at Lowood School	1.20	1.25
C1765	**£1.12**	Rev. Brocklehurst	1.65	1.70
		Set of 6	4.90	5.10
		Set of 6 Cylinder Blocks	36.50	
		Set of 6 Gutter Pairs	12.25	12.50
		First Day Cover		5.50
		Presentation Pack 369	5.20	
		PHQ Cards	3.00	5.00
MS28		Miniature Sheet	4.85	4.95
		First Day Cover		5.50

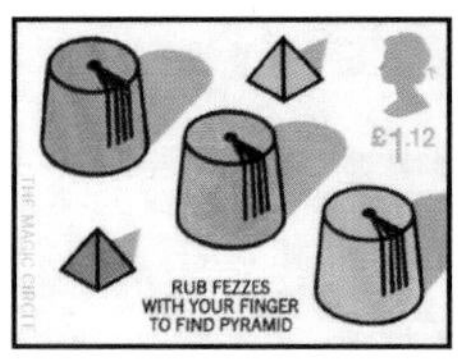

2005 (15 Mar.) Magic Perf 14½ x 14½

No.			U/M	F/U
C1766	**1st**	Heads	50	60
C1766a		Tails	50	60
C1767	**40p**	Hat and Rabbit	60	70
C1768	**47p**	Scarves and Tube	80	90
C1769	**68p**	Ace of Hearts	95	1.00
C1770	**£1.12**	Fez and Pyramid	1.65	1.70
		Set of 5	4.90	5.10
		Set of 5 Cylinder Blocks	36.50	
		Set of 5 Gutter Pairs	12.25	12.50
		First Day Cover		5.00
		Presentation Pack 370	4.80	
		PHQ Cards	3.50	5.50

2005 (15 Mar.) from 'Magic' Smilers sheet

No.		U/M	F/U
SSP23	1st Heads *plus* label (any)	2.00	
SSP23a	1st Tails *plus* label (any)	2.00	

2005 (8 Apr.) Royal Wedding 14½ x 14½

No.			U/M	F/U
C1771	30p	Prince Charles and Camilla Parker-Bowles	60	60
C1772	68p	Prince Charles and Camilla Parker-Bowles	1.40	1.40
MS30		Miniature Sheet	2.90	3.00
		First Day Cover		3.90
		Presentation Pack M10	3.50	

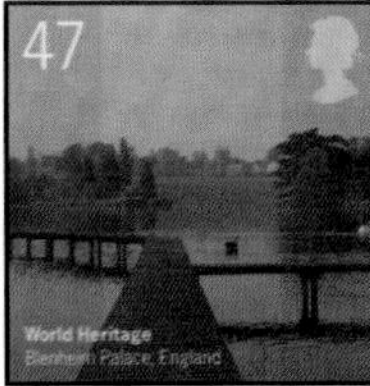

2005 (21 Apr.) World Heritage Sites Perf 14½ x 14½

No.			U/M	F/U
C1773	**2nd**	Hadrian's Wall	40	40
C1774	**2nd**	Uluru-Kata, Tjuta National Park	40	40
C1775	**1st**	Stonehenge	45	45
C1776	**1st**	Wet Tropics of Queensland	45	45
C1777	**47p**	Blenheim Palace	80	80
C1778	**47p**	Greater Blue Mountains	80	80
C1779	**68p**	Heart of Neolithic Orkney	95	95
C1780	**68p**	Purnululu National Park	95	95
		Set of 8	4.60	4.70
		Set of 4 Cylinder Blocks	13.50	
		Set of 4 Se-Tenant Pairs	5.75	5.80
		Set of 4 Gutter Pairs	6.00	6.00
		First Day Cover		6.00
		Presentation Pack 371	5.40	
		PHQ Cards	3.20	5.00

Each of the values were printed se-tenant within the sheet

2005 (7 June) Trooping the Colour Perf 14½ x 14½

No.			U/M	F/U
C1781	**2nd**	Ensign of the Scots Guards with Colour	35	40
C1782	**1st**	HM The Queen	45	50
C1783	**42p**	Trumpeter from Household Cavalry	65	70
C1784	**60p**	Welsh Guards Sgt.	90	95
C1785	**68p**	HM the Queen	1.15	1.20
C1786	**£1.12**	HM the Queen and The Duke of Edinburgh	1.60	1.65
		Set of 6	4.80	4.90
		Set of 6 Cylinder Blocks	35.50	
		Set of 6 Gutter Pairs	12.00	12.00
		First Day Cover		6.00
		Presentation Pack 372	5.40	
		PHQ Cards	2.50	4.50
MS31		Miniature Sheet	6.50	6.50

2005 (5 July) End of the War

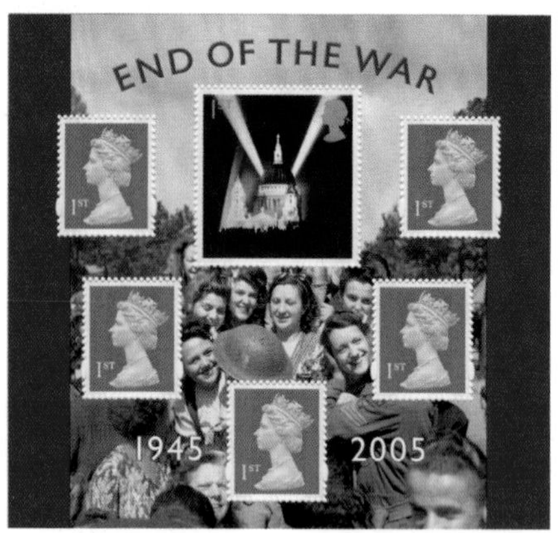

No.			U/M	F/U
C1144a	**1st**	St. Paul's Cathedral (also listed on page H - 74)	1.75	1.85
MS32		Miniature sheet	2.70	2.70

2005 (19 July) Motorcycles Perf 14½ x 14½

No.			U/M	F/U
C1787	**1st**	1991 Norton F.1	45	50
C1788	**40p**	1969 BSA Rocket 3	65	70
C1789	**42p**	1949 Vincent Black Shadow	70	80
C1790	**47p**	1938 Triumph Speed Twin	80	90
C1791	**60p**	1030 Brough Superior	90	95
C1792	**68p**	1914 Royal Enfield	95	1.00
		Set of 6	4.15	4.20
		Set of 6 Cylinder Blocks	29.50	
		Set of 6 Gutter Pairs	10.50	
		First Day Cover		5.00
		Presentation Pack 373	4.80	
		PHQ Cards	2.60	4.50

A B C D E A

2005 (5 Aug.) London 2012 Perf 14½ x 14½

No.			U/M	F/U
C1793	**1st**	Shot Putt (A)	65	65
C1794	**1st**	Javelin (B)	65	65
C1795	**1st**	Diving (C)	65	65
C1796	**1st**	Sprinting (D)	65	65
C1797	**1st**	Netball (E)	65	65
MS33		Miniature sheet	3.25	2.75
		First Day Cover	3.50	
		Presentation Pack M11	3.20	

2005(23 Aug.) Changing Tastes of Britain Perf 14½ x 14½

No.			U/M	F/U
C1798	2nd	Woman eating Rice	30	35
C1799	1st	Woman drinking tea	45	50
C1800	42p	Boy eating Suchi	65	70
C1801	47p	Woman eating Pasta	75	80
C1802	60p	Woman eating Chips	90	95
C1803	68p	Man eating Apple	1.00	1.10
		Set of 6	3.80	4.00
		Set of 6 Cylinder Blocks	27.50	
		Set of 6 Gutter Pairs	9.50	9.50
		First Day Cover	5.00	
		Presentation Pack 374	4.50	
		PHQ Cards	2.60	4.00

2005 (15 Sep.) Classic ITV Perf

No.			U/M	F/U
C1804	**2nd**	Inspector Morse	30	35
C1805	**1st**	Emmerdale	45	50
C1806	**42p**	Rising Damp	65	70
C1807	**47p**	The Avengers	70	75
C1808	**60p**	The South Bank Show	90	95
C1809	**68p**	Who Wants to be a Millionaire	1.00	1.10
		Set of 6	3.80	4.00
		Set of 6 Cylinder Blocks	27.50	
		Set of 6 Gutter Pairs	9.50	9.50
		First Day Cover		
		Presentation Pack 375	4.50	
		PHQ Cards	2.60	4.00

2005 (15 Sep.) from 'Classic ITV' Smilers sheet

No.		U/M	F/U
SSP25	1st Emmerdale *plus* label (any)	1.50	

2005 (6 Oct.) The Ashes

No.			U/M	F/U
C1810	**1st**		65	70
C1811	**1st**		65	70
C1812	**68p**		1.35	1.40
C1813	**68p**		1.35	1.40
MS34		Miniature Sheet	3.00	3.25
		First Day Cover		4.00
		Presentation Pack M12	3.50	
		PHQ Cards	2.80	4.50

This was the first issue to show recognisable living persons, apart from Royalty, on GB stamps.

A

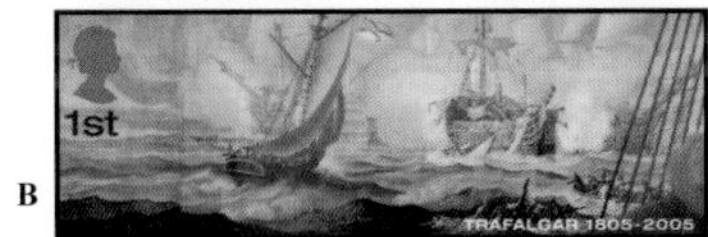

B

C

D

E

F

2005 (18 Oct.) Battle of Trafalgar

No.			U/M	F/U
C1814	**1st**	Entrepreante/Belle Isle (A)	45	50
C1815	**1st**	HMS Victory (B)	45	50
C1816	**42p**	Entrepreante/Achille (C)	65	70
C1817	**42p**	H M S Pickle (D)	65	70
C1818	**68p**	British Fleet Attacking (E)	1.00	1.10
C1819	**68p**	Franco/Spanish Fleet (F)	1.00	1.10
		Set of 6	4.00	4.50
		Set of 3 Cylinder Blocks	29.50	
		Set of Gutter Blocks	10.00	10.00
		First Day Cover		5.00
		Presentation Pack 376	4.50	
		PHQ Cards	2.60	4.00

These were issued as se-tenant pairs of each individual value

No.			U/M	F/U
MS35		Miniature Sheet	4.20	4.30

2005 (1 Nov.) Christmas Self Adhesive Perf 14 x 14.5

No.			U/M	F/U
C1820	**2nd**	Madonna and child Haiti	30	35
C1821	**1st**	Madonna and child	45	50
C1821a	**1st**	Madonna and child (Matrix intact - Post Office Staff Issue)	2.50	
C1822	**42p**	Virgin Mary/Infant Christ	65	70
C1823	**60p**	Virgin Mother/Child (Choctaw)	90	95
C1824	**68p**	Madonna and Infant Jesus	1.00	1.10
C1825	**£1.12**	Come Let Us Adore Him	1.70	1.80
		Set of 6	4.70	5.00
		Set of 6 Gutter Blocks	11.75	12.00
		First Day Cover		6.00
		Presentation Pack 377	4.75	
		PHQ Cards	3.00	5.00
MS36		Miniature Sheet	4.95	5.00
		First Day Cover		6.00

2005 (1 Nov.) Collectors Year Pack

No.		U/M	F/U
CP42	Collectors Year Pack 378	£40	

2005 (1 Nov.) Royal Mail Year Book - 22

No.		U/M	F/U
YB22	Royal Mail Year Book	£50	

Post Office Machine Labels (Framas)

Post Office machine labels have now commonly become known as 'Frama' labels, this being the machine manufacturer's name. From 1 May 1984 machines were installed on an experimental basis at five offices: Cambridge, Edinburgh, London, Southampton (Shirley Avenue) and Windsor.

The labels were dispensed from automatic machines that imprinted on command any denomination from ½p to 16p in ½p increments. On 18 August, two further values were made available, 16½p and 17p.

The Post Office supplied labels from Philatelic Bureaux in 'Packs' of either all 32 denominations or in sets of 3½p, 12½p and 16p values. The latter combination was the only type to be serviced to subscribers by the Philatelic Bureau. In early 1985 after abandonment of the ½p coin the machines were withdrawn.

Used labels with legible postmarks from any of the 5 experimental areas are worth a premium of 50%.

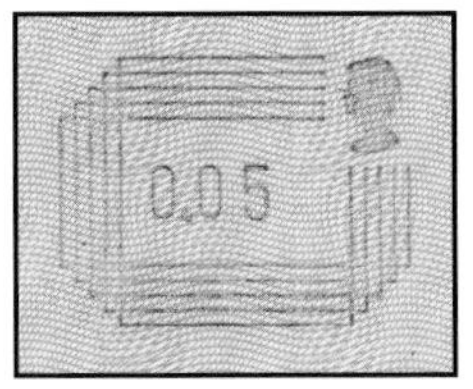

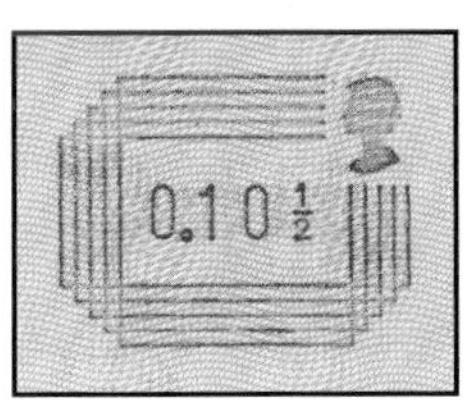

1984 (1 May) Phosphor Coated Paper. No watermark. Imperforate.

No.			U/M	F/U
FR1	½p	Red on grey	15	20
FR2	1p	Red on grey	15	20
FR3	1½p	Red on grey	15	20
FR4	2p	Red on grey	15	20
FR5	2½p	Red on grey	20	25
FR6	3p	Red on grey	20	25
FR7	3½p	Red on grey	25	30
FR8	4p	Red on grey	25	30
FR9	4½p	Red on grey	30	35
FR10	5p	Red on grey	30	35
FR11	5½p	Red on grey	35	40
FR12	6p	Red on grey	35	40
FR13	6½p	Red on grey	40	45
FR14	7p	Red on grey	40	45
FR15	7½p	Red on grey	45	50
FR16	8p	Red on grey	45	50
FR17	8½p	Red on grey	50	55
FR18	9p	Red on grey	50	55
FR19	9½p	Red on grey	55	60
FR20	10p	Red on grey	55	60
FR21	10½p	Red on grey	65	70
FR22	11p	Red on grey	65	70
FR23	11½p	Red on grey	70	75
FR24	12p	Red on grey	70	75
FR25	12½p	Red on grey	75	85
FR26	13p	Red on grey	75	85
FR27	13½p	Red on grey	80	85
FR28	14p	Red on grey	80	85
FR29	14½p	Red on grey	85	90
FR30	15p	Red on grey	85	90
FR31	15½p	Red on grey	90	95
FR32	16p	Red on grey	90	95
FR33	16½p	Red on grey	1.40	1.60
FR34	17p	Red on grey	1.40	1.60

	U/M	F/U
Set of 34	£13	£16
First Day Covers (½p to 16p)		£25
First Day Cover (3½p, 12½p and 16p)		4.00
Philatelic "Pack" (½p to 16p)	£25	
Philatelic "Pack" (3½p, 12½p and 16p)	3.50	
Philatelic "Pack" (16½p and 17p)	4.50	
NPM 'PHQ' Card (16p)*	4.50	6.00
First Day Cover (16½p and 17p)		5.00

* The National Postal Museum produced a 16p value 'PHQ' style card for this issue.

Varieties

No.			U/M
FR1a	½p	Missing "½" (label reads "0.00")	£50
FR1b	½p	Printed on white paper	£100
FR2a	1p	Printed on white paper	£100
FR2b	1p	Dry print of Red (blank label)	£20
FR4a	2p	Printed on white paper	£100
FR6a	3p	Printed on the gummed side	£225
FR25a	12½p	Printed on white paper	£100
FR25b	12½p	Printed on the gummed side	£130
FR26a	13p	Printed on the gummed side	£225
FR32a	16p	Printed on white paper	£100
FR32b	16p	Printed on the gummed side	£130
FR33a	16½p	Printed on the gummed side	£225
FR34a	17p	Printed on the gummed side	£225
		Set of 17 NPM 'Specimen' labels in red on white paper. *	£18
		Set of 17 NPM 'Specimen' labels in black on white paper. *	£14

* These were only available from a machine atThe National Postal Museum, London.

Miniature Sheets

Britains first miniature sheet was issued on 1 March 1978. The following year the second in the series was released to commemorate the death of Sir Rowland Hill; it was sold 10p above face value to help fund the London 1980 Stamp Exhibition the following year. It was another eight years (1988) before the next appeared. From 1978 to 1999 (21 years) only eight miniature sheets were issued; since then - from 2000 to 2005 there have been another 28 sheets issued in only 6 years. We predict this section will expand much more for the next edition of this catalogue!

1978 (1 March) British Architecture. Historic Buildings

No.			U/M	F/U
MS1	**53½p**	**Complete Miniature Sheet** (in original PO folder)	90	1.10
MS1a		Missing phosphor	£100	
		First Day Cover		1.00
Varieties				
MS1b	MS	Missing Red (flag on 9p)	£3500	
MS1c	MS	Missing Pale Orange (10p and 13p)	£3500	
MS1d	MS	Missing Yellow-olive (Queen's head)	£4500	
MS1e	MS	Missing Blue	£11000	
MS1f	MS	Imperforate	£4500	

1979 (22 Aug.) Sir Rowland Hill Centenary

No.			U/M	F/U
MS2	**59½p**	**Miniature sheet** (24.10.79)	70	70
MS2a		Missing phosphor	£25	
		First Day Cover		75
Varieties				
MS2b	MS	Imperforate	£2000	
MS2c	MS	Missing Black and Yellow	£12500	
MS2d	MS	Missing Yellow (10p windows, etc.)	£250	£225
MS2e	MS	Missing Yellow and phosphor	£250	
MS2f	MS	Missing Brown-ochre (15p sky, etc.)	£1750	
MS2g	MS	Missing Brown-ochre, Green and Gold	£5000	
MS2h	MS	Missing Rosine (11½p jacket, etc.)	£1000	
MS2i	MS	Missing Rosine and phosphor	£750	
MS2j	MS	Missing Blue (13p, jacket, sky, etc.)	£5500	
MS2k	MS	Missing Green (10p sky & coat, 15p etc.)	£2500	
MS2l	MS	Missing Brown (15p dress, 11½p, 13p etc.)	£750	
MS2m	MS	Missing Gold (Queen's head)	£250	£225
MS2n	MS	Missing Gold and phosphor	£250	
MS2o	MS	Shift 6mm to top of Green	£175	
MS2p	MS	Shift 2mm to right of Gold	£5	
MS2q	MS	Offset on reverse of Gold (Queen's head)	£350	

1980 (7 May) London 1980 International Stamp Exhibition

No.			U/M	F/U
MS3	**75p**	**Complete Miniature sheet**	80	1.00
		First Day Cover		75
Variety				
MS3a	MS	Imperforate sheet	£1250	£750

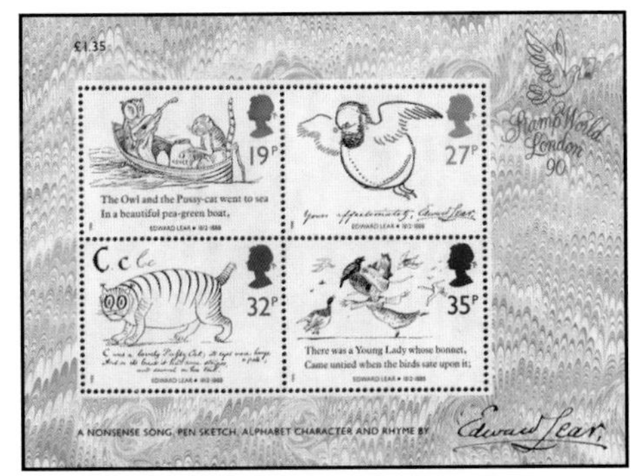

1988 (27 Sept.) Edward Lear

No.			U/M	F/U
MS4	**£1.35**	**Complete Miniature Sheet**	4.20	4.50
		First Day Cover		3.50

1989 (25 July) Industrial Archaeology

No.			U/M	F/U
MS5	**£1.40**	**Complete Miniature Sheet**	2.90	3.20
		First Day Cover		3.00

1990 (3 May) 'Stamp World 90', London

No.			U/M	F/U
MS6	**£1**	**Miniature sheet** containing 20p stamp	2.70	2.75
		First Day Cover		3.00
Varieties				
MS6a	£1	Missing Black (Recess printing)	£7500	
MS6b	£1	Missing Cream (Recess printing)	£4000	
MS6c	£1	Imperforate	£3500	
MS6d	£1	Imperforate. First Day Cover		£3500
MS6e	£1	Recess printing inverted (background)	£7500	

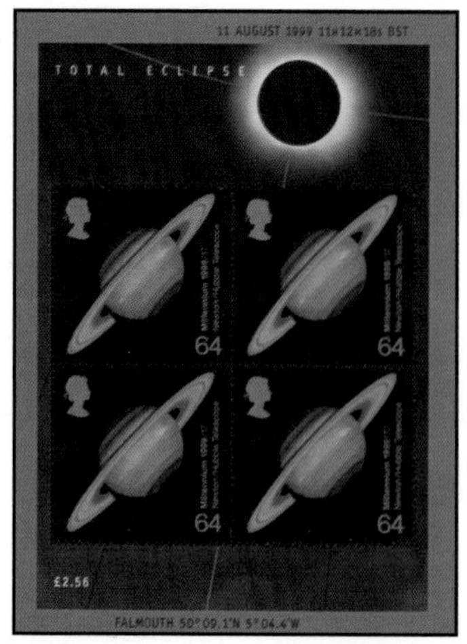

1999 (11 Aug.) Solar Eclipse

No.			U/M	F/U
MS7	**4 x 64p**	Complete Miniature Sheet	£16	£16
		First Day Cover		£16
Variety				
MS7A		Impeforate sheet (Mint & FDC)	£3250	£1750

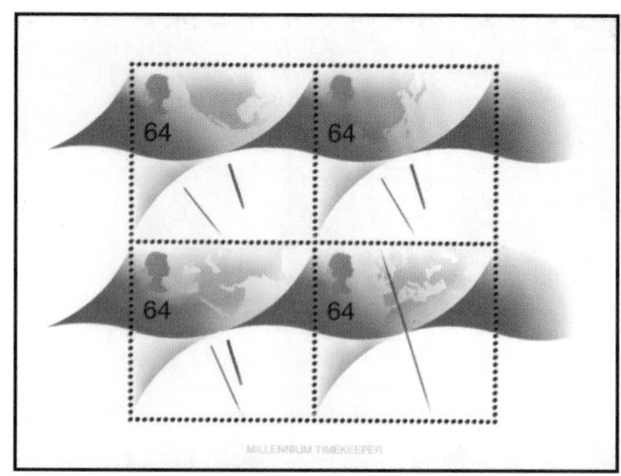

1999 (14 Dec.) Millennium Timekeeper

No.			U/M	F/U
MS8	**4 x 64p**	Complete Miniature sheeet	£15	
		First Day Cover		£15

2000 (22 May) Millennium Timekeeper Stamp Show Overprint

No.			U/M	F/U
MS9	**4 x 64p**	Stamp Show 2000 overprint	£17	
		First Day Cover		£65

2000 (22 May) Stamp Show 2000 Jeffrey Matthews Colour Pallette

No.		U/M	F/U
MS10	Complete miniature sheet	£25	£25
	First Day Cover		£25
MS10a	Souvenir Wallet	£50	

2000 (23 May) Stamp Show 2000 Her Majesty's Stamps

No.		U/M	F/U
MS11	Complete miniature sheet	£20	£20
	First Day Cover		£20
	Presentation Pack MO3	47.50	

2000 (4 Aug.) Queen Mother's Birthday

No.		U/M	F/U
MS12	Complete Miniature sheet	6.50	7.00
	Presentation Pack MO4	11.95	
	First Day Cover		4.50
Variety			
MS12a	Imperforate miniature sheet	£3750	

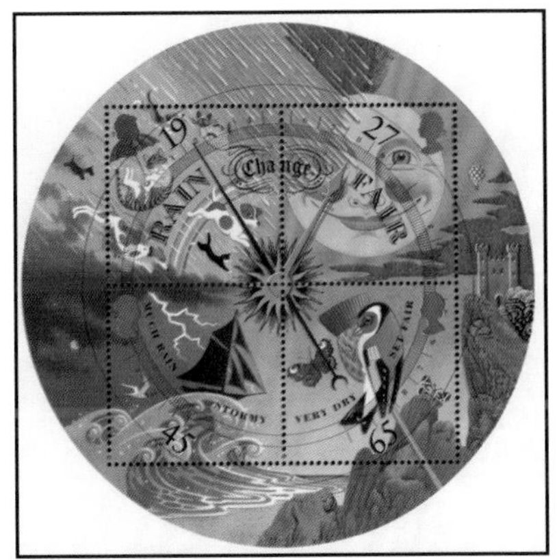

2001 (13 Mar.) The Weather

No.		U/M	F/U
MS13	Complete Miniature Sheet	8.00	8.00
	First Day Cover		8.00

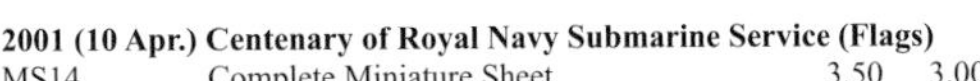

2001 (10 Apr.) Centenary of Royal Navy Submarine Service (Flags)

No.		U/M	F/U
MS14	Complete Miniature Sheet	3.50	3.00
	First Day Cover		3.50

2001 (15 May.) 150th Anniversary of First Double Decker Bus

No.		U/M	F/U
MS15	Complete Miniature Sheet	5.00	
	First Day Cover		4.50

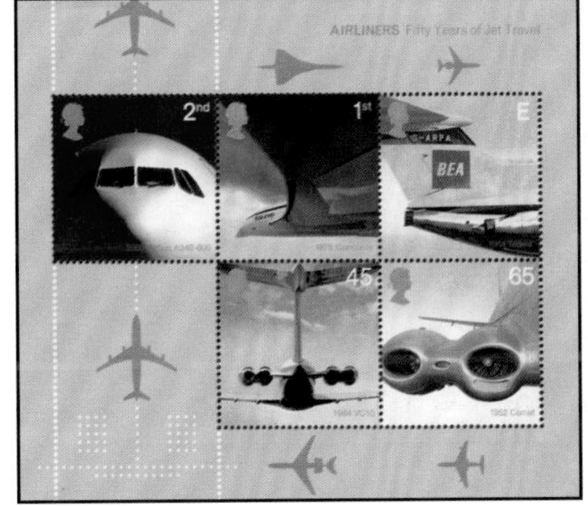

2002 (2 May) Airliners

No.		U/M	F/U
MS16	Complete Miniature Sheet	4.50	4.60
	First Day Cover		6.00

2002 (21 May) World Cup

No.		U/M	F/U
MS17	Complete Miniature Sheet	2.70	2.80
	First Day Cover		4.00

2002 (24 Sep.) Astronomy

No.		U/M	F/U
MS18	Complete Miniature Sheet	2.60	3.00
	First Day Cover		3.50

2002 (5 Dec.) Anniversary of Wilding Definitives (1st)

No.		U/M	F/U
MS19	Complete Miniature Sheet	3.40	3.80
	First Day Cover		5.00
	Presentation Pack	£45	

2003 (20 May) Anniversary of Wilding Definitives (2nd)

No.		U/M	F/U
MS20	Complete Miniature Sheet	3.80	4.20
	First Day Cover		5.00
	Presentation Pack	£10	

2003 (18 Sep.) Transports of Delight

No.		U/M	F/U
MS21	Complete Miniature Sheet	3.20	
	First Day Cover		6.25

2003 (19 Dec.) Rugby World Cup Winners

No.		U/M	F/U
MS22	Complete Miniature Sheet	2.80	2.90
	First Day Cover		4.00
	Presentation Pack	£20	

2004 (13 Jan.) Classic Locomotives

No.		U/M	F/U
MS23	Complete Miniature Sheet	17.50	17.50
	First Day Cover		20.00

2004 (13 Apr.) Ocean Liners

No.		U/M	F/U
MS24	Complete Miniature Sheet	6.00	6.00
	First Day Cover		10.00
Variety			
C1700	Error of value - The 57p printed as 53p		£6000

2004 (25 May) Bicentenary of the RHS

No.		U/M	F/U
MS25	Complete Miniature Sheet	5.50	5.50
	First Day Cover		4.95

2004 Scottish Parliament

No.		U/M	F/U
MS26	Complete Miniature sheet	2.80	2.90
	First Day Cover		4.00

2004 (2 Nov.) Christmas

No.		U/M	F/U
MS27	Complete Miniature sheet	4.90	5.10
	First Day Cover		8.00

2005 (24 Feb.) Jane Eyre

No.		U/M	F/U
MS28	Complete Miniature Sheet	4.85	4.95
	First Day Cover		5.50

2005 (22 Mar.) Castles

No.		U/M	F/U
MS29	Complete Miniature Sheet	3.95	4.20
	First Day Cover		6.50

2005 (8 Apr.) Royal Wedding

No.		U/M	F/U
MS30	Complete Miniature Sheet	2.90	3.00
	First Day Cover		3.90
	Presentation Pack M10	3.60	

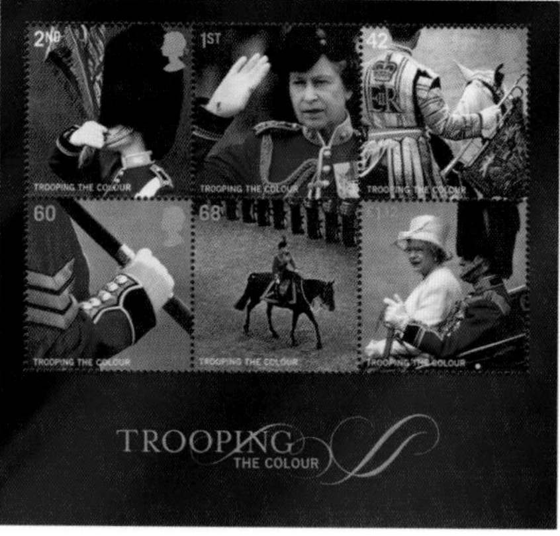

2005 (7 June) Trooping the Colour

No.		U/M	F/U
MS31	Complete Miniature Sheet	6.50	6.50
	First Day Cover		6.50

2005 (5 July) End of the War 1945 - 2005

No.		U/M	F/U
MS32	Complete Miniature Sheet	3.50	3.50
	First Day Cover		3.95

2005 (5 Aug.) London 2012 Host City

No.		U/M	F/U
MS33	Complete Miniature Sheet	2.70	2.80
	First Day Cover		4.00

2005 (6 Oct.) The Ashes

No.		U/M	F/U
MS34	Complete Miniature Sheet	3.00	3.25
	First Day Cover		4.00

2005 (18 Oct.) Battle of Trafalgar

No.		U/M	F/U
MS35	Complete Miniature Sheet	4.20	4.30
	First Day Cover		5.50

No.		U/M	F/U

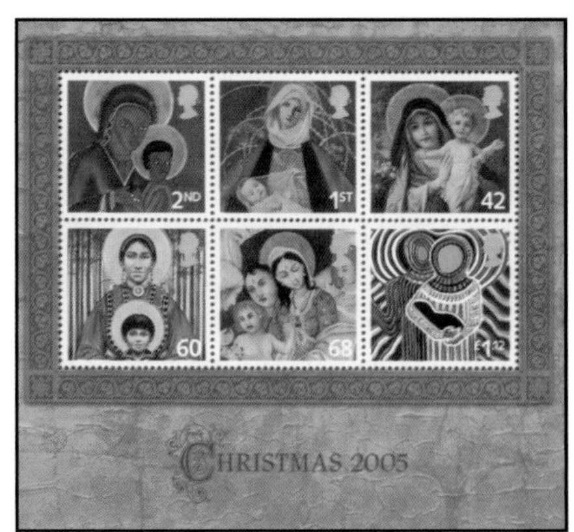

2005 (1 Nov.) Christmas

MS36	Complete Miniature Sheet	4.95	5.00
	First Day Cover		6.50

Issue date | No. | Description | Pack | Issue date | No. | Description | Pack

Royal Mail Presentation Packs

Presentation packs were first introduced in 1964 and were intially not numbered. These packs are listed in the Commemorative issues section under their respective issue details, but are repeated here in a Chronological order for the convenience of readers. We have included all presentation packs, including definitive and regional issues.

Issue date	No.	Description	Pack
23 April 1964		Shakespeare	14.50
1 July 1964		Geographical	95.00
5 August 1964		Botanical	95.00
4 September 1964		F.R. Bridge	375.00
8 July 1965		Churchill	45.00
19 July 1965		Parliament	40.00
13 September 1965		Battle of Britain	39.50
8 October 1965		Post Office Tower	3.50
25 January 1966		Burns	39.50
28 February 1966		Westminster Abbey	35.00
1 June 1966		Football World Cup	9.50
15 August 1966		Birds	4.50
19 September 1966		Technology	7.50
14 October 1966		Hastings	3.75
1 December 1966		Christmas	5.00
10 February 1967		EFTA	1.60
24 April 1967		Flowers	2.95
10 July 1967		Paintings	3.30
19 September 1967		Discoveries	2.00
29 April 1968		Bridges	2.00
29 May 1968		Anniversaries	1.75
12 August 1968	1	Paintings	1.75
25 November 1968	4	Christmas	1.75
15 January 1969	5	Ships	2.50
3 March 1969	6	Concorde	6.50
2 April 1969	9	Anniversaries	2.75
28 May 1969	10	Cathedrals	1.75
1 July 1969	11	Investiture	1.75
1 October 1969	13	PO Technology	1.75
26 November 1969	14	Christmas	1.75
11 February 1970	15	Cottages	2.95
1 April 1970	16	Anniversaries	1.75
3 June 1970	17	Dickens	2.50
15 July 1970	19	Commonwealth	1.75
18 September 1970	21	Philympia	1.75
25 November 1970	22	Christmas	1.75
16 June 1971	26A	Ulster Paintings	2.75
28 July 1971	32	Literary	2.75
25 August 1971	32A	Anniversaries	2.75
22 September 1971	33	Universities	3.50
13 October 1971	35	Christmas	2.00
16 February 1972	39	Explorers	2.25
26 April 1972	40	Anniversaries	2.25
21 June 1972	41	Churches	4.00
13 September 1972	43	BBC	2.25
18 October 1972	44	Christmas	2.25
20 November 1972	45	Silver Wedding	2.25
3 January 1973	48	EEC	1.45
28 February 1973	49	Oak Tree	1.10
18 April 1973	50	Explorers	1.50
16 May 1973	51	Cricket	2.50
4 July 1973	52	Paintings	1.60
15 August 1973	53	Inigo Jones	1.60
12 September 1973	54	Parliament	1.60
14 November 1973	56	Royal Wedding	1.25
28 November 1973	57	Christmas	1.60
27 February 1974	58	Chestnut Tree	1.10
24 April 1974	60	Fire Service	1.60
12 June 1974	64	UPU	1.60
10 July 1974	65	Great Britons	1.60
9 October 1974	66	Churchill	1.75
27 November 1974	67	Christmas	1.60
19 February 1975	69	Turner	1.60
23 April 1975	70	Architecture	1.60
11 June 1975	71	Sailing	1.30
13 August 1975	72	Railway	2.50
3 September 1975	74	Parliament	0.90
22 October 1975	75	Jane Austen	1.60
26 November 1975	76	Christmas	1.60
10 March 1976	78	Telephones	2.00
28 April 1976	79	Pioneers	1.75
2 June 1976	80	USA Bicentenary	0.75
30 June 1976	81	Roses	1.80
4 August 1976	82	Culture	2.00
20 September 1976	83	Caxton	1.80
24 November 1976	87	Christmas	2.00
12 January 1977	89	Racket Sports	1.85
2 March 1977	92	Chemistry	1.85
11 May 1977	94	Silver Jubilee	0.95
8 June 1977	95	Heads of Govt	0.50

Issue date	No.	Description	Pack
5 October 1977	96	Wildlife	0.85
23 November 1977	97	Christmas	1.25
25 January 1978	99	Energy	1.50
1 March 1978	100	Buildings	1.50
31 May 1978	101	Coronation Jubilee	1.00
5 July 1978	102	Horses	1.05
2 August 1978	103	Cycling	0.90
22 November 1978	104	Christmas	0.90
7 February 1979	106	Dogs	1.10
21 March 1979	107	Flowers	0.90
19 May 1979	108	Elections	0.90
6 June 1979	109	Derby	0.90
11 July 1979	110	Year of the Child	2.00
22 August 1979	111	Rowland Hill	0.90
26 September 1979	112	Police	0.90
21 November 1979	113	Christmas	0.95
16 January 1980	115	Birds	0.90
12 March 1980	116	Railways	0.95
9 April 1980	117	50p London	0.95
7 May 1980	118	Landmark	1.05
9 July 1980	119	Authors	1.55
10 September 1980	120	Conductors	0.90
10 October 1980	121	1980 Sport	0.90
19 November 1980	122	1980 Christmas	0.90
6 February 1981	124	1981 Folklore / Europa	1.95
25 March 1981	125	1981 Disabled	1.05
13 May 1981	126	1981 Butterflies	1.05
24 June 1981	127	1981 National Trust	1.20
22 July 1981	127A	1981 Royal Wedding	1.40
12 August 1981	128	1981 D of E Award	1.10
23 September 1981	129	1981 Fishing	1.10
18 November 1981	130	1981 Christmas	1.20
10 February 1982	132	1982 Darwin	1.20
24 March 1982	133	1982 Youth Groups	1.55
28 April 1982	134	1982 Theatre / Europa	2.75
16 June 1982	136	1982 Maritime	1.95
23 July 1982	137	1982 Textiles	1.20
8 September 1982	138	1982 Information	0.80
13 October 1982	139	1982 Cars	1.30
17 November 1982	140	1982 Christmas	1.30

Issue date	No.	Description	Pack
26 January 1983	142	1983 Fish	1.25
9 March 1983	143	1983 Commonwealth	1.25
25 May 1983	144	1983 Engineering / Europa	1.85
6 July 1983	145	1983 Army	1.60
24 August 1983	146	1983 Gardens	1.30
5 October 1983	147	1983 Fairs	1.30
16 November 1983	148	1983 Christmas	1.35
17 January 1984	150	1984 Heraldry	1.35
6 March 1984	151	1984 Cattle	1.60
10 April 1984	152	1984 Urban Renewal	1.30
15 May 1984	153	1984 Europa	2.25
26 June 1984	154	1984 Greenwich	1.35
31 July 1984	155	1984 Mail Coach	1.40
25 September 1984	156	1984 Council	1.40
20 November 1984	157	1984 Christmas	1.50
22 January 1985	159	1985 Trains	2.75
12 March 1985	160	1985 Insects	1.80
14 May 1985	161	1985 Composers / Europa	2.75
18 June 1985	162	1985 Safety at Sea	1.50
30 July 1985	163	1985 Royal Mail	1.50
3 September 1985	164	1985 Arthurian	1.50
8 October 1985	165	1985 Films	2.10
19 November 1985	166	1985 Christmas	1.60
14 January 1986	168	1986 Industry	1.60
18 February 1986	168	1986 Comet	1.60
21 April 1986	170	1986 60th Birthday	2.30
20 May 1986	171	1986 Conservation / Europa	2.75
17 June 1986	172	1986 Medieval	1.60
15 July 1986	173	1986 Sport	2.10
22 July 1986	174	1986 Royal Wedding	0.90
16 September 1986	175	1986 RAF	2.10
18 November 1986	176	1986 Christmas	1.85
20 January 1987	178	1987 Flowers	1.80
24 March 1987	179	1987 Newton	1.80
12 May 1987	180	1987 Architects / Europa	2.75
16 June 1987	181	1987 St Johns	1.80
21 July 1987	182	1987 Heraldry	1.80
8 September 1987	183	1987 Victoria	1.80
13 October 1987	184	1987 Pottery	1.80
17 November 1987	185	1987 Christmas	1.80
19 January 1988	187	1988 Linnean	1.80
1 March 1988	188	1988 Welsh Bible	1.80
22 March 1988	189	1988 Sport	1.80
10 May 1988	190	1988 Transport / Europa	2.75
21 June 1988	191	1988 Australia	1.80
19 July 1988	192	1988 Armada	1.80
6 September 1988	193	1988 Lear	1.80
15 November 1988	194	1988 Christmas	1.80
17 January 1989	196	1989 Birds	1.80
7 March 1989	197	1989 Food	1.80
11 April 1989	198	1989 Anniversaries	2.20
16 May 1989	199	1989 Toys / Europa	2.75

Issue date	No.	Description	Pack
4 July 1989	200	1989 Industry	1.90
5 September 1989	201	1989 Microscopes	1.90
17 October 1989	202	1989 Lord Mayor	1.85
14 November 1989	203	1989 Christmas	1.70
10 January 1990	21	1990 Penny Black	3.60
23 January 1990	205	1990 RSPCA	2.10
6 March 1990	206	1990 Buildings/Europa	2.75
10 April 1990	207	1990 Queens Awards	2.05
5 June 1990	208	1990 Kew Gardens	1.95
10 July 1990	209	1990 Thomas Hardy	0.80
2 August 1990	210	1990 Queen Mother	3.10
11 September 1990	211	1990 Gallantry	1.95
16 October 1990	212	1990 Astronomy	2.05
13 November 1990	213	1990 Christmas	2.00
8 January 1991	215	1991 Dogs	2.15
5 March 1991	216	1991 Science	2.05
23 April 1991	217	1991 Space/Europa	2.75
11 June 1991	218	1991 Sport	2.05
16 July 1991	219	1991 Roses	2.05
20 August 1991	220	1991 Dinosaurs	2.55
17 September 1991	221	1991 Ordnance	2.05
12 November 1991	222	1991 Christmas	2.05
14 January 1992	224	1992 Wintertime	2.05
6 February 1992	225	1992 Happy & Glorious	2.95
10 March 1992	226	1992 Tennyson	2.15
7 April 1992	227	1992 International/Europa	2.75
16 June 1992	228	1992 Civil War	2.05
21 July 1992	229	1992 Gilbert & Sull	2.15
15 September 1992	230	1992 Green	2.05
13 October 1992	231	1992 Europe	0.90
10 November 1992	232	1992 Christmas	1.95
19 January 1993	234	1993 Swans	3.45
16 February 1993	235	1993 Harrison / Timekeepers	2.55
16 March 1993	236	1993 Orchids	2.15
11 May 1993	237	1993 Art/Europa	2.75
15 June 1993	238	1993 Roman	2.05
20 July 1993	239	1993 Canals	2.05
14 September 1993	240	1993 Autumn	2.05
12 October 1993	241	1993 Holmes	2.15
9 November 1993	242	1993 Christmas	2.35

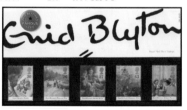

Issue date	No.	Description	Pack
18 January 1994	244	1994 Steam Trains	2.80
1 March 1994	245	1994 HRH Paintings	2.20
12 April 1994	246	1994 Postcards	2.20
3 May 1994	247	1994 Tunnel	2.20
6 June 1994	248	1994 D-Day	3.20
5 July 1994	249	1994 Golf	2.30
2 August 1994	250	1994 Summertime	2.20
27 September 1994	251	1994 Medical	2.50
1 November 1994	252	1994 Christmas	2.20
17 January 1995	254	1995 Cats	2.95
14 March 1995	255	1995 Spring	2.20
11 April 1995	256	1995 National Trust	2.20
2 May 1995	257	1995 Peace/Europa	2.60
6 June 1995	258	1995 Sci-Fi	2.35
8 August 1995	259	1995 Shakespeare	2.35
5 September 1995	260	1995 Communication	2.35
3 October 1995	261	1995 Rugby	2.70
30 October 1995	262	1995 Christmas	2.70
25 January 1996	264	1996 Burns	2.20
12 March 1996	265	1996 Wildfowl	2.20
16 April 1996	266	1996 Cinema	2.20
14 May 1996	267	1996 Football	3.00
9 July 1996	268	1996 Olympics	2.00
6 August 1996	269	1996 Women	2.30
3 September 1996	270	1996 Kids TV	2.45
1 October 1996	271	1996 Classic Cars	3.15
28 October 1996	272	1996 Christmas	2.60
21 January 1997	274	1997 Henry VIII	4.50
11 March 1997	275	1997 Missions of Faith	2.35
13 May 1997	276	1997 Legends	2.20
10 June 1997	277	1997 Air Architects	3.70
8 July 1997	278	1997 Horses	2.60
12 August 1997	279	1997 Sub PO	2.60
9 September 1997	280	1997 Enid Blyton	2.60
27 October 1997	282	1997 Christmas	2.60
13 November 1997	281	1997 Golden Wedding	3.15
20 January 1998	284	1998 Endangered Species	3.00
3 February 1998		1998 Diana	4.00
24 February 1998	285	1998 Queens Beasts	2.20
24 March 1998	286	1998 Lighthouses	2.75
23 April 1998	287	1998 Comedians	2.75
23 June 1998	288	1998 NHS	2.40
21 July 1998	289	1998 Fantasy Novels	2.70
25 August 1998	290	1998 Carnival	2.40
29 September 1998	291	1998 Speed	2.95
2 November 1998	292	1998 Christmas	2.80
12 January 1999	294	1999 Inventors' Tale	3.45
2 February 1999	295	1999 Travellers' Tale	3.45
2 March 1999	296	1999 Patients' Tale	3.45
6 April 1999	297	1999 Settlers' Tale	3.45
4 May 1999	298	1999 Workers' Tale	3.45
1 June 1999	299	1999 Entertainers' Tale	3.45

Issue date	No.	Description	Pack
15 June 1999	M01	1999 Royal Wedding	1.70
6 July 1999	300	1999 Citizens' Tale	3.45
3 August 1999	301	1999 Scientists' Tale	3.45
7 September 1999	302	1999 Farmers' Tale	3.45
5 October 1999	303	1999 Soldiers' Tale	3.45
2 November 1999	304	1999 Christians' Tale	3.45
7 December 1999	305	1999 Artists' Tale	3.45
14 December 1999	M02	1999 Millennium Timekeeper M/S	24.00
18 January 2000	307	2000 Above and Beyond	3.45
1 February 2000	308	2000 Fire and Light	3.45
7 March 2000	309	2000 Water and Coast	3.45
4 April 2000	310	2000 Life and Earth	3.45
2 May 2000	311	2000 Art and Craft	3.45
23 May 2000	M03	2000 Her Majesty's Stamps M/S	47.50
6 June 2000	312	2000 People and Place	3.45
4 July 2000	313	2000 Stone and Soil	3.45
1 August 2000	314	2000 Tree and Leaf	3.45
4 August 2000	M04	2000 Queen Mothers Birthday M/S	11.95
5 September 2000	315	2000 Mind and Matter	3.45
3 October 2000	316	2000 Body and Bone	3.45
7 November 2000	317	2000 Spirit and Faith	3.45
5 December 2000	318	2000 Sound and Vision	3.45
16 January 2001	319	2001 Hopes for the Future	3.45
6 February 2001	M05	2001 Occasions	4.50
13 February 2001	320	2001 Cats and Dogs	9.75
31 March 2001	321	2001 Weather	5.95
10 April 2001	322	2001 Royal Navy Submarines	4.95
15 May 2001	323	2001 British Double-Decker's	4.95
19 June 2001	324	2001 Fabulous Hats	3.75
10 July 2001	325	2001 Pond Life/Europa	3.75
4 September 2001	326	2001 Punch & Judy	2.95
2 October 2001	327	2001 Nobel Prizes	4.95
22 October 2001	M06	2001 Royal Navy Flags M/S	9.75
6 November 2001	328	2001 Christmas	3.40
15 January 2002	330	2002 Kipling Stories	9.95
6 February 2002	331	2002 Golden Jubilee	3.50
5 March 2002	M07	2002 Occasions	2.25
19 March 2002	332	2002 Coastlines	4.20
9 April 2002	333	2002 Circus	3.20
25 April 2002	M08	2002 Queen Mother	2.80
2 May 2002	334	2002 Aircraft	3.20
21 May 2002	335	2002 World Cup M/S	2.95
16 July 2002	336	2002 Commonwealth Games	3.20
20 August 2002	337	2002 Peter Pan	3.20
10 September 2002	338	2002 London Bridges	3.20
24 September 2002	339	2002 Astronomy M/S	2.75
8 October 2002	340	2002 Pillar Boxes	3.20
5 November 2002	341	2002 Christmas	3.20
14 January 2003	343	2003 Birds of Prey	4.25
4 February 2003	M09	2003 Occasions	2.80
25 February 2003	344	2003 The Secret of Life	3.20
25 March 2003 345	2003	Fun Fruit & Veg	32.00
29 April 2003	346	2003 Extreme Endeavours	3.80
2 June 2003	347	2003 The Coronation	12.50
17 June 2003	348	2003 HRH Prince William	16.00
15 July 2003	349	2003 Scotland	3.80
12 August 2003	350	2003 Pub Signs	3.50
18 September 2003	351	2003 Transport Toys	3.50
7 October 2003	352	2003 British Museum	3.80
4 November 2003	353	2003 Christmas	4.95
19 December 2003	M9B	2003 England Winners M/S	20.00
13 January 2004	355	2004 Classic Locomotives	27.50
3 February 2004	M10	2004 Occasions	2.80
26 February 2004	356	2004 Lord of the Rings	8.25
16 March 2004	357	2004 Northern Ireland	3.95
6 April 2004	358	2004 Entente Cordiale	12.95
13 April 2004	359	2004 Ocean Liners	4.50
25 May 2004	360	2004 Royal Horticultural Society	4.20
15 June 2004	361	2004 Wales	4.20
10 August 2004	362	2004 Royal Society of Arts	4.50
16 September 2004	363	2004 Woodland Animals	4.50
12 October 2004	364	2004 The Crimean War	5.20
2 November 2004	365	2004 Christmas	5.20
11 January 2005	367	2005 Farm Animals	4.50
8 February 2005	368	2005 South West England	4.20
24 February 2005	369	2005 Jane Eyre	5.20
15 March 2005	370	2005 Magic	4.80
8 April 2005	M10	2005 Royal Wedding M/S	3.50
21 April 2005	371	2005 World Heritage Sites	5.40
7 June 2005	372	2005 Trooping The Colour	5.40
19 July 2005	373	2005 Motorcycles	4.80
5 August 2005	M11	2005 London 2012	3.25
23 August 2005	374	2005 Changing Tastes in Britain	4.50
15 September 2005	375	2005 Classic ITV	4.50
6 October 2005	M12	2005 The Ashes M/S	3.50
18 October 2005	376	2005 The Battle of Trafalgar	4.50
1 November 2005	377	2005 Christmas	4.75
10 January 2006	379	2006 Animal Tales	5.25

Greetings Packs

Issue date	No.	Description	Pack
28 January 1992	G1	1992 Memories Greeting pack	7.00
2 February 1993	G2	1993 Greetings Giving	8.50
1 February 1994	G3	1994 Greetings. Messages	8.50
21 March 1995	G4	1995 Greetings. Art	8.50
26 February 1996	G5	1996 Greetings. Cartoons	8.50
6 January 1997	G6	1997 Greetings. Flowers	9.50

High Values Definitive Packs

Issue date	No.	Description	Pack
5 March 1969	7	1969 Machin 2/6 to £1 (pack 7)	5.00
17 July 1970	18	1970 Machin 10p - 50p (pack 18)	3.75
25 November 1971	38	1971 Machin 20p - £1 (pack 38)	6.50
2 February 1977	91	1977 Machin £1 to £5 (pack 91)	12.95
3 March 1987	13	1987 Machin £1 to £5 (pack 13)	£135
15 September 1987	14	1987 Machin £1.60 (pack 14)	17.50

Issue date	No.	Description	Pack
18 October 1988	18	1988 Castles £1 to £5 (pack18)	14.95
24 March 1992	27	1992 Castles £1 to £5 (pack 27)	22.50
2 March 1993	28	1993 Britannia £10 (pack 28)	£35
22 August 1995	33	1995 Castle £3 (pack 33)	£12
29 July 1997	40	1997 Castles £1.50 to £5 (pack 40)	£75
9 March 1999	43	1999 Machin £1.50 to £5 (pack 43)	37.50
12 March 2002	43a	2002 Machin £1.50 to £5 (pack 43a)	27.50
1 July 2003	62	2003 Machin £1.50 to £5 (pack 62)	16.50
22 March 2005	69	2005 Castles 50p to £1 (pack 69)	4.60

Regional Definitive Packs

Issue date	No.	Description	Pack
9 December 1970	25	1970 Northern Ireland (pack25)	1.10
9 December 1970	23	1970 Scotland (pack 23)	3.65
9 December 1970	24	1970 Wales (pack 24)	1.40
7 July 1971	30	1971 Isle of Man (pack 30)	1.10
7 July 1971	29	1971 Northern Ireland (pack 29)	1.50
7 July 1971	27	1971 Scotland (pack 27)	1.50
7 July 1971	28	1971 Wales (pack 28)	1.50
29 May 1974	61	1974 Northern Ireland (pack 61)	1.10
29 May 1974	62	1974 Scotland (pack 62)	1.10
29 May 1974	63	1974 Wales (pack 63)	1.10
20 October 1976	84	1976 Northern Ireland (pack 84)	1.10
20 October 1976	85	1976 Scotland (pack 85)	1.10
20 October 1976	86	1976 Wales (pack 86)	1.10
28 October 1981	129d	1981 Northern Ireland (pack 129d)	3.90
28 October 1981	129b	1981 Scotland (pack 129b)	3.90
28 October 1981	129c	1981 Wales (pack 129c)	3.90
3 August 1983	4	1983 Northern Ireland (pack 4)	8.50
3 August 1983	2	1983 Scotland (pack 2)	8.50
3 August 1983	3	1983 Wales (pack 3)	8.50
23 October 1984	8	1984 Northern Ireland (pack 8)	8.50
23 October 1984	6	1984 Scotland (pack 6)	8.50
23 October 1984	7	1984 Wales (pack 7)	8.50
3 March 1987	12	1987 Northern Ireland (pack 12)	8.75
3 March 1987	10	1987 Scotland (pack 10)	
3 March 1987	11	1987 Wales (pack 11)	8.75
8 November 1988	17	1988 3 Regions (pack 17)	8.75
28 November 1989	20	1989 3 Regions (pack 20)	8.75
4 December 1990	23	1990 3 Regions (pack 23)	8.75
3 December 1991	26	1991 3 Regions (pack 26)	8.75
7 December 1993	31	1993 3 Regions (pack 31)	8.75
23 July 1996	36	1996 3 Regions (pack 36)	13.95
1 July 1997	39	1997 Wales (pack 39)	9.50
20 October 1998	42	1998 3 Regions (pack 42)	12.50
8 June 1999	47	1999 Northern Ireland (pack 47)	6.95
8 June 1999	45	1999 Scotland (pack 45)	6.95
8 June 1999	46	1999 Wales (pack 46)	6.95
25 April 2000	52	2000 Northern Ireland (pack 52)	£12
25 April 2000	50	2000 Scotland (pack 50)	7.95
25 April 2000	51	2000 Wales (pack 51)	7.95
6 March 2001	53	2001 Northern Ireland (pack 53)	3.45
23 April 2001	54	2001 England (pack 54)	3.45
12 March 2002	55	2002 Scotland (pack 55)	2.50
12 March 2002	56	2002 Wales (pack 56)	2.50
4 July 2002 59	2002	4 Regions (pack 59)	4.50
14 October 2003	63	2003 England (pack 63)	2.50
14 October 2003	66	2003 Northern Ireland (pack 66)	3.75
14 October 2003	64	2003 Scotland (pack 64)	2.50
14 October 2003	65	2003 Wales (pack 65)	2.50
11 May 2004 68	2004	4 Regions (pack 68)	2.80
5 April 2005 70	2005	4 Regions (pack 70)	2.95

Postage Due Packs

Issue date	No.	Description	Pack
3 November 1971	36	1971 Postage Dues	11.50
30 March 1977	93	1977 Postage Dues	7.50
9 June 1982	135	1982 Postage Dues	24.50
15 February 1994	32	1994 Postage Dues	£32

Welsh Packs

Issue date	No.	Description	Pack
July 1969		1969 Investiture	£24
3 February 1998		1998 Princess Diana	£57

German Packs

Issue date	No.	Description	Pack
12 August 1968		1968 Paintings	8.50
16 September 1968		1968 Gift Pack	22.50
25 November 1968		1968 Christmas	6.00
15 January 1969		1969 Ships	18.50
3 March 1969		1969 Concorde	24.50
5 March 1969		1967 Machin - Low values	£79
5 March 1969		1969 Machin - High Values	£45
2 April 1969		1969 Anniversaries	£45
28 May 1969		1969 Cathedrals	£16
1 July 1969		1969 Investiture	£16

Japanese Packs

Issue date	No.	Description	Pack
20 November 1972		1972 Silver Wedding	4.50
22 July 1981		1981 Royal Wedding	3.50

Royal Mail Year Packs

Issue date	No.	Description	Pack
27 November 1967		1967 Year Pack	0.95
16 September 1968		1968 Year Pack - Blue	2.85
16 September 1968		1968 Year Pack - Red	1.85
15 September 1969		1969 Year Pack	8.25
14 September 1970	20	1970 Year Pack	12.50
29 September 1971	34	1971 Year Pack	24.50
20 November 1972	47	1972 Year Pack	16.00
28 November 1973	58	1973 Year Pack	11.50
27 November 1974	68	1974 Year Pack	4.00
26 November 1975	77	1975 Year Pack	3.95
24 November 1976	88	1976 Year Pack	4.95
23 November 1977	98	1977 Year Pack	3.50
22 November 1978	105	1978 Year Pack	3.50
21 November 1979	114	1979 Year Pack	4.50
19 November 1980	123	1980 Year Pack	4.95
18 November 1981	131	1981 Year Pack	6.95
17 November 1982	141	1982 Year Pack	11.50
16 November 1983	149	1983 Year Pack	11.50
20 November 1984	158	1984 Year Pack	13.50
19 November 1985	167	1985 Year Pack	13.50
18 November 1986	177	1986 Year Pack	13.50
17 November 1987	186	1987 Year Pack	13.50
15 November 1988	195	1988 Year Pack	13.50
14 November 1989	204	1989 Year Pack	13.50
13 November 1990	214	1990 Year Pack	15.95
12 November 1991		1991 Year Pack	15.95
10 November 1992	233	1992 Year Pack	15.95
9 November 1993	243	1993 Year Pack	15.95
14 November 1994	253	1994 Year Pack	£21
30 October 1995	263	1995 Year Pack	£21
28 October 1996	273	1996 Year Pack	£24
13 November 1997	283	1997 Year Pack	27.50
2 November 1998	293	1998 Year Pack	39.95
7 December 1999	306	1999 Year Pack	49.50
5 December 2000	319	2000 Year Pack	49.50
6 November 2001	329	2001 Year Pack	49.50
5 November 2002	342	2002 Year Pack	51.50
4 November 2003	354	2003 Year Pack	£41
2 November 2004	366	2004 Year Pack	£41
2 November 2005	378	2005 Year Pack	39.95

Royal Mail Year Books

20 November 1984	1	1984 Year Book	39.00
19 November 1985	2	1985 Year Book	35.95
18 November 1986	3	1986 Year Book	35.95
17 November 1987	4	1987 Year Book	16.95
15 November 1988	5	1988 Year Book	15.95
14 November 1989	6	1989 Year Book	16.95
13 November 1990	7	1990 Year Book	17.95
12 November 1991	8	1991 Year Book	17.95
11 November 1992	9	1992 Year Book	20.95
9 November 1993	10	1993 Year Book	25.95
1 November 1994	11	1994 Year Book	20.95
30 October 1995	12	1995 Year Book	20.95
28 October 1996	13	1996 Year Book	23.95
13 November 1997	14	1997 Year Book	28.95
2 November 1998	15	1998 Year Book	39.50
7 December 1999	16	1999 Year Book	49.95
7 November 2000	17	2000 Year Book	49.95
6 November 2001	18	2001 Year Book	49.95
5 November 2002	19	2002 Year Book	45.00
4 November 2003	20	2003 Year Book	49.50
2 November 2004	21	2004 Year Book	49.95
2 November 2005	22	2005 Year Book	49.95

Souvenir Packs

20 November 1972	1972 Silver Wedding	0.75
16 May 1973	1973 Cricket	2.95
12 September 1973	1973 Parliament	3.95
9 October 1974	1974 Churchill	1.75
13 August 1975	1975 Railways	1.95
11 May 1977	1977 Silver Jubilee	1.00
31 May 1978	1978 Coronation	1.20
22 July 1981	1981 Royal Wedding	1.60
31 July 1984	1984 Mail History	3.40
8 October 1985	1985 British Films	5.25
21 April 1986	1986 Queen's Birthday	3.65
21 June 1988	1988 Australian Bicentenary	7.95
10 January 1990	1990 Penny Black	9.95
13 November 1997	1997 Golden Wedding	£24

Smilers Sheets

'Smilers'sheets were first issued during the Stamp Show 2000. The designs used were from the 'Smilers' greetings book and were available with either a photograph, taken at the show, or with a Stamp Show label from Philatelic outlets or the Bureau at Edinburgh.

These Smilers sheets, as they are popularly known, have continued since with various issues and are listed chronologically here. Unlike other catalogues we have also listed se-tenant pairs or strips from these sheets - as these are sometimes different from the original sheet or book printings. They are also listed in the commemorative section together with the stamps of the original design.

2000 (2 May) The Stamp Show 2000 10 x 1st
Printer: House of Questa in Gravure

No.		U/M
SS1	Complete sheet	£25
SSP1	Se-tenant pair - stamp with label (any)	3.00

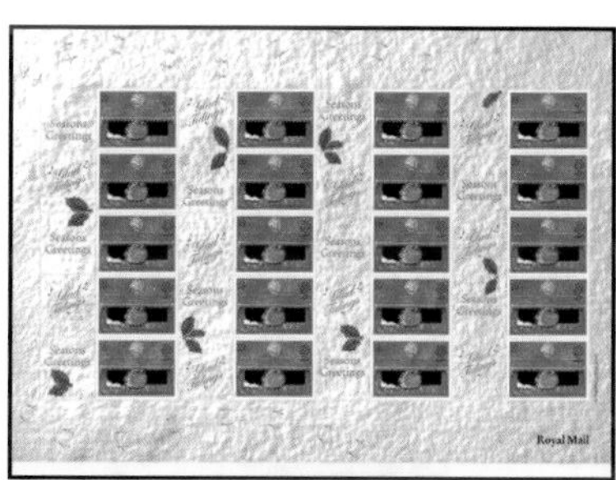

2000 (3 Oct.) Christmas 20 x 19p
Printer: House of Questa in Gravure

No.		U/M
SS2	Complete sheet	£200
SSP2	Strip of two stamps and two labels	£25

2000 (3 Oct.) Christmas 10 x 1st
Printer: House of Questa in Gravure

No.		U/M
SS3	Complete sheet	£110
SSP3	Strip of two stamps and two labels	£30

2001 (9 Oct.) Christmas 20 x 19p
As SS2 but inscribed 'Consignia 2001'
Printer: House of Questa in Gravure

No.		U/M
SS4	Complete sheet	£400
SSP2	Strip of two stamps and two labels	£25

2001 (9 Oct.) Christmas 10 x 1st
As SS2 but inscribed 'Consignia 2001'
Printer: House of Questa in Gravure

No.		U/M
SS5	Complete sheet	£450
SSP3	Strip of two stamps and two labels	£30

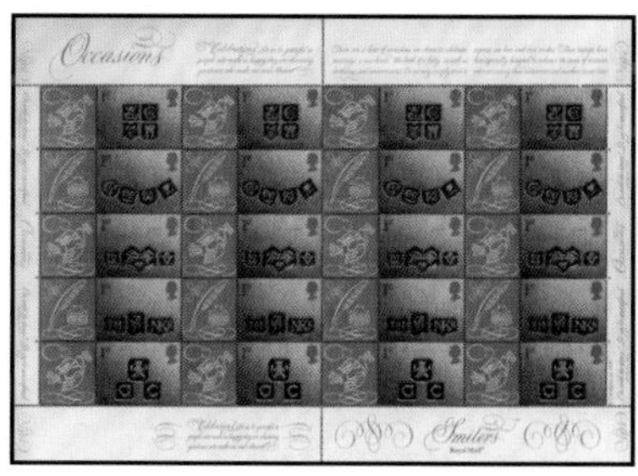

2001 (5 June) Occasions 20 x 1st
Printer: House of Questa in Lithography

No.		U/M
SS6	Complete sheet	£150
SSP4	Vertical strip of five stamps & five labels	£40

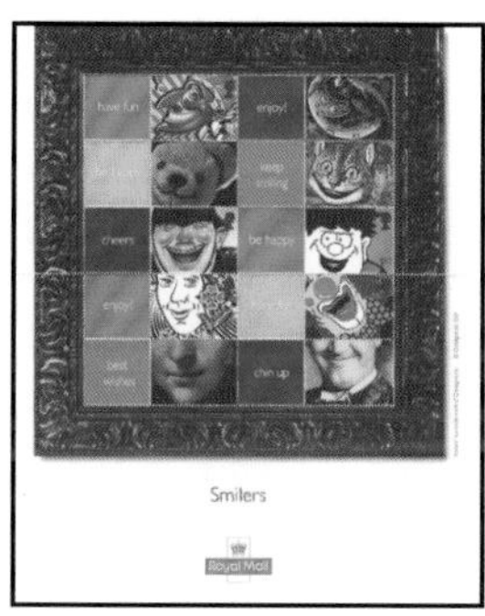

2001 (3 July) Smiles 10 x 1st
Printer: House of Questa in Lithography

No.		U/M
SS7	Complete sheet	£170
SSP5	Se-tenant pair - stamp with label (any)	£25

No. U/M

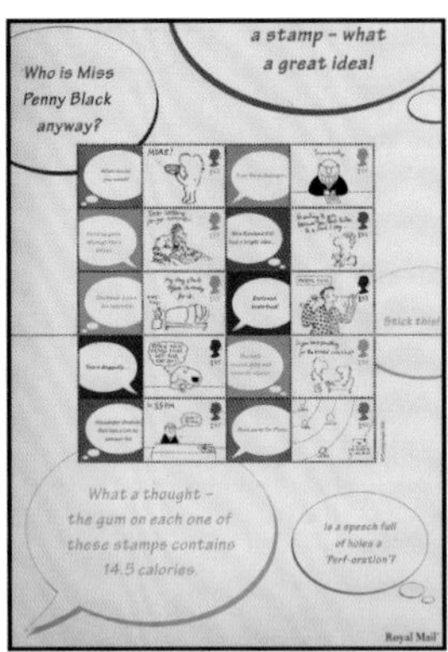

2001 (18 Dec.) Cartoons 10 x 1st
Printer: House of Questa in Lithography

No.		U/M
SS8	Complete sheet	£35
SSP6	Se-tenant pair - stamp with label (any)	4.00

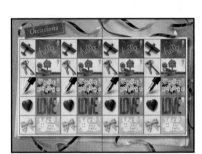

2001 (23 Apr.) Occasions 20 x 1st
Printer: House of Questa in Lithography

No.		U/M
SS9	Complete sheet	£38
SSP7	Vertical strip of five stamps & five labels	£10

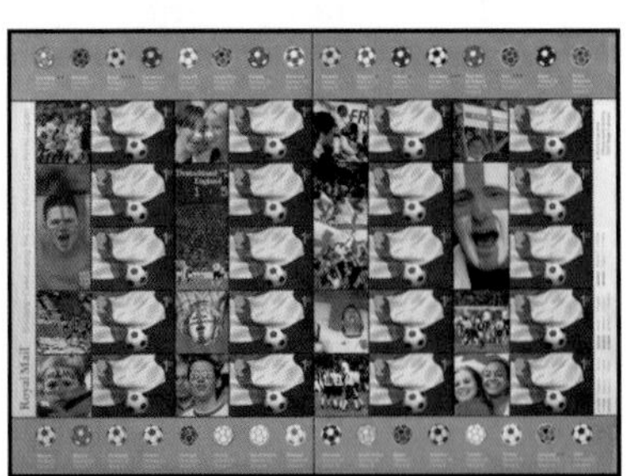

2002 (21 May) World Cup 20 x 1st
Printer: House of Questa in Lithography

No.		U/M
SS10	Complete sheet	£20
SSP8	Se-tenant pair - stamp with label (any)	2.50

No. U/M

2002 (1 Oct.) Smiles 10 x 1st
Printer: House of Questa in Lithography

No.		U/M
SS11	Complete sheet	£19
SSP9	Horizontal strip of two stamps (Teddy & Dennis) and two labels	2.00

2002 (1 Oct.) Christmas 20 x 1st
Printer: House of Questa in Lithography

No.		U/M
SS12	Complete sheet	£18
SSP10	Se-tenant pair - stamp with label (any)	1.00

2003 (21 Jan.) Flowers 20 x 1st
Printer: House of Questa in Lithography

No.		U/M
SS13	Complete sheet	£19
SS13a	Broad Centre Band	£750
SSP11	Se-tenant pair - stamp with label (any)	1.00
SSP11a	Broad Centre Band	£50

No.		U/M

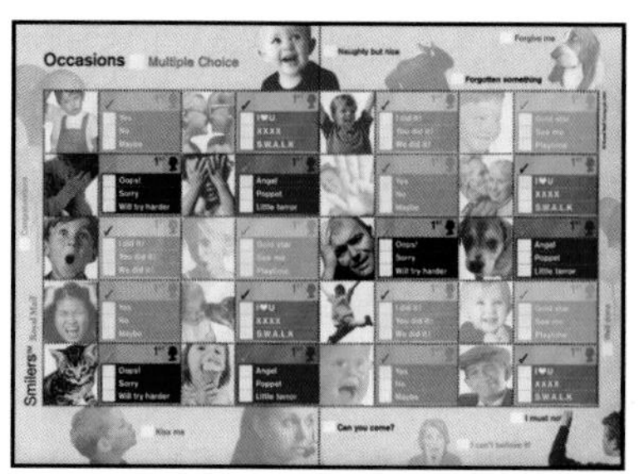

2003 (4 Feb.) Occasions 20 x 1st
Printer: House of Questa in Lithography

SS14	Complete sheet	£16
SSP12	Se-tenant pair - stamp with label (any)	1.00

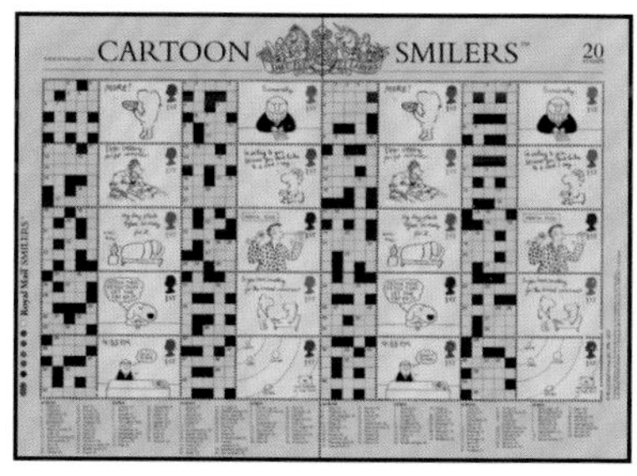

2003 (29 July) Crossword Cartoons 20 x 1st
Printer: House of Questa in Lithography

SS15	Complete sheet	£16
SS15a	Missing phosphor	£1000
SSP13	Se-tenant pair - stamp with label (any)	1.00
SSP13a	Missing phosphor	£75

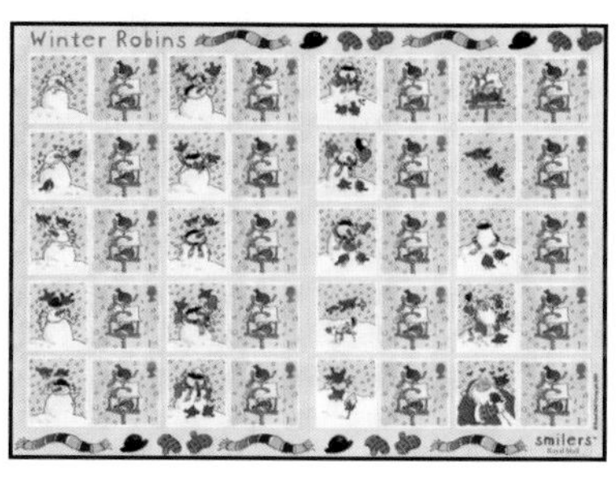

2003 (30 Sep.) Christmas 20 x 1st
Printer: De La Rue in Lithography

SS16	Complete sheet	£17
SSP14	Se-tenant pair - stamp with label (any)	1.00

No.		U/M

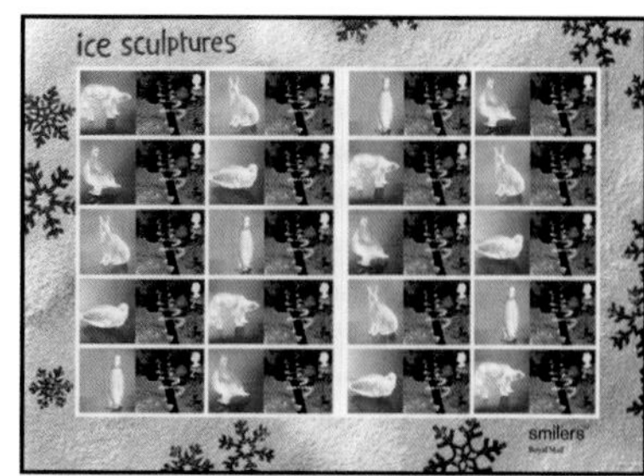

2003 (4 Nov.) Christmas 20 x 2nd
Printer: De La Rue in Lithography

SS17	Complete sheet	£25
SSP15	Se-tenant pair - stamp with label (any)	1.25

2003 (4 Nov.) Christmas 20 x 1st
Printer: De La Rue in Lithography

SS18	Complete sheet	£25
SSP16	Se-tenant pair - stamp with label (any)	1.25

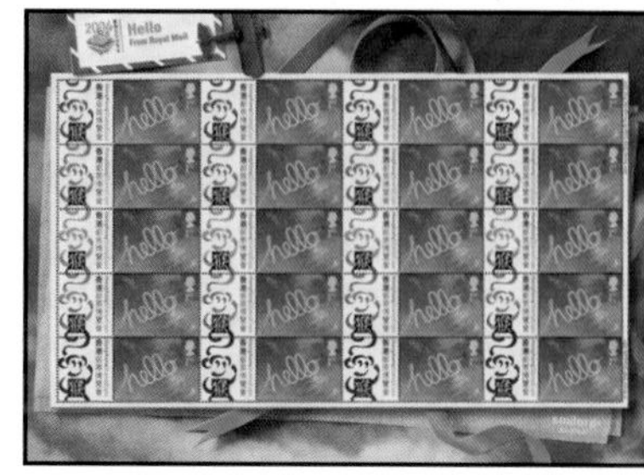

2004 (30 Jan.) Hong Kong 20 x 1st
Printer: Walsall in Lithography

SS19	Complete sheet	£11
SSP17	Se-tenant pair - stamp with label (any)	1.00

2004 (3 Feb.) Occasions 20 x 1st
Printer: De La Rue in Lithography

No.		U/M
SS20	Complete sheet	£12
SSP18	Vertical strip of five stamps & five labels	4.00

2004 (25 May) RHS 20 x 1st
Printer: Walsall in Lithography

No.		U/M
SS21	Complete sheet	£15
SSP19	Se-tenant pair - stamp with label (any)	1.00

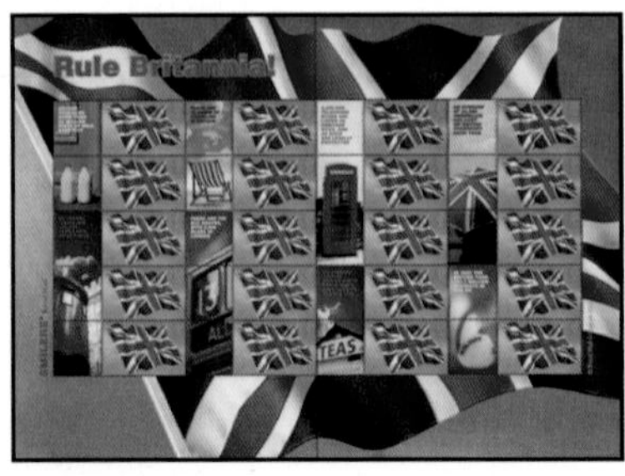

2004 (27 July) Rule Britannia 20 x 1st
Printer: Walsall in Lithography

No.		U/M
SS22	Complete sheet	11.75
SSP20	Se-tenant pair - stamp with label (any)	1.00

2004 (2 Nov.) Christmas 10 x 2nd *and* 10 x 1st
Printer: De La Rue in Lithography

No.		U/M
SS23	Complete sheet	£12
SSP21	Vertical strip of two stamps (1st and 2nd class) and two labels	7.00

2005 (11 Jan.) Farm Animals 20 x 1st
Printer: Walsall in Lithography

No.		U/M
SS24	Complete sheet	10.50
SSP22	Se-tenant pair - stamp with label (any)	1.00

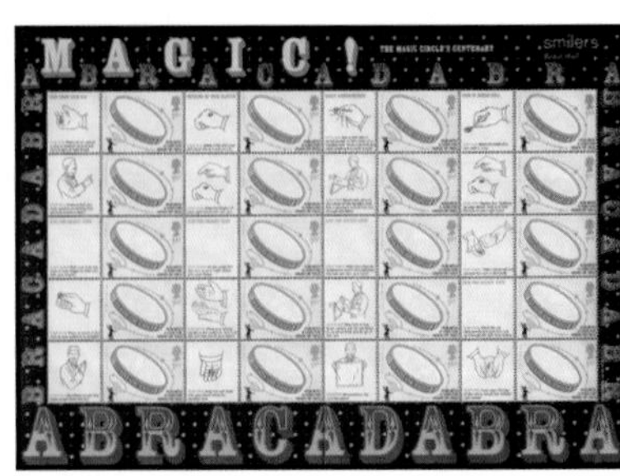

2005 (15 Mar.) Magic 20 x 1st

No.		U/M
SS25	Complete sheet	10.50
SSP23	Se-tenant pair - stamp with label (any)	1.00

No.		U/M

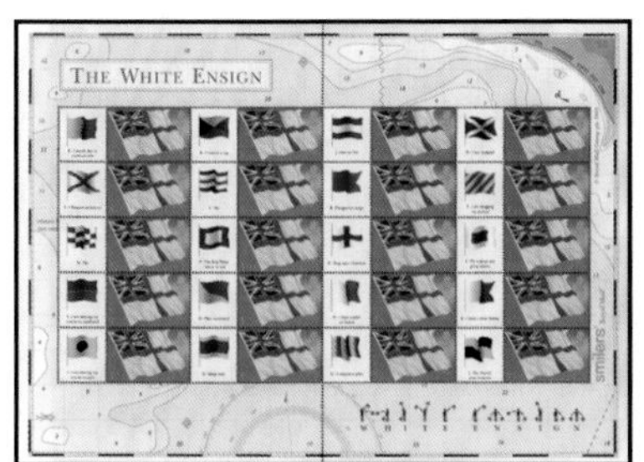

2005 (21 June) White Ensign 20 x 1st

No.		U/M
SS26	Complete sheet	10.50
SS26a	Solid all over phosphor (left 3 columns)	£150
SSP24	Se-tenant pair - stamp with label (any)	.75
SSP24a	Solid all over phosphor (strip of 5)	£45

2005 (15 Sep.) Classic ITV 20 x 1st

No.		U/M
SS27	Complete sheet	10.00
SSP25	Se-tenant pair - stamp with label (any)	.75

2005 (1 Nov.) Christmas Robins 10 x 1st *plus* 10 x 2nd

No.		U/M
SS28	Complete sheet	7.95
SSP26	Se-tenant pair - stamp with label (any)	

Stampex Smilers Sheets

2003 (28 Feb.) Spring 2003

No.		U/M
SSS1	Complete sheet	15.00

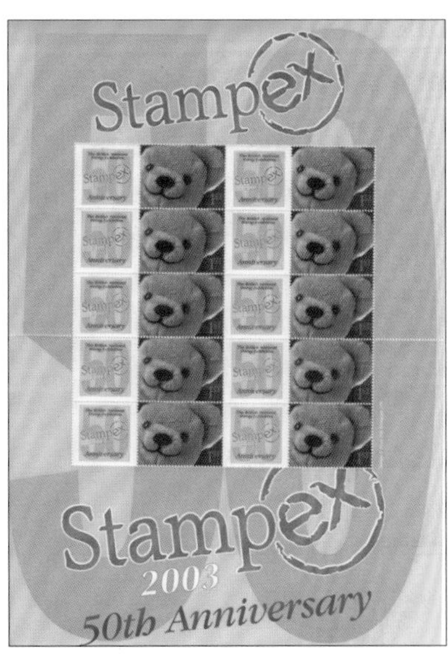

2003 (17 Sep.) Autumn 2003

No.		U/M
SSS2	Complete sheet	15.00

No. U/M

2004 (25 Feb.) Spring 2004

No.		U/M
SSS3	Complete sheet	18.50

2004 (15 Sep.) Autumn 2004

No.		U/M
SSS4	Complete sheet	13.50

No. U/M

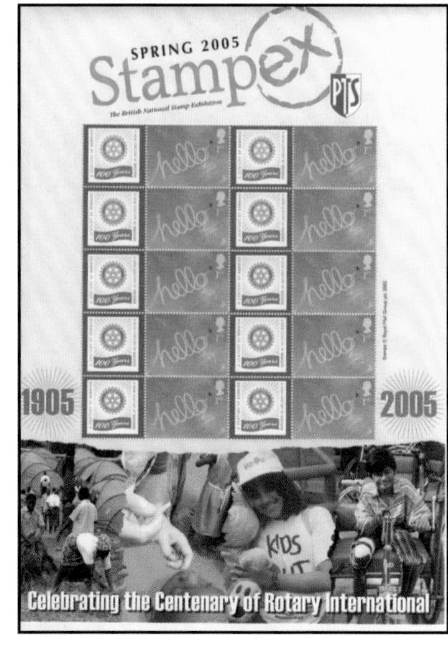

2005 (23 Feb.) Spring 2005

No.		U/M
SSS5	Complete sheet	13.50

2005 (14 Sep.) Autumn 2005

No.		U/M
SSS6	Complete sheet	10.50

Guernsey

On the 27 December 1940, authority was given to bisect British stamps as the stores of 1d stamps were almost exhausted.The locally printed 1d stamps were not issued until the 18th February 1941. Almost all examples of the bisects found are of a philatelic nature and genuine commercially used covers are of the utmost rarity and worth considerably more than the prices quoted.

1940 (27 Dec.) - 1941 (24 Feb.) Stamps of Great Britain bisected on cover or piece.

King George V

No.			Cover	Piece
GyB1	**1d**	**(2d) Orange** (1912 Wmk. Royal Cypher)	£260	£50
GyB2	**1d**	**(2d) Orange** (1924 Wmk. Block Cypher)	£225	£45
GyB3	**1d**	**(2d) Orange** (1934 Photogravure issue)	£200	£40

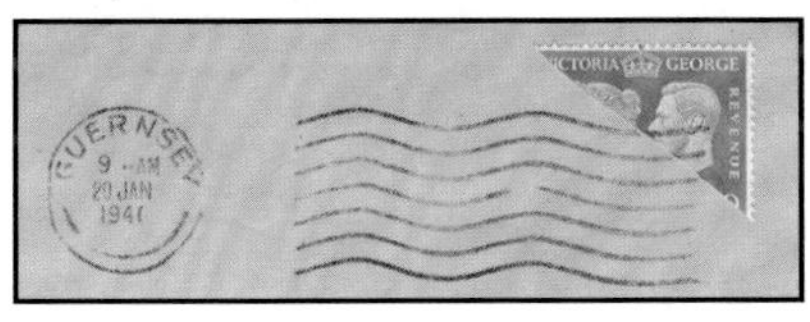

King George VI

No.			Cover	Piece
GyB4	**½d**	**(1d) Scarlet** (1937 Definitive)	£450	
GyB5	**1d**	**(2d) Orange** (1938 Definitive)	£20	4.00
GyB6	**½d**	**(1d)** (1940 Centenary)	£400	
GyB7	**1d**	**(2d)** (1940 Centenary)	£16	4.00
GyB8	**1d**	**(2½d)** (1940 Centenary)	£650	
GyB9	**1½d**	**(3d)** (1940 Centenary)	£450	

1941 (18 Feb.) - 44 Arms of Guernsey. Roulette perf.
Printer: Guernsey Press Co. Ltd in TypographyA. White Paper.
No watermark.

No.			U/M	M/M	F/U	✉
Gy1	**½d**	**Pale yellow green** (1.44)	3.00	2.20	1.50	3.00
Gy1a		Emerald green (6.4.41)	4.50	2.00	1.50	2.00
Gy1b		Light green (7.4.41)	3.50	1.25	1.20	2.00
Gy1c		Dull green (9.42)	3.50	2.00	2.00	3.00
Gy1d		Bright green (2.42)	£18	8.00	7.50	£10
Gy1e		Bluish green (11.41)	£29	£16	£18	£22
Gy1f		Olive green (2.43)	£18	£10	9.00	£20
Gy2	**1d**	**Scarlet** (18.2.41)	1.70	1.00	1.00	2.00
Gy2a		Pale vermilion (7.4.37)	1.90	1.00	1.50	3.00
Gy2b		Carmine (12.43)	2.70	1.50	2.25	4.50
Gy3	**2½d**	**Ultramarine** (12.4.44)	4.50	3.00	4.50	5.00
Gy3a		Pale ultramarine	3.50	1.75	3.50	5.00
		Set of 3	8.50	6.50	6.00	
		First Day Cover (½d)				5.00
		First Day Cover (1d)				5.00
		First Day Cover (2½d)				7.00

B. Blue French Bank Note Paper. Wmk. Loops (sideways)

No.			U/M	M/M	F/U	✉
Gy4	**½d**	**Bright green** (11.3.42)	£15	£10	£15	£27
Gy5	**1d**	**Scarlet** (9.4.42)	8.00	6.00	£15	£25
		Set of 2	20.50	£15	£28	
		First Day Cover (½d)				£70
		First Day Cover (1d)				£50

Jersey

1941 (4 April). Arms of Jersey. No watermark. Perf. 11.

White paper.

No.			U/M	M/M	F/U	✉
J1	½d	**Bright green** (29.1.42)	3.50	2.10	2.00	2.50
J2	1d	**Scarlet** (1.4.41)	3.00	1.80	2.50	3.50
		First Day Cover (½d)				3.50
		First Day Cover (1d)				2.50

Chalky Paper

No.			U/M	M/M	F/U	✉
J3	1d	**Scarlet** (10.41)	£27	£15	£25	£35

Greyish paper

No.			U/M	M/M	F/U	✉
J4	½d	**Bright green**	4.00	2.75	6.00	6.50
J5	1d	**Scarlet** (1.43)	4.00	2.75	6.00	6.50

1943 (1 June) - 44. Views of Jersey. No watermark. Perf 13½.
Printer: French Government Printing Works, Paris in Typography.

White Paper

No.			U/M	M/M	F/U	✉
J6	½d	**Green** (1.6.43)	5.00	2.00	2.50	5.00
J7	1d	**Scarlet** (1.6.43)	1.75	50	30	1.00
J8	1½d	**Brown** (8.6.43)	2.00	75	2.00	2.50
J9	2d	**Orange yellow** (8.6.43)	2.50	1.00	1.50	2.00
J10	2½d	**Blue** (29.6.43)	1.50	60	1.50	2.50
J11	3d	**Violet** (29.6.43)	75	30	3.00	3.50
		First Day Cover (½d, 1d)				3.50
		First Day Cover (1½d, 2d)				5.50
		First Day Cover (2½d, 3d)				3.50
		First Day Cover (½d, 3d)				£12

Grey Paper

No.			U/M	M/M	F/U	✉
J12	½d	**Green** (6.10.41)	6.00	3.00	6.00	£10

Newsprint

No.			U/M	M/M	F/U	✉
J13	1d	**Scarlet** (28.2.44)	6.00	3.50	6.00	3.00
J14	2½d	**Blue** (25.2.44)	2.90	1.75	3.30	3.50
		Set of 6	8.50	5.00	9.00	

Regional Stamps

The first Elizabethan regional stamps were originally issued for Guernsey, Jersey, Isle of Man, Northern Ireland, Scotland and Wales in 1958. The three small islands, Jersey, Guernsey and the Isle of Man were granted independent postal status during the 1970's. It was not until 2001 that the largest country in the UK, England, had its own country stamps.

Prices listed here are for either unmounted mint or fine used with good CDS cancels. Prices for First Day Covers are for Philatelic Bureau handstamps. Illustrated covers with regional postmarks are worth approximately double the price shown.
All stamps are from sheets unless stated otherwise.

Guernsey

Printer: Harrison & Sons in Photogravure

2½d

3d, 4d, 5d

Multiple Crown Watermark

1958 (18 Aug.) Wmk. Multiple Crowns. Perf. 15 x 14

Cream paper/GA

No.			U/M	F/U
GY6	**3d**	**Lilac**	75	50
		First Day Cover		£12

White paper/GA

No.			U/M	F/U
GY7	**2½d**	**Carmine** (8.6.64)	20	30
GY7a		Pale carmine	30	40
GY8	**3d**	**Lilac** (5.7.62)	15	20
GY9	**4d**	**Ultramarine** (7.2.66)	15	20
		Set of 3	50	55
		First Day Cover (2½d)		£15

1967 (24 May) Phosphor issue. Wmk. Multiple Crowns. Perf. 15 x 14

White paper/GA

No.			U/M	F/U
GY10	**3d**	**CB Lilac** (24.5.67)	10	20
GY10a		Reddish lilac	15	20
GY11	**4d**	**2B Ultramarine** (24.10.67)	10	20

1968 (16 April) Phosphor issue. No watermark. Perf. 15 x 14

Chalky paper/PVA

No.			U/M	F/U
GY12	**4d**	**2B Ultramarine**	10	20
GY12a		Missing phosphor	£40	
GY13	**4d**	**CB Sepia** (4.9.68)	10	20
GY13a		Missing phosphor	£40	
GY13b		Horizontal phosphor band	£400	
GY14	**4d**	**CB Vermilion** (26.2.69)	10	20
GY15	**5d**	**2B Deep blue** (4.9.68)	10	20
		Set of 4	35	70
		First Day Cover (4d sepia, 5d)		1.00

The above stamps were no longer valid on Guernsey from 30 September 1969. However, the current issues remained on sale and in use in the United Kingdom for one year until 30th September 1970.

Isle of Man

Printer: Harrison & Sons in Photogravure

2½d

3d, 4d, 5d

Multiple Crown Watermark

1958 (18 Aug.) Wmk. Multiple Crowns. Perf. 15 x 14

Cream paper/GA

No.			U/M	F/U
MX1	**3d**	**Lilac**	60	25
		First Day Cover		£17

White paper/GA

No.			U/M	F/U
MX2	**2½d**	**Carmine** (8.6.64)	20	35
MX3	**3d**	**Lilac** (1963)	20	20
MX3a		Chalky paper (17.5.63)	4.95	4.75
MX4	**4d**	**Ultramarine** (7.2.66)	75	1.00
		Set of 3	1.10	1.50
		First Day Cover (2½d)		£18

1967 (5 July) Phosphor issue. Wmk. Multiple Crowns. Perf. 15 x 14

White paper/GA

No.			U/M	F/U
MX5	**3d**	**CB Lilac** (27.6.68)	10	15
MX6	**4d**	**2B Ultramarine**	10	20
		First Day Cover (4d)		50

1968 (24 June) Phosphor issue. No watermark. Perf. 15 x 14

Chalky paper/PVA

No.			U/M	F/U
MX7	**4d**	**2B Ultramarine**	10	20
MX8	**4d**	**CB Sepia** (4.9.68)	10	20
MX8a		Missing phosphor	£20	
MX9	**4d**	**CB Vermilion** (26.2.69)	20	30
MX10	**5d**	**2B Deep blue** (4.9.68)	20	30
MX10a		Missing phosphor	£175	
		Set of 4	50	90
		First Day Cover (4d sepia, 5d)		1.00

No.			U/M	F/U

1971 (7 July) Decimal. Phosphor issue. No watermark. Perf. 15 x 14

OCP/PVA

No.			U/M	F/U
MX11	2½p	**CB Magenta**	10	10
MX11a		Missing phosphor	£1500	
MX12	3p	**2B Ultramarine**	10	10
MX13	5p	**2B Bright violet**	40	70
MX13a		Missing phosphor	£275	
MX14	7½p	**2B Chestnut**	40	70
		Set of 4	1.00	1.40
		First Day Cover		2.50
		Presentation Pack No. 30	1.10	

FCP/PVA

No.			U/M	F/U
MX15	2½p	**CB Magenta** (3.73)	25	15
MX16	3p	**2B Ultramarine** (7.73)	1.00	1.00

In 1973 the Isle of Man was granted Postal Independence and became responsible for their own stamp issues. The post 1973 issues of Isle of Man are outside the scope of this catalogue.

Jersey

Printer: Harrison & Sons in Photogravure

2½d

3d, 4d, 5d

Multiple Crown Watermark

1958 (18 Aug.) Wmk. Multiple Crowns. Perf. 15 x 14

Cream paper/GA

No.			U/M	F/U
J15	3d	**Lilac**	75	50
		First Day Cover		4.50

White paper/GA

No.			U/M	F/U
J16	2½d	**Carmine** (8.6.64)	30	45
J17	3d	**Lilac** (23.9.62)	25	10
J18	4d	**Ultramarine** (7.2.66)	12	20
		Set of 3	60	65
		First Day Cover (2½d)		£15

1967 (9 June - Sept.) Phosphor issue. Wmk. Multiple Crowns. Perf. 15 x 14

White paper/GA

No.			U/M	F/U
J19	3d	**CB Lilac** (9.6.67)	15	20
J19a		Reddish lilac	50	55
J20	4d	**2B Ultramarine** (5.9.67)	10	15

1968 (4 Sept.) - 69 Phosphor issue. No watermark. Perf. 15 x 14

Chalky paper/PVA

No.			U/M	F/U
J21	4d	**CB Sepia** (4.9.68)	10	20
J21a		Missing phosphor	£1000	
J22	4d	**CB Vermilion** (26.2.69)	10	20
J23	5d	**2B Deep blue** (4.9.68)	10	20
		Set of 3	28	55
		First Day Cover (4d sepia, 5d)		1.00

The above stamps were no longer valid on Jersey from 30 September 1969. However, the current issues remained on sale and in use in the United Kingdom for one year until 30th September 1970.

Northern Ireland

Printer: Harrison & Sons in Photogravure

3d, 4d, 5d

6d, 9d

1s3d, 1s6d

1958 (18 Aug.) Wmk. Multiple Crowns. Perf. 15 x 14

Cream paper/GA

No.			U/M	F/U
U1	3d	**Lilac**	75	25
U2	6d	**Claret** (29.9.58)	1.00	40
U3	1s3d	**Green** (29.9.58)	2.25	70
		First Day Cover (3d)		£16

White paper/GA

No.			U/M	F/U
U4	3d	**Lilac** (21.5.62)	20	15
U5	4d	**Ultramarine** (7.2.66)	10	15
U6	6d	**Claret** (4.6.62)	10	15
U7	1s3d	**Green** (9.11.62)	20	25
		Set of 4	50	60

1967 (1 Mar.) Phosphor issue. Wmk. Multiple Crowns. Perf. 15 x 14

White paper/GA

No.			U/M	F/U
U8	3d	**CB Lilac** (9.6.67)	10	15
U9	4d	**2B Ultramarine** (2.10.67)	10	15
U10	9d	**2B Deep green**	20	25
U11	1s6d	**2B Grey blue**	20	25
U11a		Missing phosphor	£200	
		Set of 4	45	60
		First Day Cover (9d, 1s6d)		4.50

1968 (27 June) Phosphor issue. No watermark. Perf. 15 x 14

Chalky paper/GA

No.			U/M	F/U
U12	4d	**2B Ultramarine** (27.6.68)	10	15

Chalky paper/PVA

No.			U/M	F/U
U13	4d	**2B Ultramarine** (23.10.68)	9.50	
U14	4d	**CB Sepia** (4.9.68)	10	15
U14a		Missing phosphor	£200	
U15	4d	**CB Vermilion** (26.2.69)	15	15
U15a		Missing phosphor	5.00	
U16	5d	**2B Deep blue** (4.9.68)	10	10
U16a		Missing phosphor	£35	
U17	1s6d	**2B Grey blue** (20.5.69)	1.30	1.40
U17a		Missing phosphor	£650	
		Set of 5	1.50	1.65
		First Day Cover (4d sepia, 5d)		1.00
		Presentation Pack 25 (9.12.70)		
		Contents: U7, 8, 10, 11, 14/16 (7v)	1.10	

Printer: Harrison & Sons in Photogravure

1971 (7 July) Decimal. Phosphor issue. No watermark. Perf. 15 x 14. Two 9.5mm phosphor bands or one 4mm centre band, unless stated otherwise.

OCP/PVA

No.			U/M	F/U
U18	2½p	**CB Magenta**	50	20
U19	3p	**2B Ultramarine**	20	120
U19a		Missing phosphor	£50	
U20	5p	**2B Bright violet**	80	85
U21	7½p	**2B Chestnut**	1.20	1.20
U21a		Missing phosphor	£95	
		First Day Cover		2.00
		Presentation Pack 29	1.50	

FCP/PVA

No.			U/M	F/U
U22	2½p	**CB Magenta** (6.73)	5.00	1.25
U23	3p	**2B Ultramarine** (4.73)	£22	1.50
U23a		'JET' yellow phosphor (7.73)	7.50	
U24	3p	**CB Ultramarine** (7.73)	10	15

FCP/PVAD

No.			U/M	F/U
U25	3p	**CB Ultramarine** (23.1.74)	1.00	
U26	3½p	**2B Bronze green** (23.1.74)	15	15
U27	3½p	**CB Bronze green** (6.11.74)	15	15
U28	4½p	**2B Steel blue** (6.11.74)	15	15
U29	5½p	**2B Violet** (23.1.74)	15	15
U29a		Missing phosphor	£300	
U29b		Missing right band	£700	
U30	5½p	**CB Violet** (21.5.75)	15	15

No.			U/M	F/U
U31	6½p	**CB Greenish blue** (14.1.76)	15	15
U32	7p	**CB Red brown** (18.1.78)	20	20
U33	8p	**2B Rose red** (23.1.74)	20	20
U33a		Missing phosphor	£85	

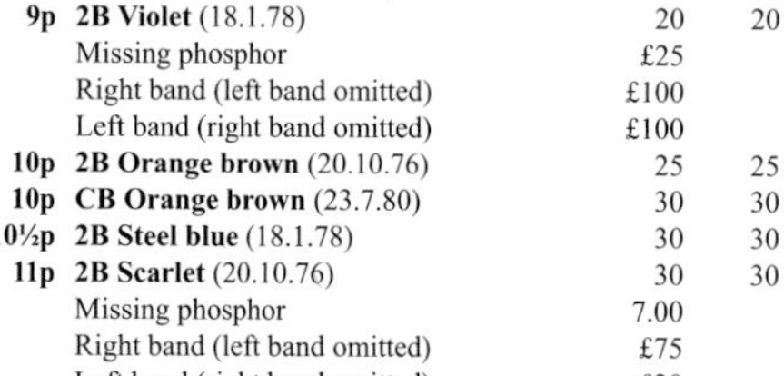

No.			U/M	F/U
U34	**8½p**	**2B Yellow green** (14.1.76)	20	20
U35	**9p**	**2B Violet** (18.1.78)	20	20
U35a		Missing phosphor	£25	
U35b		Right band (left band omitted)	£100	
U35c		Left band (right band omitted)	£100	
U36	**10p**	**2B Orange brown** (20.10.76)	25	25
U37	**10p**	**CB Orange brown** (23.7.80)	30	30
U38	**10½p**	**2B Steel blue** (18.1.78)	30	30
U39	**11p**	**2B Scarlet** (20.10.76)	30	30
U39a		Missing phosphor	7.00	
U39b		Right band (left band omitted)	£75	
U39c		Left band (right band omitted)	£20	
		First Day Cover (3p, 3½p, 5½p, 8p)		3.00
		Presentation Pack 61 (29.5.74)		
		Contents: U25, 26, 29, 33 (4v)	1.10	
		First Day Cover (3½p, 4½p)		3.00
		Presentation Pack 61 (6.11.74)		
		Contents: U24, 27/29, 33 (5v)	1.10	
		First Day Cover (6½p, 8½p)		3.00
		First Day Cover (10p, 11p)		3.00
		Presentation Pack 84 (20.10.76)		
		Contents: U31, 34, 36, 38 (4v)	1.10	
		First Day Cover (7p, 9p, 10½p)		3.00

PCP/PVAD

No.			U/M	F/U
U40	**12p**	**Yellow green** (23.7.80)	30	30
U41	**13½p**	**Red brown** (23.7.80)	40	40
U42	**15p**	**Bright blue** (23.7.80)	35	40
		First Day Cover (12p, 13½p, 15p)		3.00

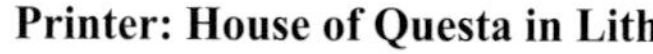

Printer: House of Questa in Litho

1981 (8 April) Decimal. Phosphor issue. No watermark. Perf. 13½ x 14. One 4mm side band on 11½p and 12½p.

OCP/PVA

No.			U/M	F/U
U43	**11½p**	**LB Drab** (8.4.81)	50	55

PCP/PVA

No.			U/M	F/U
U44	**14p**	**Grey blue** (8.4.81)	40	40
U45	**18p**	**Violet blue** (8.4.81)	60	65
U46	**22p**	**Blue** (8.4.81)	75	80
		First Day Cover (11½p, 14p, 18p, 22p)		3.00
		Presentation Pack 129d (28.10.81)		
		Contents: U32, 35, 38, 40/46 (10v)	3.90	

FCP/PVAD

No.			U/M	F/U
U47	**12½p**	**LB Light emerald** (24.2.82)	30	30

PCP/PVAD

No.			U/M	F/U
U48	**15½p**	**Pale violet** (24.2.82)	50	50
U49	**16p**	**Drab** (27.4.83)	60	60
U50	**19½p**	**Olive grey** (24.2.82)	1.10	1.51

No.			U/M	F/U
U51	20½p	**Ultramarine** (27.4.83)	2.00	2.00
U52	26p	**Rosine**. Type I (24.2.82)	65	65
U53	28p	**Violet blue**. Type I (27.4.83)	75	75
		First Day Cover (12½p, 15½p, 19½p, 26p)		3.00
		First Day Cover (16p, 20½p, 28p)		3.00
		Presentation Pack 4 (3.8.83)		
		Contents: U37, 47, 50/53 (6v)	8.50	

1984 (28 Feb.) Decimal. Phosphor issue. No watermark. Perf. 15 x 14. One 4mm phosphor band or 'bar' on 12p, 12½p, 13p, 14p and 15p.

Printer: House of Questa in Litho

Type I
Line on the hand weak or absent

Type II
Line on the hand much bolder

OCP/PVA

No.			U/M	F/U
U54	12½p	**LB Light emerald** (28.2.84)	3.50	3.25

FCP/PVAD

No.			U/M	F/U
U55	12p	**LB Emerald** (7.1.86)	50	55
U55a		Left bar (7.86)	70	75
U56	12½p	**LB Light emerald** (28.2.84)	2.90	2.50
U57	13p	**LB Pale chestnut** Type I (23.10.84)	50	55
U57a		Missing phosphor	£275	
U57b		Left bar. Type II (11.12.86)	50	55
		First Day Cover (12p)		2.00

FCP/PVA

No.			U/M	F/U
U58	13p	**LBar Pale chestnut** Type II (14.4.87)	80	40
U58a		Short band at top	£20	
U58b		Short band at bottom	6.00	
U59	14p	**CBar Dark blue** (8.11.88)	40	40
U59a		Short band at bottom	6.00	
U60	15p	**CBar Bright blue** (28.11.89)	45	45
U60a		Short band at top	1.50	
U60b		Short band at bottom	1.50	
U61	17p	**CBar Dark blue** (4.12.90)	40	40
U61a		Short band at top	4.00	
U61b		Short band at bottom	2.00	
U62	18p	**CBar Bright green** (3.12.91)	40	45
U62a		Short band at top	2.00	
U82b		Short band at bottom	2.00	
U62c		Perf error, (13½ x 14)	1.00	1.00
U62d		Short band at top	2.50	
U62e		Short band at bottom	2.50	

No.			U/M	F/U
U63	39p	**Mauve** (paper error, non-phosphor) (.91)	£30	

PCP/PVAD

No.			U/M	F/U
U64	16p	**Drab** (28.2.84)	5.00	4.00
U65	17p	**Grey blue** Type I (23.10.84)	55	50
U66	31p	**Bright purple** Type I (23.10.84)	90	90

ACP/PVA

No.			U/M	F/U
U67	19p	**Orange red** (8.11.88)	50	50
U68	20p	**Black** (28.11.89)	50	50
U68a		Low OBA	1.25	
U69	23p	**Bright green** (8.11.88)	65	65

No.			U/M	F/U
U70	24p	**Indian red** (28.11.89)	65	65
U71	24p	**Chestnut** (3.12.91)	60	65
U72	28p	**Blue grey** (3.12.91)	80	80

No.			U/M	F/U

No.			U/M	F/U
U73	**32p**	**Deep greenish blue** (8.11.88)	80	80
U74	**34p**	**Slate** (28.11.89)	90	90
U75	**39p**	**Mauve** (3.12.91)	1.20	1.30

ACP/PVAD

No.			U/M	F/U
U76	**17p**	**Grey blue** Type I (25.2.86)	75	35
U76a		Type II (10.9.86)	£80	£65
U77	**18p**	**Olive grey** (6.1.87)	50	55
U78	**22p**	**Yellow green** (23.10.84)	55	55
U79	**22p**	**Orange red** (4.12.90)	60	65
U80	**26p**	**Rosine** Type II (27.1.87)	2.50	2.50

No.			U/M	F/U
U81	**26p**	**Stone** (4.12.90)	65	65
U82	**28p**	**Violet blue** Type II (27.1.87)	75	75
U83	**31p**	**Bright purple** Type II (14.4.87)	2.50	2.50
U84	**37p**	**Red** (4.12.90)	95	95
		First Day Cover (13p, 17p, 22p, 31p) (23.10.84)		3.00
		Presentation Pack 8 (23.10.84)		
		Contents: U37, 58, 65/7, 70, 79, 81, 83 (8v)	8.50	
		First Day Cover (18p) (6.1.87)		1.50
		Presentation Pack 12 (3.3.87)		
		Contents: U56a, 58b, 66, 77, 78, 80, 81, 83 (8v)	8.75	
		First Day Cover (12p)		1.50
		First Day Cover (14p, 19p, 23p, 32p)		3.00
		First Day Cover (15p, 20p, 24p, 34p)		3.00
		First Day Cover (17p, 22p, 26p, 37p)		3.00
		First Day Cover (18p, 24p, 28p, 39p)		3.00

OFNP/PVA - C (Yellow) fluor

No.			U/M	F/U
U85	**18p**	**LB Bright green** - SP62 (B. Potter book) (10.8.93)	1.70	1.80
U86	**24p**	**2B Chestnut** - - SP62 (B. Potter book) (10.8.93)	2.00	2.00
U86a		Inset left band	4.50	4.00

For issues previously listed as U88 to U91 please see 'ellipticals' section

Scotland

Printer: Harrison & Sons in Photogravure

3d, 4d, 5d

6d, 9d

1s3d, 1s6d

1958 (18 Aug.) Wmk. Multiple Crowns. Perf. 15 x 14

Cream paper/GA

No.			U/M	F/U
S1	**3d**	**Lilac**	40	15
S2	**6d**	**Claret** (29.9.58)	75	30
S3	**1s3d**	**Green** (29.9.58)	2.25	75
		First Day Cover (3d)		£10

White paper/GA

No.			U/M	F/U
S4	**3d**	**Lilac** (9.7.62)	10	15
S5	**4d**	**Ultramarine** (7.2.66)	10	15
S6	**6d**	**Claret** (14.6.62)	10	15
S7	**1s3d**	**Green** (9.11.62)	25	20
		Set of 4	40	35

1963 (29 Jan.) Phosphor issue. Wmk. Multiple Crowns. Perf. 15 x 14

White paper/GA

No.			U/M	F/U
S8	**3d**	**2B Lilac** (29.1.63)	7.00	1.50
S9	**3d**	**LB Lilac** blue phosphor (30.4.65)	3.75	1.20
S9a		violet phosphor (16.12.65)	20	20
S10	**3d**	**RB Lilac** blue phosphor (30.4.65)	3.50	1.00
S10a		violet phosphor (16.12.65)	20	20
S11	**3d**	**CB Lilac** (6.11.67)	10	15
S12	**4d**	**2B Ultramarine** (7.2.66)	10	15
S13	**6d**	**2B Claret** (blue phosphor) (29.1.63)	15	15
S13a	**6d**	**2B Claret** (violet phosphor) (7.2.66)	75	50
S14	**9d**	**2B Deep green** (1.3.67)	25	20
S15	**1s3d**	**2B Green** (blue phosphor) (29.1.63)	1.25	60
S15a		violet phosphor (26.11.65)	25	20
S16	**1s6d**	**2B Grey blue** (1.3.67)	25	25
		Set of 6	85	90
		First Day Cover (9d, 1s6d)		4.50

1967 (28 Nov.) Phosphor issue. No watermark. Perf. 15 x 14

Chalky paper/GA

No.			U/M	F/U
S17	**3d**	**CB Lilac** (16.5.68)	10	15
S17a		Missing phosphor	7.00	
S18	**4d**	**2B Ultramarine** (28.11.67)	10	15
S18a		Missing phosphor	£10	

Chalky paper/PVA

No.			U/M	F/U
S19	**3d**	**CB Lilac** (11.7.68)	10	12
S19a		Missing phosphor	4.00	
S20	**4d**	**2B Ultramarine** (25.7.68)	10	10
S21	**4d**	**CB Sepia** (4.9.68)	10	15
S21a		Missing phosphor	3.00	
S22	**4d**	**CB Vermilion** (26.2.69)	15	15
S22a		Missing phosphor	3.00	
S23	**5d**	**2B Deep blue** (4.9.68)	15	15
S23a		Missing phosphor	£55	

No.			U/M	F/U
S24	**9d**	**2B Deep green** (28.9.70)	2.60	2.70
S24a		Missing phosphor	£250	
S25	**1s6d**	**2B Grey blue** (12.12.68)	90	60
S25a		Missing phosphor	£125	
		Set of 7	3.80	3.75
		First Day Cover (4d sepia, 5d)		1.00
		Presentation Pack 23 (9.12.70)		
		Contents: S12, 15, 19, 21/25 (8v)	3.65	

Printer: Harrison & Sons in Photogravure

1971 (7 July) Decimal. Phosphor issue. No watermark. Perf. 15 x 14. Two 9.5mm phosphor bands or one 4mm centre band, unless stated otherwise.

OCP/PVA

No.			U/M	F/U
S26	**2½p**	**CB Magenta**	20	20
S26a		Missing phosphor	8.00	
S27	**3p**	**2B Ultramarine**	20	25
S27a		Missing phosphor	£50	
S28	**5p**	**2B Bright violet**	60	70
S29	**7½p**	**2B Chestnut**	85	90
S29a		Broad band (right)	£25	
S29b		Missing phosphor	5.00	
		First Day Cover		2.00
		Presentation Pack 27	1.50	

FCP/GA

No.			U/M	F/U
S30	**2½p**	**CB Magenta** (22.9.72)	20	10
S31	**3p**	**2B Ultramarine** (14.12.72)	45	45
S31a		'JET' (yellow) phosphor	1.75	
S31b		Imperforate pair	£300	
S31c		Imperf. top margin	£200	

FCP/PVA

No.			U/M	F/U
S32	**2½p**	**CB Magenta** (6.73)	5.00	
S32a		Missing phosphor	£20	
S33	**3p**	**2B Ultramarine** (1973)	7.50	
S33a		Missing phosphor	£15	
S33b		Broad centre band	£350	
S34	**3p**	**CB Ultramarine** (23.1.74)	25	25
S35	**3½p**	**2B Bronze green** (23.1.74)	8.50	
S36	**5p**	**2B Bright violet** (6.73)	£20	£20
S36a		Broad left band	£1000	
S36b		'JET' (yellow) phosphor	6.00	
S37	**7½p**	**2B Chestnut** (11.73)	£70	

FCP/PVAD

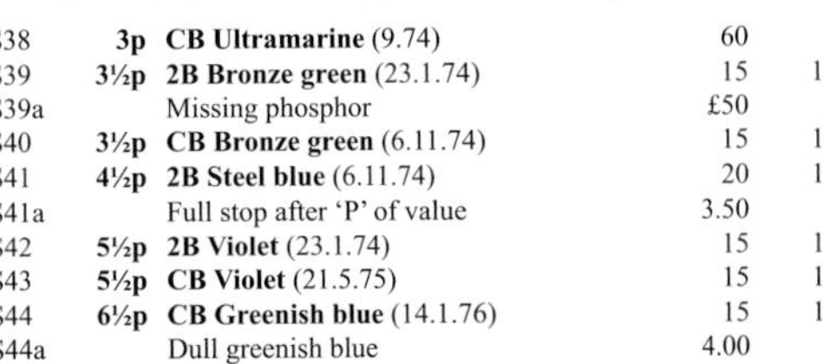

No.			U/M	F/U
S38	**3p**	**CB Ultramarine** (9.74)	60	
S39	**3½p**	**2B Bronze green** (23.1.74)	15	15
S39a		Missing phosphor	£50	
S40	**3½p**	**CB Bronze green** (6.11.74)	15	15
S41	**4½p**	**2B Steel blue** (6.11.74)	20	15
S41a		Full stop after 'P' of value	3.50	
S42	**5½p**	**2B Violet** (23.1.74)	15	15
S43	**5½p**	**CB Violet** (21.5.75)	15	15
S44	**6½p**	**CB Greenish blue** (14.1.76)	15	15
S44a		Dull greenish blue	4.00	

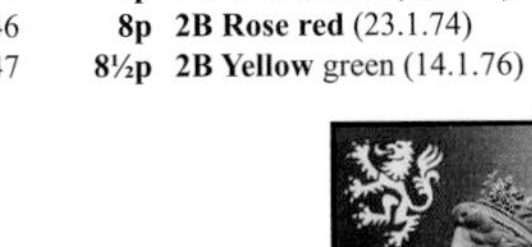

No.			U/M	F/U
S45	**7p**	**CB Red brown** (18.1.78)	15	15
S46	**8p**	**2B Rose red** (23.1.74)	20	20
S47	**8½p**	**2B Yellow** green (14.1.76)	20	20

No.			U/M	F/U
S48	**9p**	**2B Violet** (18.1.78)	20	20
S49	**10p**	**2B Orange brown** (20.10.76)	25	20
S50	**10p**	**CB Orange brown** (23.7.80)	25	25
S51	**10½p**	**2B Steel blue** (18.1.78)	30	30
S52	**11p**	**2B Scarlet** (20.10.76)	30	30
S52a		Missing phosphor	2.00	
S52b		Right band (left band omitted)	£100	
S52c		Left band (right band omitted)	£75	
		First Day Cover (3p, 3½p, 5½p, 8p)		3.00
		Presentation Pack 62 (29.5.74)		
		Contents: S34, 39, 42, 46 (4v)	1.10	
		First Day Cover (4½p)		3.00
		First Day Cover (3½p, 4½p)		3.00
		Presentation Pack 62 (6.11.74)		
		Contents: S34, 40/42, 46 (5v)	1.10	
		First Day Cover (6½p, 8½p)		3.00
		First Day Cover (10p, 11p)		3.00
		Presentation Pack 85 (20.10.76)		
		Contents: S44, 47, 49, 52 (4v)	1.10	
		First Day Cover (7p, 9p, 10½p)		3.00

PCP/PVAD

No.			U/M	F/U
S53	12p	**Yellow green** (23.7.80)	30	30
S54	13½p	**Red brown** (23.7.80)	40	40
S55	15p	**Bright blue** (23.7.80)	40	45
		First Day Cover (12p, 13½p, 15p)		3.00
		First Day Cover (10p, 12p, 13½p, 15p)		3.00

Printer: Waddington in Litho

1981 (8 April) Decimal. Phosphor issue. No watermark. Perf. 13½ x 14 One 4mm side band on 11½p, 12p, 12½p and 13p.

FCP/PVA

No.			U/M	F/U
S56	11½p	**LB Drab** (8.4.81)	50	50
S56a		Missing phosphor	£700	
S56b		Imperf. at right (marginal)	£60	
S57	12p	**LB Emerald** (7.1.86)	1.20	1.10
S58	12½p	**LB Light emerald** (24.2.82)	35	35
S58a		Varnished paper	22.50	
S59	13p	**LB Pale chestnut** Type I (23.10.84)	40	40
S59a		Missing phosphor	£700	
S59b		Type II (1.85)	4.00	3.50
S59c		Missing phosphor	£750	
		First Day Cover (12p)		2.00

PCP/PVAD

No.			U/M	F/U
S60	14p	**Grey blue** (8.4.81)	40	40
S61	15½p	**Pale violet** (24.2.82)	50	50
S62	16p	**Drab** (27.4.83)	40	40

No.			U/M	F/U
S63	17p	**Grey blue.** Type I (23.10.84)	2.00	75
S63a		Type II (1.85)	1.00	70
S64	18p	**Violet blue** (8.4.81)	60	65
S65	19½p	**Olive grey** (24.2.82)	1.10	1.10

No.			U/M	F/U
S66	20½p	**Ultramarine** (27.4.83)	2.50	2.00
S67	22p	**Blue** (8.4.81)	2.00	2.00
S68	26p	**Rosine** Type I (24.2.82)	65	65

No.			U/M	F/U
S69	28p	**Violet blue.** Type II (27.4.83)	75	75
S70	31p	**Bright purple.** Type I (23.10.84)	1.20	1.20
S70a		Type II (6.85)	£77	£45
		First Day Cover (11½p, 14p, 18p, 22p)		3.00
		Presentation Pack 129b (28.10.81)		
		Contents: S45, 48, 51, 53/55, 61, 66, 69 (10v)	3.90	
		First Day Cover (12½p, 15½p, 19½p, 26p)		3.00
		First Day Cover (16p, 20½p, 28p)		3.00
		Presentation Pack 2 (3.8.83)		
		Contents: S50, 58, 63, 68, 70, 71 (6v)	8.50	

PCP/PVA

No.			U/M	F/U
S71	17p	**Grey blue.** Type II (25.6.85)	65	65

ACP/PVAD

No.			U/M	F/U
S72	16p	**Drab** (2.11.83)	4.00	30

No.			U/M	F/U
S73	22p	**Yellow green.** Type I (23.10.84)	1.50	1.50
S73a		Type II (6.86)	£22	£22
		First Day Cover (13p, 17p, 22p, 31p) (23.10.84)		3.00
		Presentation Pack 6 (23.10.84)		
		Contents: S50, 58, 63, 64, 70/72, 76(8v)	8.50	

Printer: House of Questa in Litho

Type I
Large eye and mouth

Type II
Small eye and mouth

1986 (29 April) Decimal. Phosphor issue. No watermark. Perf. 15 x 14 One 4mm phosphor band or 'bar' on 12p, 13p, 14p, 15p, 17p and 18p.

FCP/PVAD

No.			U/M	F/U
S74	**12p**	**LBar Emerald** (29.4.86)	1.00	1.00
S74a		Short band at top	£20	
S75	**13p**	**LBar Pale chestnut** Type II (4.11.86)	40	40
S75a		Short band at top	£15	

FCP/PVA

No.			U/M	F/U
S76	**13p**	**LBar Pale chestnut** Type II (14.4.87)	60	
S76a		Short band at top	4.00	

No.			U/M	F/U
S77	**14p**	**CBar Dark blue** (8.11.88)	40	40
S77a		Short band at top	4.00	
S77b		Short band at bottom	2.00	
S77c		Cream paper. Low OBA	4.50	
S77d		CB (21.3.89)	40	40
S78	**14p**	**LB Dark blue** (21.3.89)	50	50
S78a		Short band at top	£15	
S78b		Short band at bottom	£15	
S79	**15p**	**CBar Bright blue** (28.11.89)	35	40
S79a		Short band at top	3.50	
S79b		Short band at bottom	2.00	
S80	**17p**	**CBar Dark blue** (4.12.90)	45	50
S80a		Short band at top	1.50	
S80b		Short band at bottom	1.50	

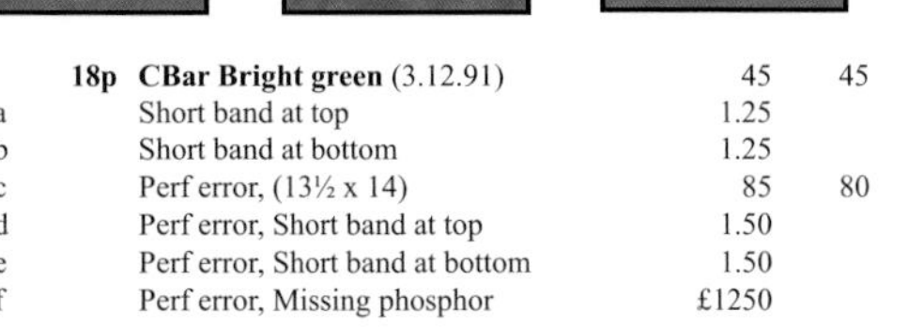

No.			U/M	F/U
S81	**18p**	**CBar Bright green** (3.12.91)	45	45
S81a		Short band at top	1.25	
S81b		Short band at bottom	1.25	
S81c		Perf error, (13½ x 14)	85	80
S81d		Perf error, Short band at top	1.50	
S81e		Perf error, Short band at bottom	1.50	
S81f		Perf error, Missing phosphor	£1250	
S82	**19p**	**2B Orange red** (21.3.89)	1.00	1.10
S83	**23p**	**2B Bright green** (21.3.89)	6.25	7.00

ACP/PVA

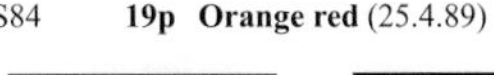

No.			U/M	F/U
S84	**19p**	**Orange red** (25.4.89)	50	50

No.			U/M	F/U
S85	**20p**	**Black** (28.11.89)	45	45
S85a		Low OBA	1.25	
S86	**22p**	**Orange red** (14.5.91)	70	
S87	**24p**	**Indian red** (28.11.89)	65	70

No.			U/M	F/U
S88	**24p**	**Chestnut** (3.12.91)	75	80
S88a		Perf error, (13½ x 14) (10.92)	1.60	1.60
S89	**26p**	**Stone** (14.5.91)	1.10	
S90	**28p**	**Blue grey** (3.12.91)	55	55
S90a		Perf error, (13½ x 14) (10.92)	2.50	2.50

No.			U/M	F/U
S91	**34p**	**Slate** (28.11.89)	90	95
S92	**37p**	**Red** (14.5.91)	95	1.00
S93	**39p**	**Mauve** (3.12.91)	1.00	1.10
S93a		Perf error, (13½ x 14) (4.92)	2.00	2.00

ACP/PVAD

No.			U/M	F/U
S94	**17p**	**Grey blue**. Type II (29.4.86)	2.20	2.20

No.			U/M	F/U
S95	**18p**	**Olive grey**. Type II (6.1.87)	50	50
S95a		Cream gum (29.3.88)	60	
S96	**19p**	**Orange red** (8.11.88)	50	30
S96a		Pale orange red (21.3.89)	50	50
S97	**22p**	**Yellow green** Type II (27.1.87)	70	75
S98	**22p**	**Orange red** (4.12.90)	55	60
S99	**23p**	**Bright green** (8.11.88)	60	65
S100	**26p**	**Rosine**. Type II (27.1.87)	1.75	1.85
S101	**26p**	**Stone** (4.12.90)	60	65
S102	**28p**	**Violet blue**. Type II (27.1.87)	60	65
S103	**31p**	**Bright purple**. Type II (29.4.86)	90	90

No.			U/M	F/U
S104	32p	**Deep greenish blue** (8.11.88)	85	90
S105	37p	**Red** (4.12.90)	1.00	
		First Day Cover (13p, 17p, 22p, 31p) (23.10.86)		3.00
		First Day Cover (18p) (6.1.87)		1.50
		First Day Cover (22p, 26p, 28p) (27.1.87)		3.00
		Presentation Pack 10 (3.3.87)		
		Contents: S78, 79, 100, 101, 103, 105, 107, 108 (8v)	8.75	
		First Day Cover (14p, 19p, 23p, 32p)		3.00
		First Day Cover (15p, 20p, 24p, 34p)		3.00
		First Day Cover (17p, 22p, 26p, 37p)		3.00
		First Day Cover (18p, 24p, 28p, 39p)		3.00

OFNP/PVA - C (Yellow) fluor

No.			U/M	F/U
S106	18p	**LB Bright green** - SP62 (B. Potter book) (10.8.93)	1.50	1.50
S107	24p	**2B Chestnut** - SP62 (B. Potter book) (10.8.93)	1.30	1.30
S107a		Inset left band	4.50	4.00

For issues previously listed as S116 to S119 please see 'ellipticals' section

Wales

Printer: Harrison & Sons in Photogravure

3d, 4d, 5d

6d, 9d

1s3d, 1s6d

1958 (18 Aug.) Wmk. Multiple Crowns. Perf. 15 x 14

Cream paper/GA

No.			U/M	F/U
WA1	3d	**Lilac**	45	25
WA2	6d	**Claret** (29.9.58)	75	40
WA3	1s 3d	**Green** (29.9.58)	2.25	1.00
		First Day Cover (3d)		£10

White paper/GA

No.			U/M	F/U
WA4	3d	**Lilac** (30.4.62)	10	15
WA5	4d	**Ultramarine** (7.2.66)	10	15
WA6	6d	**Claret** (18.7.62)	25	15
WA7	1s 3d	**Green** (11.5.64)	30	30
WA7a		Deep green	25	50
WA7b		Myrtle green	£60	£15
		Set of 4	50	50

1967 (1 Mar.) Phosphor issue. Wmk. Multiple Crowns. Perf. 15 x 14

White paper/GA

No.			U/M	F/U
WA8	3d	**CB Lilac** (16.5.67)	10	15
WA9	4d	**2B Ultramarine** (10.67)	10	10
WA10	9d	**2B Deep green** (1.3.67)	25	30
WA10a		Missing phosphor	£350	
WA11	1s 6d	**2B Grey blue** (1.3.67)	20	25
WA11a		Missing phosphor	£50	
		Set of 4	50	70
		First Day Cover (9d, 1s6d)		4.50

1967 (12 Dec.) Phosphor issue. No watermark. Perf. 15 x 14

Chalky paper/PVA

No.			U/M	F/U
WA12	3d	**CB Lilac** (6.12.67)	10	15
WA12a		Missing phosphor	£60	

Chalky paper/PVA

No.			U/M	F/U
WA13	4d	**2B Ultramarine** (21.6.68)	10	15
WA14	4d	**CB Sepia** (4.9.68)	10	15
WA15	4d	**CB Vermilion** (26.2.69)	10	15
WA15a		Missing phosphor	2.00	
WA16	5d	**2B Deep blue** (4.9.68)	15	15
WA16a		Missing phosphor	3.00	
WA17	1s 6d	**2B Grey blue** (12.12.68)	1.85	1.75
		Set of 6	2.25	2.40
		First Day Cover (4d sepia, 5d)		1.00
		Presentation Pack 24 (9.12.70)		
		Contents: WA10/12, 14/16 (6v)	1.40	

Printer: Harrison & Sons in Photogravure

1971 (7 July) Decimal. Phosphor issue. No watermark. Perf. 15 x 14. Two 9.5mm phosphor bands or one 4mm centre band, unless stated otherwise.

OCP/PVA

No.			U/M	F/U
WA18	2½p	**CB Magenta**	10	15
WA18a		Missing phosphor	6.00	
WA18b		Imperf. top margin	£175	
WA19	3p	**2B Ultramarine**	30	25
WA19a		Missing phosphor	£40	
WA20	5p	**2B Bright violet**	1.00	1.00
WA20a		Broad band	£75	
WA20b		Missing phosphor	£20	
WA21	7½p	**2B Chestnut**	1.20	1.25
WA21a		Missing phosphor	£80	
		First Day Cover		2.00
		Presentation Pack 28	1.50	

FCP/GA

No.			U/M	F/U
WA22	**2½p**	**CB Magenta** (22.9.72)	30	20
WA22a		Imperforate pair	£250	
WA23	**3p**	**2B Ultramarine** (6.6.73)	60	40
WA23a		Missing phosphor	£12	
WA23b		Right band (left band omitted)	£150	
WA23c		Left band (right band omitted)	£150	

FCP/PVA

No.			U/M	F/U
WA24	**2½p**	**CB Magenta** (1973)	1.75	
WA25	**3p**	**2B Ultramarine** (2.73)	8.00	
WA25a		Broad band	£125	
WA26	**3p**	**CB Ultramarine** (23.1.74)	30	25
WA27	**5p**	**2B Bright violet** (6.73)	17.50	
WA27a		Missing phosphor	£75	

FCP/PVAD

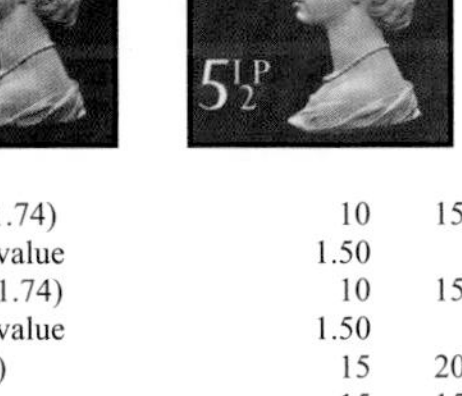

No.			U/M	F/U
WA28	**3½p**	**2B Bronze green** (23.1.74)	10	15
WA28a		Full stop before ‘P’ of value	1.50	
WA29	**3½p**	**CB Bronze green** (6.11.74)	10	15
WA29a		Full stop before ‘P’ of value	1.50	
WA30	**4½p**	**2B Steel blue** (6.11.74)	15	20
WA31	**5½p**	**2B Violet** (23.1.74)	15	15
WA31a		Missing phosphor	£175	
WA32	**5½p**	**CB Violet** (21.5.75)	15	15
WA32a		Imperf. pair	£400	

No.			U/M	F/U
WA32b		Low emblem and value (ex cyl 2)	£300	

No.			U/M	F/U
WA33	**6½p**	**CB Greenish blue** (14.1.76)	15	15
WA34	**7p**	**CB Red brown** (18.1.78)	15	15
WA35	**8p**	**2B Rose red** (23.1.74)	20	20
WA35a		Missing phosphor	£800	

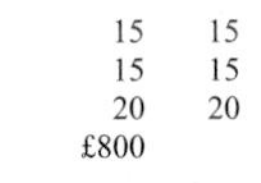

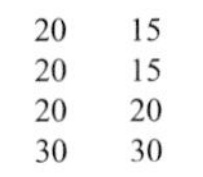

No.			U/M	F/U
WA36	**8½p**	**2B Yellow green** (14.1.76)	20	15
WA37	**9p**	**2B Violet** (18.1.78)	20	15
WA38	**10p**	**2B Orange brown** (20.10.76)	20	20
WA39	**10p**	**CB Orange brown** (23.7.80)	30	30

No.			U/M	F/U
WA40	**10½p**	**2B Steel blue** (18.1.78)	30	30
WA41	**11p**	**2B Scarlet** (20.10.76)	30	30
		First Day Cover (3p, 3½p, 5½p, 8p)		3.00
		Presentation Pack 63 (29.5.74)		
		Contents: WA26, 28, 31, 35 (4v)	1.10	
		First Day Cover (3½p, 4½p)		3.00
		Presentation Pack 63 (6.11.74)		
		Contents: WA26, 29/31, 35 (5v)	1.10	
		First Day Cover (6½p, 8½p)		3.00
		First Day Cover (10p, 11p)		3.00
		Presentation Pack 86 (20.10.76)		
		Contents: WA33, 36, 38, 41 (4v)	1.10	
		First Day Cover (7p, 9p, 10½p)		3.00

PCP/PVAD

No.			U/M	F/U
WA42	**12p**	**Yellow green** (23.7.80)	40	40
WA43	**13½p**	**Red brown** (23.7.80)	40	40
WA44	**15p**	**Bright blue** (23.7.80)	40	40
		First Day Cover (12p, 13½p, 15p)		3.00
		First Day Cover (10p, 12p, 13½p, 15p)		3.00

Printer: House of Questa in Litho

1981 (8 April) Decimal. Phosphor issue. No watermark. Perf. 13½ x 14. One 4mm side band on 11½p and 12½p.

OCP/PVA

No.			U/M	F/U
WA45	**11½p**	**LB Drab** (8.4.81)	50	50

PCP/PVA

No.			U/M	F/U
WA46	14p	**Grey blue** (8.4.81)	40	35
WA47	18p	**Violet blue** (8.4.81)	70	75
WA48	22p	**Blue** (8.4.81)	65	65
		First Day Cover (11½p, 14p, 18p, 22p)		3.00
		Presentation Pack 129c (28.10.81)		
		Contents: WA34, 37, 40, 42/48 (10v)	3.90	

FCP/PVAD

No.			U/M	F/U
WA49	12½p	**LB Light emerald** (24.2.82)	40	40

PCP/PVAD

No.			U/M	F/U
WA50	15½p	**Pale violet** (24.2.82)	50	50
WA50a		Lavender	1.50	75
WA51	16p	**Drab** (27.4.83)	90	90
WA52	19½p	**Olive grey** (24.2.82)	1.00	1.00

No.			U/M	F/U
WA53	20½p	**Ultramarine** (27.4.83)	2.00	2.00
WA54	26p	**Rosine** (24.2.82)	60	60
WA55	28p	**Violet blue** (27.4.83)	65	65
		First Day Cover (12½p, 15½p, 19½p, 26p)		3.00
		First Day Cover (16p, 20½p, 28p)		3.00
		Presentation Pack 3 (3.8.83)		
		Contents: WA39, 49, 51, 53/55 (6v)	8.50	

Type I
Thin wing-tips, tail and tongue

Type II
Thick wing-tips, tail and tongue

1984 (10 Jan) Decimal. Phosphor issue. No watermark. Perf. 15 x 14. One 4mm phosphor band or 'bar' on 12p, 12½p, 13p, 14p, 15p, 17p and 18p
Printer: House of Questa in Litho

FCP/PVAD

No.			U/M	F/U
WA58	12p	**LB Emerald** (7.1.86)	90	90
WA58a		Short left 'bar' (7.86)	2.00	1.50
WA59	12½p	**LB Light emerald** (10.1.84)	3.00	3.00
WA60	13p	**LB Pale chestnut** Type I (23.10.84)	30	40
WA60a		Type II	2.50	1.75
WA60b		LBar Type II (1.87)	2.00	55
		First Day Cover (12p)		1.50

FCP/PVA

No.			U/M	F/U
WA62	13p	**LBar Pale brown** Type II (14.4.87)	1.20	1.00
WA62a		Short band at top	2.50	
WA62b		Short band at bottom	£25	

No.			U/M	F/U
WA63	14p	**CBar Dark blue** (8.11.88)	40	40
WA63a		Short band at top	7.50	
WA63b		Short band at bottom	2.50	
WA64	15p	**CBar Bright blue** (28.11.89)	30	30
WA64a		Missing phosphor	£90	
WA64b		Short band at top	3.00	
WA64c		Short band at bottom	3.00	
WA65	17p	**CBar Dark blue** (4.12.90)	40	40
WA65a		Missing phosphor	£18	
WA65b		Short band at top	2.00	

No.			U/M	F/U
WA66	18p	**CBar Bright green** (3.12.91)	30	30
WA66a		Short band at top	2.50	
WA66b		Short band at bottom	1.50	
WA66c		Perf error (13½ x 14) (12.92)	3.60	3.60
WA66d		Perf error, Short band at top	£15	
WA66e		Perf error, Short band at bottom	4.00	
WA66f		CB (25.2.92)	65	40
WA66g		Missing phosphor	£200	
WA67	18p	**RB Bright green** - SP55 (Wales book) (25.2.92)	1.10	1.10
WA67a		Missing phosphor	£350	
WA68	24p	**2B Chestnut** - SP55 (Wales book) (25.2.92)	75	90
WA68a		Short bands at top	6.00	
WA68b		Short bands at bottom	£12	
WA68c		Missing phosphor	£350	

PCP/PVAD

No.			U/M	F/U
WA69	16p	**Drab** (10.1.84)	95	1.00

No.			U/M	F/U
WA70	17p	**Grey blue**. Type I (23.10.84)	75	30
WA71	31p	**Bright purple**. Type I (23.10.84)	70	70

ACP/PVA

No.			U/M	F/U
WA72	19p	**Orange red** (20.6.89)	65	
WA73	20p	**Black** (28.11.89)	45	45
WA73a		Low OBA	1.25	
WA74	24p	**Indian red** (28.11.89)	50	55

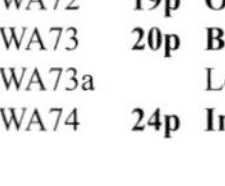

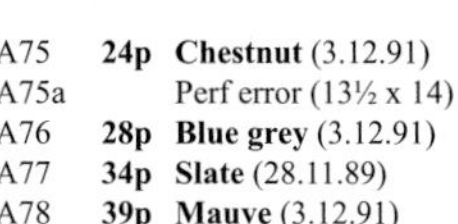

No.			U/M	F/U
WA75	24p	**Chestnut** (3.12.91)	45	45
WA75a		Perf error (13½ x 14) (10.92)	2.00	2.00
WA76	28p	**Blue grey** (3.12.91)	75	75
WA77	34p	**Slate** (28.11.89)	80	85
WA78	39p	**Mauve** (3.12.91)	1.00	1.10

ACP/PVAD

No.			U/M	F/U
WA79	17p	**Grey blue**. Type I (25.2.86)	50	50
WA79a		Type II (18.8.86)	£24	£22

No.			U/M	F/U
WA81	18p	**Olive grey**. Type II (6.1.87)	45	45
WA81a		White gum (29.3.88)	70	
WA82	19p	**Orange red** (8.11.88)	50	55
WA83	22p	**Yellow green** Type I (23.10.84)	55	55
WA84	22p	**Orange red** (4.12.90)	50	55

No.			U/M	F/U
WA85	23p	**Bright green** (8.11.88)	55	60
WA86	26p	**Rosine.** Type II (27.1.87)	3.50	3.50
WA87	26p	**Stone** (4.12.90)	70	75
WA88	28p	**Violet blue**. Type II (27.1.87)	75	80
WA89	31p	**Bright purple**. Type I (27.1.87)	70	70
WA90	32p	**Deep greenish blue** (8.11.88)	80	80
WA91	37p	**Red** (4.12.90)	1.00	1.10
		Presentation Pack 7 (23.10.84)		
		Contents: WA38, 54, 55, 60, 69/71, 85 (8v)	8.50	
		Presentation Pack 11 (3.3.87)		
		Contents: WA58, 60, 81, 83, 85, 87, 89, 90 (8v)	8.75	
		First Day Cover (13p, 17p, 22p, 31p) (23.10.84)		3.00
		First Day Cover (18p) (6.1.87)		1.50
		First Day Cover (14p, 19p, 23p, 32p)		3.00
		First Day Cover (15p, 20p, 24p, 34p)		3.00
		First Day Cover (17p, 22p, 26p, 37p)		3.00
		First Day Cover (18p, 24p, 28p, 39p)		3.00

OFNP/PVA - C (Yellow) fluor

No.			U/M	F/U
WA92	18p	**LB Bright green** - SP62 (B. Potter book) (10.8.93)	1.10	1.10
WA93	24p	**2B Chestnut** - SP62 (B. Potter book) (10.8.93)	75	80
WA93a		Inset left band	4.50	4.00

For issues previously listed as WA94 to WA97 please see 'ellipticals' section

Northern Ireland

Printer: House of Questa in Lithography

1993 (7 Dec.) Decimal. Perf. 15 x 14. Two phosphor bands, except where indicated.

OFNP/PVA - C (Yellow) fluor

No.			U/M	F/U
SLU88	**19p**	**CBar Olive-green**	50	50
SLU88a		Short band at top	2.50	2.50
SLU88b		Short band at bottom	6.00	6.00
SLU89	**19p**	**LB Olive-green** SP67, SP68 (N. Ireland book) (26.7.94)	1.30	1.30
SLU89a		Inset left band	2.75	2.75
SLU89b		Short extra band at lower right	2.75	2.75
SLU89c		Missing phosphor	£950	
SLU89d		Broad band at left	£750	
SLU90	**19p**	**RB Olive-green** - SP71 (Nat. Trust book) (25.4.95)	1.60	1.60
SLU91	**25p**	**2B 8mm Salmon-pink**	60	65
SLU91a		Short bands at top	9.50	
SLU91b		Short band at top right	4.50	4.50
SLU91c		Short band at top right and inset left band	4.50	4.50
SLU91d		Inset left band	2.50	2.50
SLU91e		Missing phosphor	£950	£375
SLU91f		Narrower gap between phosphor bands (9.5 mm bands) (25.4.95)	80	80
SLU92	**30p**	**2B Grey-green**	80	85
SLU92a		Short bands at bottom	9.50	
SLU92b		Inset left band	3.25	3.25
SLU92c		Missing phosphor	£950	
SLU93	**41p**	**2 Stone**	1.10	1.15
SLU93a		Short bands at top	3.25	3.25
SLU93b		Missing phosphor	£950	
		First Day Cover (19p, 25p, 30p, 41p)		4.00

OFNP/PVA - D (Blue) fluor

No.			U/M	F/U
SLU94	**19p**	**CBar Olive-green** (1.2.96)	90	45
SLU84a		Short band at bottom	£10	

No.			U/M	F/U
SLU95	**20p**	**CB Bright green** (23.7.96)	1.00	1.00
SLU96	**25p**	**2B 8mm Salmon-pink** (27.2.96)	80	50
SLU96a		Narrower gap between phosphor bands (9.5 mm bands) - SP76 (Euro Football book) (14.5.96)	70	90

No.			U/M	F/U
SLU97	**26p**	**2B Red-brown** (23.7.96)	1.20	1.20
SLU98	**37p**	**2B Amethyst** (23.7.96)	2.00	2.00
SLU99	**63p**	**2B Light emerald** (23.7.96)	3.00	3.00
		First Day Cover (20p,26p,37p, 63p)		4.00

Printer: Walsall Security Printers in computer engraved-gravure

OFNP/PVA - D (Blue) fluor

No.			U/M	F/U
SLU100	**19p**	**CB Olive-green** (8.6.99)	1.20	1.20
SLU100	**20p**	**CB Bright green** (1.7.97)	80	80
SLU101	**20p**	**RB Bright green** - SP86 (Breaking Barriers book) (13.10.98)	1.00	1.10
SLU101	**26p**	**2B Red-brown** (1.7.97)	70	75
SLU101a		Perf 13½ - SP87 (Breaking Barriers book) (13.10.98)	1.75	1.75
SLU102	**37p**	**2B Amethyst** (1.7.97)	1.50	1.50

No.			U/M	F/U
SLU103	**38p**	**2B Ultramarine** ((8.6.99)	1.50	1.50
SLU104	**40p**	**2B Greyish-blue** (25.4.00)	1.00	1.00
SLU105	**63p**	**2B Light emerald** (1.7.97)	2.50	2.50
SLU106	**64p**	**2B Sea green** (8.6.99)	3.00	3.00
SLU107	**65p**	**2B Greenish-blue** (25.4.00)	2.50	2.50
		First Day Cover (19p, 38p, 64p)		2.50
		First Day Cover (1st, 40p, 65p)		7.00

Printer: Harrison & Sons in computer engraved-gravure

OFNP/PVA (Layflat) - D (Blue) fluor

No.			U/M	F/U
SLU106	**26p**	**2B Red-brown** - SP77 (BBC book) (23.9.97)	1.50	1.50
SLU107	**37p**	**2B Amethyst** - SP77 (BBC book) (23.9.97)	1.10	1.10

Scotland

Printer: House of Questa in Lithography

1993 (7 Dec.) Decimal. Perf. 15 x 14. Two phosphor bands, except where indicated.

OFNP/PVA - C (Yellow) fluor

No.			U/M	F/U
SLS116	**19p**	**CBar Olive-green**	70	75
SLS116a		Short band at top	1.25	1.50
SLS116b		Short band at bottom	1.25	1.50
SLS117	**19p**	**RB Olive-green** - SP71 (Nat. Trust book) (25.4.95))	1.60	1.60
SLS117a		Short band at top	£15	
SLS118	**25p**	**2B 8mm Salmon-pink**	70	75
SLS118a		Short bands at bottom	8.50	
SLS118b		Inset left band	7.50	
SLS118c		Narrower gap between phosphor bands (9.5 mm bands) - SP71 (Nat. Trust book) (25.4.95)	90	90
SLS118d		Short bands at top	8.50	
SLS119	**30p**	**2B Grey-green**	85	90
SLS119a		Right band inset	17.50	
SLS119b		Short bands at bottom	£10	
SLS120	**41p**	**2B Stone**	1.25	1.30
SLS120a		Missing phosphor	£300	
		First Day Cover (19p, 25p, 30p, 41p)		4.00

OFNP/PVA - D (Blue) fluor

No.			U/M	F/U
SLS121	**19p**	**CBar Olive-green** (12.10.95)	1.00	1.00
SLS121a		Short band at top	7.50	
SLS121b		Short band at bottom	6.00	

No.			U/M	F/U
SLS122	**20p**	**CB 4.75mm Bright green** (23.7.96)	70	75
SLS122a		4.5 mm CB (4.12.96)	2.50	2.50
SLS123	**25p**	**2B 8mm Salmon-pink** (3.8.95)	90	90
SLS123a		Narrower gap between phosphor bands (9.5 mm bands) - SP76 (Euro Football book) (14.5.96)	90	90

No.			U/M	F/U
SLS124	**26p**	**2B Red-brown** (23.7.96)	1.20	1.20
SLS125	**37p**	**2B Amethyst** (23.7.96)	2.00	2.00
SLS126	**63p**	**2B Light emerald** (23.7.96)	2.50	2.50
		First Day Cover (20p,26p,37p, 63p)		4.00

Printer: Walsall Security Printers in computer engraved-gravure

OFNP/PVA - D (Blue) fluor

No.			U/M	F/U
SS127	**20p**	**CB Bright green** (1.7.97)	70	70
SS128	**20p**	**RB Bright green** - SP86 (Breaking Barriers book) (13.10.98)	1.00	1.10
SS128	**26p**	**2B Red-brown** (1.7.97)	1.00	1.00
SS128a		Perf 13½ - SP87 (Breaking Barriers book) (13.10.98)	1.00	1.10
SS129	**37p**	**2B Amethyst** (1.7.97)	1.50	1.50
SS130	**63p**	**2B Light emerald** (1.7.97)	2.00	2.00
		First Day Cover (19p, 38p, 64p)		2.50

Printer: Harrison & Sons in computer engraved-gravure

OFNP/PVA (Layflat) - D (Blue) fluor

No.			U/M	F/U
SS131	**26p**	**2B Red-brown** - SP77 (BBC book) (23.9.97)	90	90
SS132	**37p**	**2B Amethyst** - SP77 (BBC book) (23.9.97)	1.10	1.10

Wales

Printer: House of Questa in Lithography

1993 (7 Dec.) Decimal. Perf. 15 x 14. Two phosphor bands, except where indicated.

OFNP/PVA - C (Yellow) fluor

No.			U/M	F/U
SLWA94	**19p**	**CBar Olive-green**	50	60
SLWA94a		Short band at top	2.50	2.50
SLWA94b		Short band at bottom	2.50	2.50
SLWA95	**19p**	**RB Olive-green** SP71 (Nat. Trust book) (25.4.95)	1.70	1.75
SLWA96	**25p**	**2B 8mm Salmon-pink**	70	65
SLWA96a		Short bands at top	£20	
SLWA96b		Short bands at bottom	£10	£10
SLWA96c		Narrower gap between phosphor bands (9.5 mm bands) - SP71 (Nat. Trust book) (25.4.95)	90	90
SLWA96d		Broad left band (7.12.93)	£750	
SLWA97a	**30p**	**2B Grey-green**	85	80
SLWA97b		Short bands at bottom	12.50	
SLWA98	**41p**	**2B Stone**	1.25	90
SLWA98a		Short bands at top	£20	
SLWA98b		Short bands at bottom	12.50	
SLWA98c		Weak phosphor and fluor	17.50	
		First Day Cover (19p, 25p, 30p, 41p)		4.00

OFNP/PVA - D (Blue) fluor

No.			U/M	F/U
SLWA99	**19p**	**CBar Olive-green** (2.11.95)	90	90
SLWA99a		Short band at top	£10	

No.			U/M	F/U
SLWA100	**20p**	**CB Bright green** (23.7.96)	60	60
SLWA101	**25p**	**2B 8mm Salmon-pink** (31.7.95)	90	90
SLWA101a		Narrower gap between phosphor bands (9.5 mm bands) - SP76 (Euro Football book) (14.5.96)	70	70

No.			U/M	F/U
SLWA102	**26p**	**2B Red-brown** (23.7.96)	1.25	1.25
SLWA103	**37p**	**2B Amethyst** (23.7.96)	2.00	2.00
SLWA104	**41p**	**2B Stone** (1.2.96)	1.25	90
SLWA105	**63p**	**2B Light emerald** (23.7.96)	3.00	3.00
		First Day Cover (20p,26p,37p, 63p)		4.00

1997. Decimal, without "p" in value. Perf. 15 x 14. Two phosphor bands, except where indicated.

Printer: Walsall Security Printers in computer engraved-gravure

OFNP/PVA - D (Blue) fluor

No.			U/M	F/U
SWA106	**20(p)**	**CB Bright green** (1.7.97)	60	60
SWA106a		15-pin perforation variety	£13	
SWA107	**20(p)**	**RB Bright green** - SP86 (Breaking Barriers book) (13.10.98)	1.20	1.25
SWA107	**26(p)**	**2B Red-brown** (1.7.97)	70	70
SWA107a		Perf 13½ - SP87 (Breaking Barriers book) (13.10.98)	1.30	1.30
SWA108	**37(p)**	**2B Amethyst** (1.7.97)	1.25	1.25
SWA109	**63(p)**	**2B Light emerald** (1.7.97)	2.40	2.50
		First Day Cover (20p,26p,37p, 63p)		4.00
		First Day Cover (19p, 38p, 64p)		2.50

Printer: Harrison & Sons in computer engraved-gravure

OFNP/PVA (Layflat) - D (Blue) fluor

No.			U/M	F/U
SWA110	**26(p)**	**2B Red-brown** - SP77 (BBC book) (23.9.97)	1.10	1.10
SWA111	**37(p)**	**2B Amethyst** - SP77 (BBC book) (23.9.97)	1.75	1.75

England Pictorial

2001 (23 Apr.) Perf. 15 x 14. Two phosphor bands, except where indicated.

Printer: De La Rue Security Printers in Gravure

OFNP/PVA - D (Blue) fluor

No.			U/M	F/U
PEW2	**2nd**	**CBar Three Lions** (23.4.01)	45	45
PEW2a		Imperforate pair	£350	
PEW2b		Threee Lions, Bright fluor (10.4.03)	40	40
PEW1st	**1st**	**2B Crowned Lion** (23.4.01)	55	55
PEW1sta		Crowned Lion, Bright fluor (10.4.03)	50	50
PEWE	**E**	**2B Oak Tree** (23.4.01)	60	65
PEW65	**65p**	**2B Tudor Rose** (23.4.01)	1.20	1.30
PEW68	**68p**	**2B Tudor Rose** (4.7.02)	1.20	1.30
		First Day Cover (2nd, 1st, E, 65p)		3.00
		First Day Cover (68p)		3.00

Printer: House of Questa in Gravure

OFNP/PVA - D (Blue) fluor

No.			U/M	F/U
PEQ2	**2nd**	**CB Three Lions**, from Beyond the Universe prestige book (24.9.02)	75	85
PEQ1	**1st**	**2B Crowned Lion**,from Beyond the Universe prestige book (24.9.02)	85	95

England Pictorial
reprinted with conventional white borders

2003 (14 Oct.) Perf. 15 x 14. Two phosphor bands, except where indicated.

Printer: De La Rue Security Printers in Gravure

OFNP/PVA - D (Blue) fluor

No.			U/M	F/U
PEDW2	**2nd**	**CB Three Lions** (14.10.03)	40	45
PEDW2a		Three Lions, Layflat gum (.04)	1.00	1.00
PEDW1	**1st**	**2B Crowned Lion** (14.10.03)	55	60
PEDW1a		Short band at bottom	7.50	
PEDW1b		Layflat gum (.04)	1.25	1.25
PEDWE	**E**	**2B Oak** (14.10.03)	1.50	1.50
PEDW40	**40p**	**2B Oak** (11.5.04)	80	80
PEDW42	**42p**	**2B Oak** (7.05)	70	75
PEDW68	**68p**	**2B Tudor Rose** (24.6.03)	1.10	1.20
PEDW68a		Right band inset	4.00	
PEDW68b		Sideways print - Pane SP132 (Letters by Night book) (16.3.04)	1.25	1.25
PEDW68c		Tudor Rose, Layflat gum (.04)	1.75	1.75
		First Day Cover (2nd, 1st, E, 68p)		3.00
		First Day Cover (40p)		2.00
		First Day Cover (42p)		2.00

Printer: Walsall Security Printers in Gravure

OFNP/PVA - D (Blue) fluor

No.			U/M	F/U
PEWW2	**2nd**	**CB Three Lions** - Pane SP141 (Bronte sisters book) (24.2.05)	50	50
PEWW40	**40p**	**2B Oak** - Pane SP141 (Bronte sisters book) (24.2.05)	80	80
PEWW42	**42p**	**2B Oak** (5.4.05)	70	70
		First Day Cover (42p)		2.00

Northern Ireland Pictorial

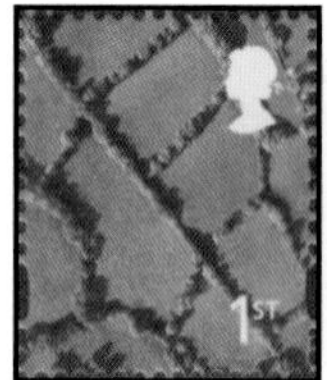

2001 (6 Mar.) - 03 Perf. 15 x 14. Two phosphor bands, except where indicated.

Printer: Walsall Security Printers in Lithography

OFNP/PVA - D (Blue) fluor

No.			U/M	F/U
PUW2	**2nd**	**CB Giant's causeway** (6.3.01)	40	45
PUW1	**1st**	**2B Patchwork fields** (6.3.01)	55	55
PUW1a		Missing phosphor	£35	
PUWE	**E**	**2B Linen** (6.3.01)	90	90
PUW65	**65p**	**2B Parian china** (6.3.01)	1.30	1.50
		First Day Cover (2nd, 1st, E, 65p)		3.00

Printer: Joh. Enschedé in Lithography

OFNP/PVA - D (Blue) fluor

No.			U/M	F/U
PUE2	**2nd**	**CB 4mm Giant's causeway** - SP124 (Microcosmos book) (25.2.03)	90	90
PUE2a		Missing phosphor	£600	
PUE1	**1st**	**2B Patchwork fields** - SP124 (Microcosmos book) (25.2.03)	1.00	1.00
PUE1a		Missing phosphor	£700	
PUE1b		Right band inset	£20	

Printer: De La Rue Security Printers in Lithography

OFNP/PVA - D (Blue) fluor

No.			U/M	F/U
PUDE	**E**	**2B Linen** (15.10.02)	90	90
PUD68	**68p**	**2B Parian china** (4.7.02)	1.30	1.40
		First Day Cover (68p)		3.00
		First Day Cover (E)		3.00

Northern Ireland Pictorial
reprinted with conventional white borders

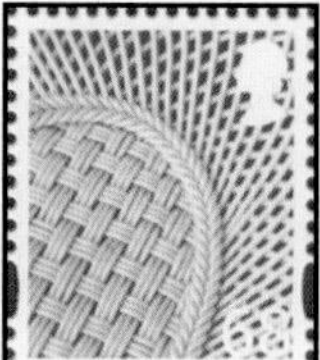

2003 (14 Oct.)-.Perf. 15 x 14. Two phosphor bands, except where indicated.

Printer: De La Rue Security Printers in Lithography

OFNP/PVA - D (Blue) fluor

No.			U/M	F/U
PUDW2	**2nd**	**CB Giant's causeway** (14.10.03)	35	35
PUDW1	**1st**	**2B Patchwork fields** (14.10.03)	50	55
PUDWE	**E**	**2B Linen** (14.10.03)	1.50	1.55
PUDW40	**40p**	**2B Linen** (11.5.04)	70	70
PUDW42	**42p**	**2B Linen** (7.05)	75	75
PUDW68	**68p**	**2B Parian china** (14.10.03)	1.20	1.20
		First Day Cover (2nd, 1st, E, 68p)		3.00
		First Day Cover (40p)		3.00

Printer: Walsall Security Printers in Lithography

OFNP/PVA - D (Blue) fluor

No.			U/M	F/U
PUWW42	**42p**	**2B Linen** (5.4.05)	70	70
		First Day Cover (42p)		4.00

Scotland Pictorial

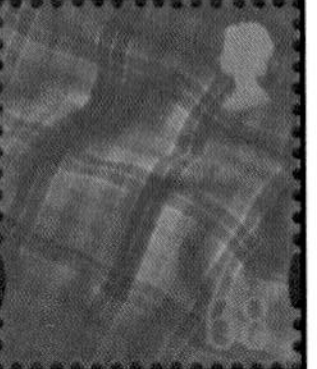

1999 (8 June) - Perf. 15 x 14. Two phosphor bands, except where indicated.

Printer: Walsall Security Printers in Gravure

OFNP/PVA - D (Blue) fluor

No.			U/M	F/U
PSW2	**2nd**	**CB Flag of St. Andrew** - Sheets (8.6.99)	45	45
PSW2a		Short band at bottom	1.20	
PSW1	**1st**	**2B Lion of Scotland** - Sheets (8.6.99)	60	60
PSW1a		Short bands at top	1.10	
PSW1b		Left band inset	£12	
PSW1c		Right band inset	7.50	
PSWE	**E**	**2B Thistle** - Sheets (8.6.99)	85	85
PSWEa		Short band at bottom	17.50	
PSWEb		Left band inset	£20	
PSWEc		Right band inset	£20	
PSW64	**64p**	**2B Tartan** - Sheets (8.6.99)	4.00	4.00
PSW65	**65p**	**2B Tartan** - Sheets (25.4.00)	1.80	1.80
PSW65a		Short bands at top	17.50	
PSW65b		Short bands at top, right band inset	£25	
PSW65c		Right band inset	£15	
		First Day Cover (2nd, 1st, E, 64p)		3.00
		First Day Cover (65p)		3.00

Printer: Questa in Gravure

OFNP/PVA - D (Blue) fluor

No.			U/M	F/U
PSQ2	**2nd**	**CB Flag of St. Andrew** (4.8.00)	1.00	1.00
PSQ2a		Pane SP103 (Life of the Century book) (4.8.00)	50	
PSQ1	**1st**	**2B Lion of Scotland** (22.10.01)	1.00	1.10
PSQ1a		Short bands at top	5.00	
PSQ1b		Short bands at top, left band inset	1.25	
PSQ1c		Left band inset	8.00	
PSQ1d		Pane SP115 (Unseen & unheard book) (22.10.01)	1.00	
PSQE	**E**	**2B Thistle** (22.10.01)	1.25	1.25
PSQEa		Short bands at top	5.00	
PSQeb		Left band inset	8.00	
PSQEc		Pane SP115 (Unseen & unheard book) (22.10.01)	1.25	
PSQ65	**65p**	**2B Tartan** (4.8.00)	2.75	2.75
PSQ65a		Left band inset	£20	
PSQ65b		Pane SP103 (Life of the Century book) (4.8.00)	1.80	

Printer: De La Rue Security Printers in Gravure

OFNP/PVA - D (Blue) fluor

No.			U/M	F/U
PSD2	**2nd**	**2B Flag of St. Andrew** (5.6.02)	45	40
PSD2a		Flag of St. Andrew (Thick '2nd') (18.7.03)	45	
PSD1	**1st**	**2B Lion of Scotland** (5.6.02)	70	70
PSD1a		Lion of Scotland (Thick '1st') (10.9.03)	70	
PSD68	**68p**	**2B Tartan** (4.7.02)	1.30	1.15
		First Day Cover (2nd, 1st)		3.00
		First Day Cover (68p)		3.00

Scotland Pictorial
reprinted with conventional white borders

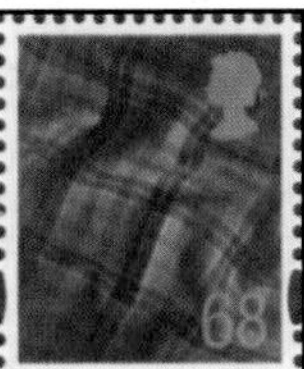

2003 (14 Oct.) - Perf. 15 x 14. Two phosphor bands, except where indicated.

Printer: De La Rue Security Printers in Gravure

OFNP/PVA - D (Blue) fluor

No.			U/M	F/U
PSDW2	**2nd**	**CB Flag of St Andrew** (14.10.03)	35	35
PSDW2a		Flag of St Andrew, Sideways print from Letters by Night prestige book (16.3.04)	65	65
PSDW2b		Flag of St Andrew. Coarse screen from Scottish Parliament min. sheet (5.10.04)	1.00	1.25
PSDW1	**1st**	**2B Lion of Scotland** (14.10.03)	55	60
PSDW1a		Lion of Scotland. Thicker neck on bandeau Scottish Parliament min. sheet (5.10.04)	65	1.00
PSDWE	**E**	**2B Thistle** (14.10.03)	1.50	1.55
PSDW40	**40p**	**2B Thistle** (11.5.04)	70	80
PSDW40a		Thistle. Coarse screen from Scottish Parliament min. sheet (5.10.04)	90	1.10
PSDW42	**42p**	**2B Thistle**	65	70
PSDW68	**68p**	**2B Tartan** (14.10.03)	1.20	1.15
PSDW68a		Right band inset	5.00	
		First Day Cover (2nd, 1st, E, 68p)		3.00
		First Day Cover (40p)		3.00
		First Day Cover (42p)		3.00

Printer: Walsall Security Printers in Gravure

OFNP/PVA - D (Blue) fluor

No.			U/M	F/U
PSWW42	**42p**	**2B Thistle** (5.4.05)	70	70
		First Day Cover (42p)		3.00

Wales Pictorial

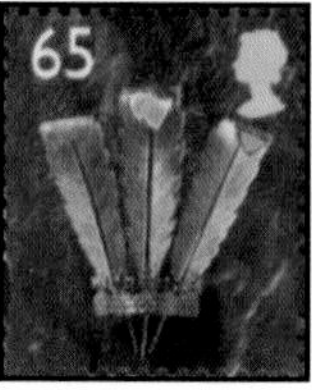

1999 (8 June) -03 Perf. 15 x 14. Two phosphor bands, except where indicated.

Printer: Walsall Security Printers in Gravure

OFNP/PVA - D (Blue) fluor

No.			U/M	F/U
PWW2	**2nd**	**CB Leek** (8.6.99)	45	45
PWW2a		**RB Leek** from Trees prestige book (18.9.00)	1.70	1.70
PWW2b		Right band inset	6.00	
PWW1	**1st**	**2B Dragon**(8.6.99)	55	65
PWWE	**E**	**2B Daffodil** (8.6.99)	1.00	1.00
PWW64	**64p**	**2B Feathers** (8.6.99)	3.60	3.60
PWW65	**65p**	**2B Feathers** (25.4.00)	1.70	1.70

Printer: De La Rue in Gravure

OFNP/PVA - D (Blue) fluor

No.			U/M	F/U
PWD2	**2nd**	**CB Leek** (28.05.03)	45	45
PWD1	**1st**	**2B Dragon** (4.3.03)	60	60
PWD68	**68p**	**2B Feathers** (4.7.02)	1.10	1.20

Wales Pictorial
reprinted with conventional white borders

2003 (14 Oct.) - Perf. 15 x 14. Two phosphor bands, except where indicated.

Printer: De La Rue in Gravure

OFNP/PVA - D (Blue) fluor

No.			U/M	F/U
PWDW2	**2nd**	**CB Leek** (14.10.03)	40	50
PWDW1	**1st**	**2B Dragon** (14.10.03)	60	60
PWDWE	**E**	**2B Daffodil** (14.10.03)	1.50	1.55
PWDW40	**40p**	**2B Daffodil** (11.5.04)	80	90
PWDW42	**42p**	**2B Daffodil**	85	85
PWDW68	**68p**	**2B Feathers** (14.10.03)	1.10	1.20

Printer: Walsall Security Printers in Gravure

OFNP/PVA - D (Blue) fluor

No.			U/M	F/U
PWWW42	**42p**	**2B Daffodil** (5.4.05)	75	75

Regional Machin NVI's

Printer: Walsall Security Printers in Gravure

2000 (15 Feb.) Two phosphor bands Perf 14

Northern Ireland

OFNP/PVA - D (Blue) fluor

No.			U/M	F/U
UW1	1st	**2B Orange-red** - Pane SP100 (Special by Design book) (15.2.00)	1.20	1.20
UW1a		Short bands at bottom	4.50	
UW1b		Right band inset	9.50	
UW1c		Perf 15 x 14 - Sheets (25.4.00)	4.50	4.50

Scotland

OFNP/PVA - D (Blue) fluor

No.			U/M	F/U
SW1	1st	**2B Orange-red** - Pane SP100 (Special by Design book) (15.2.00)	1.20	1.20
SW1a		Right band inset	9.50	

Wales

OFNP/PVA - D (Blue) fluor

No.			U/M	F/U
WW1	1st	**2B Orange-red** - Pane SP100 (Special by Design book) (15.2.00)	1.20	1.20
WW1a		Right band inset	9.50	

Postage Dues

Please note - watermarks are illustrated as seen from the back of the stamp.

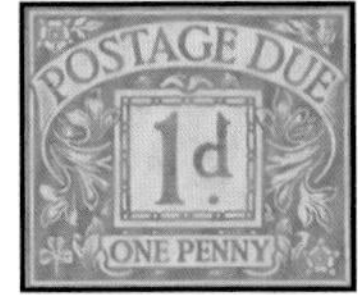

Royal Cypher Watermark
(sideways) (sideways-inverted)

1914 (20 April) Wmk. Royal Cypher (sideways). Perf. 14 x 15
Printer: Somerset House in Typo (½d, 1d, 2d, 5d and 1s)
Printer: Harrison & Sons in Typo (½d - 5d and 1d chalky)

No.			U/M	M/M	F/U
P1	**½d**	**Emerald**	80	40	30
P1a		Wmk. sideways-inverted	1.20	60	30
P2	**1d**	**Carmine**	90	35	25
P2a		Wmk. sideways-inverted	90	35	50
P2b		Pale carmine	1.20	40	40
P2c		Wmk. sideways-inverted	1.80	60	90
P2d		Carmine. Chalky paper (1924)	7.50	3.50	3.00
P3	**1½d**	**Chestnut** (1923)	£90	£30	£11
P3a		Wmk. sideways-inverted	£95	£35	£14
P4	**2d**	**Agate**	1.00	30	25
P4a		Wmk. sideways-inverted	1.25	50	25
P5	**3d**	**Violet** (1918)	14.00	4.25	50
P5a		Wmk. sideways-inverted	16.00	6.50	45
P5b		Bluish violet	16.00	6.50	1.75
P5c		Wmk. sideways-inverted	£25	8.00	3.50
P6	**4d**	**Grey green** (1921)	£65	£17	£4
P6a		Wmk. sideways-inverted	£75	£20	5.50
P7	**5d**	**Bistre brown**	7.00	3.00	1.50
P7a		Wmk. sideways-inverted	£25	£15	£15
P8	**1s**	**Bright blue** (1915)	£65	14.50	2.50
P8a		Wmk. sideways-inverted	£75	£20	3.50
P8b		Deep bright blue	£65	14.50	2.50
P8c		Wmk. sideways-inverted	£75	£13	4.00
		Set of 8	£275	£56	£19

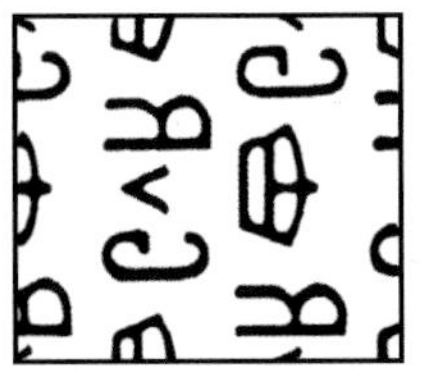
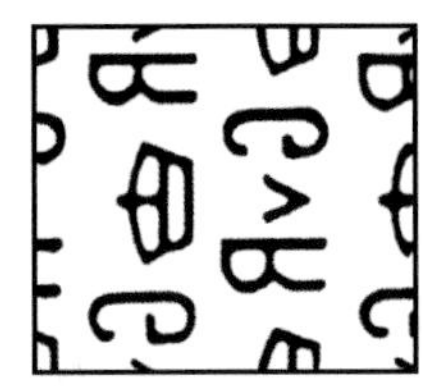

Block Cypher Watermark
(sideways) (sideways-inverted)

1924

(July) - 36 Wmk. Block Cypher (sideways). Perf. 14 x 15
Printer: Waterlow & Sons in Typo
Printer: Harrison & Sons in Typo (from 1934)

No.			U/M	M/M	F/U
P9	**½d**	**Emerald** (6.25)	1.25	40	20
P9a		Wmk. sideways-inverted	2.25	1.00	1.50
P10	**1d**	**Carmine** (4.25)	1.25	40	15
P10a		Wmk. sideways-inverted	-	-	£10
P11	**1½d**	**Chestnut** (10.24)	£72	£24	14.50
P11a		Wmk. sideways-inverted	-	-	£57
P12	**2d**	**Agate** (7.24)	5.00	80	25
P12a		Wmk. sideways-inverted	-	-	£12
P13	**3d**	**Violet** (10.24)	5.00	1.00	20
P13a		Wmk. sideways-inverted	£13	5.00	1.40
P13b		Printed on gummed side	£115	£70	-
P14	**4d**	**Grey green** (10.24)	£27	8.50	2.25
P14a		Wmk. sideways-inverted	£40	£25	-
P15	**5d**	**Bistre brown** (1.31)	£90	£35	£18
P16	**1s**	**Deep blue** (9.24)	£20	4.50	40
P16a		Wmk. sideways-inverted	-	-	£16
P17	**2s 6d**	**Purple** on yellow (10.24)	£185	£30	50
P17a		Wmk. sideways-inverted	-	-	£12
		Set of 9	£350	£85	£33

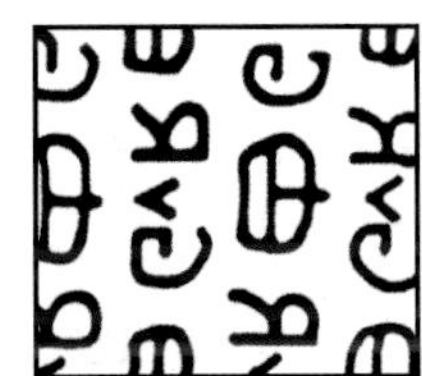

Experimental Block Cypher Watermark

1924 - 25 (?) Wmk. Experimental Block Cypher (sideways). Perf. 14 x 15
Printers: Waterlow & Sons in Typo on Experimental paper.

No.			U/M	M/M	F/U
P18	**3d**	**Violet**	£65	£40	£40

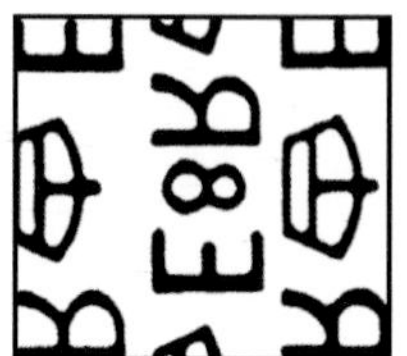

Multiple Crown E8R Watermark

1936 (Nov) - 37 Wmk. Multiple Crown E8R (sideways). Perf. 14 x 15
Printers: Harrison & Sons in Typo

No.			U/M	M/M	F/U
P19	**½d**	**Emerald** (6.37)	5.00	3.70	5.50
P20	**1d**	**Carmine** (5.37)	1.00	70	1.00
P21	**2d**	**Agate** (5.37)	4.50	4.50	4.50
P22	**3d**	**Violet** (3.37)	1.50	1.00	1.50
P23	**4d**	**Grey green** (12.36)	£15	£12	£15
P24	**5d**	**Bistre brown** (11.36)	£45	£17	£24
P24a		Yellow brown (1937)	16.50	9.50	£22
P25	**1s**	**Deep blue** (12.36)	7.00	4.50	6.00
P26	**2s 6d**	**Purple** on yellow (5.37)	£200	£65	10.25
		Set of 8	£290	£82	£73

Multiple Crown GVIRWatermark
(sideways) (sideways-inverted)

1937 - 50 Wmk. Multiple Crown G^{VI}R (sideways). Perf. 14 x 15
Printers: Harrison & Sons in Typo

No.			U/M	M/M	F/U
P27	**½d**	**Emerald** (1938)	6.00	4.00	4.25
P28	**1d**	**Carmine** (1938)	1.50	70	20
P28a		Wmk. sideways-inverted	-	-	£12
P29	**2d**	**Agate** (1938)	1.00	70	25
P29a		Wmk. sideways-inverted	-	-	£12
P30	**3d**	**Violet** (1938)	5.00	3.00	20
P30a		Wmk. sideways-inverted	-	-	£12
P31	**4d**	**Grey green**	£50	£20	5.50
P31a		Wmk. sideways-inverted	-	-	£20
P32	**5d**	**Yellow brown** (1938)	4.75	3.00	60
P32a		Wmk. sideways-inverted	-	-	7.50
P33	**1s**	**Bright blue**	£35	£14	1.00
P33a		Wmk. sideways-inverted	-	-	£10
P34	**2s 6d**	**Purple** on yellow (1938)	£36	£12	1.50
		Set of 8	£150	£44	10.50

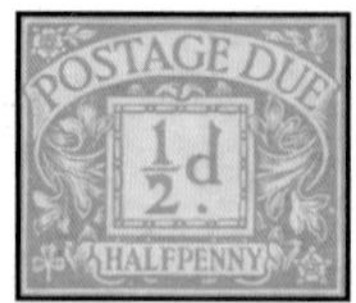

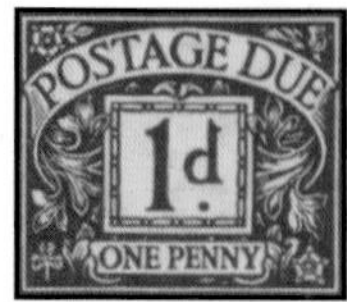

1951 (6 June) - 54 New Colours. Wmk. Multiple Crown G^{VI}R (sideways). Perf. 14 x 15

No.			U/M	M/M	F/U
P35	**½d**	**Orange** (18.9.51)	3.50	1.50	3.00
P36	**1d**	**Violet blue** (6.6.51)	1.50	70	50
P36a		Wmk. sideways-inverted	-	-	£28
P37	**1½d**	**Green** (11.2.52)	1.00	50	1.75
P37a		Wmk. sideways-inverted	9.00	4.00	£9
P38	**4d**	**Blue** (14.8.51)	£22	£12	£10
P38a		Wmk. sideways-inverted	-	-	£115
P39	**1s**	**Bistre brown** (6.12.51)	£16	9.00	2.50
P39a		Wmk. sideways-inverted	£2000	-	
		Set of 5	£39	£21	£16

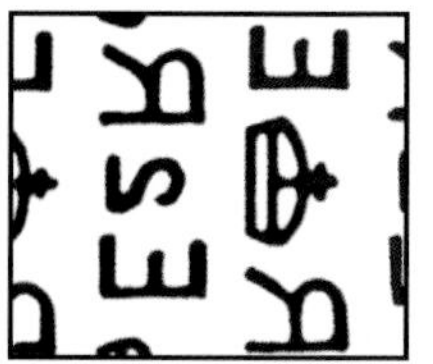

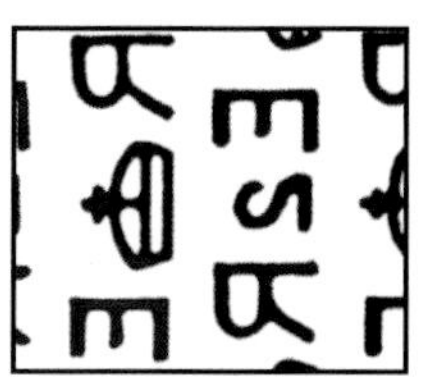

Tudor Crown Watermark
(sideways) (sideways-inverted)

1954 (Nov.) - 55 Wmk. Tudor Crown (sideways). Perf. 14 x 15

No.			U/M	M/M	F/U
P40	**½d**	**Orange** (8.6.55)	7.00	7.00	7.50
P40a		Wmk. sideways-inverted	£15	£21	£22
P41	**2d**	**Agate** (28.7.55)	£15	2.00	£14
P42	**3d**	**Violet** (4.5.55)	£20	£19	£22
P43	**4d**	**Blue** (14.7.55)	£20	£16	£15
P44	**5d**	**Yellow brown** (19.5.55)	£18	£13	£13
P45	**2s 6d**	**Purple** on yellow (11.54)	£62	£19	5.50
P45a		Wmk. sideways-inverted	-	-	£140
		Set of 6	£120	£75	£75
Variety					
P43a	4d	Imperf. pair	£195		

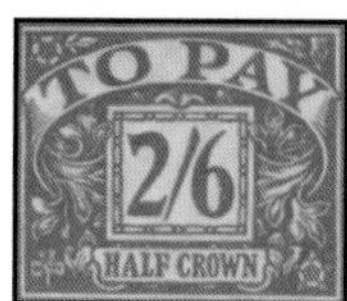

St. Edward's Crown Watermark
(sideways) (sideways-inverted)

1955 (22 Nov.) - 58 Wmk. St. Edward's Crown (sideways). Perf. 14 x 15

No.			U/M	M/M	F/U
P46	½d	**Orange** (16.7.56)	3.00	2.50	3.50
P46a		Wmk. sideways-inverted	£12	£10	£14
P47	1d	**Violet blue** (7.6.56)	2.20	1.80	1.00
P48	1½d	**Green** (13.2.56)	6.00	3.00	3.50
P48a		Wmk. sideways-inverted	£15	£10	£11
P49	2d	**Agate** (22.5.56)	£18	£10	2.20
P50	3d	**Violet** (5.3.56)	3.50	2.50	1.55
P50a		Wmk. sideways-inverted	£30	£12	£25
P51	4d	**Blue** (24.4.56)	£11	7.50	1.80
P51a		Wmk. sideways-inverted	£25	£13	£21
P52	5d	**Yellow brown** (23.5.56)	£12	8.00	1.50
P53	1s	**Ochre** (22.11.55)	£35	£15	1.50
P53a		Wmk. sideways-inverted	-	-	£120
P54	2s 6d	**Purple** on yellow (23.6.57)	£100	£38	4.50
P54a		Wmk. sideways-inverted	-	-	£120
P55	5s	**Scarlet** on yellow (25.11.55)	£49	£19	£10
P55a		Wmk. sideways-inverted	£130	£95	£90
		Set of 10	£210	£74	£27

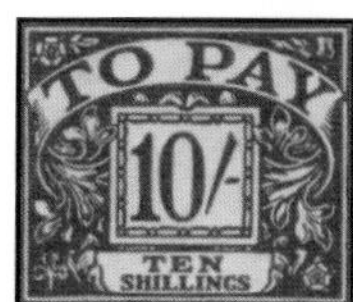

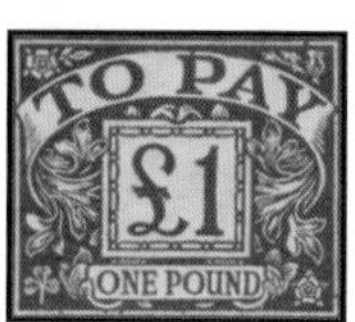

Multiple Crown Watermark
(sideways) (sideways-inverted)

1959 (24 March) - 71 Wmk. Multiple Crown (sideways). Perf. 14 x 15

A. Cream Paper (½d - 1s)

No.			U/M	M/M	F/U
P56	½d	**Orange** (8.10.61)	30	20	30
P57	1d	**Violet blue** (9.5.60)	30	20	15
P58	1½d	**Green** (5.10.60)	1.20	60	1.50
P59	2d	**Agate** (14.9.59)	2.00	1.25	50
P60	3d	**Violet** (24.3.59)	50	35	20
P61	4d	**Blue** (17.12.59)	50	35	25
P62	5d	**Yellow brown** (6.11.61)	70	60	50
P62a		Wmk. sideways-inverted	£24	£14	£18
P63	6d	**Purple** (29.3.62)	80	55	1.00
P64	1s	**Ochre** (11.4.60)	2.50	1.00	35
P65	2s 6d	**Purple** on yellow (11.5.61)	2.00	75	35
P65a		Wmk. sideways-inverted	3.50	3.50	2.00
P66	5s	**Scarlet** on yellow (8.5.61)	3.50	1.20	40
P66a		Wmk. sideways-inverted	6.00	3.00	3.00
P67	10s	**Blue** on yellow (2.9.63)	£10	4.00	2.40
P67a		Wmk. sideways-inverted	£20	£15	9.00
P68	£1	**Black** on yellow (2.9.63)	£19	£10	3.50

B. White Paper (½d - 1s)

No.			U/M	M/M	F/U
P69	½d	**Orange** (22.9.64)	10	5	20
P69a		Wmk. sideways-inverted	50	40	60
P70	1d	**Violet blue** (1.3.65)	10	5	10
P70a		Wmk. sideways-inverted	5.00	4.00	5.00
P71	2d	**Agate** (1.3.65)	50	35	20
P71a		Wmk. sideways-inverted	£13	£11	£11
P72	3d	**Violet** (1.6.64)	20	10	15
P72a		Wmk. sideways-inverted	1.25	1.00	95
P73	4d	**Blue** (3.3.64)	20	10	15
P73a		Wmk. sideways-inverted	-	-	£35
P74	5d	**Yellow brown** (9.6.64)	25	15	30
P74a		Wmk. sideways-inverted	2.90	1.90	1.50
P75	6d	**Purple** (30.1.64)	30	15	15
P75a		Wmk. sideways-inverted	£10	-	£35
P76	1s	**Ochre** (28.8.64)	70	40	15
P76a		Wmk. sideways-inverted	6.00	3.90	2.50
		Set of 13	£32	£19	£7.75

1968 (11 April) - 70 No watermark. Chalky paper. Perf. 14 x 15

A. Gum Arabic

No.			U/M	M/M	F/U
P77	2d	**Agate** (11.4.68)	15		20
P78	4d	**Blue** (25.4.68)	15		20

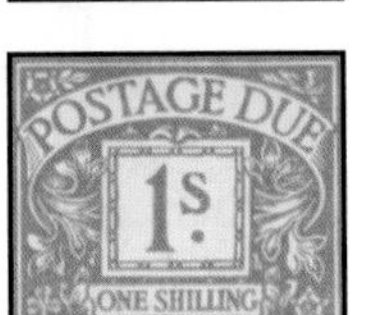

B. PVA Gum

No.			U/M	F/U
P79	**2d**	**Agate** (26.11.68)	60	
P80	**3d**	**Violet** (5.9.68)	15	25
P81	**5d**	**Orange brown** (3.1.69)	3.20	3.80
P82	**6d**	**Purple** (5.9.68)	60	70
P83	**1s**	**Ochre** (19.11.68)	1.20	1.10
		Set of 6	4.90	5.00

1968 (3 Oct.) - 70 Small Format 21 x 17mm. Chalky paper. Perf. 14 x 15
PVA Gum

No.			U/M	F/U
P84	**4d**	**Blue** (12.6.69)	5.00	5.00
P85	**8d**	**Red** (3.10.68)	40	50
		Set of 2	5.20	5.20

1970 (12 June) - 84 No watermark. Perf. 14 x 15
A. Original Coated Paper. PVA Gum

No.			U/M	F/U
P86	**½p**	**Light turquoise blue** (15.2.71)	05	20
P87	**1p**	**Crimson** (15.2.71)	07	20
P88	**2p**	**Green** (15.2.71)	07	20
P89	**3p**	**Bright blue** (15.2.71)	25	15
P90	**4p**	**Light sepia** (15.2.71)	08	10
P91	**5p**	**Pale violet** (15.2.71)	15	10
P92	**10p**	**Cerise** (12.6.70)	20	15
P93	**20p**	**Olive green** (12.6.70)	70	35
P94	**50p**	**Blue** (12.6.70)	1.40	45
P95	**£1**	**Black** (12.6.70)	3.00	65
		Set of 10	5.30	2.00
		Presentation Pack 36 *Contents: P86/95 (10v)*	£15	

B. Fluorescent Coated Paper. PVA Gum

No.			U/M	F/U
P96	**1p**	**Crimson** (10.74)	30	
P97	**3p**	**Bright blue** (10.74)	1.50	
P98	**5p**	**Pale violet** (2.74)	1.50	
P99	**10p**	**Cerise** (2.74)	£30	
P100	**20p**	**Olive green** (10.74)	£35	
P101	**£5**	**Black and orange** (2.4.73)	£17	

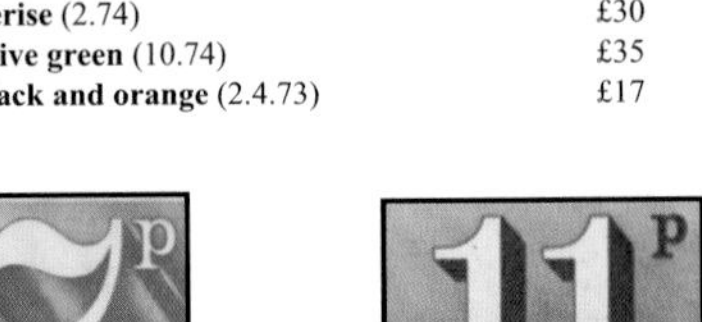

C. Fluorescent Coated Paper. PVAD Gum

No.			U/M	F/U
P102	**1p**	**Crimson** (12.74)	05	20
P103	**2p**	**Green** (12.74)	05	10
P104	**3p**	**Bright blue** (6.75)	05	10
P105	**4p**	**Light sepia** (1.78)	08	10
P106	**5p**	**Pale violet** (1.76)	08	12
P107	**7p**	**Red brown** (21.8.74)	20	30
P108	**10p**	**Cerise** (3.75)	15	15
P109	**11p**	**Brunswick green** (18.6.75)	35	50
P110	**20p**	**Olive green** (2.5.74)	35	25
P111	**50p**	**Blue** (12.74)	95	60
P112	**£1**	**Black** (3.75)	1.90	25
P113	**£5**	**Black and orange** (1.78)	£12	1.60
		Set of 12	15.50	3.25
		Presentation Pack 93 (20.3.77) *Contents : P87, 102/4, 108/12 (8v)*	7.50	

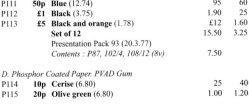

D. Phosphor Coated Paper. PVAD Gum

No.			U/M	F/U
P114	**10p**	**Cerise** (6.80)	25	40
P115	**20p**	**Olive green** (6.80)	1.00	1.20

No.			U/M	F/U

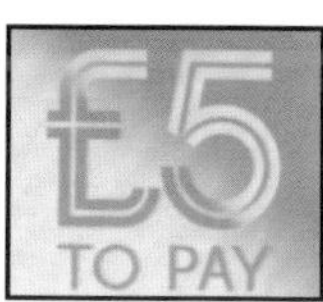

1982 (9 June) - 94 No watermark. Perf. 14 x 15
Fluorescent Coated Paper. PVAD Gum

No.			U/M	F/U
P116	**1p**	**Crimson**	20	25
P117	**2p**	**Bright blue**	20	5
P118	**3p**	**Purple**	20	25
P119	**4p**	**Blue**	20	25
P120	**5p**	**Brown**	20	25
P121	**10p**	**Light brown**	20	10
P122	**20p**	**Sage green**	30	20
P123	**25p**	**Blue grey**	40	50
P124	**50p**	**Charcoal**	95	95
P125	**£1**	**Red**	1.40	35
P126	**£2**	**Turquoise**	2.80	2.00
P127	**£5**	**Dull orange**	6.50	1.00
		Set of 12	£11.50	4.00
		Gutter pairs	£25	£10
		Presentation Pack 135	£24.50	

Variety

P117a	**2p**	**Bright blue ACP/PVAD** paper error	95.00	

No.			U/M	F/U

1994 (15 Feb.) - 94 OBA-Free non-phosphor paper PVA gum.
Perf. 15 x 14 (elliptical)
Printer: House of Questa in Lithography

No.			U/M	F/U
P128	**1p**	**Yellow, orange-red and black**	15	25
P129	**2p**	**Magenta, purple and black**	15	25
P130	**5p**	**Yellow, brown and black**	15	25
P131	**10p**	**Yellow, green and black**	30	40
P132	**20p**	**Violet, emerald-green and black**	1.00	1.00
P133	**25p**	**Magenta, claret and black**	1.50	1.00
P134	**£1**	**Reddish pink, violet and black**	5.50	5.50
P135	**£1.20**	**Green, new blue and black**	6.00	6.00
P136	**£5**	**Green, charcoal and black**	15.50	15.50
		Set of 9	£28	£29
		First Day Cover		£35
		Presentation Pack 32	£32	

Prices are for unmounted mint or fine used panes with full perforations all round plus selvedge. Lightly mounted panes at 25% less. Panes with clipped perfs are usually obtainable from 30% to 60% of the listed prices dependent on the number of stamps affected. Panes with cylinder numbers are worth considerably more, up to 150% in some cases.

King Edward VII

1904 (16 March) - 09 Wmk. Imperial Crown. Perf. 14 Printer: De La Rue

No.				
BP1	**6 x ½d**	**Yellow green** (6.06)	Upright	£55
BP1a			Inverted	£100
BP2	**5 x ½d**	**Yellow green** *plus* St. Andrew's Cross label (6.06)	Upright	£250
BP2a			Inverted	£250

No.				
BP3	**6 x 1d**	**Scarlet**	Upright	£25
BP3a			Inverted	£40

1911 Wmk. Imperial Crown. Perf. 14 Printer: Harrison & Sons

No.				
BP4	**6 x ½d**	**Yellow green**	Upright	£80
BP4a			Inverted	£180
BP5	**5 x ½d**	**Yellow green** *plus* St. Andrew's Cross label	Upright	£350
BP5a			Inverted	£350
BP6	**6 x 1d**	**Rose red**	Upright	£110
BP6a			Inverted	£120

King George V

1911 (Aug.) - 12 Wmk. Imperial Crown. Perf. 15 x 14. Die 1B

No.				
BP7	**6 x ½d**	**Green**	Upright	£65
BP7a			Inverted	£95
BP8	**6 x 1d**	**Carmine**	Upright	£65
BP8a			Inverted	£95
BP9	**6 x 1d**	**Scarlet** (6.12)	Upright	£175
BP9a			Inverted	£175
BP10		Aniline scarlet	Upright	£1500
BP10a			Inverted	£1200

1912 (Aug.) Wmk. Royal Cypher. Perf. 15 x 14. Die 1B

No.				
BP11	**6 x ½d**	**Green**	Upright	£375
BP11a			Inverted	£300
BP12	**6 x 1d**	**Scarlet**	Upright	£150
BP12a			Inverted	£140

1913 (April) - 24 Wmk. Royal Cypher. Perf. 15 x 14

No.				
BP13	**6 x ½d**	**Green**	Upright	£30
BP13a			Inverted	£40
BP14	**6 x 1d**	**Scarlet**	Upright	£30
BP14a			Inverted	£35
BP15	**6 x 1½d**	**Red brown** (10.18)	Upright	£35
BP15a			Inverted	£50
BP16	**6 x 1½d**	**Red brown** *plus* 2 x advert labels (2.24)	Upright	£400
BP16a			Inverted	£400
BP17	**6 x 2d**	**Orange**. Die I (7.20)	Upright	£110
BP17a			Inverted	£130
BP18	**6 x 2d**	**Orange**. Die II(8.21)	Upright	£150
BP18a			Inverted	£200

1924 (Feb. - June) Wmk. Block Cypher. Perf. 15 x 14

No.				
BP19	**6 x ½d**	**Green**	Upright	£25
BP19a			Inverted	£25
BP20	**6 x 1d**	**Scarlet**	Upright	£25
BP20a			Inverted	£25
BP21	**6 x 1½d**	**Red brown**	Upright	£15
BP21a			Inverted	£20
BP22	**4 x 1½d**	**Red brown** *plus* 2 advert labels (6.24)	Upright	£170
BP22a			Inverted	£170

1924 (Nov.) Wmk. Block Cypher (sideways). Perf. 15 x 14

No.				
BP23	**4 x 1½d**	**Red brown** *plus* 2 advert labels	Upright	£5000

1929 (May) Postal Union Congress. Wmk. Multiple Crown GvR. Perf. 15 x 14

No.				
BP24	**6 x ½d**	**Green**	Upright	£70
BP24a			Inverted	£140
BP25	**6 x 1d**	**Scarlet**	Upright	£70
BP25a			Inverted	£140

No.				
BP26	**6 x 1½d**	**Red brown**	Upright	£30
BP26a			Inverted	£75
BP27	**4 x 1½d**	**Red brown** *plus* 2 advert labels	Upright	£275
BP27a			Inverted	£275

1935 (Jan) Photogravure. Wmk. Block Cypher. Perf. 15 x 14

A. Intermediate Format (stamps 18.3 x 22.2mm)

No.				
BP28	**6 x ½d**	**Green**	Upright	£150
BP28a			Inverted	£250
BP29	**6 x 1d**	**Scarlet**	Upright	£175
BP29a			Inverted	£225
BP30	**6 x 1½d**	**Red brown**	Upright	£80
BP30a			Inverted	£100
BP31	**4 x 1½d**	**Red brown** *plus* 2 advert labels	Upright	£600
BP31a			Inverted	£600

B. Small Format (stamps 18 x 21.7mm)

No.				U/M
BP32	6 x ½d	**Green**	Upright	£40
BP32a			Inverted	£70
BP33	6 x 1d	**Scarlet**	Upright	£40
BP33a			Inverted	£70

No.				U/M
BP34	6 x 1½d	**Red brown**	Upright	£20
BP34a			Inverted	£25

No.				U/M
BP35	4 x 1½d	**Red brown** *plus* 2 advert labels	Upright	£120
BP35a			Inverted	£120

1935 (May) Silver Jubilee. Wmk. Multiple Crown GvR. Perf. 15 x 14

No.				U/M
BP36	4 x ½d	**Green**	Upright	£40
BP36a			Inverted	£40

No.				U/M
BP37	4 x 1d	**Scarlet**	Upright	£40
BP37a			Inverted	£45
BP38	4 x 1½d	**Red brown**	Upright	£10
BP38a			Inverted	£10

King Edward VIII

1936 (Oct.) Wmk. Multiple Crown E8R. Perf. 15 x 14

No.				U/M
BP39	6 x ½d	**Green**	Upright	£25
BP39a			Inverted	£35
BP40	6 x 1d	**Scarlet**	Upright	£25
BP40a			Inverted	£40
BP41	6 x 1½d	**Red brown**	Upright	8.00
BP41a			Inverted	8.00
BP42	2 x 1½d	**Red brown**	Upright	£30
BP42a			Inverted	£30
BP43	4 x 1½d	**Red brown** *plus* 2 advert labels	Upright	£70
BP43a				£70

King George VI

1937 (May) - 38 Dark colours. Wmk. Multiple Crown GVIR. Perf. 15 x 14

No.				U/M
BP44	6 x ½d	**Green**	Upright	£25
BP44a			Inverted	£45
BP45	2 x ½d	**Green** (2.38)	Upright	£50
BP45a			Inverted	£50
BP46	6 x 1d	**Scarlet**	Upright	£40
BP46a			Inverted	£175
BP47	2 x 1d	**Scarlet** (2.38)	Upright	£50
BP47a			Inverted	£50

No.				U/M
BP48	6 x 1½d	**Red brown**	Upright	£20
BP48a			Inverted	£50
BP49	2 x 1½d	**Red brown** (1.38)	Upright	£30
BP49a			Inverted	£30
BP50	4 x 1½d	**Red brown** *plus* 2 advert labels	Upright	£125
BP50a			Inverted	£125
BP51	6 x 2d	**Orange**	Upright	£70
BP51a			Inverted	£300

No.				U/M
BP52	6 x 2½d	**Ultramarine**	Upright	£50
BP52a			Inverted	£225

1940 (June) Wmk. Multiple Crown GVIR (sideways). Perf. 15 x 14.
Selvedge at top or bottom.

No.			Top Bottom	U/M
BP53	**4 x ½d**	**Green** (2.38)	Upright	£45
BP53a			Inverted	£45
BP54	**4 x 1d**	**Scarlet**	Upright	£60
BP54a			Inverted	£60

1942 (March) - 47 Light colours. Wmk. Multiple Crown GVIR. Perf. 15 x 14

No.				U/M
BP55	**6 x ½d**	**Pale green**	Upright	£20
BP55a			Inverted	£25
BP56	**2 x ½d**	**Pale green** (12.47)	Upright	£20
BP57	**2 x 1d**	**Pale scarlet** (12.47)		£20
BP58	**2 x 1½d**	**Pale red brown** (12.47)		£20
BP59	**6 x 2d**	**Pale orange**	Upright	£17
BP59a			Inverted	£25
BP60	**6 x 2½d**	**Light ultramarine**	Upright	£20
BP60a			Inverted	£25

1951 (May) - 54 New colours. Wmk. Multiple Crown GVIR. Perf. 15 x 14

No.				U/M
BP61	**6 x ½d**	**Pale orange**		4.00
BP61a			Inverted	5.00
BP62	**4 x ½d**	**Pale orange**. Selvedge at top		£10
BP62a			Inverted	£10
BP62b		Selvedge at bottom		£10
BP63	**2 x ½d**	**Pale orange**		£12
BP64	**6 x 1d**	**Ultramarine** (1.53)		£20
			Inverted	£30
BP65	**4 x 1d**	**Ultramarine**. Selvedge at top		£10
BP65a		Selvedge at bottom		£10
BP66	**2 x 1d**	**Ultramarine**		£10

No.				U/M
BP67	**3 x 1d**	**Ultramarine** *plus* 3 "PAPER RATE...." labels (17mm high) (3.52)		£10
BP67a			Inverted	£10
BP68	**3 x 1d**	**Ultramarine** *plus* 3 "PAPER RATE...." labels (15mm high) (3.53)		£70
BP68a			Inverted	£70
BP69	**3 x 1d**	**Ultramarine** *plus* 3 advert labels (1.54)		£60
BP69a			Inverted	£60

No.				U/M
BP70	**6 x 1½d**	**Pale green** (3.52)		6.00
BP70a			Inverted	£20
BP71	**4 x 1½d**	**Pale green**. Selvedge at top		£10
BP71a			Inverted	£12
BP71b		Selvedge at bottom		£10
BP72	**2 x 1½d**	**Pale green**		£15
BP73	**6 x 2d**	**Pale red brown**		£10
BP73a			Inverted	£40
BP74	**6 x 2½d**	**Pale scarlet**	Inverted	5.00
BP74a				5.00

Queen Elizabeth II

Prices are for unmounted mint or fine used panes with full perforations all round plus selvedge. Lightly mounted panes at 25% less. Panes with clipped perfs are usually obtainable from 30% to 60% of the listed prices dependent on the number of stamps affected. Panes with cylinder numbers are worth considerably more, up to 150% in some cases.
Watermarks are illustrated upright from the back of the stamps.

Watermark Tudor Crown

1953 (2 Sept.) - 55 Perf. 15 x 14

No.				U/M
BP75	6 x ½d	Orange (3.54)	Upright	3.00
BP75a			Inverted	3.00
BP76	4 x ½d	Orange. (7.54)	Upright	6.00
BP76a			Inverted	6.50
BP77	2 x ½d	Orange	Upright	3.00
BP78	6 x 1d	Ultramarine (3.54)	Upright	22.50
BP78a			Inverted	37.50
BP79	4 x 1d	Ultramarine (7.54)	Upright	9.00
BP79a			Inverted	£25
BP80	2 x 1d	Ultramarine	Upright	3.00
BP81	3 x 1d	Ultramarine plus 3 "PAPER RATE...." labels (3.54)	Upright	£250
BP81a			Inverted	£250

No.				U/M
BP82	**3 x 1d**	**Ultramarine** *plus* 3 "PLEASE POST EARLY...." labels (4.54)	Upright	£25
BP82a			Inverted	£25
BP83	**3 x 1d**	**Ultramarine** *plus* 3 "PLEASE PACK YOUR PARCELS...." labels (1.55)	Upright	£25
BP83a			Inverted	£25

No.				U/M
BP84	**6 x 1½d**	**Green** (5.53)	Upright	2.50
BP84a			Inverted	2.50
BP85	**4 x 1½d**	**Green** (7.54)	Upright	7.50
BP85a			Inverted	6.50
BP86	**2 x 1½d**	**Green**	Upright	3.00
BP87	**6 x 2d**	**Red brown** (3.54)	Upright	£25
BP87a			Inverted	£125
BP88	**6 x 2½d**	**Carmine red**	Upright	3.50
BP88a			Inverted	2.50

Watermark St. Edwards Crown

1955 (Aug.) - 59 Perf. 15 x 14

No.				U/M
BP89	**6 x ½d**	**Orange** (9.55)	Upright	1.50
BP89a			Inverted	1.75
BP90	**4 x ½d**	**Orange** (7.56)	Upright	6.00
BP90a			Inverted	6.00
BP91	**2 x ½d**	**Orange** (11.57)	Upright	12.50
BP92	**6 x 1d**	**Ultramarine** (3.54)	Upright	3.00
BP92a			Inverted	3.50
BP93	**4 x 1d**	**Ultramarine** (7.54)	Upright	6.00
BP93a			Inverted	6.00
BP94	**2 x 1d**	**Ultramarine** (11.57)	Upright	12.50
BP95	**3 x 1d**	Ultramarine *plus* 3 'PLEASE PACK YOUR PARCELS....' labels	Upright	£10
BP95a			Inverted	£10
BP96	**6 x 1½d**	**Green**	Upright	2.50
BP96a			Inverted	1.50
BP97	**4 x 1½d**	**Green** (7.56)	Upright	6.00
BP97a			Inverted	6.50
BP98	**2 x 1½d**	**Green**	Upright	12.50

No.				U/M
BP99	**6 x 2d**	**Red brown** (9.55)	Upright	22.50
BP99a			Inverted	£65
BP100	**6 x 2d**	**Light red brown** (1.57)	Upright	12.50
BP100a			Inverted	£30
BP101	**6 x 2½d**	**Carmine red** (9.55)	Upright	2.00
BP101a			Inverted	1.5
BP102	**6 x 3d**	**Violet** (10.57)	Upright	3.50
BP102a			Inverted	7.00
BP103	**4 x 3d**	**Violet** (4.59)	Upright	£15
BP103a			Inverted	£15

Watermark Multiple Crowns

1958 (Nov.) - 65 Perf. 15 x 14

Cream paper

No.				U/M
BP104	**6 x ½d**	**Orange**	Upright	3.50
BP104a			Inverted	3.50
BP105	**4 x ½d**	**Orange** (8.59)	Upright	3.00
BP105a			Inverted	3.00
BP105b			Sideways left	8.00
BP105c			Sideways right	8.00

No.				U/M
BP106	6 x 1d	**Ultramarine**	Upright	3.50
BP106a			Inverted	3.50
BP107	4 x 1d	**Ultramarine** (8.59)	Upright	3.00
BP107a			Inverted	3.00
BP107b			Sideays left	8.00
BP107c			Sideways right	8.00
BP108	6 x 1½d	**Green** (12.58)	Upright	8.50
BP108a			Inverted	8.50
BP109	4 x 1½d	**Green** (8.59)	Upright	3.00
BP109a			Inverted	3.00
BP109b			Sideways left	£40
BP109c			Sideways right	£35
BP110	6 x 2d	**Light red brown** (4.61)	Upright	£60
BP110a			Inverted	£625
BP111	6 x 2½d	**Carmine red**	Upright	8.00
BP112a			Inverted	£20
BP112	6 x 3d	**Violet**	Upright	1.50
BP112a			Inverted	2.00
BP113	4 x 3d	**Violet**	Upright	£15
BP113a			Inverted	£15
BP113b			Sideways left	5.00
BP113c			Sideways right	5.00

White paper

No.				U/M
BP114	6 x ½d	**Orange** (6.62)	Upright	£12
BP114a			Inverted	£12
BP115	4 x ½d	**Orange**	Sideways left	8.00
BP115a			Sideways right	8.00

No.				U/M
BP116	2 x ½d	**Orange** *plus* **2 x 2½d Carmine red** (7.64)	Sideways left	1.25
BP116a			Sideways right	1.25
BP117	6 x 1d	**Ultramarine** (4.62)	Upright	4.75
BP117a			Inverted	6.00
BP118	4 x 1d	**Ultramarine** (6.62)	Sideways left	8.00
BP118a			Sideways right	8.00
BP119	2 x 1d	**Ultramarine** *plus* **2 x 3d Violet** (1d at left)(8.65)	Sideways left	4.00
BP119a			Sideways right	4.00
BP120	2 x 3d	**Violet** *plus* **2 x 1d Ultramarine** (1d at right)(8.65)	Sideways left	4.00
BP120a			Sideways right	4.00
BP121	6 x 1½d	**Green** (4.62)	Upright	£16
BP121a			Inverted	£25
BP122	4 x 1½d	**Green**	Sideaways left	£40
BP122a			Sideways right	£40
BP123	6 x 2½d	**Carmine red** (4.62)	Upright	£25
BP123a			Inverted	37.50
BP124	6 x 3d	**Violet**	Upright	2.75
BP124a			Inverted	3.25
BP125	4 x 3d	**Violet** (6.62)	Sideways left	5.00
BP125a			Sideways right	5.00
BP126	6 x 4d	**Deep ultramarine** (6.65)	Upright	5.00
BP126a			Inverted	5.50
BP127	4 x 4d	**Deep ultramarine** (8.65)	Sideways left	2.50
BP127a			Sideways right	2.50

Chalky paper

No.				U/M
BP128	3 x ½d	**Orange** *plus* **1 x 2½d Carmine red** (7.63)	Upright	8.00
BP128a			Inverted	8.00

No.				U/M
BP129	4 x 2½d	**Carmine red** (7.63)	Upright	1.00
BP129a			Inverted	1.00

Graphite Lined Issue
Watermark Multiple Crowns

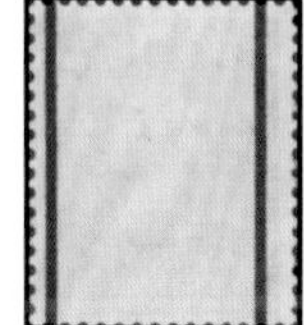

1959 (Aug.) Perf. 15 x 14

No.				U/M
BP130	6 x ½d	**Orange**	Upright	£50
BP130a			Inverted	£15
BP131	6 x 1d	**Ultramarine**	Upright	£15
BP131a			Inverted	12.50
BP132	6 x 1½d	**Green**	Upright	£425
BP132a			Inverted	£160
BP133	6 x 2½d	**Carmine red**	Upright	£65
BP133a			Inverted	£275
BP134	6 x 3d	**Violet**	Upright	3.00
BP134a			Inverted	3.00

Watermark Multiple Crowns
Green Phosphor

1960 (Aug.) - 67 Perf. 15 x 14

No.				U/M
BP135	6 x ½d	**Orange** (2B)	Upright	£15
BP135a			Inverted	£35
BP136	6 x 1d	**Ultramarine** (2B)	Upright	£15
BP136a			Inverted	£35
BP137	6 x 1½d	**Green** (2B)	Upright	17.50
BP137a			Inverted	67.50
BP138	6 x 2½d	**Carmine red**	Upright	£65
BP138a			Inverted	£950
BP139	6 x 3d	**Violet** (2B)	Upright	10.50
BP139a			Inverted	10.50

Watermark Multiple Crowns
Blue Phosphor - Cream Paper

No.				U/M
BP140	6 x ½d	**Orange**	Upright	3.00
BP140a			Inverted	5.50
BP141	4 x ½d	**Orange**	Sideways left	£35
BP141a			Sideways right	£35
BP142	6 x 1d	**Ultramarine** (2B) (6.63)	Upright	3.50
BP142a			Inverted	4.00
BP143	4 x 1d	**Ultramarine**	Sideways left	£12
BP143a			Sideways right	£12
BP144	6 x 1½d	**Green** (2B) (7.64)	Upright	7.50
BP144a			Inverted	£55
BP145	4 x 1½d	**Green**	Sideways left	£40
BP145a			Sideways right	£40
BP146	6 x 2½d	**Carmine red** (2B)	Upright	£70
BP146a			Inverted	£1000
BP147	6 x 2½d	**Carmine red** (LB)	Upright	£70
BP147a			Inverted	£160
BP148	6 x 3d	**Violet**	Upright	5.00
BP148a			Inverted	5.00
BP149	4 x 3d	**Violet**	Sideways left	£15
BP149a			Sideways right	£15

Watermark Multiple Crowns
Blue Phosphor - Whiter Paper

No.				U/M
BP150	6 x ½d	**Orange**	Upright	£10
BP150a			Inverted	12.50
BP151	4 x ½d	**Orange**	Sideways left	37.50
BP151a			Sideways right	£35
BP152	6 x 1d	**Ultramarine** (2B) (6.63)	Upright	6.00
BP152a			Inverted	6.00
BP153	4 x 1d	**Ultramarine**	Sideways left	£12
BP153a			Sideways right	£12
BP154	2 x 1d	**Ultramarine** *plus* **2 x 3d Violet** (1d at left)	Sideways left	£60
BP154a			Sideways right	£60
BP155	2 x 3d	**Violet** (1d at left) *plus* **2 x 1d Ultramarine**	Sideways left	£60
BP155a			Sideways right	£60
BP156	6 x 1½d	**Green** (2B) (7.64)	Upright	£75
BP156a			Inverted	£175
BP157	4 x 1½d	**Green**	Sideways left	£40
BP157a			Sideways right	£40
BP158	6 x 2½d	**Carmine red** (LB)	Upright	£60
BP158a			Inverted	£175
BP159	6 x 3d	**Violet**	Upright	4.50
BP159a			Inverted	4.50
BP160	4 x 3d	**Violet**	Sideways left	18.50
BP160a			Sideways right	18.50
BP161	6 x 4d	**Deep ultramarine** (2B) (6.65)	Upright	£10
BP161a			Inverted	12.50
BP162	4 x 4d	**Deep ultramarine**	Sideways left	8.00
BP162a			Sideways right	8.00

Watermark Multiple Crowns
Violet Phosphor 8mm Bands

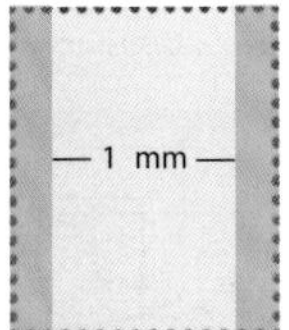

No.				U/M
BP163	6 x 1d	**Ultramarine**	Upright	6.00
BP163a			Inverted	6.00
BP164	2 x 1d	**Ultramarine** *plus* **2 x 3d Violet** (LB) (1d at left)	Sideways left	10.50
BP164a			Sideways right	10.50
BP165	2 x 3d	**Violet** (RB) (1d at left) *plus* **2 x 1d Ultramarine**	Sideways left	10.50
BP165a			Sideways right	10.50
BP166	2 x 3d	**Violet** (LB) *plus* **4 x 3d Violet (RB)**	Upright	£20
BP166a			Inverted	£95
BP167	6 x 4d	**Deep ultramarine** (2B)	Upright	4.50
BP167a			Inverted	4.50
BP168	4 x 4d	**Deep ultramarine** Photogravure phosphor	Sideways left	3.50
BP168a		Photogravure phosphor	Sideways right	3.50
BP168b		Typo phosphor	Sideways left	£50
BP168c		Typo phosphor	Sideways right	£50

Watermark Multiple Crowns
Violet Phosphor 9.5mm Bands

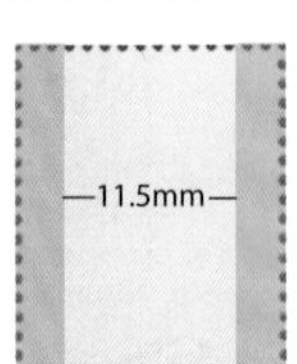

No.				U/M
BP169	6 x 1d	**Ultramarine**	Upright	5.00
BP169a			Inverted	5.00
BP170	2 x 1d	**Ultramarine** *plus* **2 x 3d Violet** (2B) (1d at left)	Sideways left	4.50
BP170a			Sideways right	4.50
BP171	2 x 3d	**Violet** (2B) (1d at left) *plus* **2 x 1d Ultramarine**	Sideways left	4.50
BP171a			Sideways right	4.50
BP172	6 x 3d	**Violet (CB)**	Upright	6.00
BP172a			Inverted	£15
BP173	6 x 4d	**Deep ultramarine** (2B) (6.65)	Upright	2.50
BP173a			Inverted	2.50
BP174	4 x 4d	**Deep ultramarine**	Sideways left	1.50
BP174a			Sideways right	1.50

Pre-Decimal Machin Booklet Panes

1967 (Sept.) - 69 Machin series. No watermark. Perf. 15 x 14. Two phosphor bands, except where stated.

Gum Arabic (GA)

No.			U/M
BP175	**6 x 4d**	**Sepia** (9.67)	8.00
BP175a		Missing phosphor	£20
BP175b		Deep olive brown (2.68)	9.00
BP175c		Missing phosphor	£22
BP176	**6 x 4d**	**Vermilion** (CB) (2.69)	£120

PVA

No.			U/M
BP177	**6 x 1d**	**Olive** (3.68)	1.25
BP177a		Missing phosphor	£20
BP178	**4 x 1d**	**Olive** (CB) *plus* **2 x 4d** Sepia (CB) (9.68)	3.50
BP178a		Missing phosphor	£25

No.			U/M
BP179	**4 x 1d**	**Olive** (CB) *plus* **2 x 4d** Vermilion (LB) (6.1.69)	3.00
BP179a		Missing phosphor	£150

No.			U/M
BP180	**2 x 1d**	**Olive** (CB) *plus* **2 x 3d** Violet (1d at left) (4.68)	2.50
BP180a		Broad bands	£16
BP180b		Missing phosphor	£40

No.			U/M
BP181	**2 x 1d**	**Olive** (CB) *plus* **2 x 3d** Violet (1d at right) (4.68)	2.50
BP181a		Broad bands	£12
BP181b		Missing phosphor	£40
BP182	**6 x 3d**	**Violet** (CB) (3.68)	£15
BP182a		Missing phosphor	£800
BP183	**6 x 4d**	**Deep Olive-brown** (2B) (3.68)	1.00
BP183a		Broad bands	£175
BP183b		Missing phosphor	£20
BP184	**6 x 4d**	**Deep olive** (CB) (9.68)	1.50
BP184a		Missing phosphor	£25

No.			U/M
BP185	**4 x 4d**	**Deep Olive-sepia** (2B) (4.68)	1.00
BP185a		Broad bands	8.00
BP185b		Missing phosphor	8.00
BP186	**4 x 4d**	**Sepia** (CB) (9.68)	2.00
BP186a		Missing phosphor	

£4,315
FOR YOU
AT
AGE 55
SEE
OTHER
PAGES

No.			U/M
BP187	**2 x 4d**	**Sepia** (CB) *plus* 2 '£4,315....' labels (16.9.68)	2.50
BP187a		Missing phosphor	£70
BP188	**6 x 4d**	**Vermilion**, Head A (CB) (1.69)	2.00
BP188a		Missing phosphor	£40
BP188b		Pale vermillion	4.50
BP188c		Vermilion, Head B2	1.25
BP188d		Missing phosphor	£40
BP189	**4 x 4d**	**Vermilion** (CB) (3.69)	1.00
BP189a		Missing phosphor	£45
BP190	**2 x 4d**	**Vermilion** (CB) *plus* 2 '£4,315....' labels (3.69)	1.00
BP190a		Missing phosphor	£50

No.			U/M
BP191	**6 x 5d**	**Deep blue** (2B) (11.68)	1.00
BP191a		Missing phosphor	£30
		First Day Cover (pane BP178)	2.25
		First Day Cover (pane BP170)	£12

Decimal Machin Booklet Panes

1971 (15 Feb.) - 74. Decimal Machin series. No watermark. Perf. 15 x 14. Two 9.5mm phosphor bands except where stated.

OCP/PVA

No.			U/M
MP1	5 x ½p	**Turquoise** (2B) *plus* 'B. Alan Ltd......' label	4.00
MP1a		Missing phosphor	£300
MP2	5 x ½p	**Turquoise** (2B) *plus* 'B. Alan Ltd......' blind label (17.9.71)	6.00
MP3	5 x ½p	**Turquoise** (2B) *plus* 'Lick.....' label	3.75
MP3a		Missing phosphor	£80

No.			U/M
MP4	2 x ½p	**Turquoise** (2B) *plus* **2 x 2p dark green** (2B) (½p below 2p)	3.75
MP4a		Broad bands	£60
MP4b		Missing phosphor	£300
MP5	2 x ½p	**Turquoise** (2B) *plus* **2 x 2p dark green** (2B) (½p at right) (14.7.71)	7.50
MP5a		Broad bands	£400
MP5b		Missing phosphor	£400

No.			U/M
MP6	2 x 1p	**Crimson** (2B) *plus* **2 x 1½p black** (2B) (1p above 1½p)	3.75
MP6a		Broad bands	£125
MP7	2 x 1p	**Crimson** (2B) *plus* **2 x 1½p black** (2B) (1p at right) (14.7.71)	3.00
MP7a		Broad bands	£225

No.			U/M
MP8	4 x 2½p	**Magenta** (CB) *plus* 2 x 'UNIFLO.....' labels	3.00
MP8a		Missing phosphor	£275
MP9	4 x 2½p	**Magenta** (CB) *plus* 2 x 'UNIFLO.....' blind labels	5.00
MP9a		Missing phosphor	£250
MP10	5 x 2½p	**Magenta** (CB) *plus* 'STICK.....' label	3.75

No.			U/M
MP11	5 x 2½p	**Magenta** (CB) *plus* 'STICK.....' blind label (17.9.71)	4.50
MP12	5 x 2½p	**Magenta** (CB) *plus* *'TEAR OFF.....' label*	3.75
MP12a		Missing phosphor	

No.			U/M
MP13	2 x 2½p	**Magenta** (LB) *plus* **4 x 3p** ultramarine (2B) (2½p at right)	3.50
MP13a		Missing phosphor	£275
MP13b		JET Phosphor	
MP14	5 x 3p	**Ultramarine** (2B) *plus* £4315.....' label (15.2.71)	1.50
MP14a		Broad bands	£900
MP14b		Missing phosphor	£300

No.			U/M
MP15	5 x 3p	**Ultramarine** (2B) *plus* £4315.....' blind label (23.7.71)	5.50
MP16	6 x 3p	**Ultramarine** (2B)	3.50
MP16a		Broad bands	£600
MP16b		Missing phosphor	£200
MP16c		JET Phosphor	

FCP/PVA

No.			U/M
MP17	5 x ½p	**Turquoise** (2B) *plus* 'LICK.....' blind label (17.9.71)	6.00
MP18	5 x ½p	**Turquoise** (2B) *plus* 'MAKE YOUR LUCKY.....' blind label (23.12.71)	2.00
MP18a		Missing phosphor	£525
MP18b		Thin paper	7.50
MP18c		JET Phosphor	
MP19	2 x½p	**Turquoise** (2B) *plus* **2 x 2p** dark green (2B) (½p at right) (6.10.71)	2.00
MP19a		Broad bands	£50
MP19b		Missing phosphor	£200
MP19c		JET Phosphor	
MP20	2 x 1p	**Crimson** (2B) *plus* **2 x 1½p** black (2B) (1p at right) (6.10.71)	2.00
MP20a		Broad bands	£120
MP20b		Missing phosphor	£300
MP20c		JET Phosphor	
MP21	4 x 2½p	**Magenta** (CB) *plus* **2 x** 'DO YOU COLLECT.....' blind labels (23.12.71)	2.75
MP21a		Missing phosphor	£250
MP22	5 x 2½p	**Magenta** (CB) *plus* 'TEAR OFF.....' blind label (17.9.71)	5.00
MP23	5 x 2½p	**Magenta** (CB) *plus* 'STAMP COLLECTIONS.....' blind label(23.12.71)	2.50
MP23a		Missing phosphor	£300
MP24	5 x 2½p	**Magenta** Type I (CB) *plus* 'B. ALAN for.....' blind label (23.12.71)	2.50
MP24a		Missing phosphor	£30
MP25	5 x 2½p	**Magenta** Type II (CB) *plus* 'B. ALAN for.....' blind label	£90
MP26	2 x 2½p	**Magenta** (LB) *plus* **4 x 3p** ultramarine (2B) (2½p at right) (17.9.71)	4.00
MP26a		Missing phosphor	£100
MP27	5 x 3p	**Ultramarine** (2B) *plus* '£4315.....' blind label (1.10.71)	2.25
MP27a		Missing phosphor	£300
MP27b		Thin paper	8.50
MP27c		Missing phosphor	£200

No.			U/M
MP28	5 x 3p	**Ultramarine** (CB) *plus* blind label (14.11.73)	6.00
MP29	6 x 3p	**Ultramarine** (2B) (17.9.71)	1.50
MP30	5 x 3½p	**Olive-green** (2B) *plus* 'blind' label (14.11.73)	£10
MP30a		Missing phosphor	

FCP/PVAD

No.			U/M
MP31	2 x ½p	**Turquoise** (2B) *plus* **2 x 2p dark green** (2B) (½p at right) (12.11.73)	60
MP31a		Broad bands	£28
MP32	2 x 1p	**Crimson** (2B) *plus* **2 x 1½p black** (2B) (1p at right) (12.11.73)	50
MP32a		Broad bands	£50
MP32b		Missing phosphor	£375
MP33	5 x 3p	**Ultramarine** (CB) *plus* 'blind' label (14.11.73)	3.00

No.			U/M
MP34	5 x 3½p	**Olive green** (2B) *plus* 'blind' label (14.11.73)	1.50
MP34a		Missing phosphor	£30
MP35	5 x 3½p	**Olive green** (CB) *plus* 'blind' label (23.10.74)	1.50
MP35a		Miscut (label at top)	£12
MP35b		Missing phosphor	

No.			U/M
MP36	5 x 4½p	**Grey blue** (2B) *plus* blind label (9.10.74)	2.00
MP36a		Missing phosphor	£400
MP36b		Phosphor under ink (white bands)	£50

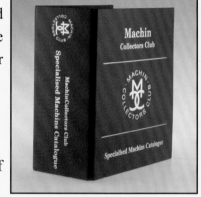

Decimal Machin Booklet Panes

1976 (3 Mar) - 95 Decimal Machin series. No watermark. Perf. 15 x 14.

Two phosphor bands or one CB except where stated. Panes are listed in order of paper/gum combination, size (panes of 4, 6, 10 etc.) and then in ascending order of face values, i.e. panes containing ½p are listed before panes containing 1p. There are two types of perforation used on the machine booklet panes and both are illustrated below. Usually the first pane listed has a single perforation hole extending into the Margin of the pane. Fully perforated margins are then listed within the grouping of that pane. Where a booklet pane exists in only one perf. type it is listed without perf. details.

All books are illustrated with the margins to the left. This means that all Vending (Machine) books show the Queen's portrait to the left; On Counter and Window books the Queen's portrait appears upright.

Single extension hole

Perforated margin

Printed by Harrison in Photogravure

FCP/PVAD

Panes of 4

FP1 **2 x 1p CB Crimson**, Type I and **8p CB** (short at top) **Rosine** (17.10.79)
FP1a Perforated margin
FP1b Miscut (8p at right)
FP2 Chambon printing (1p crimson, Type II) (4.8.80)
FP2a Perforated margin
FP2b Miscut (8p at right)

FP3 **1p LB Crimson, 13p RB pale chestnut** and **2 x 18p 2B dull olive-grey** (20.10.86)
FP3a Missing phosphor
FP3b Reversed bands (1p RB and 13p LB) (20.10.86)
FP3c 'A' phosphor (27.1.87)
FP3d Missing phosphor
FP3e Reversed bands (1p RB and 13p LB) (27.1.87)

FP4 **4 x 13p CB Pale chestnut**, margins all round (4.8.87)

FP5 **4 x 14p CB Dark blue**, margins all round (23.8.88)
FP5a Missing phosphor

FP6 **4 x 14p CB Dark blue**, imperf. top and bottom (11.10.88)

FP7 **4 x 14p CB Dark blue**, imperf. on three sides (24.1.89)
FP7a Missing phosphor

No.

FP8 14p **RB Dark blue** and **2 x 19p 2B Orange-red** (2B) *plus* "Please use the postcode" label (5.9.88)
FP8a Perforated margin
FP8b Missing phosphor
FP8c Miscut (14p at right)

FP9 **2 x 15p LB Light blue, 20p 2B Black** *plus* "Please use the postcode" label (2.10.89)
FP9a Missing phosphor

FP10 **3 x 17p 2B Grey-blue** *plus* "Please use the postcode" label (12.8.86)
FP11 Multiple star underprint in blue (4.11.85)
FP11a Missing phosphor

FP12 **2 x 17p LB Dark blue, 17p RB Dark blue** *plus* "Please use the postcode" label (4.9.90)
FP12a Missing phosphor

No.

Panes of 6

FP13 **2 x ½p 2B Turquoise, 3 x 1p 2B Crimson** and **6p 2B Light green** with 12mm margin and cutting lines (8.2.78)
FP13a Perforated margin
FP13b Miscut (6p at right)
FP14 **Margin 5mm**
FP14a Miscut (6p at right)
FP14b Perforated margin
FP14c Miscut (6p at right)

FP15 **2 x ½p CB Turquoise, 2 x 1p CB Crimson, 7p CB Purple-brown** *plus* "remember the postcode" label (8.2.78)
FP15a Miscut (label at left)
FP15b Perforated margin
FP15c Missing phosphor
FP15d Miscut (label at left)

FP16 ½p **2B Turquoise, 1p 2B Crimson, 3 x 11½p (side band) Drab** and **14p 2B Grey-blue** (26.1.81). 11½p (RB) at left
FP16a Perforated margin
FP16b Missing phosphor
FP17 11½p (LB) at right
FP17a Perforated margin
FP17b Missing phosphor
FP17c Miscut (2 x ½p, 2 x 1p and 2 x 14p)
FP17d Miscut (6 x 11½p)

No.

FP18 **1p CB Crimson**, **2 x 5p CB Claret** and **3 x 13p CB Pale chestnut** (20.10.86)
FP18a 'A' phosphor (27.1.87)

FP19 Imperf. left and right sides (29.9.87)
FP19a Missing phosphor
FP19b 4mm CB (29.9.87)

FP20 **2 x 1p CB Crimson** and **4 x 12p CB Emerald** (29.7.86)

FP21 **13p LB Pale chestnut** and **5 x 18p 2B Olive-grey** (2B) (20.1.86)
FP21a 'A' phosphor (27.1.87)

FP22 Imperf. left and right sides (29.9.87)

No.

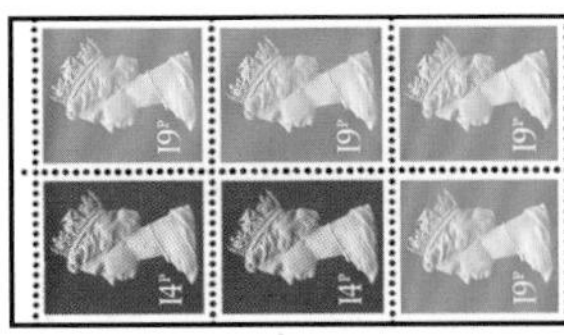

FP23 **2 x 14p RB Dark blue** and **4 x 19p 2B Orange-red** (narrow at right), imperf. left and right sides (5.9.88)
FP23a Missing phosphor

Panes of 8

FP24 **½p 2B Turquoise**, **4 x 3p 2B Bright magenta** and **3 x 12½p (side band) Light emerald** (1.2.82). 12½p (RB) at left
FP24a Missing phosphor
FP25 12½p (LB) at right
FP25a Missing phosphor
FP25b Miscut (2 x ½p and 6 x 12½p)
FP25c Miscut (8 x 3p)

FP26 **2 x 1p CB Crimson**, **3 x 3½p CB Chestnut** and **3 x 12½p CB Light emerald** at right (5.4.83)
FP26a Missing phosphor
FP26b Miscut (3½p at right)

FP27 **3 x 1p CB Crimson**, **2 x 4p CB Greenish blue** and **3 x 13p CB Pale chestnut** at right (3.9.84)
FP27a Missing phosphor

No.

Thick value

Thin value

FP28 2 x 1p **2B Crimson, 3 x 7p (side band) purple-brown** and **3 x 9p 2B Dull violet** (13.6.77). 7p (RB) at left
FP28a Thin value on 7p, Type III
FP29 7p (LB) at right
FP29a Thin value on 7p, Type III

FP30 2 x 2p **2B Dark green, 2 x 8p (side band) Rosine** and **3 x 10p 2B Orange-brown** *plus* "don't forget the postcode" label (28.8.79). 8p (RB) at left
FP30a Missing phosphor
FP31 8p (LB) at right
FP31a Missing phosphor
FP31b Miscut (2 x 2p and 4 x 8p)
FP31c Miscut (2 x 2p and 6 x 10p)

Normal printing

Chambon printing

FP32 3 x 2p **2B Dark green, 2 x 10p (side band) Orange-brown** and **2 x 12p 2B Yellow-green** *plus* "don't forget the postcode" label (4.2.80). 10p (RB) at left
FP32a Missing phosphor
FP33 **10p LB Orange brown** at right, Chambon printing. Lower set value on 12p (25.6.80)
FP33a Missing phosphor
FP34 **10p RB Orange brown** at left
FP34a Missing phosphor

No.

FP35 **10p RB Orange brown** at left, Chambon printing. Lower set value on 12p (25.6.80)
FP35a Missing phosphor

FP36 3 x 2½p **2B Rose-red, 2 x 4p 2B Green-blue** and **3 x 11½p (side band) Drab** (26.8.81). 11½p (RB) at left
FP36a Perforated margin
FP37 **11½p drab** (LB) at right
FP37a Perforated margin

FP38 2 x 17p **RB Dark blue, 3 x 22p 2B Orange-red** *plus* 3 x "Please use the postcode" labels, imperf. left and right sides (4.9.90)
FP38a Missing phosphor

Panes of 10

FP39 2 x ½p **2B Turquoise, 2 x 1p 2B Crimson, 2 x 6½p (side band) Greenish-blue** and **4 x 8½p 2B Yellow-green** (26.1.77). 6½p (RB) at left
FP40 6½p (LB) at right

FP41 10 x 6½p **CB Greenish blue** (14.7.76). Left margin
FP41a Left margin - Miscut
FP41b Left perforated margin
FP41c Left perforated margin - Miscut
FP42 Right margin
FP42a Right margin - Miscut
FP42b Right perforated margin
FP42c Right perforated margin - Miscut

No.

FP43 **10 x 7p** **CB Purple-brown** (13.6.77). Left margin
FP43a Miscut
FP44 Right margin
FP44a Miscut

FP45 **10 x 8p** **CB Rosine** (3.10.79). Left margin
FP46 Right margin

FP47 **10 x 8½p** **2B Yellow-green** (14.7.76). Left margin
FP47a Left margin - Miscut
FP47b Left perforated margin
FP47c Left perforated margin - Miscut
FP48 Right margin
FP48a Right margin - Miscut
FP48b Right perforated margin
FP48c Right perforated margin - Miscut

FP49 **10 x 9p** **2B Deep violet** (13.6.77). Left margin
FP49a Experimental fold between columns 2 and 3
FP49b Miscut
FP50 Right margin
FP50a Miscut

No.

FP51 **10 x 10p** **CB Orange-brown** (4.2.80) Left margin
FP51a Miscut
FP52 Right margin
FP53a Miscut

FP54 **10 x 11½p** **CB Drab** (26.1.81). Left margin
FP55 Right margin

FP56 **4 x 11½p** **Drab (side band)** (2 left and 2 right bands) and **6 x 14p 2B Grey blue** (6.5.84). Left margin
FP57 Right margin

FP58 **10 x 12p** **CB Emerald** (14.1.86). Left margin
FP58a Missing phosphor
FP59 Right margin
FP59a Missing phosphor (on 8 stamps)
FP59b Miscut

No.

FP60 **4 x 12p** **(side band) Emerald** (2 left and 2 right bands) and **6 x 17p 2B Grey blue** (14.1.86). Left margin
FP61 Right margin

FP62 **10 x 12½p** **CB Light emerald** (1.2.82). Left margin
FP62a Missing phosphor
FP63 Right margin
FP63a Missing phosphor

FP64 **4 x 12½p** **(side band) Light emerald** (2 left and 2 right bands) and **6 x 15½p 2B Pale violet** (1.2.82). Left margin
FP64a Missing phosphor
FP64b Transposed phosphor bands
FP65 Right margin
FP65a Missing phosphor
FP65b Transposed phosphor bands

FP66 **4 x 12½p** **(side band) Light emerald** (2 left and 2 right bands) and **6 x 16p 2B Drab** (5.4.83). Left margin
FP66a Missing phosphor
FP67 Right margin
FP67a Missing phosphor

No.

FP68 **10 x 13p** **CB Chestnut** (3.9.84). Left margin
FP68a 'A' phosphor (27.1.87)
FP68b Missing phosphor
FP69 Star underprint in blue (2.12.86)
FP70 Right margin
FP70a 'A' phosphor (27.1.87)
FP70b Missing phosphor
FP71 Star underprint in blue (2.12.86)

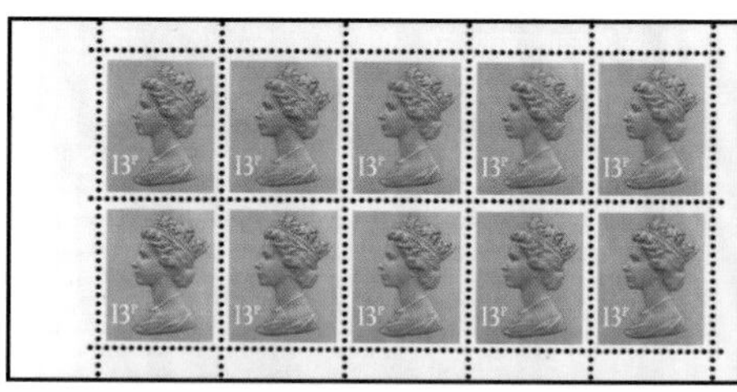

FP72 **10 x 13p** **CB Pale chestnut**, margins all round (4.8.87)

FP73 **4 x 13p** **(side band) Pale chestnut** (2 left and 2 right bands) and **6 x 17p 2B Grey blue** (3.9.84). Left margin
FP73a Transposed phosphor bands
FP74 Right margin
FP74a Transposed phosphor bands

FP75 **10 x 14p** **CB Dark blue** (5.9.88). Left margin
FP75a Missing phosphor
FP76 Right margin
FP76a Missing phosphor

No.

FP77 **10 x 14p** **CB Dark blue**, margins all round (23.8.88)

FP78 **10 x 14p** **CB Dark blue**, imperf. top and bottom (11.10.88)
FP78a Missing phosphor

Panes of 20

FP79 **10 x 7p** **CBar Purple brown** and **10 x 9p 2Bars Dull violet** (15.11.78)

FP80 **10 x 8p** **CBar Rosine** and **10 x 10p 2Bars Orange brown** (14.11.79)
FP80a Miscut (8p above 10p)

No.

FP81 **10 x 10p** **CBar Orange brown** and **10 x 12p 2Bars Yellow green** (12.11.80)
FP81a Missing phosphor

FP82 **10 x 11½p** **CBar Drab** and **10 x 14p grey blue 2Bars** (11.11.81)
FP82a Miscut (11½p above 14p)

FP83 **10 x 12½p** **CBar Light emerald** and **10 x 15½p pale violet 2Bars** with blue ten point star underprint (10.11.82)
FP83a Missing phosphor

FP84 **20 x 12½p** **CB Light emerald** with 5 point star underprint in blue (9.11.83)
FP84a Miscut
FP84b Thin value, Type I
FP84c Thin value, Type I, Miscut

No.

PPP/PVAD

FP85 **10 x 10p** **Orange brown** (3.10.79). Left margin
FP85a Miscut
FP86 Right margin
FP86a Miscut

PCP1/PVAD

FP87 **3 x 17p** **Grey blue** (2B) *plus* 'Please use the postcode' label. Error (12.8.86)

FP88 **6 x 17p** **Grey blue** (29.7.86)

FP89 **10 x 12p** **Yellow green** (4.2.80). Left margin
FP89a Miscut
FP90 Right margin
FP90a Miscut

No.

FP91 **10 x 14p** **Pale grey blue** (6.5.81). Left margin
FP91a Fluorescent Brightener Omitted
FP92 Right margin
FP92a Fluorescent Brightener Omitted

FP93 **10 x 15½p** **Pale violet** Type II (1.2.82). Left margin
FP94 Right margin

FP95 **10 x 16** **Pale drab** (5.4.83). Left margin
FP95a Deep drab
FP96 'D' underprint in blue
FP96a Miscut
FP97 Right margin
FP97a Deep drab
FP98 'D' underprint in blue

FP99 **10 x 17p** **Grey blue** (3.9.84). Left margin
FP100 'D' underprint in blue (5.3.85)
FP101 Right margin
FP102 'D' underprint in blue (5.3.85)

FP103 **10 x 18p** **Olive grey** (20.10.86). Left margin
FP104 Right margin

PCP2/PVAD

FP106 **10 x 14p** **Grey blue** (26.1.81). Left margin
FP107 Right margin
FP107a Miscut

FP108 **10 x 15½p** **Dull violet**, Type II (1.2.82). Left margin
FP109 Right margin

FP110 **10 x 18p** **Olive grey** (20.10.86). Left margin
FP111 Right margin

ACP/PVAD

FP112 **2 x 1p** **Crimson** and **2 x 24p chestnut** (10.9.91)
Miscut

FP113 **2 x 2p** **Deep green** and **4 x 24p chestnut** *plus*
2 x "Please use the postcode" labels (10.9.91)

FP114 **4 x 18p** **Dull grey olive**, margins all round (4.8.87)

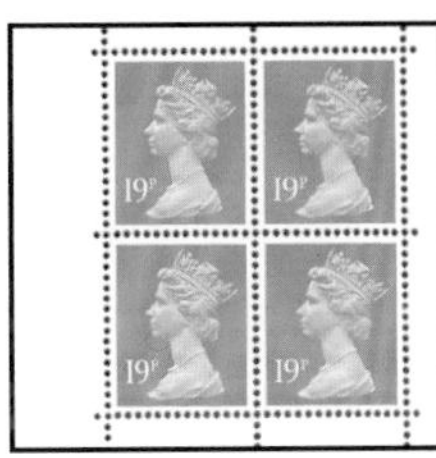

FP115 **4 x 19p** **Orange red**, margins all round (23.8.88)

No.

FP116 **4 x 19p** **Orange red**, imperf. top and bottom (11.10.88)

FP117 **4 x 19p** **Orange red**, imperf. on three sides (24.1.89)

FP118 **4 x 26p** **Red**, margins all round (4.8.87)

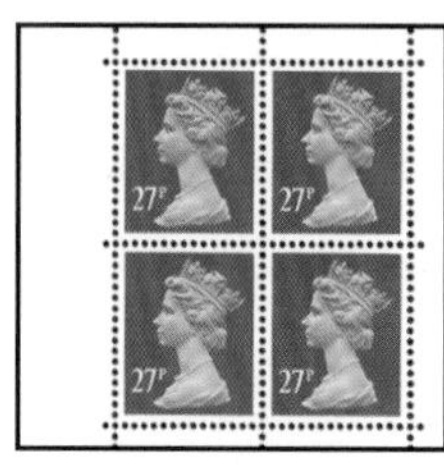

FP119 **4 x 27p** **Rust brown**, margins all round (23.8.86)

FP120 **4 x 27p** **Rust brown**, imperf. top and bottom (11.10.88)

No.

FP121 **5 x 20p** **Black**, imperf. left and right sides *plus* 'Please use the postcode' label (2.10.89)

FP122 **10 x 18p** **Dull olive grey** (27.1.87). Left margin
FP123 Right margin
FP123a Miscut

FP124 **10 x 18p** **Dull grey olive**, margins all round (4.8.87)

FP125 **10 x 19p** **Orange red** (5.9.88). Left margin
FP126 Right margin

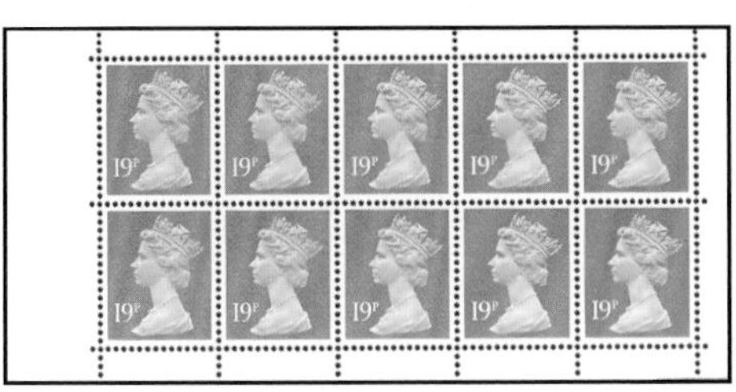

FP127 **10 x 19p Orange red**, margins all round (23.8.88)

FP128 **10 x 19p Orange red**, imperf. top and bottom (11.10.88)

Printed by Questa in Lithography

1988 (11 Oct.) Perf. 15 x 14

FCP/PVA

LP1 **10 x 14p CBar Dark blue**

ACP/PVA

LP2 **10 x 19p Orange red**

Printed by Walsall in Lithography

1989 (25 April) Perf. 14

FCP/PVA

LP3 **2 x 14p RB Dark blue** and **4 x 19p 2B Orange red** imperf. left and right sides

LP3a Missing phosphor

LP4 **4 x 29p 2B Purple** imperf. on three sides (2.10.89)

ACP/PVA

LP5 **2 x 2p Deep green** and **4 x 24p Chestnut** *plus* 2 x "Please use the postcode" labels (9.2.93)

LP6 **4 x 29p Purple** imperf. on three sides (17.4.90) Pane layout as LP4, but ACP

LP7 **4 x 31p Bright blue**, imperf. top and bottom (17.9.90)

LP7a Low OBA

LP8 **4 x 33p** **Emerald**, imperf. top and bottom (16.9.91)

LP9 **2 x 39p** **Pale mauve**, imperf. top and bottom (28.7.92)

LP10 **4 x 39p** **Deep mauve**, imperf. top and bottom (16.9.91)

ACP/PVAD

LP11 **4 x 33p** **Emerald**, imperf. top and bottom (8.9.92)
Pane layout as LP8, but ACP

Printed by Harrison in Photogravure

1993(1 Nov.) Perf. 15 x 14 elliptical

OFPP/PVAD

EP1 **2 x 25p** **Salmon pink** *plus* 2 x "Postcode Helpline" label
EP1a Miscut

EP2 **4 x 25p** **Salmon pink** (26.4.94)

EP3 **8 x 25p** **Salmon pink**

OFNP/PVAD

(The layout of panes EP4, EP5 and EP6 is the smae as EP1, EP2 and EP3 respectively.)

EP4 **2 x 25p** **2B Salmon pink** C (Yellow) fluor
plus 2 x 'Postcode Helpline' label
EP4a Miscut
EP4b D (Blue) fluor

EP5 **4 x 25p** **2B Salmon pink** C (Yellow) fluor
EP5a D (Blue) fluor

EP6 **8 x 25p** **2B Salmon pink** C (Yellow) fluor
EP6a D (Blue) fluor

No.

Printed by Walsall in Lithography

1993 (1 Nov.) No wmk. Perf. 15 x 14 elliptical

OFNP/PVA

EP7 **4 x 25p 2B Salmon pink** - C (Yellow) fluor (As EP2)

EP8 **4 x 35p 2B Yellow** - C (Yellow) fluor
EP8a D (Blue) fluor

EP9 **4 x 37p 2B Amethyst** D (Blue) fluor

EP10 **4 x 41p 2B Stone** - C (Yellow) fluor
EP10a D (Blue) fluor

EP11 **4 x 60p 2B Slate blue** - C (Yellow) fluor (9.8.94)
EP11a D (Blue) fluor

No.

EP12 **4 x 63p 2B Light emerald** D (Blue) fluor
EP12a Missing phosphor

Printed by Questa in Lithography

1996 (16 Jan.) Perf. 15 x 14 elliptical

OFNP/PVA (Blue) fluor

EP13 **4 x 25p 2B Salmon pink**

EP14 **3 x 26p 2B Red-brown** and **2 x 1p 2B Crimson** and **1 x 20p CB Bright green** *plus* two labels (8.7.96)
EP14a Missing phosphor
EP14b Miscut

EP15 **8 x 25p 2B Salmon-pink**

EP16 **7 x 26p 2B Red-brown** and **1 x 20p CB Bright green** (8.7.96)
EP16a Missing phosphor

Printed by Walsall in Gravure

(Gravure is also sometimes refered to as EME or Computer engraved)

1997 (26 Aug.) Perf. 15 x 14 elliptical

OFNP/PVA - D (Blue) fluor

EP17 **4 x 30p 2B Grey-green** (5.5.98)

EP18 **4 x 37p 2B Amethyst** (26.8.97)

EP19 **4 x 38p 2B Ultramarine** (5.5.98)

EP20 **4 x 40p 2B Greyish blue** (27.4.00)

EP21 **4 x 63p 2B Light emerald** (26.8.97)

EP22 **4 x 64p 2B Sea green** (5.5.98)

EP23 **4 x 65p 2B Greenish blue** (27.4.00)

Printed by Questa in Gravure

OFNP/PVA - D(Blue) fluor

1998 (1Dec.) No Wmk. Perf 15 x 14 elliptical

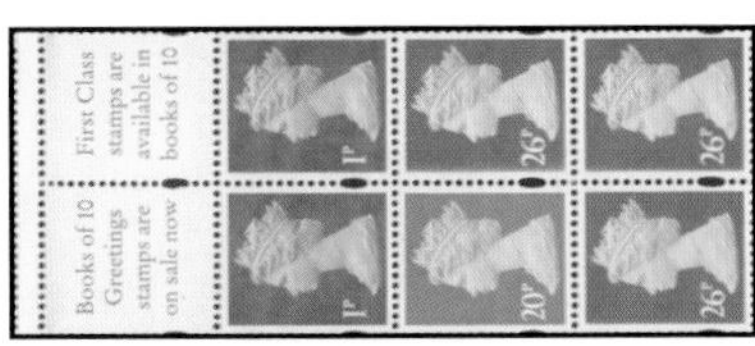

EP24 **3 x 26p 2B Red-brown** and **2 x 1p 2B Crimson** and **1 x 20p CB Bright green** *plus* two labels
EP24a Miscut

1999 (26 Apr.) No Wmk. Perf 15 x 14 elliptical

EP25 **3 x 26p 2B Red-brown**, **1 x 1p 2B Deep Crimson**, **1 x 2p CB Green** and **1 x 19p CB Olive-green**
EP25a Miscut

1998 (1 Dec.) No Wmk. Perf 15 x 14 elliptical

EP26 **1 x 20p CB Bright green** and **7 x 26p 2B Red-brown**
EP26a Miscut

1999 (26 Apr.) No Wmk. Perf 15 x 14 elliptical

EP27 **1 x 19p CB Olive green** and **7 x 26p 2B Red-brown**

Double Head (1d Black Anniversary) Panes

Printed by Harrison in Photogravure

1990 (30 Jan.) 150th Anniversary of the Penny Black

FCP/PVAD

AP1 **2 x 15p LB Bright blue, 20p 2B Black and buff** *plus* 'Please use the postcode' label

AP2 **10 x 15p CB Bright blue**, imperf. top and bottom

ACP/PVAD

AP3 **4 x 20p Black & buff**, imperf. on three sides (17.4.90)

AP4 **5 x 20p Black & buff**, imperf. left and right sides *plus* 'Please use the postcode' label

AP5 **10 x 20p Black & buff**, imperf. top and bottom

Printed by Questa in Lithography

Printed in Lithography. Perf. 15 x 14

FCP/PVA

AP6 **10 x 15p CBar Bright blue** (17.4.90)

ACP/PVA

AP7 **10 x 20p Black**. (17.4.90)
AP7a ACP/Low OBA

Printed by Walsall in Lithography

Perf. 14

FCP/PVA

AP8 **4 x 15p CB Bright blue**, imperf. on three sides (30.1.90)

AP9 **10 x 15p CB Bright blue**, imperf. on three sides (12.6.90)

ACP/PVA

AP10 **5 x 20p Black & buff**, imperf. left and right sides *plus* "Please use the postcode" label (As AP4)

ACP/PVAD

AP11 **4 x 20p Black & buff**, imperf. on three sides (30.1.90)

AP12 **10 x 20p Black & buff**, imperf. on three sides (12.6.90)

Standard Perforations

NVI Machin Booklet Panes

No.

Printed by Harrison in Photogravure

1989 (22 Aug.) Perf. 15 x 14

FCP/PVAD

CP1 **4 x 2nd** **CB Bright blue**, imperf. on three sides (28.11.89)

CP2 **10 x 2nd** **CB Bright blue**, imperf. at top and bottom

CP3 **10 x 2nd** **CB Dark blue**, imperf. at top and bottom (7.8.90)

ACP/PVAD

CP4 **4 x 1st** **Black**, imperf. on three sides (5.12.89)

No.

CP5 **10 x 1st** **Black**, imperf. at top and bottom

CP6 **10 x 1st** **Orange red**, imperf. top and bottom (7.8.90)

Printed by Questa in Lithography

Perf. 15 x 14

FCP/PVA

CP7 **10 x 2nd** **CBar Bright blue,** Perf. margin (19.8.89)

CP7a **10 x 2nd** **CBar Bright blue**, Imperf. margin

CP8 **10 x 2nd** **CBar Dark blue** (7.8.90)

No.

ACP/PVA

CP9 **10 x 1st** **Black**. Perf. margin (19.9.89)
CP9a Low OBA
CP9b Imperf. margin
CP9c Low OBA

CP10 **10 x 1st** **Orange red** (6.8.91)

ACP/PVAD

CP11 **10 x 1st** **Orange red** (7.8.90) As CP10 above

Printed by Walsall in Lithography

Perf. 14

FCP/PVA

CP12 **4 x 2nd** **CB Bright blue**. Imperf. on three sides (22.8.89)

CP13 **4 x 2nd** **CB Dark blue**. Imperf. at top and bottom (7.8.90)

No.

CP14 **4 x 2nd** **CB Bright blue**. Imperf. at top and bottom (6.8.91)

CP15 **4 x 1st** **2B Black**. Imperf. on three sides (22.8.89)
CP15a Missing phosphor

CP16 **10 x 2nd** **CB Dark blue**. Imperf. at top and bottom (7.8.90)

CP17 **10 x 2nd** **CB Bright blue**. Imperf. at top and bottom (6.8.91)

FCP/PVAD

CP18 **10 x 2nd** **CB Bright blue**. Imperf. at top and bottom (16.3.93) As CP17 above

No.

ACP/PVA

CP19 **4 x 1st** **Orange red**. Imperf. at top and bottom (7.8.90)
CP19a Low OBA

CP20 **10 x 1st** **Orange red**. Imperf. at top and bottom (7.8.90)
CP20a Low OBA

Perf. 13 in error

CP21 4 x 1st **Orange red**. Imperf. at top and bottom (10.90)
CP21a Low OBA

ACP/PVAD

CP22 **4 x 1st** **Orange red.** Imperf. at top and bottom
Pane layout as CP 19 (16.3.93)

CP23 **10 x 1st** **Orange red**. Imperf. at top and bottom
Pane layout as CP20 (9.2.93)

Printed by Harrison in Photogravure

1993 (6 April) Perf. 15 x 14 elliptical

OFNP/PVAD

CP24 **4 x 2nd** **CB Bright blue** (7.9.93)
C (Yellow) fluor

CP24a **4 x 2nd** **CB Bright blue** (7.9.93)
D (Blue) fluor

No.

CP25 **10 x 2nd** **CB Bright blue** (7.9.93)
D (Blue) fluor

CP26 **10 x 1st** **2B Orange red** (4.4.95)
C (Yellow) fluor

CP26a **10 x 1st** **2B Orange red** (4.4.95)
D (Blue) fluor

OFPP/PVAD

CP27 **4 x 1st** **Orange red**
CP28 **10 x 1st** **Orange red,** Pane layout as CP26

OFNP/PVA (Layflat)

CP29 **10 x 2nd** **CB Bright blue,** Pane layout as CP25
CP30 **10 x 1st** **2B Orange-red,** Pane layout as CP26

No.

Printed by Questa in Lithography

Perf. 15 x 14 elliptical

OFNP/PVA

CP31 **10 x 2nd** **CBar Bright blue** (6.4.93)
CP31a Missing phosphor
CP32 **10 x 2nd** **CB Bright blue** (1.11.93)
C (Yellow) fluor.As CP31
CP32a **10 x 2nd** **CB Bright blue** (.7.95)
D (Blue) fluor.As CP31

CP33 **10 x 1st** **2B Orange red** (1.11.93)
C (Yellow) fluor
CP33a **10 x 1st** **2B Orange red** (.7.95)
D (Blue) fluor

Commemorative issue

CP34 **4 x 1st** **2B Orange red** *plus* '300 years of The Bank of England' label (27.7.94)
CP34a Missing phosphor

No.

Printed by Walsall in Lithography

Perf. 15 x 14 elliptical

OFNP/PVA

CP35 **4 x 2nd** **CB Bright blue** (6.4.93)
C (Yellow) fluor
CP35a **4 x 2nd** **CB Bright blue** (.7.95)
D (Blue) fluor

CP36 **10 x 2nd** **CB Bright blue** (1.11.93)
C (Yellow) fluor
CP36a **10 x 2nd** **CB Bright blue** (.7.95)
D (Blue) fluor

CP37 **4 x 1st** **2B Orange red**
C (Yellow) fluor
CP38 **4 x 1st** **2B Orange red**
D (Blue) fluor

CP39 **10 x 1st** **2B Orange red** (6.4.93)
C (Yellow) fluor
CP39a Missing phosphor
CP39b Broad band
CP40 **10 x 1st** **2B Orange red**
D (Blue) fluor

No.

Commemorative issues

CP41 **4 x 1st** **2B Orange red** *plus* 'R. J. Mitchell' label (16.5.95)

CP41A **4 x 1st** **2B Orange red** *plus* 'Queen's 70th Birthday' label (16.4.96)

CP41B **4 x 1st** **2B Orange red** *plus* 'Hong Kong 97' label (12.2.97)

CP41C **4 x 1st** **2B Orange red** *plus* 'Heads of Government' label (21.10.97)

CP41D **4 x 1st** **2B Orange red** *plus* 'Prince's Trust' label (14.11.98)

No.

CP41E **4 x 1st** **2B Orange red** *plus* 'Berlin Airlift' label (12.5.99)

CP41F **4 x 1st** **2B Orange red** *plus* 'Rugby World Cup' label (1.10.99)

CP41G **4 x 1st** **2B Millennium** *plus* 'Postman Pat' label (21.3.00)

CP41H **4 x 1st** **2B Millennium** *plus* 'Botanical' label (4.4.00)

Printed by Harrison/De La Rue in Gravure

1997 (21 April) Perf. 15 x 14 elliptical

OFNP/PVA (Layflat) - D (Blue) fluor

CP42 **10 x 2nd CB Bright-blue**

CP43 **10 x 1st 2B Orange-red**

CP44 **10 x 1st 2B Gold** (21.4.97)

Printed by Walsall in Gravure

Perf. 15 x 14 elliptical

OFNP/PVA - D (Blue) fluor

CP45 **4 x 2nd CB Bright blue** (26.8.97)

CP46 **4 x 1st 2B Bright orange red** (26.8.97)
CP46a Missing phosphor

CP47 **4 x E 2B Dark blue**

CP48 **10 x 1st 2B Gold**

CP49 **10 x 1st 2B Bright orange red** (18.11.97)

CP50 **10 x 1st 2B Millennium** (6.1.00)

No. No.

Printed by Questa in Gravure

Perf. 15 x 14 elliptical

OFNP/PVA - D (Blue) fluor

CP51 **10 x 2nd** **CB Bright-blue** (1.12.98)
CP51a Miscut

CP52 **10 x 1st** **2B Bright orange red** (1.12.98)
CP52a Miscut

CP53 **10 x 1st** **2B Millennium** (6.1.00)
CP53a Missing phosphor

2000 (27 Apr.) No Wmk. Perf 15 x 14 elliptical

CP54 **1 x 2nd** **CB Bright blue**, **3 x 1st 2B Orange-red** and four labels (Postcode) (27.4.00)
CP54a Miscut

2000 (27 Apr.) No Wmk. Perf 15 x 14 elliptical

CP55 **2 x 2nd** **CB Bright blue** and **6 x 1st 2B Orange-red**
CP55a Broad band left

2001 (17 Apr.) No Wmk. Perf 15 x 14 elliptical

CP56 **1 x 2nd** **CB Bright blue**, **3 x 1st 2B Orange-red** and four labels (Postcodes)

King Edward VII

1904 (16 March) - 09 Printed by De La Rue. Sold with ½d premium for the booklet. Grease-proof paper interleaving. *Contents* BP3/3/3/3

BK1 **2s 0½d Black on red** £275

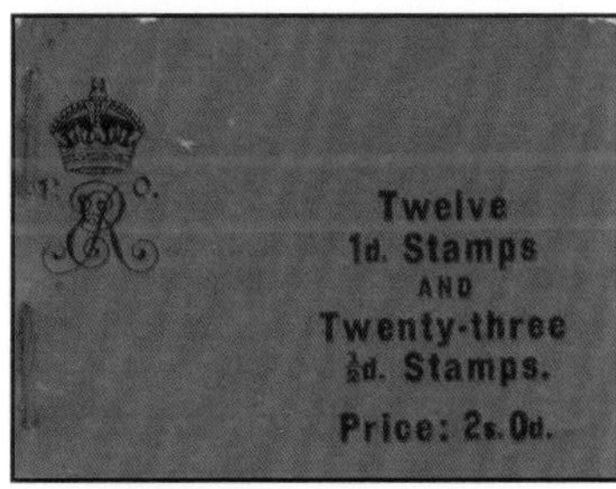

1906 (June) *Contents* BP3/3/1//1/1/2

BK2 **2s Black on red** £850

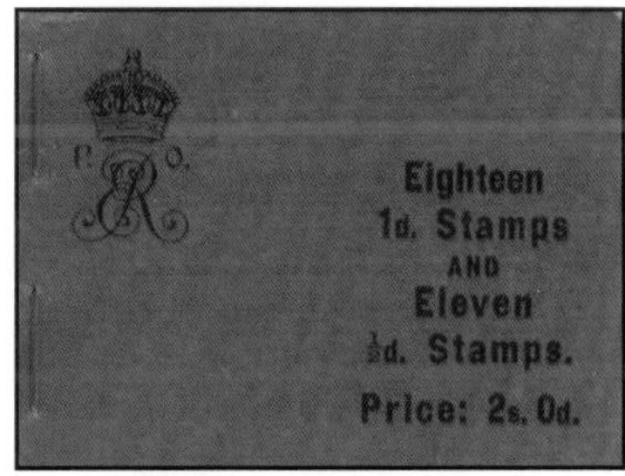

1907 (Aug.) *Contents* BP3/3/3/1/2

BK3 **2s Black on red** £1500

1908 (Aug) Interleaving printed in red. *Contents* BP3/3/3/1/2

BK4 **2s Black on red** £1100

1909 (Aug) Interleaving printed in green. *Contents* BP3/3/3/1/2

BK5 **2s Black on red** £850

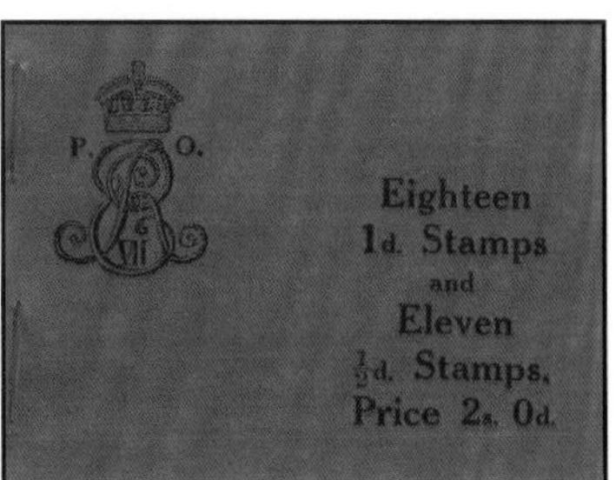

1911 (June) Printed by Harrison & Sons. *Contents* BP6/6/6/4/5

BK6 **2s Black on red** £900

King George V

All booklets were printed by Harrison & Sons unless otherwise stated.

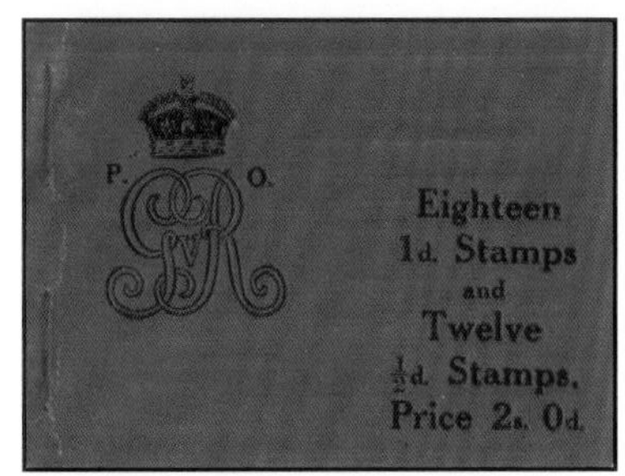

1911 (Aug.) *Contents* BP8/8/8/7/7

BK7 **2s Black on red** £600

EIGHTEEN 1d. and TWELVE ½d. Stamps. PRICE 2s. 0d.

INLAND RATES OF POSTAGE.

Letters.	Not exceeding 4 oz. 1d.; for every additional 2 oz. ½d.		
Parcels. Not exceeding	1 lb. 3d.	5 lb. 6d.	9 lb. 9d.
	2 „ 4d.	7 „ 7d.	10 „ 10d.
	3 „ 5d.	8 „ 8d.	11 „ 11d.

1912 (April) Redrawn cover design. *Contents* BP8/8/8/7/7

BK8 **2s Black on red** £750

1912 (Sept.) *New contents* BP12/12/12/11/11

BK9 **2s Black on red** £650

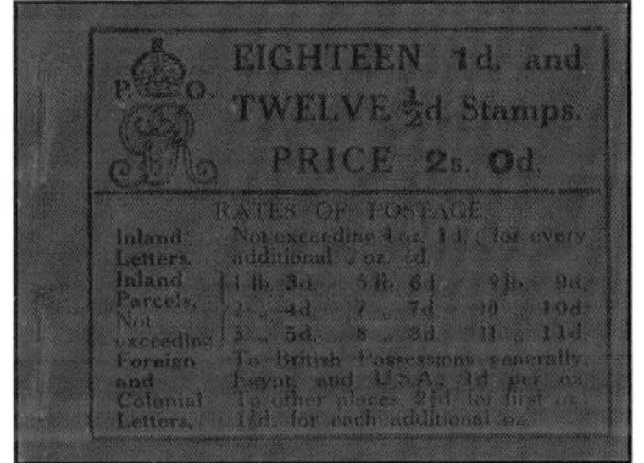

Inscribed 'RATES OF POSTAGE'

1912 (Nov.) *Contents* BP12/12/12/11/11

BK10 **2s Black on red** £750

1913 (Jan.) Edition Nos. 8 and 9 added to cover. *Contents* BP12/12/12/11/11

BK11 **2s Black on red** £750

1913 (April) Edition Nos. 10-35. *Contents* BP14/14/14/13/13

BK12 **2s Black on red** £475

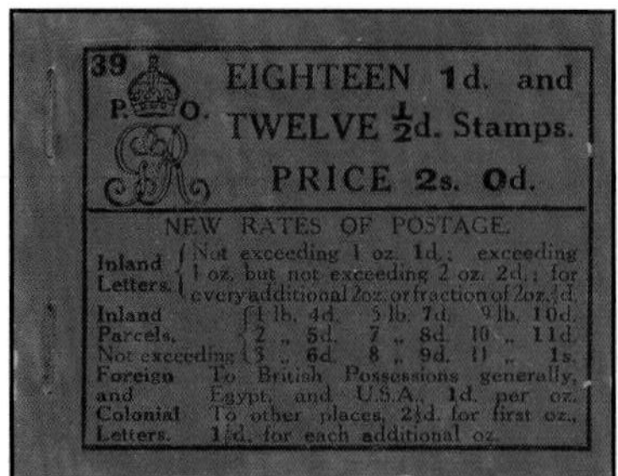

Inscribed 'NEW RATES OF POSTAGE'

1915 (Nov.) Edition Nos. 36-42. *Contents* BP14/14/14/13/13
BK13 **2s Black on red** £525

1916 (May) Black interleaving. Edition Nos. 43-45.
Contents BP14/14/14/13/13
BK14 **2s Black on red** £650

1916 (July) Edition Nos. 46-64. *Contents* BP14/14/14/13/13
BK15 **2s Black on orange** £475

Advertisement on cover

1917 (Sept.) Edition Nos. 65-81. *Contents* BP14/14/14/13/13
BK16 **2s Black on orange** £475

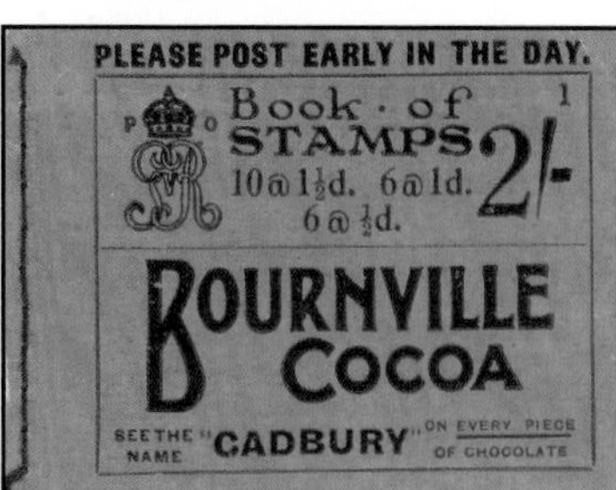

Inscribed 'Book of STAMPS'

1924 (Feb.) Edition Nos. 1 and 2. *Contents* BP16/15/14/13
BK17 **2s Black on blue** £1100

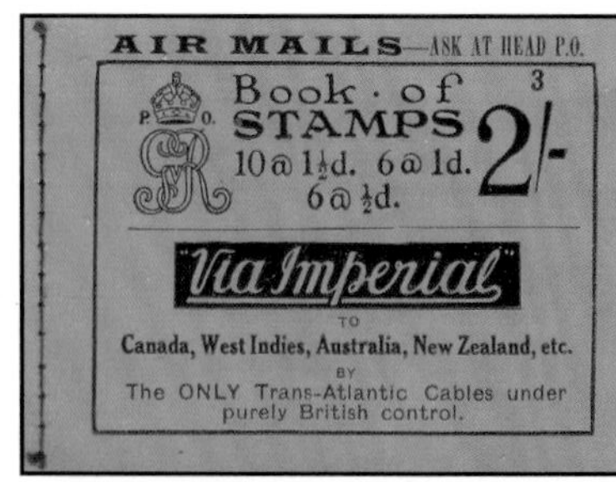

1924 (June) Printed by Waterlow & Sons Ltd. Edition Nos. 3-102, 108-254.
Contents BP22/21/20/19
BK18 **2s Black on blue** £450

1924 (Nov.) Printed by Waterlow & Sons Ltd. Edition No. 15.
Contents BP23/21/20/19
BK19 **2s Black on blue** £4000

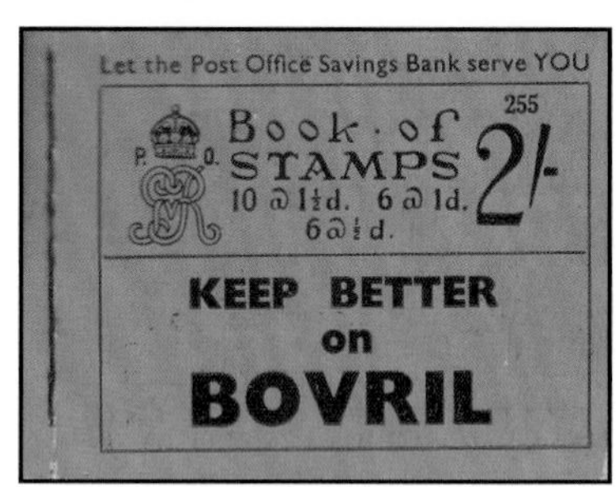

1934 (Feb.) Edition Nos. 255-287.
Contents BP22/21/20/19
BK20 **2s Black on blue** £475

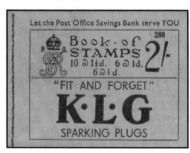

1935 (Jan.) Photogravure intermediate format. Edition Nos. 288-297.
Contents BP31/30/29/28
BK21 **2s Black on blue** £1000

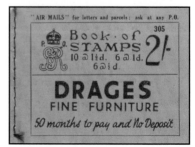

1935 (July) Photogravure small format. Edition Nos. 305-353. *Contents* BP35/34/33/32

BK22 **2s Black on blue** £300

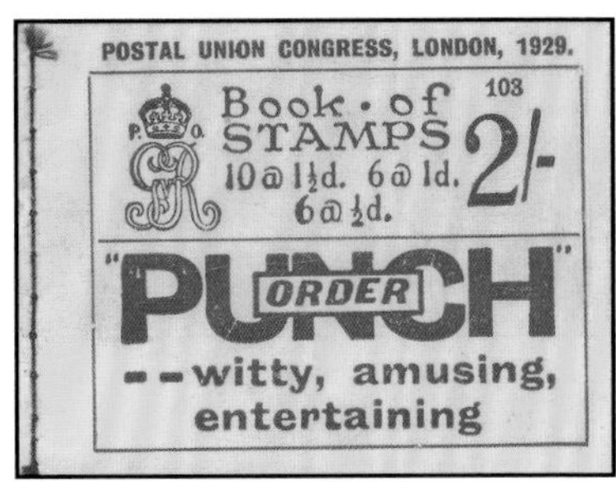

1929 (May) Postal Union Congress. Printed by Waterlow & Sons Ltd. Edition Nos. 103-107. *Contents* BP27/26/25/24

BK23 **2s Blue on buff** £375

1935 (May) Silver Jubilee. Edition Nos. 298-304. *Contents* BP38/38/38/37/36

BK24 **2s Blue on buff** £75

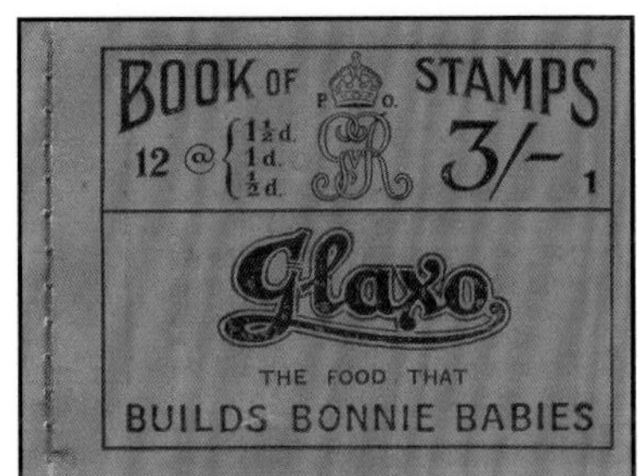

1918 (Oct.) Edition Nos. 1-11. *Contents* BP15/15/14/14/13/13

BK25 **3s Black on orange** £600

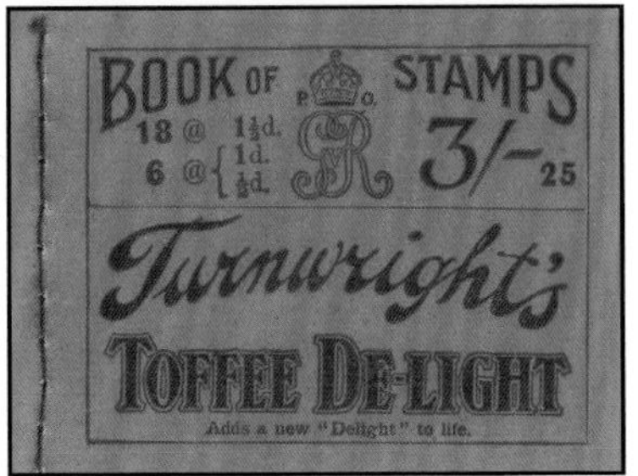

1919 (July) Edition Nos. 12-28. *Contents* BP15/15/15/14/13

BK26 **3s Black on orange** £600

1921 (April) Edition Nos. 35 and 37. *Contents* BP17/17/17

BK27 **3s Black on blue** £750

1921 (Dec.) Edition Nos. 12, 13 and 37. *Contents* BP18/18/18

BK28 **3s Black on blue** £800

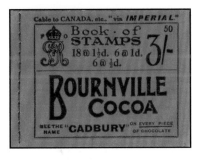

1922 (May) Edition Nos. 19, 20, 22, 23 and 25-54. *Contents* BP15/15/15/14/13

BK29 **3s Black on scarlet** £750

1922 (June) Edition Nos. 21 and 24. *Contents* BP15/15/15/15

BK30 **3s Black on blue** £800

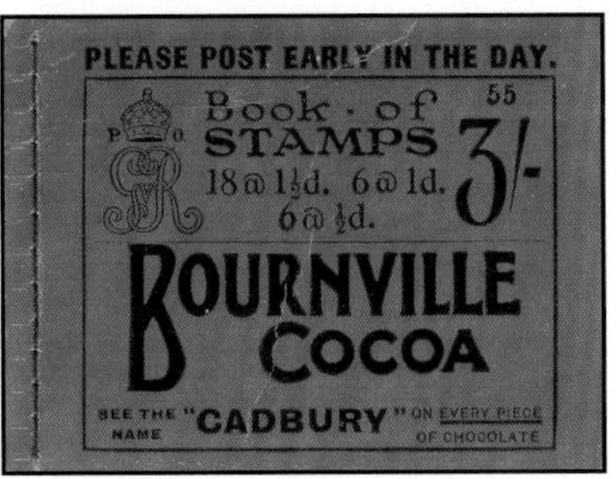

1924 (Feb.) Printed by Waterlow & Sons Ltd. Edition Nos. 55-167 and 173-273. *Contents* BP21/21/21/20/19

BK31 **3s Black on scarlet** £275

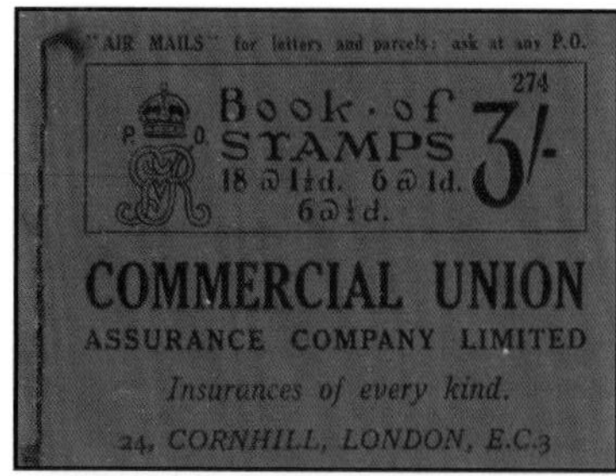

1934 (March) Edition Nos. 274 - 288.

BK32	**3s Black on scarlet**	£350

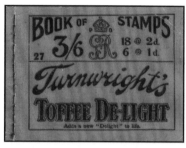

1935 (Jan.) Photogravure intermediate format. Edition Nos. 289-293. *Contents* BP30/30/30/29/28

BK33	**3s Black on scarlet**	£1100

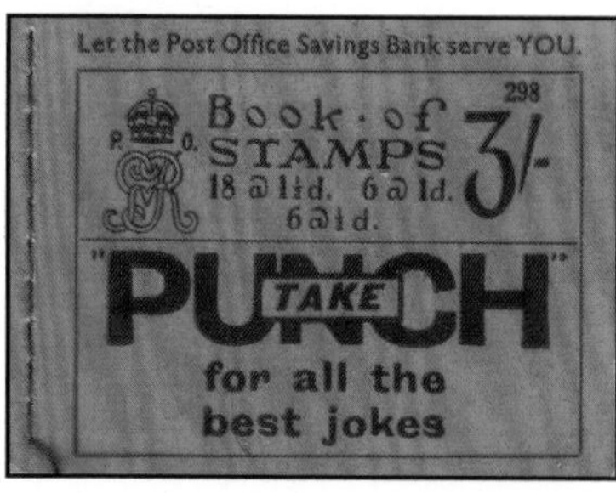

1935 (July) Photogravure small format. Edition Nos. 298-319. *Contents* BP34/34/34/33/32

BK34	**3s Black on scarlet**	£275

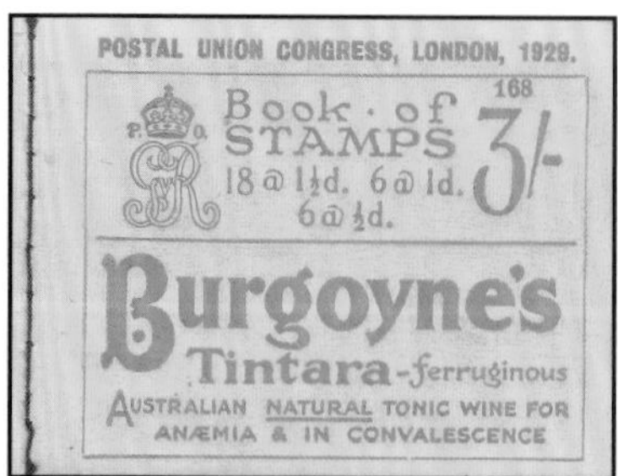

1929 (May) Postal Union Congress. Printed by Waterlow & Sons Ltd. Edition Nos. 168-172. *Contents* BP26/26/26/25/24

BK35	**3s Red on buff**	£300

1935 (May) Silver Jubilee. Edition Nos. 294-297. *Contents* BP38/38/38/38/38/37/36

BK36	**3s Red on buff**	£75

1920 (July) Edition Nos. 27-32. *Contents* BP17/17/17/14

BK37	**3s6d Black on orange**	£800

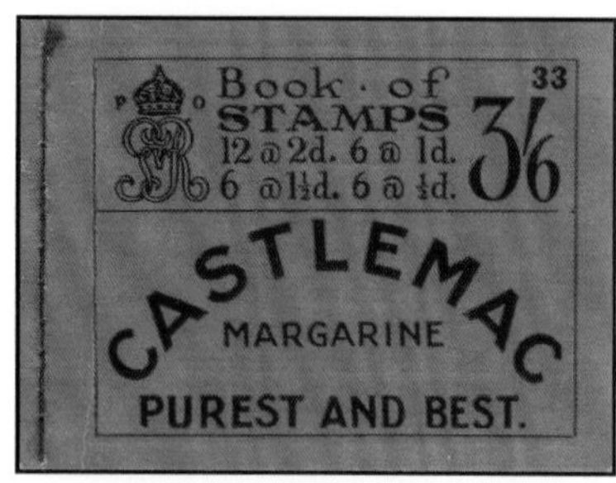

1921 (April) Edition Nos. 33, 34, 36 and 38. *Contents* BP17/17/15/14/13

BK38	**3s6d Black on orange**	£800

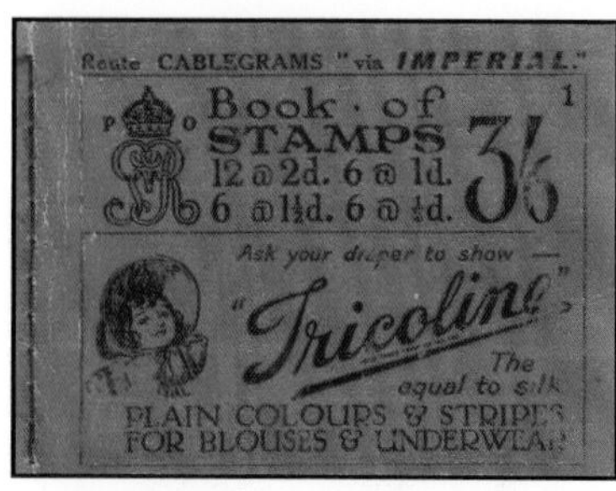

1921 (Aug.) Edition Nos. 1-11 and 14-18. *Contents* BP17/17/15/14/13

BK39	**3s6d Black on orange**	£800
BK39a	*Contents* BP18/18/15/14/13	£800

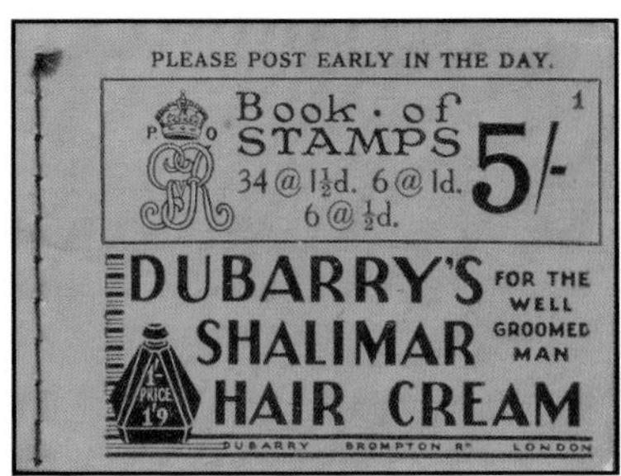

1931 (Aug.) Printed by Waterlow & Sons Ltd. Edition No. 1.
Contents BP22/21/21/21/21/21/20/19
BK40 **5s Black on green** £3000

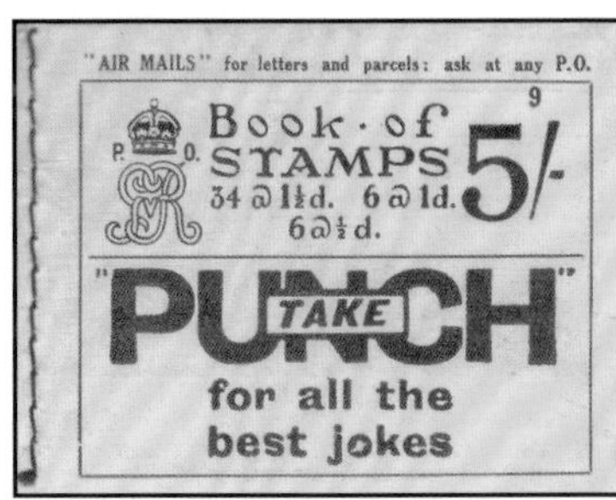

1932 (June) Printed by Waterlow & Sons Ltd. Edition Nos. 2-6.
BK41 **5s Black on buff** £1250

1934 (July) Edition Nos. 7 and 8.
BK42 **5s Black on buff** £900

1935 (Feb.) Photogravure intermediate format. Edition No. 9.
Contents BP31/30/30/30/30/30/29/28
BK43 **5s Black on buff** £2000

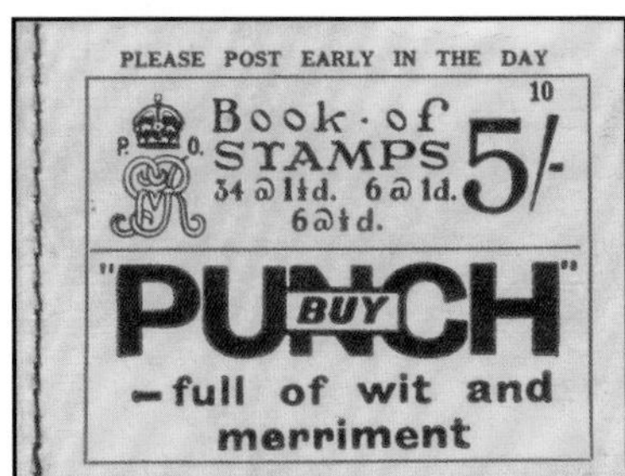

1935 (July) Photogravure small format. Edition Nos. 10-15.
Contents BP35/34/34/34/34/34/33/32
BK44 **5s Black on buff** £300

King Edward VIII

1936 Plain cover. *Contents* BP42/42
BK45 **6d Buff** £40

1936 (Oct.) Edition Nos. 354-385. *Contents* BP43/41/40/39
BK46 **2s Black on scarlet** £80

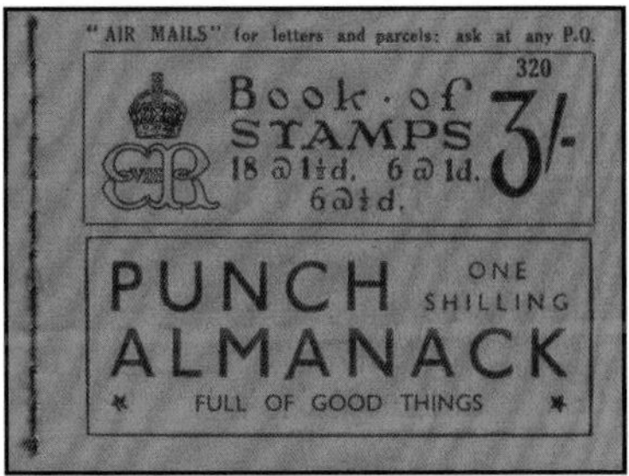

1936 (Nov.) Edition Nos. 320-332. *Contents* BP41/41/41/40/39
BK47 **3s Black on scarlet** £65

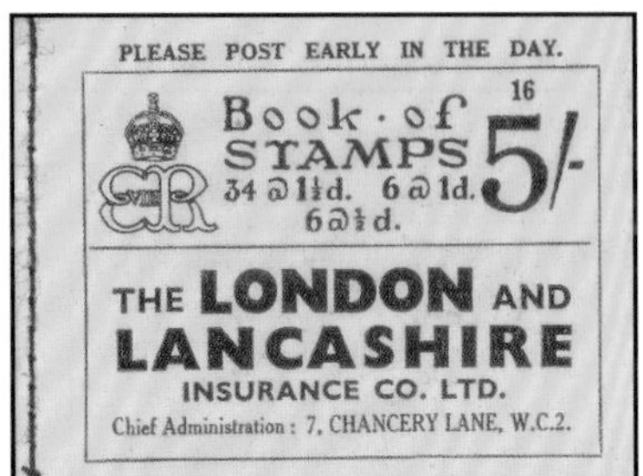

1937 (March) Edition Nos. 16 and 17.
Contents BP41/41/41/41/41/43/40/39
BK48 **5s Black on buff** £180

King George VI

1938 (Jan.) Plain cover. *Contents* BP49/49
BK49 **6d Buff cover** £40

1938 (Feb.) Plain cover. *Contents* BP49/47/45
BK50 **6d Pink cover** £250

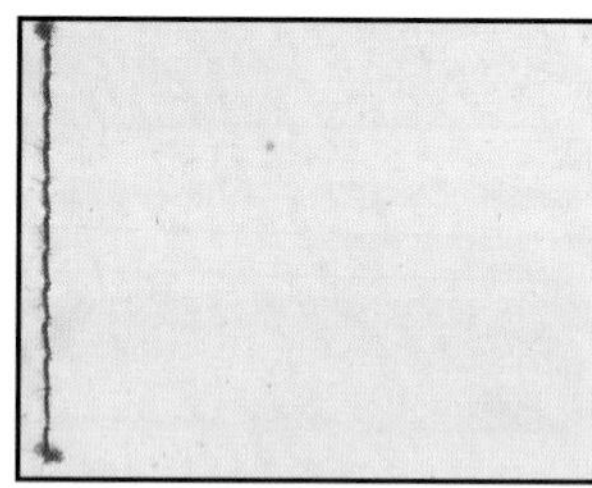

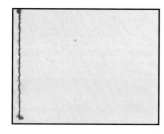

1940 (June) Plain cover. *Contents* BP54/53
BK51 **6d Green cover** £80

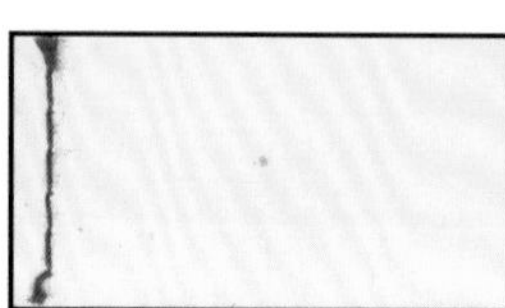

1947 (Dec.) Plain cover. *Contents* BP56/56/57/57/58/58
BK52 **1s Cream cover** £10

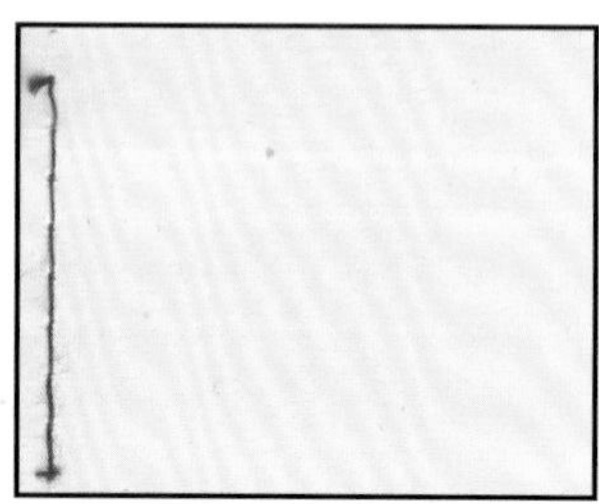

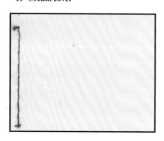

1951 (May) Plain cover. *Contents* BP63/63/66/66/72/72
BK53 **1s Cream cover** £10
1951 (May) Plain cover. *Contents* BP62/65/71. Selvedge at top or bottom
BK54 **1s Cream cover** £10

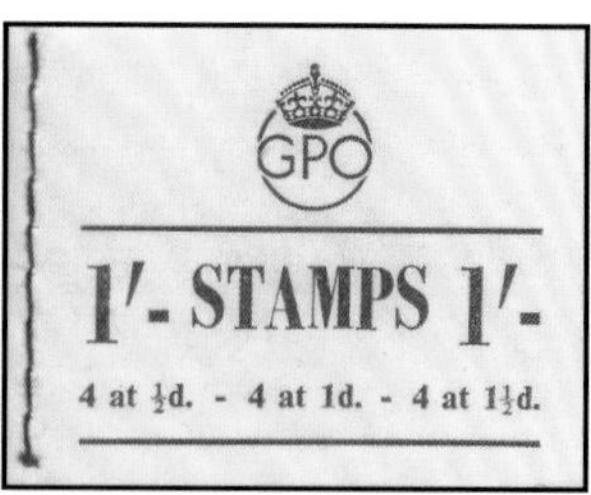

1952 (Dec.) Round G.P.O. emblem. *Contents* BP62/65/71.
BK55 **1s Cream cover** £10

1954 Oval G.P.O. emblem. *Contents* BP62/65/71.
BK56 **1s Cream cover** £12

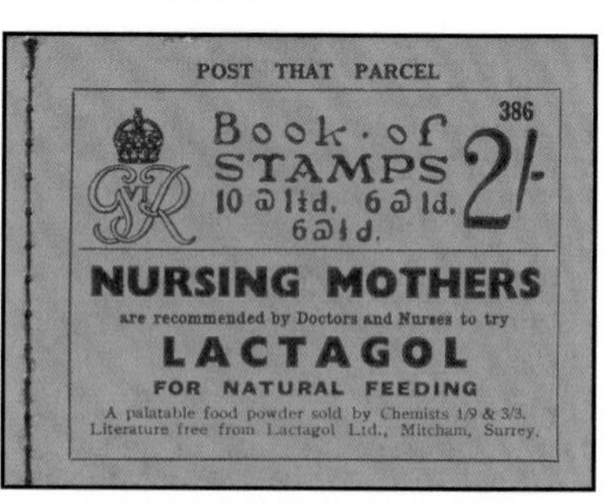

1937 (Aug.) Edition Nos. 386-412. *Contents* BP50/48/46/44.
BK57 **2s Black on blue** £400

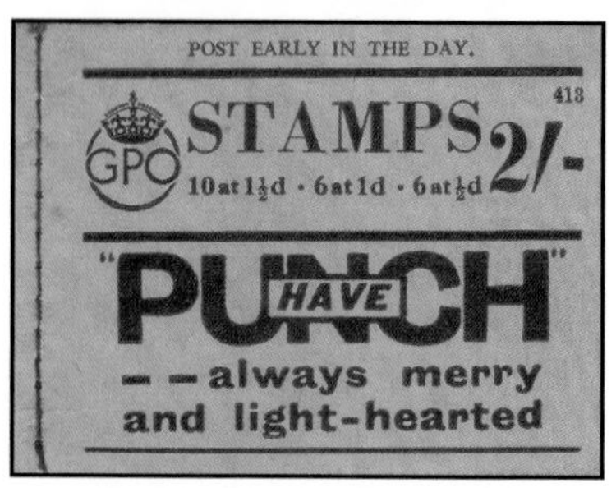

1938 (April) G.P.O. emblem added to cover. Edition Nos. 413-508.
Contents BP50/48/46/44.
BK58 **2s Black on blue** £400

1940 (June) Edition Nos. 1-7. *Contents* BP52/51/44.

BK59 **2s6d Black on scarlet** £800

1940 (Sept.) Edition Nos. 8-13.

BK60 **2s6d Black on blue** £800

1940 (Oct.) Edition Nos. 14-94. *Contents* BP52/51/44

BK61 **2s6d Black on green** £425

1942 (March) Edition Nos. 95-214. *Contents* BP60/59/55

BK62 **2s6d Black on green** £460

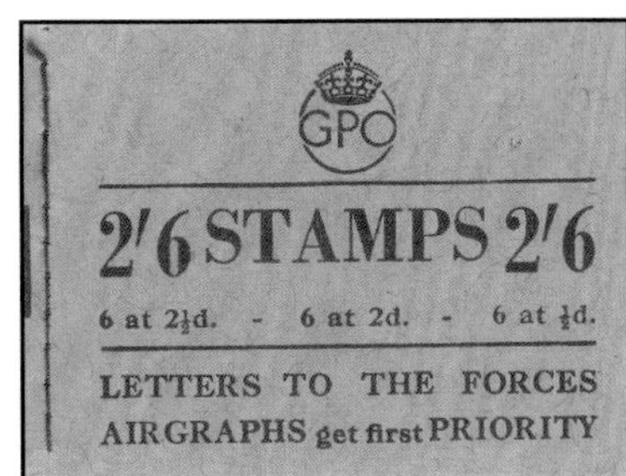

1943 (Aug.) Introduction of dated editions and G.P.O. emblem placed centrally. Edition dates Aug. 1943 - Feb. 1951 (90). *Contents* BP60/59/55

BK63 **2s6d Black on green** From £45 to £100

1951 (May) Edition dates May 1951 - Feb. 1952 (10). *Contents* BP74/73/61

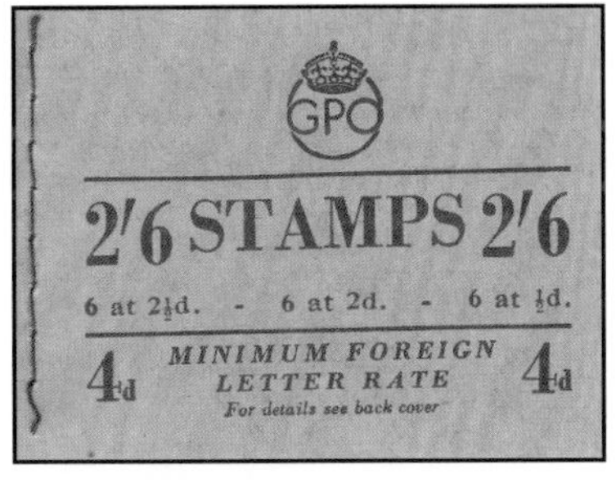

BK64 **2s6d Black on green** £25

1952 (March) Edition dates Mar. 1952 - May 1953 (15). *Contents* BP74/70/67/61

BK65 **2s6d Black on green** £25

Composite Booklets

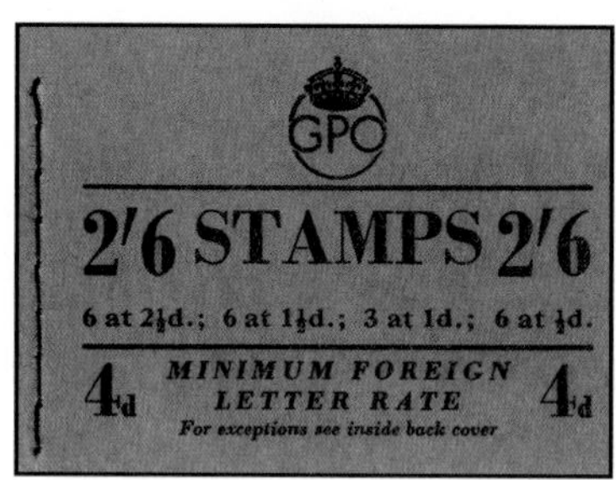

1953 (May). Edition dates May - Sept. 1953 (5). *Contents* BP88/84/67/61
BK66 **2s6d Black on green** From £20
1953 (Sept.) Edition date Sept. 1953. *Contents* BP88/84/68/61
BK67 **2s6d Black on green** £60

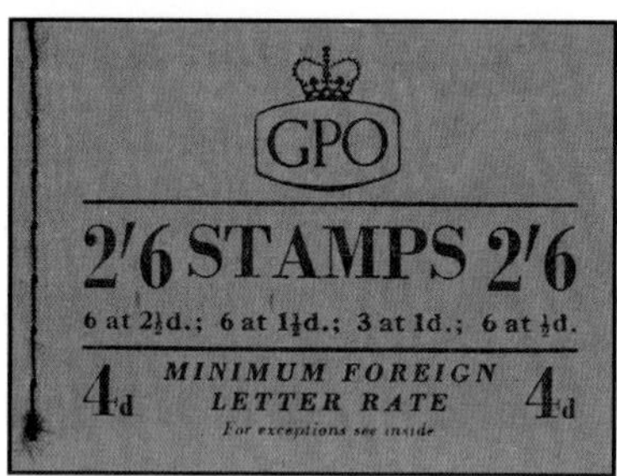

1953 (Oct.) Edition dates Oct. - Dec. 1953 (3). *Contents* BP88/84/67/61
BK68 **2s6d Black on green** From £20
1953 (Oct.) Edition dates Oct. - Nov. 1953 (2). *Contents* BP88/84/68/61
BK69 **2s6d Black on green** From £50
1954 (Jan.) Edition dates Jan. - Feb. 1954 (2). *Contents* BP88/84/69/61
BK70 **2s6d Black on green** £40
1954 (March) Edition date Mar. 1954. *Contents* BP88/84/67/75
BK71 **2s6d Black on green** £400
1954 (March) Edition date Mar. 1954. *Contents BP88/84/69/75*
BK71a **2s6d Black on green** £2500

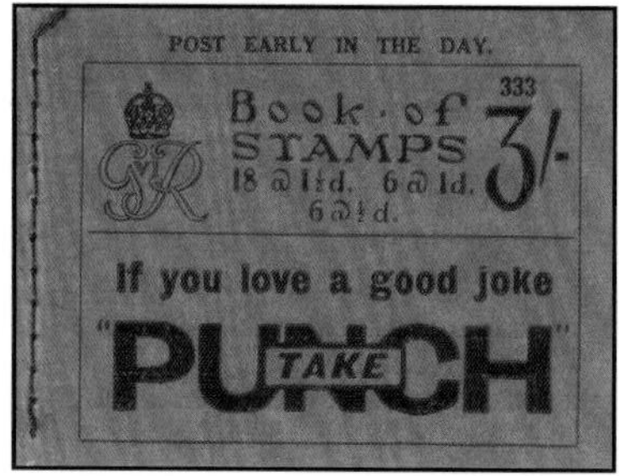

1937 (Aug.) Edition Nos. 333-343. *Contents* BP48/48/48/54/53
BK72 **3s Black on scarlet** £375

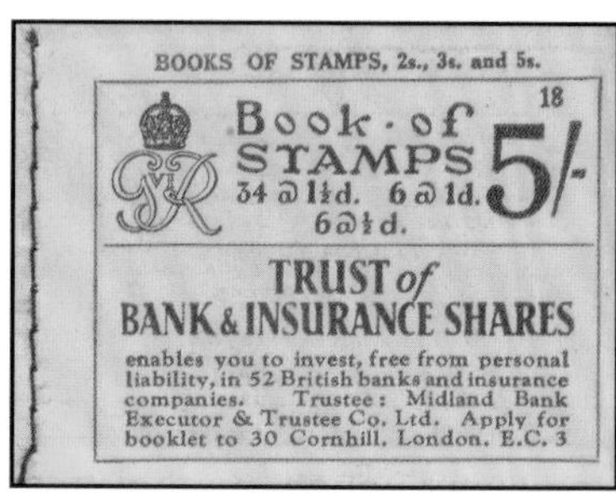

1938 (April) Edition Nos. 344-377. *Contents* BP48/48/48/54/53
BK73 **3s Black on scarlet** £650

1937 (Aug.) Edition Nos. 18-20. *Contents* BP50/48/48/48/48/48/46/44
BK74 **5s Black on buff** £850

1938 (May) Edition Nos. 21-29. *Contents* BP50/48/48/48/48/48/46/44
BK75 **5s Black on buff** £750

1940 (July) Edition Nos. 1-16. *Contents* BP52/52/52/51/44
BK76 **5s Black on buff** £800

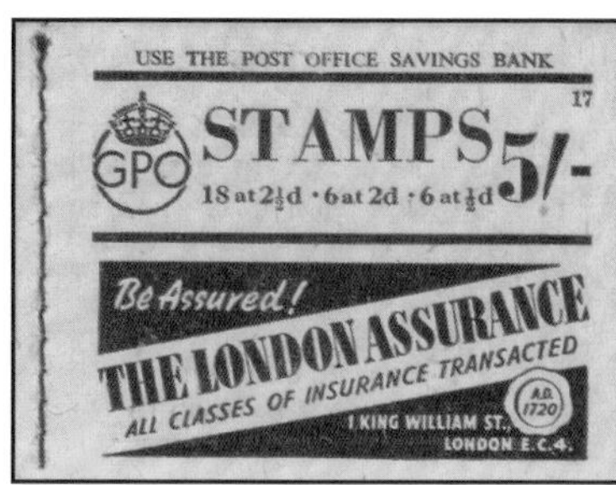

1942 (March) Edition Nos. 16-36. *Contents* BP60/60/60/59/55

BK77	**5s Black on buff**	£800

1943 (Sept.) Edition dates Sept. 1943 - Dec. 1950 (49). *Contents* BP60/60/60/59/55

BK78	**5s Black on buff**	From £60 to £120

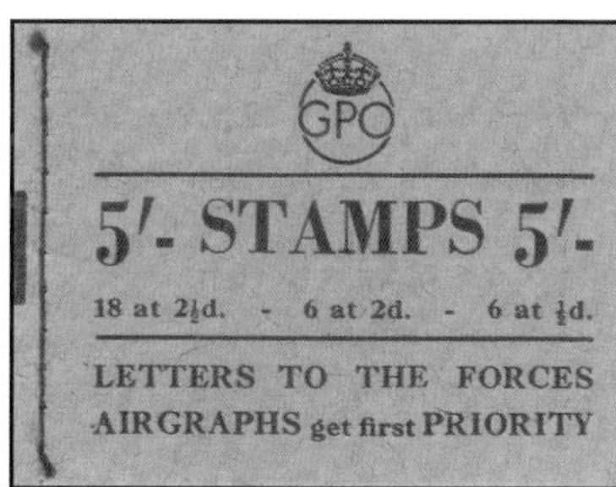

1951 (May) Edition dates May 1951 - Jan. 1952 (5). *Contents* BP74/74/74/73/61

BK79	**5s Black on buff**	£40

1952 (March) Edition dates Mar. - Nov. 1952 (5). *Contents* BP74/74/74/70/67/67/61

BK80	**5s Black on buff**	£30

1953 (Jan.) Edition dates Jan. - Mar. 1953 (2). *Contents* 74/74/73/70/64/61

BK81	**5s Black on buff**	£35

1944 (April) Edition dates Apr. - June 1944 (2). *Contents* BP60/60/60/59/55

BK82	**5s Black on buff**	£1250

1953 (May) Edition dates May - Sept. 1953 (3). *Contents* BP88/88/73/84/64/61

BK83	**5s Black on buff**	From £25

1953 (Nov.) Edition dates Nov. 1953 - Jan. 1954 (2). *Contents* BP88/88/73/84/64/61

BK84	**5s Black on buff**	From £25

1954 (March) Edition date Mar. 1954. *Contents* BP88/88/73/84/64/75

BK85	**5s Black on buff**	£600

1954 (March) Edition date Mar. 1954. *Contents* BP88/88/73/84/78/75

BK86	**5s Black on buff**	£125

Queen Elizabeth II Wilding Booklets

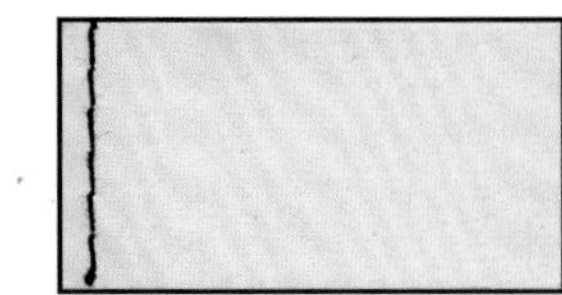

1953 (Sept.) Plain cover. *Contents* BP86/86/80/80/77/77

BK87	**1s White cover**	2.00

1957 (Nov.) Plain cover. *Contents* BP98/98/94/94/91/91

BK88	**1s White cover**	£10

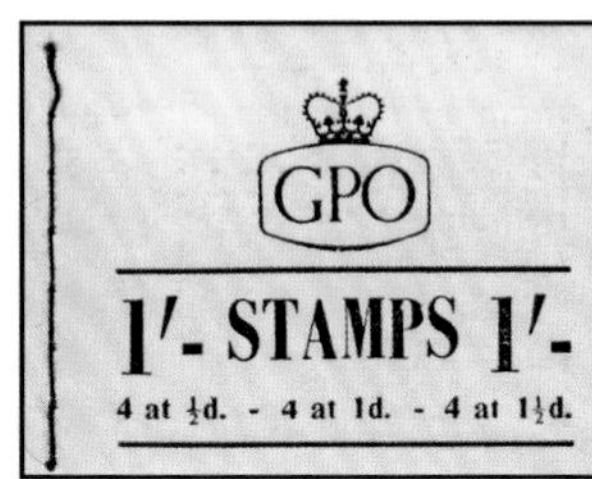

1954 (July) Oval G.P.O. emblem. *Contents* BP85/79/76

BK89	**1s Black on white**	3.00

1956 (July) *Contents* BP97/93/90

BK90	**1s Black on white**	2.50

1959 (Aug.) *Contents* BP109/107/105

BK91	**1s Black on white**	2.75

1959 (22 April) *Contents* BP103/97/93/90

BK92	**2s Black on salmon**	4.00

1960 (Nov.) Small G.P.O. emblem. *Contents* 113/109/107/105

BK93	**2s Black on salmon**	6.00
BK94	**2s Black on lemon** (2.61)	3.00

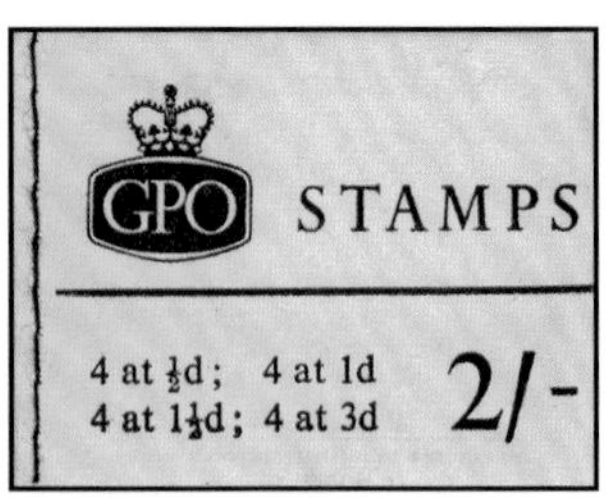

1961 (April) Edition dates Apr. 1961 - Apr. 1965 (17).
Contents BP125/124/123/122 or BP132/131/128/126

BK95	**2s Black on lemon**	£25

1961 (April). Phosphor issue. Edition dates Apr. 1961 - Apr. 1965 (13).
Contents BP156/155/154/153 or BP164/163/158/157

BK96	**2s Black on lemon**	From £45

BK97 Black stitching

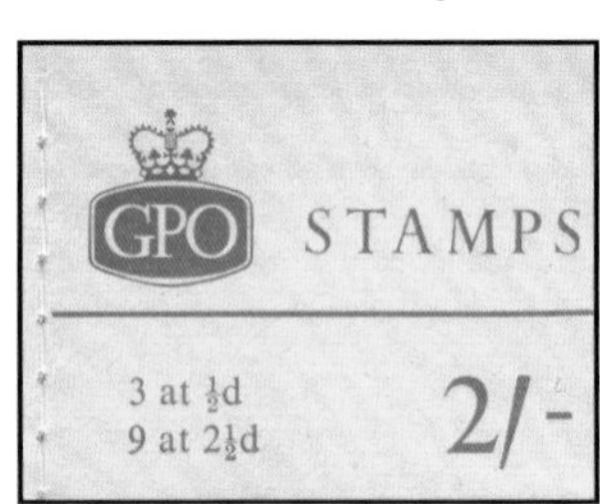

BK98 White stitching

1963 (July) Holiday resorts issue. *Contents* BP121/121/120

BK97	**2s Red on lemon** (black stitching)	1.75
BK98	**2s Red on lemon** (white stitching)	2.25

1964 (July) Holiday resorts issue. *Contents* BP127/127/127/127

BK99	**2s Red on lemon**	3.00

1965 (Aug.) Edition dates July 1965 - Jan. 1967 (7).
Contents BP133/129 or 130

BK100	**2s Black on orange**	1.25

1965 (Aug.) Phosphor issue. Edition dates July 1965 - Oct. 1967 (10).
Contents BP165/159 or 160

BK101	**2s Black on orange**	From 3.00

1965 (Dec.) Christmas Cards issue. *Contents* BP132/132

BK102	**2s Red on orange**	50

1967 (Nov.) Edition dates Jan. - Mar. 1968 (2). *Contents* BP165/161 or 162

BK103	**2s Black on orange**	1.50

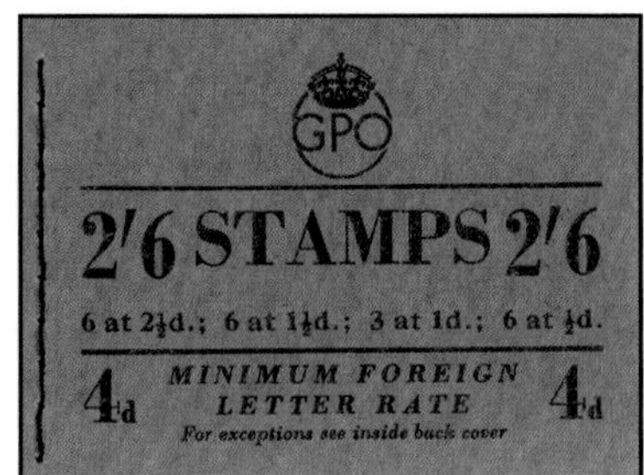

1954 (March) Edition date Mar. 1954. *Contents* BP88/84/81/75
BK104 **2s6d Black on green** £200

1954 (April) Edition dates Apr. 1954 - Jan. 1955 (10).
Contents BP88/84/82/75
BK105 **2s6d Black on green** £25

1955 (Jan.) Edition dates Jan. - Aug. 1955 (8). *Contents* BP88/84/83/75
BK106 **2s6d Black on green** £25

1955 (Aug.) Edition dates Aug. 1955 - June 1956 (8).
Contents BP88/84/83/75 or BP101/96/95/89 or mixed
BK107 **2s6d Black on green** £20

1956 (Feb.) Edition dates Feb.1956 - Mar. 1957 (12).
Contents BP101/96/95/89
BK108 **2s6d Black on green** £15

1957 (April) Edition dates Apr. - Dec. 1957 (9). *Contents* BP101/100/89
BK109 **2s6d Black on green** £15

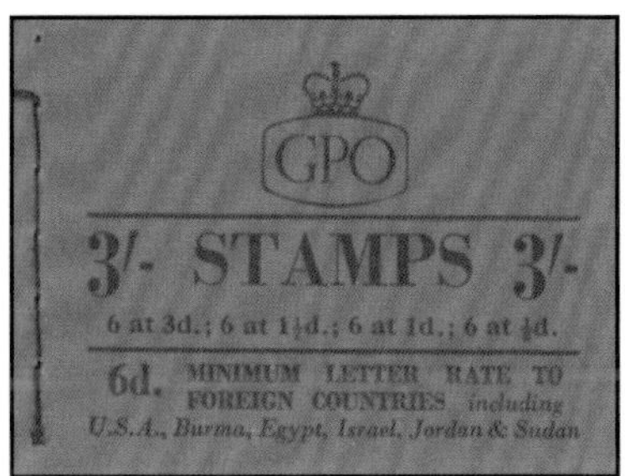

1958 (Jan.) Edition dates Jan. - Nov. 1958 (9). *Contents* BP102/96/92/89
BK110 **3s Black on red** £12

1958 (Nov.) Edition dates Nov.1958 - Jan. 1959 (3).
Contents BP102/96/92/89 or BP112/108/106/104 or mixed
BK111 **3s Black on red** £15

1958 (Dec.) Edition dates Dec. 1958 - Sept. 1959 (5).
Contents BP112/108/106/104
BK112 **3s Black on red** £15

1959 (Aug.) Graphite lined issue. Edition dates Aug. - Sept. 1959 (2).
Contents BP138/136/135/134
BK113 **3s Black on red** £125

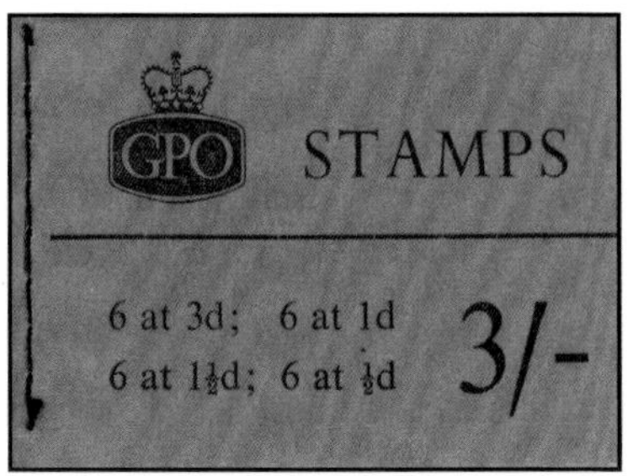

1959 (Oct.) Small G.P.O. emblem. Edition dates Oct. 1959 - Nov. 1960 (14). *Contents* BP112/108/106/104
BK114 **3s Black on brick red** £20

1959 (Oct.) Graphite lined issue. Edition dates Oct. 1959 - Apr. 1960 (4).
Contents BP138/136/135/134
BK115 **3s Black on brick red** £140

1960 (Aug.) Phosphor issue. Edition dates Aug. & Nov. 1960 (2).
Contents BP144/141/140/139
BK116 **3s Black on brick red** £35

1960 (Dec.) Large G.P.O. emblem. Edition dates Dec. 1960 - May 1965 (46). *Contents* BP112/108/106/104 or BP118/116/115/114
BK117 **3s Black on brick red** From £25

1960 (Dec.) Phosphor issue Edition dates Dec. 1960 - May 1965 (34).
Contents BP144/141/140/139 or BP149/147/146/145
BK118 **3s Black on brick red** From £35

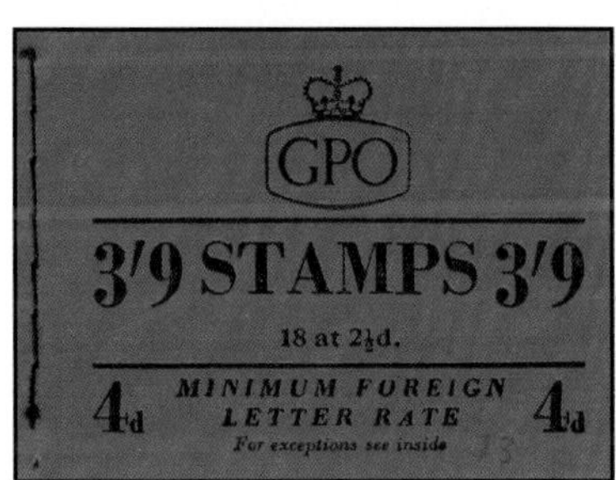

1953 (Nov.) Edition dates Nov. 1953 - Dec. 1955 (10).
Contents BP88/88/88
BK119 **3s9d Black on red** £20

1955 (Oct.) Edition dates Oct. and Dec. 1955 (2).
Contents BP88/88/88 or BP101/101/101 or mixed
BK120 **3s9d Black on red** £20

1955 (Oct.) Edition dates Oct. 1955 - Aug. 1957 (12).
Contents BP101/101/101
BK121 **3s9d Black on red** £15

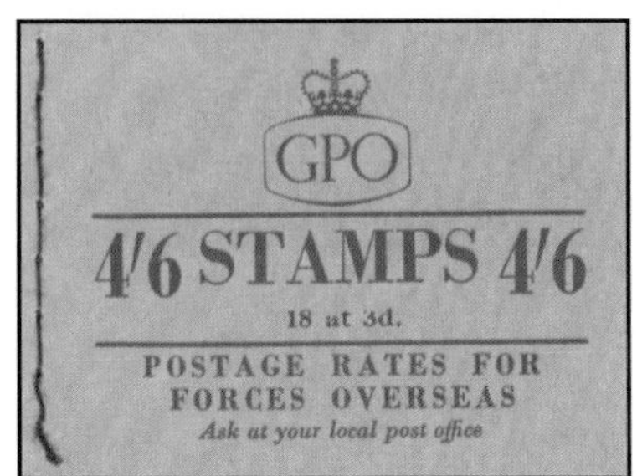

1957 (Oct.) Edition dates Oct. 1957 - Dec. 1958 (7).
Contents BP102/102/102
BK122 **4s6d Black on purple** £15
1958 (Oct.) Edition date Dec. 1958. *Contents* BP112/112/112
BK123 **4s6d Black on purple** £60

1959 (Feb.) Small G.P.O. emblem**.** Edition dates Feb. - Dec. 1959 (5).
Contents BP112/112/112
BK124 **4s6d Black on purple** £18
1959 (Feb.) Edition dates Feb.1959 - Oct. 1960 (9).
Contents BP112/112/112
BK125 **4s6d Black on violet** £18
1959 (April) Edition dates Apr.1959 - Apr. 1960 (4).
Contents BP138/138/138
BK126 **4s6d Black on violet** £18
1959 (Aug.) Edition date Aug. 1959 (5). *Contents* BP138/138/138
BK127 **4s6d Black on purple** £15
1960 (Aug.) Edition date Aug. 1960. *Contents* BP144/144/144
BK128 **4s6d Black on violet** £20

1960 (Dec.) Large G.P.O. emblem**.** Edition dates Dec. 1960 - Apr. 1965 (36). *Contents* BP112/112/112 or BP118/118/118
BK129 **4s6d Black on violet** £20
1961 (Feb.) Phosphor issue Edition dates Feb. 1961 - Mar. 1965 (31).
Contents BP144/144/144 or BP149/149/149
BK130 **4s6d Black on violet** £30

1965 (July) New contents. Edition dates July 1965 - Mar. 1967 (7).
Contents BP119/119/115
BK131 **4s6d Black on slate blue** £10
1965 (July) Phosphor issue. Edition dates July 1965 - Mar. 1968 (13).
Contents BP152/152/146
BK132 **4s6d Black on slate blue** £10

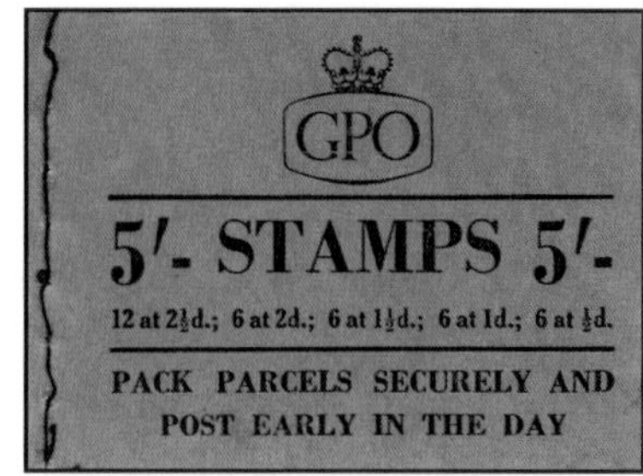

1954 (Mar.) Edition dates Mar. 1954 - Sept. 1955 (10).
Contents BP88/88/87/84/78/75
BK133 **5s Black on buff** From £25
1955 (Sept.) Edition dates Sept. 1955 - May 1956 (4)
Contents BP88/88/87/84/78/75 or BP101/101/99/96/92/89 mixed
BK134 **5s Black on buff** From £25
1955 (Sept.) Edition dates Sept. 1955 - Jan. 1957 (9).
Contents BP101/101/99/96/92/89
BK135 **5s Black on buff** From £20
1957 (Jan.) Edition dates Jan. - Nov. 1957 (6).
Contents BP101/101/100/96/92/89
BK136 **5s Black on buff** From £15
1958 (Jan.) Edition dates Jan. - Nov. 1958 (5).
Contents BP102/102/101/92/89
BK137 **5s Black on buff** From £15
1958 (July) Edition dates July - Nov. 1958 (2).
Contents BP102/102/101/92/89 or BP112/112/111/106/104 mixed
BK138 **5s Black on buff** From £15

1958 (Jan.) Small G.P.O. Cypher. Edition date Jan. 1959
Contents BP112/112/92/89 or BP112/112/111/106/104 mixed
BK139 **5s Black on buff** £15

1959 (Jan.) Edition dates Jan. 1959 - Nov. 1960 (10)
Contents BP112/112/111/104
BK140 **5s Black on blue** From £20

1959 (July) Graphite lined issue. Edition dates July 1959 - Sept. 1960 (3)
Contents BP138/138/137/134
BK141 **5s Black on blue** From £75

1960 (Sept.) Phosphor issue. Edition dates Sept. 1960.
Contents BP144/144/142/140/139
BK142 **5s Black on blue** £60

1961 (Jan.) Large G.P.O. Cypher. Edition dates Jan. 1961 - May 1965 (27). *Contents* BP112/112/111/106/104 cream or whiter paper.
BK143 **5s Black on blue** From £25

1961 (Mar.) Phosphor issue. Edition dates Mar. 1961 - Jan. 1962 (4). *Contents* BP144/144/142/140/139
BK144 **5s Black on blue** From £65
1962 (Mar.) Edition dates Mar. 1962 - May 1965 (20). *Contents* BP144/143/140/139 cream or whiter paper.
BK145 **5s Black on blue** From £50

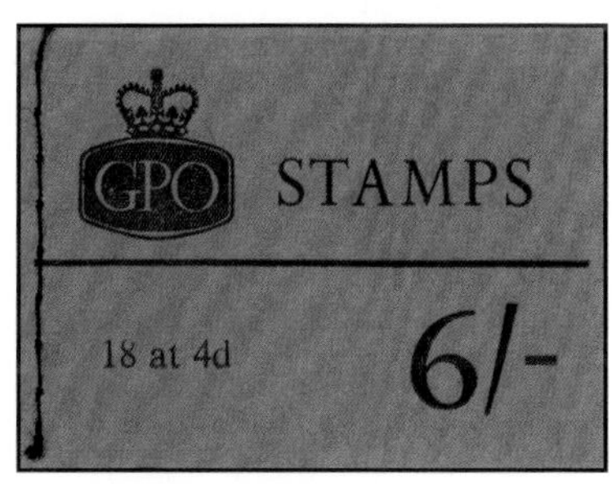

965 (June) Large G.P.O. Cypher. Edition dates June 1965 - Apr. 1967 (23). *Contents* BP119/119/119
BK146 **6s Black on claret** From £20

1965 (June) Phosphor issue. Edition dates June 1965 - Aug. 1967 (27). *Contents* BP152/152/152
BK147 **6s Black on claret** From £20

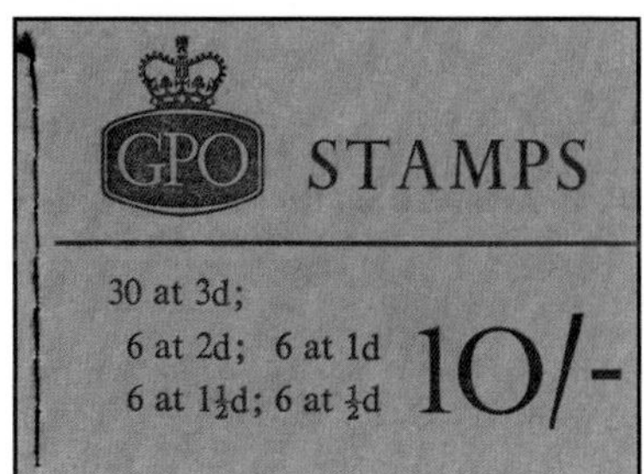

1961 (April) Undated. *Contents* BP112/112/112/112/112/110/108/106/104
BK148 **10s Black on green** £75

1961 (Oct.) Edition date Oct. 1961. *Contents* BP112/112/112/112/112/1 10/106/104
BK149 **10s Black on green** £85

1961 (April) Edition dates Apr. 1962 - Dec. 1964 (7). *Contents* BP118/118/118/118/118/117/116/115
BK150 **10s Black on green** From £55

1965 (Aug.) Edition dates Aug. 1965 - Nov. 1966 (5). *Contents* BP119/119/119/119/118/115
BK151 **10s Black on ochre** £15

1967 (Feb.) Edition date Feb. 1967. *Contents* BP152/152/152/152/150/146
BK152 **10s Black on buff** 5.00
1967 (Aug.) Edition dates Aug. 1967 and Feb. 1968 (2). *Contents* BP152/152/152/152/150/146
BK153 **10s Black on buff** 5.00

Machin Issues 1968 – 70

1968 (6 April) No watermark. Edition dates May - Aug. 1968 (3).
Contents BP176/171 or 172

BK154	2s	**Black on orange**	75

1968 (16 Sept.) Edition dates Sept. 1968 & Jan. 1969 (2).
Contents BP176/178

BK155	2s	**Black on grey**, Sept. 1968	60
BK155a		Jan. 1969	£130

1968 (16 Sept.) Edition dates Sept. 1968 & Jan. 1969 (3)
Contents BP177/178

BK156	2s	**Black on grey**	60
BK156a		Sept. 1968	£350

1969 (3 March) Edition dates Mar. - Dec. 1970 (12).
Contents BP180/181

BK157	2s	**Black on grey**	1.50

1968 (1 May) Large G.P.O. Cypher. Edition date May 1968.
Contents BP174/174/168

BK158	4s6d	**Black on slate blue**	6.00

1968 (July) - 70 Ships series. Printed in black on blue cover. G.P.O. emblem. *Contents* BP174/174/168

BK159	4s6d	**The Cutty Sark**, July 1968	1.50
Contents BP175/175/168			
BK160	4s6d	**Golden Hind**, Sept. 1968 (16.9.68)	1.50
BK161	4s6d	**Discovery**, Nov. 1968	1.50
Contents BP179/179/168			
BK162	4s6d	**Queen Elizabeth 2**, Jan. 1968 (6.1.69)	1.50
BK163	4s6d	**Sirius**, Mar. 1969	1.80
BK163a		May 1969	2.20
BK164	4s6d	**Dreadnought**, July 1969	2.20
BK164a		Sept. 1969	4.00
BK165	4s6d	**Mauretania**, Nov. 1969	3.50
BK165a		Jan. 1970	4.00
BK166	4s6d	**Victory**, Mar. 1970	3.00
BK166a		May 1970	7.00

1970 (Aug.) Crown emblem. *Contents* BP179/179/168

BK167	4s6d	**The Sovereign of the Seas**, Aug. 1970	3.00
BK167a		Oct. 1970	8.00

1968 (27 Nov.) - 69 English Homes series. Printed in black on cinnamon cover. G.P.O. emblem. *Contents* BP182/182

BK168	5s	**Igtham Mote**, Dec. 1968	1.75
BK169	5s	**Little Moreton Hall**, Feb. 1969	1.50
BK170	5s	**Long Melford Hall**, Apr. 1969	2.50
BK170a		June 1969	2.50
BK170b		Aug. 1969	3.00

1969 (Oct.) - 70 Crown emblem. *Contents* BP182/182

BK171	**5s**	**Mompesson House**, Oct. 1969	2.50
BK171a		Dec. 1969	2.75
BK172	**5s**	**Cumberland Terrace**, Feb. 1970	2.50
BK173	**5s**	**The Vineyard**, Saffron Waldon, June 1970	2.40
BK173a		Aug. 1970	2.40
BK174	**5s**	**Mereworth Castle**, Oct. 1970	3.50
BK174a		Dec. 1970	3.50

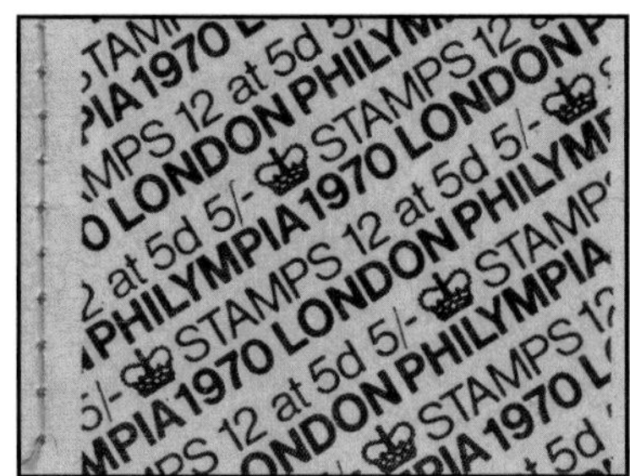

1970 (3 March) Philympia 1970, London. Red stitching.
Contents BP182/182

BK175	**5s**	Black on cinnamon	1.50

1967 (21 Sept.) - 68 Edition dates Sept. 1967 - Jan. 1968 (5).
Contents BP166/166/166

BK176	**6s**	**Black on claret**	£28

1968 (Feb.) Edition dates Feb. - May 1968 (4).
Contents BP166b/166b/166b

BK177	**6s**	**Black on claret**	£20

1968 (May) - 68 Edition date May 1968. *Contents* BP174/174/174

BK178	**6s**	**Black on claret**	£215

1968 (4 June) - 69 Birds series. Printed in black on orange cover. G.P.O. emblem. *Contents* BP174/174/174

BK179	**6s**	**Kingfisher**, June 1968	1.80
BK179a		July 1968	4.00
BK180	**6s**	**Peregrine Falcon**, Aug. 1968	1.50

Contents BP175/175/175

BK181	**6s**	**Peregrine Falcon**, Sept. 1968	2.00
BK182	**6s**	**Pied Woodpecker**, Oct. 1968	2.00
BK182a		Nov. 1968	2.25
Bk183	**6s**	**Great Crested Grebe**, Dec. 1968	2.25
Bk184	**6s**	**Barn Owl**, Jan. 1969	2.25

Contents BP167/167/167 (Gum Arabic)

BK185	**6s**	**Barn Owl**, Feb. 1969	£150

Contents BP167/167/167 or BP179/179/179 mixed

BK186	**6s**	**Barn Owl**, Feb. 1969	£50
BK187	**6s**	**Jay**, Mar. 1969	£50

Contents BP179/179/179 (PVA Gum)

BK188	**6s**	**Barn Owl**, Feb. 1969	2.00
BK189	**6s**	**Jay**, Mar. 1969	2.25
BK189a		May 1969	2.50
BK190	**6s**	**Puffin**, July 1969	2.50
BK190		Sept. 1969	4.50

1969 (Nov.) - 70 Crown emblem. *Contents* BP179/179/179

BK191	**6s**	**Cormorant**, Nov. 1969	3.00
BK191a		Jan. 1970	3.90
BK192	**6s**	**Wren**, Apr. 1970	3.00
BK193	**6s**	**Golden Eagle**, Aug. 1970	3.00
BK193a		Oct. 1970	3.90

1968 (25 Mar.) Explorers series. Printed in black on purple cover. G.P.O. emblem. *Contents* BP174/174/174/174/173/168

BK194	**10s**	**Livingstone**, May 1968	5.50
BK194a		Aug. 1968	5.50

1968 (16 Sept.) Printed in black on yellow green cover.

Contents BP182/182/175/175/169			
BK195	**10s**	**Scott**, Sept. 1968	3.75
Contents BP182/182/179/179/170			
BK196	**10s**	**Mary Kingsley**, Feb. 1969 (1.69)	3.00
BK196a		May 1969	4.50
BK197	**10s**	**Shackleton**, Aug. 1969	4.50
BK197a		Nov. 1969	5.25
Contents BP182/182/179/167/170 or BP182/182/167/179/170			
BK198	**10s**	**Mary Kingsley**, May 1969	£75

1970 (2 Feb.) Crown emblem. *Contents* BP182/182/179/179/170

BK199	**10s**	**Frobisher**, Feb. 1970	6.00
BK200	**10s**	**Captain Cook**, Nov. 1970	6.50

Decimal Machin Stitched Booklets

1971 (15 Feb.) - 74 Pillar Box series. Printed in black on old gold cover. *Contents* 2 x ½p *plus* 2 x 2p (½p below 2p), 2 x 1p *plus* 2 x 1½p (1p above 1½p). Panes MP4/MP6 (OCP/PVA)

MB1	**10p**	**London Pillar Box 1855**, Feb. 1971	2.75
MB2		April 1971 (19.3.71)	2.75
MB3	**10p**	**Giant Pillar Box 1856**, June 1971 (1.6.71)	2.75

Contents 2 x ½p *plus* 2 x 2p (½p at right), 2 x 1p *plus* 2 x 1½p (1p at right). Panes MP5/MP7 (OCP/PVA)

MB4	**10p**	**Giant Pillar Box 1856**, Aug. 1971 (14.7.71)	3.50
MB5	**10p**	**Standard Pillar Box 1857**, Oct. 1971 (27.8.71)	3.50

Contents Panes MP19/MP20 (FCP/PVA)

MB6	**10p**	**Standard Pillar Box 1857**, Dec. 1971	£25
MB6a		*Panes* OCP/PVA, FCP/PVA	£40
MB6b		*Panes* OCP/PVA, OCP/PVA	5.00
MB7	**10p**	**Penfold Pillar Box 1866**, Feb. 1972 (8.12.71)	8.00
MB7a		*Panes* OCP/PVA, FCP/PVA	£40
MB7b		*Panes* FCP/PVA, OCP/PVA	£25
MB8	**10p**	**April 1972** (24.2.72)	2.75
MB8a		*Panes* FCP/PVA, OCP/PVA	£25
MB9	**10p**	**Double Aperture Box 1899**, June 1972 (12.4.72)	2.25
MB10		Aug. 1972 (8.6.72)	2.25
MB11	**10p**	**Mellor Pillar Box 1968**, Oct. 1972 (2.8.72)	2.25
MB12		Dec. 1972 (30.10.72)	2.25
MB13	**10p**	**King Edward VIII 1936**, Feb. 1973 (5.1.73)	2.25
MB14		April 1973	2.25
MB15	**10p**	**Standard Pillar Box 1952**, June 1973 (18.4.73)	2.25
MB16		Aug. 1973 (4.7.73)	£12
MB17	**10p**	**Double Aperture Mellor Box**, Oct. 1973 (16.8.73)	2.25
MB18		Dec. 1973 (12.11.73)	4.50
MB18a		*Panes* FCP/PVA, FCP/Dex	£10
MB18b		*Panes* FCP/Dex, FCP/PVA	
MB18c		*Panes* FCP/Dex, FCP/Dex	2.50

Contents Panes MP31/MP32 (FCP/Dex)

MB19	**10p**	**Double Aperture Mellor Box**, Feb. 1974 (17.12.79)	1.25
MB19a		*Panes* FCP/PVA, FCP/PVA	12.50
MB19b		*Panes* FCP/PVA, FCP/Dex	£10
MB19c		*Panes* FCP/Dex, FCP/PVA	3.00
MB20	**10p**	**Philatelic Posting Box 1974**, April 1974 (22.2.74)	1.25
MB20a		*Panes* FCP/PVA, FCP/PVA	12.50
MB20b		*Panes* FCP/PVA, FCP/Dex	£10
MB20c		*Panes* FCP/Dex, FCP/PVA	3.00
MB21		June 1974 (23.4.74)	1.75

1974 (23 July) - 76 Postal Uniforms series. Printed in black on old gold cover. *Contents* 2 x ½p *plus* 2 x 2p (½p at right), 2 x 1p *plus* 2 x 1½p (1p at right). Panes MP31/MP32 (FCP/Dex)

MB22	**10p**	**General Letter Carrier 1793**, Aug. 1974	1.50
MB23		Oct. 1974 (27.8.74)	1.50
MB24	**10p**	**District Letter Carrier 1837**, Dec. 1974 (25.10.74)	1.50
MB25		Feb. 1975, (12.1.74)	1.50
MB26	**10p**	**Letter Carrier 1855**, April 1975 (26.3.75)	1.50
MB27		June 1975 (21.5.75)	1.50
MB28		Aug. 1975 (27.6.75)	1.25
MB29		Oct. 1975 (3.10.75)	95
MB30		Jan. 1976 (16.3.76)	95

1971 (15 Feb.) - 73 Veteran Transport series. Printed in black on mauve cover.

Contents 5 x 2½p *plus* label, 4 x 2½p *plus* labels, 5 x ½p *plus* label. Panes MP10 or 11/MP8 or 9/MP1 or 2 (OCP/PVA)

MB31	**25p**	**Knife-board Omnibus 1850**, Feb. 1971	5.50
MB32	**25p**	**B.-type Omnibus 1910**, June 1971 (11.6.71)	5.50
MB33		Aug. 1971 (17.9.71)	7.50
MB34	**25p**	**Showman's Engine 1886**, Oct. 1971 (22.11.71)	7.00

Contents Panes MP24 or 25/MP21/MP18 (FCP/PVA)

MB35	**25p**	**Royal Mail Van 1913**, Feb. 1972 (23.12.71)	6.00
MB36		April 1972 (13.3.72)	7.50
MB37	**25p**	**Motor Wagonette 1901**, June 1972 (24.4.72).	6.50
MB38		Aug. 1972 (14.6.72)	6.50
MB39	**25p**	**London Taxi Cab 1913**, Oct. 1972 (17.7.72)	6.50
MB40		Dec. 1972 (19.10.72)	6.00
MB41		Dec. 1972 Issue 'S' (6.11.72)	6.50
MB42	**25p**	**Norwich Tramcar**, Feb. 1973 (26.2.73)	8.00

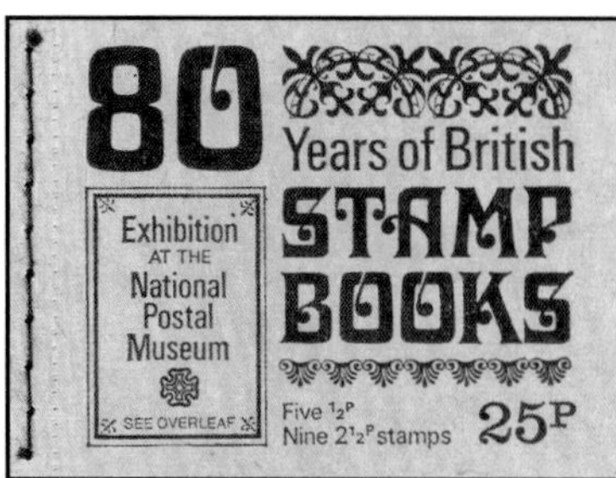

1971 (19 March) '80 Years of British Stamp Books'
Contents 5 x ½p *plus* label, 4 x 2½p *plus* labels, 5 x ½p *plus* label.
Panes MP10/MP8/MP1 (OCP/PVA)

MB43	**25p**	**Black on mauve**, April 1971	4.50

Help children
If it's children you care about most, help through Save the Children.
Help bring food, shelter, medical care, education and training–to millions of children throughout the world, including U.K.
Dept.SB5, The Save the Children Fund, 29 Queen Anne's Gate, London, SW1H 9DH.
Save the Children
STAMPS: 9at 2½P: 5at ½P
25P

1973 (7 June) 'Save the Children Fund'.
Contents 5 x ½p *plus* label, 4 x 2½p *plus* labels, 5 x ½p *plus* label.
Panes MP25/MP21/MP18 (FCP/PVA)

MB44	**25p**	**Black on mauve**, June 1973	8.00

1971 (15 Feb.) - 73. British Birds series. Printed in black on cerise cover.
Contents 5 x 3p *plus* label, 5 x 3p *plus* label. Panes MP14 or 15 (OCP/PVA)

MB45	**30p**	**Curlew**, Feb 1971	4.00
MB46	**30p**	**Lapwing**, June 1971 (26.5.71)	4.00
MB47		Aug. 1971 (23.7.71)	4.50
Contents Panes MP27/MP27 (FCP/PVA)			
MB48	**30p**	**Robin**, Oct. 1971 (1.10.71)	4.00
MB49		Dec. 1971 (10.11.71)	4.00
MB49a		*Panes* OCP/PVA, OCP/PVA	£10
MB50	**30p**	**Pied Wagtail**, Feb. 1972 (21.12.71)	4.00
MB51		April 1972 (9.2.72)	4.00
MB52	**30p**	**Kestrel**, June 1972 (12.4.72)	4.00
MB53		Aug. 1972 (8.6.72)	4.75
MB54	**30p**	**Black Grouse**, Oct. 1972 (31.7.72)	4.00
MB55		Dec. 1972 (30.10.72)	4.00
MB56		Dec. 1972 Issue 'S' (6.12.72)	4.00
MB57	**30p**	**Skylark**, Feb. 1973 (29.1.73)	4.00
MB58		April 1973 (2.4.73)	5.00
MB59	**30p**	**Oyster Catcher**, June 1973 (8.5.73)	4.75
MB60		Aug. 1973 (7.6.73)	6.00

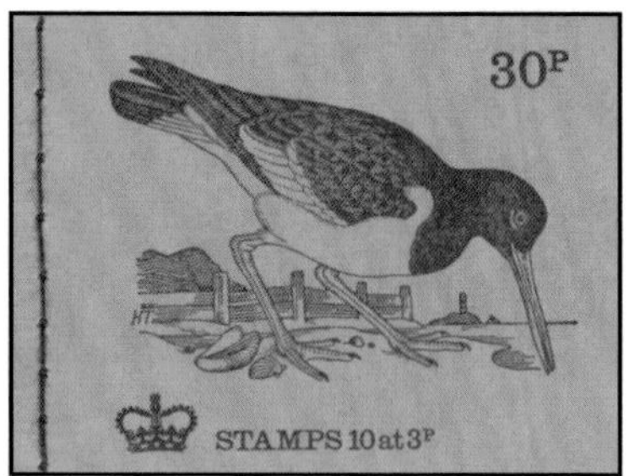

1973 (10 Aug.) Cover colours changed to black on buff.
Contents Panes MP27/MP27 (FCP/PVA)

MB61	**30p**	**Oyster Catcher**, Aug. 1973	5.00

1971 (19 March) '80 Years of British Stamp Books'.
Contents Panes MP14/MP14 (FCP/PVA)

MB62	**30p**	**Black on cerise**, April 1971	4.50

30P
Help children
If it's children you care about most, help through Save the Children.
Help bring food, shelter, medical care, education and training–to millions of children throughout the world, including U.K.
Dept.SB5, The Save the Children Fund, 29 Queen Anne's Gate, London, SW1H 9DH.
Save the Children
STAMPS 10 at 3P

1974 (30 Jan.) 'Save the Children Fund'. *Contents* 5 x 3p CB *plus* label, 5 x 3p CB *plus* label. Panes MP28/MP28 (FCP/Dex)

MB63	**30p**	**Black on red**, Spring 1974	8.00
MB63a		*Panes* FCP/PVA, FCP/PVA	5.00
MB63b		*Panes* FCP/PVA, FCP/Dex	£30
MB63c		*Panes* FCP/Dex, FCP/PVA	£20

1974 (21 June) 'Canada Life'. *Contents* Panes MP28/MP28 (FCP/Dex)

MB64	**30p**	**Black on red**, June 1974	4.50

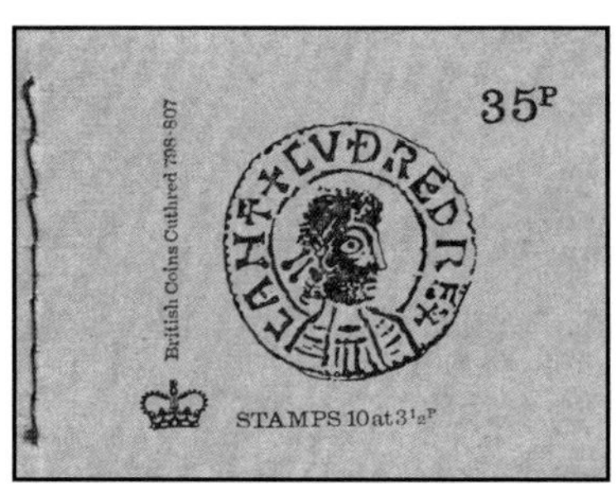

1973 (12 Dec.) - 74. British Coins series. Printed in black on blue cover. *Contents* 5 x 3½p *plus* label, 5 x 3½p *plus* label. Panes MP34/MP34 (FCP/Dex)

MB65	**35p**	**Cuthred Penny 798-807**, Autumn 1973	4.00
		Panes FCP/PVA, FCP/PVA	6.00
		Panes FCP/PVA, FCP/Dex	9.00
		Panes FCP/Dex, FCP/PVA	7.25
MB66		April 1974 (10.4.74)	4.75
		Panes FCP/PVA, FCP/PVA	6.00
		Panes FCP/PVA, FCP/Dex	12.50
		Panes FCP/Dex, FCP/PVA	£10
MB67	**35p**	**Silver Groat 1279**, June 1974 (4.7.74)	3.00
		Panes FCP/PVA, FCP/PVA	£15
		Panes FCP/PVA, FCP/Dex	9.00
		Panes FCP/Dex, FCP/PVA	9.00

1974 (23 Oct.) 'Canada Life'. *Contents* 5 x 3½p CB *plus* label, 5 x 3½p CB *plus* label. Panes MP35/MP35 (FCP/Dex)

MB68	**35p**	**Black on blue**, Sept. 1974	2.75

1974 (9 Oct.) British Coins series continued. Printed in black on buff cover. *Contents* 5 x 4½p *plus* label, 5 x 4½p *plus* label. Panes MP36/MP36 (FCP/Dex)

MB69	**45p**	**Gold Crown 1592-5**, Sept. 1974	4.50
MB70		Dec. 1974 (1.11.74)	7.50

1974 (26 Nov.) Cover colours changed to black on orange-brown

MB71	**45p**	**Gold Crown 1592-5**, Dec. 1974	6.00

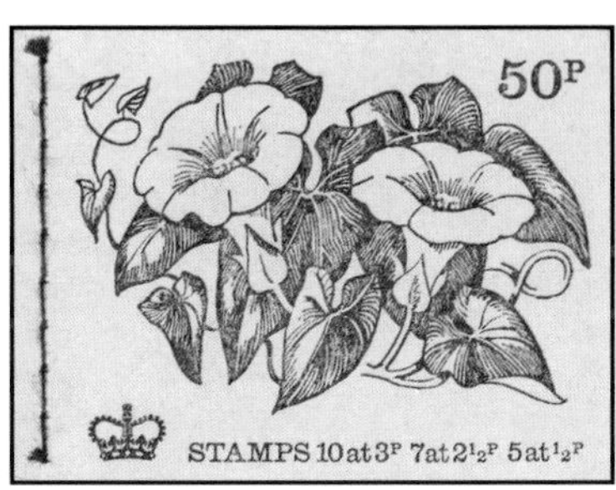

1971 (15 Feb.) - 72. British Flowers series. Printed in black on apple-green cover.
Contents 6 x 3p, 4 x 3p *plus* 2 x 2½p, 5 x 2½p *plus* label, 5 x ½p *plus* label. Panes MP16/MP13/MP12/MP3 (OCP/PVA)

MB72	**50p**	**Large Bindweed**, Feb. 1971	8.00
MB73	**50p**	**Primrose**, May 1971 (24.3.71)	7.50
MB74	**50p**	**Honeysuckle**, Aug. 1971 (28.6.71)	7.50

Contents Panes MP29/MP26/MP22/MP17 (FCP/PVA)

MB75	**50p**	**Hop**, Nov. 1971 (17.9.71)	8.25
		Panes OCP/OCP/FCP/FCP	£45
		Panes OCP/FCP/FCP/FCP	£75

Contents Panes MP29/MP26/MP23/MP18 (FCP/PVA)

MB76	**50p**	**Common Violet**, Feb. 1972 (24.12.71)	8.25
MB77	**50p**	**Lords and Ladies**, May 1972 (13.3.72)	7.50
MB78	**50p**	**Wood Anemone**, Aug. 1972 (31.5.72)	7.50
MP79	**50p**	**Deadly Nightshade**, Nov. 1972 (15.9.72)	7.50

1973 (19 Jan.) - 74. 'Canada Life'.
Contents Panes MP29/MP26/MP23/MP18 (FCP/PVA)

MB80	**50p**	**Black on apple-green**, Feb. 1973	6.00
MB81		April 1973 (26.2.73)	8.00
MB82		May 1973 (2.4.73)	8.50
MB83		Aug 1973 (14.6.73)	11.50

Contents 5 x 3½p *plus* label, 5 x 3p *plus* label, 5 x 3p CB *plus* label.
Panes MP34/MP34/MP33 (FCP/Dex)

MB84	50p	**Black on moss-green**, Autumn 1973 (14.11.73)	
		Panes PVA/PVA/PVA	7.50
		Panes PVA/PVA/Dex	£12
		Panes PVA/Dex/Dex	17.50
		Panes PVA/Dex/PVA	£25
		Panes Dex/PVA/PVA	£20
		Panes Dex/PVA/Dex	17.50
		Panes Dex/Dex/PVA	£12
MB85		**March 1974** (18.2.74)	4.50
		Panes PVA/PVA/Dex	£15
		Panes PVA/Dex/Dex	£15

1974 (13 Nov.) 'Canada Life'.
Contents 5 x 4½p *plus* label, 5 x 4½p *plus* label, 5 x 4½p *plus* label, 5 x 3½p CB *plus* label. Panes MP36/MP36/MP35 (FCP/Dex)

MB86	85p	**Black on cerise**, Sept. 1974	8.00

Prestige Books and Panes

Prices for panes are for the complete pane including stubs

1969 £1 'Stamps for Cooks'

1969 (1 Dec.) £1 'Stamps for Cooks' booklet. No watermark. Perf. 15 x 14

No.		U/M
PB1	Complete Book, stitched	7.50
PB1a	Complete book stapled	£250

Pane printed by Harrison on OCP/PVA

No.		U/M
SP1	**6 x 1d 2B Olive, 3 x 4d LB Vermillion, 3 x 4d RB Vermillion, 3 x 5d 2B Deep blue. Stitched.**	7.50
SP1a	Missing phosphor	£150
SP1b	Uncoated paper	£750
SP1c	**Stapled**	£35
SP1d	Missing phosphor (stapled)	£350

Pane printed by Harrison on OCP/PVA

No.		U/M
SP2	**15 x 4d CB Vermillion. Stitched.**	1.50
SP2a	Missing phosphor	£75
SP2b	Uncoated paper	£200
SP2c	**Stapled**	£20

No.		U/M
SP3	15 x 4d Red (CB) *plus* 'Method.....' label. **Stitched.**	1.50
SP3a	Missing phosphor	£100
SP3b	Uncoated paper	£110
SP3c	**Stapled**	£20

Pane printed by Harrison on OCP/PVA

No.		U/M
SP4	**15 x 5d 2B Deep blue** *plus* 'Method.....' label. **Stitched.**	1.50
SP4a	Broad bands	£550
SP4b	Missing phosphor	£110
SP4c	Uncoated paper	£200
SP4d	**Stapled**	£28
SP4e	Uncoated paper	£200
	First Day Covers (4)	£18
Varieties		
SP1e	'Specimen' overprint	£1400
SP2d	'Specimen' overprint	£325
SP3d	'Specimen' overprint	£325
SP4f	'Specimen' overprint	£450

1972 £1 'The Story of Wedgwood'

1972 (24 May). £1 'The Story of Wedgwood' booklet. No Wmk. Perf. 15 x 14

No.		U/M
PB2	Complete book	38.00

Pane printed by Harrison on FCP/PVA

No.		U/M
SP5	**12 x 3p 2B Ultramarine** plus label	2.75
SP5a	Broad bands	£165
SP5b	Missing phosphor	£175

No.		U/M

Pane printed by Harrison on FCP/PVA

No.		U/M
SP6	**3 x 2½p CB Magenta, 3 x 2½p RB Magenta and 6 x 3p 2B Ultramarine**	5.00
SP6a	Missing phosphor	
SP6b	Broad bands	

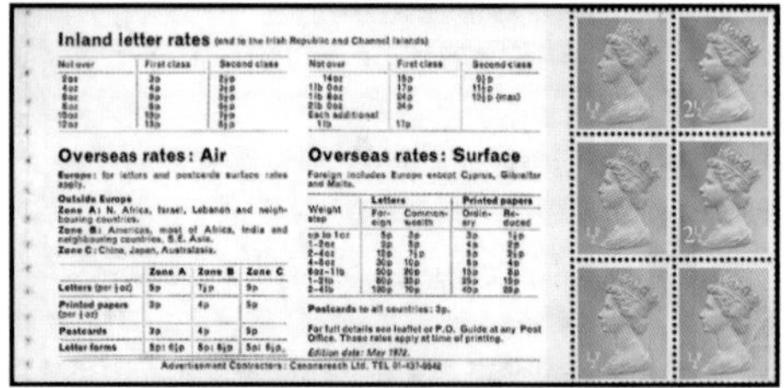

Pane printed by Harrison on FCP/PVA

No.		U/M
SP7	**3 x ½p 2B Turquoise, 3 x 2½p LB Magenta, 3 x 2½p CB Magenta** and **3 x 2½p RB Magenta**	6.00
SP7a	Missing phosphor	£1750
SP7b	Phosphor bands are printed on the back	£2500
SP7c	Broad bands	£375

Pane printed by Harrison on FCP/PVA

No.		U/M
SP8	**3 x ½p 2B Turquoise, ½p LB Turquoise** and **2 x 2½p LB Magenta**	£48
SP8a	Broad band left	
SP8b	Missing phosphor	

1980 £3 'The Story of Wedgwood'

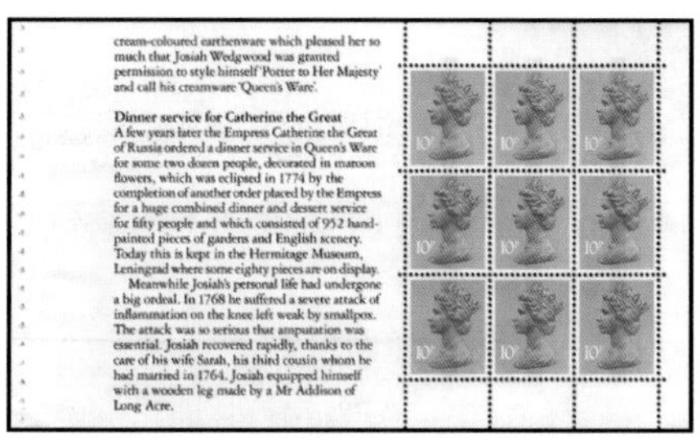

£3 book of stamps and story of Wedgwood
13 at 12p 13 at 10p 7 at 2p

1980 (16 April). £3 'The Story of Wedgwood' booklet. No wmk. Perf. 15 x 14

No.		U/M
PB3	Complete book	3.50

Pane printed by Harrison on FCP/PVAD

No.		U/M
SP9	**9 x 12p 2B Yellow green**	1.50
SP9a	Broad bands	£220
SP9b	Missing phosphor	£35
SP9c	Phosphor bands also printed on the back	£650

Pane printed by Harrison on FCP/PVAD

No.		U/M
SP10	**9 x 10p CB Orange**	1.40
SP10a	Missing phosphor	£40
SP10b	Phosphor bands also printed on the back	£600

Pane printed by Harrison on FCP/PVAD

No.		U/M
SP11	**6 x 2p 2B Deep green**	30
SP11a	Broad bands	£250
SP11b	Missing phosphor	£45
SP11c	Phosphor bands also printed on the back	£600
SP11d	6 x 2p Missing red (£1 Royal Mail Stamps, etc.) from booklet illustration on label.	£1300

Pane printed by Harrison on FCP/PVAD

No.		U/M
SP12	**2p 2B Deep green**, **10p LB Orange**, **3 x 10p CB Orange** and **4 x 12p 2B Yellow green** plus label	1.55
SP12a	Missing phosphor	£40
SP12b	Phosphor bands also printed on the back	£950
SP12c	Broad band	

1982 £4 'Story of Stanley Gibbons'

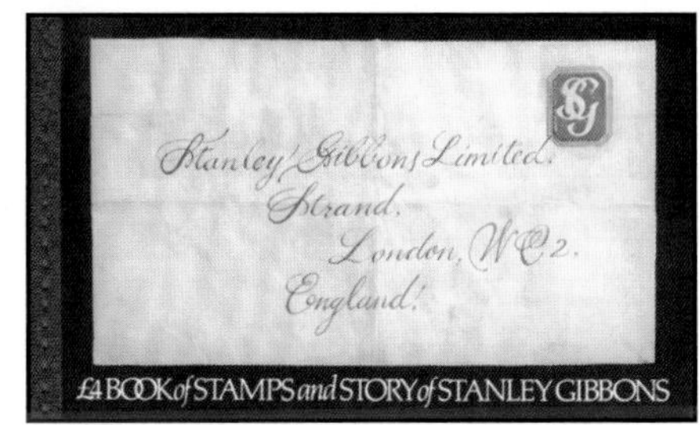

1982 (19 May) £4 'Story of Stanley Gibbons' booklet. No wmk. Perf. 15 x 14

No.		U/M
PB4	Complete book	4.50

Pane printed by Harrison on FCP/PVAD

No.		U/M
SP13	**6 x 15½p 2B Pale violet**	1.40
SP13a	Broad bands	£135
SP13b	Missing phosphor	£65
SP13c	Phosphor bands also printed on the back	£350

Pane printed by Harrison on FCP/PVAD

No.		U/M
SP14	**3 x 12½p LB Light emerald** and **3 x 12½p RB Light emerald**	1.40
SP14a	Broad bands	£500
SP14b	Missing phosphor	£40
SP14c	Phosphor bands also printed on the back	£375

Pane printed by Harrison on FCP/PVAD

No.		U/M
SP15	**2p 2B Deep green**, **3p 2B Magenta**, **3 x 12½p LB Light emerald**, **12½p CB Light emerald** and **3 x 12½p RB Light emerald**	2.20
SP15a	Broad bands	£150
SP15b	Missing phosphor	£75
SP15c	Phosphor bands also printed on the back	

Pane printed by Harrison on FCP/PVAD

No.		U/M
SP16	**9 x 2B 15½p Pale violet**	2.05
SP16a	Broad bands	£200
SP16b	Missing phosphor	£40
SP16c	Two phosphor bands also printed on the back	£950

1983 £4 'Story of the Royal Mint'

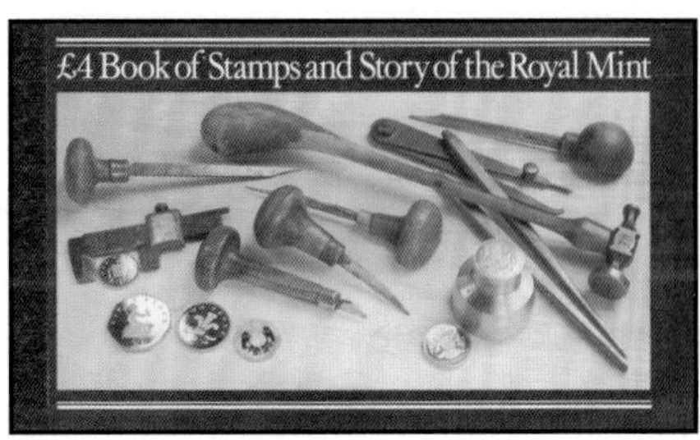

1983 (14 Sept.) £4 'The Story of the Royal Mint' booklet. Perf. 15 x 14

No.		U/M
PB5	Complete book	4.50

No. U/M

Pane printed by Harrison on FCP/PVAD

No.		U/M
SP17	**3 x 12½p LB Light emerald** and **3 x 12½p RB Light emerald**	1.20
SP17a	Broad band on column 2	£595
SP17b	Missing phosphor	£400
SP17c	Phosphor bands also printed on the back	£600

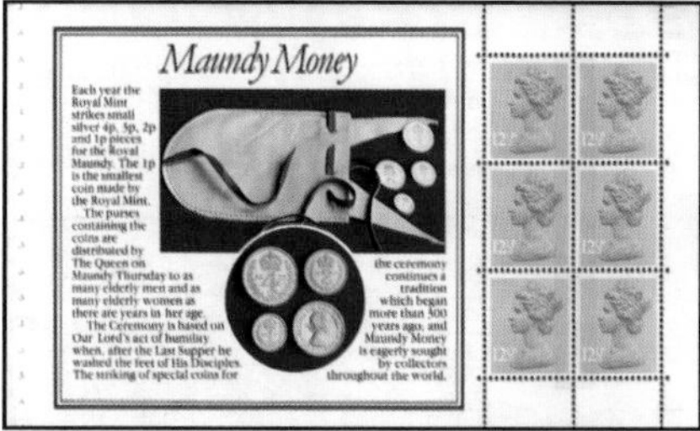

Pane printed by Harrison on FCP/PVAD

No.		U/M
SP18	**3 x 12½p LB Light emerald** and **3 x 12½p RB Light emerald**	1.20
SP18a	Broad band on column 2	£375
SP18b	Missing phosphor	£400
SP18c	Phosphor bands also printed on the back	£600

Pane printed by Harrison on ACP/PVAD

No.		U/M
SP19	**3p Magenta**, **3½p Dull chestnut** and **6 x 16p Deep drab**	2.40

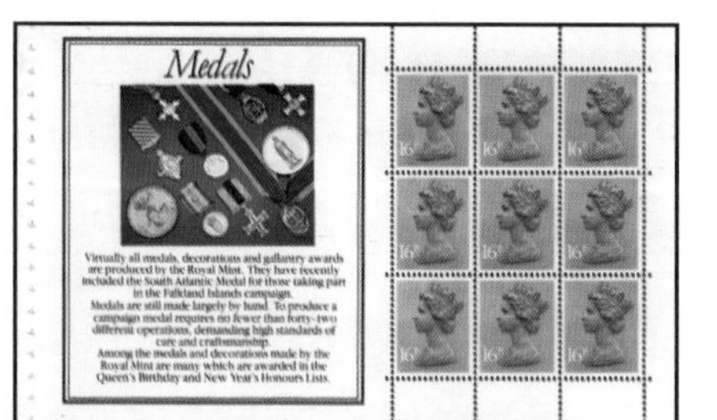

Pane printed by Harrison on ACP/PVAD

No.		U/M
SP20	**9 x 16p Deep drab**	1.90

No. U/M

1984 £4 'The Story of our Christian Heritage'

1984 (4 Sept.). £4 'The Story of our Christian Heritage' booklet. Perf. 15 x 14

No.		U/M
PB6	Complete book	15.50

Pane printed by Harrison on ACP/PVAD

No.		U/M
SP21	**6 x 17p Grey blue**	1.40
	First Day Cover (pane SP21 - stamps only)	4.50
	First Day Covers (4)	£13

Pane printed by Harrison on FCP/PVAD

No.		U/M
SP22	**3 x 13p LB Chestnut** and **3 x 13p RB Chestnut**	1.20
SP22a	Missing phosphor	£290

No.		U/M

Pane printed by Harrison on FCP/PVAD

SP23	**10p 2B Orange**, Type II, **13p Deep chestnut LB** and **7 x 17p 2B Grey blue**	£14
SP23a	Missing phosphor	
SP23b	Phosphor bands also printed on the back	

Pane printed by Harrison on FCP/PVAD

SP24	**3 x 13p LB Chestnut** and **3 x 13p RB Chestnut**	1.20
SP24a	Broad band on column 2	£400
SP24b	Missing phosphor	£325

1985 £5 'The Story of The Times'

1985 (8 Jan.) £5 'The Story of The Times' booklet. Perf. 15 x 14

PB7	Complete book	9.95

Pane printed by Harrison on ACP/PVAD

SP25	**6 x 17p Grey blue**	1.45

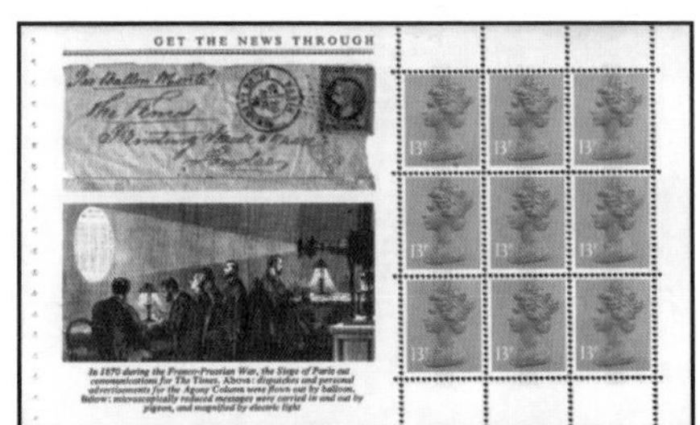

No.		U/M

Pane printed by Harrison on FCP/PVAD

SP26	**9 x 13p CB Chestnut**	1.70
SP26a	Missing phosphor	£550
SP26b	Phosphor bands also printed on the back	£1000

Pane printed by Harrison on FCP/PVAD

SP27	**4p LB Greenish blue, 4p RB Greenish blue, 2 x 13p LB Chestnut, 2 x 13p RB Chestnu, 2 x 17p 2B Grey blue** and **34p 2B Ochre brown**	5.95
SP27a	Broad bands on columns 2 and 3	£1350
SP27b	Missing phosphor	£2000
SP27c	Phosphor bands also printed on back	£3000

Pane printed by Harrison on ACP/PVAD

SP28	**9 x 17p Grey blue**	1.95

1986 £5 'The Story of British Rail'

1986 (18 March) £5 'The Story of British Rail' booklet. Perf. 15 x 14

PB8	Complete book	15.00

No. U/M

Pane printed by Harrison on ACP/PVAD

SP29	**9 x 17p Grey blue**	1.95
SP29a	9 x 17p Missing yellow from label (inscription, etc.)	£1250

Pane printed by Harrison on FCP/PVAD

SP30	**9 x 12p CB Emerald**	1.40
SP30a	Missing phosphor	£200
SP30b	Phosphor bands also printed on the back	£700

Pane printed by Harrison on FCP/PVAD

SP31	**3 x 12p LB Emerald**, **3 x 12p RB Emerald**, **2 x 17p 2B Grey blue** and **31p 2B Mauve**	8.50
SP31a	Broad bands	£1500
SP31b	Missing phosphor	£1400
SP31c	Phosphor bands also printed on the back	£1300

Pane printed by Harrison on FCP/PVAD

SP32	**6 x 17p 2B Grey blue**	1.45

No. U/M

1987 £5 The Story of P & O'

1987 (3 March) £5 'The Story of P & O' booklet. No wmk. Perf. 15 x 14

'A' phosphor ink.

PB9	Complete book	9.95

Pane printed by Harrison on ACP/PVAD

SP33	**9 x 18p Olive grey**	2.10

Pane printed by Harrison on FCP/PVAD.

SP34	**9 x 13p CB Pale chestnut**	1.60

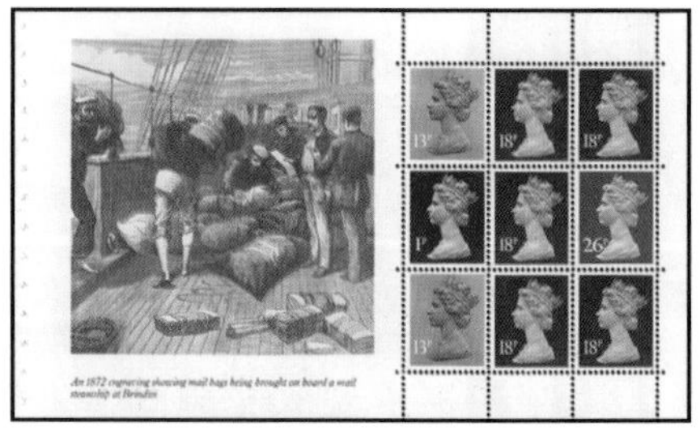

No.		U/M

Pane printed by Harrison on FCP/PVAD.

SP35	**1p Crimson** (RB), **2 x 13p Pale chestnut** (RB), **5 x 18p Olive grey** (2B) and **26p Rosine** (2B)	6.50

Pane printed by Harrison on FCP/PVAD.

SP36	**6 x 13p CB Pale chestnut** *plus* label	1.20

1989 £5 ' The Story of The Financial Times'

1988 (9 Feb.) £5 'The Story of The Financial Times' booklet. Perf. 15 x 14
Printer: House of Questa in Lithography

PB10	Complete book	16.00

Pane printed by Questa on ACP/PVAD

SP37	**9 x 18p Grey olive**	2.20
	First Day Cover (pane SP38 - stamps only)	4.50
	First Day Covers (4)	£14

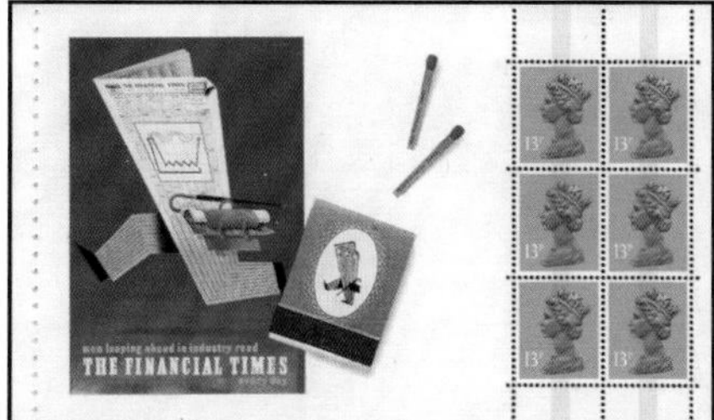

No.		U/M

Pane printed by Questa on FCP/PVA

SP38	**6 x 13p CB Pale chestnut**	1.70
SP38a	Missing phosphor	£500

Pane printed by Questa on FCP/PVA

SP39	**3 x 13p LB Pale chestnut, 3 x 13p RB Pale chestnut, 18p 2B Deep grey-olive, 22p 2B Yellow green** and **34p 2B Ochre brown**	10.75
SP39a	Broad bands	£1150
SP39b	Missing phosphor	£1150
SP39c	18p printed in blackish olive	£25
SP39d	Double print of 18p *1	£750

*1 This variety varies considerably due to the position of the second print

Pane printed by Questa on ACP/PVAD

SP40	**6 x 18p Grey olive**	1.50

1989 £5 'The Scots Connection'

1989 (21 Mar.) £5 'The Scots Connection' booklet. No wmk. Perf. 15 x 14
Printer: House of Questa in Lithography

PB11	Complete book	10.95

No.		U/M

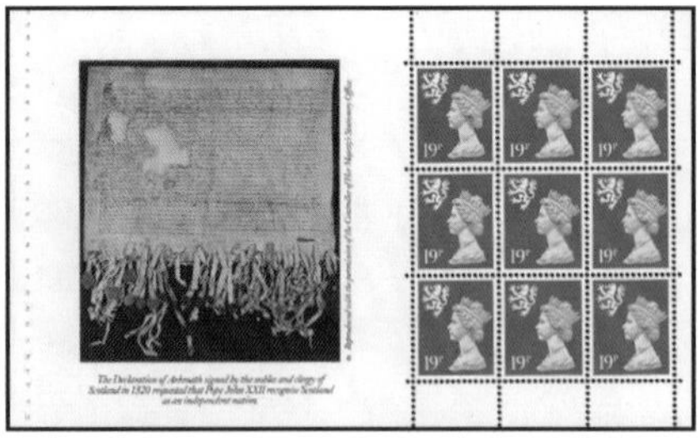

Pane printed by Questa on ACP/PVAD

SP41	**9 x 19p Orange red**	2.30
	First Day Cover (pane SP42 - stamps only	4.50
	First Day Covers (4)	£14

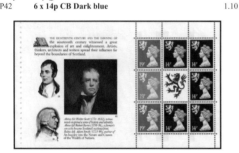

Pane printed by Questa on FCP/PVA

SP42	**6 x 14p CB Dark blue**	1.10

Pane printed by Questa on FCP/PVA

SP43	**5 x 14p LB Dark blue, 2 x 19p 2B Orange red** and **23p 2B Bright green** *plus* label	8.25
	Imperforate	£1400
	Error. Perforated as a pane of six	£2000

Pane printed by Questa on ACP/PVAD

SP44	**6 x 19p Scotland Orange red**	1.20

No.		U/M

1990 £5 'London Life'

1990 (20 Mar.) £5 'London Life' booklet. No wmk. Perf. 15 x 14
Printer: Harrison & Sons in Photogravure

PB12	Complete book	13.00

Pane printed by Harrison on ACP/PVAD

SP45	**4 x 20p Alexandra Palace**	1.10

Pane printed by Harrison on ACP/PVAD

SP46	**6 x 20p Black** Penny Black Anniversary stamp	1.40
	First Day Cover (pane SP45 - stamps only)	5.00
	First Day Covers (4)	£14

Pane printed by Harrison on FCP/PVAD

SP47	**15p RB Light blue, 20p 2B Black, 50p 2B Bistre, 2nd RB Light blue, 1st 2B Black, 15p 2B Light blue & 20p Black** (Penny Black Anniversary stamps), **20p 2B Black, 29p 2B Purple** *plus* label	9.90

No. | U/M

Pane printed by Harrison on ACP/PVAD

SP48 **6 x 20p Black** Penny Black Anniversary stamp 1.40

1991 £6 'Alias Agatha Christie'

1991 (19 March) £6 'Alias Agatha Christie' booklet. Perf. 15 x 14
Printer House of Questa in Lithography

PB13 Complete book 8.50

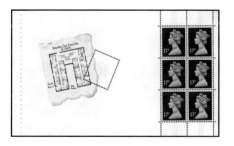

Pane printed by Questa on FCP/PVA

SP49 **6 x 17p CB Dark blue** 1.30
SP49a Missing phosphor

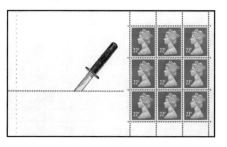

Pane printed by Questa on ACP/PVA

SP50 **9 x 22p Orange red** *plus* label 2.50
First Day Cover (pane SP51 - stamps only) 5.00
First Day Covers (4) £14

No. | U/M

Pane printed by Questa on ACP/PVA

SP51 **6 x 22p Orange red, 2 x 33p Emerald** *plus* label 4.40

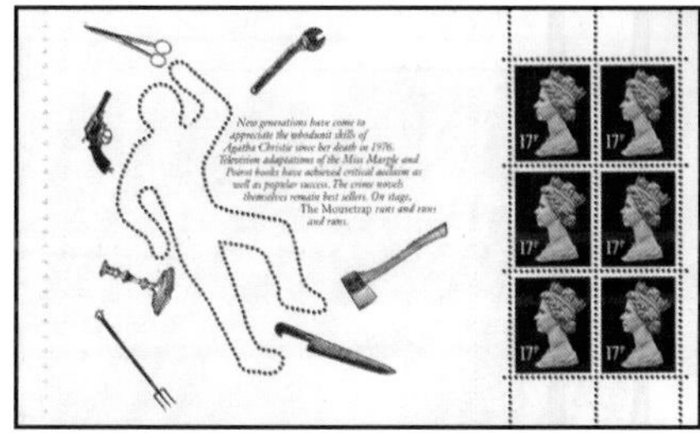

Pane printed by Questa on FCP/PVA

SP52 **6 x 17p CB Dark blue** 1.30
SP52a Missing phosphor

1992 £6 'Cymru Wales'

1992 (25 Feb.) £6 'Cymru Wales' booklet. Perf 15 x 14

PB14 Complete book 8.00

Pane printed by Harrison on ACP/PVAD

SP53 **4 x 39p 1992 Wintertime** 1.85

No.		U/M

Pane printed by Questa on FCP/PVA

SP54	**6 x 18p CBar Bright green**	1.10
SP54a	Missing phosphor	

Pane printed by Questa on FCP/PVA

SP55	**1 x 2nd RB Bright blue, 1st 2B Orange red, 2 x 33p 2B Emerald, Wales 2 x 18p RB Bright green, 2 x 24p 2B Chestnut**	5.90
SP55a	Missing phosphor	£3000
SP55b	Solid all over phosphor	£2500

Pane printed by Questa on ACP/PVA

SP56	**6 x 24p Wales Chestnut**	1.70

1992 £6 'Tolkien'

No.		U/M

1992 (27 Oct.) £6 'Tolkien' booklet. Perf. 15 x 14
Printer: House of Questa in Lithography

PB15	Complete book	8.00

Pane printed by Questa on ACP/PVA

SP57	**6 x 24p Brown**	1.70

Pane printed by Questa on FCP/PVA

SP58	**6 x 18p CB Bright green**	1.45

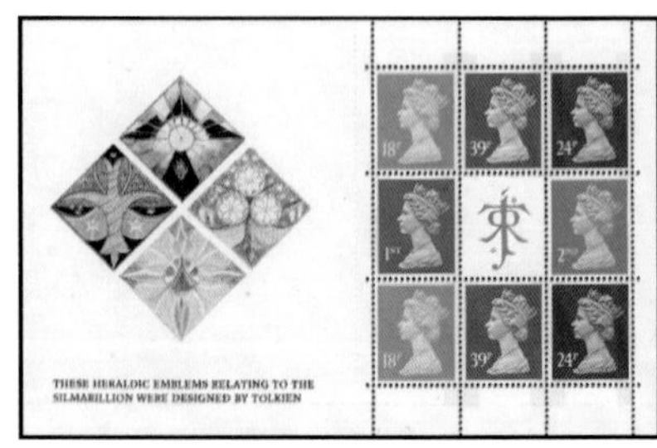

Pane printed by Questa on FCP/PVA

SP59	**2 x 18p RB Bright green, 2 x 24p 2B Chestnut, 2 x 39p 2B Bright mauve, 2nd CB Bright blue, 1st 2B Orange red**	5.70

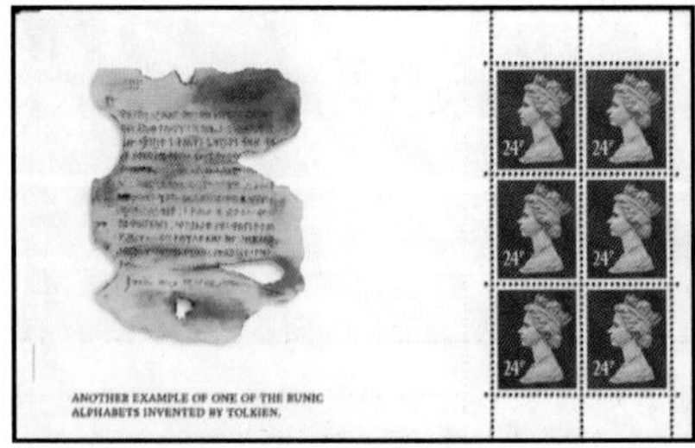

Pane printed by Questa on ACP/PVA

SP60	**6 x 24p Chestnut**	1.70

No.		U/M

1993 £6 'The Story of Beatrix Potter'

1993 (10 Aug.) £6 'The Story of Beatrix Potter' booklet. Perf. 15 x 14

PB16	Complete book	8.50

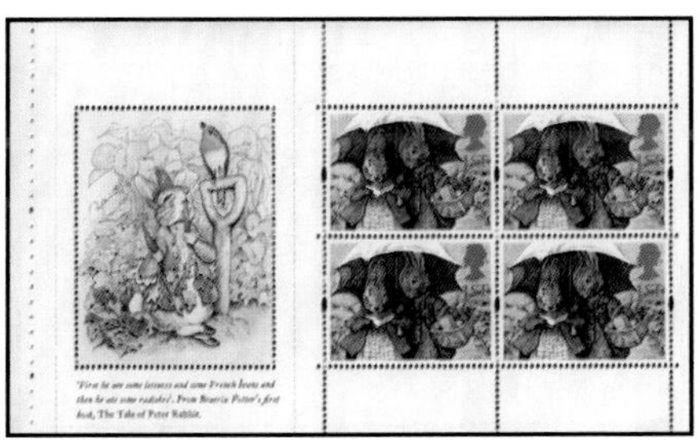

Pane printed by Harrison on OFNP/PVAD

SP61	**4 x 1st 2B 1994 Greetings**	1.10

Pane printed by Questa on OFNP/PVA

SP62	**3 x 18p LB Bright green, 3 x 24p 2B Chestnut** from Northern Ireland, Scotland and Wales	2.40

Pane printed by Questa on OFNP/PVA

SP63	**3 x LB 2nd Bright blue, 3 x 1st 2B Orange red**	2.20

No.		U/M

Pane printed by Questa on OFNP/PVA

SP64	**2 x 18p LB Bright green, 2 x 33p 2B Emerald, 2 x 39p 2B Mauve, 2nd LB Bright blue,** *plus label*	4.75
SP64a	Missing phosphor	£2250

1994 £6.04 'Northern Ireland'

1994 (26 July) £6.04 'Northern Ireland' booklet
Printer: Harrison & Sons in photogravure. Perf. 15 x 14

PB17	Complete book	12.00

Pane printed by Harrison on OFPP/PVAD

SP65	**4 x 30p Mourne Mountains**	1.40

No. U/M

Pane printed by Questa on OFNP/PVA

No.		U/M
SP66	**6p 2B Lime green, 19p LB Bistre, 4 x 25p 2B Salmon pink**	6.50
SP66a	6p Misplaced left	

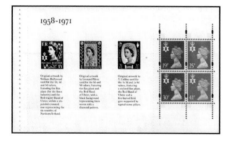

Pane printed by Questa on OFNP/PVA

No.		U/M
SP67	**2 x 19p LB Bistre, 4 x 25p 2B Salmon pink, 30p 2B Sage green, 41p 2B Stone** *plus* label	3.30

Pane printed by Questa on OFNP/PVA

No.		U/M
SP68	**19p LB Bistre, 25p 2B Salmon pink, 30p 2B Sage green 41p 2B Stone**	3.50
SP68a	Missing phosphor	

1995 £6 'The National Trust'

No. U/M

1995 (25 April) £6 'The National Trust' booklet

No.		U/M
PB18	Complete book	12.00

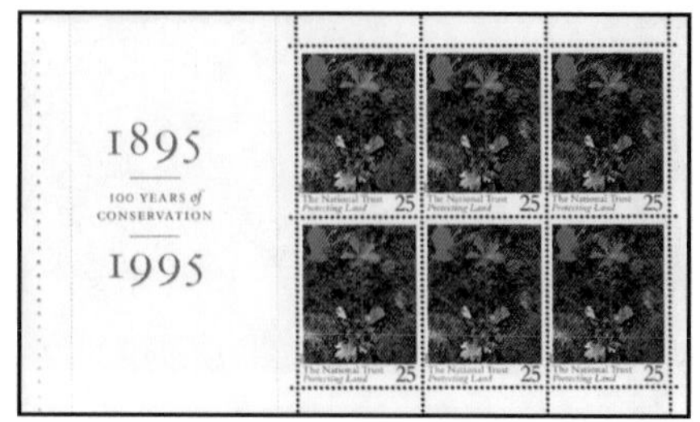

Pane printed by Harrison on OFNP/PVAD

No.		U/M
SP69	**6 x 25p 2B 1995 National Trust**	1.30

Pane printed by Questa on OFNP/PVA

No.		U/M
SP70	**10p 2B Dull orange, 19p LB Bistre, 19p RB Bistre, 2 x 25p 2B Salmon pink, 30p 2BSage green, 35p 2B Yellow, 41p 2B Stone** *plus* label	8.25
SP70a	Missing phosphor	

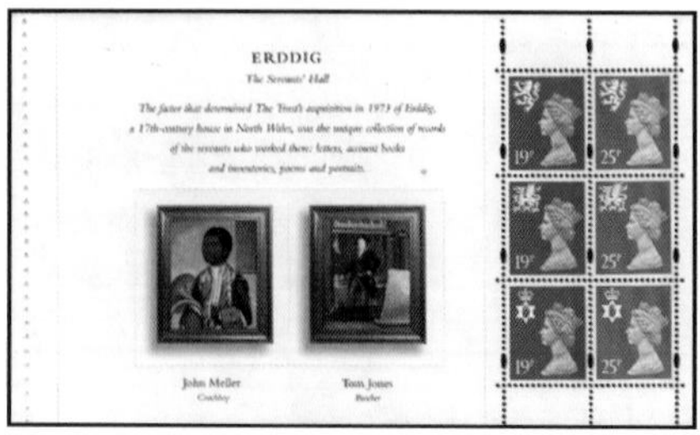

Pane printed by Questa on OFNP/PVA

No.		U/M
SP71	**3 x 19p RB Bistre, 3 x 25p 2B Salmon pink** from Northern Ireland, Scotland and Wales	3.50

Pane printed by Questa on OFNP/PVA

No.		U/M
SP72	**3 x 19p LB Bistre, 3 x 19p RB Bistre**	5.20

No.		U/M

1996 £6.48 'European Football Championship'

1996 (14 May) £6.48 'European Football Championship' booklet
Printer: House of Questa in Lithography. Perf. 14½ x 14

PB19	Complete book	8.00

Pane printed by Questa on OFNP/PVA

SP73	**4 x 19p CB 1996 Football**	1.40
SP73a	Missing phosphor	

Pane printed by Questa on OFNP/PVA

SP74	**4 x 25p 2B 996 Football**	1.40
SP74a	Missing phosphor	

Pane printed by Questa on OFNP/PVA

SP75	**2 x 35p 2B , 2 x 41p 2B , 2 x 60p 2B 1996 Football**	3.70

No.		U/M

Pane printed by Questa on OFNP/PVA

SP76	**2 x 25p 2B Salmon-pink, and 2 each x 25p** from Northern Ireland, Scotland and Wales (all 2B) *plus* label	2.30

1997 £6.15 '75 Years of the BBC'

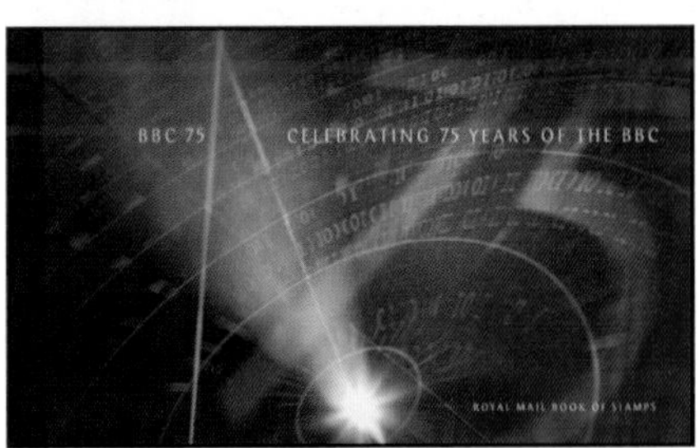

1997 (23 Sept.) £6.15 '75 years of the BBC' booklet
Printer: Harrison & Sons in computer-engraved gravure.
Perf. 15 x 14 elliptical

PB20	Complete book	9.25

Pane printed by Harrison on OFNP/PVA

SP77	**1 each x 26p 2B Red-brown** and **37p 2B Amethyst** from Northern Ireland, Scotland and Wales	2.90

No. U/M

Pane printed by Harrison on OFNP/PVA
SP78 **4 x 26p 2B Gold, 4 x 1st 2B Gold** *plus* label 2.70

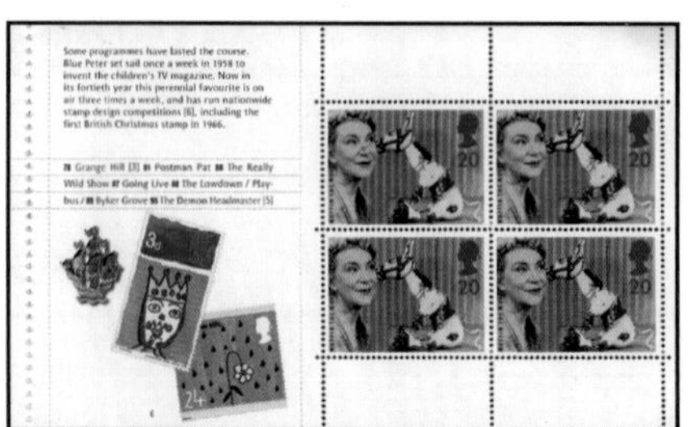

Pane printed by Harrison on OFNP/PVA
SP79 **3 x 20p RB Bright green, 3 x 26p 2B Reddish brown** 2.40

Pane printed by Harrison on OFNP/PVA
SP80 **4 x 20p CB 1996 Television** 3.50

1998 £7.49 'The Definitive Portrait'

1998 (10 Mar.) £7.49 'The Definitive Portrait' booklet
Printer: Walsall Security Printers in gravure.
Perf. 15 x 14 elliptical

PB21 Complete book 11.75

No. U/M

Pane printed by Walsall on OFNP/PVA
SP81 **9 x 26p 2B Brown** (wilding design) 3.40

Pane printed by Walsall on OFNP/PVA
SP82 **3 x 20p LB Pastel green, 3 x RB Pastel green** (Wilding design) 2.50

Pane printed by Walsall on OFNP/PVA
SP83 **2 x 20p LB Bright green, 2 x 20p RB Bright green** (Wilding design), **2 x 26p 2B Brown** (Wilding design), **2 x 37p 2B Red-purple** (Wilding design) *plus* 'National symbols' label 4.35

Pane printed by Walsall on OFNP/PVA
SP84 **3 x 26p 2B Brown** (wilding design), **3 x 37p 2B Red-purple** (wilding design) 4.20

No. U/M

1998 £6.16 'Breaking Barriers'

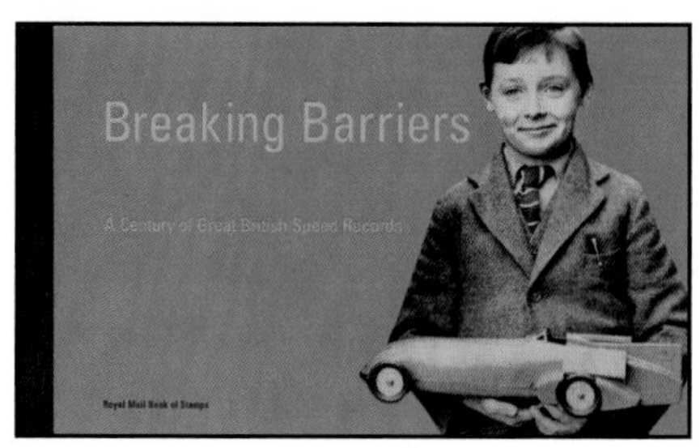

1998 (13 Oct.) £6.16 'Breaking Barriers' Booklet
Printer; Walsall Security Printers in gravure.
Perf. 15 x 14 elliptical

PB22 Complete book 13.50

Pane printed by Walsall on OFNP/PVA
SP85 **2 x 20p LB Multicoloured** and **2 x 20p RB Multicoloured** 2.20

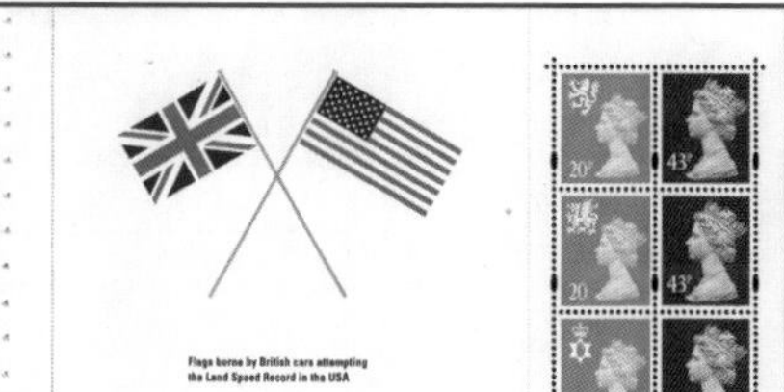

Pane printed by Walsall on OFNP/PVA
SP86 **1 x 20p RB** Country stamp from each of Scotland, Wales and Northern Ireland and **3 x 43p 2B Sepia-brown** 3.40

Pane printed by Walsall on OFNP/PVA
SP87 **3 x 2nd RB Bright blue** plus **1 x 26p 2B** Country stamp each from Scotland, Wales and N. Ireland 3.80

No. U/M

Pane printed by Walsall on OFNP/PVA
SP88 **2 x 10p 2B Deep orange, 3 x 2nd LB Bright blue, 3 x 43p 2B Chocolate-brown** *plus* label 5.50

1999 £7.54 'Profile on Print'

1999 (16 Feb.) £7.54 'Profile on Print' Booklet

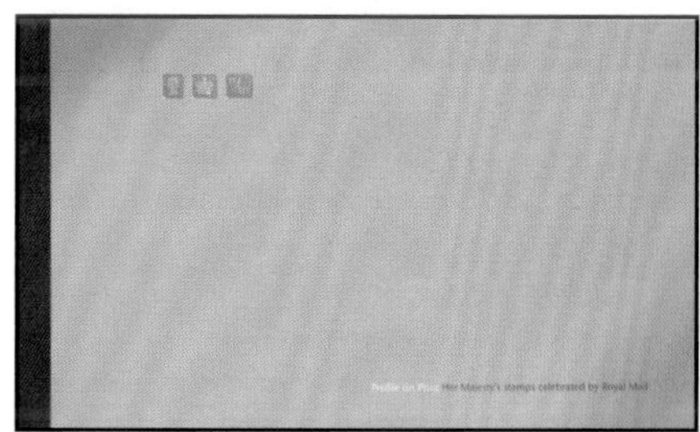

PB23 Complete book 14.50

Pane printed by De La Rue on OFNP/PVA
SP89 **8 x 1st 2B Orange red** *plus* label 3.00
SP89a Broad band left £80

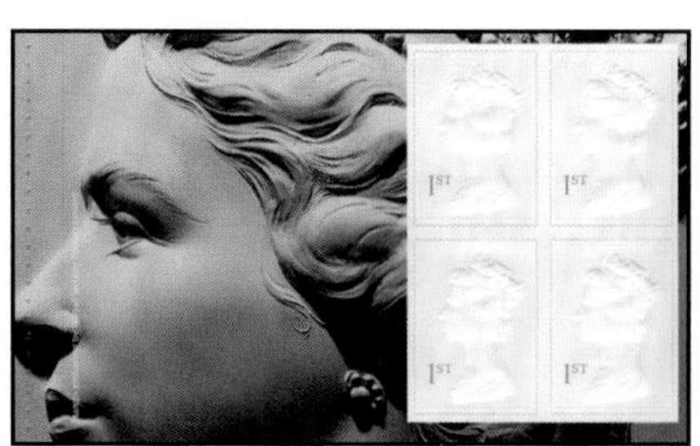

Pane printed by Walsall, Litho and embossed, on OFNP/PVA
SP90 **4 x 1st** 4.20

No.		U/M

Pane printed by Enschedé in Intaglio on Uncoated paper/PVA

SP91	**4 x 1st 2B Greyish-black**	4.20

Pane printed by Harrison by Letterpress on Uncoated paper/PVA

SP92	**4 x 1st 2B Black**	4.00
SP92a	Missing phosphor	

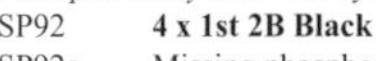

Pane printed by Questa in Litho on OFNP/PVA

SP93	**9 x 1st 2B Orange-red**	3.00

1999 £6.99 'World Changers'

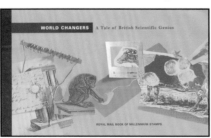

1999 (21 Sep.) £6.99 'World Changers' Booklet
Printer: Questa in gravure.

PB24	Complete book	15.00

No.		U/M

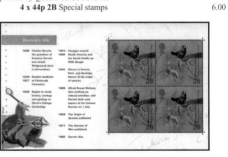

Pane printed by Questa on OFNP/PVA

SP94	**4 x 20p CB** Special stamps	1.20

Pane printed by Questa on OFNP/PVA

SP95	**4 x 44p 2B** Special stamps	6.00

Pane printed by Questa on OFNP/PVA

SP96	**4 x 26p 2B** Special stamps	4.90

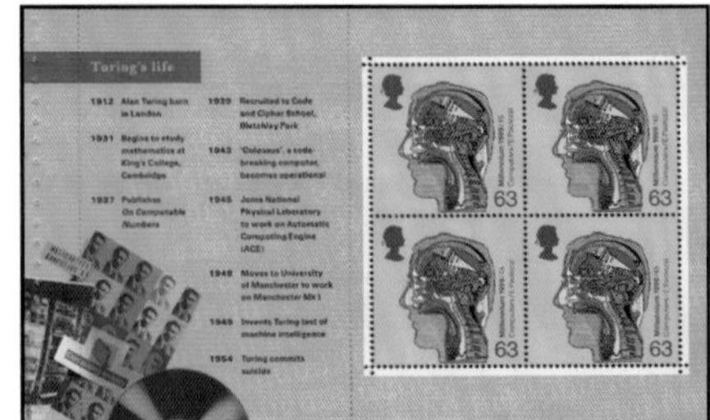

Pane printed by Questa on OFNP/PVA

SP97	**4 x 63p 2B** Special stamps	7.00

No. U/M

Pane printed by Questa on OFNP/PVA

SP98 **4 x 1p 2B Crimson, 3 x 19p CB Bistre, 1 x 26p 2B Chestnut** *plus* label 2.00

2000 £7.50 'Special by Design'

2000 (15 Feb.) £7.50 'Special by Design' Booklet
Printer: Walsall Security Printers in gravure.

PB25 Complete book 16.50

Pane printed by Walsall on OFNP/PVA

SP99 **8 x 1st 2B Millennium** *plus* label 3.20

Pane printed by Walsall on OFNP/PVA

SP100 **3 x 1st 2B Orange-red Scotland, 3 x 1st 2B Orange-red Wales** and **3 x 1st 2B Orange-red N. Ireland** 6.50

No. U/M

Pane printed by Walsall on OFNP/PVA

SP101 **4 x 19p RB Bistre** and **2 x 38p 2B Ultramarine** 7.50

Pane printed by Walsall on OFNP/PVA

SP102 **6 x 1st 2B Black & buff** 3.70

2000 £7.03 'The Life of the Century'

2000 (4 Aug.) £7.03 'The Life of the Century' booklet
Printer: Walsall Security Printers in gravure.

PB26 Complete book 12.50

Pane printed by Walsall on OFNP/PVA

SP103 **6 x 2nd CB Scotland emblem, 2 x 65p 2B Scotland emblem** *plus* label 3.60

No.		U/M

Pane printed by Walsall on OFNP/PVA
SP104 **9 x 1st 2B Millennium** 3.75

Pane printed by Walsall on OFNP/PVA
SP105 **4 x 27p 2B Special stamps** 5.00

Pane printed by Walsall on OFNP/PVA
SP106 **4 x 27p 2B Special stamps** 4.60

2000 £7 'A Treasury of Trees'

2000 (18 Sep.) £7.00 'A Treasury of Trees' Booklet
Printer: Walsall Security Printers in gravure.

PB27 Complete book 12.95

No.		U/M

Pane printed by Walsall on OFNP/PVA
SP107 **2 x 65p 2B Special stamps** 2.00

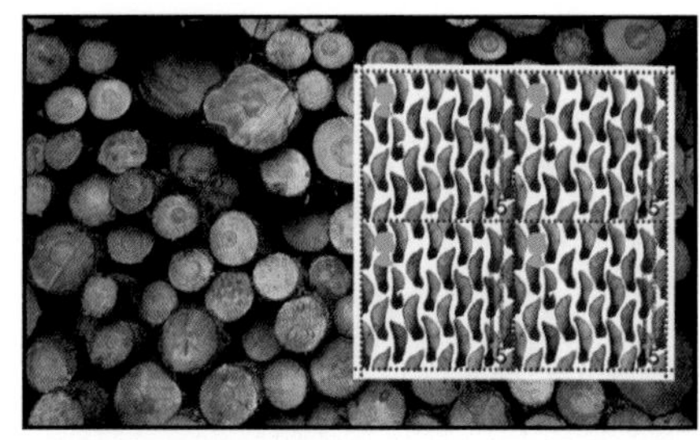

Pane printed by Walsall on OFNP/PVA
SP108 **4 x 45p 2B Special stamps** 2.80

Pane printed by Walsall on OFNP/PVA
SP109 **2 x 65p 2B Special stamps** 2.10

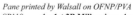

Pane printed by Walsall on OFNP/PVA
SP110 **4 x 1st 2B Millennium, 4 x 2nd CB Wales emblem** *plus* label 4.20

No.		U/M

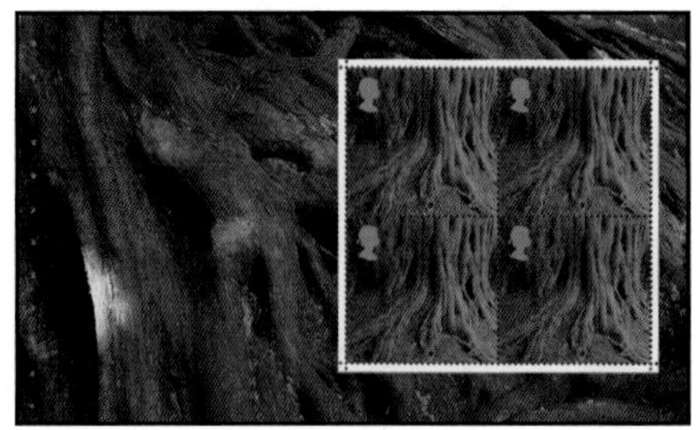

Pane printed by Walsall on OFNP/PVA
SP111 **4 x 2nd CB Special stamps** 1.70

2001 £6.76 'Unseen and Unheard'

2001 (22 Oct.) £6.76 'Unseen and Unheard' Booklet
Printer: Walsall Security Printers in gravure.

PB28 Complete book 14.50

Pane printed by Walsall on OFNP/PVA
SP112 **2 x 1st 2B Special stamps** and **2 x 65p 2B Special stamps** 5.20

Pane printed by Walsall on OFNP/PVA
SP113 **2 x 2nd CB Special stamps** and **2 x 45p 2B Special stamps** 4.50

No.		U/M

Pane printed by Walsall on OFNP/PVA
SP114 **4 x 1st 2B Special stamps** 2.40

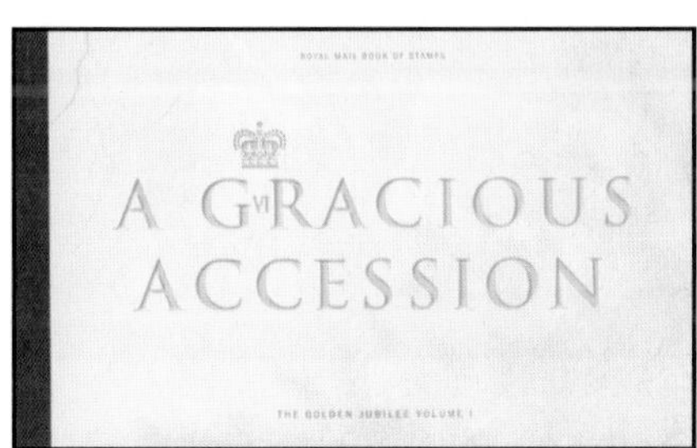

Pane printed by Walsall on OFNP/PVA
SP115 **4 x 1st 2B Scotland emblem, 4 x 'E' 2B Scotland emblem** *plus* label 4.00

2002 £7.29 'A Gracious Accession'

2002 (6 Feb) £7.29 'A Gracious Accession' Booklet
Printer: Walsall Security Printers in gravure.

PB29 Complete book 15.00

Pane printed by Walsall on OFNP/PVA
SP116 **4 x 'E' 2B Dark blue, 4 x 2nd CB Bright blue** *plus* label 4.50

No.		U/M

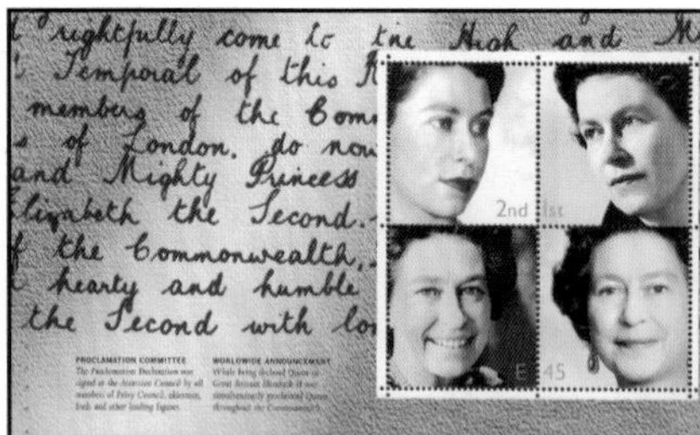

Pane printed by Walsall on OFNP/PVA

No.		U/M
SP117	**1 x 2nd CB**, **1 x 1st 2B**, 1 x **'E' 2B** and **1 x 45p 2B** Special stamps	3.80

Pane printed by Walsall on OFNP/PVA

No.		U/M
SP118	**1 x 1st 2B, 1 x 'E' 2B**, 1 x **45p 2B** and **1 x 65p 2B** Special stamps	3.80

Pane printed by Walsall on OFNP/PVA

No.		U/M
SP119	**4 x 1st 2B (Wilding), 4 x 2nd CB (Wilding)** *plus* blank label	4.50

2002 £6.83 'Across the Universe'

2002 (24 Sep.) £6.83 'Across the Universe' Booklet
Printer: Walsall Security Printers in gravure.

No.		U/M
PB30	Complete book	11.25

Pane printed by Walsall on OFNP/PVA

No.		U/M
SP120	**4 x 1st 2B England emblem, 4 x 2nd CB England emblem** and **1 x 1st 2B Scotland emblem**	4.00

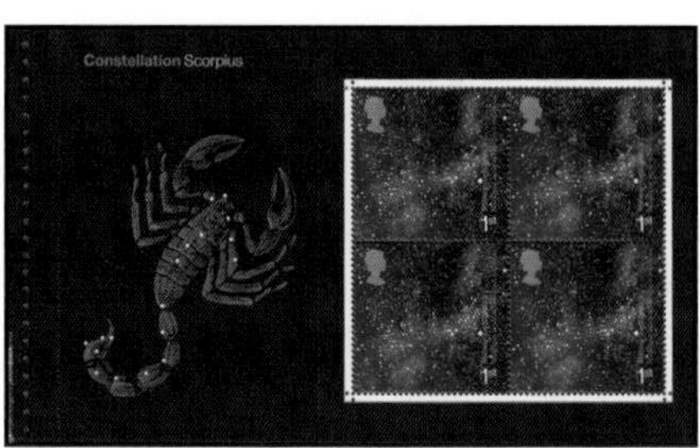

Pane printed by Walsall on OFNP/PVA

No.		U/M
SP121	**4 x 1st 2B Special stamps**	2.25

Pane printed by Walsall on OFNP/PVA

No.		U/M
SP122	**4 x 1st 2B Gold**, **4 x 'E' 2B** *plus* label	3.25

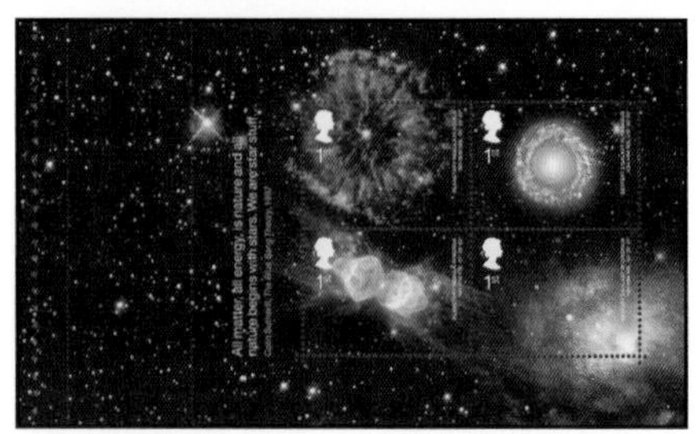

Pane printed by Walsall on OFNP/PVA

No.		U/M
SP123	**4 x 1st 2B Special stamps**	2.25

No. U/M

2003 £6.99 'Microcosmos'

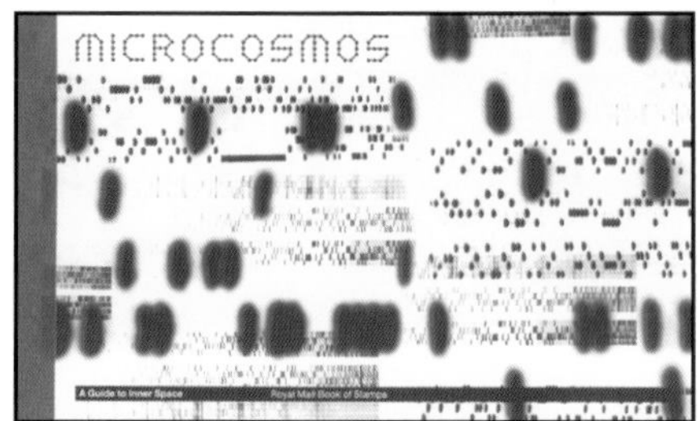

2003 (25 Feb.) £6.99 'Microcosmos' Booklet

PB31 Complete book 10.00

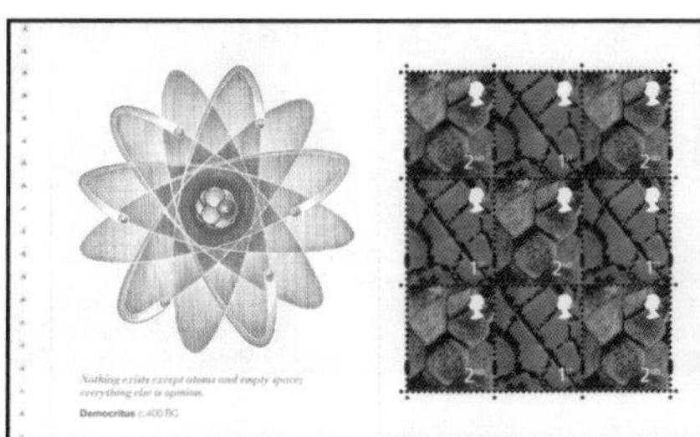

Pane printed by Enschedé in Litho on OFNP/PVA

SP124 **4 x 1st 2B N. Ireland emblem, 5 x 2nd CB N. Ireland emblem** 3.00

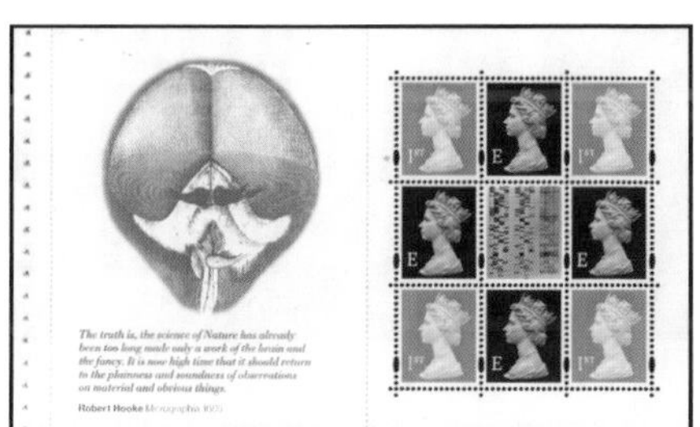

Pane printed by Enschedé in Gravure on OFNP/PVA.

SP125 **4 x 1st 2B Gold, 4 x 'E' 2B Dark blue** *plus* label 3.75

Pane printed by Enschedé in Litho on OFNP/PVA

SP126 **2 x 2nd CB Special stamps** and **2 x 1st 2B Special stamps** 1.25

No. U/M

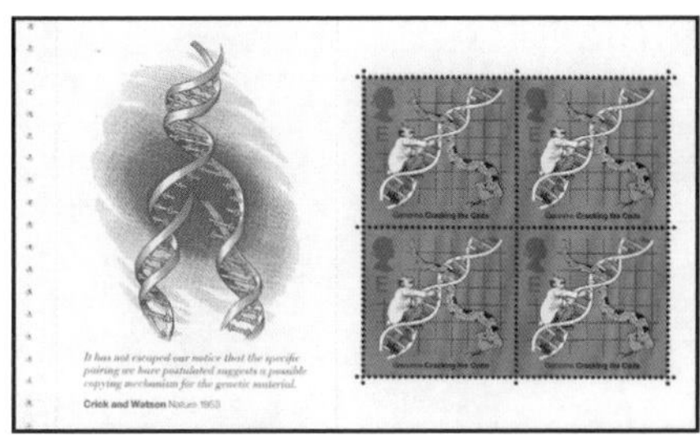

Pane printed by Enschedé in Litho on OFNP/PVA

SP127 **4 x E 2B Special stamps** 2.60

2003 £7.46 'A Perfect Coronation'

2003 (2 June) £7.46 'A Perfect Coronation'

Printer: Walsall Security Printers in gravure.

PB32 Complete book 35.00

Pane printed by Walsall on OFNP/PVA

SP128 **4 x 1st 2B Gold, 4 x 2nd CB Bright blue** *plus* label 3.75

Pane printed by Walsall on OFNP/PVA

SP129 **4 x 1st 2B Special stamps** 1.80

No. U/M

Pane printed by Walsall on OFNP/PVA

SP130 **4 x 1st 2B Special stamps** 1.80

Pane printed by Walsall on OFNP/PVA

SP131 **2 x 47p 2B Wilding design, 2 x 68p 2B Wilding design** and **£1 2B 'Dulac' design** 27.00

2004 £7.44 'Letters by Night'

2004 (16 Mar.) £7.44 'Letters by Night'
Printer: De La Rue in gravure.

PB33 Complete book 11.50
PB33a Pane 6 omitted plus 2 copies of Pane 5 35.00

Pane printed by De la Rue in Gravure on OFNP/PVA

SP132 **3 x 2nd CB Scotland emblem** and **3 x 68p 2B England emblem** (2B) 4.00

No. U/M

Pane printed by De la Rue in Litho on OFNP/PVA

SP133 **1 x 28p 2B Locomotive, 1 x 'E' 2B Locomotive** and **1 x 42p 2B Locomotive** 3.00

Pane printed by De la Rue in Gravure on OFNP/PVA

SP134 **4 x 1st 'The station' 2B** 2.00

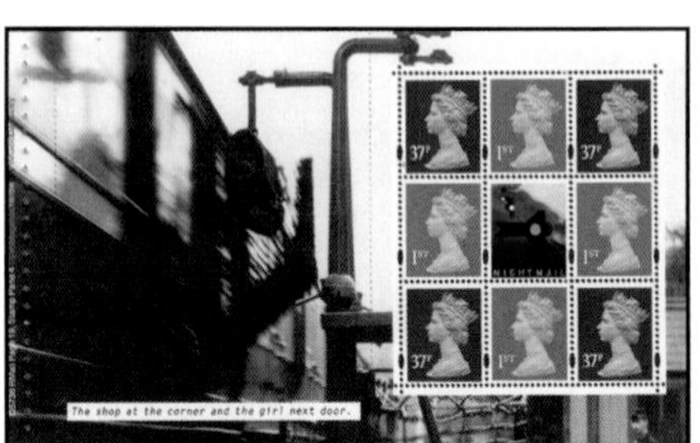

Pane printed by De la Rue in Gravure on OFNP/PVA

SP135 **4 x 37p 2B Black, 4 x 1st 2B Gold** *plus* label 4.00

2004 £7.23 'The Glory of the Garden'

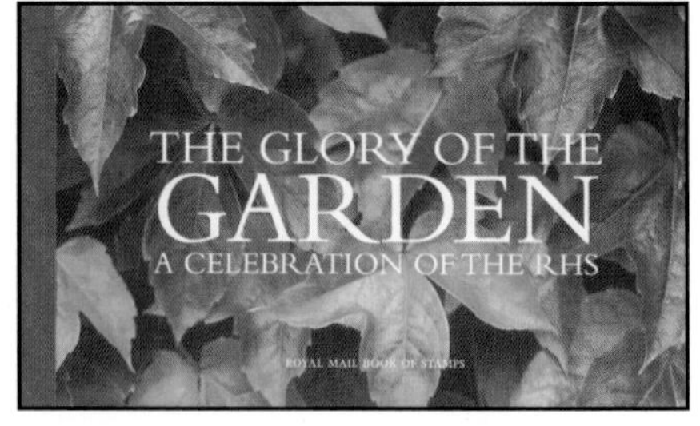

2004 (25 May) £7.23 'The Glory of the Garden'
Printer: Enschedé in gravure.

PB34 Complete book 12.00

No. | U/M

Pane printed by Enschedé in Gravure on OFNP/PVA
SP136 **4 x 1st 2B Gold, 2 x 42p 2B Sage-green, 2 x 47p 2B Sea green** *plus label* 4.50

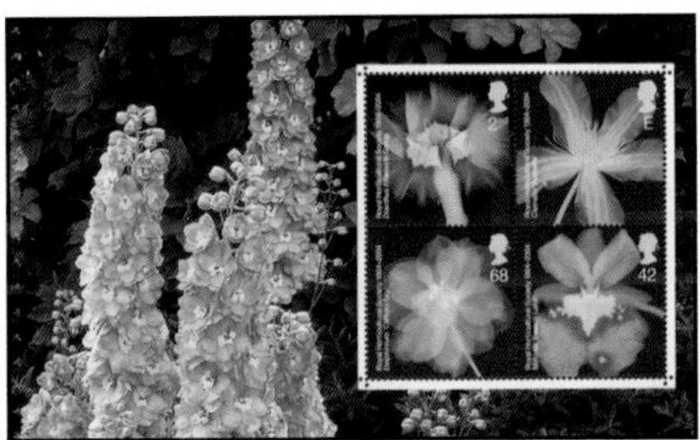

Pane printed by Enschedé in Gravure on OFNP/PVA
SP137 **1 x 2nd CB 1 x 'E' 2B , 1 x 68p 2B** and **1 x 42p 2B** Special stamps 3.00

Pane printed by Enschedé in Gravure on OFNP/PVA
SP138 **4 x 1st 2B 'Flowers'** Special stamps 4.50

Pane printed by Enschedé in Gravure on OFNP/PVA
SP139 **4 x 47p 2B** Special stamps 4.00

No. | U/M

2005 £7.47 'The Bronte Sisters'

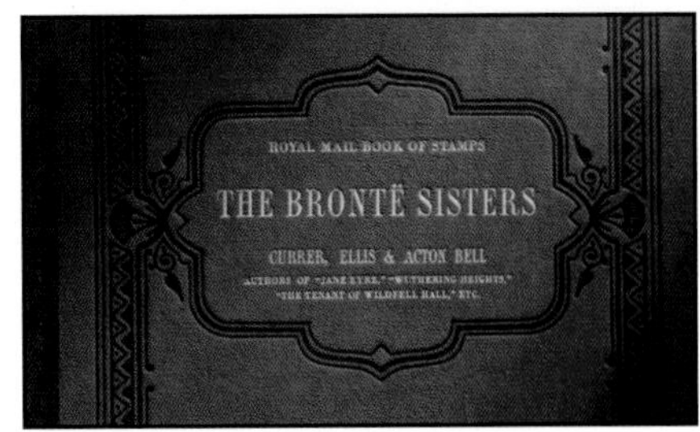

2005 (Feb. 24) £7.47 'The Bronte Sisters' Booklet
Printer: Walsall Security Printers in gravure.

PB35 Complete book 11.50

Pane printed by Walsall on OFNP/PVA
SP140 **4 x 2nd CB Bright blue, 2 x 39p 2B Light grey, 2 x 42p 2B Sage green** *plus* label 4.00

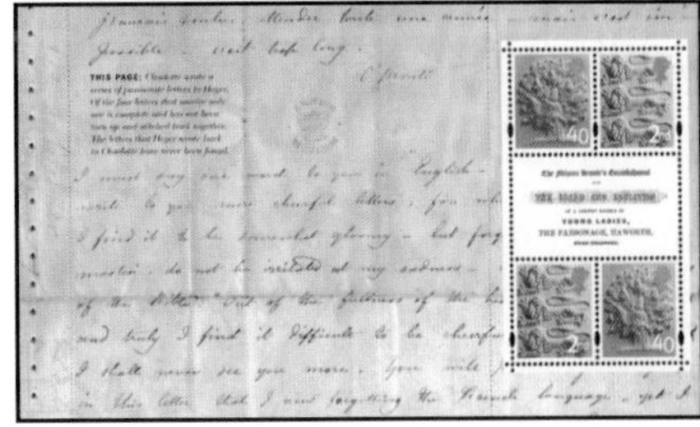

Pane printed by Walsall on OFNP/PVA
SP141 **2 x 2nd CB England emblem, 2 x 40p 2B England emblem** *plus* label 3.00

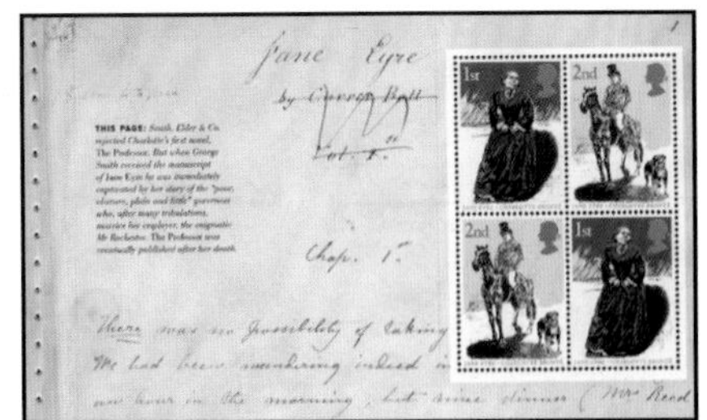

Pane printed by Walsall on OFNP/PVA
SP142 **2 x 1st 2B** and **2 x 2nd CB** Special stamps 2.25

No. U/M

Pane printed by Walsall on OFNP/PVA

SP143 **1 x 40p 2B**, **1 x 57p 2B**, **1 x 68p** 2B and **1 x £1.12 2B** special stamps 4.50

2005 £7.26 'Battle of Trafalgar'

2005 (18 Oct.) £7.26 'Battle of Trafalgar

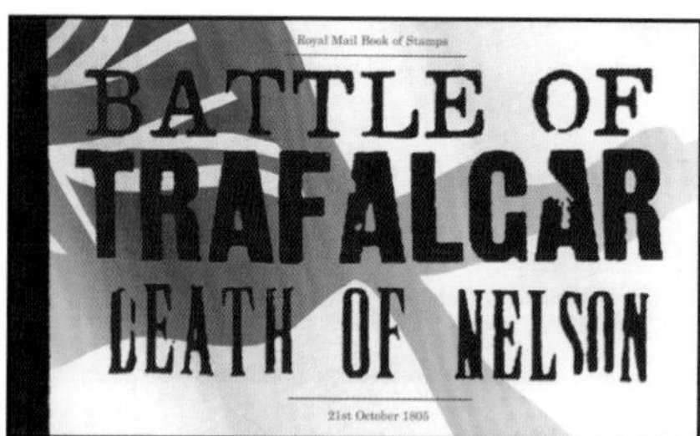

PB36 Conplete book 11.50

Pane printed by Cartor Security Printing in Litho on OFNP/PVA.

SP144 **3 x 1st 2B Special stamps** 1.50

Pane printed by Walsall in Gravure on OFNP/PVA..

SP145 **4 x 1st 2B Gold), 2 x 50p 2B Ochre, 2 x 68p 2B Stone** *plus* label 5.25

No. U/M

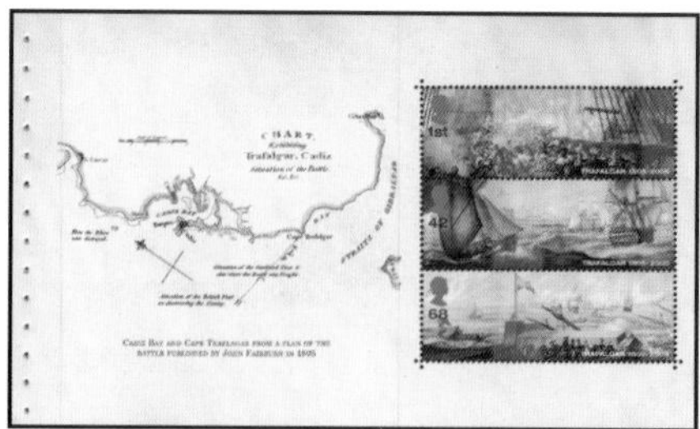

Pane printed by Cartor Security Printing in Litho on OFNP/PVA.

SP146 **1 x 1st 2B**, **1 x 42p 2B** and **1 x 68p 2B** Special stamps 2.75

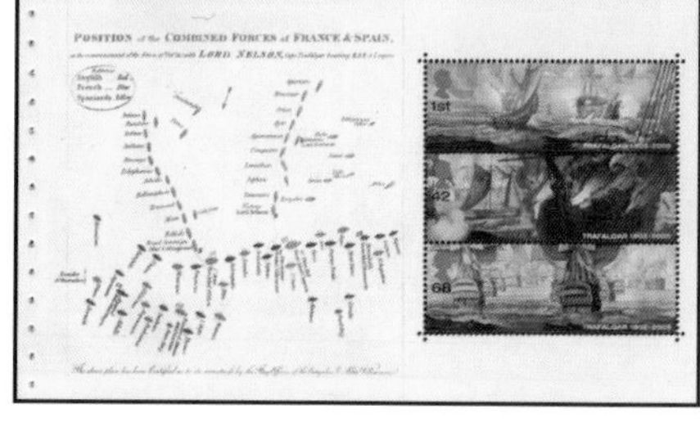

Pane printed by Cartor Security Printing in Litho on OFNP/PVA.

SP147 **1 x 1st 2B**, **1 x 42p 2B** and **1 x 68p 2B** Special stamps 2.75

Christmas Books

1978 (15 Nov.)

Contents 10 x 7p CB below 10 x 9p 2B. Pane FP79

No.			Plain	Cyl.
FC1	**£1.60**	**Greetings**, August 1978	3.00	4.50

1979 (15 Nov.)

Contents 10 x 8p CB below 10 x 10p 2B. Pane FP80

No.			Plain	Cyl.
FC2	**£1.80**	**Christmas cracker**, Oct. 1979	3.25	5.00
C2a		Miscut pane	£75	£145

1980 (12 Nov.)

Contents 10 x 10p CB below 10 x 12p 2B. Pane FP81

No.			Plain	Cyl.
FC3	**£2.20**	**Nativity**, Sept 1980	4.00	5.00
FC3a		Missing phosphor (Partial)	£125	£275

1981 (11 Nov.)

Contents 10 x 11½p CB below 10 x 14p 2B. Pane FP82

No.			Plain	Cyl.
FC4	**£2.55**	**Ice-skaters**, Jan 1981	6.00	-
FC4a		Miscut pane	£1000	-

1982 (10 Nov.) .

Contents 10 x 12½p CB below 10 x 15½p 2B, with 'star' underprint (£2.80). Pane FP83

No.			Plain	Cyl.
FC5	**£2.80**	**Christmas mummers**, Feb. 1982	6.00	6.50

1983 (9 Nov.)

Contents 20 x 12½p with 'star' underprint (£2.50). Pane FP84

No.			Plain	Cyl.
FC6	**£2.50**	**Pantomimes**, April 1983	5.00	6.00
FC6a		Miscut pane	£3500	
FC6b		Thin value, Type 1	9.00	£19

1984 (20 Nov.)

Contents 20 x 13p Christmas commemorative with 'star' underprint (£2.60)

No.			Plain	Cyl.
FC7	**£2.60**	**The Nativity**, Sept. 1984	6.00	6.50
FC7a		Miscut pane	£20	

No.			Plain	Cyl.

1985 (19 Nov.)

Contents 20 x 12p Christmas commemorative with 'star' underprint.

FC8	**£2.40**	**The Pantomime**	5.50	6.00

1986 (2 Dec.)

Contents 10 x 13p CB with 'star' underprint (£1.30). Pane FP69 or FP71

FC9	**£1.30**	**Shetland Yule Cakes**. Left margin	4.50	5.00
FC9a		Right margin	4.50	5.00

1990 (13 Nov.)

Contents 20 x 17p Christmas commemorative, imperf. at top or bottom.

FC10	**£3.40**	**Snowman**	7.00	7.50

1991 (12 Nov.)

Contents 20 x 18p Christmas commemorative

FC11	**£3.60**	**Holly**	6.00	7.00

1992 (10 Nov.)

Contents 20 x 18p Christmas commemorative

FC12	**£3.60**	**Santa Claus**	5.50	6.00

1993 (9 Nov.)

Contents 10 x 25p Christmas commemorative

FC13	**£2.50**	**Santa Claus**	5.00	7.00

Contents 20 x 19p Christmas commemorative

FC14	**£3.80**	**Santa Claus**	7.00	8.00

No. | Plain | Cyl.

1994 (1 Nov.)

Contents 10 x 25p Christmas commemorative

No.		Plain	Cyl.
FC15	**£2.50 Christmas play props**	4.25	6.75

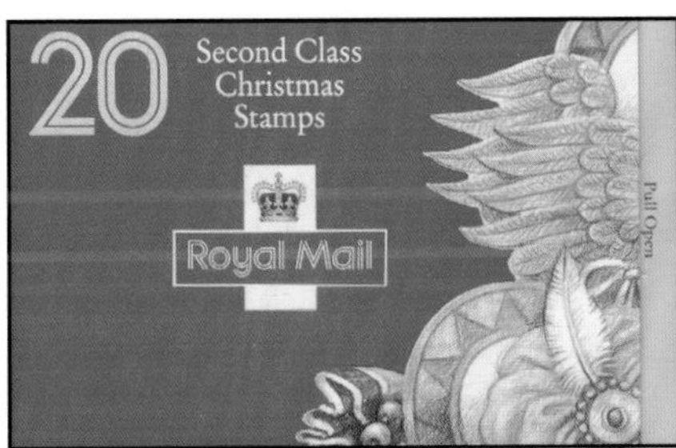

Contents 20 x 19p Christmas commemorative

No.		Plain	Cyl.
FC16	**£3.80**	6.00	7.50

1995 (30 Oct.)

Contents 4 x 60p 2B

No.		Plain	Cyl.
FC17	**£2.40 Robins**	4.50	5.50

Contents 10 x 25p Christmas commemorative

No.		Plain	Cyl.
FC18	**£2.50 Robins**	4.50	6.50

Contents 20 x 19p Christmas commemorative

No.		Plain	Cyl.
FC19	**£3.80 Robins**	7.00	8.00

1996 (28 Oct.)

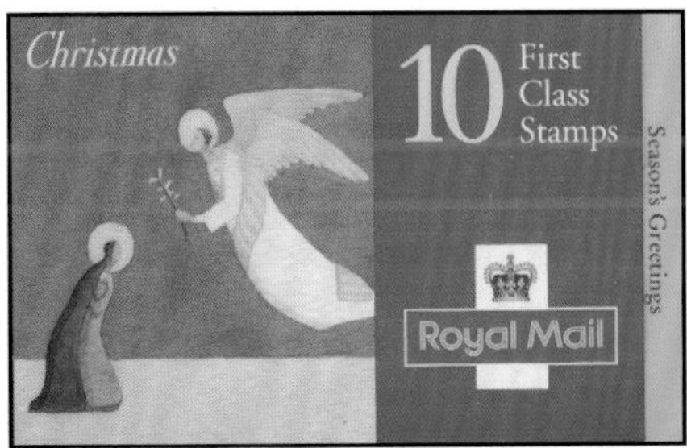

Contents 10 x 1st

No.		Plain	Cyl.
FC20	**£2.60 Nativity**	4.50	6.50

Contents 20 x 2nd

No.		Plain	Cyl.
FC21	**£4.00 Nativity**	7.00	7.75

1997 (27 Oct.)

Contents 10 x 1st

No.		Plain	Cyl.
FC22	**£2.60 Father Christmas & crackers**	4.50	5.50

No. | Plain | Cyl.

Contents 20 x 2nd
FC23 **£4.00 Father Christmas & crackers** 6.50 7.00

1998 (2 Nov.)

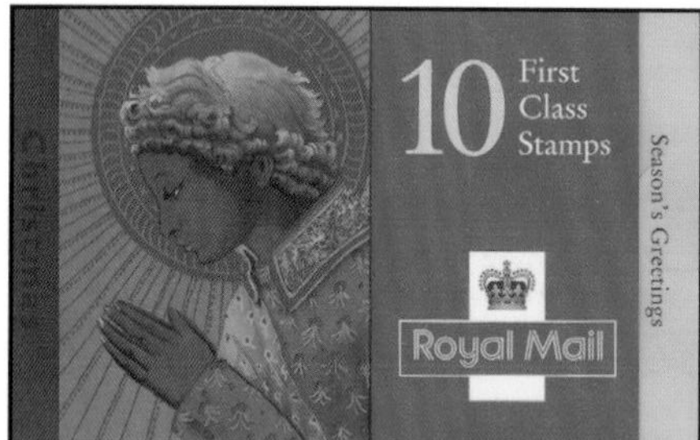

Contents 10 x 26p
FC24 **£2.60 Angels** 5.00 6.00

Contents 20 x 20p
FC25 **£4 Angels** 6.50 7.00

1999 (2 Nov.)

Contents 10 x 26p
FC26 **£2.60 King James's Bible** 4.50 5.50

No. | Plain | Cyl.

Contents 20 x 19p
FC27 **£1.90 Hark the Herald Angels Sing** 6.00 7.00

2000 (7 Nov.)

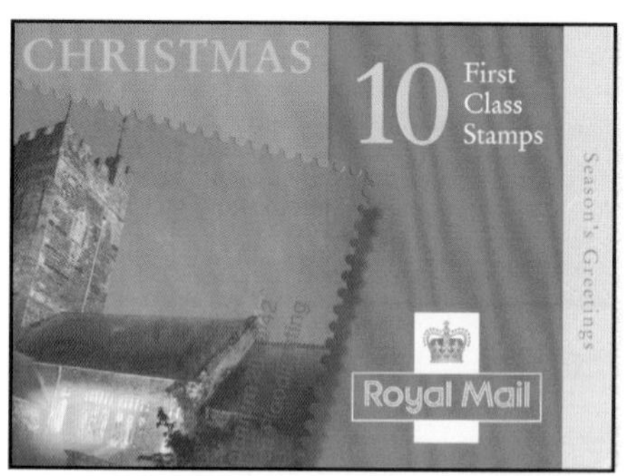

Contents 10 x 1st
FC28 **£2.70 Spirit and Faith** 5.50 6.50

Contents 20 x 2nd
FC29 **£4.00 Spirit and Faith** 5.50 6.50

Christmas books from 2001 onwards are of the self adhesive type and are listed from Page S - 5 in Section S

No. | No. Plain Cyl.

Greetings Stamp Books

1989 (31 Jan.) Cover with various designs.

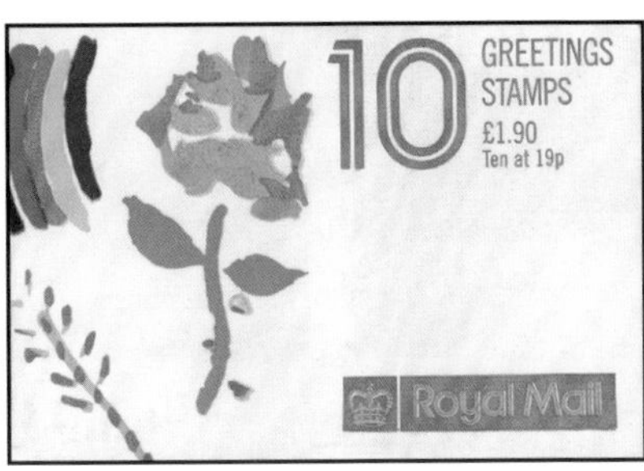

Contents 10 x 19p Greetings stamps *plus* 12 x labels.

No.			Plain	Cyl.
GB1	**£1.90**	**Sept. 1988**	£30	£35

1990 (6 Feb.)

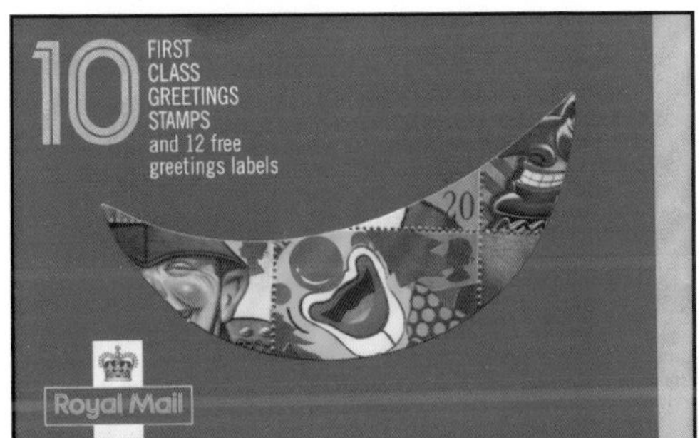

Contents 10 x 20p Greetings stamps *plus* 12 x labels. Loose in folder.

No.			Plain	Cyl.
GB2	**£2**	**"Smiles"**	£19	-

1991 (5 Feb.)

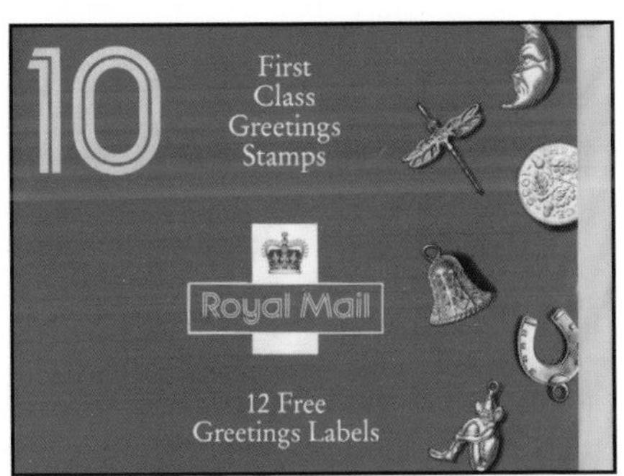

Contents 10 x 1st Greetings stamps *plus* 12 x labels.

No.			Plain	Cyl.
GB3	**£2.20**	**"Good Luck"** charms	6.50	7.00

1991 (26 March)

Contents 10 x 1st Greetings stamps *plus* 12 x labels.

No.			Plain	Cyl.
GB4	**£2.20**	**Laughing letter box**	5.50	6.50
GB4a		Reprint. Revised instructions on use of NVI stamps on overseas mail (3.3.92)	7.50	9.50

1992 (28 Jan.)

Contents 10 x 1st Greetings stamps *plus* 12 x labels.

No.			Plain	Cyl.
GB5	**£2.40**	**Memories**	5.50	6.00

1993 (2 Feb.)

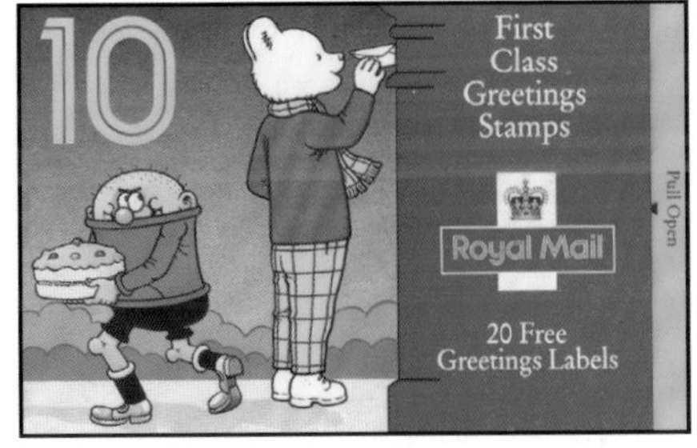

Contents 10 x 1st Greetings stamps *plus* 20 x labels.

No.			Plain	Cyl.
GB6	**£2.40**	**Rupert Bear and Wilfrid**	6.50	7.50
GB6a		Reprint. 'Thompson' corrected to 'Thomson'	8.00	£12
GB6b		Reprint. Revised text and spelling of 'Sorrell'	8.00	£12

No.			Plain	Cyl.

1994 (1 Feb.)

Contents 10 x 1st Greetings stamps *plus* 20 x labels.

GB7	**£2.50**	**Rupert Bear and Paddington Bear**	5.00	5.50

1995 (21 March)

Contents 10 x 1st Greetings stamps *plus* 20 x labels.

GB8	**£2.50**	**Noted Art Works**	5.00	6.00
GB8a		Alteration to event dates in inside cover - 'Pull open' removed from yelow strip	6.00	7.00

1996 (26 Feb.)

Contents 10 x 1st Greetings stamps (All over phosphor) *plus* 20 x labels.

GB9	**£2.50**	**More! Love**	5.00	6.50

1996 (11 Nov.)

Contents 10 x 1st Greetings stamps (2 x D (Blue) phosphor bands) *plus* 20 x labels.

GB10	**£2.60**	**More! Love**	5.00	6.50

No.			Plain	Cyl

1997 (6 Jan.)

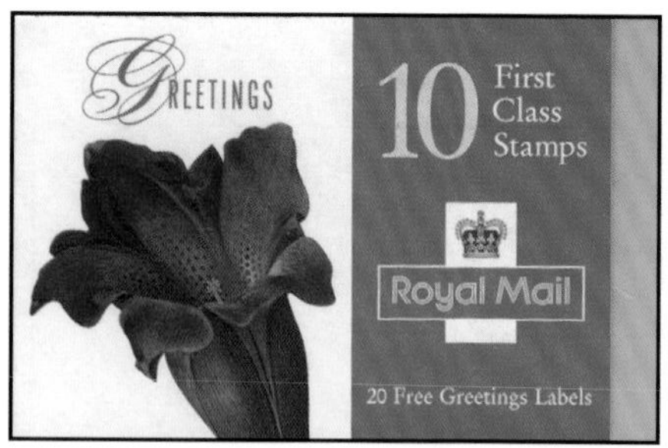

Contents 10 x 1st Greetings stamps *plus* 20 x labels.

GB11	**£2.60**	**19th Century Flower Paintings**	5.00	6.00

1997 (3 Feb)

GB12	**£2.60**	**19th Century Flower Paintings**	5.00	6.00

1997 (3 Feb.)

Contents 10 x 1st Greetings stamps *plus* 20 x labels.

GB12	**£2.60**	**19th Century Flower Paintings**	5.00	6.50

No.			Plain	Cyl.	No.	Plain	Cyl

1998 (5 Jan.)

Contents 10 x 1st Greetings stamps *plus* 20 x labels.

No.			Plain	Cyl.
GB13	**£2.60**	**19th Century Flower Paintings**	5.00	6.00

Folded (Counter) Books

First issued on 14 July 1976, these Swedish style books were introduced as a convenient method for the public to buy a small supply of the more common denominations that they required. They were eventually replaced by the now familiar 'Window' books which are listed elsewhere.

The panes of stamps in these books are attached by either the left or right margins and are listed simply as Left or Right. Please note that a dash '-' in the price column denotes that this does not exist.

There are wide number of varieties to be found in these books and many collections have been assembled based on this area of GB alone. In this new edition we have now included the price of the cheapest cylinder book, and also miscut panes, missing and displaced phosphors bands, but a complete listing of these fascinating books can be found in the Machin Collectors Club Specialised Catalogue featured at the beginning of this book.

Left margin plain normal pane - guillotine marks at top and bottom

Left margin cylinder 11 Dot pane

Left margin miscut - guillotine mark in centre

1976 (14 July) 'Royal Mail Stamps' design
Contents 10 x 6½p CB. Pane FP41 or FP42

			Plain	Cyl.
FB1	**65p**	**March 1976,** Left	7.50	10.00
FB1a		Miscut pane	8.50	35.00
FB1b		Perforated margin	25.00	15.00
FB1c		Miscut pane	8.00	45.00
FB2		Right	5.00	-
FB2a		Miscut pane	6.00	-
FB2b		Perforated margin	12.50	-
FB2c		Miscut pane	10.00	-

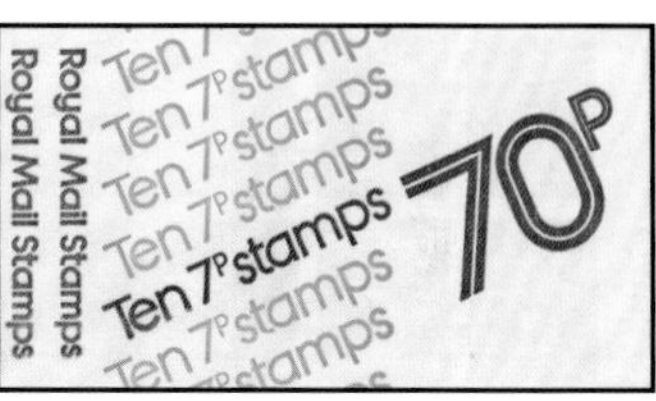

1977 (13 June) 'Royal Mail Stamps' design
Contents 10 x 7p CB. Pane FP43 or FP44.

			Plain	Cyl.
FB3	**70p**	**June 1977**. Left	4.00	4.50
FB3a		Miscut pane	6.00	25.00
FB4		Right	3.75	-
FB4a		Miscut pane	7.75	-

1978 (8 Feb.) Country Crafts.
Contents 10 x 7p CB. Pane FP43 or FP44

			Plain	Cyl.
FB5	**70p**	**Horse-shoeing**, 1st Left	20.00	25.00
F5aa		Miscut pane	5.50	20.00
FB6		Right	3.75	-
FB6a		Miscut pane	7.00	-

			Plain	Cyl.
FB7	**70p**	**Thatching**, 2nd (3.5.78). Left	95.00	95.00
FB8		Right	3.75	-

			Plain	Cyl.
FB9	**70p**	**Dry-stone walling**, 3rd (9.8.78). Left	150.00	195.00
FB10		Right	3.75	-

			Plain	Cyl.
FB11	**70p**	**Wheel making**, 4th (25.10.78). Left	4.50	6.00
FB12		Right	3.75	-

			Plain	Cyl.
FB13	**70p**	**Wattle fence making**, 5th (10.1.79). Left	12.50	17.50
FB14		Right	3.75	-
FB14a		Miscut pane	£150	-

			Plain	Cyl.
FB15	**70p**	**Basket making**, 6th (4.4.79). Left	6.00	7.50
FB16		Right	3.50	-

1979 (5 Feb.) Derby Letter Office.
Contents 10 x 7p CB. Pane FP43 or FP44

			Plain	Cyl.
FB17	**70p**	**Kedlestone Hall,** Left	5.00	8.00
FB18		Right	5.50	-

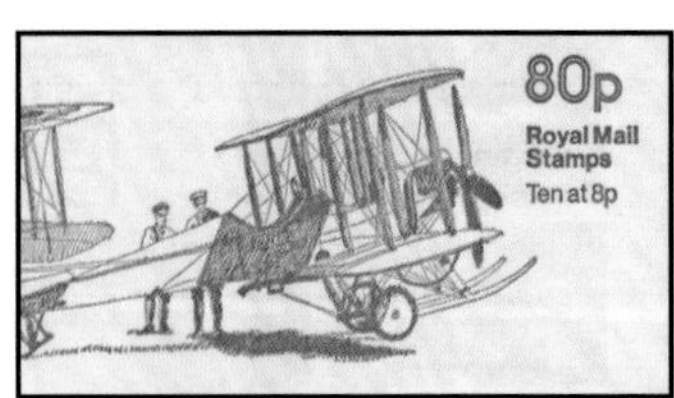

1979 (3 Oct.) Military Aircraft.
Contents 10 x 8p CB. Pane FP45 or FP46

			Plain	Cyl.
FB19	**80p**	**BE2B 1914**, Vickers Gun Bus 1915, 1st. Left	3.00	2.50
FB20		Right	3.00	-

1976 (14 July) 'Royal Mail Stamps' design
Contents 10 x 8½p 2B. Pane FP47 or FP48.

			Plain	Cyl.
FB21	**85p**	**March 1976,** Left	7.50	10.00
FB21a		Miscut pane	12.00	37.50
FB21b		Perforated margin	20.00	10.50
FB21c		Miscut pane	200.00	350.00
FB22		Right	6.00	-
FB22a		Miscut pane	29.50	-
FB22b		Perforated margin	20.00	-
FB22c		Miscut pane		-

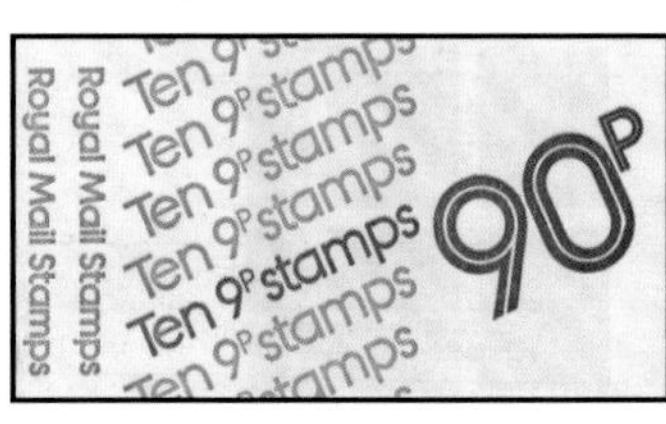

1977 (13 June) 'Royal Mail Stamps' design
Contents 10 x 9p 2B. Pane FP49 or FP50.

			Plain	Cyl.
FB23	**90p**	**June 1977**, Left	4.00	5.00
FB23a		Miscut pane	17.00	85.00
FB24		Right	4.50	-
FB24a		Miscut pane	10.00	-

1978 (8 Feb.) British Canals.
Contents 10 x 9p 2B. Pane FP49 or FP50

			Plain	Cyl.
FB25	**90p**	**Grand Union Canal**, (8.1.78) 1st Left	20.00	22.00
FB25a		Miscut pane	25.00	
FB26		Right	4.00	-
FB26a		Miscut pane	10.00	-

			Plain	Cyl.
FB27	**90p**	**Llangollen Canal**, 2nd (3.5.78) Left	3.50	4.75
FB28		Right	275.00	-

			Plain	Cyl.

			Plain	Cyl.
FB29	**90p**	**Kennet & Avon Canal**, 3rd (9.8.78) Left	10.00	17.50
FB30		Right	6.50	-

			Plain	Cyl.
FB31	**90p**	**Caledonian Canal**, 4th (25.10.78) Left	3.75	6.00
FB32		Right	6.00	-

			Plain	Cyl.
FB33	**90p**	**Regents Canal**, 5th (10.01.79) Left	8.50	10.00
FB33a		Experimental fold between cols. 2 & 3	25.00	28.00
FB34		Right	5.50	-
FB34a		Miscut pane	350.00	

			Plain	Cyl.
FB35	**90p**	**Leeds and Liverpool Canal**, 6th (4.4.79). Left	4.00	5.00
FB35a		Miscut pane	50.00	175.00
FB36		Right	4.50	-

1979 (5 Feb.) Derby Letter Office.
Contents 10 x 9p 2B. Pane FP49 or FP50

			Plain	Cyl.
FB37	**90p**	**Tramway Museum**, Crich. Left	6.00	12.50
FB38		Right	6.00	-

1979 (3 Oct.) Industrial Archaeology.
Contents 10 x 10p PPP. Pane FP85 or FP86

			Plain	Cyl.
FB39	**£1**	**Ironbridge**, Telford, 1st Left	3.50	4.25
FB39a		Miscut pane	12.00	60.00
FB40		Right	3.50	-
FB40a		Miscut pane	5.00	-

1980 (4 Feb) Military Aircraft.
Contents 10 x 10p CB. Pane FP51 or FP52.

			Plain	Cyl.
FB41	**£1**	**Sopwith Camel**, 2nd (4.2.80) Left	3.25	4.00
FB41a		Miscut pane	27.50	
FB42		Right	3.25	-
FB42a		Miscut pane	20.00	-

			Plain	Cyl.
FB43	**£1**	**Hawker Fury**, 3rd (25.6.80). Left	3.25	4.50
FB43a		Right	3.25	-

			Plain	Cyl.
FB44	**£1**	**Hurricane**, 4th (24.9.80). Left	3.25	6.00
FB44a		Right	3.25	-

1981 (26 Jan.) Military Aircraft.

Contents 10 x 11½p CB. Pane FP54 or FP55.

			Plain	Cyl.
FB45	**£1.15**	**Spitfire & Lancaster**, 5th. (26.1.81) Left	3.50	4.00
FB45a		Right	3.50	-

			Plain	Cyl.
FB46	**£1.15**	**Lightning and Vulcan**, 6th (18.3.81). Left	4.00	5.00
FB46a		Right	3.75	-

1981 (6 May - Sept.) Museums.

Contents 10 x 11½p CB. Pane FP54 or FP55

			Plain	Cyl.
FB47	**£1.15**	**Natural History Museum**, 1st, Left	3.50	5.00
FB48		Right	3.50	

			Plain	Cyl.
FB49	**£1.15**	**The National Museum of Antiquities of Scotland**, 2nd (30.9.81). Left	3.50	4.50
FB50		Right	3.50	

1980 (4 Feb. - Sept.) Industrial Archaeology.

Contents 10 x 12p PCP1. Pane FP89 or FP90

			Plain	Cyl.
FB51	**£1.20**	**Beetle Mill**, 2nd. Left	3.75	4.50
FB51a		Miscut pane	4.50	17.50
FB52		Right	3.75	-
FB52a		Miscut pane	4.75	-

			Plain	Cyl.
FB53	**£1.20**	**Tin Mines**, 3rd (25.6.80). Left	4.00	4.50
FB54		Right	4.00	-

			Plain	Cyl.
FB55	**£1.20**	**Bottle Kilns**, 4th (24.9.80). Left	4.00	4.75
FB56		Right	4.00	-

1986 (14 Jan.) Pillar Box.

Contents 10 x 12p CB. Pane FP58 or FP59

			Plain	Cyl.
FB57	**£1.20**	**Pillar Box**. Left	3.50	4.00
FB58		Right	3.25	3.75
FB58a		Miscut pane	195.00	575.00

1986 (29 April) National Gallery.

Contents 10 x 12p CB. Pane FP58 or FP59

			Plain	Cyl.
FB59	**£1.20**	**National Gallery**. Left Margin	3.25	3.75
FB59a		Missing phosphor	60.00	85.00
FB60		Right	3.25	3.75
FB60a		Missing phosphor	175.00	250.00

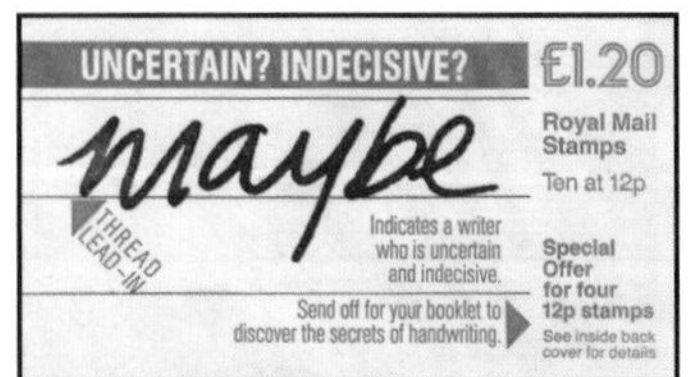

1986 (29 July) Graphology.

Contents 10 x 12p CB. Pane FP58 or FP59

			Plain	Cyl.
FB61	**£1.20**	**"Maybe"**. Left	3.25	3.75
FB62		Right	3.25	3.75

1982 (1 Feb.) Museums Series.
Contents 10 x 12½p CB. Pane FP62 or FP63

			Plain	Cyl.
FB63	**£1.25**	**The Ashmolean Museum**, 3rd. Left	3.50	-
FB64		Right	3.50	-

			Plain	Cyl.
FB65	**£1.25**	**National Museum of Wales**, 4th (6.5.82).		
		Left	3.50	-
FB66		Right	3.75	-

			Plain	Cyl.
FB67	**£1.25**	**Ulster Museum**, 5th (11.8.82). Left	3.50	350.00
FB68		Right	3.50	-

			Plain	Cyl.
FB69	**£1.25**	**Castle Museum**, 6th (6.10.82). Left	3.50	4.00
FB70		Right	3.50	4.00

1983 (16 Feb) Railway Engines.
Contents 10 x 12½p CB. Pane FP62 or FP63

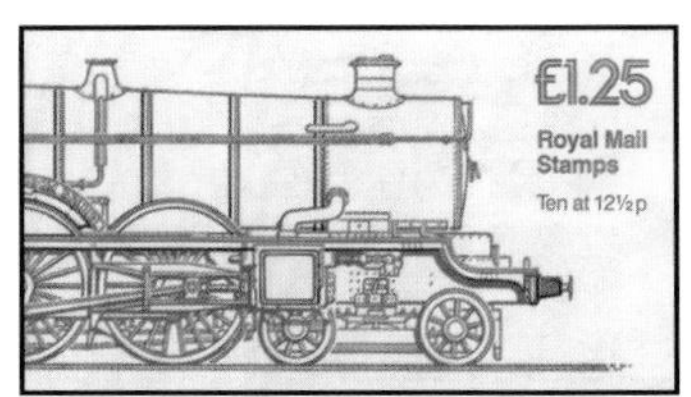

			Plain	Cyl.
FB71	**£1.25**	**GWR Isambard Kingdom Brunel**, 1st.		
		Left	4.00	5.00
FB72		Right	3.50	4.50

			Plain	Cyl.
FB73	**£1.25**	**LMS Class 4P Passenger Tank Engine**, 2nd (5.4.83).		
		Left	3.75	5.00
FB74		Right	4.00	4.75
FB74a		Rate corrected to "36p" (200g). Left	37.00	35.00
FB74b		Right	55.00	45.00

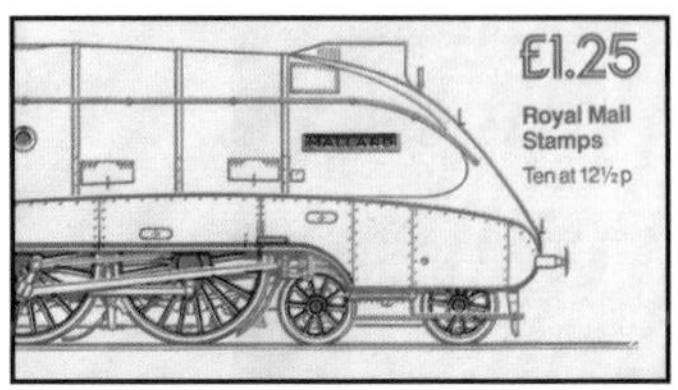

			Plain	Cyl.
FB75	**£1.25**	**LNER Mallard**, 3rd (27.7.83). Left	4.00	4.50
FB76		Right	4.00	4.50

			Plain	Cyl.
FB77	**£1.25**	**SR/BR Clan Line**, 4th (26.10.83). Left	4.00	5.00
FB78		Right	4.00	4.25

1981 (6 May) Postal History.
Contents 4 x 11½p SB and 6 x 14p 2B. Pane FP56 or FP57

			Plain	Cyl.
FB79	**£1.30**	**The Penny Black** 1840/41, 1st. Left	3.75	-
FB80		Right	4.00	-

			Plain	Cyl.
FB81	**£1.30**	**The Downey Head 1911**, 2nd (30.9.81).		
		Left	4.75	-
FB82		Right	12.00	-

1984 (3 Sept.) Trams Series
Contents 10 x 13p CB. Pane FP68 or FP70

			Plain	Cyl.
FB83	**£1.30**	**Swansea/Mumbles**, 1st. Left	3.25	3.75
FB84		Right	3.25	3.75

			Plain	Cyl.
FB85	**£1.30**	**Glasgow**, 2nd (15.1.85). Left	4.00	4.00
FB86		Right	3.50	4.00

			Plain	Cyl.
FB87	**£1.30**	**Blackpool**, 3rd (23.4.85). Left	3.25	3.75
FB88		Right	3.25	3.75

			Plain	Cyl.
FB89	**£1.30**	**London**, 4th (23.7.85). Left	3.25	3.75
FB90		Right	3.25	3.75

1986 (20 Oct.) Special Offer series.
Contents 10 x 13p CB. Pane FP68 or FP70

			Plain	Cyl.
FB91	**£1.30**	**Bears**. "My Day" work book. Left	3.00	3.75
FB91a		All over phos. (2), streaks (6)	£25	
FB92		Right	3.25	3.75

1987 (27 Jan.) Special Offer series.
Contents 10 x 13p CB, 'A' phosphor. Pane FP68a or FP70a.

			Plain	Cyl.
FB93	**£1.30**	**"Keep in Touch"** pack. Left	3.25	4.50
FB94		Right	3.25	3.75

1987 (14 April) Special Offer series.
Contents 10 x 13p CB. 'A' phosphor. Pane FP68a or FP70a

			Plain	Cyl.
FB95	**£1.30**	**"Ideas for your Garden"**. Left	3.25	4.75
FB96		Right	3.25	3.75

1987 (14 July) Special Offer series.
Contents 10 x 13p CB 'A' phosphor. Pane FP68a or FP70a

			Plain	Cyl.
FB97	**£1.30**	**"Brighter Writer"** pack. Left	3.25	3.75
FB98		Right	3.25	3.50

1987 (29 Sept.) Special Offer series.
Contents 10 x 13p CB. 'A' phosphor. Pane FP68a or FP70a

			Plain	Cyl.
FB99	**£1.30**	**"Jolly Postman"** pack. Left	3.25	3.75
FB99a		Missing phosphor	30.00	45.00
FB100		Right	3.25	3.75
FB100a		Missing phosphor	75.00	175.00

1986 (26 Jan.) Special Offer series.
Contents 10 x 13p CB, 'A' phosphor. Pane FP68a or FP70a

			Plain	Cyl.
FB101	**£1.30**	Natural History Postcards (Linnean Society). Left	3.50	3.75
FB102		Right	3.50	3.75

1988 (12 April) Special Offer series.
Contents 10 x 13p CB. 'A' phosphor. Pane FP68a or FP70a

			Plain	Cyl.
FB103	**£1.30**	**Recipe Cards**. Left	3.25	3.75
FB104		Right	3.25	3.75

1988 (5 July) Special Offer series.
Contents 10 x 13p CB. 'A' phosphor. Pane FP68a or FP70a

			Plain	Cyl.
FB105	**£1.30**	**Children's party pack**. Left	3.25	3.75
FB105a		All over phosphor error on 6 stamps	7.50	
FB106		Right	3.25	3.75
FB106a		All over phosphor error	£10	

1981 (26 Jan Industrial Archaeology.
Contents 10 x 14p PCP2. Pane FP106 or FP107

			Plain	Cyl.
FB107	**£1.40**	**Preston Mill**, 5th. Left	3.75	4.00
FB108		Right	3.50	-

			Plain	Cyl.
FB109	**£1.40**	**Talyllyn Railway**, 6th (18.3.81). Left	4.00	4.50
FB110		Right	4.00	-
FB110a		Miscut pane	500.00	-

1981 (6 May) Nineteenth Century Women's Costume.
Contents 10 x 14p PCP2. Pane FP106 or FP107

			Plain	Cyl.
FB111	**£1.40**	**1800 - 1815**, 1st. Left	3.50	3.75
FB111a		PCP1. Pane FP91	45.00	47.50
FB112		Right	3.50	-
FB112a		Fluorescent Brightener Omitted.	15.00	-
FB112b		PCP1. Pane FP92	37.00	-

			Plain	Cyl.
FB113	**£1.40**	**1815 - 1830**, 2nd (20.9.81). Left	3.50	5.50
FB113a		PCP1. Pane FP91	32.00	37.00
FB114		Right	4.00	-
FB114a		Fluorescent Brightener Omitted	30.00	-
FB114b		PCP1. Pane FP92	27.00	-

1988 (5 Sept.) Special Offer series.
Contents 10 x 14p CB. 'A' phosphor. Pane FP73 or FP74

			Plain	Cyl.
FB115	**£1.40**	**'Pocket Planner'**. Left	3.75	4.00
FB115a		Missing phosphor	150.00	200.00
FB116		Right	3.75	4.00

1989 (24 Jan.) 'William Henry Fox Talbot'
Contents 10 x 14p CB. 'A' phosphor. Pane FP73 or FP74

			Plain	Cyl.
FB117	**£1.40**	**William Henry Fox Talbot**. Left	3.75	4.50
FB118		Right	3.75	4.50

1982 (1 Feb.) - 83 Postal History.
Contents 4 x 12½p SB and 6 x 15½p 2B. Pane FP64 or FP65

			Plain	Cyl.
FB119	**£1.43**	**James Chalmers**, 3rd. Left	3.75	-
FB120		Right	3.75	-

			Plain	Cyl.
FB121	**£1.43**	**Edmund Dulac**, 4th (6.5.82). Left	3.75	8.00
FB121a		Transposed phosphor bands	195.00	260.00
FB122		Right	3.75	8.00

			Plain	Cyl.
FB123	**£1.43**	**Forces Postal Service**, 5th (21.7.82). Left	3.50	
FB124		Right	3.50	

			Plain	Cyl.
FB125	**£1.43**	**The £5 Orange**, 6th (6.10.82). Left	3.75	5.50
FB126		Right	3.75	7.00

			Plain	Cyl.
FB127	**£1.43**	**Postmark History**, 7th (16.2.83). Left	3.75	7.00
FB128		Right	3.75	5.50

1982 (12 July) The Holiday Postcard Stamp Book.
Contents 4 x 12½p SB and 6 x 15½p 2B. Pane FP64 or FP65

			Plain	Cyl.
FB129	**£1.43**	**The Golden Hinde** (replica). Left	3.50	4.00
FB130		Right	3.75	4.25

1983 (10 Aug.) Britain's Countryside.
Contents 10 x 16p PCP1 with 'D' underprint (£1.60). Pane FP96 or FP98

			Plain	Cyl.
FB131	**£1.45**	**Lyme Regis**, Dorset. Left	4.50	5.00
FB131a		Miscut	1250.00	1500.00
FB132		Right	4.50	6.00

1983 (5 April - Oct.) Postal History.
Contents 4 x 12½p SB and 6 x 16p 2B. Pane FP66 or FP67

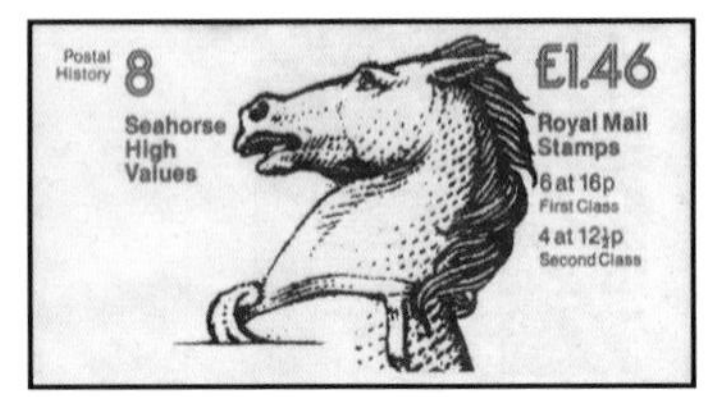

			Plain	Cyl.
FB133	**£1.46**	**Seahorse High Values**, 8th. Left	7.50	8.00
FB133a		Rate corrected to '36p' (200g). Left	20.00	25.00
FB134		Right	7.50	8.50
FB134a		Rate corrected to '36p' (200g). Right	14.00	15.00

			Plain	Cyl.
FB135	**£1.46**	**Parcel Post**, 9th (27.7.83). Left	6.50	7.00
FB136		Right	6.50	7.00

			Plain	Cyl.
FB137	**£1.46**	**Regional Stamps**, 10th (26.10.83). Left	6.50	7.00
FB138		Right	7.50	8.00

1986 (14 Jan.) Special Offer series.
Contents 4 x 12p SB and 6 x 17p 2B. Pane FP60 or FP61

			Plain	Cyl.
FB139	**£1.50**	**Pillar Box**. 'Write Now' Letter-pack. Left	3.75	4.25
FB140		Right	3.75	4.00

1986 (29 April) Special Offer series.
Contents 4 x 12p SB and 6 x 17p 2B. Pane FP60 or FP61

			Plain	Cyl.
FB141	**£1.50**	**National Gallery**. Left	3.75	4.50
FB142		Right	3.75	4.75

1986 (29 July) Graphology. Special Offer series.
Contents 4 x 12p SB and 6 x 17p 2B. Pane FP60 or FP61

			Plain	Cyl.
FB143	**£1.50**	**'No'**. Left	4.00	4.50
FB144		Right	4.00	5.00

1985 (30 July) Royal Mail, 350 years of service to the public.
Contents 10 x 17p PCP commemorative with 'D' underprint (£1.70).

			Plain	Cyl.
FB145	**£1.53**	**Datapost van and aircraft**	4.50	6.50

1984 (3 Sept.) Postal History.
Contents 4 x 13p SB and 6 x 17p 2B. Pane FP73 or FP74

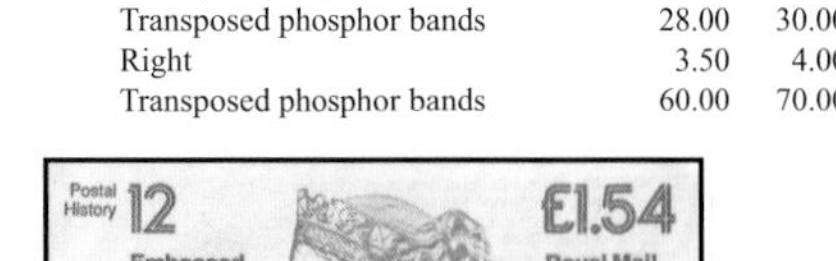

			Plain	Cyl.
FB146	**£1.54**	**To Pay Labels**, 11th. Left	3.50	4.00
FB146a		Transposed phosphor bands	28.00	30.00
FB147		Right	3.50	4.00
FB147a		Transposed phosphor bands	60.00	70.00

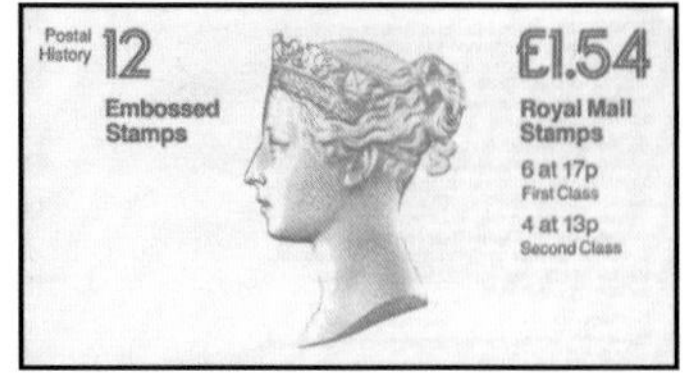

			Plain	Cyl.
FB148	**£1.54**	**Embossed Stamps**, 12th (15.1.85). Left	3.50	4.00
FB149		Right	3.50	4.00

			Plain	Cyl.
FB150	**£1.54**	**Surface Printed Stamps** 13th (23.4.85).		
		Left	3.50	4.00
FB151		Right	3.50	4.00

			Plain	Cyl.
FB152	**£1.54**	**350 Years of Service to the Public**, 14th (23.7.85).		
		Left	3.50	4.00
FB153		Right	3.50	4.50

1982 (1 Feb.) Nineteenth Century Women's Costume.
Contents 10 x 15½p PCP1. Pane FP93 or FP94

			Plain	Cyl.
FB154	**£1.55**	**1830 - 1850**, 3rd. Left	3.50	-
FB154a		PCP2. Pane FP108	60.00	-
FB155		Right	3.50	-
FB155a		PCP2. Pane FP109	95.00	-

FB156	**£1.55**	**1850 - 1860**, 4th (6.5.82). Left	3.50	25.00
FB156a		PCP2. Pane FP108	150.00	200.00
FB157		Right	3.50	17.50
FB157a		PCP2. Pane FP109	80.00	125.00

FB158	**£1.55**	**1860 - 1880**, 5th (11.8.82). Left	3.75	9.00
FB158a		PCP2. Pane FP108	250.00	300.00
FB159		Right.	3.75	5.50
FB159a		PCP2. Pane FP109	250.00	300.00

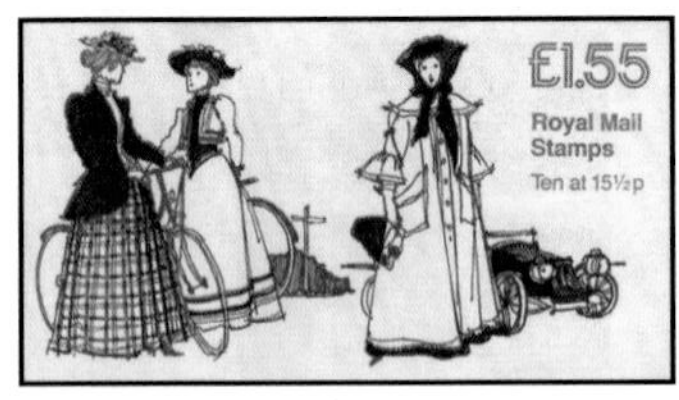

FB160	**£1.55**	**1880 - 1900**, 6th (6.10.82) Left	4.00	5.50
FB160a		PCP2. Pane FP108	40.00	60.00
FB161		Right	4.00	5.50
FB161a		PCP2. Pane FP109	35.00	39.50

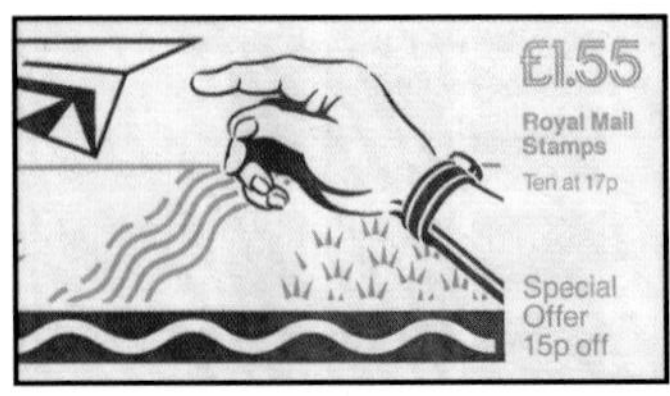

1985 (5 March) Social Letter Writing.

Contents 10 x 17p PCP1 with 'D' underprint (£1.70). Panes FP100 or FP102

FB162	**£1.55**	**Letters abroad**, 2nd. Left	5.00	5.50
FB163		Right	5.00	5.50

1983 (5 April) Special Offer series.

Contents 10 x 16p PCP1. Pane FP95 or FP97

FB164	**£1.60**	**'Birthday Box'** Left	5.00	5.50
FB164a		Rates corrected to '36p' (200g) Left	35.00	35.00
FB165		Right	5.00	7.00
FB165a		Rates corrected to '36p' (200g) Right	45.00	45.00

1983 (21 Sept.) Britain's Countryside.

Contents 10 x 16p PCP1. Pane FP95 or FP97

FB166	**£1.60**	**Cotswolds Arlington Row**, 2nd. Left	4.00	4.25
FB167		Right	4.00	4.50

1984 (14 Feb.) Special Offer series.

Contents 10 x 16p PCP1. Pane FP95 or FP97

FB168	**£1.60**	**'Write it'** wallet. Left	4.00	4.50
FB169		Right	4.00	4.50

1984 (3 Sept.) Social Letter Writing.

Contents 10 x 17p PCP1. Pane FP99 or FP101

FB170	**£1.70**	**Love letters**, 1st. Left (3.9.84)	4.00	4.50
FB171		Right	4.00	5.00

FB172	**£1.70**	**Fan letters**, 3rd. Left (9.4.85)	3.75	4.25
FB173		Right	3.75	4.25

1985 (8 Oct.) Special Offer series.
Contents 10 x 17p PCP1. Pane FP99 or FP101

FB174	**£1.70**	**Pillar Box**. 'Write Now' letter pack. Left	4.00	4.50
FB175		Right	4.00	6.00
FB176	**£1.70**	**Revised rate '12p'** (60g) and BBC copyright on back cover. Left	10.00	15.00
FB177		Right	10.00	12.00

1986 (29 April) Special Offer series.
Contents 10 x 17p PCP1. Pane FP99 or FP101. Cover as £1.20 booklet

FB178	**£1.70**	**National Gallery**. Left	4.00	4.50
FB179		Right	4.00	4.50

1986 (28 July) Graphology. Special Offer series.
Contents 10 x 17p PCP1. Pane FP99 or FP101

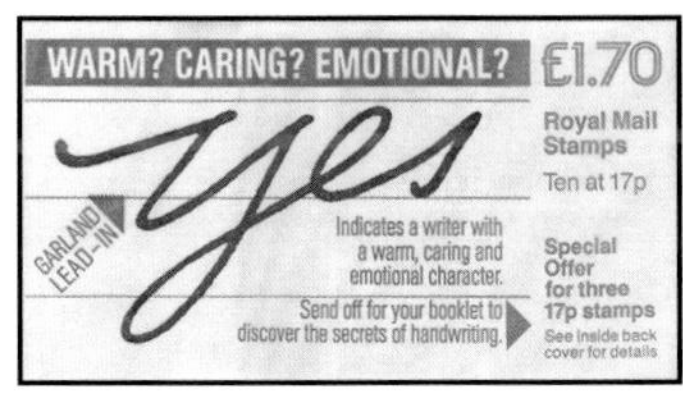

FB180	**£1.70**	**"Yes"**. Left	4.00	4.50
FB181		Right	3.00	3.50

1986 (20 Oct.) Special Offer series.
Contents 10 x 18p PCP1. Pane FP103 or FP104

FB182	**£1.80**	**Rabbits**. 'My Day' word book. Left	5.00	5.25
FB182a		PCP2. Pane FP110	20.00	45.00
FB183		Right	5.00	5.50
FB183a		PCP2. Pane FP111	17.50	19.50

1987 (27 Jan.) Special Offer series.
Contents 10 x 18p PCP1. Pane FP103 or FP104

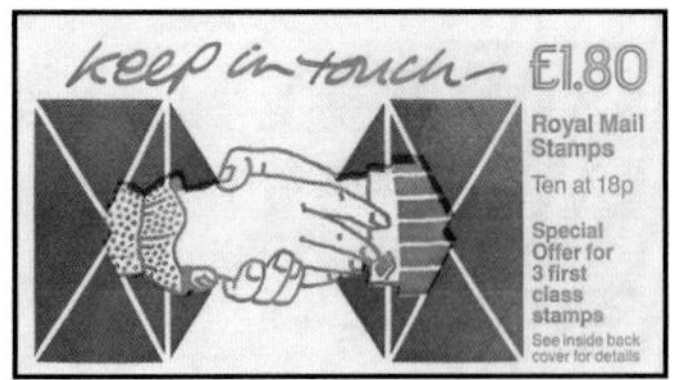

FB184	**£1.80**	**'Keep in touch'** pack. Left	5.25	8.00
FB184a		ACP. Pane FP122	6.50	7.00
FB185		Right	7.00	7.50
FB185a		ACP. Pane FP123	7.50	

1987 (14 April) Special Offer series.
Contents 10 x 18p ACP. Pane FP122 or FP123

FB186	**£1.80**	**'Ideas for your Garden'**. Left	4.75	5.25
FB187		Right	4.75	5.25

1987 (14 July) Special Offer series.
Contents 10 x 18p ACP. Pane FP122 or FP123

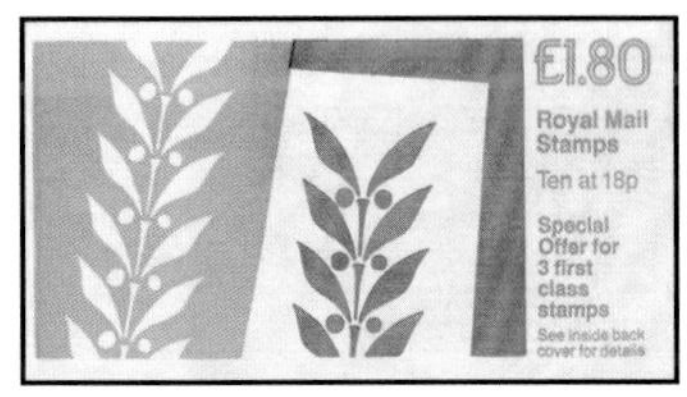

FB188	**£1.80**	**'Brighter Writer'** pack. Left	5.00	5.50
FB189		Right	5.00	5.50

1987 (29 Sept.) Special Offer series.
Contents 10 x 18p ACP. Pane FP122 or FP123

FB189	**£1.80**	**'Jolly Postman'** pack. Left	4.75	4.00
FB190		Right	4.75	5.25
FB190a		Miscut	118.00	450.00

1988 (26 Jan.) Special Offer series.
Contents 10 x 18p ACP. Pane FP122 or FP123

FB191	**£1.80**	**Natural History Postcards** (Linnean Society) 'for three 18p stamps (54p)'. Left	4.75	5.25
FB191a		Miscut pane	125.00	500.00
FB192		Right	4.75	5.50
FB193		Error '...for four 13p stamps (52p)'. Left	12.00	12.00
FB194		Right	11.00	12.00

1988 (12 April) Special Offer series.
Contents 10 x 18p ACP. Pane FP122 or FP123

FB195	**£1.80**	**Recipe Cards**. Left	4.75	5.25
FB196		Right	4.75	5.25

1988 (5 July) Special Offer series.
Contents 10 x 18p ACP. Pane FP122 or FP123

FB197	**£1.80**	**Children's party pack**. Left	5.00	5.50
FB197a		All over phosphor (6 stamps)		
FB198		Right	5.00	5.50
FB198a		All over phosphor		

1988 (5 Sept.) Special Offer series.
Contents 10 x 19p ACP. Pane FP125 or FP126

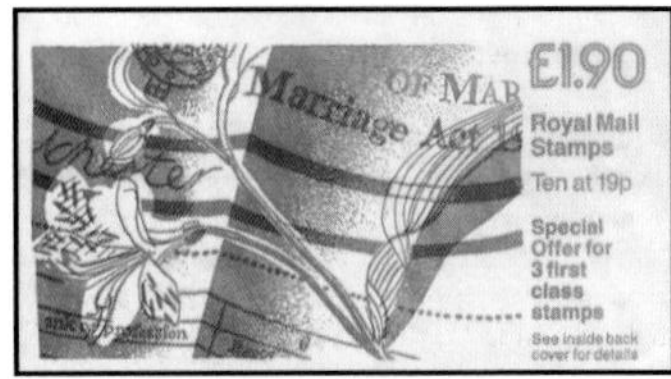

FB199	**£1.90**	**Pocket Planner**. Left	5.25	5.75
FB200		Right	5.25	6.00

1989 (24 Jan.). .

FB201	**£1.90**	**William Henry Fox Talbot**. Left	5.25	5.75
FB102		Right	5.25	5.75

Machine (Vending) Books

The notes on the decimal booklet panes are applicable to this listing of booklets and the numbers quoted for panes are taken from that section of the catalogue. A short description of the pane is included for ease.

There are wide number of varieties to be found in these books and many collections have been assembled based on this area of GB alone. In this new edition we have now included the price of the cheapest cylinder book, and also miscut panes and missing phosphor books, but a complete listing of these fascinating books can be found in the Machin Collectors Club Specialised Catalogue featured at the beginning of this book.

Miscut books are easily identified by the misplaced 'guillotine' line. On a normal book these are at each side, but on a miscut book this line is at the centre as illustrated below. Another feature of these issues is a Black or Red Back Marker Bar (BMB) which is printed on the spine of the book. These are printed every 25th book as an aid in the packing process.

Please note that a dash '-' in the price column denotes that this variety does not exist.

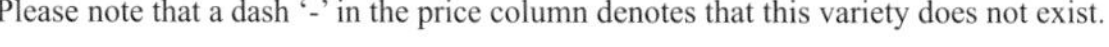

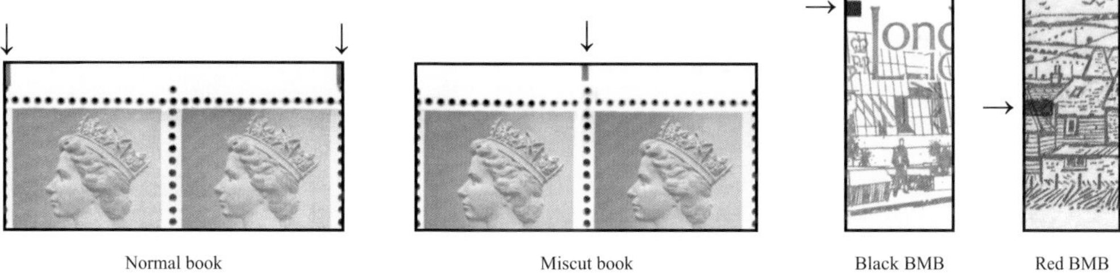

Normal book   Miscut book   Black BMB   Red BMB

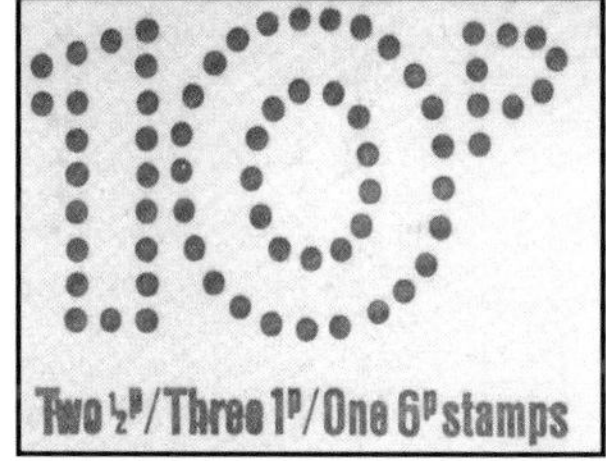

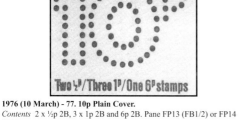

1976 (10 March) - 77. 10p Plain Cover.
Contents 2 x ½p 2B, 3 x 1p 2B and 6p 2B. Pane FP13 (FB1/2) or FP14 (FB3)

			Plain	Cyl.
FB1	**10p**	**White card**, Nov. 1975	1.20	-
FB1a		Perforated margin	1.00	-
FB1b		Cream card cover	1.25	-
FB1c		Perforated margin	1.50	-
FB2	**10p**	**Thin card cover**, Mar. 1976 (9.6.76)	1.00	-
FB2a		Perforated margin	1.00	-
FB2b		Thick card cover	5.00	-
FB2c		Perforated margin	£35	-
FB2d		Missing pale blue from cover	£75	-
FB2e		Miscut pane	£1450	-

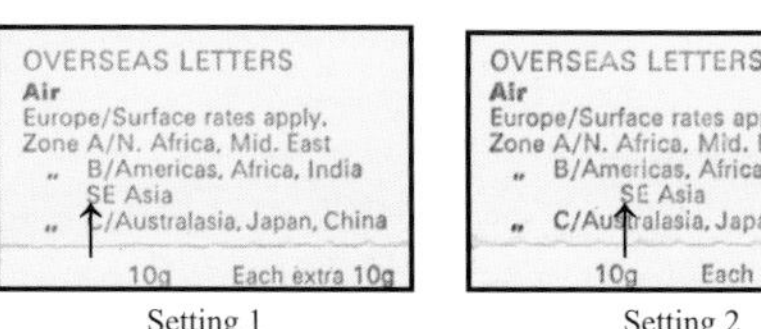

Setting 1   Setting 2

			Plain	Cyl.
FB3	**10p**	**June**, 1977 "S.E. Asia" at left-Setting 1	7.50	-
FB3a		Miscut pane	£25	-
FB3b		Perforated margin	2.00	-
FB3c		Miscut pane	4.75	-
FB3d		"S.E. Asia" at right-Setting 2	1.00	-
FB3e		Miscut pane	3.50	-
FB3f		Perforated margin	0.50	-
FB3g		Miscut pane	7.50	-

1978 (8 Feb.) - 79. Farm Buildings.
Contents 2 x ½p CB, 2 x 1p CB and 7p CB. Pane FP15.

			Plain	Cyl.
FB4	**10p**	**Oast houses**, 1st (8.2.78)	75	-
FB4a		Perforated margin	60	-
FB4b		Miscut pane	£35	-
FB5	**10p**	**Northern Ireland**, 2nd (3.5.78)	75	-
FB5a		Perforated margin	75	-
FB5b		Missing phosphor	£25	-
FB5c		Miscut pane	£120	-

			Plain	Cyl.
FB6	**10p**	**Yorkshire**, 3rd (9.8.78)	90	-
FB6a		Perforated margin	75	-

			Plain	Cyl.
FB7	**10p**	**Wales**, 4th (25.10.78)	75	-
FB7a		Missing turquoise from cover	£95	-
FB7b		Perforated margin	75	-

			Plain	Cyl.
FB8	**10p**	**Scotland**, 5th (10.1.79)	65	-
FB8a		Perforated margin	50	-
FB8b		Miscut pane	12.00	-

			Plain	Cyl.
FB9	**10p**	**Sussex**, 6th (4.4.79)	75	-
FB9a		Miscut pane	£275	
FB9b		Perforated margin	60	

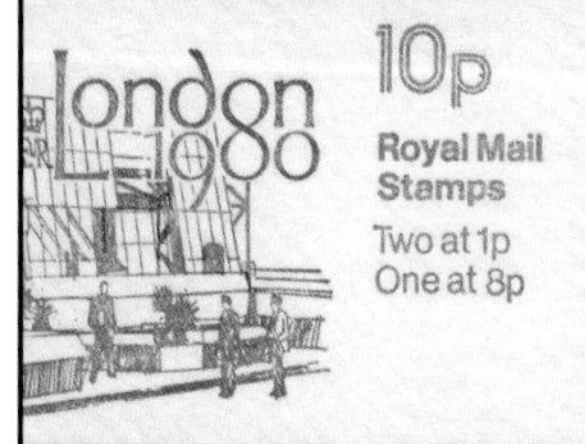

1979 (17 Oct.) - 80 "London 1980".

Contents 2 x 1p CB and 8p CB *plus* label. Panes FP1 or FP2 (FB12)

			Plain	Cyl.
FB10	**10p**	**Aug. 1979** (17.10.79)	50	-
FB10a		Miscut pane	7.00	-

1p Jumelle

1p Chambon

			Plain	Cyl.
FB11	**10p**	**Jan. 1980**, Jumelle (12.1.80)	50	-
FB11a		Miscut pane	3.50	-
FB12	**10p**	**Jan. 1980**, Chambon (4.8.80)	1.25	-
FB12a		Perforated margin	1.00	-
FB12b		Miscut pane	£350	-

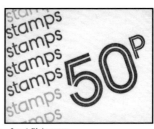

1977 (26 Jan. - June) Plain cover.

Contents 2 x ½p 2B, 2 x 1p 2B, 2 x 6½p SB and 4 x 8½p 2B. Pane FP39 or FP40.

			Plain	Cyl.
FB13	**50p**	**March 1976** (26.1.77). 6½p (right band) at left	2.50	-
FB13a		6½p (left band) at right	2.50	-

Setting 1

Setting 2

Contents 2 x 1p 2B, 3 x 7p SB and 3 x 9p 2B. Pane FP28 or FP29.

Setting 1

			Plain	Cyl.
FB14	**50p**	**June 1977** (13.6.77). 7p (right band) at left	7.50	-
FB14a		Thin value on 7p's	15.00	-
FB14b		7p (left band) at right	7.50	-
FB14c		Thin value on 7p's	10.00	-

Setting 2

			Plain	Cyl.
FB14	**50p**	**June 1977** (13.6.77). 7p (right band) at left	4.50	-
FB14a		Thin value on 7p's	9.00	-
FB14b		7p (left band) at right	3.00	-
FB14c		Thin value on 7p's	9.50	-

1978 (2 Aug.) - 79 Commercial Vehicles.
Contents 2 x 1p 2B, 3 x 7p SB and 3 x 9p 2B. Pane FP28 or FP29.

			Plain	Cyl.
FB15	**50p**	**Clement-Talbot van**, 1st (8.2.78). 7p (right band) at left	4.50	-
FB15a		Thin value on 7p's	7.00	-
FB15b		7p (left band) at right	2.50	-
FB15c		Thin value on 7p's	6.00	-
FB15d		Missing bistre-yellow from cover	£60	

			Plain	Cyl.
FB16	**50p**	**Austin Cape taxi**, 2nd (3.5.78) 7p (right band) at left	4.50	-
FB16a		7p (left band) at right	2.75	

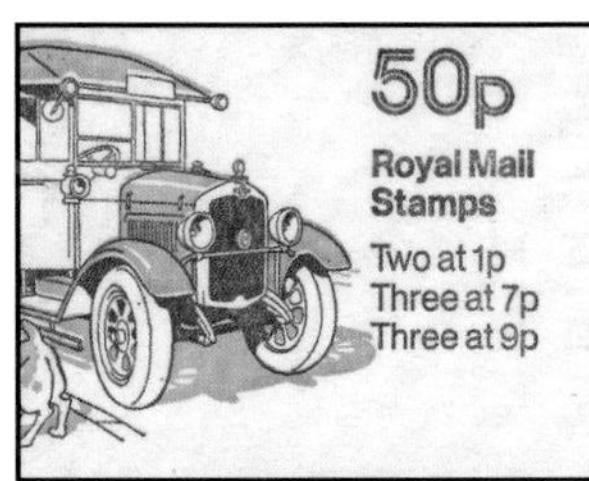

			Plain	Cyl.
FB17	**50p**	**Morris Royal Mail van**, 3rd (9.8.78) 7p (right band) at left	4.50	-
FB17a		Thin value on 7p's	8.00	-
FB17b		7p (left band) at right	3.00	-
FB17c		Thin value on 7p's	8.00	-

			Plain	Cyl.
FB18	**50p**	**Guy Electric dustcart**, 4th (25.10.78) 7p (right band) at left	4.50	-
FB18a		Thin value on 7p's	8.00	-
FB18b		7p (left band) at right	3.50	-
FB18c		Thin value on 7p's	7.50	-

			Plain	Cyl.
FB19	**50p**	**Albion Van**, 5th (10.1.79) 7p (right band) at left	6.00	-
FB19a		Thin value on 7p's	£25	-
FB19b		7p(left band) at right	5.00	-
FB19c		Thin value on 7p's	£17.50	-

			Plain	Cyl.
FB20	**50p**	**Leyland Fire engine**, 6th (4.4.79) 7p (right band) at left	4.50	-
FB20a		7p (left band) at right	2.75	-

Contents 2 x 2p 2B. 2 x 8p SB and 3 x 10p 2B *plus* label. Pane FP30 or FP31.

			Plain	Cyl.
FB21	**50p**	**Leyland Fire engine**, 6th (28.8.79) 8p (right band) at left	1.50	-
FB21a		8p (left band) at right	1.50	-

1979 (3 Oct.) - 81. Veteran Cars.
Contents 2 x 2p 2B, 2 x 8p SB and 3 x 10p 2B *plus* label. Pane FP30 or FP31.

			Plain	Cyl.
FB22	**50p**	**1907 Rolls Royce Silver Ghost**, 1st (3.10.79). 8p (right band) at left	2.00	-
FB22a		Miscut (2 x 2p & 4 x 8p)	£2250	-
FB22b		8p (left band) at right	2.00	-
FB22c		Miscut pane	£2250	-

Contents 3 x 2p 2B, 2 x 10p SB and 2 x 12p 2B *plus* label. Panes FP32/33 or FP34/35 (FB24/25)

			Plain	Cyl.
FB23	50p	**1908 Grand Prix Austin**, 2nd (4.2.80). 10p (right band) at left	2.75	-
FB23a		10p (left band) at right	2.25	-

			Plain	Cyl.
FB24	50p	**1905 Vauxhall**, 3rd (25.6.80) 10p (right band) at left	1.50	-
FB24a		Missing phosphor	£50	-
FB24b		10p (left band) at right	1.50	-
FB24c		Missing phosphor	£50	-

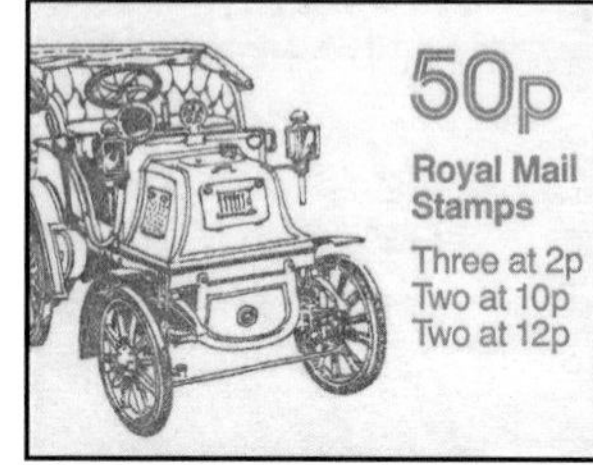

			Plain	Cyl.
FB25	50p	**1897 - 1900 Daimler**, 4th (24.9.80) 10p (right band) at left	1.50	-
FB25a		Missing phosphor	£60	-
FB25b		10p (left band) at right	1.50	-
FB25c		Missing phosphor	£60	-

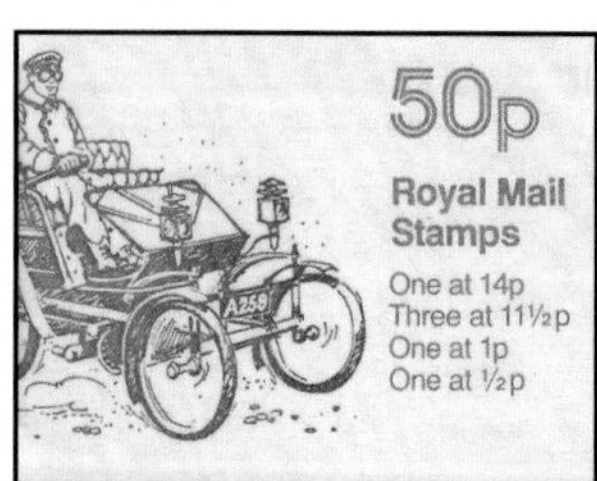

Contents ½p 2B, 1p 2B, 3 x 11½p SB and 14p 2B. Pane FP16 or FP17

			Plain	Cyl.
FB26	50p	**1896 Lanchester**, 5th (26.1.81). 11½p (right band) at left	1.95	-
FB26a		Perforated margin	1.75	-
FB26b		Missing phosphor	£50	-
FB26c		Missing phosphor, Perforated margin	£35	-
FB26d		Miscut (6 x 11½p)	£4000	-
FB26e		11½p (left band) at right	1.95	-
FB26f		Perforated margin	1.75	-
FB26g		Missing phosphor	£50	-
FB2h		Missing phosphor, Perforated margin	35.00	-
FB26i		Miscut (2 x ½p, 2 x 1p & 2 x 14p)	£3000	-

			Plain	Cyl.
FB27	50p	**1913 Bullnose Morris**, 6th (18.3.81). 11½p (right band) at left	4.00	-
FB27a		Perforated margin	2.25	-
FB27b		11½p (left band) at right	3.75	-
FB27c		Perforated margin	2.25	-

1981 (6 May) - 82 Follies.

Contents ½p 2B, 1p 2B, 3 x 11½p SB and 14p 2B. Pane FP16 or FP17

			Plain	Cyl.
FB28	50p	**Mugdock Castle**, 1st (6.5.81). 11½p (right band) at left	3.75	-
FB28a		Perforated margin	1.75	-
FB28b		Missing phosphor	£60	-
FB28c		11½p (left band) at right	3.75	-
FB28d		Perforated margin	1.75	-
FB28e		Missing phosphor	£60	-

Contents 3 x 2½p 2B, 2 x 4p 2B and 3 x 11½p SB. Pane FP36 or FP37

			Plain	Cyl.
FB29	50p	**Mugdock Castle**, 1st (26.8.81). 11½p (right band) at left	2.75	-
FB29a		Perforated margin	£20	-
FB29b		11½p (left band) at right	5.00	-
FB29c		Perforated margin	£60	-

			Plain	Cyl.
FB30	50p	**Mow Cop Castle**, 2nd (30.9.81). 11½p (right band) at left	3.00	-
FB30a		11½p (left band) at right	3.00	-

Contents ½p 2B, 4 x 3p 2B and 3 x 12½p SB. Pane FP24 or FP25

			Plain	Cyl.

			Plain	Cyl.
FB31	50p	**Paxton's Tower**, 3rd (1.2.82) 12½p (right band) at left	1.50	-
FB31a		Miscut (2 x ½p & 6 x 12½p)	£400	-
FB31b		12½p (left band) at right	1.50	-
FB31c		Miscut (8 x 3p)	£400	-

			Plain	Cyl.
FB32	50p	**Temple of the Winds**, 4th (6.5.82) 12½p (right band) at left	1.50	-
FB32a		12½p (left band) at right	1.50	-

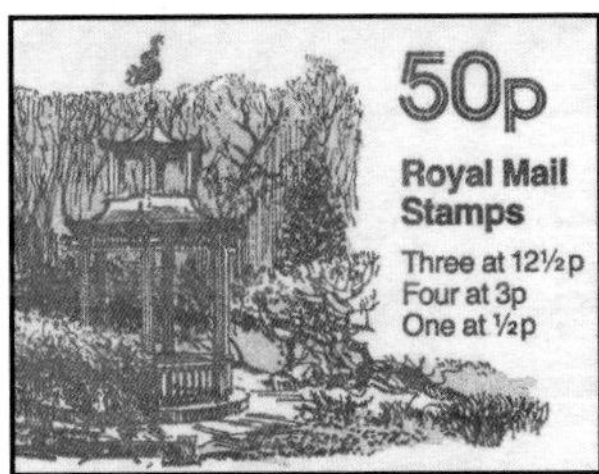

			Plain	Cyl.
FB33	50p	**Temple of the Sun**, 5th (11.8.82) 12½p (right band) at left	1.50	-
FB33a		12½p (left band) at right	1.75	-

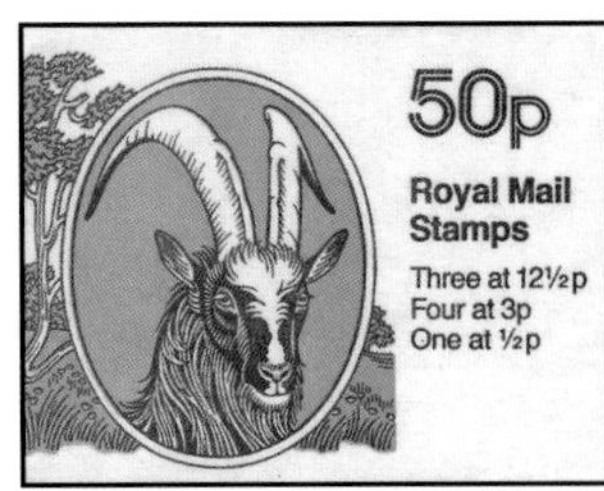

1983 (16 Feb. - Oct.) Rare Farm Animals.
Contents ½p 2B, 4 x 3p 2B and 3 x 12½p SB. Pane FP24 or FP25

			Plain	Cyl.
FB35	50p	**Bagot Goat**, 1st (16.2.83). 12½p (right band) at left	2.50	-
FB35a		12½p (left band) at right	2.25	-

Contents 2 x 1p CB, 3 x 3½p CB and 3 x 12½p CB at right. Pane FP26

			Plain	Cyl.
FB36	50p	**Gloucester Old Spot Pig**, 2nd (5.4.83)	3.00	-
FB36a		Missing phosphor	£12	-
FB36b		Miscut 12½p CB at left	£220	-
FB36c		Rate corrected to '36p' (200g)	6.00	-

			Plain	Cyl.
FB37	50p	**Toulouse Goose**, 3rd (27.7.83)	3.00	-

			Plain	Cyl.
FB38	50p	**Orkney Sheep**, 4th (26.10.83)	3.00	-
FB38a		Missing phosphor	£450	-

1984 (3 Sept.) - 85. Orchids. Printed in yellow-green and light violet.
Contents 3 x 1p CB, 2 x 4p CB and 3 x 13p CB. Pane FP27

			Plain	Cyl.
FB39	50p	**Dendrobium**, 1st (3.9.84)	1.50	1.75
FB39a		Missing phosphor	£200	£250
FB40	50p	**Cypripedium**, 2nd (15.1.85)	1.50	1.75
FB41	50p	**Bifrenaria**, 3rd (23.4.85)	1.50	1.75

			Plain	Cyl.
FB42	50p	**Cymbidium**, 4th (23.7.85)	1.50	2.25

1985 (4 Nov.) Special Offer series. Printed in grey-black and light scarlet.
Contents 3 x 17p 2B *plus* label with 'stars' underprint (51p). Pane FP11

			Plain	Cyl.
FB43	50p	**Pillar Box**, Nov. 1985 (4.11.85)	2.00	2.25
FB43a		Missing phosphor	£33	£50

1986 (20 May) - 87. Pond Life. Printed in dull blue and light blue-green.
Contents 3 x 17p 2B *plus* label with 'stars' underprint (51p). Pane FP11

			Plain	Cyl.
FB44	50p	**Emperor Dragonfly**, 1st (20.5.86)	1.80	1.75
FB44a		Missing phosphor	£50	£95

Contents 3 x 17p 2B *plus* label with 'stars' underprint (51p). Pane FP10

			Plain	Cyl.
FB45	50p	**Common frog**, 2nd (29.7.86)	2.50	2.75

Contents 3 x 17p 2B *plus* label without 'stars' underprint (51p). Pane FP10

			Plain	Cyl.
FB46	50p	**Common frog**, 2nd (12.8.86)	1.80	2.75
FB46a		Error. PCP1 paper. Pane FP87	£190	£195

Contents 1p CB, 2 x 5p CB and 3 x 13p CB. Pane FP18

			Plain	Cyl.
FB47	50p	**Moorhen**, 3rd (20.10.86) 'A' phosphor. Pane FP18a	4.00	4.50

			Plain	Cyl.
FB48	50p	**Giant Pond Snail**, 4th (27.1.87)	3.50	3.75

1986 (29 July) - 87. Roman Britain.

Contents 2 x 1p CB and 4 x 12p CB. Pane FP20

			Plain	Cyl.
FB49	50p	**Hadrian's Wall**, 1st (29.7.86)	3.50	4.00

Contents 1p LB, 13p RB and 2 x 18p 2B. Pane FP3

			Plain	Cyl.
FB50	50p	**Roman Theatre**, St. Albans, 2nd (20.10.86)	2.50	3.00
FB50a		Broad bands	£595	£750
FB50b		Missing phosphor	£275	£550
FB50c		Reversed phosphor bands	£30	£50

Contents 1p LB, 13p RB and 2 x 18p 2B. 'A' phosphor. Pane FP3c

			Plain	Cyl.
FB51	50p	**Portchester Castle**, 3rd (27.1.87)	2.25	2.95
FB51a		Reversed phosphor bands	£125	£175

1987 (14 April) - 88. MCC Bicentenary.

Contents 1p LB, 13p RB and 2 x 18p 2B. Pane FP3c

			Plain	Cyl.
FB52	50p	**Father Time**, 1st	1.95	3.00
FB52a		Missing phosphor	£75	£120
FB52b		Error. Old phosphor ink	4.50	£12

			Plain	Cyl.
FB53	50p	**Ashes urn**, 2nd (14.7.87)	2.00	3.00
FB53a		Error. Old phosphor ink	£145	£295
FB54	50p	**Lord's Pavillion**, 3rd (29.9.87)	1.95	2.50
FB54a		Missing phosphor	£55	£125
FB54b		Reversed phosphor bands	£40	£65
FB55	50p	**England Badge**, 4th (26.1.88)	2.00	2.50

1987 (14 April) - 86. Botanical Gardens.

Contents 1p CB, 2 x 5p CB and 3 x 13p CB. Pane FP18

			Plain	Cyl.
FB56	50p	**Bodnant**, 1st (14.4.87)	3.00	3.75

			Plain	Cyl.
FB57	50p	**Edinburgh**, 2nd (14.7.87) Imperf. sides. Pane FP19	3.00	4.00

			Plain	Cyl.

			Plain	Cyl.
FB58	**50p**	**Mount Stuart** (Incorrect spelling), 4.5mm Phosphor band 3rd (29.9.87)	3.00	4.00
FB58a		4mm Phosphor band	4.50	10.00
FB59	**50p**	**Mount Stewart** (Corrected spelling), 4.5mm Phosphor band 3rd (30.10.87)	3.00	3.75
FB59a		4mm Phosphor band	4.00	4.75
FB59b		Missing phosphor	£225	£325

			Plain	Cyl.
FB60	**50p**	**Kew**, 4.5mm Phosphor band 4th (26.1.88)	2.50	3.00
FB60a		4mm Phosphor band	£15	£20

1988 (12 April - 5 July) London Zoo.
Contents 1p LB, 13p RB and 2 x 18p RB. Pane FP3c

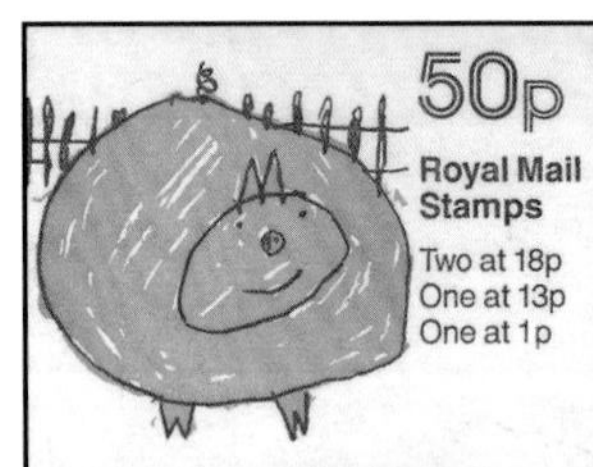

			Plain	Cyl.
FB61	**50p**	**Pigs**, 1st	2.00	2.25
FB61a		Missing phosphor	£45	£75

Contents 1p CB, 2 x 5p CB and 3 x 13p CB. Pane FP19

			Plain	Cyl.
FB62	**50p**	**Birds**, 4.5mm Phosphor band, 2nd	2.50	3.00
FB62a		4mm Phosphor band	10.00	12.50

Contents 1p LB, 13p RB and 2 x 18p 2B. Pane FP3c

			Plain	Cyl.
FB63	**50p**	**Elephants**, 4th (5.7.88)	2.00	2.50

1988 (5 July) - 89 Marine Life. Printed in dull blue and light orange-brown.
Contents 1p CB, 2 x 5p CB and 3 x 13p CB. Pane FP19

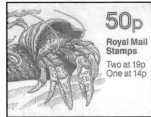

			Plain	Cyl.
FB64	**50p**	**Parasitic anemone**, 1st	2.00	2.25

Contents 14p RB and 2 x 19p 2B *plus* label. Pane FP10

			Plain	Cyl.
FB65	**50p**	**Common hermit crab**, 2nd (18.7.89). APS perf	2.00	2.50
FB65a		Reprint. Comb perf (8.8.89)	2.75	4.00

1988 (5 Sept.) - 89 Gilbert and Sullivan. Printed in salmon and black.
Contents 14p RB and 2 x 19p 2B *plus* label. Pane FP8a

			Plain	Cyl.
FB66	**50p**	**The Yeoman of the Guard**, 1st	1.75	2.50
FB66a		Missing phosphor	7.50	17.50
FB66b		Miscut pane	£950	£1200

			Plain	Cyl.

			Plain	Cyl.
FB67	**50p**	**The Pirates of Penzance**, 2nd (24.1.89)	2.50	2.75
FB67a		Missing phosphor	£95	£145
FB67b		Miscut	£1200	-

			Plain	Cyl.
FB68	**50p**	**The Mikado**, 3rd (25.4.89)	3.00	£25
FB68a		Missing phosphor	£35	£60

1989 (2 Oct.) - 91 Aeroplanes. Printed in blue-green and brown.
Contents 2 x 15p LB and 20p 2B *plus* label. Pane FP9

			Plain	Cyl.
FB69	**50p**	**HP42**, 1st	3.75	7.00
FB69a		Missing phosphor	£400	£500

Contents 2 x 15p LB and 20p 2B Anniversary stamps *plus* label. Pane AP1

			Plain	Cyl.
FB70	**50p**	Vickers Viscount 806, 2nd (30.1.90)	3.50	5.00

Contents 2 x 17p LB and 17p RB *plus* label. Pane FP12

			Plain	Cyl.
FB71	**50p**	BAC1-11, 3rd (4.9.90)	2.50	2.75
FB71a		Missing phosphor	£35	£70

			Plain	Cyl.
FB72	**50p**	BAe ATP, 4th (25.6.91)	2.75	3.00

1991 (10 Sept.) - 92 Archaeology.
Contents 2 x 1p, 2 x 24p ACP. Pane FP112

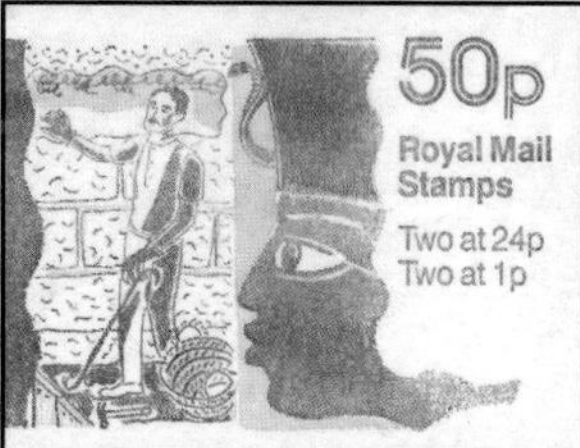

			Plain	Cyl.
FB73	**50p**	**Sir Arthur Evans**, 1st. 100g @ 35p	1.75	2.25
FB73a		Miscut	£135	£295
FB73b		Rates corrected. 100g @ 36p (10.91)	1.75	2.25

			Plain	Cyl.
FB75	**50p**	**Howard Carter**, 2nd (21.1.92)	1.75	2.25

50p
Royal Mail
Stamps
Two at 24p
Two at 1p

			Plain	Cyl.
FB76	**50p**	**Sir Austen Layard**, 3rd (28.4.92)	1.50	2.25

		Plain	Cyl.

		Plain	Cyl.
FB77	**50p Sir Flinders Petrie**, 4th (28.7.92)	2.00	2.25

1992 (22 Sept.) Sheriff's Millennium.
Contents 2 x 1p, 2 x 24p. Pane FP112

		Plain	Cyl.
FB78	**50p Crest**	1.50	2.25

1993 (9 Feb.) Postmarks.
Contents 2 x 1p, 2 x 24p ACP. Pane FP112

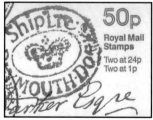

		Plain	Cyl.
FB79	**50p Airmail**, 1st	1.50	2.25
FB80	**50p Ship mail**, 2nd (6.4.93)	1.50	2.25
FB81	**50p Registered mail**, 3rd (6.7.93)	1.50	2.25

Contents 2 x 25p OFPP *plus* 2 x labels. Pane EP1

		Plain	Cyl.
FB82	**50p 'Paid'**, 4th (1.11.93)	1.50	2.25
FB82a	Miscut	£45	£150

1994 (25 Jan.) Coaching Inn Signs.
Contents 2 x 25p OFPP *plus* 2 x labels. Pane EP1

		Plain	Cyl.
FB83	**50p 'Swan with Two Necks'**, 1st	1.50	2.25
FB84	**50p 'Bull and Mouth'**, 2nd (26.4.94)	1.50	2.25

		Plain	Cyl.
FB85	**50p 'Golden Cross'**, 3rd (6.6.94)	1.50	2.25
FB86	**50p 'Pheasant Inn'**, 4th (6.9.94)	1.50	2.50

Plain Cyl.

1995 (7 Feb.) Sea Charts.
Contents 2 x 25p OFPP *plus* 2 x labels. Pane EP1

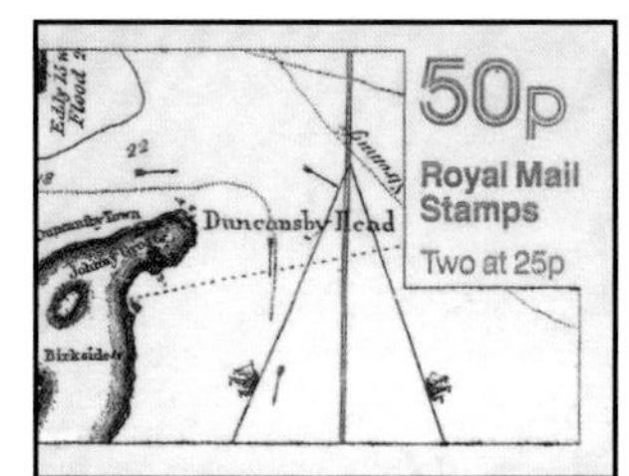

FB87 **50p John o' Groats**, 1st 1.50 2.25

FB88 **50p Land's End**, 2nd (4.4.95) 1.50 2.25

FB89 **50p St. David's Head,** 3rd (6.6.95) 2.75 3.25

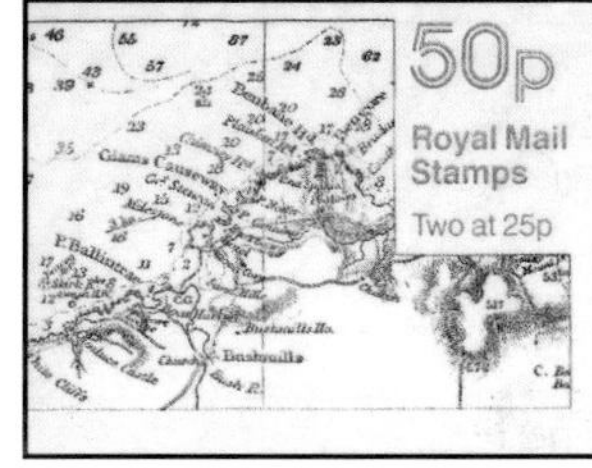

FB90 **50p Giant's Causeway**, 4th (4.9.95) 3.00 3.50

1986 (29 July) - 87. Musical Instruments. Printed in red and black.

Contents 6 x 17p PCP1 (£1.02). Pane FP88
FB114 **£1 Violin**, 1st 3.50 5.00

Plain Cyl.

Contents 13p LB and 5 x 18p 2B. Pane FP21
FB115 **£1 French horn**, 2nd (20.10.86) ' 5.00 5.50

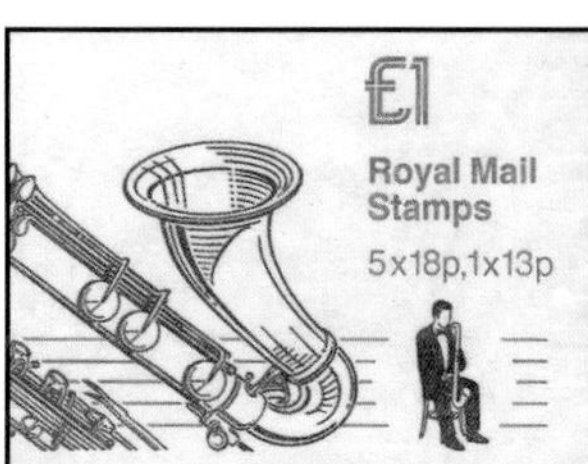

A' phosphor. Pane FP21a
FB116 **£1 Bass clarinet**, 3rd (27.1.87) 3.50 4.00

1987 (14 April) - 88 Sherlock Holmes.
Contents 13p LB and 5 x 18p 2B. Pane FP21a

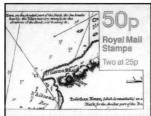

FB117 **£1 A Study in Scarlet**, 1st 5.00 5.50

FB118 **£1 The Hound of the Baskervilles**, 2nd (14.7.87) 4.50 5.00

Plain Cyl.

FB119 **£1 The Adventure of the Speckled Band**, 3rd (29.9.87) 4.50 5.00

FB120 **£1 The Final Problem**, 4th (26.1.88) 4.00 4.25

1988 (12 April) London Zoo. Drawings by children. Printed in black and brown. *Contents* 13p LB and 5 x 18p 2B, imperf. sides. Pane FP22

FB121 **£1 Bears**, 3rd 4.00 4.25

1988 (5 July) - 89 Charles Dickens.
Contents 13p LB and 5 x 18p 2B, imperf. sides. Pane FP22

FB122 **£1 Oliver Twist**, 1st 4.00 4.25

Plain Cyl.

Contents 2 x 14p RB and 4 x 19p 2B, imperf. sides. Pane FP23

FB123 **£1 Nicholas Nickleby**, 2nd (5.9.88). APS perf. 4.5. 4.75

FB123a Comb perf £45 £145

FB124 **£1 David Copperfield**, 3rd (24.1.89). Comb perf. 3.00 3.75

FB124a APS perf. (3.89) 9.50 £45

Contents 2 x 14p RB and 4 x 19p 2B, imperf. sides. Pane LP3
Printer: Walsall in Lithography.

FB125 **£1 Great Expectations**, 4th (25.4.89) 4.00 4.50

FB125a Missing phosphor £1100 £1500

1989 (18 July) Marine Life.
Contents 2 x 14p RB and 4 x 19p 2B, imperf. sides. Pane FP23

FB126 **£1 Edible sea urchin**, 3rd 3.00 3.50

Plain Cyl.

1989 (2 Oct.) - 91 Mills.
Contents 5 x 20p imperf sides *plus* label. Pane FP121

			Plain	Cyl.
FB127	**£1**	**Wicken Fen**, 1st	4.00	4.50

Printer: Walsall in Lithography. Printed on glossy card.
Contents 5 x 20p Anniversary stamp *plus* label. Pane AP10

			Plain	Cyl.
FB128	**£1**	**Wicken Fen**, 1st (30.1.90)	10.00	12.00

Contents 5 x 20p Anniversary stamps *plus* label. Pane AP4

			Plain	Cyl.
FB129	**£1**	**Click Mill**, 2nd (30.1.90)	3.50	3.75

Contents 2 x 17p RB and 3 x 22p 2B *plus* 3 x labels. Pane FP38

			Plain	Cyl.
FB130	**£1**	**Jack and Jill Mills**, 3rd (4.9.90)	2.50	7.00
FB130a		Missing phosphor	£60	£85

			Plain	Cyl.
FB131	**£1**	**Howell Mill**, 4th (25.6.91)	2.00	3.00

Plain Cyl.

1991 (10 Sept.) - 92 'Punch'.
Contents 2 x 2p, 4 x 24p imperf sides *plus* 2 x labels. Pane FP113

			Plain	Cyl.
FB132	**£1**	**1st**. 100g @ 35p	3.00	3.50
FB132a		Rates corrected 100g @ 36p	3.00	3.50

			Plain	Cyl.
FB133	**£1**	**2nd** (21.1.92)	2.75	3.00

			Plain	Cyl.
FB134	**£1**	**3rd** (28.4.92) 2.75	3.00	3.50

			Plain	Cyl.
FB135	**£1**	**4th** (28.7.92)	2.75	3.00

1992 (22 Sept.) Sheriff's Millennium.
Contents 2 x 2p, 4 x 24p imperf sides *plus* 2 x labels. Pane FP113

			Plain	Cyl.
FB136	**£1**	**Crest**	2.75	3.00

1993 (9 Feb.) Educational Institutions.
Contents 2 x 2p, 4 x 24p imperf sides *plus* 2 x labels. Pane LP5
Printer: Walsall in Lithography

		Plain	Cyl.
FB137	£1 **University of Wales**, 1st	3.50	4.00
FB138	£1 **St. Hilda's College**, 2nd (6.4.93)	3.50	4.00
FB139	£1 **Marlborough College**, 3rd (6.7.93)	3.50	4.00

Contents 4 x 25p (2 bands). Pane EP4

		Plain	Cyl.
FB140	£1 **University of Edinburgh**, 4th (1.11.93)	3.50	3.50

1994 (25 Jan.) British Prime Ministers.
Contents 4 x 25p (2 bands). Pane EP4
Printer: Walsall in Lithography

		Plain	Cyl.
FB141	£1 **Asquith,** 1st	2.75	3.00

Contents 4 x 25p OFPP. Pane EP2
Printer: Harrison

		Plain	Cyl.
FB142	£1 **Lloyd-George**, 2nd (26.4.94)	2.50	3.00
FB143	£1 **Churchill**, 3rd (6.6.94)	2.50	2.75
FB143a	Miscut	£725	£1250
FB144	£1 **Attlee**, 4th (6.9.94)	2.50	3.00

1995 (7 Feb.) 'Inspiration for Victory'.
Contents 4 x 25p OFPP. Pane EP2

		Plain	Cyl.
FB145	£1 **Violette Szabo**, 1st	2.50	3.00
FB145a	Miscut	£350	£400

			Plain	Cyl.

			Plain	Cyl.
FB146	£1	**Dame Vera Lynn**, 2nd (4.4.95)	2.50	3.00
FB146a		Miscut	£375	£1250
FB146b		4 x 25p 2B Yellow fluor	£75	£150

			Plain	Cyl.
FB147	£1	**R J Mitchell**, 4 x 25p 2B Yellow fluor 3rd (16.5.95) 2.50	3.00	
FB147a		Miscut	£150	£350
FB147b		4 x 25p 2B Blue fluor	3.00	3.50

			Plain	Cyl.
FB148	£1	**Archibald McIndoe,** 4th (4.9.95)	3.00	3.50
FB148a		Miscut	£450	£1200
FB148b		Missing phosphor	£85	£145

1996 (16 Jan.) Varnished Cover
Contents 4 x 25p 2B. Pane EP2

			Plain	Cyl.
FB149	£1	**Multicoloured**	3.00	3.50

1996 (8 July) Varnished Cover
Contents 3 x 26p 2B, 1 x 20p CB, 2 x 1p 2B. Pane EP Printed in Litho. Pane EP14

			Plain	Cyl.
FB150	£1	**Multicoloured**	2.75	3.25
FB150a		Corrected rate (4.2.97)	2.50	3.00
FB150b		'Textphone' inscription added (5.5.98)	2.50	2.75

1998 (1 Dec.) Varnished Cover
Contents 2 x 1p 2B, 1 x 20p CB, 3 x 26p 2B Printed in Gravure. Pane EP19

			Plain	Cyl.
FB151	£1	**Multicoloured**	2.25	2.75
FB151a		Miscut	£2750	£3000

1999 (26 Apr.) Varnished Cover
Contents 1 x 1p 2B, 1 x 2p 2B, 1 x 19p CB, 3 x 26p 2B Printed in Gravure. Pane EP20

			Plain	Cyl.
FB151	£1	**Multicoloured**	2.00	2.50
FB151a		Miscut	£1750	£2000

2000 (27 Apr.) Varnished Cover
Contents 1 x 2nd CB, 3 x 1st 2B and two lables. Pane CP49

			Plain	Cyl.
FB152	£1	Multicoloured (Postcode) (27.4.00) *1	2.25	3.50
FB152a		Miscut	£350	£1250

2001 (17 Apr.) Varnished
Contents 1 x 2nd CB, 3 x 1st 2B and two lables. Pane CP51

			Plain	Cyl.
FB153	£1	Multicoloured (Postcode<u>s</u>) (17.4.01) *2	2.25	3.50
FB153a		Miscut	£1000	£1750

*1 Web address is www.postcode.royalmail.co.uk on label 2
*2 Web address is www.postcodes.royalmail.co.uk on label 2

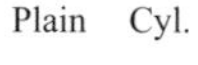

			Plain	Cyl.

1993 (1 Nov.) - 94 Postal Vehicles.
Contents 8 x 25p OFPP. Pane EP3

			Plain	Cyl.
FB230	£2	**Motorised Cycle**, 1st	3.75	4.00
FB230a		Miscut	12.50	£55

			Plain	Cyl.
FB231	£2	**Experimental Motor Mail Van**, 2nd (26.4.94)	3.00	4.00

			Plain	Cyl.
FB232	£2	**Experimental Electric Mail Van**, 3rd (6.9.94)	3.00	4.00

1995 (7 Feb.) Rowland Hill Birth Bicentenary.
Contents 8 x 25p OFPP. Pane EP3

			Plain	Cyl.
FB233	£2	**London and Brighton Railway**, 1st	3.00	4.00

			Plain	Cyl.
FB234	£2	**Hill's Educational Reform**, 2nd (4.4.95)	3.75	4.25
FB234a		Miscut	£300	£350
FB235	£2	**Postal Districts**, 3rd (6.6.95)	4.50	5.00
FB235a		Miscut		-

FB235a was confirmed in April 2004 - only one copy known.

			Plain	Cyl.
FB236	£2	**Uniform Penny Postage**, 4th (4.9.95)		
		Yellow fluor	4.50	5.00
FB236a		Blue fluor	6.00	7.00

1996 (16 Jan.) Varnished Cover
Contents 8 x 25p 2B. Pane EP15

			Plain	Cyl.
FB237	£2	**Multicoloured**	4.00	4.50

			Plain	Cyl.

1996 (8 July) Varnished Cover
Contents 7 x 26p 2B, 1 x 20p CB, Printed in Litho. Pane EP16

			Plain	Cyl.
FB238	£2	**Multicoloured**	4.00	5.00
FB238a		Corrected rate (4.2.97)	29.50	55.00
FB238b		'Textphone' inscription added (5.5.98)	3.75	4.25

1998 (1 Dec.) Varnished Cover
Contents 7 x 26p 2B 1 x 20p CB, Printed in Gravure. Pane EP23

			Plain	Cyl.
FB239	£2	**Multicoloured**	3.50	4.25
FB239a		Miscut	£1250	£1750

1999 (26 Apr.) Varnished Cover
Contents 1 x 19p CB and 7 x 26p 2B Printed in Gravure. Pane EP24

			Plain	Cyl.
FB240	£2	**Multicoloured**	3.25	3.75

2000 (27 Apr.) Varnished Cover
Contents 2 x 2nd CB and 6 x 1st 2B Printed in Gravure. Pane CP55

			Plain	Cyl.
FB241	£2	**Multicoloured**	3.25	4.00

Pane Plain Cyl.

Window Books

Window booklets made their appearance on 4 August 1987. They were designed for sale through the usual Post Office counters and supermarkets, stationers and similar retail outlets. The term "window" was applied because of the transparent "window" through which an example of the stamp contents could be viewed. The idea has been dropped and the booklets now have a printed 'stamp' on the cover. The term 'window' appears to have stayed and the booklets are now referred to as 'window' or 'bar code' booklets.

On the reverse of each booklet cover is a Bar Code moreover, on the early booklets, a Code Letter in the lower right hand corner. The code letter has since been dropped but it is important for sorting the earlier booklets and is therefore included in the listings. The early booklets can also be sorted by the locking 'tab' designed to keep the contents secure. The first 'tab' was square and this was altered to a round 'tab' on the first reprint.

The booklets have since moved on, and some covers adapted to promotions for leading retailers or Post Office promotions. The cover designs in later years were aimed at 'the high street' and the greetings books especially, have included eye catching characters, familiar to the great British public.

Window books were superceded by Self Adhesive books from 29 January 2001.

Square tab

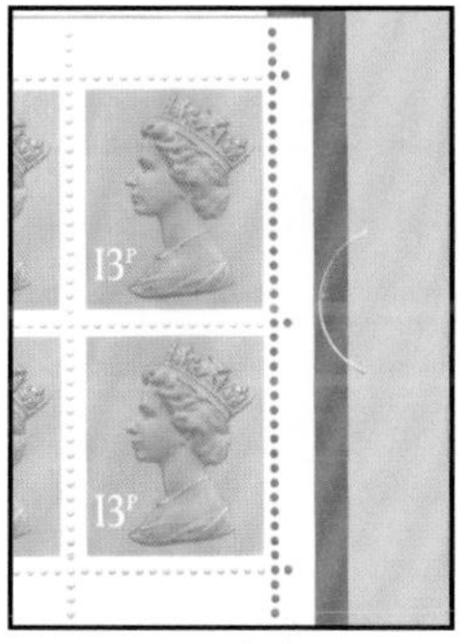

Round tab

1987 (4 Aug.) Large Format Booklets. Covers printed in red, yellow and black with a laminated finish and transparent 'window'. Perf. 15 x 14
Printer: Harrison & Sons in Photogravure

A. Window booklets with square tab (60mm high)

		Pane	Plain	Cyl.
WB1	**4 x 13p Chestnut** CB. Code E	FP4	2.50	2.75
WB2	**4 x 13p Chestnut** CB. Code F	FP4	2.50	2.75
WB3	**4 x 18p Grey-green** ACP. Code A	FP114	2.75	3.00
WB4	**4 x 18p Grey-green** ACP. Code B	FP114	2.75	3.00
WB5	**4 x 26p Red** ACP. Code I	FP118	9.00	9.50
WB6	**4 x 26p Red** ACP. Code J	FP118	9.00	9.50
WB7	**10 x 13p CB Chestnut** Code G	FP72	3.75	6.00
WB8	**10 x 13p CB Chestnut** Code H	FP72	3.25	4.50
WB9	**10 x 18p Grey-green** ACP. Code C	FP124	4.50	4.75
WB10	**10 x 18p Grey-green** ACP. Code D	FP124	4.75	6.50

B. Window booklets with round tab (60mm high) (1.88)

		Pane	Plain	Cyl.
WB11	**4 x 13p CB Chestnut** Code E	FP4	8.50	12.50
WB12	**4 x 13p CB Chestnut** Code F	FP4	£10	£15
WB13	**4 x 18p Grey-green** ACP. Code A	FP114	£11	£25
WB14	**4 x 18p Grey-green** ACP. Code B	FP114	6.50	8.50
WB15	**4 x 26p Red** ACP Code I	FP118	£14	£15
WB16	**10 x 13p CB Chestnut** Code G	FP72	£11	£11
WB17	**10 x 13p CB Chestnut** Code H	FP72	£11	£11
WB18	**10 x 18p Grey-green** ACP. Code C	FP124	£15	£15
WB19	**10 x 18p Grey-green** ACP. Code D	FP124	£14	£15

1988 (23 Aug.) Slightly smaller booklets with a reduced margin around the pane and new code letters. Round tab (56mm high). Perf. 15 x 14
Printer: Harrison & Sons in Photogravure

		Pane	Plain	Cyl.
WB20	**4 x 14p CB Dark blue** Code O	FP5	4.50	4.50
WB20a	Error of contents (4 x 19p) Code O	FP115	£345	£500
WB20b	Missing phosphor	FP5a		
WB21	**4 x 14p CB Dark blue** Code P	FP5	4.50	4.50
WB22	**4 x 19p Orange-red** ACP. Code K	FP115	4.00	4.25
WB23	**4 x 19p Orange-red** ACP. Code L	FP115	4.00	4.25
WB24	**4 x 27p CB Red-brown** Code S	FP119	8.50	8.50
WB24a	**4 x 27p CB Red-brown** Code S - Error Blank inside back cover	FP119	£20	£20
WB25	**4 x 27p CB Red-brown** Code T	FP119	8.50	8.50
WB26	**10 x 14p CB Dark blue** Code Q	FP77	6.00	7.00
WB27	**10 x 14p CB Dark blue** Code R	FP77	7.50	7.75
WB28	**10 x 19p Orange-red** ACP. Code M	FP127	9.50	9.50
WB28a	**10 x 19p Orange-red** ACP/ Low OBA, Code M	FP127	9.50	9.50
WB29	**10 x 19p Orange-red** ACP. Code N	FP127	9.50	9.50
WB29a	**10 x 19p Orange-red** ACP/ Low OBA, Code N	FP127	£95	9.50

1988 (11 Oct.)
Printer: House of Questa in Lithography

		Pane	Plain	Cyl.
WB30	**10 x 14p CB Dark blue** Code Q	LP1	£11	-
WB31	**10 x 14p CB Dark blue** Code R	LP1	£11	-
WB32	**10 x 19p Orange-red** ACP. Code M	LP2	12.50	-
WB33	**10 x 19p Orange-red** ACP. Code N	LP2	12.50	-

Booklet covers printed by Walsall Security Printers Ltd.
Stamps printed by Harrison & Sons in Photogravure Perf. 15 x 14.

		Pane	Plain	Cyl.
WB34	**4 x 14p CB Dark blue** Code O	FP5	4.00	3.25
WB35	**4 x 14p CB Dark blue** Code P	FP5	4.00	3.25
WB36	**4 x 19p Orange-red** ACP. Code K	FP115	4.50	3.75
WB37	**4 x 19p Orange-red** ACP. Code L	FP115	4.50	3.75

1988 (11 Oct.) Small Format Booklets with printed 'stamp' (48mm high)
Printer: Harrison & Sons in Photogravure. Perf. 15 x 14

		Pane	Plain	Cyl.
WB38	**4 x 14p CB Dark blue**	FP6	4.50	6.00
WB39	**4 x 19p Orange-red** ACP.	FP116	5.00	5.50
WB39a	Error of contents (10 x 19p)		£800	£1300
WB40	**4 x 27p Red-brown** ACP.	FP120	£20	£20
WB41	**10 x 14p CB Dark blue** - Bar code 100104	FP78	8.00	7.50
WB42	**10 x 14p CB Dark blue** - Bar code 200101	FP78	£15	£10
WB42a	Missing phosphor		£180	£250
WB42c	Error of contents (4 x 14p)	FP6	£850	£1200

Contents FP128

		Pane	Plain	Cyl.
WB43	**10 x 19p Orange-red** ACP. - Bar code 200088	FP128	6.50	7.50
WB43b	Plain - Error of contents (4 x 19p)	FP116	£1200	£1200
WB44	**10 x 19p Orange-red** ACP. - Bar code 100081	FP128	8.00	9.50

Printer: House of Questa in Lithography. Perf. 15 x 14

		Pane	Plain	Cyl.
WB45	**10 x 14p CB Dark blue**	LP1	£11	-
WB46	**10 x 19p Orange-red** ACP. Plain	LP2	£11	-

1989 (24 Jan.)
Booklet covers printed by Walsall Security Printers Ltd.
Stamps Printed by Harrison & Sons in Photogravure Perf. 15 x 14

		Pane	Plain	Cyl.
WB47	**4 x 14p CB Dark blue** Imperf. on three sides	FP7	£15	-
WB47a	**4 x 14p Dark blue**. Imperf. on three sides Missing phosphor	FP7a	£20	-
WB48	**4 x 19p Orange-red** ACP. Imperf. on three sides.	FP117	£15	-

1989 (2 Oct.) Worldwide postcards. Perf. 14
Printer: Walsall in Lithography

		Pane	Plain	Cyl.
WB49	**4 x 29p 2B Purple**	LP4	7.50	8.00
WB50	**4 x 29p Purple** ACP. (17.4.90)	LP6	6.50	7.00

1990 (17 Sep.) Worldwide Postcard Books

		Pane	Plain	Cyl.
WB51	**4 x 31p Ultramarine** ACP.	LP7	3.50	5.00
WB51a	**4 x 31p Ultramarine** ACP./Low OBA	LP7a	5.00	9.50
WB51b	**4 x 31p Ultramarine** ACP./Low OBA New revised locking tab without side slits	LP7a	3.50	5.00

1991 (16 Sept.) Worldwide postcards and Airmail stamps. Perf. 14
Printer: Walsall in Lithography

		Pane	Plain	Cyl.
WB52	**4 x 33p Light emerald** PVA gum.	LP8	2.50	3.50
WB52a	Error. PVAD gum. No text on postcard rate.	LP11	6.00	8.50

Reprint.

		Pane	Plain	Cyl.
WB53	**4 x 33p Light emerald** PVAD gum.. Text - postcard rate is 33p	LP11	2.50	3.50
WB54	**4 x 39p Bright mauve** ACP	LP10	2.75	4.00

1992 (28 July) Kellogs Overseas Rate. Perf. 14
Printer: Walsall in Lithography

		Pane	Plain	Cyl.
WB55	**2 x 39p Bright mauve** ACP.	LP9	1.75	3.00

1993 (1 Nov.) - 94 Worldwide postcards and Airmail stamps.
Printer: Walsall in Lithography. Perf. 15 x 14 elliptical

		Pane	Plain	Cyl.
WB56	**4 x 35p 2B Yellow** (Yellow fluor).	EP8	3.50	3.75
WB57	**4 x 41p 2B Stone** (Yellow fluor).	EP10	3.75	4.00

		Pane	Plain	Cyl.
WB58	**4 x 60p 2B Slate-blue** (Yellow fluor). (9.8.94)	EP11	4.50	5.00

		Pane	Plain	Cyl.
WB59	**4 x 60p 2B Slate-blue** (Yellow fluor). Christmas edition (4.10.94)	EP11	4.50	5.50

1995 (16 May) Worldwide postcards and Airmail stamps.
Printer: Walsall in Lithography. Perf. 15 x 14 elliptical.

		Pane	Plain	Cyl.
WB60	**4 x 35p 2B Yellow** (Yellow fluor).	EP8	3.50	4.00
WB60b	**4 x 35p 2B Yellow** (Blue fluor) (10.10.94)	EP8a	3.00	4.00
WB61	**4 x 41p 2B Drab** (Yellow fluor).	EP10	3.75	4.25
WB62	**4 x 60p 2B Slate-blue** (Yellow fluor).	EP11	4.50	5.50

1996 (19 Mar.) Worldwide postcards and Airmail stamps. Olympics.
Printer: Walsall in Lithography. Perf. 15 x 14 elliptical.

		Pane	Plain	Cyl.
WB63	**4 x 35p 2B Deep yellow** (Blue fluor).	EP8a	6.00	7.50
WB64	**4 x 41p 2B Stone** (Blue fluor).	EP10a	6.75	7.25
WB65	**4 x 60p 2B Slate-blue** (Blue fluor).	EP11a	7.50	7.75

1996 (8 July) Worldwide postcards and Airmail stamps. Cover as WB63
Printer: Walsall in Lithography. Perf. 15 x 14 elliptical.

		Pane	Plain	Cyl.
WB66	**4 x 37p 2B Amethyst** (Blue fluor).	EP9	3.50	4.50
WB67	**4 x 63p 2B Light emerald** (Blue fluor).	EP12	4.50	5.50
	Missing Phosphor	EP12a	£1200	£1200

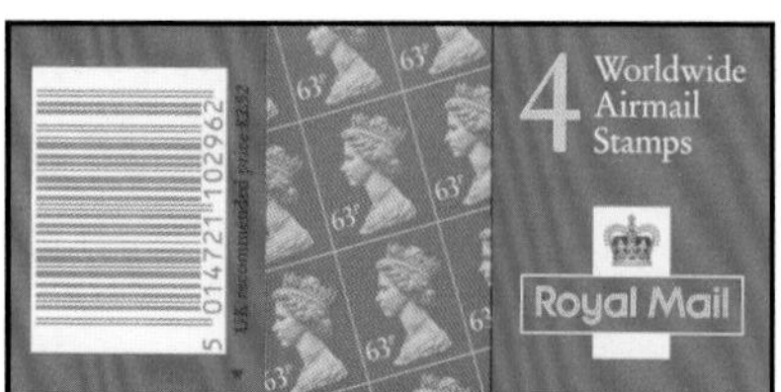

1997 (4 Feb.) Worldwide postcards and Airmail stamps. Text 'Worldwide Airmail Stamps' ranged to the left and 'International' omitted.
Printer: Walsall in Photogravure

		Pane	Plain	Cyl.
WB68	**4 x 37p 2B Amethyst** (Blue fluor).	EP9	3.00	3.50
WB69	**4 x 63p 2B Light emerald** (Blue fluor).	EP12	4.00	4.50

1997 (26 Aug.) Worldwide postcards and Airmail stamps with table of postage rates
Printer: Walsall in computer-engraved gravure. Perf. 15 x 14 elliptical.

		Pane	Plain	Cyl.
WB70	**4 x 37p 2B Amethyst** (Blue fluor).	EP9	2.50	3.50
WB71	**4 x 63p 2B Light emerald** (Blue fluor). Cover as WB69	EP12	3.50	4.50

1998 (5 May) European Airmail stamps.

		Pane	Plain	Cyl.
WB72	**4 x 30p 2B Grey-green** (Blue fluor).	EP14	2.50	3.25
WB73	**4 x 63p 2B Light emerald** (Blue fluor).	EP18	3.75	4.50
WB74	**4 x 38p 2B Ultramarine** (Blue fluor). (26.4.99)	EP16	2.75	3.50
WB75	**4 x 64p 2B Sea green** (Blue fluor). (26.4.99)	EP19	3.75	4.50

It pays to get the postage right when sending mail abroad

Valid for sending Postcards to anywhere in the World by Airmail*

- Please check and ensure that you have paid the correct postage.
- Always use Airmail labels on Airmail items.
- Always put your name, address and postcode on the back of the envelope.
- A range of international pre-paid Aircards, Aerogrammes and gift Airpacks are available from most main post offices.

For further information about Royal Mail's international services and postage rates please refer to the International Prices leaflet available at your local post office, or alternatively telephone your local Royal Mail Customer Services on 0345 740 740.

*Details correct at time of printing.

For Worldwide Postcards

1998 (5 May) Worldwide postcards and Airmail stamps.

Cover as WB70 but *without* table of postal rates (above)

		Pane	Plain	Cyl.
WB76	**4 x 37p 2B Amethyst** (Blue fluor).	EP15	2.75	3.50

1998 (3 Aug.) Worldwide postcards and Airmail stamps Create-a-Card

		Pane	Plain	Cyl.
WB77	**4 x 30p 2B Grey-green** (Blue fluor)	EP14	2.50	3.25
WB78	**4 x 37p 2B Amethyst** (Blue fluor)	EP15	2.75	3.50

These have a revised telephone number beginning with 0845

2000 (27 Apr.) European Airmail stamps.

		Pane	Plain	Cyl.
WB79	**4 x 40p 2B Greyish-blue** (Blue fluor).	EP17	2.75	3.50
WB80	**4 x 65p 2B Greenish-blue** (Blue fluor).	EP20	3.75	4.50

Penny Black Anniversary Books

1990 (30 Jan. - 12 June) Printer: Harrison & Sons in Photogravure

		Pane	Plain	Cyl.
AB1	**10 x 15p CB Bright blue**	AP2	5.50	6.00
AB2	**10 x 20p Black & buff** ACP.	AP5	6.00	6.50

Printer: House of Questa in Lithography

		Pane	Plain	Cyl.
AB3	**10 x 15p CB Bright blue** (17.4.90)	AP6	£11	-
AB4	**10 x 20p Black & buff** ACP. (17.4.90)	AP7	£700	-
AB4a	**10 x 20p Black & buff** ACP/Low OBA	AP7a	9.00	-

Printer: Walsall Security Printers Ltd in Lithography

		Pane	Plain	Cyl.
AB5	**4 x 15p CB Bright blue**	AP8	3.50	3.75
AB5a	Yellow Queen Victoria head on cover	AP8	4.50	7.50
AB6	**4 x 20p Black & buff** ACP.	AP11	3.75	3.75
AB7	**10 x 15p CB Bright blue** (12.6.90)	AP9	5.75	5.75
AB7a	Incorrect rates on inside cover	AP9a	8.50	£10
AB8	**10 x 20p Black & buff** ACP. (12.6.90)	AP12	7.50	7.50

1990 (17 April) Booklet covers printed by Walsall Security Printers Ltd Stamps printed by Harrison & Sons in Photogravure

Contents

		Pane	Plain	Cyl.
AB9	**4 x 20p Black & buff** ACP	AP3	4.50	-
AB9a	Missing cream from Queen Victoria head on cover	AP3	6.50	-

Non Value Indicator (NVI) Books

1989 (22 Aug.) - 90 Printer: Harrison & Sons in Photogravure. Perf. 15 x 14

		Pane	Plain	Cyl.
CB1	**10 x 2nd CB Bright blue**	CP2	5.00	5.00
CB1a	Reprint. Full postal rates	CP2	5.25	6.00
CB2	**10 x 1st Black** ACP.	CP5	6.50	7.00
CB2a	Reprint. Full postal rates	CP5	6.75	7.00

Printer: House of Questa in Lithography. Perf. 15 x 14

		Pane	Plain	Cyl.
CB3	**10 x 2nd CB Bright blue**			
	Perforated margin (19.9.89)	CP7	8.50	-
CB3a	Imperf. margin	CP7a	£60	-
CB4	**10 x 1st Black** ACP.			
	Perforated margin (19.9.89)	CP9	8.50	-
CB4a	Perforated margin - Low OBA	CP9a	£15	-
CB4b	Imperf. margin	CP9b	9.00	-
CB4c	Imperf margin - Low OBA	CP9c	£15	-

Printer: Walsall Security Printers Ltd in Lithography. Perf. 14

		Pane	Plain	Cyl.
CB5	**4 x 2nd CB Bright blue**	CP12	2.75	3.75
CB6	**4 x 1st 2B Black**	CP15	4.00	4.25

1989 (28 Nov.) Booklet covers printed by Walsall Security Printers Ltd. Stamps printed by Harrison & Sons in Photogravure. Perf. 15 x 14

		Pane	Plain	Cyl.
CB7	**4 x 2nd CB Bright blue**	CP1	8.50	-
CB8	**4 x 1st Black** ACP.	CP4	9.75	-

		Pane	Plain	Cyl.

1990 (7 Aug.) - 91 New 'Royal Mail' logo. Perf. 15 x 14
Printer: Harrison & Sons in Photogravure.

		Pane	Plain	Cyl.
CB9	**10 x 2nd CB Dark blue**.	CP3	4.50	5.00
CB10	**10 x 1st Orange-red** ACP.	CP6	4.75	5.00

Printer: House of Questa in Lithography. Perf. 15 x 14

		Pane	Plain	Cyl.
CB11	**10 x 2nd CB Dark blue**	CP8	5.75	-
CB12	**10 x 1st Orange-red** ACP.	CP11	5.00	-

Printer: Walsall Security Printers Ltd in Lithography. Perf. 14

		Pane	Plain	Cyl.
CB13	**4 x 2nd CB Dark blue**	CP13	2.00	2.75
CB14	**4 x 1st Orange-red** ACP.	CP19	2.25	3.00
CB14a	**4 x 1st Orange-red** ACP./Low OBA	CP19a	2.75	4.50
CB15	**4 x 1st Orange-red** ACP. Perf 13. (10.90)	CP21	6.00	7.50
CB15a	**4 x 1st Orange-red** ACP/Low OBA. Perf 13	CP21a	6.00	7.50
CB16	**10 x 2nd CB Dark blue**	CP16	4.25	4.75
CB17	**10 x 1st Orange-red** ACP.	CP20	4.50	5.00
CB17a	**10 x 1st Orange-red** ACP./Low OBA	CP20a	7.00	7.50

Without side slits - Newcastle address on inside cover

Printer: Walsall Security Printers Ltd in Lithography. Perf. 14

		Pane	Plain	Cyl.
CB18	**4 x 2nd CB Dark blue**	CP13	2.25	2.75
CB19	**4 x 1st Orange-red** ACP.	CP19	2.50	3.00
CB20	**10 x 2nd CB Dark blue**	CP16	4.75	5.00
CB21	**10 x 1st Orange-red** ACP.	CP20	3.75	4.50

Without side slits - London address on inside cover

1991 (6 Aug.)
Printer: House of Questa in Lithography. Perf. 15 x 14

		Pane	Plain	Cyl.
CB22	**10 x 2nd CB Bright blue**	CP7	4.00	5.00
CB23	**10 x 1st Orange-red** ACP.	CP11	4.50	5.00

Printer: Walsall Security Printers Ltd in Lithography. Perf. 15

		Pane	Plain	Cyl.
CB24	**4 x 2nd CB Bright blue**	CP12	1.50	2.75
CB25	**4 x 1st Orange-red** ACP.	CP19	2.50	3.00
CB26	**10 x 2nd CB Bright blue**	CP17	3.75	4.00
CB27	**10 x 1st Orange-red** ACP.	CP20	4.50	4.50

Printer: Harrison & Sons in Photogravure. Perf 15 x 14

Contents

		Pane	Plain	Cyl.
CB28	**10 x 1st Orange-red** ACP.	CP6	5.25	6.00

1992 (21 Jan.) British Olympic and Paralympic teams logo.
Printer: Harrison & Sons in Photogravure. Perf. 15 x 14

		Pane	Plain	Cyl.
CB29	**10 x 1st Orange-red** ACP.	CP6	4.00	4.50

Printer: House of Questa in Lithography. Perf. 15 x 14

		Pane	Plain	Cyl.
CB30	**10 x 2nd CB Bright blue** (31.3.92)	CP7	4.00	4.50

Printer: Walsall Security Printers in Lithography. Perf. 14

		Pane	Plain	Cyl.
CB31	**4 x 2nd CB Bright blue**	CP14	1.50	2.75
CB32	**4 x 1st Orange-red** ACP.	CP19	2.00	3.00
CB33	**10 x 2nd CB Bright blue**	CP17	3.25	4.00
CB34	**10 x 1st Orange-red** ACP.	CP20	3.75	4.50

1993 (9 Feb.) Rupert Bear Promotion. Perf. 14
Printer: Walsall Security Printers in Lithography

		Pane	Plain	Cyl.
CB35	**10 x 1st Orange-red** ACP.	CP23	3.75	4.50
CB36	**10 x 1st 2B Orange-red** 'C' Yellow fluor. (1.11.93)	CP39	4.00	5.00

1993 (6 April) Security booklets Type 1.
These books have a single line of text at left of inside cover

Printer: Harrison & Sons in Photogravure. Perf. 15 x 14 elliptical

		Pane	Plain	Cyl.
CB37	**4 x 1st Orange-red** OFPP.	CP27	2.00	3.25
CB38	**10 x 1st Orange-red** OFPP.	CP28	4.00	5.00

		Pane	Plain	Cyl.

Printer: House of Questa in Lithography. Perf. 15 x 14 elliptical

		Pane	Plain	Cyl.
CB39	**10 x 2nd CB Bright blue**	CP31	3.50	4.50
CB39a	Missing phosphor		£1250	£1400

Printer: Walsall Security Printers Ltd in Lithography. Perf. 15 x 14 elliptical

		Pane	Plain	Cyl.
CB40	**4 x 2nd CB Bright blue**	CP35	3.00	3.25
CB41	**4 x 1st 2B Orange-red**	CP37	2.00	3.50
CB42	**10 x 1st 2B Orange-red**	CP39	4.50	5.00
CB42a	Missing phosphor	CP39a	£1000	£1200

↑

1993 (17 Aug.) Security Booklets Type 2
These books have two lines of text at left of inside cover

Printer: Walsall Security Printers in Lithography. Perf. 15 x 14 elliptical

		Pane	Plain	Cyl.
CB43	**4 x 2nd CB Bright blue** C(Yellow) fluor.	CP35	2.00	3.25
CB44	**4 x 1st 2B Orange-red** C(Yellow) fluor.	CP37	3.00	4.00
CB45	**10 x 2nd CB Bright blue** C(Yellow) fluor.	CP36	3.50	4.50
CB46	**10 x 1st 2B Orange-red** C(Yellow) fluor.	CP39	4.50	5.00

Printer: House of Questa in Lithography. Perf. 15 x 14 elliptical

		Pane	Plain	Cyl.
CB47	**10 x 2nd CB Bright blue** C(Yellow) fluor	CP32	3.50	4.50
CB48	**10 x 1st 2B Orange-red** C(Yellow) fluor	CP33	4.50	5.00

Printer: Harrison & Sons in Photogravure. Perf. 15 x 14 elliptical

		Pane	Plain	Cyl.
CB49	**4 x 2nd CB Bright blue** (7.9.93)	CP24	1.75	3.25
CB50	**10 x 1st Orange-red** OFPP.	CP28	4.50	5.00

↑

1993 (17 Aug.) Security Booklets Type 3
These books have three lines of text at left of inside cover

Printer: House of Questa in Lithography. Perf. 15 x 14 elliptical

		Pane	Plain	Cyl.
CB51	**10 x 2nd CB Bright blue**	CP32	3.50	5.00
CB52	**10 x 1st 2B Orange-red** C (Yellow) fluor.	CP33	4.50	6.00

1994 (22 Feb.) Free Postcards (text on tab at right). Perf. 15 x 14 elliptical
Printer: Walsall Security Printers in Lithography

		Pane	Plain	Cyl.
CB53	**10 x 1st 2B Orange-red** CP39 *plus* additional pane detailing 'Free Greetings Postcards' offer	CP39	4.50	5.50
CB53a	Broad band	CP39a	£750	£850

1994 (1 July) W H Smith free kite offer. OPEN NOW Chance to win a kite (text on tab at right).
Printer: Walsall Security Printers in Lithography Perf 15 x 14 elliptical

		Pane	Plain	Cyl.
CB54	**10 x 1st 2B Orange-red**	CP39		
	Better Luck Next Time (text on inside back cover)		4.50	5.00
	You've Won! (text on inside back cover)		4.50	5.50

1994 (27 July) Bank of England. Perf. 15 x 14 elliptical
Printer: House of Questa in Lithography.

		Pane	Plain	Cyl.
CB55	**4 x 1st 2B Orange-red**	CP34	2.50	3.50
CB55a	Missing phosphor	CP34a	£950	£1250

1994 (6 Sept.) STAMPERS™.
Printer Walsall Security Printers in Lithography. Perf. 15 x 14 elliptical

		Pane	Plain	Cyl.
	10 x 1st 2B Orange-red	CP39.		
CB56	* Do not open until.....		4.50	5.00
CB57	* Keep in Touch		4.50	5.00
CB58	* Happy birthday		4.50	5.00
CB59	* What's Happenin'?		4.50	5.00

1995 (10 Jan.) New cover designs.
Printer: Harrison & Sons in Photogravure. Perf. 15 x 14 elliptical

C (Yellow) fluor phosphor

		Pane	Plain	Cyl.
CB60	**4 x 2nd CB Bright blue**	CP24	2.25	3.25
CB61	**10 x 1st Orange-red** OFPP.	CP28	4.50	5.00
CB62	**10 x 1st 2B Orange-red** (4.4.95)	CP26	4.50	5.00

Printer: House of Questa in Lithography. Perf. 15 x 14 elliptical

		Pane	Plain	Cyl.
CB63	**10 x 2nd CB Bright blue**	CP32	4.00	5.00
CB64	**10 x 1st CB Orange-red**	CP33	4.50	5.00

Printer: Walsall Security Printers Ltd in Lithography. Perf. 15 x 14 elliptical

		Pane	Plain	Cyl.
CB65	**4 x 1st 2B Orangre-red**	CP37	2.00	3.75
CB66	**10 x 1st 2B Orange-red**	CP39	4.50	5.00

D (Blue) fluor phosphor

Printer: Harrison & Sons in Photogravure. Perf. 15 x 14 elliptical

		Pane	Plain	Cyl.
CB67	**4 x 2nd CB Bright blue**	CP24a	2.25	3.25
CB68	**10 x 1st 2B Orange-red**	CP26a	4.50	4.50
CB69	**10 x 2nd CB Bright blue**	CP25	3.50	4.50

Printer: House of Questa in Lithography. Perf. 15 x 14 elliptical

		Pane	Plain	Cyl.
CB70	**10 x 2nd CB Bright bl**ue	CP32a	3.50	4.50
CB71	**10 x 1st 2B Orange-red**	CP33a	5.00	6.00

Printer: Walsall Security Printers Ltd in Lithography. Perf. 15 x 14 elliptical

		Pane	Plain	Cyl.
CB72	**4 x 1st 2B Orange-red**	CP38	2.50	3.50
CB73	**10 x 1st 2B Orange-red**	CP40	4.50	5.50
CB74	**4 x 2nd CB Bright blue**	CP35a	2.25	3.00

1995 (14 Feb.) Thorntons Sun Chocolates.
Printer: Walsall Security Printers in Lithography. Perf. 15 x 14 elliptical

		Pane	Plain	Cyl.
CB75	**10 x 1st 2B Orange-red**	CP39	4.50	5.00
CB75a	Missing phosphor	CP39a	£1000	£1200

1995 (24 April) W H Smith Special Offer. (text on tab at right)
Printer: Walsall Security Printers in Lithography. Perf. 15 x 14 elliptical

		Pane	Plain	Cyl.
CB76	**10 x 1st 2B Orange-red**	CP39	4.50	6.00

1995 (16 May) R J Mitchell. (label attached to stamps)
Printer: Walsall Security Printers in Lithography. Perf. 15 x 14 elliptical

		Pane	Plain	Cyl.
CB77	**4 x 1st 2B Orange-red**	CP41	3.00	3.50

1995 (26 June) Sainsbury's Promotion. (text on tab at right)
Printer: House of Questa in Lithography. Perf. 15 x 14 elliptical

		Pane	Plain	Cyl.
CB78	**10 x 1st 2B Orange-red**	CP33	7.00	7.50

		Pane	Plain	Cyl.

1995 (4 Sept.) Someone special. (Royal Mail)
Printer: Harrison & Sons in Photogravure. Perf. 15 x 14 elliptical

		Pane	Plain	Cyl.
CB79	**10 x 1st 2B Orange-red**	CP26a	4.00	5.00

1996 (6 Feb.) Olympic Symbols. (on reverse)
Printer: Walsall Security Printers in Lithography. Perf. 15 x 14 elliptical

		Pane	Plain	Cyl.
CB80	**4 x 2nd CB Bright blue**	CP35a	1.75	3.00
CB81	**4 x 1st 2B Orange-red**	CP38	2.50	3.25
CB82	**10 x 1st 2B Orange-red**	CP40	4.50	5.00

Printer: Harrison & Sons/De La Rue in Photogravure

		Pane	Plain	Cyl.
CB83	**10 x 2nd CB Bright blue**	CP25	3.00	5.00
CB84	**10 x 1st 2B Orange-red** (19.3.96)	CP26a	4.50	5.50

Printer: House of Questa in Lithography

		Pane	Plain	Cyl.
CB85	**10 x 2nd CB Bright blue**	CP32a	3.00	4.50

1996 (19 Feb.) Promotional. Perf. 15 x 14 elliptical
Printer: Harrison & Sons/De La Rue in Photogravure

		Pane	Plain	Cyl.
CB86	**10 x 1st 2B Orange-red**	CP26a	4.50	5.00

1996 (16 April) Queen's 70th Birthday. (label attached to stamps) Perf. 15 x 14 elliptical
Printer: Walsall Security Printers in Lithography

		Pane	Plain	Cyl.
CB87	**4 x 1st Orange-red** 2B.	CP41A	2.00	3.50

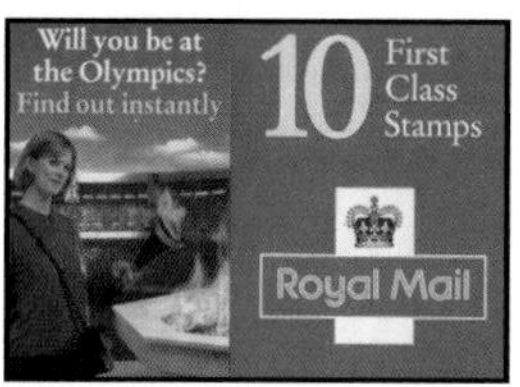

1996 (13 May.) Olympics. Perf. 15 x 14 elliptical
Printer: Harrison & Sons in Photogravure

		Pane	Plain	Cyl.
CB88	**10 x 1st 2B Orange-red** Shot Put	CP26a	4.50	5.00
CB89	**10 x 1st 2B Orange-red** Hurdles	CP26a	4.50	5.00
CB90	**10 x 1st 2B Orange-red** Archery	CP26a	4.50	5.00

1996 (15 July) W H Smith/Olympic Symbols. (on reverse)
Perf. 15 x 14 elliptical
Printer: Walsall Security Printers in Lithography

		Pane	Plain	Cyl.
CB91	**10 x 1st 2B Orange-red**	CP39	4.50	5.50

Printers Initial added to bottom right corner of reverse

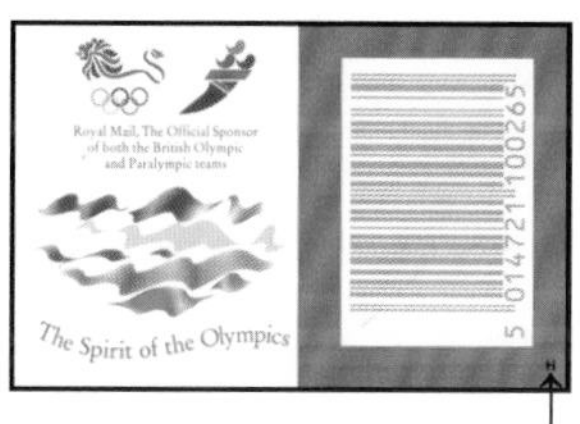

1996 (6 Aug.) (New Rates) Olympic Symbols and printer's intial on reverse)
Perf. 15 x 14 elliptical
Printer: Harrison & Sons/De La Rue in Photogravure

		Pane	Plain	Cyl.
CB92	**10 x 2nd CB Bright blue**	CP25	3.25	4.00
CB93	**10 x 1st 2B Orange-red** (16.8.96)	CP26a	4.50	5.00

Diagonal line on stamp omitted and printers initial added

		Pane	Plain	Cyl.
Printer: House of Questa in Lithography				
CB94	**10 x 2nd CB Bright blue**	CP32a	3.50	6.50
Printer: Walsall Security Printers in Lithography				
CB95	**10 x 1st 2B Orange-red** (6.8.96)	CP40	4.50	5.50

1996 (9 Sept.) Promotional. Perf. 15 x 14 elliptical
Printer: Walsall Security Printers in Lithography

		Pane	Plain	Cyl.
CB96	**10 x 1st 2B Orange-red**	CP40	4.50	5.50

1996 (7 Oct.) ASDA ('Offer inside' on tab)/**Olympic Symbols.** (on reverse) Perf. 15 x 14 elliptical
Printer: Walsall Security Printers Ltd in Lithography

		Pane	Plain	Cyl.
CB97	**10 x 1st 2B Orange-red**	CP40	4.50	5.50

1997 (4 Feb.) New Cover (no diagonal line across stamp) Perf. 15 x 14 elliptical
Printer: Harrison & Sons in Photogravure

		Pane	Plain	Cyl.
CB98	**10 x 2nd CB Bright blue**	CP25	4.00	4.50
CB99	**10 x 1st 2B Orange-red**	CP26a	4.50	5.50

		Pane	Plain	Cyl.
Printer: House of Questa in Lithography				
CB100	**10 x 2nd CB Bright blue**	CP32a	3.50	5.00
Printer: Walsall Security Printers in Lithography				
CB101	**4 x 2nd CB Bright blue**	CP35a	2.00	2.50
CB102	**4 x 1st 2B Orange-red**	CP38	3.25	3.50
CB103	**10 x 1st 2B Orange-red**	CP40	4.50	5.00
Printer: Walsall Security Printers in Gravure				
CB104	**4 x 2nd CB Bright blue** 26.8.97	CP45	1.75	2.50
CB105	**4 x 1st 2B Orange-red** (26.8.97)	CP46	2.00	3.00
CB106	**10 x 1st 2B Orange-red** (18.11.97)	CP49	4.50	5.50
CB107	**10 x 1st 2B Gold**	CP48	4.25	5.00
Printer: Harrison & Sons in Gravure				
CB108	**10 x 1st 2B Gold** (21.4.97)	CP44	5.00	5.50
CB109	**10 x 2nd CB Bright blue** (29.4.97)	CP42	3.50	4.50
CB110	**10 x 1st 2B Orange-red** (18.11.97)	CP43	4.50	5.00

1997 (12 Feb.) Hong Kong 97. (label attached to stamps) Perf. 15 x 14 elliptical
Printer: Walsall Security Printers in Lithography

		Pane	Plain	Cyl.
CB111	**4 x 1st 2B Orange-red**	CP41B	2.25	3.25

1997 (15 Sept.) First Class Travel ('Open for details' on tab) Perf. 15 x 14 elliptical
Printer: Harrison & Sons in Gravure

		Pane	Plain	Cyl.
CB112	**10 x 1st 2B Gold**	CP44	5.00	5.50

		Pane	Plain	Cyl.

1997 (21 Oct.) Heads of Government. (label attached to stamps)
Perf. 15 x 14 elliptical
Printer: Walsall Security Printers Ltd in Lithography

CB113	**4 x 1st 2B Orange-red** + Label	CP41C	2.00	3.00

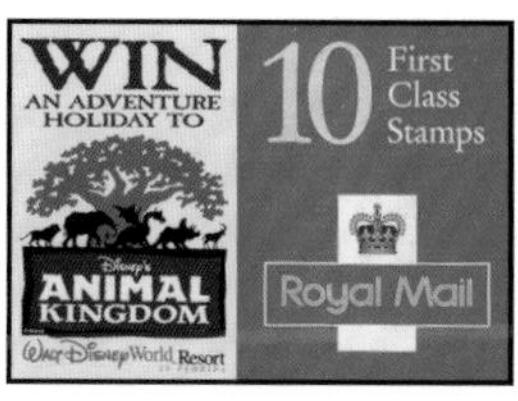

1998 (2 Feb.) Disney ('See reverse…' on tab) Perf. 15 x 14 elliptical
Printer: De La Rue in Gravure

CB114	**10 x 1st 2B Orange-red**	CP43	3.75	4.50

1998 (April) Woolworths Perf. 15 x 14 elliptical
Printer: De La Rue in Gravure

CB115	**10 x 1st 2B Orange-red**	CP43	4.00	4.50

These stamps are valid whatever the current postage rate and may be used for second class items up to 60g within the UK. They can also be used as payment for postage on any item to any country provided the full cost of postage is paid. Information on postage rates is available from post offices.

Postcode enquiries tel: 0345 111 222
Customer Services Helpline tel: 0345 740 740
Monday to Friday (calls charged at local rates)
Textphone 0845 600 0606 (for the deaf and hard of hearing)

1998 (5 May) New Inscriptions (textphone for hard of hearing)
Perf. 15 x 14 elliptical

Printer: Walsall Security Printers in Gravure

CB116	**4 x 1st 2B Orange-red**	CP46	2.50	3.50
CB117	**4 x 2nd CB Bright blue**	CP45	2.00	2.50
CB118	**10 x 1st 2B Orange-red**	CP49	4.00	4.50

		Pane	Plain	Cyl.

Printer: De La Rue in Gravure

CB119	**10 x 2nd CB Bright blue**	CP42	3.50	4.00
CB120	**10 x 1st 2B Orange-red**	CP43	4.00	4.50

Printer: The House of Questa in Gravure

CB121	**10 x 2nd CB Bright blue** (1.12.98)	CP51	3.50	4.00
CB121a	Miscut	CP51a	£15	£20
CB122	**10 x 1st 2B Orange-red**	CP52	4.00	5.00
CB122a	Miscut	CP52a	£25	£100

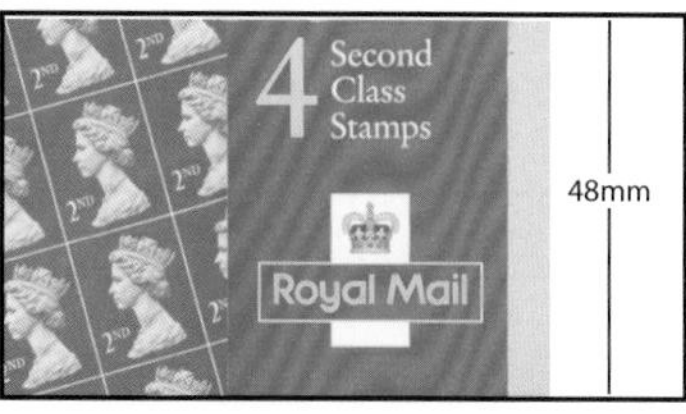

1998 (5 May) Smaller Covers (cover 48mm deep)

Printer: Walsall Security Printers Ltd in Gravure

CB123	**4 x 2nd CB Bright blue**	CP45	2.50	3.50
CB124	**4 x 1st 2B Orange-red**	CP46	2.25	3.25

Printer: The House of Questa in Lithography

CB125	**10 x 2nd CB Bright blue**	CP32a	3.50	4.00
CB126	**10 x 1st 2B Orange-red** (7.09.98)	CP33a	4.00	4.50

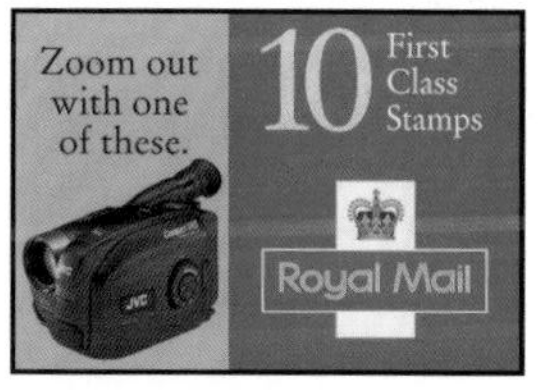

1998 (1 July) JVC Perf. 15 x 14 elliptical
Printer: De La Rue in gravure

CB127	**10 x 1st 2B Orange-red**	CP43	4.00	4.50

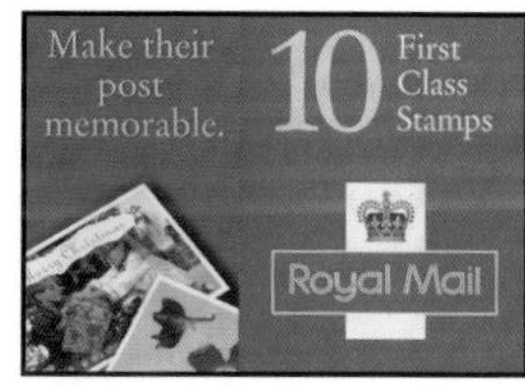

1998 (3 Aug.) Create - a - Card
Printer: De La Rue in gravure

CB128	**10 x 1st 2B Orange-red**	CP43	4.00	4.50

1998 (14 Nov.) **Princes Trust**
Printer: Walsall Security Printers in Lithography

		Pane	Plain	Cyl.
CB129	**4 x 1st 2B Orange-red** + Label	CP41D	2.00	3.00

These stamps are valid whatever the current postage rate and may be used for First Class items up to 60g within the UK. **Please note that the First Class rate is no longer valid to Europe.** However, these stamps can be used as part payment for postage on any item to any country provided the full cost of postage is paid. Information on postage rates is available from post offices.

Postcode enquiries tel: 0345 111 222
Customer Services Helpline tel: 0345 740 740
Monday to Friday (calls charged at local rates)
Textphone 0845 600 0606 (for the deaf and hard of hearing)

1999 (16 Mar.) Revised Validity on inside cover
Printer: Walsall Security Printers in Gravure

		Pane	Plain	Cyl.
CB130	**10 x 1st 2B Orange-red**	CP49	5.00	5.50

These stamps are valid whatever the current postage rate and may be used for First Class items up to 60g within the UK. **Please note that the First Class rate is no longer valid to Europe.** However, these stamps can be used as part payment for postage on any item to any country provided the full cost of postage is paid. Information on postage rates is available from post offices.

Postcode enquiries tel: 0345 111 222
Customer Services Helpline tel: 0345 740 740
Monday to Friday (calls charged at local rates)
Textphone 0845 600 0606 (for the deaf and hard of hearing)

1999 (16 Mar,) Smaller Covers with Revised Validity on Inside Cover
Printer: Walsall Security Printers Ltd.in Gravure

		Pane	Plain	Cyl.
CB131	**4 x 1st 2B Orange-red**	CP46	2.25	3.00
CB132	**10 x 1st 2B Orange-red**	CP49	9.50	15.00

Printer: The House of Questa in Gravure

		Pane	Plain	Cyl.
CB133	**10 x 1st 2B Orange-red**	CP52	4.00	4.50

1999 (12 May) Berlin Airlift
Printer: Walsall Security Printers in Gravure

		Pane	Plain	Cyl.
CB134	**4 x 1st 2B Orange-red** + Label	CP41E	2.25	4.50

1999 (1 Oct.) Rugby Union World Cup
Printer: Walsall Security Printers in Gravure

		Pane	Plain	Cyl.
CB135	**4 x 1st 2B Orange-red** + Label	CP41F	2.25	3.00

To commemorate the Year 2000, Royal Mail issues a special Millennium edition of the famous 'Machin definitive' stamp.

These stamps are valid whatever the current postage rate and may be used for First Class items up to 60g within the UK. Please note that the First Class rate is no longer valid to Europe. However, these stamps can be used as part payment for postage on any item to any country provided the full cost of postage is paid. Information on postage rates is available from post offices.

Postcode enquiries www.postcodes.royalmail.co.uk
or tel: 08457 111 222
Customer Services Helpline tel: 08457 740 740
Textphone 0845 600 0606 (for the deaf and hard of hearing)

2000 (6 Jan.) Millennium Cover with Revised Validity Notice
Printer: Walsall Security Printers in Gravure

		Pane	Plain	Cyl.
CB136	**10 x 1st 2B Millennium**	CP50	5.00	5.50

To commemorate the Year 2000, Royal Mail issues a special Millennium edition of the famous 'Machin definitive' stamp.

These stamps are valid whatever the current postage rate and may be used for First Class items up to 60g within the UK. Please note that the First Class rate is no longer valid to Europe. However, these stamps can be used as part payment for postage on any item to any country provided the full cost of postage is paid. Information on postage rates is available from post offices.

Postcode enquiries www.postcodes.royalmail.co.uk
or tel: 0345 111 222
Customer Services Helpline tel: 08457 740 740
Textphone 0845 600 0606 (for the deaf and hard of hearing)

2000 (6 Jan.) Millennium Cover with Revised Text
Printer: The House of Questa in Gravure

		Pane	Plain	Cyl.
CB137	**10 x 1st 2B Millennium**	CP53	5.00	5.50

To commemorate the Year 2000, Royal Mail issues a special Millennium edition of the famous 'Machin definitive' stamp.

These stamps are valid whatever the current postage rate and may be used for First Class items up to 60g within the UK. Please note that the First Class rate is no longer valid to Europe. However, these stamps can be used as part payment for postage on any item to any country provided the full cost of postage is paid. Information on postage rates is available from post offices.

Postcode enquiries www.postcodes.royalmail.co.uk
or tel: 08457 111 222
Customer Services Helpline tel: 08457 740 740
Textphone 0845 600 0606 (for the deaf and hard of hearing)

2000 (14 Mar.) Millennium Cover with Revised Telephone Number (Number changed to 08457 111 222)
Printer: Walsall Security Printers in Gravure

		Pane	Plain	Cyl.
CB138	**10 x 1st 2B Millennium**	CP50	5.00	5.50

		Pane	Plain	Cyl.

These stamps are valid whatever the current postage rate and may be used for Second Class items up to 60g within the UK. They can also be used as part payment for postage on any item to any country provided the full cost of postage is paid. Information on postage rates is available from post offices.

Postcode enquiries www.postcodes.royalmail.co.uk
or tel: 08457 111 222
Customer Services Helpline tel: 08457 740 740
Textphone 0845 600 0606 (for the deaf and hard of hearing)

2nd class book -Inside cover
1st class has similar layout but text refers to 1st class items.

2000 (14 Mar.) Revised Telephone Number
Printer: Walsall Security Printers in Gravure

		Pane	Plain	Cyl.
CB139	**4 x 2nd CB Bright blue**	CP45	2.50	3.50
CB140	**4 x 1st 2B Orange-red**	CP46	2.25	3.00

Printer: The House of Questa in Gravure

		Pane	Plain	Cyl.
CB141	**10 x 2nd CB Bright blue**	CP51	3.50	4.00
CB142	**10 x1st 2B Millennium**	CP53	4.00	5.00
CB142a	Missing Phosphor	CP53a	£40	£45

2000 (21 Mar.) Postman Pat
Printer: Walsall Security Printers in Gravure

		Pane	Plain	Cyl.
CB143	**4 x 1st 2B Millennium** + Label	CP41G	2.25	3.00

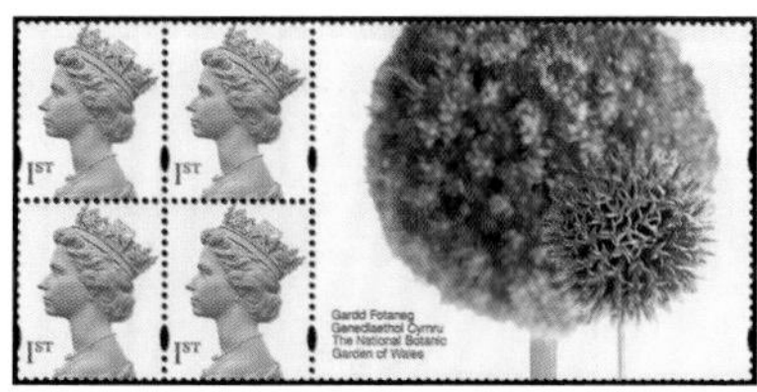

2000 (4 Apr.) National Botanical Garden of Wales
Printer: Walsall Security Printers in Gravure

		Pane	Plain	Cyl.
CB144	**4 x 1st 2B Millennium** + Label	CP41H	2.25	3.00

Single Self Adhesive Stamps

Self adhesive un-mounted mint stamps are assumed to have the 'backing' attached. In general, the backing paper will be square cut around the stamp giving a distinct border. Original printings came with the surplus paper surrounding the stamps (the matrix) still attached. However the norm is now for this paper surplus (matrix) to be stripped away during stamp production. Singles from some presentation packs have been prepared specially in that the die-cutting has been punched through the backing paper giving true 'stamp' shapes.

Landscape Design

Printer: Walsall in Lithography

Matrix intact, Perf 14 x 15

S1	1st	**2B Orange-red** - Book (19.10.93)	**60**
S1a		Missing phosphor	£150

Printer: Joh. Enschedé in Gravure
Matrix removed, Perf 14 x 15

S2	2nd	**CB Bright blue** - Coil (18.3.97)	75
S2a		Larger sized 'frame' of stamp - Coil (Used only)	£135
S3	1st	**2B Orange-red** - Coil (18.3.97)	90

Portrait Design

Printer: Enschedé in Gravure

Matrix removed, Perf 15 x 14

S4	2nd	**CB Bright blue** - Translucent backing paper - Coil (6.4.98)	1.25
S4a		Yellow translucent backing paper - Coil (.11.05)	1.25
S5	1st	**2B Orange-red** - Translucent backing paper - Coil (6.4.98)	90

Printer: Enschedé, Questa or Walsall in Gravure

Matrix intact

S6	2nd	**CB Bright blue** - Unprinted backing - Bus. sheets (22.6.98)	40
S6a		Imperforate	
S6b		'Dagger' perfs	£125
S6c		Orange-red printed backing paper (29.1.01) - Booklets	40
S6d		Imperforate	
S6e		Missing phosphor	
S7	1st	**2B Orange-red** - Unprinted backing - Bus. sheets (25.6.98)	60
S7a		Imperforate	
S7b		'Dagger' perfs	£125
S7c		Orange-red printed backing paper (29.1.01) - Booklets	60
S7d		Imperforate	£125
S7e		Missing phosphor	£125
S7f		Grey/white printed backing paper (13.2.01) - Booklets	2.00
S14	1st	**2B Gold** - Unprinted backing - Bus. sheets (4.7.02)	60

Printer: De La Rue, Questa or Walsall in Gravure

Matrix stripped

S9	1st	**2B Gold** - Printed backing paper - Booklets (5.6.02)	60
S9a		Imperforate	
S9b		Unprinted backing - Bus. sheets (18.3.02)	60
S9c		Die cut through, unprinted backing - Presentation Packs (6.9.05)	1.00
S10	2nd	**CB Bright blue** - Printed backing paper - Booklets (4.7.02)	45
S10a		Unprinted backing - Bus. sheets (18.9.03)	45
S10b		Imperforate	
S10c		Missing colour	£150
S10d		Die cut through, unprinted backing - Presentation Packs (6.9.05)	1.00
S11	E	**2B Dark blue** - Printed backing paper - Booklets (4.7.02)	75
S12	42p	**2B Sage** - Printed backing paper - Booklets (4.7.02)	90
S13	68p	**2B Stone** - Printed backing paper - Booklets (4.7.02)	1.50

S15 **Eur.** **2B Ultramarine & Red** - Printed backing paper - Booklets (27.3.03) 80
S15a Die cut through - Printed backing paper - Presentation Packs (27.3.03) 1.75
S15b Die cut through - Unprinted backing paper - Presentation Packs (6.9.05) 1.75
S16 **W/W** **2B Red & Ultramarine** - Printed backing paper - Booklets (27.3.03) 1.60
S16a Die cut through - Printed backing paper - Presentation Packs (27.3.03) 2.00
S16b Die cut through - Unprinted backing paper - Presentation Packs (6.9.05) 1.75

S17 **Post.** **2B Grey, Red & Blue** - Printed backing paper - Booklets (1.4.04) 80
S17a Die cut through - Unprinted backing paper - Presentation Packs (1.4.04) 1.75

Large Portrait Design

Printer: Walsall in Lithography and Embossing

S8 **1st** **White** - Phosphor printed background - Pane SP90, Profile on Print Prestige book (16.2.99) 2.50

Definitive Sized 'Smilers' design

Printer: Walsall in Gravure

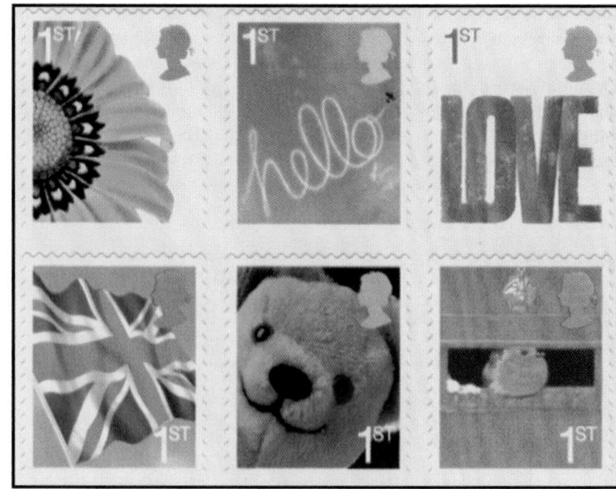

Definitive 'Smilers' as issued in booklet

S18 **1st** **Flower** - Printed backing paper - Booklet (4.10.05) 55
S19 **1st** **Hello** - Printed backing paper - Booklet (4.10.05) 55
S20 **1st** **Love** - Printed backing paper - Booklet (4.10.05) 55
S21 **1st** **Flag** - Printed backing paper - Booklet (4.10.05) 55
S22 **1st** **Bear** - Printed backing paper - Booklet (4.10.05) 55
S23 **1st** **Robin** - Printed backing paper - Booklet (4.10.05) 55

Self Adhesive Issues

These are arranged in issue date order and include all the basic types. There are many varieties on these which are beyond the scope of this catalogue, but full details can be found in the Machin Collectors Club Specialised catalogue.

Details of some of the varieties known to date are indicated by the following abbreviations at the right of the *Contents* line:-
MP-Missing phosphor ILB-Inset Left Band IRB-Inset Right Band
SBT-Short Band Top SBB-Short Band Bottom
IMP-Imperforate (Kiss die-cut omitted)

1993 (19 Oct.) 20 x 1st class Sheet

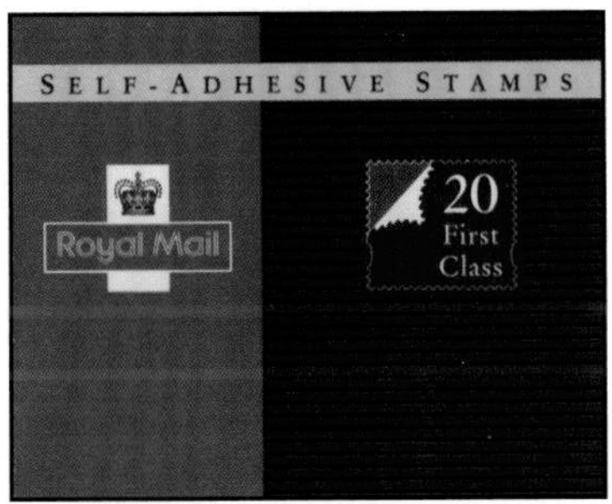

Printer: Walsall Security Printers in Lithography
Contents 20 x 1st Orange-red 2B. - Pane SB1 MP - SBT

SAB1	Complete Book	8.00
	Double print of phosphor	65.00

1998 (22 June) 100 x 2nd class Business sheet

Printer: Walsall Security Printers in Gravure
Contents 100 x 2nd Bright blue CB. - Pane SS1 SBT - SBB

SAS1	Complete sheet	40.00
	Top panel of four	7.50

100 x 1st class Business sheet

Printer: Walsall Security Printers in Gravure
Contents 100 x 1st Orange-red 2B. - Pane SS2

SAS2	Complete sheet	50.00
	Top panel of four	12.50

2000 (4 Sep.) 100 x 2nd class Business sheet

Printer: Walsall Security Printers in Gravure
Contents 100 x 2nd Bright blue CB. - Pane SS3 SBT - SBB

SAS3	Complete sheet	35.00
	Top panel of four	

2000 (4 Sep.) 100 x 1st class Business sheet

Printer: House of Questa in Gravure
Contents 100 x 1st class Orange-red 2B - Pane SS4 ILB - IRB -IMP

SAS4	Complete sheet	43.00
	Top panel of four	9.50

2001 (29 Jan.) 6 x 2nd class book - Walsall

Printer: Walsall Security Printers in Gravure
Contents 6 x 2nd Bright blue CB. - Pane SB2

SAB2	Complete book	3.00

10 x 2nd class book - Questa

Printer: House of Questa in Gravure
Contents 10 x 2nd class Bright blue CB - Pane SB3

SAB3	Complete book	3.00

2 x 2nd class book - Questa

Printer: House of Questa in Gravure
Contents 12 x 2nd class Bright blue CB - Pane SB4 IMP

SAB4 Complete book 3.60

6 x 1st class book - Walsall

Printer: Walsall Security Printers in Gravure
Contents 6 x 1st class Orange-red 2B - Pane SB5 ILB - IRB - IMP

SAB5 Complete book 3.50

6 x 1st Victoria label

Printer: Walsall Security Printers in Gravure
Contents 6 x 1st Orange-red 2B. - Pane SB6 ILB

SAB6 Complete book 4.00

10 x 1st class book - Questa

Printer: House of Questa in Gravure
Contents 10 x 1st class Orange-red 2B. - Pane SB7

SAB7 Complete book 4.40

12 x 1st class book - Questa

Printer: House of Questa in Gravure
Contents 12 x 1st class Orange-red 2B - Pane SB8

SAB8 Complete book 6.00

12 x 1st class book - Walsall

Printer: Walsall Security Printers in Gravure
Contents 12 x 1st Orange-red 2B. Pane - SB9 ILB - IRB - MP - IMP

SAB9 Complete book 6.00

2001 (13 Feb.) 10 x 1st Cats and Dogs

Printer: Walsall Security Printers in Gravure
Contents 10 x 1st Cats and Dogs designs 2B. - Pane SB10 IMP

SAB10 Complete book 10.00

12 x 1st Cats and Dogs

Printer: Walsall Security Printers in Gravure
Contents 10 x 1st Cats and Dogs designs 2B plus 2 x 1st Orange-red 2B.
Pane SB11 ILB

SAB11 Complete book 18.00

2001 (17 Apr.) 6 x 1st Submarines

Printer: House of Questa in Gravure
Contents 2 x 1st Submarines stamps plus 4 x 1st Orange-red 2B
Pane SB12 IMP

SAB12 Complete book 60.00

2001 (1 Aug.) Revised Text on Back Covers

6 x 2nd book - Questa

Printer: House of Questa in Gravure - Revised text on back cover
Contents 6 x 2nd Bright blue CB - Pane SB2

SAB2a Complete book` 3.00

12 x 2nd book - Questa

Front of cover as SAB4 - Back of cover as SAB2a (above)

Printer: House of Questa in Gravure - Revised text on back cover
Contents 12 x 2nd Bright blue CB - Pane SB4

SAB4a Complete book 3.60

6 x 1st book - Walsall

Front of cover as SAB5 - Back of cover as SAB2a (above)

Printer: Walsall Security Printers in Gravure - Revised text on back cover
Contents 6 x 1st Orange-red 2B - Pane SB5

SAB5a Complete book 3.50

12 x 1st book - Walsall

Front of cover as SAB9 - Back of cover as SAB2a (above)

Printer: Walsall Security Printers in Gravure - Revised text on back cover
Contents 12 x 1st Orange-red 2B - Pane SB9 ILB

SAB9a Complete book 4.75

12 x 1st book - Questa

Front of cover as SAB8 - Back of cover as SAB2a (above)

Printer: House of Questa in Gravure - Revised text on back cover
Contents 12 x 1st Orange-red 2B - Pane SB8

SAB8a Complete book 5.75

2001 (4 Sep.) 6 x 1st Punch & Judy

Printer: House of Questa in Gravure
Contents 2 x 1st Punch & Judy stamps plus 4 x 1st Orange-red 2B -
Pane SB13

SAB13 Complete book 14.00

2001 (22 Oct.) 6 x 1st Flags & Ensigns

Printer: House of Questa in Gravure
Contents 2 x 1st Flag stamps plus 4 x 1st Orange-red 2B - Pane SB14 IMP

SAB14 Complete book 14.00

2001 (6 Nov.) 24 x 2nd Christmas

Printer: De La Rue in Gravure
Contents 24 x 2nd Christmas stamps - Pane SS5

SAS5 Complete sheet 6.50

12 x 1st Christmas

Printer: De La Rue in Gravure
Contents 12 x 1st Christmas stamps - Pane SS6

SAS6 Complete sheet 4.75

2002 (15 Jan.) 10 x 1st Kipling - Just So stories

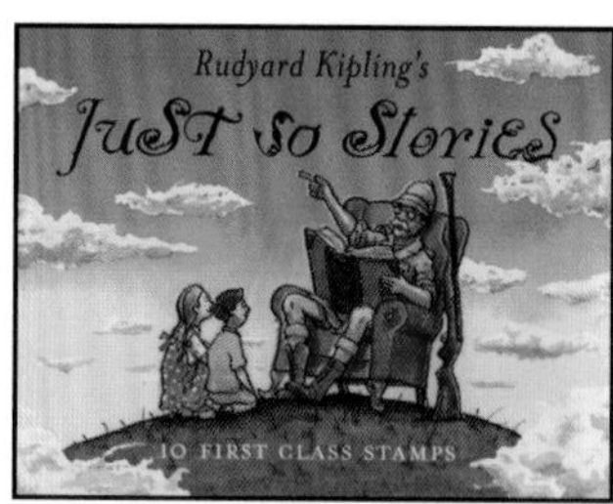

Printer: Walsall Security Printers in Gravure
Contents 10 x 1st Special stamps 2B - Pane SB15

SAB15	Complete book	7.00

2002 (2 May) Airliners

Printer: House of Questa in Gravure
Contents 2 x 1st Special stamps 2B plus 4 x 1st Orange-red 2B - Pane SB16

SAB16	Complete book	5.00

2002 (9 May) 100 x 2nd Business sheet - Enschedé

Printer: Joh. Enschedé in Gravure
Contents 100 x 2nd Bright blue CB - Business sheet SS7

SAS7	Complete sheet	30.00
	Top panel of four	6.50

100 x 1st Business sheet

Printer: Joh. Enschedé in Gravure
Contents 100 x 1st Orange-red 2B - Business sheet SS8

SAS8	Complete sheet	42.50
	Top panel of four	12.00

2002 (21 May) 6 x 1st World Cup

Printer: Walsall Security Printers in Gravure
Contents 2 x 1st Special stamps 2B plus 4 x 1st Orange-red 2B - Pane SB17 ILB - IRB - SBB

SAB17	Complete book	3.50

2002 (5 June) 6 x 1st Book - Questa

Printer: House of Questa in Gravure
Contents 6 x 1st Gold 2B - Pane SB18

SAB18	Complete book	3.50

6 x 1st book - Walsall

Printer: Walsall Security Printers in Gravure
Contents 6 x 1st Gold 2B - Pane SB19 SBT - SBB

SAB19	35mm Printers imprint, Complete book	3.50
SAB19a	29mm Printers imprint, Complete book (15.1.04)	3.50
SAB19b	'Hello' label	
SAB19s	'Love' label	

12 x 1st book - Walsall

Printer: Walsall Security Printers in Gravure
Contents 12 x 1st Gold 2B - Pane SB20 SBT - SBB

SAB20	35mm Printers imprint, Complete book	6.00
SAB20a	29mm Printers imprint, Complete book (15.1.04)	6.00

2002 (4 July)

12 x 2nd - Questa

Printer: House of Questa in Gravure
Contents 12 x 2nd Bright blue CB - Pane SB21

SAB21	Complete book	4.50

6 x 1st - Questa

Printer: House of Questa in Gravure
Contents 6 x 1st Orange-red 2B - Pane SB22

SAB22	Complete book	3.50

100 x 2nd Business sheet - Enschedé

Printer: Joh. Enschedé in Gravure
Contents 100 x 2nd Bright blue CB - Business sheet SS9

SAS9	Complete sheet	40.00
	Top panel of four	6.50

100 x 1st Business sheet - Enschedé

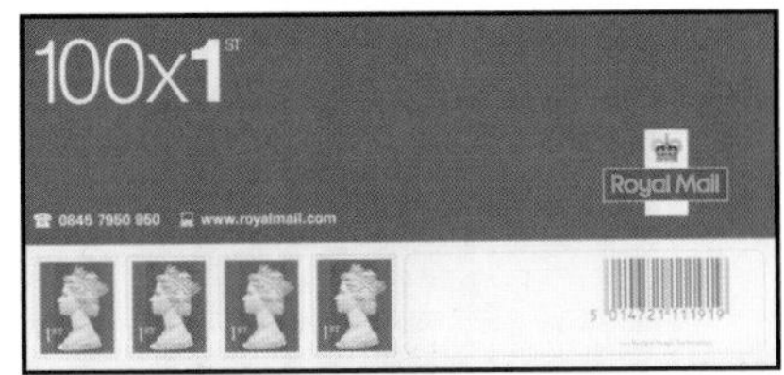

Printer: Joh. Enschedé in Gravure
Contents 100 x 1st Gold 2B - Business sheet SS10 SBT - SBB

SAS10	Complete sheet	42.50
	Top panel of four	7.50

6 x E European - Walsall

Printer: Walsall Security Printers in Gravure
Contents 6 x E stamps 2B - Pane SB23 SBB

SAB23	Complete book	4.50

6 x 42p - Walsall

Printer: Walsall Security Printers in Gravure
Contents 6 x 42p stamps 2B - Pane SB24 SBT

SAB24	Complete book	4.50

6 x 68p - Walsall

Printer: Walsall Security Printers in Gravure
Contents 6 x 68p stamps 2B - Pane SB25 SBB

SAB25	Complete book	7.00

2002 (10 Sep.) 6 x 1st Bridges of London

Printer: House of Questa in Gravure
Contents 2 x 1st Bridges stamps plus 4 x 1st Gold 2B - Pane SB26

SAB26	Complete book	5.00

2002 (5 Nov.) 24 x 2nd Christmas

Printer: De La Rue in Gravure
Contents 24 x 2nd Christmas stamps - Pane SS11

SAS11	Complete sheet	6.00

12 x 1st Christmas

Printer: De La Rue in Gravure
Contents 12 x 1st Christmas stamps - Pane SS12

SAS12	Complete sheet	4.50

2003 (4 Mar.) 6 x 1st Hello - Questa

Printer: House of Questa in Gravure
Contents 2 x 1st Hello stamps plus 4 x 1st Gold 2B - Pane SB27

SAB27	Complete book	7.50

2003 (18 Mar.) 100 x 2nd Business sheet

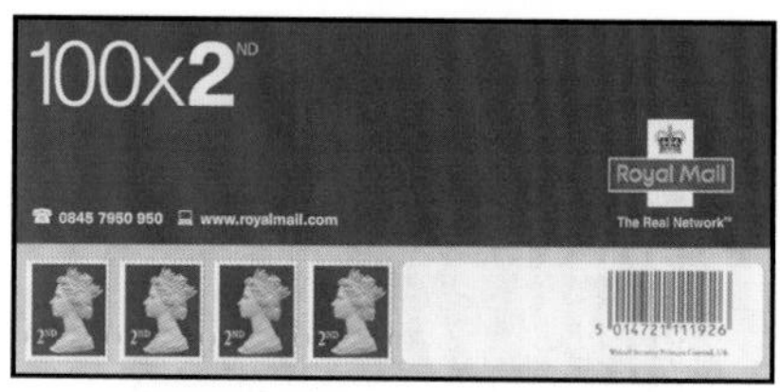

Printer: Walsall Security Printers in Gravure
Contents 100 x 2nd Bright blue CB - Business sheet SS13

SAS13	Complete sheet	35.00
	Top panel of four	6.50

100 x 1st Business sheet

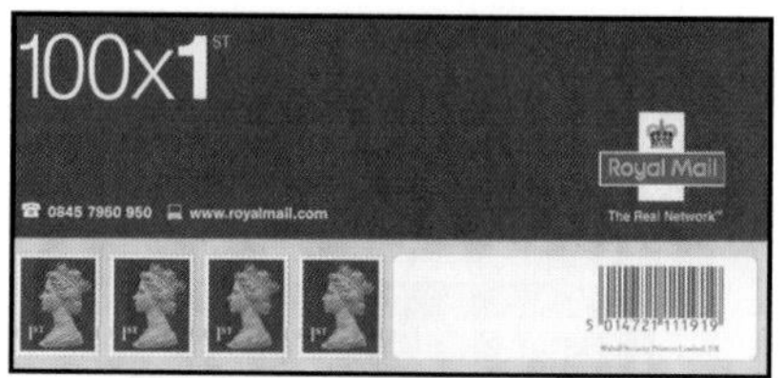

Printer: Walsall Security Printers in Gravure
Contents 100 x 1st Gold 2B - Business sheet SS14

SAS14	Complete sheet	42.50
	Top panel of four	7.50

2003 (25 Mar.) **Fruit & Veg Pack**

There are two versions of this pack.The post office version which is a plain pack and a second type sold by Sainsbury's which has a cut-out at the top of the pack for display purposes (shown below).

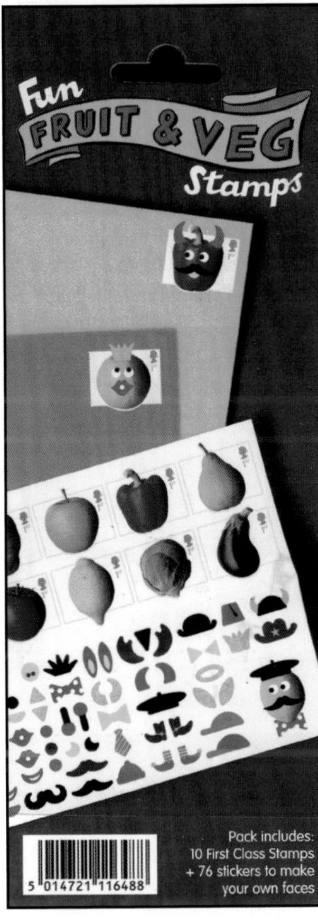

Printer: Walsall Security Printers in Gravure
Contents 10 x 1st Multi-coloured Fruit & Veg stamps 2B - Pane SB28

SAB28	Complete pack - Post Office version	6.50
SAB28a	Complete pack - Sainsbury's version	6.50

2003 (27 Mar.)

12 x 2nd book - The Real Network TM added

Printer: Walsall Security Printers in Gravure
Contents 12 x 2nd Bright blue CB - Pane SB29 SBB

SAB29	Complete book	4.50

6 x 1st book - The Real Network TM added

Printer: Walsall Security Printers in Gravure
Contents 6 x 1st Gold 2B - Pane SB19a

SAB30	Complete book	2.50

12 x 1st book - The Real Network TM added

Printer: Walsall Security Printers in Gravure
Contents 12 x 1st Gold 2B - Pane SB20a SBB

SAB31	Complete book	6.00

4 x Europe book - The Real Network TM sdded

Printer: Walsall Security Printers in Gravure
Contents 4 x Europe 2B - Pane SB30 SBT - SBB - ILB - IRB

SAB32	Complete book	2.80

4 x Worldwide book - The Real Network TM added

Printer: Walsall Security Printers in Gravure
Contents 4 x Worldwide 2B - Pane SB31 SBT - SBB

SAB33	Complete book	6.70

2003 (29 Apr.) 6 x 1st Extreme Endeavours

Printer: De La Rue in Gravure
Contents 2 x 1st Special stamps plus 4 x 1st Gold 2B - Pane SB32

SAB34 Complete book 4.50

2003 (28 May) 6 x E The Real Network TM added

Printer: Walsall Security Printers in Gravure
Contents 6 x E 2B - Pane SB23

SAB35 Complete book 5.00

6 x 42p The Real Network TM added

Printer: Walsall Security Printers in Gravure
Contents 6 x 42p 2B -Pane SB24

SAB36 Complete book 4.50

6 x 68p The Real Network TM added

Printer: Walsall Security Printers in Gravure
Contents 6 x 68p 2B - Pane SB25

SAB37 Complete book 7.00

2003 (15 July) 6 x 1st Scotland

Printer: De La Rue in Gravure
Contents 2 x 1st Special stamps plus 4 x 1st Gold 2B- Pane SB33

SAB38 Complete book 2.80

2003 (18 Sep) 6 x 1st Transports of Delight

Printer: De La Rue in Gravure
Contents 2 x 1st Special stamps plus 4 x 1st Gold 2B -Pane SB34

SAB39 Complete book 7.50

2003 (4 Nov.) 24 x 2nd Christmas

Printer: De La Rue in Gravure
Contents 24 x 2nd Christmas stamps - Pane SS15

SAS15 Complete sheet 6.25

12 x 1st Christmas

Printer: De La Rue in Gravure
Contents 12 x 1st Christmas stamps - Pane SS16

SAS16 Complete sheet 4.50

2004 (16 Mar.) **6 x 1st Northern Ireland**

Printer: De La Rue in Gravure
Contents 2 x 1st Special stamps plus 4 x 1st Gold 2B - Pane SB35

SAB40 Complete book 2.80

2004 (1 Apr.) **4 x Postcard**

Printer: Walsall Security Printers in Gravure
Contents 4 x Postcard 2B - Pane SB36 SBB

SAB41 Complete book 3.50

2004 (13 Apr.) **6 x 1st Ocean Liners**

Printer: De La Rue in Gravure
Contents 2 x 1st Special stamps plus 4 x 1st Gold 2B -Pane SB37

SAB42 Complete book 4.00

2004 (15 June) 12 x 2nd book - The Real Network TM removed

Printer: Walsall Security Printers in Gravure
Contents 12 x 2nd Bright blue CB - Pane SB29a

SAB43 Complete book 4.50

6 x 1st Wales

Printer: De La Rue in Gravure
Contents 2 x 1st Special stamps plus 4 x 1st Gold 2B - Pane SB38

SAB46 Complete book 4.50

4 x Europe - The Real Network TM removed

Printer: Walsall Security Printers in Gravure
Contents 4 x Europe 2B - Pane SB30a SBT

SAB44 Complete book 4.00

4 x Worldwide - The Real Network TM removed

Printer: Walsall Security Printers in Gravure
Contents 4 x Worldwide 2B - Pane SB31a SBB

SAB45 Complete book 4.50

6 x 1st Olympic

Printer: Walsall Security Printers in Gravure
Contents 6 x 1st Gold 2B -Pane SB39

SAB47 Complete book 3.50

100 x 2nd Business sheet - The Real Network TM removed

Printer: Walsall Security Printers in Gravure
Contents 100 x 2nd Bright blue CB - Business sheet SS17

SAS17	Complete sheet	35.00
	Top panel of four	5.00

100 x 1st Business sheet - The Real Network TM removed

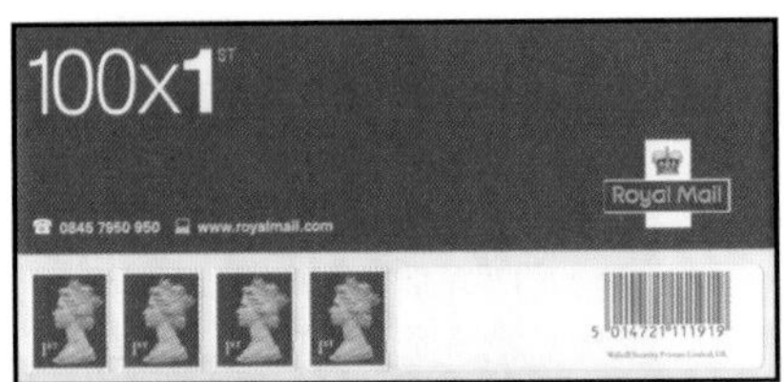

Printer: Walsall Security Printers in Gravure
Contents 100 x 1st Gold 2B - Business sheet SS18

SAS18	Complete sheet	42.50
	Top panel of four	6.50

2004 (2 Nov.) 24 x 2nd Christmas

Printer: De La Rue in Gravure
Contents 24 x 2nd Christmas stamps - Pane SS19

SAS19	Complete sheet	6.25

12 x 1st Christmas

Printer: De La Rue in Gravure
Contents 12 x 1st Christmas stamps - Pane SS20

SAS20	Complete sheet	4.50

2005 (1 Nov.) 24 x 2nd Christmas

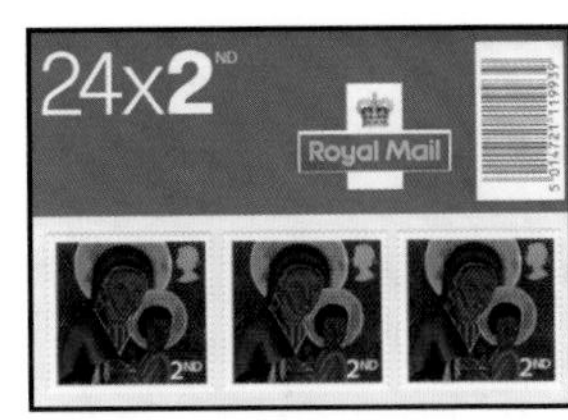

Printer: De La Rue in Gravure
Contents 24 x 2nd Christmas stamps - Pane SS21

SAS21	Complete sheet	6.25

12 x 1st Christmas

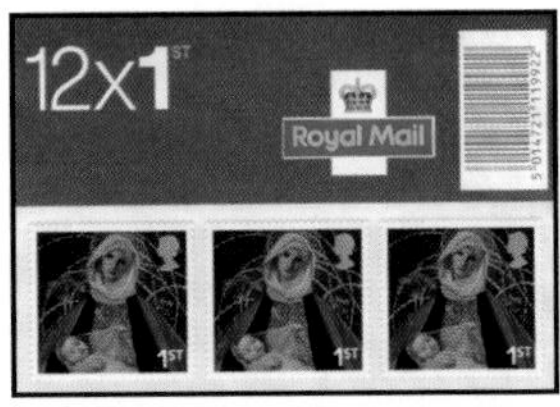

Printer: De La Rue in Gravure
Contents 12 x 1st Christmas stamps - Pane SS22

SAS22	Complete sheet	4.50

6 x 1st 'Smilers'

Printer: Walsall Security Printers in Gravure
Contents 6 x 1st 2B Multicoloured - Pane SB42

SAB48	Complete book	7.00

Coil Issues

1997 (18 Mar.) **100 x 2nd - Horizontal**

Printer: Joh. Enschedé in Gravure
Contents 100 x 2nd Bright blue CB

SAC1	Complete box of 100	
	Strip of 4	4.00

100 x 1st - Horizontal

Printer: Joh. Enschedé in Gravure
Contents 100 x 1st Orange-red 2B

SAC2	Complete box of 100	
	Strip of 4	4.00

1998 (6 Apr.) **200 x 2nd - Vertical**

Printer: Joh. Enschedé in Gravure
Contents 200 x 2nd Bright blue CB

SAC3	Complete box of 200	
	Strip of 4	5.00

200 x 1st - Vertical

Printer: Joh. Enschedé in Gravure
Contents 200 x 1st Orange-red 2B

SAC4	Complete box of 200	
	Strip of 4	5.00

2005 (Apr.) **10,000 x 2nd - Vertical**

Printer: Joh. Enschedé in Gravure
Contents: 10,000 x 2nd Bright blue CB

SAC5	2 x Strips of five (with and without number)	£20

Appendix 1 - Panes and Single Reference					
Book Pane		Description	Process	Printer	Single No.
SB1		20 x 1st Orange-red	Litho	Walsall	S1
SB1a		Missing phosphor			S1a
SP90		4 x 1st (Large format)	Emb/Litho	Walsall	S8
SB2		6 x 2nd	Gravure	Walsall	S6c
SB2a		Missing phosphor			S6e
SB3		10 x 2nd		Questa	S6c
SB4		12 x 2nd		Questa	S6c
SB4a		Imperforate			S6d
SB5		6 x 1st Orange-red	Gravure	Walsall	S7c
SB5a		Imperforate			S7d
SB6		6 x 1st Orange-red - Victoria label		Walsall	S7c
SB7		10 x 1st Orange-red		Questa	S7c
SB8		12 x 1st Orange-red		Questa	S7c
SB9		12 x 1st Orange-red		Walsall	S7c
SB9a		Missing phosphor			S7e
SB9b		Imperforate			S7d
SB10		10 x 1st Cats & Dogs		Walsall	
SB10a		Imperforate			
SB11		10 x 1st Cats & Dogs / 2 x 1st Orange-red		Walsall	S7f
SB12		6 x 1st Orange-red / Submarines		Questa	S7c
SB12a		Imperforate			
SB13		6 x 1st Orange-red / Punch & Judy		Questa	S7c
SB14		6 x 1st Orange-red / Flags & Ensigns		Questa	S7c
SB14a		Imperforate			
SB15		10 x 1st Kiplimg		Walsall	
SB16		6 x 1st Orange-red / Airliners		Questa	S7c
SB17		6 x 1st Orange-red / World Cup		Walsall	S7c
SB18	*	6 x 1st Gold		Questa	S9
SB19	*	6 x 1st Gold - 35mm Printers imprint		Walsall	S9
SB19a	*	'The Real Network' Strap-line on cover		Walsall	S9
SB19b		Imperforate			S9a
SB19c	*	'The Real Network' removed - 29mm Printers imprint		Walsall	S9
SB20	*	12 x 1st Gold - 35mm Printers imprint		Walsall	S9
SB20a	*	'The Real Network' Strap-line on cover		Walsall	S9
SB20b	*	'The Real Network' removed - 29mm printers imprint		Walsall	S9
SB21	*	12 x 2nd		Questa	S10
SB22		6 x 1st Orange-red		Questa	S7c
SB23	*	6 x E		Walsall	S11
SB24	*	6 x 42p		Walsall	S12
SB25	*	6 x 68p		Walsall	S13
SB26	*	6 x 1st Gold / London Bridges		Questa	S9
SB27	*	6 x 1st Gold / Hello		Questa	S9
SB28		10 x 1st Fruit & Veg		Walsall	
SB28a		Imperforate			
SB29	*	12 x 2nd 'The Real Network' Strap-line on cover		Walsall	S10
SB29a	*	'The Real Network' removed		Walsall	S10
SB30	*	4 x Europe		Walsall	S15
SB30a	*	'The Real Network' removed - Labels spaced wider		Walsall	S15

* Indicates the matrix has been stripped away during manufacture

Book Pane		Description	Process	Printer	Single No.
SB31	*	4 x Worldwide	Gravure	Walsall	S16
SB31a	*	'The Real Network' removed		Walsall	S16
SB32	*	6 x 1st Gold / Endeavours		De La Rue (Byfleet)	S9
SB33	*	6 x 1st Gold / Scotland		De La Rue (Byfleet)	S9
SB34	*	6 x 1st Gold / Toy Transport		De La Rue (Byfleet)	S9
SB35	*	6 x 1st Gold / Northern Ireland		De La Rue	S9
SB36	*	4 x Postcard		Walsall	S17
SB37	*	6 x 1st Gold / Ocean Liners		De La Rue	S9
SB38	*	6 x 1st Gold / Wales		De La Rue	S9
SB39	*	6 x 1st Gold ' Support London 2012' label		Walsall	S9
SB40	*	6 x 1st Gold 'Smilers - Hello' label		Walsall	S9
SB41	*	6 x 1st Gold 'Smilers - Love' label		Walsall	S9
SB42	*	6 x 1st Definitive sized 'Smilers'		Walsall	S18, S19, S20, S21, S22, S23
Z Folded Sheets					
SS1		100 x 2nd Business sheets	Gravure	Walsall	S6
SS2		100 x 1st Orange-red Business sheets		Walsall	S7
SS3		100 x 2nd Business sheets		Walsall	S6
SS3a		Imperforate			
SS4		100 x 1st Orange-red Business sheets		Questa	S7
SS4a		Imperforate			
SS5		24 x 2nd Christmas 2001		De La Rue (High Wycombe)	
SS6		12 x 1st Christmas 2001		De La Rue (High Wycombe)	
SS7		100 x 2nd Business sheets		Enschedé	S6
SS8		100 x 1st Orange-red Business sheets		Enschedé	S7
SS9		100 x 2nd Business sheets		Enschedé	S6
SS10		100 x 1st Gold Business sheets		Enschedé	S14
SS11		24 x 2nd Christmas 2002		De La Rue (High Wycombe)	
SS12		12 x 1st Christmas 2002		De La Rue (High Wycombe)	
SS13	*	100 x 2nd Business sheets 'The Real Network'		Walsall	S10a
SS14	*	100 x 1st Gold Business sheets 'The Real Network'		Walsall	S9b
SS15	*	24 x 2nd Christmas 2003		De La Rue (Byfleet)	
SS16	*	12 x 1st Christmas 2003		De La Rue (Byfleet)	
SS17	*	100 x 2nd ('The Real Network' removed)		Walsall	S10a
SS17a		Imperforate			S10b
SS17b	*	Missing colour			S10c
SS18	*	100 x 1st Gold ('The Real Network' removed)		Walsall	S9b
SS19	*	24 x 2nd Christmas 2004		De La Rue	
SS20	*	12 x 1st Christmas 2004		De La Rue	
SS21	*	24 x 2nd Christmas 2005		De La Rue	
SS22	*	12 x 1st Christmas 2005		De La Rue	
Coils					
SC1	*	100 x 2nd (Landscape design)	Gravure	Enschedé	S2
SC2	*	100 x 1st Orange-red (Landscape design)		Enschedé	S3
SC3	*	200 x 2nd (Portrait design)		Enschedé	S4
SC3a	*	10,000 x 2nd (Portrait design)		Enschedé	S4a
SC4	*	200 x 1st Orange-red (Portrait design)		Enschedé	S5

* Indicates the matrix has been stripped away during manufacture

Appendix 2 - Complete Books and Pane Reference				
Book No.	Description	Process	Printer	Pane No.
SAB1	20 x 1st Orange-red	Litho	Walsall	SB1
	Missing phosphor			SB1a
SAB2	6 x 2nd	Gravure	Walsall	SB2
	Missing phosphor			SB2a
SAB2a	6 x 2nd Revised text on back cover		Walsall	SB2
SAB3	10 x 2nd		Questa	SB3
SAB4	12 x 2nd		Questa	SB4
	Imperforate			SB4a
SAB4a	12 x 2nd - Revised text on back cover		Questa	SB4
SAB5	6 x 1st Orange-red	Gravure	Walsall	SB5
	Imperforate			SB5a
SAB5a	6 x 1st Orange-red - Revised text on back cover		Walsall	SB5
SAB6	6 x 1st Orange-red Victoria label		Walsall	SB6
SAB7	10 x 1st Orange-red		Questa	SB7
SAB8	12 x 1st Orange-red		Questa	SB8
SAB8a	12 x 1st Orange-red - Revised text on back cover		Questa	SB8
SAB9	12 x 1st Orange-red		Walsall	SB9
	Missing phosphor			SB9a
	Imperforate			SB9b
SAB9a	12 x 1st Orange-red - Revised text on back cover		Walsall	SB9
SAB10	10 x 1st Cats & Dogs		Walsall	SB10
	Imperforate			
SAB11	10 x 1st Cats & Dogs / 2 x 1st Orange-red Machin		Walsall	SB11
SAB12	6 x 1st Orange-red / Submarines		Questa	SB12
	Imperforate			
SAB13	6 x 1st Orange-red / Punch & Judy		Questa	SB13
SAB14	6 x 1st Orange-red / Flags & Ensigns		Questa	SB14
	Imperforate			
SAB15	10 x 1st Kipling		Walsall	SB15
SAB16	6 x 1st Orange-red / Airliners		Questa	SB16
SAB17	6 x 1st Orange-red / World Cup		Walsall	SB17
SAB18	6 x 1st Gold - Re-branded cover		Questa	SB18
SAB19	6 x 1st Gold - 35mm Printers imprint - Re-branded cover		Walsall	SB19
SAB19a	'The Real Network' removed - 29mm printers imprint		Walsall	SB19c
SAB19a	6 x 1st Gold with 'Smilers - Hello' label inside		Walsall	SB40
SAB19c	6 x 1st Gold with 'Smilers - Love' label inside		Walsall	SB41
SAB20	12 x 1st Gold - 35mm Printers imprint - Re-branded cover		Walsall	SB20
SAB20a	'The Real Network' removed - 29mm Printers imprint		Walsall	SB20b
SAB21	12 x 2nd - Re-branded cover		Questa	SB21
SAB22	6 x 1st Orange-red		Questa	SB22
SAB23	6 x E		Walsall	SB23
SAB24	6 x 42p		Walsall	SB24
SAB25	6 x 68p		Walsall	SB25
SAB26	6 x 1st Gold / London Bridges		Questa	SB26
SAB27	6 x 1st Gold / Hello		Questa	SB27
SAB28	10 x 1st Fruit & Veg		Walsall	SB28
	Imperforate			SB28a
SAB29	12 x 2nd 'The Real Network' Strap line on cover		Walsall	SB29
SAB30	6 x 1st Gold 'The Real Network' strap line on cover		Walsall	SB19a
	Imperforate			SB19b

SAB31	12 x 1st Gold 'The Real Network' strap line on cover	Gravure	Walsall	SB20a
SAB32	4 x Europe 'The Real Network' strap line on cover		Walsall	SB30
SAB33	4 x Worldwide - 'The Real Network' strap line on cover		Walsall	SB31
SAB34	6 x 1st Gold / Endeavours		De La Rue (Byfleet)	SB32
SAB35	6 x E 'The Real Network' strap line on cover		Walsall	SB22
SAB36	6 x 42p 'The Real Network' strap line on cover		Walsall	SB23
SAB37	6 x 68p 'The Real Network' strap line on cover		Walsall	SB24
SAB38	6 x 1st Gold / Scotland		De La Rue (Byfleet)	SB33
SAB39	6 x 1st Gold / Toy Transport		De La Rue (Byfleet)	SB34
SAB40	6 x 1st Gold / Northern Ireland		De La Rue (Byfleet)	SB35
SAB41	4 x Worldwide Postcard		Walsall	SB36
SAB42	6 x 1st Gold / Ocean Liners		De La Rue (Byfleet)	SB37
SAB43	12 x 2nd 'The Real Network' removed		Walsall	SB29a
SAB44	4 x Europe The Real Network' removed; Labels spaced wider		Walsall	SB30a
SAB45	4 x Worldwide 'The Real Network' removed; Labels spaced wider		Walsall	SB31a
SAB46	6 x 1st Gold / Wales		De La Rue (Byfleet)	SB38
SAB47	6 x 1st Gold ' Support London 2012'		Walsall	SB39
SAB48	6 x 1st Definitive sized 'Smilers'		Walsall	SB42
Z Folded (Business) Sheets and Pane References				
SAS1	100 x 2nd Business sheet		Walsall	SS1
SAS2	100 x 1st Orange-red Business sheet		Walsall	SS2
SAS3	100 x 2nd Business sheet		Walsall	SS3
	Imperforate			
SAS4	100 x 1st Orange-red Business sheet		Questa	SS4
	Imperforate			
SAS5	24 x 2nd Christmas 2001		De La Rue (High Wycombe)	SS5
SAS6	12 x 1st Christmas 2001		De La Rue (High Wycombe)	SS6
SAS7	100 x 2nd Business sheet		Enschedé	SS7
SAS8	100 x 1st Orange-red Business sheet		Enschedé	SS8
SAS9	100 x 2nd Business sheet - Re-branded cover		Enschedé	SS9
SAS10	100 x 1st Gold Business sheet - Re-branded cover		Enschedé	SS10
SAS11	24 x 2nd Christmas 2002		De La Rue (High Wycombe)	SS11
SAS12	12 x 1st Christmas 2002		De La Rue (High Wycombe)	SS12
SAS13	100 x 2nd Business sheet - 'The Real Network'		Walsall	SS13
SAS14	100 x 1st Gold Business sheet - 'The Real Network'		Walsall	SS14
SAS15	24 x 2nd Christmas 2003		De La Rue (Byfleet)	SS15
SAS16	12 x 1st Christmas 2003		De La Rue (Byfleet)	SS16
SAS17	100 x 2nd - 'The Real Network' removed		Walsall	SS17
	Imperforate			
	Missing colour			
SAS18	100 x 1st Gold - 'The Real Network' removed		Walsall	SS18
SAS19	24 x 2nd Christmas 2004		De La Rue (Byfleet)	SS19
SAS20	12 x 1st Christmas 2004		De La Rue (Byfleet)	SS20
SAS21	24 x 2nd Christmas 2005		De La Rue (Byfleet)	SS21
SAS22	12 x 1st Christmas 2005		De La Rue (Byfleet)	SS22
Complete Coils and References				
SAC1	100 x 2nd (Landscape Design)		Enschedé	SC1
SAC2	100 x 1st Orange-red (Landscape Design)		Enschedé	SC2
SAC3	200 x 2nd (Portrait Design)		Enschedé	SC3
SAC3a	10,000 x 2nd (Portrait Design)		Enschedé	SC3a
SAC4	200 x 1st Orange-red (Portrait Design)		Enschedé	SC4

Stamps of issues 1841-1901 used in offices abroad.
Compiled by Paul Dauwalder

British stamps were sent to various agencies mainly in the Americas, Mediterranean, North Africa and Mesopotamia usually through British Consulate Appointments and mail distributed via British Packet Mail Boat lines.

The system carried on in embryonic form until the various countries established their own postal service and postage labels. D65 is known to be used at Pisagua, Peru on 2/- blue and various GB stamps were used with local non numerical cancels in Nigeria, Niger Coast, Egypt and Ionian Islands.

This listing is by no means exhaustive. We have detailed numeral cancels only and illustrate some typical cancels employed. Various barred cancels may be found freely from each office.

Prices are estimates of values of clearly legible postmarks on stamps only, but please note the operative word ‘from’. Stamps on cover are worth considerably more. An asterisk thus * indicates that a cancel is known on stamp or cover. For more information we refer the reader to Stanley Gibbons British Commonwealth Catalogue 1840 - 1952.

We welcome further information of incidence of cancels within the territories shown below.

Stamp Face value	Comments and thoughts
4d, 6d and 1s	By far the commonest three values encountered, the 4d value is slightly more difficult from west coast offices and vice versa for the 6d but certainly not difficult. The early 1862 issues are generally very difficult, which to be expected as the offices were not open, the obvious exception being Buenos Ayres.
3d, 9d, 10d, 2s and 5s	Still fairly easy values to obtain, varies from office to office but generally regularly seen, the comments about the 1862 issues apply here as well.
1d, 2d, 1½d and ½d (Line engraved)	Surprisingly difficult at times, it is infinitely easier to find a 2s or 5s used abroad than it is a 1d plate. The scarcest is the ½d mainly due to its size and getting a legible strike of the postmark.
½d - 5d (1880 issue) Lilac & Green issue	Very tricky. The only one that commonly appears is the 1½d Venetian red used in Greytown, the rest are much rarer. The Lilac & Green issue is only found in Panama and really are an abnormal usage from Naval mail. We don’t actually list them here but they definitely exist
8d	This is one of the key values used abroad from this area. The only ones seen with any regularity are, as you would expect, St. Thomas, Callao and Valparaiso. Never underestimate this value!
2½d Rosy mauve	This is a major rarity and a surprise for most people. The writer has only seen 4 or 5 used in Valparaiso and a couple used in Panama. Do not underestimate this stamp - it is very common used in Malta, Gibraltar etc, and the exact opposite in South America.
10s & £1	Vary rare as to be expected. Six 10s used in Valparaiso (2 reperfed and 2 badly damaged) are known; The 10s for Greytown is believed unique. The 10s listed for Port Au Prince is very rare and three £1 used in Valparaiso are known (they all have faults!)

Comparative Rarity

In this section we endeavour to give an idea of the rarity of one office to another, as we feel it is this balance which is most important - and most difficult to obtain. Please read this in combination with the priced tables

Letter	Rarity	Letter	Rarity	Letter	Rarity
A	Very Common	B	Common	C	Scarce
D	Very Scarce	E	Rare	F	Almost Impossible

Country	Office	Comments
Argentine	Buenos Ayres	Rarity B. Nothing is particularly difficult here. Even the 1d plates and 1862 issues can be found. Good strikes abound. About 10% of cancels are in blue.
Bolivia	Cobija	Rarity F. Very rare for all values. Less than a dozen genuine examples have been seen by the author in twenty years. No matter what value you put on these it is not enough! 3 types of canceller known.
Brazil	Rio, Bahia, Pernambuco	Rarity B-C. Nothing that difficult here. Bahia and Pernambuco are slightly scarcer than Rio but still nothing that difficult.
Chile	Valparaiso	Rarity A. Nothing difficulty here except the 2½d, 10s, £1 and 1880 issues for the reasons stated above. Even the 2s Brown is quite easy to find used here. The 1862 4d is know on a cover with 3 x 4d and 2 x 1s. 1862 3d known on cover in pair with 1858 1d plate 89
	Caldera, Coquimbo	Rarity C-D. Coquimbo is more difficult than Caldera, and both can be found cancelled in blue. If anything C37 in black is more difficult than blue. The 1862 4d and 1865 1s used in Caldera are known from three covers to Germany in 1866. Loose examples have not been seen by the author. Both these places are 20 times scarcer than Valparaiso. The ½d - 2d values are particularly difficult here especially from Coquimbo.
Columbia	Carthagena	Rarity C. Nothing unusual here. The C65 error is at least 2 - 3 times scarcer than the C56
	Panama	Rarity A-B. Apart from the 2½d and 1880 issues as already mentioned, nothing is particularly difficult.
	Colon, Santa, Martha & Savanilla	Rarity C-D. Colon is surprisingly difficult, the 4d value is by far the commonest for all offices. The 4d Sage green used in Savanilla being far easier than the earlier 4d Vermilion. Nothing particularly unusual, nevertheless all are difficult in any quantity.
Cuba	Havana	Rarity D. Surprisingly difficult for what was such a large office, especially the 6d and 8d.
	St. Jago	Rarity E. Very difficult - at least five times rarer than Havana. The vast majority of stamps offered are smudgy strikes of Rio C83. A very difficult one to price as only a few are known.
DWI	St. Thomas	Rarity A. Very common.
Dominican Republic	Porto Plata, St. Domingo	Rarity D-E. A very difficult area. The 1s used in Porto Plata is by far the commonest value seen. St. Domingo is the more difficult of the two. We think they would fit between Havana and St. Jago in terms of rarity.
Ecuador	Guayaquil	Rarity B. Nothing really that difficult here - slightly scarcer than Valparaiso and Callao and probably on a similar par to Panama. Plenty of forgeries seen particularly on the 1d plates, most of which are relatively easy to detect.
Haiti	Jacmel, Port Au Prince	Rarity B. Jacmel is relatively common, Port Au Prince is slightly more difficult. Each listing is probably unique.
Mexico	Tampico	Rarity D-E. This is really very difficult, the 1d and 4d values being the commonest. Several 2s values with poor C83 strikes offered as C63 have been seen. Do not underestimate Tampico.
Nicaragua	Greytown	Rarity C. An odd one this, the latter issues are ten times easier than the earlier ones with most stamps encountered with CDS's for 1879-82. Beware of suspect circular cancels. Anything earlier is much more difficult and is cancelled by the C57 duplex. The 5s plate 4 and 10s are probably both unique. The 5s has been seen and its authenticity is dubious. Also seen is the 1s green with the C57 horizontal oval numeral which is supposedly the unique example of this.
Peru	Callao	Rarity A. Apart from the early 1862-65 issues nothing difficult. The duplex cancel is very scarce.
	Arica, Iquique and Islay	Rarity C-D. These three are all about equal, Iquique is slightly scarcer than the other two. Arica and Iquique can be found cancelled in blue 40-50% of the time and Islay very rarely. These three should probably be placed on a par with, or fractionally easier than, Caldera and Coquimbo. Iquique cancels on piece are always used with Peruvian stamps. It is difficult to find C42 on one stamp - the mark covers 2 stamps
	Paita	Rarity E. Very rare - at least 4-5 times more difficult than Arica etc.

Peru (continued)	Pisagua	It is not believed that the cover with the 2s blue was cancelled in Peru, more likely by an inspector in transit in London. 1d and 2d plates exist cancelled D65 in red - who knows??
	Pisco	Rarity F. Without doubt the rarest os all the South American Offices. All values are priced at different levels, but that could all be the same as we doubt whether more than 10-15 examples exist with genuine cancels. There are a lot of fakes about usually on stamps that were issued after the office shut!
Porto Rico	San Juan	Rarity A-B Relatively common the 1862 and 1865 9d are the only difficult stamps here.
	Mayaguez	Rarity B-C. Not as easy as San Juan but still not difficult.
	Ponce, Arroyo	Rarity C-D. Getting progressively more difficult. F83 in red is vary rare. It is known on the 9d and 1s values both cancelled by an additional C51 in black.
	Naguabo	Rarity F. Very difficult, on a par with Coboja, although 20 years ago a page of 20 10d values used here were found.
		Due to the high volume of mail with Spain the 10d value is easier in Porto Rico than some other offices.
Uruguay	Montevideo	Rarity D-E. This office is very hard to find, at least 10 times rarer than Argentina or Brazil. The very early 1857 and 1862 issues being particularly difficult. This office is on a par with Havana or Aguadilla.
Venezuela	La Guayra	Rarity C-D. Not too bad but as superb cds's are found from 1877 onwards, huge premiums normally apply. The 4d Vermilion is by far the commonest stamp seen here. The use of the Crowned Circle to cancel stamps is a major rarity.
	Cuidad Bolivar	Rarity E-F. Very difficult, the 4d Sage green with a red cds is by far the commonest. Some of the stamps are really scarce. Among those seen by the author are three 1d Pl.133 (on cover, D22 numeral), three 2s blue (all off centre red cds), two 1s Pl.8 and 13 (Red cds) and one 5s (black cds without PAID at base). The numeral cancellation is far scarcer than the cds, although nowhere near as attractive.

Type	AO1 Kingston Jamaica		AO2 St. Johns Antigua	AO3 -AO4 Georgetown	AO5 Nassau Bahamas	AO6 Belize	AO7 Dominica	AO8 Montseratt	AO9 Charlestown Nevis	A10 Kingstown St. Vincent
	Single Cancel	Double Cancel								
½d Rose (1870 - 79)										
1d Red (1841) Imperf										
1d Red-brown 1855 p16 Die II										
1d Red-brown 1855 p14 Die II										
1d Red-brown 1855 Die II p16 LC										
1d Red 1857 LC p14	£150	£200	£400	From £300	£1750	£750	£200	£1000	£375	£500
1d Red Plate 1864 - 79										
1½d Rose -red, Plate 1 or 3										
2d Blue 1841 Imperf										
2d Blue 1855 LC p14			£750							
2d Blue 1858 LC p16										
2d Blue 1858 Pl 7-15			£500	From £700	From £1000		Plate 7 - £600		Plate 7 & 8 £1500	
2½d Rosy-mauve 1875 Blue paper										
2½d Rosy-mauve 1876 Plates 3 - 17										
2½d Blue 1880 Plates 17 - 20										
2½d Blue 1881 Plates 21 - 23										
3d Carmine 1862										
3d Rose 1865 Plate 4										
3d Rose 1867 Plates 4 - 10										
3d Rose 1873 Plates 11 - 20										
3d Rose 1881 Plate 20/21										
3d on 3d Lilac 1883										
4d Rose 1857	£140	£120	£400	£120	£350	£300	£300	*	£300	£325
4d Rose 1857 Glazed paper										
4d Red Plate 3 or 4 1862										
4d Vermillion 1865 Plate 7 - 14										
4d Vermillion Plate 15 1876										
4d Sage-green (1877) Plate 15 & 16										
4d Grey-brown 1880 Wmk. Garter Pl17										

Type	AO1 Kingston Jamaica Single Cancel	Double Cancel	AO2 St. Johns Antigua	AO3 -AO4 Georgetown	AO5 Nassau Bahamas	AO6 Belize	AO7 Dominica	AO8 Montseratt	AO9 Charlestown Nevis	A10 Kingstown St. Vincent
4d Grey-brwon 1880 Wmk. Cross Plates 17 & 18										
6d Lilac Embossed 1854					£3250					
6d Lilac 1856	£35	£110	£130	From £100	£275					
6d 1862 Plates 3 & 4										
6d 1865 Plates 5 & 6										
6d 1865 Wmk. error										
6d Lilac 1867 Plate 6										
6d Lilac 1867 Plate 6, 8 or 9										
6d Buff 1872 Plates 11 & 12										
6d Chestnut 1872 Plate 11										
6d Grey 1873 Plate 12										
6d Grey 1873 Plates 13-17										
6d Grey 1881 - 2 Plates 17 & 18										
6d on 6d Lilac										
8d Orange 1876										
9d Straw 1862										
9d Bistre 1862										
9d Straw 1867										
10d Red-brown 1867										
1/- 1847 Embossed										
1/- Green (1856)	£300	*	£1500	£1000	£1800	£1200	£1200	£1200	*	
1/- Green (1856)Thick paper										
1/- Green 1862										
1/- Green 1862 K Variety										
1/- Green 1865 Plate 4										
1/- Green Plates 4, 5, 6, 7 (1867)										
1/- Green 1873 Plates 8 - 13										
1/- Orange-brown Plate 13										

Type	AO1 Kingston Jamaica Single Cancel Double Cancel	AO2 St. Johns Antigua	AO3 -AO4 Georgetown	AO5 Nassau Bahamas	AO6 Belize	AO7 Dominica	AO8 Montserat	AO9 Charlestoen Nevis	A10 Kingstown St. Vincent
1/- Orange-brown 1881 Plates 13 & 14									
2/- Blue 1867									
2/- Brown 1880									
5/- Rose 1867 Plates 1 and 2									
5/- Rose Plate 4 1882 Blued paper									
5/- Rose Plate 4 1882 White paper									
10/- Grey-green 1878									
10/- Grey-green 1883									
£1 Brown-lilac 1878									
£1 Brown-lilac 1882									
1880 ½d Deep green									
1880 ½d Pale green									
1880 1d Venetian red									
1880 1½d Venetian red									
1880 2d Pale rose									
1880 2d Deep rose									
1880 5d Indigo									
1881 1d Lilac 14 dots									
1881 1d Lilac 16 dots									
1883 - 4 ½d Slate blue									
1883 - 4 1½d Lilac									
1883 - 4 2d Lilac									
1883 - 4 2½d Lilac									
1883 - 4 3d Lilac									
1883 - 4 Dull green									
1883 - 4 5d Dull green									
1883 - 4 6d Dull green									
1883 - 4 9d Dull green									
1883 - 4 1/- Dull green									

Type	A11 Castries St. Lucia	A12 Basse Terre St Christopher	A13 Tortola Virgin Islands	A14 Scarborough Tobago	A15 St' George Grenada	A18 English Harbour Antigua	A25 Malta	A26 Gibraltar	A27-78 Jamaica
½d Rose (1870 - 79)							From £18	From £20	
1d Red (1841) Imperf							From £2000	From £1100	
1d Red (1854) p16 Die I SC							£250		
1d Red-brown 1855 p16 Die II SC									
1d Red-brown 1855 p14 Die II LC						£4500		£130	
1d Red-brown 1855 Die II p16 LC							£55		
1d Red 1857 LC p14	£850	£500	£3250	£650	£350		£7	£10	£100
1d Red 1861 Alph IV									
1d Red Plate 1864 - 79							From £10	From £15	
1½d Rose-red Plate 1 or 3							£300	Plate 13 - £375	
2d Blue 1841 Imperf							£3000		
2d Blue 1854 SC Die I p16									
2d Blue 1855 LC p14	*						£50	£100	
2d Blue 1858 LC p16								From £15	£400
2d Blue 1858 Plates 7 - 15		Plate 7 £850			Plate 7 - £850	Plate 7 - £4500	From £12		
2½d Rosy-mauve 1875 Blue paper							£50	From £75	
2½d Rosy-mauve 1876 White paper							£25	From £20	
2½d Rosy-mauve 1876 Plates 3 - 17							From £20	From £15	
2½d Blue 1880 Plates 17 - 20							From £10	From £10	
2½d Blue 1881 Plates 21 - 23							from £10	From £12	
3d Carmine 1862							£85	£120	
3d Rose 1865 Plate 4							£40	£45	
3d Rose 1867 Plates 4 - 10							From £20	From £25	
3d Rose 1873 Plates 11 - 20							From £25	From £32	
3d Rose 1881 Plate 20/21							£600	*	
3d on 3d Lilac 1883							£350	£115	
4d Rose 1857	£350	£300	£3500	£275	£225		£28	£40	£95
4d Rose 1857 Glazed paper							£90		
4d Red Plate 3 or 4 1862							£25	£35	

Type	A11 Castries St. Lucia	A12 Basse Terre St Christopher	A13 Tortola Virgin Islands	A14 Scarborough Tobago	A15 St' George Grenada	A18 English Harbour Antigua	A25 Malta	A26 Gibraltar	A27-78 Jamaica
4d Vermillion 1865 Palte 7 - 14							From £15	From £20	
4d Vermillion Plate 15 1876							From £120	£200	
4d Sage green (1877) Plates 15 & 16							£65	£85	
4d Grey-brown 1880 Wmk. Garter Pl. 17							£125	£185	
4d Grey-brown 1880 Wmk. Crown Plates 17 & 18							£30	£35	
6d Lilac Embossed 1854							£1850		
6d Lilac 1856	£195	£165	£1100	£220	£150	£140	£35	£35	£225
6d 1862 Plates 3 & 4							£28	£28	
6d 1865 Plates 5 & 6							£27	£25	
6d 1865 Wmk. Error							£1000		
6d Lilac 1867 Plate 6							£30	£35	
6d Violet 1867 Plate 8 or 9							From £20	£25	
6d Buff 1872 Plates 11 & 12							£80	From £110	
6d Chestnut 1872 Plate 11							£25	£25	
6d Grey 1873 Plate 12							£85	£85	
6d Grey 1873 Plates 13 - 17							£25	£25	
6d Grey 1881 - 2 Plates 17 & 18							£50	£150	
6d on 6d Lilac							£90	£80	
8d Orange 1876							£250	£350	
9d Straw 1862							£400	£200	
9d Bistre 1862							£400	£450	
9d Straw 1865							£500	£550	
9d Straw 1867							£100	£130	
10d Red-brown 1867							£100	£110	
1/- 1847 Embossed							£2000		
1/- Green (1856)	£1000	£1200	*	£1100	£1000	*	£65	£75	£500
1/- Green (1856) Thick paper							£220		
1/- Green 1862							£50	£60	

Type	A11 Castries St. Lucia	A12 Basse Terre St Christopher	A13 Tortola Virgin Islands	A14 Scarborough Tobago	A15 St' George Grenada	A18 English Harbour Antigua	A25 Malta	A26 Gibraltar	A27-78 Jamaica
1/- Green 1862 K Variety							£2500	£1600	
1/- Green 1865 Plate 4							£50	£60	
1/- Green Plates 4, 5, 6 & 7 (1867)							From £20	From £22	
1/- Green 1873 Plates 8 - 13							From £35	From £40	
1/- Orange-brown Plate 13							£225	£250	
1/- Orange-brown 1881 Plates 13 & 14							£60	£75	
2/- Blue 1867							£150	£170	
2/- Brown 1880							£2000		
5/- Rose 1867 Plates 1 and 2							£275	Plate 1 - 500	
5/- Rose Plate 41882 Blued paper							£1100		
5/- Rose Plate 4 1882 White paper							£1000		
10/- Grey-green 1878							£2000		
10/- Grey-green 1883									
£1 Brown-lilac 1878									
£1 Brown-lilac 1882									
1880 ½d Deep green							£10	£17	
1880 ½d Pale green							£10	£17	
1880 1d Venetian red							£8	£17	
1880 1½d Venetian red							£275	£190	
1880 2d Pale rose							£30	£40	
1880 2d Deep rose							£30	£40	
5d Indigo							£50	£85	
1881 1d Lilac 14 dots							£25	£20	
1881 1d Lilac 16 dots							£6	£7	
1883-4 ½d Slate blue							£10	£15	
1883-4 1½d Lilac							*		
1883-4 2d Lilac							£60	£60	
1883-4 2½d Lilac							£15	£12	

Type	A11 Castries St. Lucia	A12 Basse Terre St Christopher	A13 Tortola Virgin Islands	A14 Scarborough Tobago	A15 St' George Grenada	A18 English Harbour Antigua	A25 Malta	A26 Gibraltar	A27-78 Jamaica
1883-4 3d Lilac							*	*	
1883-4 4d Dull green							£120	£120	
1883-4 5d Dull green							£120	*	
1883-4 6d Dull green							*		
1883-4 9d Dull green							*		
1883-4 1/- Dull green							*		
1883 5/- Blued							£1200		
1883 5/- White							£750		

Type	A80 - A99 Mailboats	B01 Alexandria Egypt	B02 Suez Egypt	B03 B12 B56 B57 Mailboats	B32 Buenos Ayres	C Constantinople	C28 Montivideo Uruguay	C30 Valparaiso Chile
½d Rose (1870 - 79)		£15	£25			From £20		
1d Red (1841) Imperf								
1d Red (1854) p16 Die I SC						*		
1d Red-brown 1855 p16 Die II SC						*		
1d Red-brown 1855 p14 Die II LC						£15		
1d Red-brown 1855 Die II p16 LC								
1d Red 1857 LC p14	From £25	£5	£8	From £40	£40			
1d Red 1861 Aph IV						*		
1d Red Plate 1864-79	From £20	£8	£10	From £40	£30	From £8	£60	£20
1½d Rose-red Plate 1 or 3						£150		£40
2d Blue 1841 Imperf								
2d Blue 1854 SC Die I p16								
2d Blue 1855 LC p14						*		
2d Blue 1858 LC p16								
2d Blue 1858 Plates 7-15	From £40	£8	£12	From £50	£30	From £10	Plate 9 & 13 £60	£30
2½d Rosy-mauve 1875 Blue paper		£50	£45			From £40		
2½d Rosy-mauve 1875 White paper		£30	£30			From £25		Plate 2 £150
2½d Rosy-mauve 1876 Plates 3-17						£15		Plates 4 & 8 £150
2½d Blue 1880 Plates 17-20						£12		
2½d Blue 1881 Plates 21-23						8.50		
3d Carmine 1862	From £200	£85	£100		£350	£95		*
3d Rose 1865 Plate 4	From £200	£40	£55	From £75	£80	£50	*	*
3d Rose 1867 Plates 4-10	From £50	£40	£20	From £75	£35	£40	£50	£30
3d Rose 1873 Plates 11-20		£20	£30			£20		£25
3d Rose 1881 Plates 20/21						Plate 21 *		
3d on 3d Lilac 1883						*		
4d Rose 1857	From £150	£30	£40		£80	£30	*	
4d Rose 1857 Glazed paper								
4d Red Plate 3 or 4 1862	From £85	£35	£35	From £90	£65	£25	Plate 4 *	*

Type	A80 - A99 Mailboats	B01 Alexandria Egypt	B02 Suez Egypt	B03 B12 B56 B57 Mailboats	B32 Buenos Ayres	C Constantinople	C28 Montivideo Uraguay	C30 Valparaiso Chile
4d Vermillion 1865 Plates 7-14	From £50	From £20	£20	From £55	£35	From £15	From £35	From £30
4d Vermillion Plate 15 1876		£130	*			£110		£200
4d Sage green (1877) Plates 15 & 16		£100	£100			£65		£125
4d Grey-brown 1880 Wmk. Garter Pl 17						*		
4d Grey-brown 1880 Wmk. Cross Plates 17 & 18						£25		
6d Lilac Embossed 1854								
6d Lilac 1856	From £120	£38	£40	From £120	£70	£45	*	
6d 1862 Plates 3 & 4	From £85	£30	£30	From £100	*	£25	Plate 4 £120	£40
6d 1865 Plates 5 & 6	From £80	Plate 6 £30	£30	From £80	£60	£25	£65	*
6d 1865 Wmk. error								
6d Lilac 1867 Plate 6	From £75	£30	£35	From £75	£60	£25	*	*
6d Lilac 1867 Plate 6, 8 or 9	From 350	£28	£20	From £55	£50	£20	Plates 8 & 9 £65	£40
6d Buff 1872 Plates 11 & 12		£45	£45		Plate 11 £60	£40	*	£50
6d Chestnut 1872 Plate 11		£25	£30		£35	£20	*	£30
6d Grey 1873 Plate 12		£55	£75			£50		£140
6d Grey 1873 Plates 13-17		£20	£20			£20		£30
6d Grey 1881-2 Plates 17 & 18						£30		*
6d on 6d Lilac						£55		
8d Orange 1876			*			£250		£220
9d Straw 1862	*	£120	£140		£375		*	*
9d Bistre 1862		*	*		£375			
9d Straw 1865	*	*			£375		*	*
9d Straw 1867	*	*	*		£200		£300	£140
10d Red-brown 1867	From £400	£120	£130	From £400	£200	£100	£300	£200
1/- 1847 Embossed								
1/- Green (1856)	From 3200	£100	£110		£200	£80		
1/- Green (1856) Thick paper								
1/- Green 1862	From £200	£50	£70		£120	£45	£150	

Type	A80 - A99 Mailboats	B01 Alexandria Egypt	B02 Suez Egypt	B03 B12 B56 B57 Mailboats	B32 Buenos Ayres	C Constantinople	C28 Montivideo Uraguay	C30 Valparaiso Chile
1/- Green 1862 K Variety		*	*			*		
1/- Green 1865 Plate 4		£30	£40		£150	£45	£200	*
1/- Green Plates 4, 5, 6, 7 (1867)		£12	£12		From £50	From £10	Plates 4 & 5 £60	£30
1/- Green 1873 Plates 8-13		From 322	From £22		Plate 8 -*	From £25		£40
1/- Orange-brown Plate 13						£130		£250
1/- Orange-brown 1881 Plates 13 & 14						£40		
2/- Blue 1867		£90	£120		£100	£75	£170	£90
2/- Brown 1880								£1500
5/- Rose 1867 Plates 1 & 2		£150	£200		£250	£175	Plate 1 £350	Plate 1 & 2 £220
5/- Rose Plate 4 1882 Blued paper						£750		
5/- Rose Plate 4 White paper						£700		
1/- Grey-green 1878								£2500
10/- Grey-green 1883								
£1 Brown-lilac 1878								£3500
£1 Brown-lilac 1882								
1880 ½d Deep green						£8		
1880 ½d Pale green						£10		
1880 1d Venetian red						£8		
1880 1½d Venetian red						£120		
1880 2d Pale rose						£40		
1880 2d Deep rose						£40		
1880 5d Indigo						£65		
1881 1d Lilac 14 dots						*		
1881 1d Lilac 16 dots						£5		
1883-4 ½d Slate-blue						£12		
1883-4 1½d Lilac						£60		
1883-4 2d Lilac						£45		
1883-4 2½d Lilac						£7		
1883-4 3d Lilac								

Type	A80 - A99 Mailboats	B01 Alexandria Egypt	B02 Suez Egypt	B03 B12 B56 B57 Mailboats	B32 Buenos Ayres	C Constantinople	C28 Montivideo Uruguay	C30 Valparaiso Chile
1883-4 4d Dull green						£125		
1883-4 5d Dull green						£90		
1883-4 6d Dull green						£200		
1883-4 9d Dull green								
1883-4 1/- Dull green								

Type	C35 Panama Columbia	C36 Arica Peru	C37 Caldera	C38 Callao	C39 Cobija Bolivia	C40 Coquimbo Chile	C41 Guayaquil Ecuador	C42 Islay Peru	C43 Paita Peru
½d Rose (1870-79)	£35	£70		£35		*	£40	£40	
1d Red (1841) Imperf									
1d Red (1854) p16 Die I									
1d red-brown 1855 p16 Die II									
1d Red-brown 1855 p14 Die II									
1d Red-brown 1855 Die II p16 LC									
1d Reed 1857 LC p14						*	*		
1d Red 1861 Alph IV									
1d Red Plate 1864-79	£20	£55	£35	From £25		*	£30		Pl 127 & 147 £90
1½d Rose-red Plate 1 or 3	£45	*	*	*			Plate 3 £65	*	
2d Blue 1841 Imperf									
2d Blue 1854 SC Die I p16									
2d Blue 1855 LC p14									
2d Blue 1858 LC p16					*				
2d Blue 1858 Plates 7-15	$30	Plate 14 £80	Plate 6 & 9 £40	From £20	Plate 14 *	*	£25	£40	Plates 9 & 14 £90
2½d Rosy-mauve 1875 Blue paper									
2½d Rosy-mauve 1875 White paper	£150								
2½d Rosy-mauve 1876 Plates 3-17	£150								
2½d Blue 1880 Plates 17-20	Plate 19 *								
2½d Blue 1881 Plates 21-23	*								
3d Carmine 1862	£175			*				£80	
3d Rose 1865 Plate 4	*		£55	£50		*	£90		
3d Rose 1867 Plates 4-10	£30	*	Plates 5 & 7 *	From £25	Plate 6 *	Plate 8 *	£30	£40	
3d Rose 1873 Plates 11-20	£30	£50	From £40	From £25	*	£60	£40		£90
3d Rose 1881 Plate 20/21	*								
3d on 3d Lilac 1883									
4d Rose 1857									
4d Rose 1857 Glazed paper									
4d Red Plate 3 or 4 1862	£75		*	*		*	£80	£90	

Type	C35 Panama Columbia	C36 Arica Peru	C37 Caldera	C38 Callao	C39 Cobija Bolivia	C40 Coquimbo Chile	C41 Guayaquil Ecuador	C42 Islay Peru	C43 Paita Peru
4d Vermillion 1865 Plate 7-14	£30	£45	From £40	From £20		£60	£30	£40	£90
4d Vemillion Plate 15 1876	£200	*		£200			£225	*	
4d Sage green (1877) Plate 15 & 16	£130	£160	Plate 16 *	£120	Plate 15 £500	£140	£140	£120	*
4d Grey-brown 1880 Wmk. Garter Pl 17									
4d Grey-brown 1880 Wmk. Crown Plates 17 & 18	£35								
6d Lilac Embossed									
6d Lilac 1856									
6d 1862 Plates 3 & 4	£55	*	Plate 4 £70	*		£70	£100	£60	Plate 3 £120
6d 1865 Plates 5 & 6	£50	*	*	*		*	£55	£60	£90
6d 1865 Wmk. error									
6d Lilac 1867 Plate 6	*		£60	£50			*		
6d Violet 1867 Plate 8 or 9	£40	£55	£60	£40	Plate 9 £450	£60	£50	£150	£90
6d Buff 1872 Plates 11 & 12	£40	£70	*	From £45	Plate 11 -*	£60	£50		£100
6d Chestnut 1872 Plate 11	£35	£70	Plate 11 *	£30		*	*	*	£100
6d Grey 1873 Plate 12	£140	£130	*	£130			*	*	*
6d Grey 1873 Plates 13-17	£30	£50	From £40	From £30	£350		£40	£40	*
6d Grey 1881-2 Plates 17 & 18	Plate 17 £50								
6d on 6d Lilac									
8d Orange 1876	£220	*	£350		£400	*	£250		
9d Straw 1862	£200	*			£300		£220		*
9d Bistre 1862						*			
9d Straw 1865		*			£200			£300	
9d Straw 1867	£175	£175	£150	£150		*	£120	£130	
10d Red-brown 1867	£200	*	£220	£220		£250	£220	£150	£350
1/- 1847 Embossed									
1/- Green (1856)									
1/- Green (1856) Thick paper									
1/- Green 1862		*							

Type	C35 Panama Columbia	C36 Arica Peru	C37 Caldera	C38 Callao	C39 Cobija Bolivia	C40 Coquimbo Chile	C41 Guayaquil Ecuador	C42 Islay Peru	C43 Paita Peru
1/- Green 1862 K Variety									
1/- Green 1865 Plate 4	£100	*	*	*		£120	£120		*
1/- Green Plates 4, 5, 6, 7 (1867)	£30	£50	From £40	From £30	Plate 4 & 5 £350	£60	£30	£60	Plate 4 £100
1/- Green 1873 Plates 8-13	£40	£50	From £50	From £40	£350	£70	£50	£70	£80
1/- Orange-brown Plate 13	£260								
1/- Orange-brown 1881 Plates 13 & 14	Plate 13 £85								
2/- Blue 1867	£100	£150	£150	£100	£350	£125	£120	*	£225
2/- Brown 1880	£1500		£1500			£1500	£1600		
5/- Rose 1867 Plates 1 & 2	Plate 1 & 2 £250	Plate 1 & 2 £275	Plate 2 £350	£250	Plate 2 £500	£275	£290	Plate 1 *	Plate 1 £450
5/- Rose Plate 4 1882 Blued paper									
5/- Rose Plate 4 1882 White paper									
10/- Grey-green 1878									
10/- Grey-green 1883									
£1 Brown lilac 1878									
£1 Brown-lilac 1882									
1880 ½d Deep green									
1880 ½d Pale green									
1880 1d Venetian red	£40								
1880 1½d Venetian red									
1880 2d Pale rose									
1880 2d Deep rose	£70								
1880 5d Indigo									
1881 1d Lilac 14 dots	£130								
1881 1d Lilac 16 dots									
1883-4 ½d Slate-blue									
1883-4 1½d Lilac									
1883-4 2d Lilac									
1883-4 2½d Lilac									
1883-4 3d Lilac									

Type	C35 Panama Columbia	C36 Africa Peru	C37 Caldera	C38 Callao	C39 Cobija Bolivia	C40 Coquimbo Chile	C41 Guayaquil Ecuador	C42 Islay Peru	C43 Paita Peru
1883-4 Dull green									
1883-4 5d Dull green									
1883-4 6d Dull green									
1883-4 9d Dull green									
1883-4 1/- Dull green									

Type	C51 St. Thomas (BWI)	C56/C65 Carthagena Columbia	C57 Greytown Nicaragua	C58 Havana Cuba	C59 Jacmel (Haiti)	C60 La Guayra Venezuela	C61 San Juan Porto Rico	C62 Santa Martha Columbia	C63 Tampico Mexico
½d Rose (1870-79)	£25	*	£55	£55	£40	*	£35	Plate 6 £70	
1d Red (1841) Imperf									
1d Red (1854) p16 Die I									
1d Red-brown 1855 p16 Die II									
1d Red-brown p14 Die II									
1d Red-brown 1855 Die II p16 LC									
1d Red-brown LC p14	*						*		
1d Red 1861 Alph IV									
1d Red Plate 1864-79	£20	£40	£35	£40	£30	£35	£25	Plate 106 £50	£75
1½d Rose-red Plate 1 or 3	£40		Plate 3 £50		Plate 3 £50	*	£40		
2d Blue 1841 Imperf									
2d Blue 1854 SC Die I p16									
2d Blue 1855 LC p14									
2d Blue 1858 LC p16									
2d Blue 1858 Plates 7-15	£20	£40	*	£50	£30	£40	£25	£65	£120
2½d Rosy-mauve 1875 Blue paper									
2½d Rosy-mauve 1875 White paper					Plate 4 *				
2½d Rosy-mauve 1876 Plates 3-17									
2½d Blue 1880 Plates 17-20									
2½d Blue 1881 Plates 21-23									
3d Carmine 1862									
3d Rose 1865 Plate 4	£50	*		£90			£55		
3d Rose 1867 Plates 4-10	£25	*			£30		£30		
3d Rose 1873 Plates 11-20	£20	£40	£35	*	£30	£40	£30		
3d Rose 1881 Plates 20/21			*						
3d on 3d Lilac 1883									
4d Rose 1857									
4d Rose 1857 Glazed paper									
4d Red Plate 3 or 4 1862	£25				Plate 4 £75				

Type	C51 St. Thomas (BWI)	C56/C65 Carthagena Columbia	C57 Greytown Nicaragua	C58 Havana Haiti	C59 Jacmel (Haiti)	C60 La Guayra Venezuela	C61 San Juan Porto Rico	C62 Santa Martha Columbia	C63 Tampico Mexico
4d Vermillion 1865 Plates 7-14		£40	£35	£35	£30	£35	£30	£45	Plate 12 & 13 £60
4d Vermillion Plate 15 1876	£100	£200	£175	£200	£220	£220	£200		
4d Sage green (1877) Plates 15 & 16	£120	£140	£120		£140			£140	£75
4d Grey-brown 1880 Wmk. Garter Pl 17			£225		£250			£250	
4d Grey-brown 1880 Wmk. Crown Plates 17 & 18			Plate 17 £50		Plate 17 £40				
6d Lilac Embossed 1854									
6d Lilac 1856									
6d 1862 Plates 3 & 4	£100								
6d 1865 Plates 5 & 6	£50	*		Plate 15 *	£40	*	£50	£65	
6d 1865 Wmk. error									
6d Lilac 1867 Plate 6	£50						£55		
6d Violet 1867 Plate 8 or 9	£40	£50			Plates 8 & 9 £45	*	£40		
6d Buff 1872 Plates 11 & 12	£50				£45	£75	£50		
6d Chestnut 1872 Plate 11	£25				*		£30		
6d Grey 1873 Plate 12	£120	£140			*	£130	*	*	
6d Grey 1873 Plates 13-17	£25	£40	£50	Plate 15 *	£30	£40	£35	Plate 14 *	
6d Grey 1881-2 Plates 17 & 18									
6d on 6d Lilac									
8d Orange 1876	£225	£300	£225		£250	£225		£250	
9d Straw 1862	£200				£170	*	£200	*	
9d Bistre 1862	£200								
9d Straw 1865	£300	*					£300		
9d Straw 1867	£120			£220	£120	*	£130		
10d Red-brown 1867	£150			£240	£220	*	£300		
1/- 1847 Embossed									
1/- Green (1856)									
1/- Green (1856) Thick paper									
1/- Green 1862									

Type	C51 St. Thomas (BWI)	C56/C65 Carthagena Columbia	C57 Greytown Nicaragua	C58 Havana Cuba	C59 Jacmel (Haiti)	C60 La Guayra Venezuela	C61 San Juan Porto Rico	C62 Santa Martha Columbia	C63 Tampico Mexico
1/- Green 1862 K Variety									
1/- Green 1865 Plate 4	£80	*	*	£110	£80	£110	£80	£120	
1/- Green Plates 4, 5, 6, 7 (1867)	£20	£40	*	£40	£25	Plate 4 & 7 *	£30	£50	£100
1/- Green 1873 Plates 8-13	£30	£50	£40	£50	£40	£45	£40	Plate 8 *	Plate 8 £150
1/- Orange-brown Plate 13		*	£300		£275				
1/- Orange-brown 1881 Plates 13 & 14			Plate 13 £75						
2/- Blue 1867	£90	£200	£110	£160	£90	£150	£100	£200	£400
2/- Brown 1880			£1600		£1500				
5/- Rose 1867 Plates 1 & 2	£200	Plate 1 £375	£250	£300	£270	£250	£275	Plate 2 £375	
5/- Rose Plate 4 1882 Blued paper			£1500						
5/- Rose Plate 4 1882 White paper									
10/- Grey-green 1878			£2250						
10/- Grey-green 1883									
£1 Brown-lilac 1878									
£1 Brown-lilac 1882									
1880 ½d Deep green					£40				
1880 ½d Pale green									
1880 1d Venetian red			£55		£40				
1880 1½d Venetian red			£55		£60				
1880 2d Pale rose									
1882 2d Deep rose					£80				
1880 5d Indigo									
1881 1d Lilac 14 dots									
1881 1d Lilac 16 dots									
1883-4 1½d Lilac									
1883-4 2d Lilac									
1883-4 2½d Lilac									
1883-4 3d Lilac									
1883-4 Dull green									

Type	C79 Mailboat	C81 Bahia Brazil	C82 Pernambuco Brazil	C83 Rio de Janeiro	C86 Porto Plata Dominican Rep	C87 St Domingo Dominican Rep	C88 St Jago de Cuba	D22 Cuidad Bolivar Venezeula	D26 Mailboat
½d Rose (1870-79					£80	£90	*		
1d Red (1841) Imperf									
1d Red (1854) p16 Die I									
1d Red-brown 1855 p16 Die II									
1d Red-brown 1855 Die II p16 LC									
1d Red 1857 LC p14				£30					
1d Red 1861 Alph IV									
1d Red Plate 1864-79		£30	£30	£25	£45	£50	£150	Plate 133 £175	Plate 98 & 125*
1½d Rose-red Plate 1 or 3		Plate 3 £75			£90		Plate 3 -*		
2d Blue 1841 Imperf						£100	£150		
2d Blue 1854 SC Die I p16									
2d Blue 1855 LC p14									
2d Blue 1858 LC p16									
2d Blue 1858 Plates 7-15		£40	£40	£25	Plate 14 & 15 £55	£75		*	
2½d Roay-mauve 1875 Blue paper									
2½d Roay-mauve 1875 White paper									
2½d Rosy-mauve 1876 Plates 3-17					£140				
2½d Blue 1880 Plates 17-20									
2½d Blue 1881 Plates 21-23									
3d Carmine 1862									
3d Rose 1865 Plate 4		*	£80						
3d Rose 1867 Plates 4-10		£35	£35	£25			Plate 5 *	Plate 5 - *	
3d Roase 1873 Plates 11-20		Plate 11 - *	Plate 11 *	Plate 11 *	£70	Plate 18 *		Plate 11 £125	
3d Rose 1881 Plate 20/21									
3d on 3d Lilac 1883									
4d Rose 1857									
4d Rose 1857 Glazed paper									
4d Red Plate 3 or 4 1862									
4d Vermillion 1865 Plate 7-14		£40	£40	£35	£80	£70	£150	£60	£500

Type	C79 Mailboat	C81 Bahia Brazil	C82 Pernambuco Brazil	C83 Rio de Janeiro	C86 Porto Plata Dominican Rep	C87 St Domingo Dominican Rep	C88 St Jago de Cuba	D22 Cuidad Bolivar Venezeula	D26 Mailboat
4d Vermillion Plate 15 1876					£250	£300	£400		
4d Sage green (1877) Plate 15 & 16					£200	£200		£150	
4d Grey-brown 1880 Wmk. Garter pl 17									
4d Grey-brown 1880 Wmk. Crown Plates 17 & 18								Plate 17 *	
6d Lilac Embossed 1854									
6d Lilac 1856									
6d 1862 Plates 3 & 4									
6d 1865 Plates 5 & 6			*	Plate 5 £70					
6d 1865 Wmk. error									
6d Lilac 1867 Plate 6		£60	£60	£55					
6d Violet 1867 Plate 8 & 9	£65	£50	£50	£40	Plate 8 *		£250		Plate 8 *
6d Buff 1872 Plates 11 & 12		£65	£50	Plate 11 £40			Plate 11 *		
6d Chestnut 1872 Plate 11		£65	£40	£35					
6d Grey 1873 Plate 12		*	*	*					
6d Grey 1873 Plates 13-17		Plate 13 *			£90	*			
6d Grey 1881-2 Plates 17 & 18									
6d on 6d Lilac									
8d Orange 1876					£350				
9d Straw 1862									
9d Bistre 1862									
9d Straw 1865		£300	£300	£250			*		
9d Straw 1867		£180	£180	£120		*	*	*	
10d Red-brown 1867	£300		£220	£200			£500	*	
1/- 1847 Embossed									
1/- Green (1856)									
1/- Green (1856) Thick paper									
1/- Green 1862									
1/- Green 1862 K variety									

Type	C79 Mailboat	C81 Bahia Brazil	C82 Pernambuco Brazil	C83 Rio de Janeiro	C86 Porto Plata Dominican Rep	C87 St Domingo Dominican Rep	C88 St Jago de Cuba	D22 Cuidad Bolivar Venezeula	D26 Mailboat
1/- Green 1865 Plate 4		£120	£120	£90		*	£300		*
1/- Green Plates 4, 5, 6, 7 (1867)		£40	£40	£30	Plate 4 & 7 £90		*	£120	
1/- Green 1873 Plates 8-13		Plate 8 & 9 £55		£45	£90	£90		£400	
1/- Orange-brown Plate 13									
1/- Orange-brown 1881 Plates 13 & 14									
2/- Blue 1867		£180	£170	£100	£250	*	*	£600	
2/- Brown 1880									
5/- Rose 1867 Plates 1 & 2		Plate 1 £275	£275	Plate 1 & 2 £275	*		Plate 1 *	£950	
5/- Rose Plate 4 1882 Blued paper									
5/- Rose Plate 4 1882 White paper									
10/- Grey-green 1878									
10/- Grey-green 1883									
£1 Brown-lilac 1878									
£1 Brown-lilac 1882									
1880 ½d Deep green									
1880 ½d Pale green									
1880 1d Venetian red									
1880 1½d Venetian red									
1880 2d Pale rose									
1880 2d Deep rose									
1880 5d Indigo									
1881 1d Lilac 14 dots									
1881 1d Lilac 16 dots									
1883-4 ½d Slate-blue									
1883-4 1½d Lilac									
1883-4 2d Lilac									
1883-4 2½d Lilac									
1883-4 3d Lilac									
1883-4 Dull green									

D74 of forged cancels on this office

Type	D74 Pisco & Chincha Islands - Peru	D87 Iquique Peru	E53 Port au Prince Haiti	E88 Colon Columbia	F69 Savanilla Columbia	F83 Arroyo Porto Rico	F84 Aquadilla Porto Rico	F85 Mayaquez Porto rico
½d Rose (1870-79)		£80	£45		£85	£50	Plate 6 £75	£40
1d Red (1841) Imperf								
1d Red (1854) p16 Die I								
1d Red-brown 1855 p16 Die II								
1d Red-brown 1855 p14 Die II								
1d Red-brown 1855 Die II p16 LC								
1d Red 1857 LC p14								
1d Red 1861 Alph IV								
1d Red Plate 1864-79		£60	£30	£35	£60	£40	£60	£25
1½d Rose-red Plate 1 or 3			£60	£75	£100	*		£35
2d Blue 1841 Imperf								
2d Blue 1854 SC Die I p16								
2d Blue 1855 LC p14								
2d Blue 1858 LC p16								
2d Blue 1858 Plates 7-15	*	£90	£40	£40		Plate 14 - *	Plate 14 - *	£30
2½d Roay-mauve 1875 Blue paper								
2½d Rosy-mauve 1876 Plates 3-17			£250					
2½d Blue 1880 Plates 17-20								
2½d Blue 1881 Plates 21-23								
3d Carmine 1862								
3d Rose 1865 Plate 4								
3d Rose 1867 Plates 4-10		£70	Plate 6 & 7 £35	*	*	£45	*	£35
3d Rose 1873 Plates 11-20		£170	£30	£40	Plate 20 £100	£45	Plate 12 - *	£35
3d Rose 1881 Plate 20/21					Plate 20 £100			
3d on 3d Lilac 1883								
4d Roase 1857								
4d Rose 1857 Glazed paper								
4d Red Plate 3 or 4 1862								
4d Vermillion 1865 Plates 7-14	£1000	£50	£35	£40	£45	£40	£100	£30

Type	D74 Pisco & Chincha Islands - Peru	D87 Iquique Peru	E53 Port au Prince Haiti	E88 Colon Columbia	F69 Savanilla Columbia	F83 Arroyo Porto Rico	F84 Aquadilla Porto Rico	F85 Mayaquez Porto rico
4d Vermillion Plate 15 1876		£225	£225	*	£225	£225	*	£85
4d Sage green (1877) Plate 15 & 16		£150	£110	£150	£150			Plate 15 - *
4d Grey-brown 1880 Wmk. Garter Pl 17			£200	£275	£300			
4d Grey-bown 1880 Wmk. Cross Plates 17 & 18			£40	£55	Plate 17 £55			
6d Lilac Embossed 1854								
6d Lilac 1856 Thick paper								
6d 1862 Plates 3 & 4								
6d 1865 Plates 5 & 6	£1000							
6d 1865 Wmk error								
6d Lilac 1867 Plate 6								
6d Lilac 1867 Plate 6, 8 or 9		*		*				Plate 9 £650
6d Buff 1872 Plates 11 & 12		£80			*	£50	*	£50
6d Chestnut 1872 Plate 11		*				£45		£40
6d Grey 1873 Plate 12		£150		*		*		£120
6d Grey 1873 Plates 13-17		£75	*	£40	£60	£40	*	£35
6d Grey 1881-2 Plates 17 & 18								
6d on 6d Lilac								
8d Orange 1876		£300	£275	*	£275			£225
9d Straw 1862								
9d Bistre 1862								
9d Straw 1867		£150		*		£220	£275	£150
10d Red-brown 1867		*		*		£220	£275	£200
1/- 1847 Embossed								
1/- Green (1856)								
1/- Green (1856) Thick paper								
1/- Green 1862								
1/- Green 1862 K Variety								
1/- Green 1865 Plate 4	*					*		

Type	D74 Pisco & Chincha Islands - Peru	D87 Iquique Peru	E53 Port au Prince Haiti	E88 Colom Columbia	F69 Savanilla Columbia	F83 Arroyo Porto Rico	F84 Aquadilla Porto Rico	F85 Mayaquez Porto rico
1/- Green Plates 4, 5, 6, 7 (1867)		£60		£35	£55	£40	£85	£30
1/- Green 1873 Plates 8-13		£55	£50	£50	£60	£50	£85	£35
1/- Orange-brown Plate 13			£300	£275	£300			
1/- Orange-brown 1881 Plates 13 & 14			£90	£120	£170			
2/- Blue 1867	£1000	£150	£120	£120		£170	£220	£120
2/- Brown 1880			£1700	£1500				
5/- Rose 1867 Plates 1 & 2			£300	£350	Plate 2 £375	Plate 2 - *		
5/- Rose Plate 4 1882 Blued paper								
5/- Rose Plate 4 1882 White paper								
10/- Grey-green 1878			£3500					
10/- Grey-green 1883								
£1 Brown-lilac 1878								
£1 Brown-lilac 1882								
1880 ½d Deep green								
1880 ½d Pale green			£50					
1880 1d Venetian red			£60	£100				
1880 1½d Venetian red			£70					
1880 2d Pale rose			£80	*				
1880 2d Deep rose								
1880 5d Indigo								
1881 1d Lilac 14 dots								
1881 1d Lilac 16 dots								
1883-4 ½d Slate-blue								
1883-4 1½d Lilac								
1883-4 2d Lilac								
1883-4 2½d Lilac								
1883-4 3d Lilac								
1883-4 Dull green								
1883-4 5d Dull green								

Type	D74 Pisco & Chincha Islands - Peru	D87 Iquique Peru	E53 Port au Prince Haiti	E88 Colom Columbia	F69 Savanilla Columbia	F83 Arroyo Porto Rico	F84 Aquadilla porto Rico	F85 Mayaquez porto rico
1883-4 6d Dull green								
1883-4 9d Dull green								
1883-4 1/- Dull green								

Type	F87 Smyrna	F88 Ponce Porto Rico	G Gibraltar	G06 Beyrout Lebanon	M Malta	247 Fernando Poo	582 Naguabo Porto Rico	942 969 974 975 981 982 Cyprus	0X0 Crimea
½d Rose (1870-79)	£20	£40		£25			*	£200	
1d Red (1841) Imperf					£1200				*
1d Red (1854) p16 Die I			£250		£100				£50
1d Red-brown 1855 p16 Die II			£450		£650				
1d Red-brown 1855 p14 Die II			£250		£150				£5
1d Red-brown 1855 Die II p16 LC					£45				£80
1d Red 1857 LC p14			£20		£15				
1d Red 1861 Alph IV									
1d Red Plate 1864-79	£10	£30		£12			£250	£120	
1½d Rose-red Plate 1 or 3	£165	£80		£175				£1200	
2d Blue 1841 Imperf					£2000				£700
2d Blue 1854 SC Die p16			£300		£500				£600
2d Blue 1855 LC p14			£45		£40				£90
2d Blue 1858 LC p16	*		£275		£175				£175
2d Blue 1858 Plates 7-15	£12	£40	£250	£15	£30			£150	
2½d Rosy-mauve 1875 Blue paper	£45			£50					
2½d Rosy-mauve 1875 White paper	£22			£20					
2½d Rosy-mauve 1876 Plates 3-17	£12			£15				£45	
2½d Blue 1880 Plates 17-20	£9			£10					
2½d Blue 1881 Plates 21-23	£8			£9				£350	
3d Carmine 1862									
3d Rose 1865 Plate 4									
3d Rose 1867 Plates 4-10	£20	*		Plate 10 - *					
3d Rose 1873 Plates 11-20	*	£40		£25			£400		
3d Rose 1881 Plates 20/21									
3d on 3d Lilac 1883									
4d Rose 1857			£40		£25				£500
4d Rose 1857 Glazed paper			*		£120				
4d Red Plate 3 or 4 1862									

Type	F87 Smyrna	F88 Ponce Porto Rico	G Gibraltar	G06 Beyrout Lebanon	M Malta	247 Fernando Poo	582 Naguabo Porto Rico	942 969 974 975 981 982 Cyprus	0X0 Crimea
4d Vermillion 1865 Plate 7-14	£20	£40		£25		*	£600		
4d Vermillion Plate 15 1876	£120	£200		£125		*	*		
4d Sage green (1877) Plates 15 & 16	£75	£150		£85				£400	
4d Grey-brown Wmk. Garter Pl 17	*			*					
4d Grey-brown 1880 Wmk. Crown Plates 17 & 18	£25			£35					
6d Lilac Embossed 1854					£2500				£800
6d Lilac 1856			£30		£30				
6d 1862 Plates 3 & 4									
6d 1865 Plates 5 & 6									
6d 1865 Wmk. error									
6d Lilac 1867 Plate 6									
6d Violet 1867 Plate 8 or 9				*					
6d Buff 1872 Plates 11 & 12	£50	£60		£55				£1500	
6d Chestnut 1872 Plate 11	*	£60		£30					
6d Grey 1873 Plate 12	£65	*		*				£300	
6d Grey 1873 Plates 13-17	£20	£50		£20		*	*		
6d Grey 1881-2 Plates 17-18	£35								
6d on 6d Lilac	£75								
8d Orange 1876	*			£275				£4000	
9d Straw 1862									
9d Bistre 1862									
9d Straw 1867	£200			£220			*		
10d Red-brown 1867	£100	£225		£120			£550		
1/- 1847 Embossed									£800
1/- Green (1856)			£80		£100				
1/- Green (1856) Thick paper			*		£130				
1/- Green 1862									
1/- Green 1862 K Variety									

Type	F87 Smyrna	F88 Ponce Porto Rico	G Gibraltar	G06 Beyrout Lebanon	M Malta	247 Fernando Poo	582 Naguabo Porto Rico	942 969 974 975 981 982 Cyprus	0X0 Crimea
1/- Green 1865 Plate 4									
1/- Green Plates 4, 5, 6, 7 (1867)	*	£35		£22					
1/- Green 1873 Plates 8-13	£25	£45		£30			*	£650	
1/- Orange-brown Plate 13	£125			*					
1/- Orange-brown `88` Plates 13 & 14	£35			£40					
2/- Blue 1867		*		£110			£550		
2/- Brown 1880									
5/- Rose 1867 Plates 1 & 2	*	£250		£400			Plate 2 £3500		
5/- Rose Plate 4 1882 Blued paper									
5/- Rose Plate 4 1882 White paper									
10/- Grey-green 1878									
10/- Grey-green 1883									
£1 Brown-lilac 1878									
£1 Brown-lilac 1882									
1880 ½d Deep green	£7			£8					
1880 ½d Pale green	£7			£9					
1880 1d Venetian red	£12			£10					
1880 1½d Venetian red	£80			£120					
1880 2d Pale rose	£35			£40					
1880 2d Deep rose	£35			£40					
1880 5d Indigo	£50			£65					
1881 1d Lilac 14 dots				*					
1881 1d Lilac 16 dots	£4			£5					
1883-4 ½d Slate-blue	£12			£15					
1883-4 1½d Lilac	£50			£50					
1883-4 2d Lilac				£40					
1883-4 2½d Lilac	£10			£8					
1883-4 3d Lilac									
1883-4 4d Dull green	*			£125					

Type	F87 Smyrna	F88 Ponce Porto Rico	G Gibraltar	G06 Beyrout Lebanon	M Malta	247 Fernando Poo	582 Naguabo Porto Rico	942 969 974 975 981 982 Cyprus *	0X0 Crimea
1883-4 5d Dull green	£80			£75					
1883-4 6d Dull green									
1883-4 9d Dull green									
1883-4 1/- Dull green	£200			£175					
1887 ½d Orange	£5			£7					
1887 6d Purple	£15			£20					
1887 1/- Green	£90			£100					
1887 ½d Blue-green	£7			£15					
1887 1/- Green & red	*			£150					

* It should be noted prices can vary dependant on office location in Cyprus

					'Jubilee' Line added to selvedge			
	½d		1d		½d		1d	
Control	I	P	I	P	I	P	I	P
None		* £85		* £350				* £750
A		£15		£100				
B		£22		£30		£140		
C		£15		£30		£12		
D		£15		£12	£14	£12		
E		£160	£95	£14		5.00		
F				£14	£50	4.50		
G				£14	£110	4.50		£10
H				8.00	5.00	4.50		£10
I				£30	£10	4.50	£70	3.00
J				£25	£20	4.50	£70	3.00
K					£16	4.50	£70	3.00
L					£16	4.50	7.00	3.00
M					5.00	4.50	7.00	3.00
N					5.00	4.50	5.00	3.00
O					5.00	4.50	2.50	3.00
O over N							£1500	£1500
P					5.00	4.50	£25	3.00
Q					5.00	4.50	5.00	3.00

Control	½d Blue green		1d	
R	5.00	4.00	7.50	3.00
S			3.00	3.00
T			3.00	3.00
U			3.00	3.00
V			3.00	3.00
W			3.00	3.00
X			3.00	4.50

Prices shown are for single stamp with control, mounted mint

* Price for a lower right hand corner pair, with selvedge intact

I = Imperforate through margin

P = Perforated through margin

	Continuous 'Jubilee' line						Interupted 'Jubilee' line					
	½d E1		½d E2		1d E3		½ E1		½d E2		1d E3	
Control	I	P	I	P	I	P	I	P	I	P	I	P
A	4.00	5.00			5.00	£15						
B	4.00	£20			5.00	£15	£25					
C	5.00	£95			5.00	£12	6.00	£75			£14	£70
C4	4.00	£75			£5	£15	5.00	£95			6.00	£75
5.00		£45					4.00	£95	4.00	£75	6.00	£70
D5									4.00	£35	6.00	£75
E5									4.00	£15	6.00	6.00
E6									4.00	£95	6.00	£75
F6									4.00	£18	6.00	6.00
F7									4.00	£15	6.00	6.00
G7									5.00	4.00	6.00	6.00
G8									5.00	5.00	6.00	6.00
H8									4.00	4.00	6.00	6.00
H9									5.00	5.00	6.00	6.00
I9									5.00	4.00	6.00	6.00
I10									4.00	5.00	5.00	6.00
J10									4.00	4.00	5.00	6.00

Perf. 14	½d E27		1d E28	
A 11(c)			£12	5.00
A 11(w)	6.00	6.00	£60	£15

Perf. 15 x 14	½d E32		1d E33	
A 11 (c)	£85	£125	£35	£45

Prices shown are for a mounted mint single stamp with control

(c) denotes close spacing between the figures - 1.5mm (1d vlues only)

(w) denotes wide spacing between the figures - 2mm (1d values only)

1911 - 1912 Definitives

Prices shown are for single stamp with control, mounted mint

Watermark Imperial Crown. Die 1A

	A. 11		A 11 (w)		A 11 (c)	
Control	I	P	I	P	I	P
½d			£20	£10	*	*
1d	£200	£125	£12	£12	£50	£100

Watermark Imperial Crown. Die 1B

	A. 11		A 11 (w)		A 11 (c)	
Control	I	P	I	P	I	P
½d			£15	£15	£15	£10
1d	£17	£17	£55	£275	£12	£20

Watermark Imperial Crown. Die 2

	B.11		B 11		B. 12		B 12 (w)		B 12 (c)		B13	
Control	I	P	I	P	I	P	I	P	I	P	I	P
½d			£10	£20		£15000	£15	£12	6.00	6.00		
1d	£25	£30	£10	£10	£20	£25	8.00	8.00	£12	£10		

Watermark Royal Cypher. Die 2

	B.11		B 11		B. 12		B 12 (w)		B 12 (c)		B13	
Control	I	P	I	P	I		I	P	I	P	I	P
½d							£10	£10	£12	£10	£10	£10
1d							£10	£12			£17	£17

Watermark Multiple Cypher. Die 2

	B.11		B 11		B. 12		B 12 (w)		B 12 (c)		B13	
Control	I	P	I	P	I		I	P	I	P	I	P
½d					£3000	£3000	£12	£15	£12	£12		
1d					£4000	£4000	£20	£20				

Notes: All controls with dot between letter and number were Somerset House printings

A 11 (w) denotes wide spacing - 2mm

B 12 (w) denotes wide spacing - 6mm

A 11 (c) denotes close spacing - 1½mm

B 12 (c) denotes close spacing - 4½mm

Control B12 Wide (I)

B12 Narrow (I)

B12 Wide (P)

1912 - 1924 Wmk. Royal Cypher

	½d		1d		1 ½d		2d Die 1		2d Die II		2 ½d		3d		4d	
Control	I	P	I	P	I	P	I	P	I	P	I	P	I	P	I	P
A. 12 (w)					8.00	£250							£15	£150		
A. 12 (c)					£10						£10	£650	£20	£25		
B.13	2.00	£325											£12	£20	7.00	£65
C 12			1.00	1.00												
C 13	1.00	1.00	1.00	1.00	6.00	6.00					7.00	7.00	5.00	5.00	6.00	6.00
C.13							5.00	5.00					£12	£45		
C 14	8.00	8.00	5.00	5.00			4.00	5.00			£15	9.00				
D 14	1.00	1.00	1.00	1.00	5.00	7.00	3.00	3.00			£35	£35	5.00	5.00	6.00	6.00
E 14	1.00	1.00	1.00	1.00							8.00	7.00	5.00	6.00		
F 15	1.00	1.00	1.00	1.00	£12	£15	3.00	£10					5.00	5.00	6.00	6.00
G 15	2.00	2.00	1.00	1.00	£12	£20	5.00	5.00			7.00	8.00	£17	£17	6.00	6.00
H 16	1.00	5.00	1.00	1.00	6.00	£20	3.00	£250			7.00	7.00	£15	£50	6.00	£55
I 16	1.00	1.00	1.00	1.00			3.00	£35			7.00	£12	5.00	5.00	6.00	9.00
J 17	1.00	1.00	1.00	1.00	8.00	£10	3.00	7.00			8.00	£12	6.00	7.00	6.00	6.00
J. 17											£450					
K 17	9.00	£12	2.00	2.00			8.00	£22			8.00	£250			£10	£1500
K 18	4.00	5.00	1.00	1.00	8.00	£12									6.00	£10
18					£1350	£1350										
L 18	5.00	6.00	2.00	2.00	3.00	3.00	4.00	6.00			£10	9.00	8.00	8.00		
M 18	7.00	7.00	£10	£10	6.00	5.00					£20	£15	7.00	7.00	6.00	6.00
M			£8000													
19					£7500	£7500										
M 19	1.50	1.00	2.00	2.00	4.00	4.00	£15	£20			£15	£15				
N 19	2.00	2.00	1.00	1.00	4.00	4.00	3.00	8.00			8.00	8.00	5.00	5.00	7.00	7.00
O 19	6.00	6.00	5.00	5.00	4.00	4.00	£12	£70			9.00	9.00				
O 20	3.00	3.00	£10	£10	4.00	4.00	4.00	4.00			£10	£10	6.00	6.00	6.00	6.00
P 20	1.00	1.00	1.00	1.00			3.00	3.00			7.00	9.00	6.00	6.00		
Q20	6.00	6.00	1.00	1.00	9.00	9.00	3.00	3.00								
Q 21	1.00	2.00	9.00	8.00	8.00	8.00	3.00	3.00			£25	£25	8.00	8.00	£55	£55
R 21	1.50	1.50	6.00	6.00			3.00	3.00			£12	£12	6.00	6.00	6.00	6.00
S 21	£12	£12	£15	£15			7.00	7.00	£20	£17	£20	£17	£15	£12	£60	£40
S 22	£12	£12	8.00	8.00			6.00	6.00	7.00	7.00	£35	£40	6.00	6.00	£30	£30
T 22	3.00	2.00	2.00	1.00	4.00	4.00	£15	£20	£10	8.00	£12	£12	£10	£10	6.00	6.00
U 22	2.00	2.00	5.00	5.00	5.00	5.00			£12	£12			7.00	7.00	£45	£35
U 23	1.50	1.50	£10	£10	4.00	4.00			7.00	7.00	£10	£10	7.00	6.00	£25	£15
V 23	1.00	1.00	1.00	1.00	4.00	4.00			8.00	7.00	£12	£12	7.00	7.00	8.00	8.00
W 23	9.00	£12	4.00	3.00	5.00	6.00			7.00	7.00			£10	£10		
W 24	£165	£165	£15	£15	£165	£165			£165	£195						
No control *							£40	£40								

* Price is for bottom left hand pair with selvedge

All controls with dot between letter and number were Somerset House printings.

A. 12 (w) denotes wide spacing between 'A' and '1' - 4mm

A. 12 (c) denotes close spacing between 'A' and '1' - 1 ½mm

1912 - 1924 Wmk. Royal Cypher

	5d		6d			7d		8d		9d		10d		1s	
Control	I	P	I		P	I	P	I	P	I	P	I	P	I	P
B.13	£10	£12								£12					
C.13			£12		£12	£25		£22				£30	£850	£20	£30
C 13						£15	£15								
C 14	7.00	7.00													
D 14	7.00	7.00	9.00			£15	£15	£30	£22			£25	£25	£20	£25
E 14			9.00		8.00						9.00			£450	£450
F 15	7.00	7.00	£25		£650	£25	£35	£20	£20	£10	£25	£30	£25	£20	£18
G 15	7.00	7.00	8.00			£15	£15	£20	£20	£10	£15	£30	£25	£15	£15
H 16	7.00	9.00	8.00			£12	£12	£20	£20	£15	£10	£20	£30	£15	£20
I 16	8.00	£10	8.00					£25	£25	£10	£30	£20	£30	£15	£35
J 17	7.00	7.00	8.00			£13	£13	£20	£20	£10	£10	£20	£18	£15	£18
K 17	7.00	£35	9.00							£10	£10			£15	£85
K 18								£275	£20	£35	£12	£35	£20		
L. 18			8.00		£35										
L 18	7.00	8.00	£10			£12	£140			£10	£10			£12	£12
M 18			8.00		£850										
M 19												£20	£30	£18	£15
N 19	7.00	8.00	8.00		£75					£10	£10			£15	£15
O 19	£12	£12	8.00							£10	£12	£20	£20	£15	£18
O 20										£10	£10			£15	£15
P 20			9.00							£10	£10			£20	£20
Q20			£10							£15	£40			£18	£15
Q21	£10	£15										£20	£40		
R 21	£30	£40	£10							£15	£10			£15	£15
S 21	£15	£20	£10		£175					£10	£10	£25	£20	£15	£15
S 22	8.00	£225								£12	£12	£25	£35	£15	£15
T 22	7.00	7.00	£11		£450					£60	£50	£45	£60	£15	£15
U 22			£10											£20	£30
U 23	£10	£10								£50	£60	£25	£25	£15	£15
V 23	8.00	£20	9.00							£50	£50			£20	£20
W.23			8.00												
A.24			£10												
B.24			£85												

			6d	
Control			I	P
Q.20			£50	
R.21			£60	

All 6d values were printed by Somerset House and all controls had dot bewteen the control letter and the control number, except for L. 18 imperf which exists with or without the dot.

1924 - 1935 Watermark Multiple Block Cypher

	½d		1d		1 ½d		2d		2 ½d		3d		4d	
Control	I	P	I	P	I	P	I	P	I	P	I	P	I	P
A 24	1.50	£10	3.00	£15	1.00	£10	£20							
A 24 EP					£350									
B 24	1.50	£40	2.00	£35	1.00	£85	3.00	£95	6.00		8.00		£11	
B 24 EP			£225		£350									
C 25	1.50	£60	2.00	£15	1.00		3.00		6.00		£25		£11	
D 25	1.50		£45		1.00		3.00		£10		8.00			
D 25 EP					£350									
E 26	1.50	£200	2.50		1.00		3.00		6.00		8.00		£16	
E.26					£850									
F 26	1.50	£75	2.00		1.00	£65	3.00							
G 27	1.50	£45	2.00		1.00		3.00		6.00	£150	8.00	£200	£11	
H 27	1.50	£45	2.00		1.00	£65	8.00		£25					
I 28	1.50		2.00		1.00	£85	6.00	£175	8.00		8.00		£11	
J 28	1.50		2.00		1.00		8.00							
K 29	4.00		5.00		2.50	£125	4.00		7.00		£25		£15	
L 29	75	£175	2.50	£175	1.00		4.00							
M 30	1.50		3.00		1.00		4.00		6.00		£10		£11	
N 30	1.50		2.00		1.00	*	3.00		6.00		£15			
O 31	1.50	*	2.50		1.00		8.00		£1500				£11	
P 31	1.50		2.00		1.00		3.00				£10			
Q 32	1.50		2.00		1.00		3.00		£10				£11	
R 32	1.50		8.00		2.00		4.00	£250	£10		£10		£15	
S 33	1.50		3.00		1.00		£25		£22		£30			
T 33	1.50		2.00		1.00		3.00		£15		£18		£11	
U 34	2.50		5.00		5.00		6.00							
V 34	2.00	£40	5.00	£75	5.00	*	5.00		£12		£15		£15	
W 35									£15	£150			£55	
X 35													£11	£850

EP - Denotes the experimental paper printings.

1924 - 1935 Watermark Multiple Block Cypher

	5		6d (c)		6d (o)		9d		10d		1s	
Control	I	P	I	P	I	P	I	P	I	P	I	P
A 24	£25	£85					£15	£10	£80	£60	£20	£65
B 24			£15								£85	
C 25	£20		£15	*			£10					
D 25			£20		£135				£45		£30	
E 26					7.00	£750						
F 26	£20				9.00		£10		£95		£25	
G 27					7.00				£45			
H 27	£40				7.00						£35	
I 28	£15				£10	£20	£10				£25	
J 28					8.00	£20	£12		£45		£35	
K 29	£20				7.00						£95	
L 29	£20				7.00		£10		£45		£25	
M 30	£50				7.00	£600						
N 30					£10		£12				£25	
O 31	£22				£10				£85			
P 31					7.00		£10				£30	
Q 32	£30				7.00				£80			
R 32					£12		£12				£30	
S 33	£25				£12	*			£75		£75	
T 33	£275				7.00		£50					
U 34	£55								£185		£35	
V 34	£25				£12		£18		£175		£35	£125
W 35					£12	£15	£30		£50		£40	
X 35	£20				£10	£15	£12	£45			£35	
Y 36			£50		7.00							
Z 36			£20		7.00							
A 37					8.00							
B 37					£100	£450						
C 38					£15							
D 38					£15	£75						

All 6d values were Somerset House with dot bewteen letter and figures, except from V 34 and after which were Harrison

1934 - 1937 Photogravure

All prices on this page are for mounted mint Cylinder control blocks of four or six, unmounted mint at 50% more.

Control	U34 (A)		V34 (A)		V34 (B)		V34 (D)		W35 (C)		W35 (D)	
	No dot	Dot	No dot	Dot	No dot	Dot	No dot	Dot	No dot	Dot	No dot	Dot
Large Format												
1d					£15	£15						
1½d	£30	£30	£25	£25	£20	£20						
Intermediate Format												
½d					£15	£15			£35	£35		
1d					£50	£50			£185	£185		
1½d					£40	£40						
1½d											£150	£125
2d											£40	£40

			Fractional Controls							
Control	W35 (D)		X35 (D)		Y36 (D)		Z36 (D)		A37 (D)	
	No dot	Dot	No dot	Dot	No dot	Dot	No dot	Dot	No dot	Dot
Small Format										
½d	£12	£12	£10	£10	£10	£10	£20	£20		
1d	£85	£85	£10	£10	£10	£10				
1½d	£40	£20	£10	£10	£10	£10	£12	£12		
2d			£12	£12	£12	£12	£15	£15	£15	£15
2½d	£25	£25			£40	£40				
3d	£50	£35	£40	£40	£25	£25	£25*	£25*		
4d	£675	£50	£35	£25	£25 *	£25*				
5d			£225	£225	£75	£75	£50 *	£50 *		
9d			£125*	£125*						
10d					£115 *	£125*				
1s					£140	£140	£140 *	£140*		

The letter in brackets after the control shows the layout of the control/cylinder block, as illustrated below.
* Denotes control exists with varying degrees of 'boxing'.

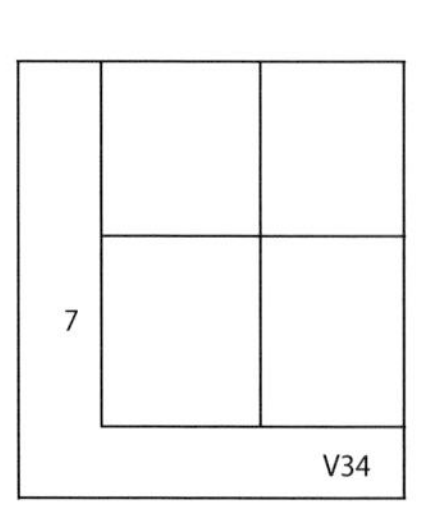

Position A

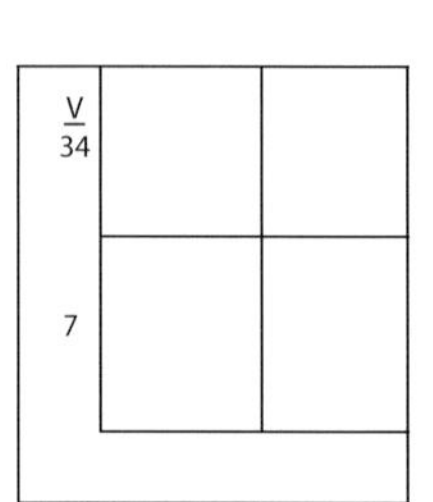

Position B

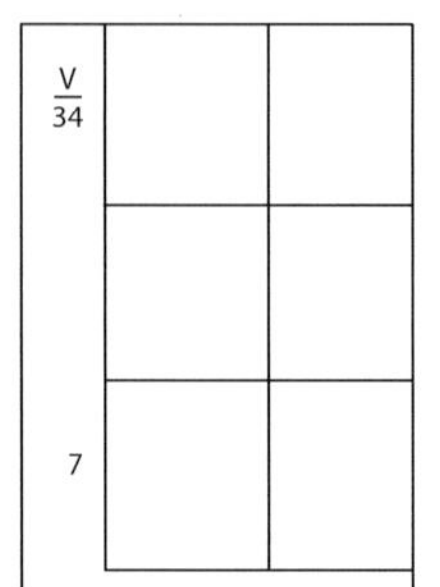

Position C

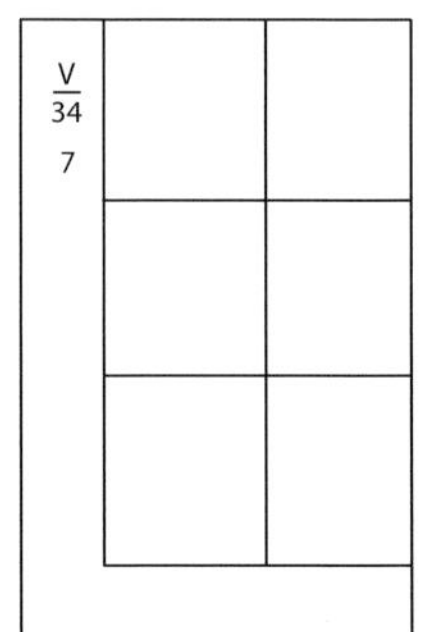

Position D

1936 - 1937 Watermark Block Cypher KVII

All prices on this page are for mounted mint Cylinder control blocks of six, unmounted mint at 50% more.

Control	A36		A37	
	No dot	Dot	No dot	Dot
½d	£10	£10	£10	£10
1d	£10	£10	£12	£12
1½d	£10	£10	£10	£10
2½d	£15*	£15*		

1937 - 1947 Watermark Block Cypher GVIR

All prices on this page are for mounted mint Cylinder control blocks of six, unmounted mint at 50% more.

Dark Colours

Control		Marginal Rule			A37	B37	C38	D38	E39	F39	G40	H40	I41
		A37	B37	D38									
½d	No dot	5.00	6.00		2.00	2.00	2.00	2.00	2.00	2.00	2.00		2.00
	Dot	5.00	6.00		3.50								
1d	No dot	5.00	5.00		2.00	2.00	2.00	2.00	2.00	2.00	2.00	2.00	2.00
	Dot	5.00	5.00			4.50							
1½d	No dot	8.00	7.00		2.00	2.00	2.00	2.00	2.00	2.00	2.00		
	Dot	8.00	7.00					3.50	3.50				
2d	No dot					4.00	5.50	4.00	4.00	4.00	4.00	4.00	4.00
	Dot					£12	£200	£12	£12	£15	£12	£15	£15
2½d	No dot	£20	£20	£35					9.00		2.50	2.50	2.50
	Dot	7.00	7.00	£25					£15		£15	£10	£10
3d	No dot						£20	£20	£20		£20	£20	
	Dot						£45	£45	£45		£45	£45	

Control		D38	E39	F39	G40	H40	I41	J41	K42	L42	M43	N43	O44	P44	Q45	R45	S46	T46	U47	None
4d	No dot	900	9.00		9.00		900		9.00*				9.00							9.00
	Dot												9.00							9.00
5d	No dot	£20	£20		£20		£20		£20	£20*										
	Dot								£40	£20*										
6d	No dot	£30	£15	£15	£15	8.00	£20	£15	£15	£15	£17	£15	£15		£15			£15	£15	£15
7d	No dot		£55*														£75			£55
	Dot																£55			£55
8d	No dot		£55*										£55				£55*			£60
	Dot																			£60
9d	No dot		£60		£60	£60	£60		£60	£80		£80	£60	£65		£60				£70
	Dot																			£60
10d	No dot		£55	£90		£55	£90	£65	£55	£55	£65	£55	£55		£55			£55	£65	£55
	Dot														£55			£55	£65	£65
11d	No dot																			£40
	Dot																			£35
1s	No dot		£60		£60	£65		£65	£60		£65		£60		£60		£65		£60	£40
	Dot														£60		£85		£85	£35

* An astrerisk next to a price denotes that the control exists with varying degrees of 'boxing'

All prices on this page are for mounted mint Cylinder control blocks of six, unmounted mint at 50% more.

Pale Colours

Control	J41	K42	L42	M43	N43	O44	P44	Q45	R45	S46	T46	U47	None
½d	8.00	£10	£20	£10	£10	8.00	£10	8.00	8.00	£12	£10	8.00	8.00
1d	7.00	£10	7.00	7.00	7.00	7.00	7.00	7.00	7.00	8.00	7.00	7.00	7.00
1½d			£12		£12	£15	£50	£12	£22	£12		£12	£12
2d	£11	£12	£15	£12	£12	£12	£15	£20	£20	£12	£11	£15	£12
2½d	6.00	7.00	£12	£15	£12	£10	£12	£12	£10	7.00	7.00	7.00	7.00
3d No dot	£18	£18	£18	£18	£18	£18	£20	£20	£20			£18	

New Colours

	No Dot	Dot
½d	£15	£15
1d	£15	£15
1½d	£13	£13
2d	£15	£15
2½d	£11	£11
4d	£22	£22

1914 - 1925 Watermark Royal Cypher (Sideways)

Prices are for mounted mint singles

	½d		1d		1d chalky		1½d		2d		3d		4d		5d		1s	
Control	I	P	I	P	I	P	I	P	I	P	I	P	I	P	I	P	I	P
D.14		£12		£12						£10						£45		
D 14	2.00	2.00	3.00	3.00					3.50	3.50					£38	£120		
E 14			3.00	2.00														
F.15																		£55
G 15			2.00	£27														
H 16									3.00	3.00								
I 16	2.00	2.00	2.00	3.00					3.50	3.50								
K 17			2.00	2.00					6.00	3.00								
L 18											9.00	£15						
N 19	2.00	2.00	2.50	2.00														
O.19																		£40
O 19									3.50	3.50								
O 20											8.00	£12						
P 20			3.00						3.00	4.50								
Q 20			9.00										£45	£38				
Q 21			£10	£23														
R 21	2.00	£18	2.00	4.00					3.00	9.00								
S .21																		£50
S 21			2.00	3.00														
S 22		3.00	3.00	3.00														
T 22			3.00	2.00							9.00	£12						
U 22	2.00	£18					£75											
U 23			2.00	2.00			£75		£12	9.00								
V.23																	£75	
V 23							£75	£75			£10	£12						
W23	8.00	£11									£12	£18						
B 24					£12													
C 25					£12													

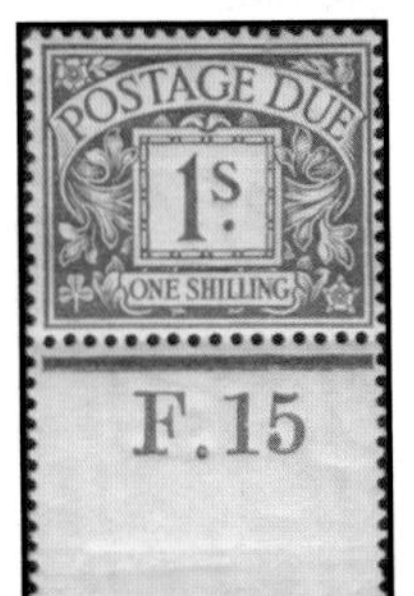

1914 - 1925 Watermark Multiple Block (Sideways)

Prices are for mounted mint singles

	½d		1d		1½d		2d		3d		4d		5d		1s		2s 6d	
Control	I	P	I	P	I	P	I	P	I	P	I	P	I	P	I	P	I	P
A 24							6.00				£38				£375			
B 24		3.00	£12		£75				9.00		£15				£18		£50	
B 24 EP									£90									
C 25							6.00								£18			
D 25									£12									
E 26							8.00		9.50		£18				*	£22		
F 26							6.00		8.50		£30				£18			
G 27									9.00						£18			
H 27							£38			£20							£50	
I 28	1.50		2.50				8.00		£12			£30			£18		£50	
K 29		£12	2.50	£22			7.00		£12		£18				£18		£50	
L 29	2.00		2.50				5.00		£12		£15						£50	
M 30	2.00						6.00								£18			
N 30			3.50						9.00		£38		£45				£38	
O 31	3.00		2.00				6.00		9.00				£45		£18		£50	
P 31	3.00						£10											
Q 32	2.00		3.00				6.00		£10		£38		£45		£18		£50	
R 32							6.00		£10		£38				£18		£50	
S 33	1.50		3.00	£26									£45		£18		£50	
T 33							£33		£12		£60							
U 34	8.50		£18	£18									£50		£28		£60	
V 34							£22				£38						£60	
W 35	4.00		£11						£12				£50		£28			
X 35							9.00				£38				£22		£60	
Y 36	3.00		4.00	*			9.00		9.00	£12								
Z 36																	£60	

EP - Denotes the experimental paper printing.

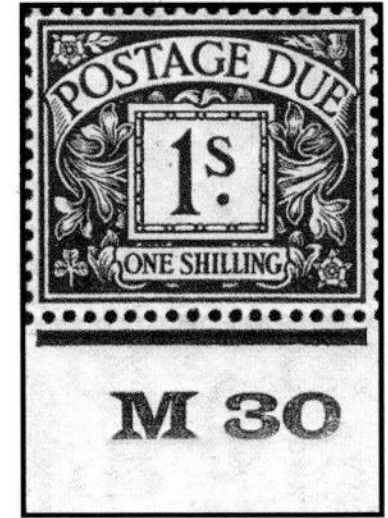

1936 - 1937 Watermark Multiple E8R Crown (Sideways)

Prices are for unmounted mint singles, lightly mounted approximately 30% less

	½d		1d		2d		3d		4d		5d		1s		2s 6d	
Control	I	P	I	P	I	P	I	P	I	P	I	P	I	P	I	P
A 36									£45		£45		£24			
A 37	£22	3.00	7.00		£12		9.00				£60				£300	
C 38															£450	

Postage Due Controls — King George VI

1937 - 1938 Watermark Multiple GVIR Crown (Sideways)

Prices are for unmounted mint singles, lightly mounted approximately 30% less

	½d		1d		2d		3d		4d		5d		1s		2s 6d	
Control	I	P	I	P	I	P	I	P	I	P	I	P	I	P	I	P
B37							£15		£100				£90			
C 38	£12		7.00		7.00		£15		£100		£23		£90		£90	
D38							£18								£90	£150
E 39	£12	£250	7.00		7.00				£100		£18		£100		£120	
F 39								£70								
G40	£35	£65	7.00	*	*	7.00				£140	£23		£23			
H 40									£140							
I 41			7.00	7.00	*	£30		£16		£18		£18			£190	*
J 41													£90			
K 42				7.00	*	7.00	£70	*		£100			£90		£260	£250
L 42															£200	
M 43			7.00		7.00		£16		£100		£30		£90			
O 44			9.00		£45		£18		£150		£30		£90		£100	
P 44									£100		£18		£90		£110	*
Q 44			*			*										
Q 45			£60		7.00										£350	
R 45							£18						£90			
S 46													£100		£330	
T 46									£100		£18					
U 47			7.00		7.00		£16	*							*	
'None' (pair)	£22	£22	£11	£11	£11	£11	£24	£24	£150	£150	£24	£24	£130	£130	£150	£200

No.			M/M	Used	✉

In 1881 Parliament passed 'The Customs and Inland Revenue Act' which authorised the use of 1d postage stamps to pay fiscal duties and certain 1d revenue stamps to be used for postal purposes. This authorisation came into effect from 1st June 1881 and the latter part of the year saw widespread use of the current 1d Inland Revenue stamp to pay postage. The new combined "Postage and Inland Revenue" 1d lilac was not issued until about 12th July 1881. The authorisation for dual purposes was extended to all values up to 2s6d with effect from 1st January 1883.

The fiscal stamps allowed for postage were those inscribed "Inland Revenue", although the fact that the post office notice announcing the change referred to "Receipt Stamps" vicariously allowed the earlier "Receipt", "Receipt and Draft" and "Draft" stamps to be used for postage. Copies are seen of Customs, Foreign Bill, Law Courts etc. stamps used postally but these were never authorised, although many seem not to have been surcharged.

The pricing basis for Fiscal stamps is as follows:
1. Be guided by notes for surface printed issues.
2. The price for postally used is based on fine used.

Illustrations of stamps and watermarks are reduced in size.

Please note that there is a wide range of shades - most of which are worth much the same.

Surface Printed Issues

Authorised 1 June 1881
Printer: De La Rue & Co.

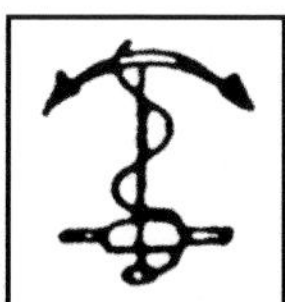

Ornate Cabled Anchor Watermark

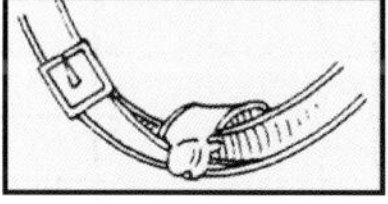

Die I. Square buckle, lighter shading as shown.

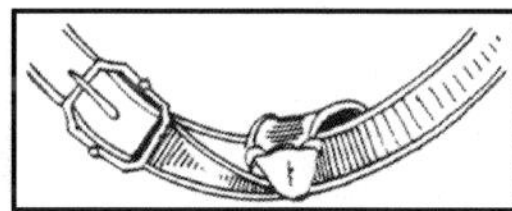

Die II. Octagonal buckle, heavier or solid shading as shown.

Receipt Stamps. Wmk. Ornate Cabled Anchor (inverted). Perf. 15½ x 15

No.			M/M	Used	✉
F1	1d	**Blue** (Die I)	£15	£20	£100
F1a		Watermark reversed (Die I)	£60	£80	-
F1b		Watermark upright (Die I)	£60	£80	-
F2	1d	**Blue** (Die II)	£14	£20	£100
F3	1d	**Blue** on blued paper (Die II)	£30	£35	£200
F3a		Watermark upright (Die II)	£70	£70	-

Draft Stamps. Wmk. Ornate Cabled Anchor (inverted). Perf. 15½ x 15

No.			M/M	Used	✉
F4	1d	**Brown**	£40	£40	£200
F4a		Watermark upright	£120	£120	-
F4a		Ochre brown	£40	£40	£200
F4b		Tete-beche pair (Brown)	£5000	-	-

Simple Cabled Anchor Watermark

Draft or Receipt Stamps. (a) Wmk. Ornate Cabled Anchor (inverted). Perf. 15½ x 15

No.			M/M	Used	✉
F5	1d	**Reddish lilac** on blued paper	£50	£25	£200
F5a		Watermark upright	£100	£50	-

(b) Wmk. Simple Cabled Anchor. Perf. 15½ x 15

No.			M/M	Used	✉
F6	1d	**Lilac**	5.00	7.00	£60
F6a		Watermark inverted	£80	-	-
F6b		'SPECIMEN'	From £60	-	-
F7	1d	**Lilac** on blued paper	5.00	7.00	£70

Inland Revenue Stamps Provisional. F7 overprinted 'INLAND REVENUE' in red in two lines.

No.			M/M	Used	✉
F8	1d	**Reddish lilac**	£250	£225	£450
F8a		Watermark reversed	£400	£350	-

(a) Wmk. Simple Cabled Anchor. Perf. 15½ x 15

No.			M/M	Used	✉
F9	1d	**Reddish lilac**	5.00	6.00	£50
F9a		Watermark inverted	£75	-	-
F9s		'SPECIMEN'	From £50	-	-
F10	1d	**Reddish lilac** on bluish paper	6.00	6.00	£50
F11	3d	**Pale reddish lilac**	£200	£100	£200
F11s		'SPECIMEN'	From £60	-	-
F12	3d	**Pale reddish lilac** on bluish paper	£200	£110	£200
F13	6d	**Reddish lilac**	£70	£75	£150
F13s		'SPECIMEN'	From £75	-	-
F14	6d	**Reddish lilac** on bluish paper	£85	£75	£150

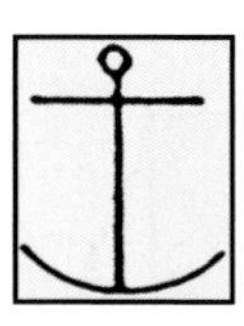
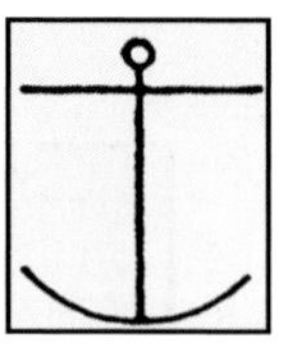

Anchor Watermark

Height: 16mm 18mm 20mm

(b) Wmk. Anchor (16mm). Perf. 15½ x 15

No.			M/M	Used	✉
F15	1d	**Reddish lilac**	4.00	6.00	£50
F16	1d	**Reddish lilac** on bluish paper	5.00	7.00	£50
F17	3d	**Pale reddish lilac**	£80	£60	£110
F17s		'SPECIMEN'	From £100	-	-
F18	3d	**Pale reddish lilac** on bluish paper	£100	£60	£120
F19	6d	**Reddish lilac**	£60	£70	£115
F19a		Watermark inverted	£200	-	-
F20	6d	**Reddish lilac** on bluish paper	£70	£70	£120

(c) Wmk. Anchor (18mm). Perf. 15½ x 15

No.			M/M	Used	✉
F21	1d	**Reddish lilac** on bluish paper	£10	£10	£90
F21s		'SPECIMEN'	From £80	-	-
F22	3d	**Pale reddish lilac** on bluish paper	£70	£70	£120
F22s		'SPECIMEN'	From £80	-	-
F23	6d	**Reddish lilac** on bluish paper	£60	£50	£150

(d) Wmk. Anchor (18mm). Perf. 14

No.			M/M	Used	✉
F24	3d	**Pale reddish lilac** on bluish paper	£300	£175	£300
F25	6d	**Reddish lilac** on bluish paper	£140	£60	£150

(e) Wmk. Anchor (20mm). Perf. 14

No.			M/M	Used	✉
F26	3d	**Reddish purple** on bluish paper	£225	£90	£150
F26s		'SPECIMEN'	From £90	-	-
F27	6d	**Reddish lilac** on bluish paper	£100	£90	£150

Small Anchor Watermark

(f) Wmk. Small Anchor. Perf. 14

No.			M/M	Used	✉
F28	1d	**Purple**	5.00	£10	£45
F29	1d	**Purple** on bluish paper	5.00	£10	£45
F29a		Watermark inverted	£40	-	-

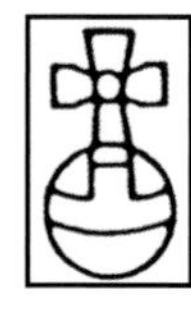
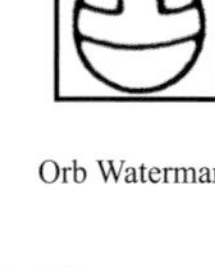

Orb Watermark

Corner Ornaments

Small sometimes broken — Small always broken — Large — Very large

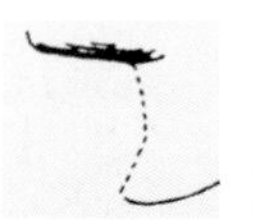
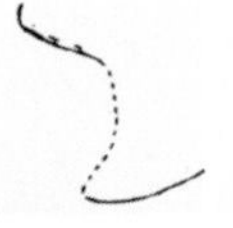

Chin: Shaded Die I — Unshaded Die II
Neck: Half outline Die III — Full outline Die IV

New design. (a) Wmk. Small Anchor. Perf. 14

No.			M/M	Used	✉
		Die I			
F30	1d	**Purple**	1.50	4.00	£40
F30a		Wmk. inverted	£40	£30	
F30s		'SPECIMEN'	From £20	-	-
F31	1d	**Purple** on bluish paper	3.00	2.00	£30
		Die II			
F32	1d	**Purple**	£12	£15	£150
F32s		'SPECIMEN'	From £20	-	-
F33	1d	**Purple** on bluish paper	£12	£15	£150
		Die III			
F34	1d	**Purple**	3.00	4.00	£50
F34s		'SPECIMEN'	From £20	-	-
F35	1d	**Purple** on bluish paper	3.00	4.00	£50
		Die IV			
F36	1d	**Purple**	2.00	1.00	£25
F37	1d	**Purple** on bluish paper	2.00	1.00	£25

(b) Wmk. Orb. Perf. 14

No.			M/M	Used	✉
		Die IV			
F38	1d	**Purple**	4.00	3.00	£25
F38a		Wmk. inverted	£75		
F39	1d	**Purple** on bluish paper	4.00	3.00	£25

Coloured Embossed Issues

Authorised 1 January 1881
Printer: Somerset House

Each stamp has a single capital letter in the design, which shows the die used.

Inland Revenue Stamps

(a) Bluish paper. No watermark. Imperforate

No.			M/M	Used
F40	2d	**Pink.** Die A	£250	£500
F41	3d	**Pink.** Die C	£100	£250
F41a		Pink. Die D	£275	
F41b		Tete-beche pair, Die C	£1200	
F42	6d	**Pink.** Die T	£750	
F42a		Pink. Die U	£150	£400
F42b		Tete-beche pair, Die U	£2000	
F43	9d	**Pink.** Die C	£250	
F43a		Tete-beche pair, 'SPECIMEN'	£750	
F44	1s	**Pink.** Die E	£400	£500
F44a		Pink. Die F	£150	£300
F45	2s	**Pink.** Die K	£400	£600
F46	2s6d	**Pink.** Die N	£750	
F46a		Pink. Die O	£200	£450

Thick letters

Thin letters

(b) 'INLAND REVENUE'(thick letters) underprint in green. Bluish paper. No watermark. Perf 12½

No.			M/M	Used
F47	2d	**Pink.** Die A	£200	£500
F46a		Tete-beche pair	£2000	
F48	3d	**Pink.** Die C	£750	
F48a		Pink. Die D	£750	
F49	9d	**Pink.** Die C	£750	£300
F50	1s	**Pink.** Die E	£400	£600
F50a		Pink. Die F	£200	£450
F51	2s 6d	**Pink.** Die O	£100	£250

(c) 'INLAND REVENUE'(thin letters) underprint in green. White paper. Wmk. Small Anchor. Perf. 12½

No.			M/M	Used
F52	1s	**Pink.** Die F	£200	£400

(d) 'INLAND REVENUE'(thin letters) underprint in green. White paper. Wmk. Small Anchor. Perf. 12½

No.			M/M	Used
F53	2d	**Vermilion.** Die A	£200	£350
F53a		Vermilion on bluish paper. Die A	£200	£350
F54	9d	**Vermilion.** Die C	£250	£450
F54a		Vermilion on bluish paper. Die C	£250	£450
F55	1s	**Vermilion.** Die E	£175	£300
F55a		Vermilion on bluish paper. Die E	£175	£300
F55b		Vermilion. Die F	£500	
F55c		Vermilion on bluish paper. Die F	£500	
F56	2s 6d	**Vermilion.** Die O	£175	£300
F56a		Vermilion on bluish paper. Die O	£175	£300

(e) 'INLAND REVENUE'(thin letters) underprint in green. White paper. Wmk. Orb. Perf. 12½

No.			M/M	Used
F57	2d	**Vermilion.** Die A, 'SPECIMEN'		
F58	9d	**Vermilion.** Die C, 'SPECIMEN'		
F59	1s	**Vermilion.** Die E, 'SPECIMEN'		
F60	2s 6d	**Vermilion.** Die O	£450	£600
F60a		Vermilion on bluish paper. Die O	£450	£600

Please note. All the above Embossed issues are rare on cover and are worth 2-3 times the postally used price.

In 1870 the many private telegraph companies, then in existence, were nationalised and a unified Government service introduced. Ordinary postage stamps were used for accountancy and a large proportion of the stamps of this period bearing circular date stamps were used for this purpose.

This form of accountancy proved inadequate and large losses were being made. To help clarify the exact income, special Telegraph stamps were issued in 1876. These had no other use, although they were sometimes wrongly used as postage stamps and passed through the postal system incorrectly, particularly after 1881 when the stamps were discontinued and of no other use.

Surface printed by De La Rue & Co. with check letters in the two lower corners and plate numbers shown in the two upper corners, where appropriate. All watermarks have been illustrated in the normal position, as seen from the back of the stamp, to ease identification for the collector. Sideways watermarks are shown in the direction they appear as sideways watermark, sideways-inverted therefore face the opposite direction.

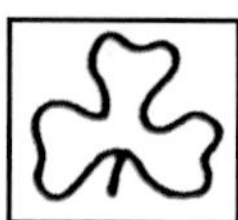

Shamrock Watermark

1876 (1 Feb.) Wmk. Shamrock. Perf. 14

No.			M/M	F/U
T1	**½d**	**Orange.** Plate 5 (1.4.80)	3.00	8.00
T1s		'SPECIMEN'	£14	-
T2	**1d**	**Brown.** Plate 1	4.00	3.00
T2a		Wmk. inverted	£75	-
T2s		'SPECIMEN'	£15	-
T3	**1d**	**Brown.** Plate 2	6.00	3.00
T3a		Wmk. inverted	£100	£50
T3s		'SPECIMEN'	£16	-
T4	**1d**	**Brown.** Plate 3	6.00	4.00
T4s		'SPECIMEN'	£20	-

Spray Watermark

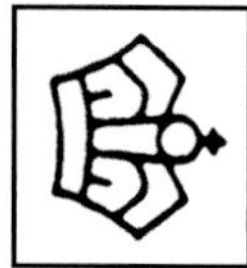

Imperial Crown Watermark

1876 (1 Feb.) Wmk. Spray (sideways). Perf. 14

No.			M/M	F/U
T5	**3d**	**Carmine.** Plate 1	£15	£12
T5a		Wmk. sideways inverted	£100	£60
T5s		'SPECIMEN'	£18	-
T6	**3d**	**Carmine.** Plate 2	£15	£10
T6a		Wmk. sideways inverted	-	£150
T6s		'SPECIMEN'	£20	-
T7	**3d**	**Carmine.** Plate 3	£25	£15
T7a		Wmk. sideways inverted	£160	
T7s		'SPECIMEN'	£25	-

1881 (March) Wmk. Imperial Crown (sideways). Perf. 14

No.			M/M	F/U
T8	**3d**	**Carmine.** Plate 3	£25	£20
T9	**3d**	**Carmine.** Plate 4	£100	£60
T10	**3d**	**Carmine.** Plate 5	£80	£50

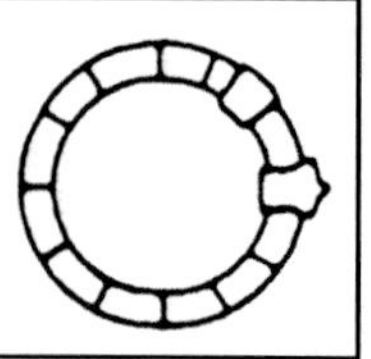

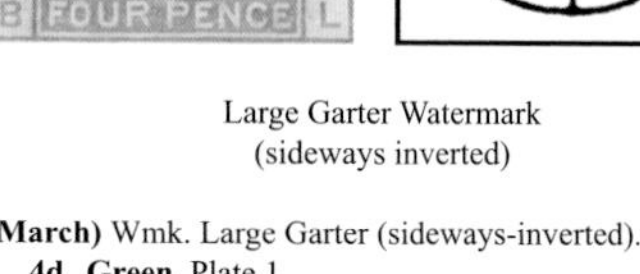

Large Garter Watermark (sideways inverted)

1877 (1 March) Wmk. Large Garter (sideways-inverted). Perf. 14

No.			M/M	F/U
T11	**4d**	**Green.** Plate 1	£20	£20
T11s		'SPECIMEN'	From £20	-

1877 (1 March) Wmk. Spray (sideways). Perf. 14

No.			M/M	F/U
T12	**6d**	**Grey.** Plate 1	£18	6.00
T12s		'SPECIMEN'	From £18	-
T13	**6d**	**Grey.** Plate 2	£75	£30

1881 (March) Wmk. Imperial Crown (sideways). Perf. 14

No.			M/M	F/U
T14	**6d**	**Grey.** Plate 2	£50	£25

1876 (1 Feb.) Wmk. Spray (sideways). Perf. 14

No.			M/M	F/U
T15	**1s**	**Dark green.** Plate 1	£35	£12
T15s		'SPECIMEN'	From £20	-
T16	**1s**	**Dark green.** Plate 2	£20	£12
T16a		Wmk. sideways inverted	£100	£70
T16s		'SPECIMEN'	From £25	-
T17	**1s**	**Dark green.** Plate 3	£25	£10
T17s		'SPECIMEN'	From £25	-
T18	**1s**	**Green.** Plate 4	£40	6.00
T18a		Wmk. sideways inverted	-	-
T18s		'SPECIMEN'	From £75	-
T19	**1s**	**Green.** Plate 5	£18	6.00
T19a		Wmk. sideways inverted	-	-
T19s		'SPECIMEN'	From £20	-
T20	**1s**	**Green.** Plate 6	£25	6.00
T20a		Wmk. sideways inverted	-	-
T20s		'SPECIMEN'	From £25	-
T21	**1s**	**Green.** Plate 7	£80	£10
T22	**1s**	**Green.** Plate 8	£35	£12
T22s		'SPECIMEN'	From £25	-
T23	**1s**	**Green.** Plate 9	£35	£10
T24	**1s**	**Green.** Plate 10	£40	£10

1880 (Oct.) New colour. Wmk. Spray (sideways). Perf. 14

No.			M/M	F/U
T25	1s	**Brown orange.** Plate 10	£70	£40
T25s		'SPECIMEN'	From £20	-
T26	1s	**Brown orange.** Plate 12	£70	£40

1881 (Feb.) Wmk. Imperial Crown (sideways). Perf. 14

No.			M/M	F/U
T27	1s	**Brown orange.** Plate 10	£45	£30
T27a		Wmk. sideways inverted	£70	£35
T27s		'SPECIMEN'	From £50	-
T28	1s	**Brown orange.** Plate 12	£120	£35

1877 (1 March) Wmk. Spray (sideways). Perf. 14

No.			M/M	F/U
T29	3s	**Blue.** Plate 1	£22	8.00
T29a		Wmk. sideways inverted	-	£125
T29s		'SPECIMEN'	£25	-

1881 (Feb.) Wmk. Imperial Crown (sideways-inverted). Perf. 14

No.			M/M	F/U
T30	3s	**Blue.** Plate 1	£2500	£1200
T30a		Wmk. sideways inverted		

Maltese Cross Watermark

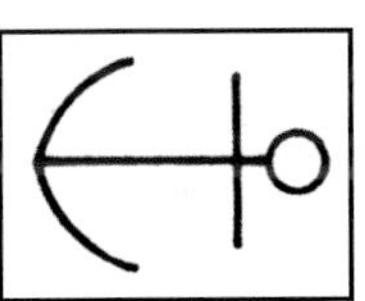

Large Anchor Watermark

1876 (1 Feb.) Wmk. Maltese Cross. Perf. 15 x 15½

No.			M/M	F/U
T31	5s	**Rose.** Plate 1	£280	£15
T31a		Pale rose	£200	£10
T31s		'SPECIMEN'	From £35	-
T32	5s	**Rose.** Plate 2	£550	£70

1880 (Nov.) Wmk. Maltese Cross. Perf. 14

No.			M/M	F/U
T33	5s	**Rose.** Plate 2	£1800	£90

1881 (May) Wmk. Large Anchor (sideways). Perf. 14

No.			M/M	F/U
T34	5s	**Rose.** Plate 3	£1800	£220
T35	5s	**Rose.** Plate 3 on bluish paper	£1800	£220
T35s		'SPECIMEN'	From £300	-

1877 (1 March) Wmk. Maltese Cross. Perf. 15 x 15½

No.			M/M	F/U
T36	10s	**Grey green.** Plate 1	£400	£65
T36s		'SPECIMEN'	£85	-

1877 (1 March) Wmk. Three Shamrocks (sideways). Perf. 14

No.			M/M	F/U
T37	£1	**Brown lilac.** Plate 1	£1500	£180
T37s		'SPECIMEN'	From £200	

1877 (1 March) Wmk. Three or more Shamrocks (sideways-inverted). Perf. 15 x 15½

No.			M/M	F/U
T38	£5	**Orange.** Plate 1	£5500	£850
T38s		'SPECIMEN'	From £800	-

Before the issue of the ½d postage stamp on 1 October 1870, for use on printed matter, there was no cheap way of distributing circulars, etc. through the postal system. There was a great need and in 1865 private enterprise decided to fill the gap in the form of the 'Edinburgh and Leith Circular Delivery Company'. They were quickly followed by many others.

In 1868 the Post Office went to Law to regain their monopoly, winning their case and an Appeal heard in June 1869. As a final attempt to remain in business, before the Appeal hearing, a Limited Circular Delivery Company was registered in February 1868 and incorporated under 'The Companies' Act of 1862. New stamps were produced including two new towns, Birmingham and Manchester, but were not used pending the Appeal Court judgement. These stamps, sometimes thought of as forgeries, are more correctly described as 'prepared to use but not issued'. As they never served a postal use we do not list them here.

Many forgeries exist, some contemporary to the genuine issues. Most are easily recognised by their crude production, the paper used or bogus colours and values. Over a period of twenty years and including the contemporary types, six series of forgeries have been identified. Their continued appearance was almost certainly due to the lack of information at this time about the genuine issues.
Circular Delivery Company Stamps used on cover are very rare and few stamps off cover are found with a handstamp cancellation although two types are known to have been issued. Stamps with coloured pencil lines, usually blue, are virtually all from a dealer's stock defaced at the request of Post Office Officials. They informed him that it was a serious offence to have mint undesirable items in stock.

The Circular Delivery Companies effectively ceased trading from June 1868 having provided a cheap and useful service to the public for just over two years. That this fulfilled a genuine commercial need cannot be doubted since public protests were made at every level when the Post Office took further legal action in 1868. The matter was taken up in the House of Commons in April 1869, when it was demonstrated that many countries had stamps with face values well below one penny. The Postmaster-General promised to look into the matter. On 1 October 1870 the first ½d rate for postcards and printed paper up to 2 ounces was introduced, which could, at least indirectly, be attributed to the initiative of the Brydones local delivery services.

Printed in Lithography. Imperforate, unless otherwise stated.

1867 Aberdeen. Perf. 13

CD1	**¼d**	Orange brown	£60
CD2	**½d**	Blue	5.00

1867 Dundee. Imperf.

CD3	**¼d**	Maroon	£60
CD4	**½d**	Vermilion	£60

1866 Clark & Co., Edinburgh. Imperf.

CD5	**¼d**	Blue	£15
CD5a		Pale blue	£15

CD6

CD15

CD16

1865 Edinburgh & Leith. Type A. Imperf.

CD6	**¼d**	Green. Roulette 7	£15
CD7	**¼d**	Green. Perf. 12	£60
CD8	**¼d**	Slate blue. Roulette 7	8.00
CD9	**¼d**	Grey lilac	£10
CD9a		Greenish grey	5.00
CD10	**¼d**	Pearl grey. Perf. 12	£100
CD11	**¼d**	Greenish grey. Perf. 11¾	£8
CD12		Greenish grey. Pin perf. 10½	£40
CD13		Greenish grey. Roulette 7	£40

1866 Colours changed.

CD14	**¼d**	Rosy mauve	2.50
CD15		Mauve. Perf. 11¾ - 12	£60

Type B

CD16	**¼d**	Grey lilac	3.00
CD17	**½d**	Green	£12
CD18	**¼d**	Pin perf. 10½	7.00
CD18a		Reddish lilac. Pin perf. 10½	7.00
CD19	**¼d**	Green. Pin perf. 10½	£18

1867 12 Elder Street. Type C

CD20	**¼d**	Red brown	2.50
CD21	**¼d**	Black on yellow. Roulette 7	£90
CD22	**¼d**	Black on yellow. Imperf.	£150
CD23	**¼d**	Red brown. Roulette 7	£100

No.			M/M
1865 12 St. Andrews' Square. Type D			
CD24	¼d	Green. Roulette 7	£100
CD25	¼d	Green. Imperf.	£125
CD26	2d	Yellow. Roulette 7	8.00
CD27	3d	Brown red. Roulette 7	£100
CD27a		Imperf	£125
1866 Parcel Delivery Co. Type E			
CD28	2d	Orange	4.00
CD29	3d	Brick red	5.00
CD30	2d	Orange. Roulette 7	£50
CD31	3d	Brick red. Roulette 7	£50
CD32	2d	Orange. Pin perf. 10½	£50
CD33	3d	Brick red. Pin perf. 10½	£50

CD34

CD38

1867 Glasgow. Horizontal laid paper. Imperf.

CD34	¼d	Black	2.50
CD35	½d	Vermilion	2.50
CD36	¼d	Black. Pin perf. 10½	£15
CD37	½d	Vermilion. Pin perf. 10½	£15

1866 Liverpool. Imperf.

CD38	¼d	Dark brown	£10
1867 Perf. 13			
CD39	¼d	Red brown	3.00
CD40	½d	Lilac	4.00

CD41

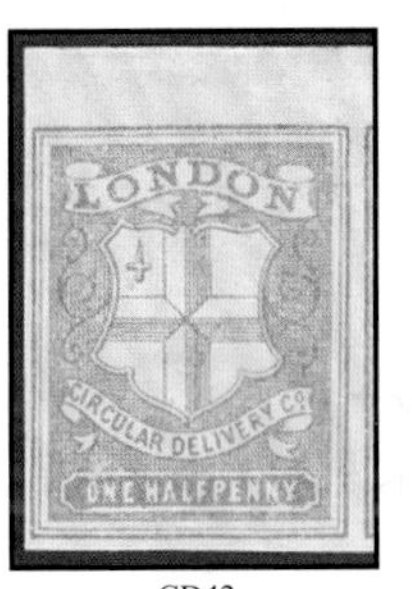

CD42

1866 London. Imperf. Thick soft wove paper

CD41	¼d	Deep blue	4.00
CD42	½d	Blue grey	3.00
CD43	½d	Dull purple	3.00
CD43a		Pale lilac	£15
CD44	¼d	Deep blue. Clean perf. 11½	6.00
CD45	½d	Blue grey. Clean perf. 11½	6.00
CD46	¼d	Deep blue. Rough perf. 11½	£100
CD47	½d	Deep blue (error of colour). Rough perf. 11½	£100
CD48	¼d	Deep blue. Pin perf. 10½ - 11	8.00
CD49	½d	Blue grey. Pin perf. 10½ - 11	£100
CD50	½d	Dull purple. Pin perf. 10½ - 11	8.00

No.			M/M
1867 Thinner hard wove paper. Rough perf. 11½			
CD51	¼d	Deep blue	£25
CD52	½d	Reddish lilac	6.00
CD52a		Showing papermakers watermark *	£18
CD52b		Watermarked paper *	£18

1867 London and District. Imperf.

CD53	¼d	Green	£10
CD54	½d	Brown rose	£50
CD55	¼d	Brown rose (error of colour)	£150
CD56	¼d	Green. Perf. 13	2.50
CD57	½d	Pink. Perf. 13	3.00
CD58	¼d	Pink (error of colour). Perf. 13	£20
CD59	½d	Brown purple. Perf. 13	£25
CD60	¼d	Brown purple (error of colour). Perf. 13	£130
CD61	½d	Lilac rose. Perf. 13	£14
CD62	¼d	Lilac rose (error of colour). Perf. 13	£80

CD64

CD69

1867 Metropolitan. Rough perf. 11½

CD63	¼d	Rose (thick hard wove paper)	4.00
CD63a		Showing papermakers watermark *	£12
CD64	¼d	Rose (pelure paper)	4.00
CD65	¼d	Rose (pelure paper). Imperf.	£100
CD66	¼d	Orange yellow (error of colour)	£100
CD67	½d	Orange (Thick hard wove paper)	£12
CD67a		Showing papermakers watermark *	£30

1867 National. Perf. 13

CD68	¼d	Green	£60
CD69	½d	Blue	6.00
CD70	¾d	Yellow	£14
CD71	1d	Red	6.00

* The watermark found on the stamps listed is that of the paper maker and reads 'A. COWAN & SON' or 'EXTRA SUPERFINE' in double lined letters with 'A C & S' script monogram.

The Colleges of Oxford and Cambridge Universities were allowed the privilege of running their own local postal service. This practice generally ceased in 1886, although Keble continued until 1890.
Used should be collected on cover (all scarce to rare) as generally the stamps were uncancelled or marked in manuscript. Used prices are for stamps on cover.

Oxford University

Keble Type A

Keble Type B

Keble Type C

Keble Type B1 with round O's in Spiers & Son, etc.
Keble Type B2 with oval O's in Spiers & Son, etc.

No.		M/M	✉
1871 - 82 Keble College. Type A			
C1	Vermilion. Perf. 10½	£175	£600
C2	Vermilion. Perf. 11¾ (1872)	£130	£700
C3	Rosy magenta. Perf. 10¾ (1873)	£140	£900
C4	Magenta. Perf. 10¾ x imperf. (1876)	£320	£2500
	Type B		
C5	Ultramarine (1). Perf. 11½ (1876)	£30	£400
C6	Ultramarine (2). Perf. 11½ (1879)	£30	£300
	Type C		
C7	Ultramarine. Perf. 12 (1882)	2.50	£250

Merton Type A

Merton Type B

Merton Type C

No.		M/M	✉
1876 - 83 Merton College. Type A			
C8	Royal blue. Perf. 12½ x imperf. (1876)	£200	£1100
C9	Milky blue. Perf. 11¾ x imperf. (1877)	£220	£800
	Type B		
C10	Dull blue. Perf. 12½ x imperf. (1876)	£600	£2000
	Type C		
C11	Mauve. Perf. 12 (1883)	£10	£300

Lincoln

Hertford

Exeter

No.		M/M	✉
1877 Lincoln College			
C12	(1d) Indigo. Perf. 14½	£45	£600
1879 Hertford College			
C13	Mauve. Perf. 11½	6.00	£1200
C13a	Imperforate	4.00	
1882 Exeter College			
C14	Salmon. Perf. 11¾	£10	£400

All Souls

St. John's

Balliol

No.		M/M	✉
1884 All Souls College			
C15	Ultramarine. Perf. 11½	£22	£800
1884 St. John's College			
C16	Dull blue. Perf. 12	4.00	£300
1885 Balliol College			
C17	Scarlet. Perf. 11½ x imperf.	£45	

Cambridge University

Selwyn

Queen's

St. John's

No.		M/M	✉
1882 Selwyn College			
C18	Black. on pink paper Imperf.	£42	£2500
1883 Queen's College			
C19	Green. Perf. 11½	£20	£2500
1884 St. John's College			
C20	Scarlet. Perf. 12	£10	£3000

SPECIMEN	SPECIMEN	SPECIMEN	SPECIMEN	SPECIMEN
Type 1	**Type 2**	**Type 3**	**Type 4**	**Type 5**
19.75 x 2.5 mm	20 x 2.75-3 mm	21 x 2.5 mm	18 x 2.5 mm	18.25 x 2.75-3 mm

SPECIMEN	SPECIMEN	SPECIMEN	SPECIMEN	SPECIMEN
Type 6	**Type 7**	**Type 8**	**Type 9**	**Type 10**
18.25 x 3 mm	16.5 x 2.75 mm	19.5 x 2.5 mm	14.75 x 1.75-2 mm	20 x 2.5 mm

SPECIMEN	SPECIMEN	SPECIMEN	SPECIMEN	SPECIMEN
Type 11	**Type 12**	**Type 13**	**Type 14**	**Type 15**
20.25 x 3 mm	15.5 x 1.75 mm	15.25 x 1.5 mm	14.5 x 2-2.25 mm	15.5 x 2.5 mm

SPECIMEN	SPECIMEN	SPECIMEN	SPECIMEN	SPECIMEN
Type 16	**Type 17**	**Type 18**	**Type 19**	**Type 20**
16 x 2.75 mm	14.75 x 2 mm	9.75-10 x 1.75 mm	12.5 x 2 mm	11.25 x 1.25 mm

SPECIMEN	SPECIMEN	SPECIMEN
Type 21	**Type 22**	**Type 23**
13 x 1.75 mm	12.25 x 1.75 mm	10.5 x 2 mm

Specimen Overprints

Where ‘SPECIMEN’ overprints are known on both imperforate and perforate stamps of the same issue or the issue exists in more than one colour, the price quoted is for the cheapest only.

Queen Victoria

		Type 1	Type 2	Type 3	Type 4	Type 5	Type 6	Type 7	Type 8	Type 9	Type 10	Type 11	Type 12	Type 13	Type 14	Type 15
V22	1d Red brown	£1500														
V23	2d Blue, plate 3	£2500														
V24	2d Blue, plate 4	£2500														
V27	2d Deep blue, plate 4	£1600														
V31	2d Blue, plate 4	£1600														
V41	1d Red brown		£900													
V44	1d Rose red					£300	£300				£180					
V50	½d Rose red, plate 3		£200													
V55	½d Rose red, plate 9		£2000													
V56	½d Rose red, plate 10								£200	£180						
V57	½d Rose red, plate 11								£200		£250					
V59	½d Rose red, plate 13									£180						
V62	½d Rose red, plate 19									£180						
V113	1d Rose red, plate 121		£300			£200										
V139	1d Rose red, plate 146									£180						
V154	1d Rose red, plate 164								£180							
V173	1d Rose red, plate 183									£180						
V188	1d Rose red, plate 198									£180						
V197	1d Rose red, plate 207									£180						
V214	1d Rose red, plate 224									£180						
V216	1½d Rose red, plate 1		£200			£200										
V217	1½d Rose red, plate 3								£200	£180	£200					
V220	2d Blue, plate 9						£300									
V221	2d Blue, plate 12	£250														
V222	2d Blue, plate 13		£400													
V223	2d Blue, plate 14					£250			£200							
V224	2d Blue, plate 15					£250				£180	£250					
V225	6d embossed	£1500	£1500													
V226	10d embossed, die 1	£1500														
V229	10d embossed, die 4		£2000													
V231	1s embossed, die 1	£1500														
V232	1s embossed, die 2		£2000													
V234	4d small garter		£500	£500												
V236	4d medium garter		£500													
V237	4d medium garter		£500													
V238	4d medium garter				£500											
V239	4d large garter		£350				£250									
V241	6d emblems		£250		£250		£250		£200							